D1517178

The University of Chicago School Mathematics Project

Geometry

Second Edition

Teacher's Edition

Part 2, Chapters 8-14

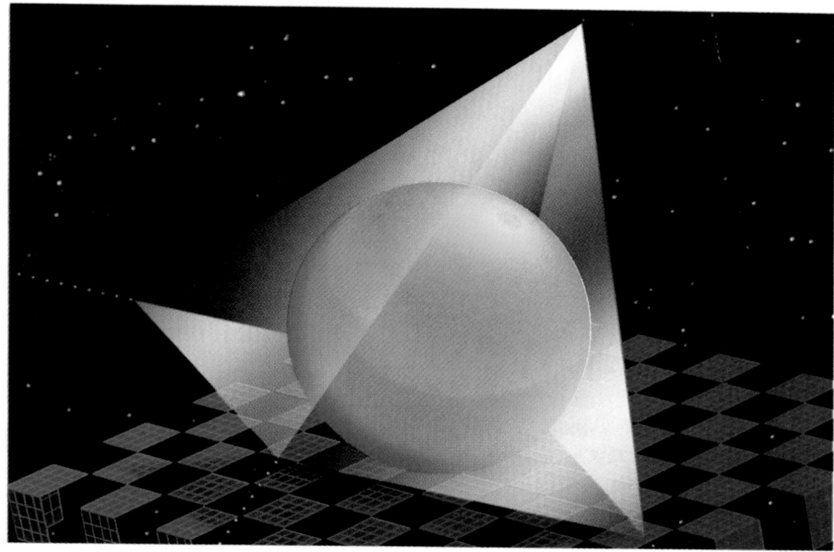

About the Cover The computer-generated art on the cover connects shapes studied by ancient geometers to the present and to the future. *UCSMP Geometry* integrates geometry with algebra, functions, and discrete mathematics.

Authors

Zalman Usiskin Daniel Hirschhorn
Arthur Coxford Virginia Highstone Hester Lewellen
Nicholas Oppong Richard DiBianca Merilee Maeir

Scott Foresman
Addison Wesley

Editorial Offices: Glenview, Illinois • Menlo Park, California
Sales Offices: Reading, Massachusetts • Atlanta, Georgia • Glenview, Illinois
Carrollton, Texas • Menlo Park, California

http://www.sf.aw.com

Contents

of Teacher's Edition

The complete Table of Contents for the Student Edition begins on page *vi*.

Your UCSMP Professional Sourcebook is found at the back of Part 1, starting on page T20.

ISBN: 0-673-45958-6

4 5 6 7 8 9—DR—0 3 0 2 0 1 0 0

CONTENTS

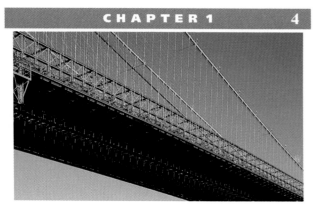

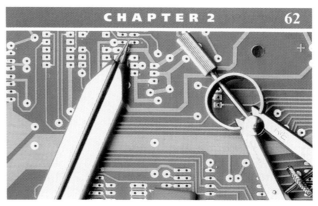

POLYGONS AND SYMMETRY

TRIANGLE CONGRUENCE

PERIMETERS AND AREAS

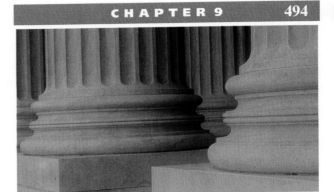

CHAPTER 12 684

SIMILARITY

CHAPTER 13 736

SIMILAR TRIANGLES AND TRIGONOMETRY

CHAPTER 14 798

FURTHER WORK WITH CIRCLES

Chapter 8 Planner

Adapting to Individual Needs

The student text is written for the vast majority of students. The chart at the right suggests two pacing plans to accommodate the needs of your students. Students in the Full Course should complete the entire text by the end of the year. Students in the Minimal Course will spend more time when there are quizzes and more time on the Chapter Review. Therefore, these students may not complete all of the chapters in the text.

Options are also presented to meet the needs of a variety of teaching and learning styles. For each lesson, the Teacher's Edition provides a section entitled *Adapting to Individual Needs.* This section regularly includes **Optional Activities, Challenge** problems, **English Language Development** suggestions, and suggestions for providing **Extra Help.** The Teacher's Edition also frequently includes an **Error Alert,** an **Extension,** and an **Assessment** alternative. The options available in Chapter 8 are summarized in the chart below.

Chapter 8 Pacing Chart

Day	Full Course	Minimal Course
1	8-1	8-1
2	8-2	8-2
3	8-3	8-3
4	Quiz*; 8-4	Quiz*; begin 8-4.
5	8-5	Finish 8-4.
6	8-6	8-5
7	Quiz*; 8-7	8-6
8	8-8	Quiz*; begin 8-7.
9	Self-Test	Finish 8-7.
10	Review	8-8
11	Test*	Self-Test
12		Review
13		Review
14		Test*

*in the Teacher's Resource File

In the Teacher's Edition...

Lesson	Optional Activities	Extra Help	Challenge	English Language Development	Error Alert	Extension	Cooperative Learning	Ongoing Assessment
8-1	●	●	●	●	●	●	●	Oral/Written
8-2	●	●	●			●		Written
8-3	●		●	●		●	●	Written
8-4	●	●	●	●	●	●	●	Oral/Written
8-5	●	●	●	●	●	●		Oral/Written
8-6	●	●	●			●	●	Oral/Written
8-7	●	●	●			●	●	Oral/Written
8-8	●	●	●	●		●		Written

Chapter 8 Block Schedule

Day	Recommended Pacing
1	Lesson 8-1
2	Lessons 8-2, 8-3
3	Lessons 8-4, 8-5
4	Lesson 8-6
5	Lesson 8-7
6	Lesson 8-8, Self-Test, Chapter Review
7	Chapter Review, Chapter Test

In the Additional Resources...

	In the Teacher's Resource File								
Lesson	Lesson Masters, A and B	Teaching Aids*	Activity Kit*	Answer Masters	Technology Sourcebook	Assessment Sourcebook	Visual Aids**	Technology	Video Segments
8-1	8-1	101, 104, 105		8-1			101, 104, 105, AM		
8-2	8-2	101, 105, 106	18	8-2			101, 105, 106, AM		
8-3	8-3	102, 104, 105, 107, 108		8-3		Quiz	102, 104, 105, 107, 108, AM		
8-4	8-4	102, 109		8-4			102, 109, AM		
8-5	8-5	102, 104, 105, 110, 111		8-5			102, 104, 105, 110, 111, AM		
In-class Activity		112		8-6			112, AM		
8-6	8-6	103, 113	19	8-6	16	Quiz	103, 113, AM	GeoExplorer	
In-class Activity				8-7			AM		
8-7	8-7	103		8-7	17		103, AM	GeoExplorer	
In-class Activity		112		8-8			112, AM		
8-8	8-8	103, 114–116		8-8	18		103, 114–116, AM	GeoExplorer	8-8
End of Chapter				Review		Tests			

*Teaching Aids, except for Warm-ups, are pictured on pages 434C and 434D. The activities in the Activity Kit are pictured on page 434C. Teaching Aid 112, which accompanies the In-class Activities for Lessons 8-6 and 8-8, is pictured with the lesson notes on page 465.

**Visual Aids provide transparencies for all Teaching Aids and all Answer Masters.

Also available is the Study Skills Handbook which includes study-skill tips related to reading, note-taking, and comprehension.

Integrating Strands and Applications

	8-1	8-2	8-3	8-4	8-5	8-6	8-7	8-8
Number Sense	●	●	●		●		●	●
Algebra	●	●	●	●	●	●	●	●
Geometry	●	●	●	●	●	●	●	●
Measurement	●	●	●	●	●	●	●	●
Logic and Reasoning	●	●	●	●	●	●	●	●
Probability								●
Statistics/Data Analysis	●					●		
Patterns and Functions	●	●	●	●	●	●	●	●
Discrete Mathematics	●							
Art	●	●						
Music						●		
Science	●							
Social Studies	●	●	●	●	●	●	●	●
Multicultural	●		●		●	●	●	●
Technology			●	●		●	●	●
Career	●					●		
Consumer		●	●		●		●	
Sports		●						●

Teaching and Assessing the Chapter Objectives

Chapter 8 Objectives (Organized into the SPUR categories—Skills, Properties, Uses, and Representations)	**Lessons**	**Progress Self-Test Questions**	**Chapter Review Questions**	**In the Teacher's Resource File: Chapter Test, Forms A and B**	**Chapter Test, Forms C**	**Chapter Test, Forms D**
Skills						
A: Calculate perimeters of parallelograms, kites, and equilateral polygons given appropriate lengths, and vice versa.	8-1	1, 4, 10, 14	1–8	1, 4, 11	1	
B: Describe or apply a method for determining the area of an irregularly shaped region.	8-3	12	9–12	20		✓
C: Calculate areas of squares, rectangles, parallelograms, trapezoids, and triangles given relevant length of sides, and vice versa.	8-2, 8-4, 8-5	2, 3, 5, 6, 14	13–22	2, 3, 5, 11, 22	2	
D: Apply the Pythagorean Theorem to calculate lengths and areas in right triangles and other figures.	8-6	9, 10	23–28	7, 8, 9	3, 6	
E: Apply the Pythagorean Converse Theorem.	8-6	11	29–32	17	6	
F: Calculate lengths and measures of arcs, the circumference, and the area of a circle given measures of relevant lengths and angles, and vice versa.	8-7, 8-8	7, 8	33–37	6, 10		
Properties						
G: Relate various formulas for area.	8-2, 8-4, 8-5, 8-8	13	38–44	16	4	✓
Uses						
H: Apply the Pythagorean Theorem and perimeter formulas for parallelograms, kites, and equilateral polygons to real-world situations.	8-1, 8-6	15, 16, 19	45–50	12, 15	5	✓
I: Apply formulas for areas of squares, rectangles, parallelograms, trapezoids, and triangles to real-world situations.	8-2, 8-4, 8-5	18, 19	51–54	13	5	✓
J: Apply formulas for the area and circumference of a circle to real situations.	8-7, 8-8	17, 20	55–58	19, 21	4	✓
Representations						
K: Determine the areas of polygons on a coordinate plane.	8-2, 8-4, 8-5	21, 22	59–62	14, 18	3	
Culture						
L: Identify cultures in which the Pythagorean Theorem is known to have been studied.	8-6	23	63–66	23		

Assessment Sourcebook
Quiz for Lessons 8-1 through 8-3
Quiz for Lessons 8-4 through 8-6
Chapter 4 Test, Forms A–D
Chapter 4 Test, Cumulative Form

Quiz and Test Writer

Activity Kit

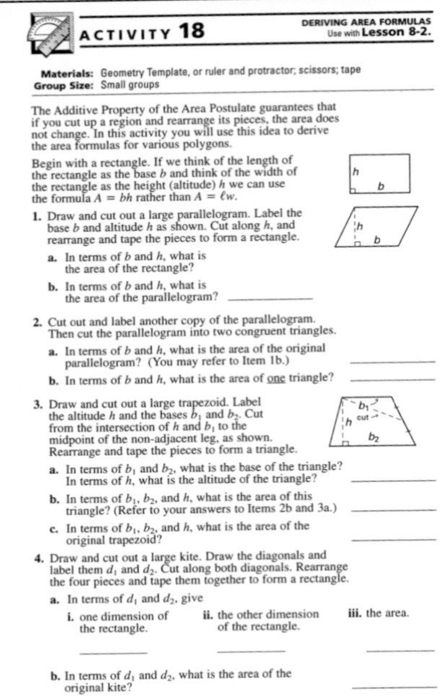

ACTIVITY 18 — DERIVING AREA FORMULAS
Use with **Lesson 8-2.**

Materials: Geometry Template, or ruler and protractor; scissors; tape
Group Size: Small groups

The Additive Property of the Area Postulate guarantees that if you cut up a region and rearrange its pieces, the area does not change. In this activity you will use this idea to derive the area formulas for various polygons.

Begin with a rectangle. If we think of the length of the rectangle as the base b and think of the width of the rectangle as the height (altitude) h we can use the formula $A = bh$ rather than $A = \ell w$.

1. Draw and cut out a large parallelogram. Label the base b and altitude h as shown. Cut along h, and rearrange and tape the pieces to form a rectangle.

   a. In terms of b and h, what is the area of the rectangle?
   b. In terms of b and h, what is the area of the parallelogram? ________

2. Cut out and label another copy of the parallelogram. Then cut the parallelogram into two congruent triangles.
   a. In terms of b and h, what is the area of the original parallelogram? (You may refer to Item 1b.) ________
   b. In terms of b and h, what is the area of <u>one</u> triangle? ________

3. Draw and cut out a large trapezoid. Label the altitude h and the bases b_1 and b_2. Cut from the intersection of h and b_1 to the midpoint of the non-adjacent leg, as shown. Rearrange and tape the pieces to form a triangle.

   a. In terms of b_1 and b_2, what is the base of the triangle? In terms of h, what is the altitude of the triangle? ________
   b. In terms of b_1, b_2, and h, what is the area of this triangle? (Refer to your answers to Items 2b and 3a.) ________
   c. In terms of b_1, b_2, and h, what is the area of the original trapezoid? ________

4. Draw and cut out a large kite. Draw the diagonals and label them d_1 and d_2. Cut along both diagonals. Rearrange the four pieces and tape them together to form a rectangle.
   a. In terms of d_1 and d_2, give
      i. one dimension of the rectangle. ________
      ii. the other dimension of the rectangle. ________
      iii. the area. ________
   b. In terms of d_1 and d_2, what is the area of the original kite? ________

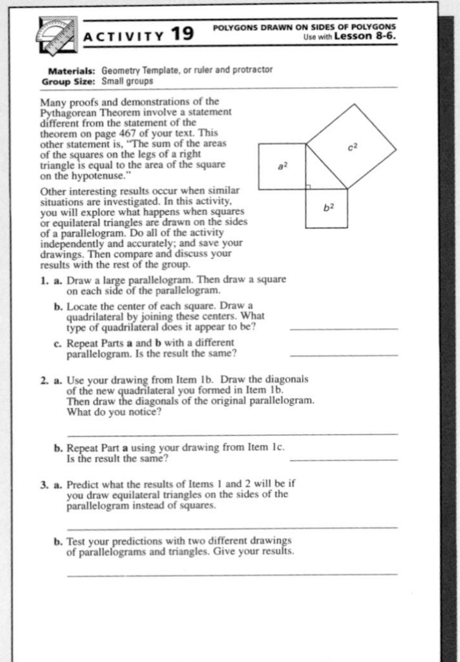

ACTIVITY 19 — POLYGONS DRAWN ON SIDES OF POLYGONS
Use with **Lesson 8-6.**

Materials: Geometry Template, or ruler and protractor
Group Size: Small groups

Many proofs and demonstrations of the Pythagorean Theorem involve a statement different from the statement of the theorem on page 467 of your text. This other statement is, "The sum of the areas of the squares on the legs of a right triangle is equal to the area of the square on the hypotenuse."

Other interesting results occur when similar situations are investigated. In this activity, you will explore what happens when squares or equilateral triangles are drawn on the sides of a parallelogram. Do all of the activity independently and accurately; and save your drawings. Then compare and discuss your results with the rest of the group.

1. a. Draw a large parallelogram. Then draw a square on each side of the parallelogram.
   b. Locate the center of each square. Draw a quadrilateral by joining these centers. What type of quadrilateral does it appear to be? ________
   c. Repeat Parts **a** and **b** with a different parallelogram. Is the result the same? ________

2. a. Use your drawing from Item 1b. Draw the diagonals of the new quadrilateral you formed in Item 1b. Then draw the diagonals of the original parallelogram. What do you notice?
   ____
   b. Repeat Part **a** using your drawing from Item 1c. Is the result the same? ________

3. a. Predict what the results of Items 1 and 2 will be if you draw equilateral triangles on the sides of the parallelogram instead of squares.
   ____
   b. Test your predictions with two different drawings of parallelograms and triangles. Give your results.
   ____

Teaching Aids

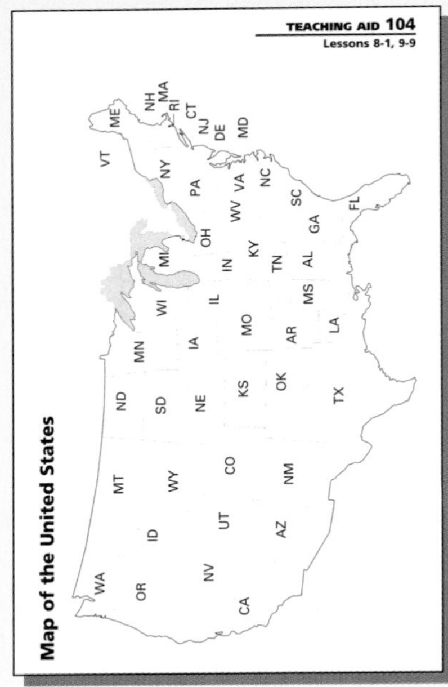

TEACHING AID 104
Lessons 8-1, 9-9

Map of the United States

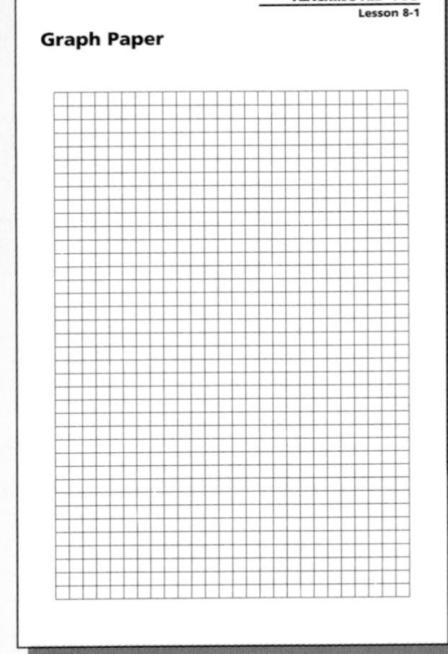

TEACHING AID 105
Lesson 8-1

Graph Paper

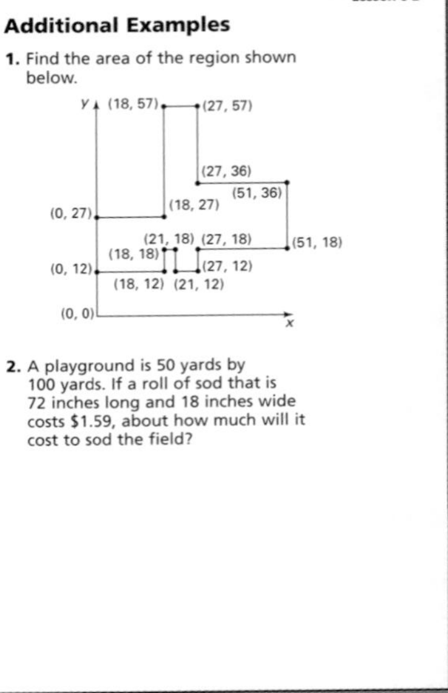

TEACHING AID 106
Lesson 8-2

Additional Examples

1. Find the area of the region shown below.

2. A playground is 50 yards by 100 yards. If a roll of sod that is 72 inches long and 18 inches wide costs $1.59, about how much will it cost to sod the field?

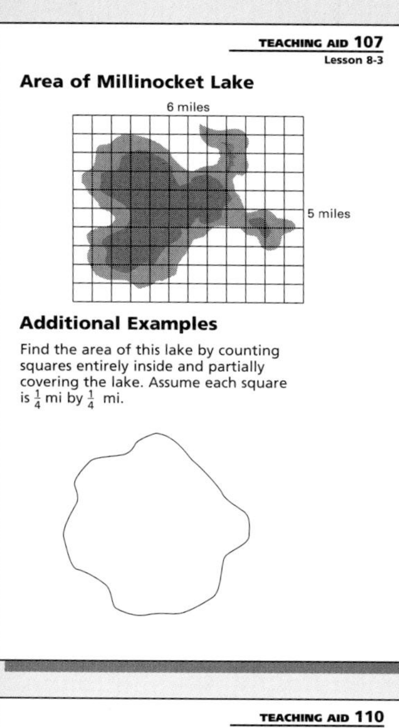

TEACHING AID 107
Lesson 8-3

Area of Millinocket Lake

6 miles

5 miles

Additional Examples

Find the area of this lake by counting squares entirely inside and partially covering the lake. Assume each square is $\frac{1}{4}$ mi by $\frac{1}{4}$ mi.

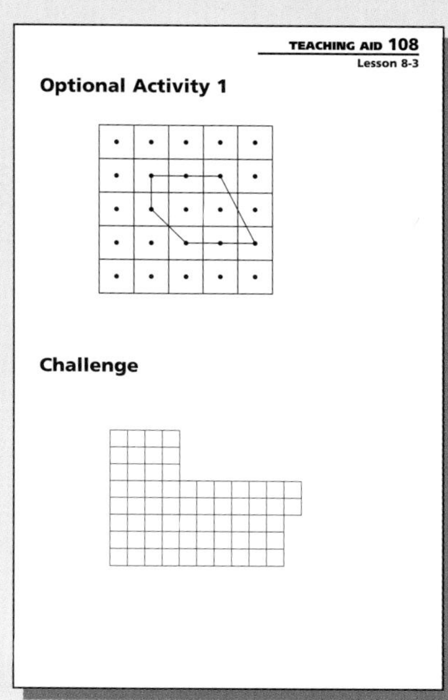

TEACHING AID 108
Lesson 8-3

Optional Activity 1

Challenge

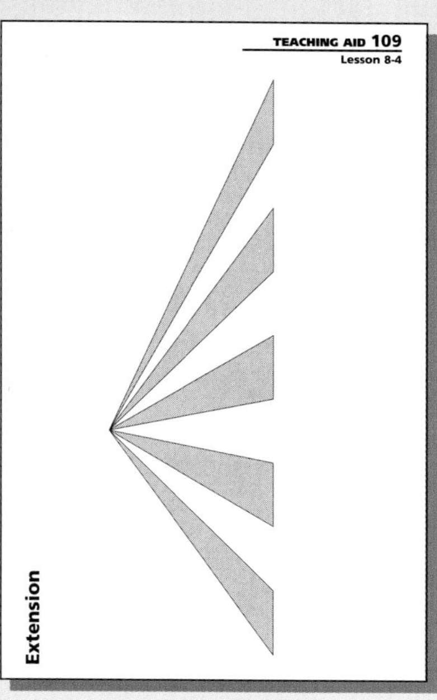

TEACHING AID 109
Lesson 8-4

Extension

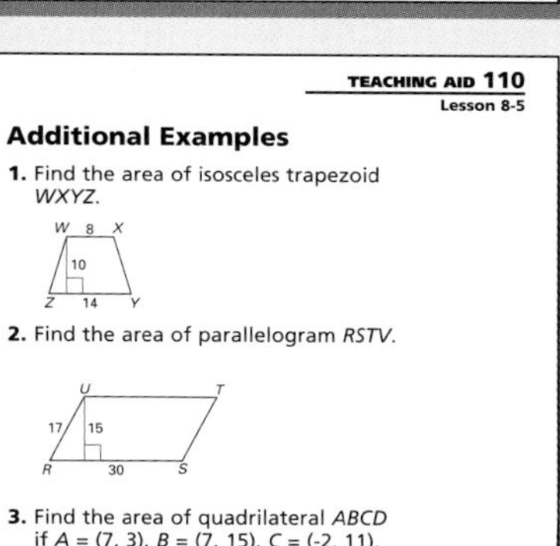

TEACHING AID 110
Lesson 8-5

Additional Examples

1. Find the area of isosceles trapezoid *WXYZ*.

2. Find the area of parallelogram *RSTV*.

3. Find the area of quadrilateral *ABCD* if *A* = (7, 3), *B* = (7, 15), *C* = (-2, 11), and *D* = (-2, 5).

4. Show that the Trapezoid Area Formula can be used to find the area of a square with side *s*.

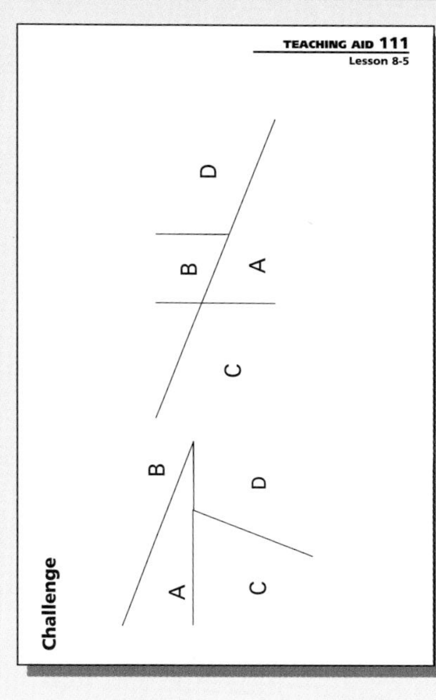

TEACHING AID 111
Lesson 8-5

Challenge

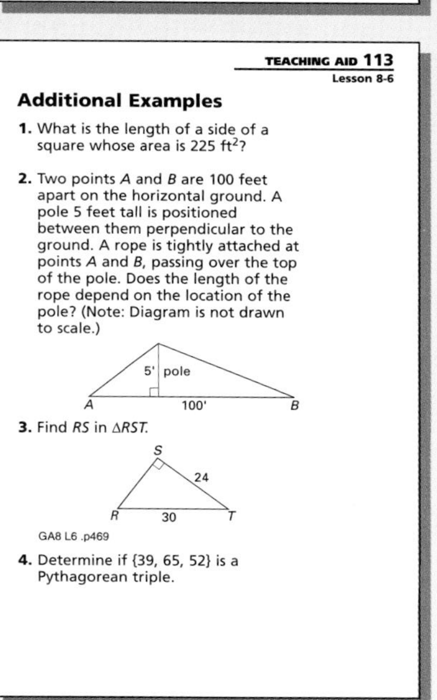

TEACHING AID 113
Lesson 8-6

Additional Examples

1. What is the length of a side of a square whose area is 225 ft^2?

2. Two points *A* and *B* are 100 feet apart on the horizontal ground. A pole 5 feet tall is positioned between them perpendicular to the ground. A rope is tightly attached at points *A* and *B*, passing over the top of the pole. Does the length of the rope depend on the location of the pole? (Note: Diagram is not drawn to scale.)

3. Find *RS* in $\triangle RST$.

GA8 L6 .p469

4. Determine if {39, 65, 52} is a Pythagorean triple.

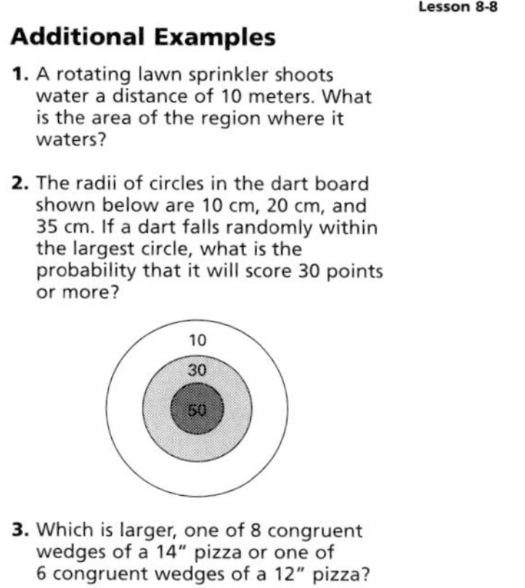

TEACHING AID 114
Lesson 8-8

Additional Examples

1. A rotating lawn sprinkler shoots water a distance of 10 meters. What is the area of the region where it waters?

2. The radii of circles in the dart board shown below are 10 cm, 20 cm, and 35 cm. If a dart falls randomly within the largest circle, what is the probability that it will score 30 points or more?

3. Which is larger, one of 8 congruent wedges of a 14" pizza or one of 6 congruent wedges of a 12" pizza?

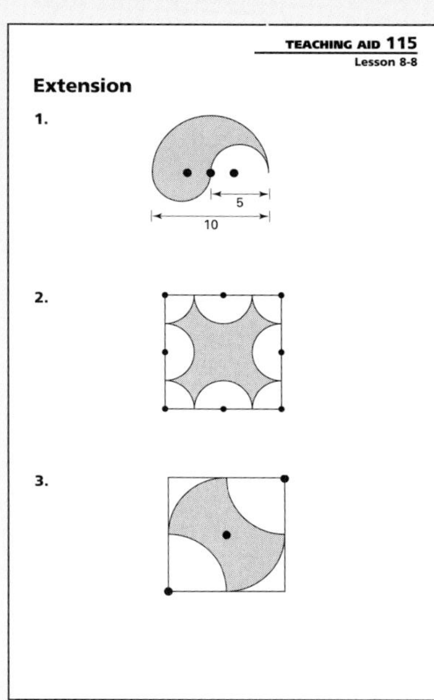

TEACHING AID 115
Lesson 8-8

Extension

1.

2.

3.

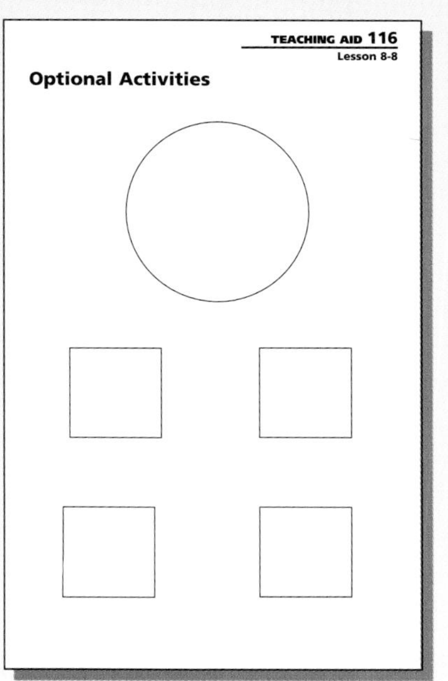

TEACHING AID 116
Lesson 8-8

Optional Activities

Chapter 8 Opener

Pacing

All lessons in this chapter are designed to be covered in one day. At the end of the chapter, you should plan to spend 1 day to review the Progress Self-Test, 1–2 days for the Chapter Review, and 1 day for a test. You may want to spend a day on projects, and possibly a day is needed for quizzes. Therefore, this chapter should take 11–15 days. We strongly advise you not to spend more than 16 days on this chapter. There is ample opportunity to review ideas in later chapters, particularly in Chapter 10.

Using Pages 434–435

The opener discusses the difference between the perimeter and the area of the museum. It provides a lead-in to Lesson 8-1 and gives a preview of the area ideas covered in the chapter.

Emphasize that although perimeter and area both indicate something about the size of a figure, they measure different things. Use the museum to point out the difference: the perimeter measures the distance a person would travel if he or she walked around the museum, whereas the area measures how much ground the museum covers.

Another example of two different quantities that are used to measure size involves the height and the weight of people—just as a person can be tall and not heavy or heavy and not tall, a figure can have a large perimeter but not a large area. However, if a figure has a large area, then it has to have at least a certain perimeter, an idea that is developed in detail in Chapter 14.

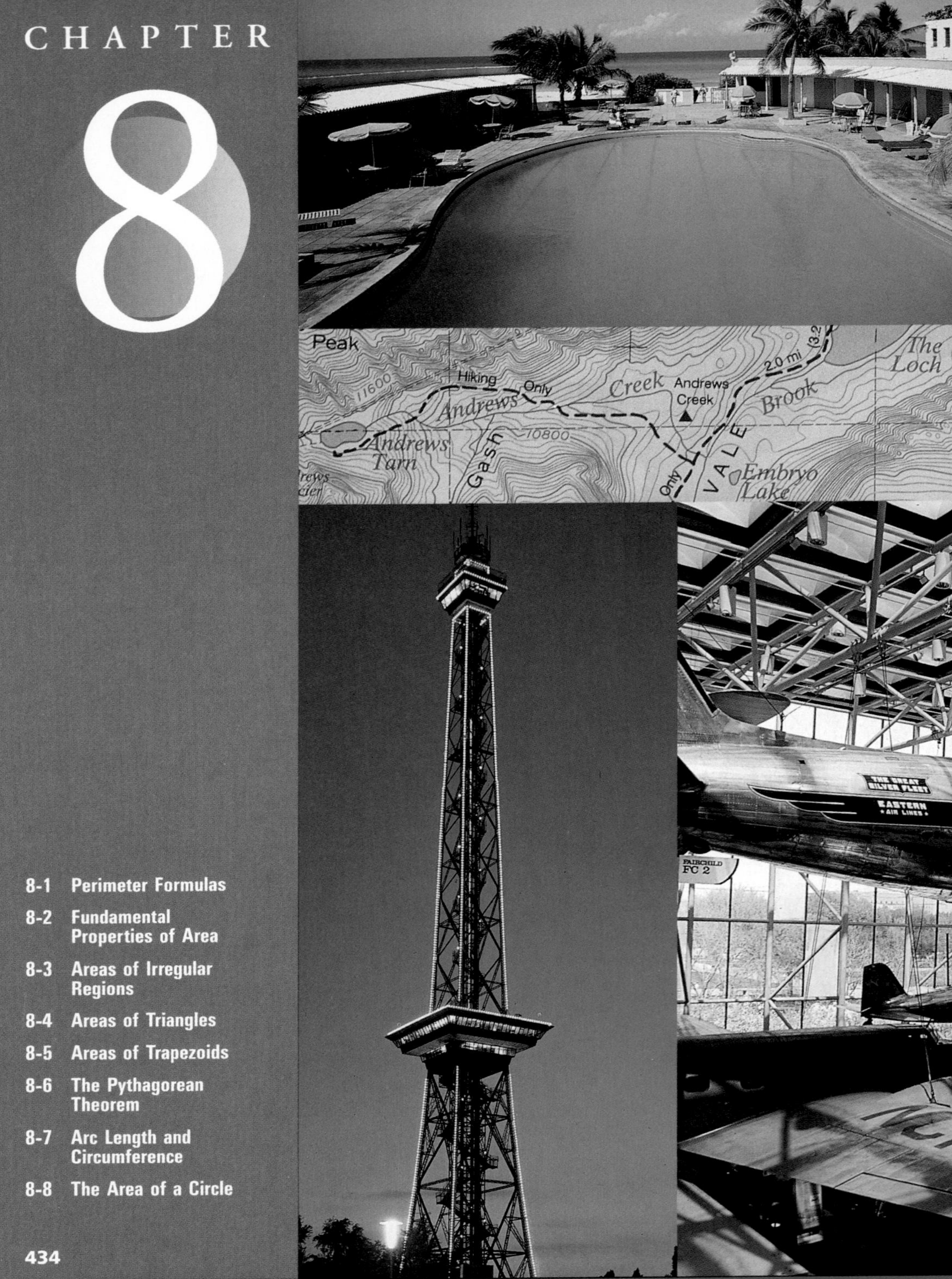

CHAPTER 8

434

Chapter 8 Overview

The measurement formulas discussed in this chapter involve length, angle measure, and area. The content covers some of the most famous and most familiar theorems in all of geometry, the formulas for area and perimeter, and the Pythagorean Theorem. One purpose of this chapter is to help students become more competent with all sorts of problems involving measure relationships. Another purpose is to help the students understand how the different formulas are related and how they follow from each other and from relationships among figures.

Much of the content of this chapter may have been studied by students in previous years. In fact, many, if not most, students coming into geometry are familiar with formulas for the area and perimeter of a rectangle and with the Pythagorean Theorem. It is unlikely, however, that they have seen any logical development of these ideas. Proof may seem unnecessary because students learned these results earlier. However, the use of formulas for one shape to justify formulas for another shape should put proof into perspective.

The chapter begins with the concept of perimeter, and then moves on to area. Lessons 8-1 to 8-3 should be viewed as concept-building lessons. Lessons 8-4

PERIMETERS AND AREAS

Pictured below is an aerial view of a museum surrounded by an elliptical walkway. The museum and the walkway both lie inside a large rectangle that is 2 blocks long and 1 block wide.

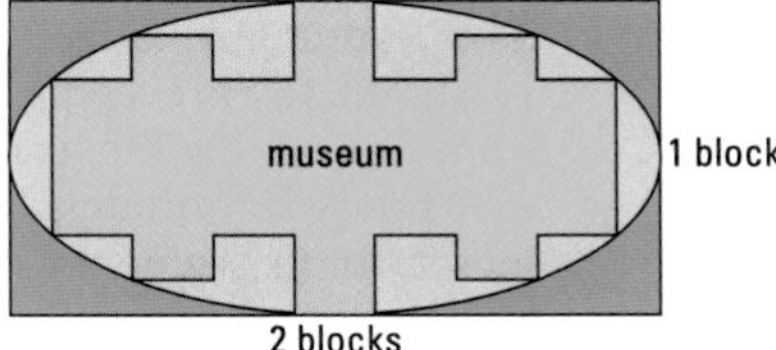

Area is a measure of the space occupied by a two-dimensional region. The area of the rectangle is 2 square blocks. So the area of the museum is less than 2 square blocks. The area of the elliptical region is larger than the area of the museum but smaller than the area of the rectangle. All of this can be seen by separating the three regions.

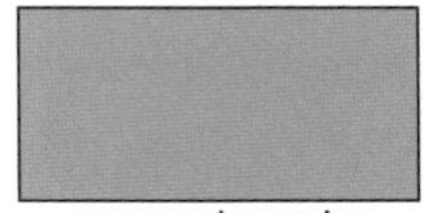
rectangular region

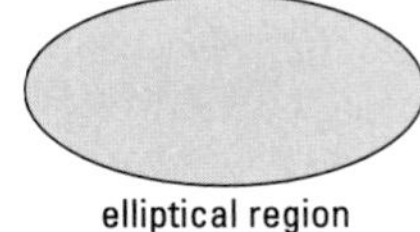
elliptical region

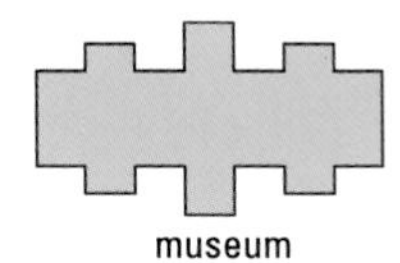
museum

Perimeter is different from area. The perimeter of a region is the length of its boundary. It tells you how far it would be to walk along the boundary. The perimeter of the rectangle is 6 blocks. It is harder to calculate the perimeter of the museum because the museum is a nonconvex 28-gon. But you can see that it would take longer to walk around all the walls of the museum than to walk around either the rectangle or the ellipse. The perimeter of the museum is larger than the perimeter of either the rectangle or the ellipse.

Thus the museum has the smallest area but the largest perimeter. So, although area and perimeter both measure how big something is, they are quite different.

In this chapter, you will learn formulas for the areas of many of the figures you have studied so far in this book. You will also learn how these formulas are related to each other, so that if you forget one of them, you may be able to derive it.

Students who have studied from *Transition Mathematics* should be familiar with the ideas mentioned here.

Photo Connections

The photo collage makes real-world connections to the content of the chapter: perimeters and areas.

Pools: Not all swimming pools are rectangular or oval—many of them have irregular shapes like the one pictured. In this chapter you will find the area of irregular shapes.

Bicycles: What is the distance between two spokes on a bicycle wheel? How far will the bicycle travel in one revolution of the wheel? The answers depend on arc length and circumference of circles.

Maps: The map shows lakes in Rocky Mountain National Park. You will estimate the areas of lakes in Lesson 8-3.

Radio Towers: In Project 3 on page 485 you will investigate the area covered by radio signals sent out from radio towers.

Museums: The wall area and the perimeter of rooms and hallways in a museum influence the exhibits that can be displayed. This picture shows one of many bureaus of the Smithsonian known as the National Air and Space Museum.

Chapter 8 Projects

At this time you might want to have students look over the projects on pages 485–486.

and 8-5 develop area formulas by beginning with the area of a rectangle. Lesson 8-6 develops the Pythagorean Theorem by using what is known about the area of a square. The last two lessons, Lessons 8-7 and 8-8, cover the circumference and area of a circle.

Students will need calculators throughout the chapter.

Lesson 8-1

Objectives

A Calculate perimeters of parallelograms, kites, and equilateral polygons given appropriate lengths, and vice versa.

H Apply perimeter formulas for parallelograms, kites, and equilateral polygons to real-world situations.

Resources

From the ***Teacher's Resource File***
- Lesson Master 8-1A or 8-1B
- Answer Master 8-1
- Teaching Aids
  101 Warm-up
  104 Map of the United States
  105 Graph Paper

Additional Resources
- Visuals for Teaching Aids 101, 104–105

Teaching Lesson 8-1

Warm-up

Would you measure the area or the perimeter to find the answer?

1. How many exhibits is a museum able to hold? Area
2. How many signs could be placed around the inside or outside of the museum? Perimeter
3. How much would a sidewalk surrounding the museum cost? Perimeter and area
4. How many people could visit the museum at a given time? Area
5. How many people are in a line that stretches around the museum? Perimeter

LESSON

8-1 *Perimeter Formulas*

Time and Mileage Map

Below is a portion of a United States mileage and driving-time map. It is a network whose nodes are cities. The lengths of arcs in this network are given in miles and in hours and minutes. For instance, the length of the arc from Charleston to Lexington is 177 miles or 2 hours 48 minutes.

There are many paths on this network. For instance, there is a path from Nashville to Shreveport through Little Rock. The length of that path is found by adding the lengths of the individual segments. It is 562 miles or 9 hours 35 minutes. In general, the length of a path is the sum of the lengths of its segments.

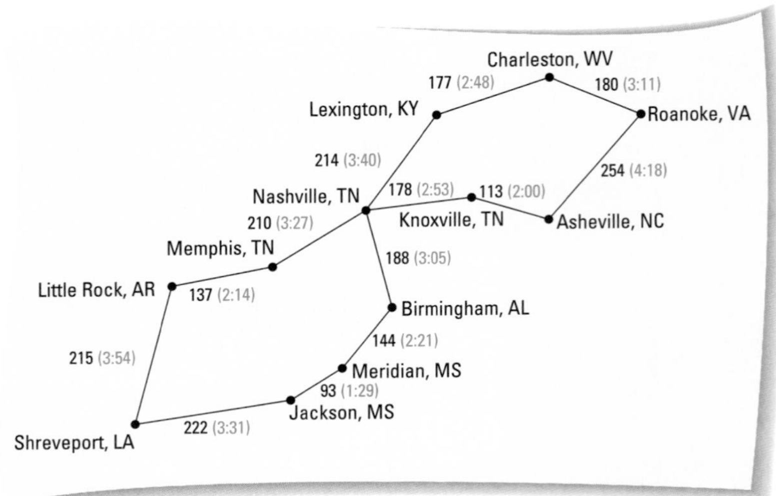

The network can be thought of as the union of two polygons, a heptagon and a hexagon, which share a vertex at Nashville. Think of traveling along the sides of one of these polygons, the hexagon *NLCRAK* (named using the first letters of the cities). You will have taken a tour through six cities (the vertices), ending where you started. According to this map, you will have traveled about 1116 miles and it would take you a little under 19 hours. In calculating the sum of the distances, you have calculated the *perimeter* of *NLCRAK*.

Definition
The perimeter of a polygon is the sum of the lengths of its sides.

Lesson 8-1 Overview

Broad Goals There are three goals in this lesson: (1) to review the perimeter formulas for a polygon and for polygons with sides of equal length (parallelograms, kites, equilateral polygons), (2) to emphasize the difference between perimeter and area, and (3) to review the requisite algebra and arithmetic skills.

Perspective The most general perimeter formula for polygons is given by the definition on page 437. If the sides of an n-gon have lengths $a_1, a_2, \ldots a_n$, then the perimeter is $a_1 + a_2 + \ldots + a_n$. All other formulas are derived from this.

The formula for the perimeter of a rectangle, $p = 2(\ell + w)$, with which students are familiar, is a special case of the formula $p = 2a + 2b$, which holds for any quadrilateral with two distinct pairs of congruent sides. These two formulas are both discussed in this lesson.

Also, the formula for the perimeter of an equilateral polygon is covered. Notice that in these cases we emphasize the formula for the more general type of figure (quadrilateral with two pairs of congruent sides; equilateral polygon) rather than for the more specific type of figure (rectangle; regular polygon). This is a pattern maintained

Biltmore House, Asheville, NC. *George Vanderbilt's summer house, constructed in 1895, contains art treasures, rare books, and more in its 250 rooms.*

The driving-time map illustrates that the length of a side of a polygon may be measured in various units. Usually the units are those of length in the metric system (meters, centimeters, and so on) or in the customary system (inches, miles, and so on). When calculating the perimeter of a polygon, it is important that the units for each side be the same.

If all the sides of a polygon have different lengths, there is no special formula for its perimeter. A formula for the perimeter p of a triangle with sides x, y, and z is just $p = x + y + z$.

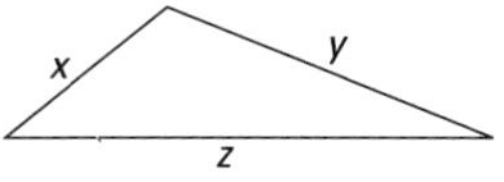

Perimeters of Kites and Rectangles

When a polygon has some sides equal, then the calculations of the perimeter can be shortened. For instance, we know that a kite has two pairs of equal sides. If the lengths of these sides are a and b, then its perimeter p can be given by the formula

$$p = a + a + b + b$$

or, using repeated addition, $p = 2a + 2b$

or, factoring, using the Distributive Property, $p = 2(a + b)$.

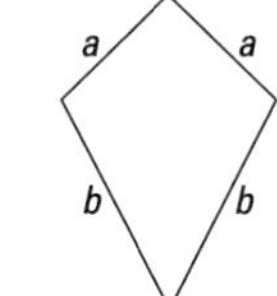

Example 1

Kite $WXYZ$ with ends X and Z has side lengths as shown at the right. Find its perimeter.

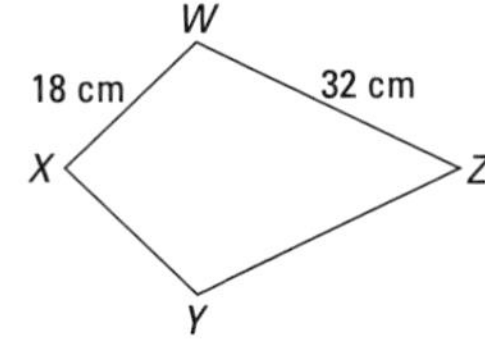

Solution 1

Use the definition of perimeter.
Perimeter of $WXYZ = WX + XY + YZ + ZW$.
Since X and Z are ends of the kite,
$WX = XY$ and $YZ = ZW$. Substituting,
perimeter of WXYZ = 18 cm + 18 cm + 32 cm + 32 cm
WXYZ = 100 cm.

Solution 2

Use the formula $p = 2(a + b)$. If $a = WX$ and $b = ZW$, then
$p = 2(a + b)$
$= 2(18 \text{ cm} + 32 \text{ cm})$
$= 2(50 \text{ cm})$
$= 100 \text{ cm}$.

The lengths of two adjacent sides of a rectangle are the dimensions of the rectangle. Sometimes they are called the rectangle's length and width. Since the opposite sides of a rectangle are congruent, the perimeter of a rectangle with length ℓ and width w is $\ell + w + \ell + w$, or $2\ell + 2w$, or $2(\ell + w)$. So a formula for the perimeter of a rectangle is $p = 2(\ell + w)$. Formulas are nice to have because they allow you to apply what you know about algebra to geometry, and thus shorten calculations.

Notes on Reading

Geography Connection You may want to have students use a map of the U.S. to locate the states involved in the time-and-mileage map on page 436. **(Teaching Aid 104)** You might also want to discuss situations for which the distance in miles is the more important measure, and other situations for which the distance in time is more important.

In **Example 2,** emphasize that the length can be any side of the rectangle, and so can the width. This notion will be important because it will extend to parallelograms in which any side can be the base.

In **Example 2,** the ratio of dimensions of the flag is 1.6, approximately the golden ratio: $\frac{\sqrt{5} + 1}{2} \approx 1.6180$. Another interesting fact is that the ratio of kilometers to miles, 1.609 km per 1 mile, is also approximately the golden ratio. The fact that the dimensions of typical flags are in this ratio is not coincidence; but the fact that the kilometer-to-mile ratio is close to the golden ratio is a coincidence.

Error Alert Students sometimes confuse "equilateral," "equiangular," and "regular." When discussing equilateral polygons on page 438, make sure to discuss the differences among these terms. Give labeled examples to help students visualize the differences.

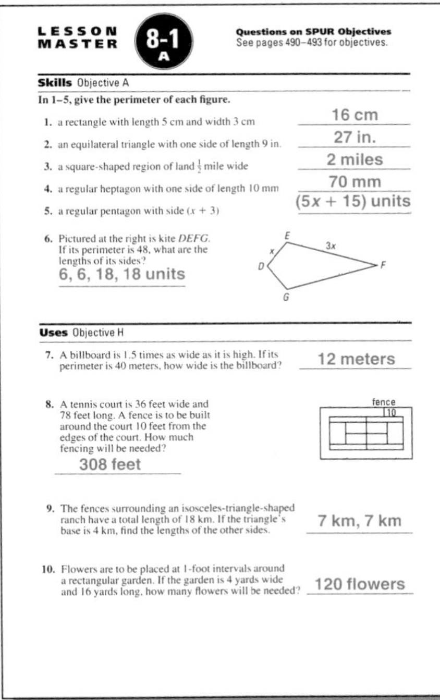

LESSON MASTER 8-1 A

Questions on SPUR Objectives
See pages 490–493 for objectives.

Skills Objective A

In 1–5, give the perimeter of each figure.

1. a rectangle with length 5 cm and width 3 cm — 16 cm
2. an equilateral triangle with one side of length 9 in. — 27 in.
3. a square-shaped region of land $\frac{1}{2}$ mile wide — 2 miles
4. a regular heptagon with one side of length 10 mm — 70 mm
5. a regular pentagon with side $(x + 3)$ — $(5x + 15)$ units
6. Pictured at the right is kite $DEFG$. If its perimeter is 48, what are the lengths of its sides? — 6, 6, 18, 18 units

Uses Objective H

7. A billboard is 1.5 times as wide as it is high. If its perimeter is 40 meters, how wide is the billboard? — 12 meters
8. A tennis court is 36 feet wide and 78 feet long. A fence is to be built around the court 10 feet from the edges of the court. How much fencing will be needed? — 308 feet

9. The fences surrounding an isosceles-triangle-shaped ranch have a total length of 18 km. If the triangle's base is 4 km, find the lengths of the other sides. — 7 km, 7 km
10. Flowers are to be placed at 1-foot intervals around a rectangular garden. If the garden is 4 yards wide and 16 yards long, how many flowers will be needed? — 120 flowers

throughout this chapter and followed in Chapter 10 for the formulas for surface area and volume. By concentrating on formulas for the more general figures, students need to remember fewer formulas.

Students who have taken previous UCSMP courses will be familiar with the concept of perimeter but will not have seen the formulas for the perimeter of a kite or of an equilateral polygon.

We want to have students become more intuitive about perimeter so that they understand how area and perimeter are different. One way of doing this is to show that different figures can have the same perimeter. Another way is through examples, such as the museum situation on page 435. Students who have taken *Transition Mathematics* should be familiar with these ideas. They may remember seeing a drawing of a lake which has a small area but a large perimeter.

Remind students that lengths are added to get perimeter. So the formulas for perimeter, such as $2(\ell + w)$, never involve the multiplication of lengths. In contrast, formulas for area *always* involve, or can be traced back to, the multiplication of two lengths.

Additional Examples

1. A rectangular park is 500 ft long and 220 feet wide. What is the perimeter of the park? 1440 ft
2. A flower garden is shaped like a kite and requires 50 feet of edging to surround it. If one side is 4 times as long as the other, what are the dimensions? 5 ft and 20 ft

Notes on Questions

Cooperative Learning All questions in this lesson should be discussed in class.

Question 2 Ask if the trucker's decision should be based on distance or time. [Time, if the load is perishable] Note that four routes are shown from Roanoke to Shreveport.

Questions 8–9 Error Alert If students cannot answer these questions with variables, suggest that they look at special cases (see **Questions 6–7**) and find a pattern.

Example 2

Most rectangular flags are about 1.6 times as long as they are wide. If you have 10 meters of border material to strengthen the edges of a flag, about how large a flag can you make?

Solution

First, draw a picture. The edges are the length ℓ and width w of the rectangle. The perimeter p satisfies

$$p = 2(\ell + w).$$

Using $\ell = 1.6w$ and $p = 10$, substitute for p and ℓ.

$$10 = 2(1.6w + w)$$
$$10 = 2(2.6w)$$
$$10 = 5.2w$$

So $w = \frac{10}{5.2} \approx 1.923$ meters. Since $\ell = 1.6w$, $\ell \approx 3.077$ meters.
From 10 meters of border material, you can make a flag about 1.92 meters wide and 3.08 meters long.

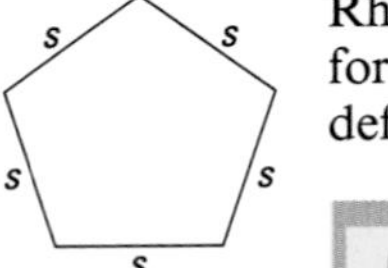

equilateral pentagon

Equilateral Polygons

Rhombuses, squares, and regular polygons are all equilateral. A formula for the perimeter of an equilateral polygon follows directly from the definition of perimeter.

Equilateral Polygon Perimeter Formula
The perimeter p of an equilateral n-gon with sides of length s is given by the formula $p = ns$.

Since all regular polygons are equilateral, this formula applies to every regular polygon. For instance, in an equilateral triangle, $p = 3s$. In a square, $p = 4s$. In a regular octagon, $p = 8s$.

QUESTIONS

Covering the Reading

In 1–3, use the network pictured in this lesson.

1. What does the number 2:21 on the segment from Meridian, MS, to Birmingham, AL, mean?
It takes 2 hr 21 min to drive from Meridian to Birmingham.
2. A trucker with a perishable load should choose which route from Roanoke, VA, to Shreveport, LA?
the route through Asheville, Knoxville, Nashville, Memphis, and Little Rock
3. Give the perimeter of the heptagon
   a. in miles. 1209 miles
   b. in hours. 20 hours 1 minute

Optional Activities

Cooperative Learning You might use this activity after students have discussed the lesson. Have students **work in groups** and make a table showing the dimensions and perimeters of rectangles with an area of 360 square units. After students have done several examples, ask the class to make a conjecture about which rectangle would have the least perimeter. [The rectangle with congruent sides; that is, a square.] Ask which rectangle would have the greatest perimeter. [There is none; the perimeter can be as large as one wishes. For instance, a length of 1000 yields a width of 0.36 and a perimeter of 2000.72.] Some possible entries in the students' tables are shown at the right. The beginning of the table suggests that the perimeter could increase without limit. The last entry suggests that when the length and width of the rectangle are $\sqrt{360}$, the perimeter is the least.

LESSON MASTER 8-1 B Questions on SPUR Objectives

Skills Objective A: Calculate perimeters of parallelograms, kites, and equilateral polygons given appropriate lengths and vice versa.

In 1–9, give the perimeter of each figure.

1. a rectangle with length 8 cm and width 2.5 cm — 21 cm
2. an equilateral triangle with one side of length 15 in. — 45 in.
3. a square-shaped region $\frac{1}{4}$ yard on a side — 1 yard
4. a regular hexagon with one side of length 16 mm — 96 mm
5. a parallelogram with one side of length 12 and the adjacent side half as long — 36 units
6. a regular octagon with side $(y + 7)$ — $(8y + 56)$ units
7. an equilateral pentagon with side length $(4a + 13)$ — $(20a + 65)$ units
8. a rectangle with one dimension $n + 2$ and the other dimension $2n - 1$ — $(6n + 2)$ units
9. a kite with the length of a shorter side $4m$ and the length of a longer side 5 more than twice the length of a shorter side — $(24m + 10)$ un.
10. The perimeter of an equilateral triangle is 13.5 m. Find the length of a side. — 4.5 m
11. The perimeter of a parallelogram is 48, with the length of a shorter side 10. Find the length of a longer side. — 14 units
12. The perimeter of a rhombus is 34 mm. What is the length of a side? — $8\frac{1}{2}$, or 8.5, mm
13. The longer sides of a rectangle are 3 times as long as the shorter sides. If the perimeter is 100 feet, what are the dimensions of the rectangle? — 12.5 ft, 37.5 ft
14. The perimeter of a regular hexagon is $84h + 12$. What is the length of a side? — $(14h + 2)$ units
15. Pictured at the right is kite *KITE*. If its perimeter is 72 cm, what are the lengths of its sides? — 24 cm, 12 cm

K I T E 8y 4y

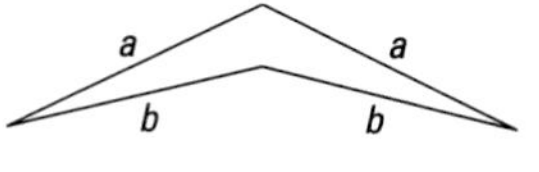

4. Give three different algebraic expressions for the perimeter of the polygon pictured at the left. $a + b + b + a$, $2a + 2b$, $2(a + b)$

5. State the Distributive Property. $a(b + c) = ab + ac$

In 6–9, give the perimeter of each figure.

6. a rectangular-shaped piece of land $3\frac{1}{2}$ miles long and $\frac{1}{2}$ mile wide 8 miles

7. an equilateral hexagon with one side of length 14 mm 84 mm

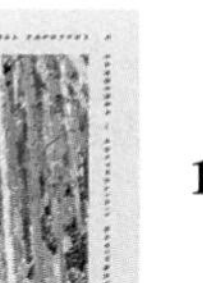

This poster shows a tapestry which hangs in the Parliament House in Canberra, Australia. Can you find a bird and Halley's comet woven into the eucalyptus forest?

8. a square with side t $4t$

9. a regular heptagon with side $(x + 1)$ $7(x + 1)$ or $7x + 7$

10. The perimeter of a rectangle is 70. One side of the rectangle is 3 times the length of the other. What are the lengths of the sides? 8.75 and 26.25

11. A poster is to be 1.5 times as wide as it is high. If its edges total 3 meters in length, how wide will the poster be? 0.9 meters

Applying the Mathematics

12. The perimeter of a rhombus is 2 feet.
- **a.** Is this enough information to find the length of a side of the rhombus? Yes
- **b.** If so, find that length. If not, why not? 0.5 ft

13. A stop sign is a regular octagon. If the total length of its edges is 10′, what is the length of each side? 1.25 ft

14. The perimeter of an equilateral triangle is p. What is the length of each side? $\frac{p}{3}$

15. The boundary of the museum on page 435 has sides of three different lengths. Let the smallest sides have length s, the middle sides have length m, and the largest sides have length ℓ.
- **a.** What is a formula for the perimeter of the museum? $8s + 18m + 2\ell$
- **b.** If $s = 25$ meters, $m = 50$ meters, and $\ell = 100$ meters, what is the perimeter of the museum? 1300 meters

16. Suppose the dimensions of a rectangle are multiplied by 5. What happens to its perimeter? Its perimeter is multiplied by 5.

17a)

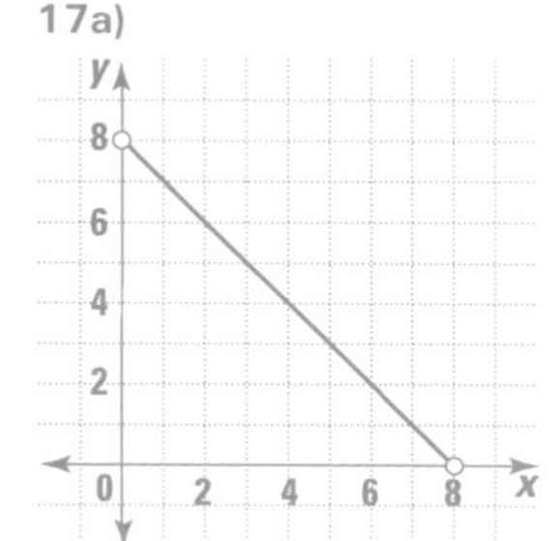

17. A rectangle has perimeter 16.
- **a.** Graph all possible pairs of lengths x and widths y. See left.
- **b.** Give an equation for the graph. $x + y = 8$ $(x > 0$ and $y > 0)$
- **c.** Find one possible length and width where both are not integers. Sample: $x = 4.5$, $y = 3.5$

18. One side of an equiangular pentagon has measure 7″. Can you compute its perimeter? Why or why not?
No; an equiangular pentagon is not necessarily equilateral.

Question 10 Encourage students to solve this problem in various ways: (1) Substitute in the formula $p = 2\ell + 2w$ to get $70 = 2(3s + s)$, and solve for s. (2) Use the fact that one length plus one width equals half the perimeter: $3s + s = 35$. (3) Let x and y be the dimensions and solve a system: $x + y = 35$ and $y = 3x$.

Question 14 Most students need practice solving for variables in formulas. Here $p = 3s$, so $s = \frac{p}{3}$. In conversion formulas, 1 in. = 2.54 cm, so 1 cm ≈ .3937 in. Also, 1 sq mi = 640 acres and so 1 acre = 0.0015625 sq mi. The coefficients are reciprocals—this is one reason for having a reciprocal key on scientific calculators.

Question 17 Students will need graph paper or **Teaching Aid 105.** To show a connection to area, choose a point on the graph, such as (3, 5). Draw the rectangle with vertices (0, 0), (3, 0), (3, 5), and (0, 5). This rectangle has perimeter 16 units and area 15 square units.

Question 18 Stress the difference between "equilateral" and "equiangular."

(Notes on Questions continue on page 440.)

Length	Width	Area	Perimeter
18,000	0.02	360	36,000.04
7,200	0.05	360	14,400.10
1,000	0.36	360	2,000.72
360	1	360	722
90	4	360	188
36	10	360	92
20	18	360	76
19	≈18.95	360	≈75.9
$\sqrt{360}$	$\sqrt{360}$	360	≈75.88

Adapting to Individual Needs

Extra Help

Point out to students that the formulas for perimeter in this lesson all relate to polygons. But it is possible to find the perimeter of figures that are not polygons. You might draw a kidney-shaped swimming pool on the board. Discuss how one might find the perimeter of the pool. [Sample: lay a rope around the edge of the pool, and then measure the length of the rope.]

▸ **LESSON MASTER 8-1B** *page 2*

16. The perimeter of a kite is 120 inches, and the length of one side is 18 inches. Is this enough information to find the lengths of the other three sides of the kite? If so, find the lengths. If not, tell why not.
Yes; the longer sides measure 42 inches, and the other short side measures 18 inches.

Uses Objective H: Apply perimeter formulas for parallelograms, kites, and equilateral polygons to real-world situations.

17. The Parthenon in Athens, Greece, was completed in 432 B.C. It is about 69.5 m long and 30.9 m wide. Find its perimeter. 200.8 m

18. The Pentagon, outside Washington, D.C., is shaped like a regular pentagon with each side 921 feet long. Find the perimeter. 4605 feet

19. The base of the Great Pyramid of Khufu, near Cairo, Egypt, is shaped like a square. If the perimeter is about 922.4 m, find the length of a side. 230.6 m

20. The Taj Mahal in Agra, India, is octagonal, with a perimeter of 212 m. Four sides each measure about 44.5 m, and the remaining sides are each the same length. Find the length of a remaining side. 8.5 m

21. A stockade fence is to be supported at 6-foot intervals by vertical posts. If the area to be fenced is a rectangle 54 feet by 72 feet, how many posts will be needed? 42 posts

22. Sue Ling wishes to sew braid trim 3 inches from the edges of a 72-in. × 108-in. table cloth. How many yards of trim will she need? $9\frac{1}{3}$ yards

23. The molding for an ornate gold picture frame with outside dimensions of 5 inches and 7 inches costs $12. At this rate, what will the same molding cost for a frame whose outside dimensions are 3 times as long? $36

24. For an outdoor display, Jose wishes to outline a large 6-pointed star with small lights. The sides of each point are $3\frac{1}{2}$ feet long, and he plans to place the lights 4 inches apart. How many lights will he need? 126 lights

Notes on Questions

Question 19 Note that (c) is the sum of the measures of the angles of an *n*-gon; (b) gives the number of its diagonals.

Question 22–24 These questions cover units of length and may be a review for some students.

Follow-up for Lesson 8-1

Practice

For more questions on SPUR Objectives, use **Lesson Master 8-1A** (shown on page 437) or **Lesson Master 8-1B** (shown on pages 438–439).

Assessment

Oral/Written Communication Have students **work in groups** to prepare a written list of as many everyday situations as possible where it is useful to find perimeter. Then have the class compile a master list. [Students provide meaningful situations where perimeter might be useful. Allow any reasonable situations.]

Extension

This problem involves nonregular equilateral polygons. Suppose *ABCDE* is an equilateral pentagon with perimeter 100. What are the possible values of *AC*? Think of connecting five new congruent pencils, and then collapsing them in the plane. [$0 < AC < 40$]

Project Update Project 1, *Perimeter of Your School*, on page 485, relates to the content of this lesson.

Review

19. *Multiple choice.* The measure of each angle of a regular *n*-gon is: d

(a) $\frac{360}{n}$ (b) $\frac{n(n-3)}{2}$

(c) $(n-2) \cdot 180$ (d) $\frac{(n-2) \cdot 180}{n}$ *(Lesson 6-7)*

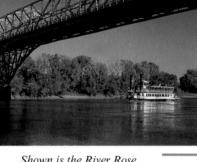

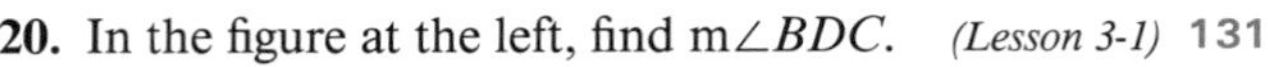

20. In the figure at the left, find m$\angle BDC$. *(Lesson 3-1)* 131

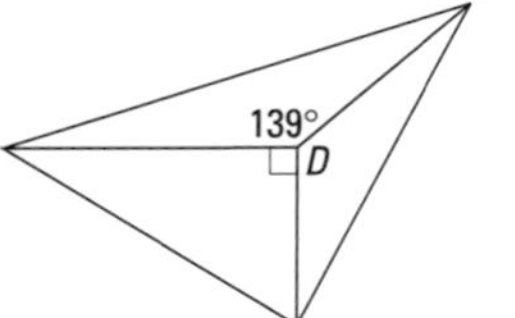

21. Is the network in the map on page 436 traversable? *(Lesson 1-4)* Yes

22. Fill in the blanks of these conversion formulas. *(Previous course)*
a. 1 yard = _?_ feet 3
b. 1 kilometer = _?_ meters 1000
c. 1 mile = _?_ feet 5280

23. One inch is exactly 2.54 centimeters. About what part of an inch is two centimeters? *(Previous course)* ≈ .79

24. Do the calculations, which are of a type often found when adding lengths. *(Previous course)*
a. 3 feet 6 inches + 8 feet 11 inches 12 feet 5 inches
b. 8 · (2 feet 3 inches) 18 feet
c. 2.4 meters + 62 centimeters 3.02 meters or 302 centimeters

25. If $p = 2\ell + 2w$, $\ell = 11$, and $p = 25$, find w. *(Previous course)* 1.5

26. Solve $x^2 = 200$. Give your answer to the nearest hundredth. *(Previous course)* $x \approx \pm 14.14$

27. Is $(x + 1)(2x - 3)$ the same as $2x^2 - 3$? Why or why not? *(Previous course)* No; Sample counterexample: If $x = -1$, $(x + 1)(2x - 3) = 0$, but $2x^2 - 3 = -1$.

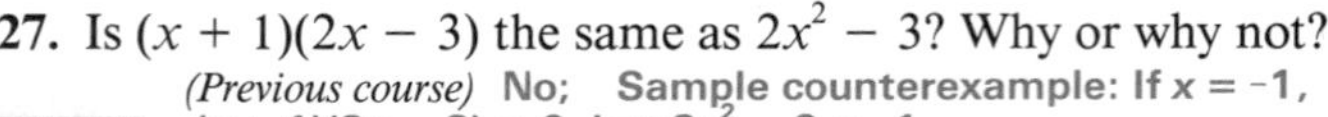

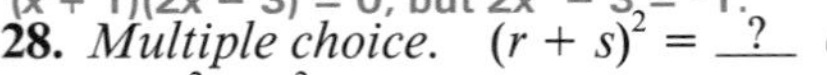

28. *Multiple choice.* $(r + s)^2 =$ _?_ c
(a) $r^2 + s^2$ (b) $r^2 + rs + s^2$
(c) $r^2 + 2rs + s^2$ (d) none of these
(Previous course)

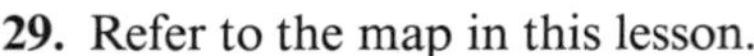

29. Refer to the map in this lesson.
a. What average speed did the map makers assume in the trip from Shreveport, LA, to Jackson, MS? ≈ 63 mph
b. What average speed is assumed in the trip from Shreveport, LA, to Little Rock, AR? ≈ 55 mph
c. What conditions could account for the different rates? *(Previous course)*
Sample: one route has more stops or slower speed limits.

Shown is the River Rose cruising down the Red River in Shreveport, Louisiana.

Exploration

30. If your school has one building, estimate the perimeter of that building. If your school has more than one building, estimate the perimeter of the largest building.
Answers will vary from school to school.

Adapting to Individual Needs

English Language Development
Very often the phrase "distance around" is used to describe the perimeter of a figure. Students with limited English proficiency might associate "around" with a circle. Have a students walk around the perimeter of the classroom and explain that the distance he or she walked is the "distance around" or the perimeter of the room. Explain that the distance around a polygon is its perimeter.

Challenge
1. A blanket was folded in half three times so that it fit snugly in a box that was 16 inches by 24 inches. What were the original dimensions of the blanket? [64 in. by 48 in.]
2. All angles in the figure at the right are right angles. When asked to find the perimeter of the figure, a student said there was not enough information. Explain whether or not the student was correct.

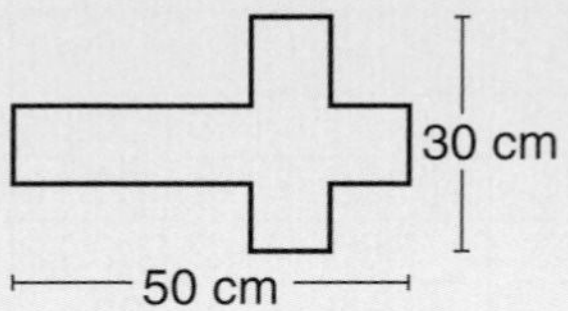

[The student was incorrect. The perimeter of the figure is 160 cm, the same as a rectangle that is 50 cm by 30 cm. The given dimensions are used, and the perimeter is found by adding up the lengths of all the sides.]

LESSON

8-2

Fundamental Properties of Area

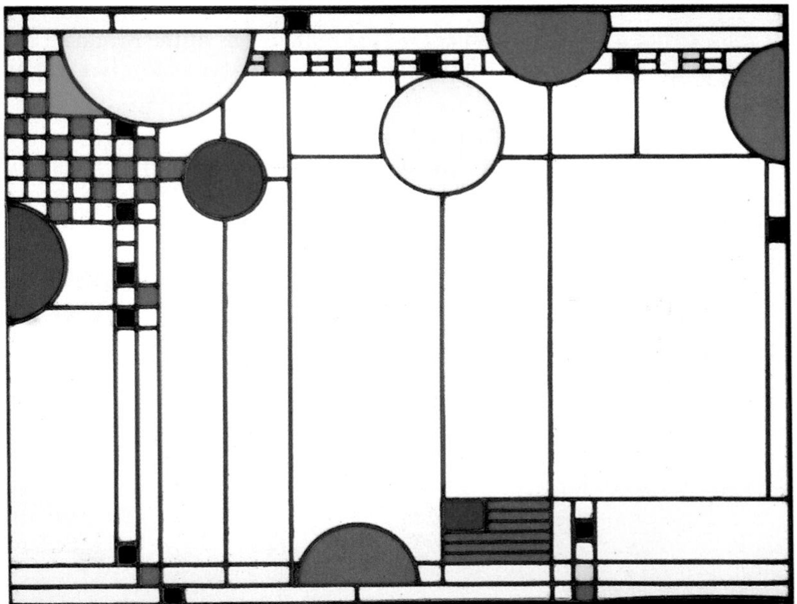

The Wright Way. *Frank Lloyd Wright (1867–1959) designed windows and furniture as well as buildings for which he is famous. He was conscious of area and lights as demonstrated by this center window of a stained-glass window triptych.*

What Is Area?

Area is a measure of the space covered by a two-dimensional region. The region may be small, like a microchip in a computer, or it may be large, like a country. The idea of area is the same. Tessellate the region with a fundamental region. Then count the number of copies of the fundamental region needed to cover the region. That count is the area.

Usually, the fundamental region is a square, and so we say that area is measured in **square units.** For instance, the rectangular region below at the left has dimensions 11 units and 8 units. Its area is 88 square units because 88 unit squares cover the region.

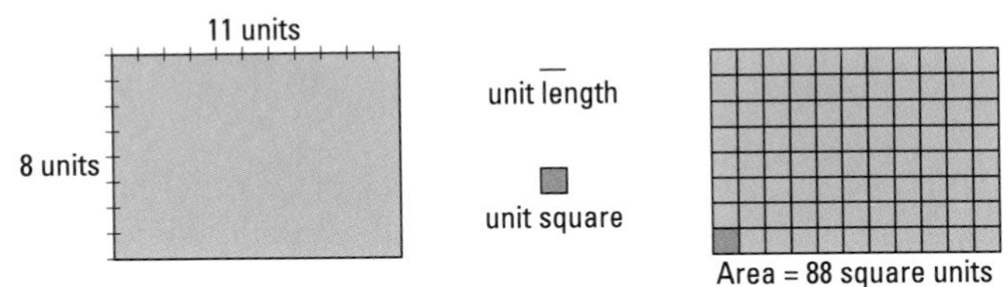

Lesson 8-2

Objectives

C Calculate areas of squares and rectangles given relevant lengths of sides, and vice versa.

G Relate various formulas for area.

I Apply formulas for areas of squares and rectangles to real-world situations.

K Determine the areas of polygons on a coordinate plane.

Resources

From the ***Teacher's Resource File***

- Lesson Master 8-2A or 8-2B
- Answer Master 8-2
- Teaching Aids
  - 101 Warm-up
  - 105 Graph Paper
  - 106 Additional Examples
- Activity Kit, Activity 18

Additional Resources

- Visuals for Teaching Aids 101, 105–106

Teaching Lesson 8-2

Warm-up

Only two noncongruent rectangles with dimensions that are whole numbers have the same number of units in their perimeter as the number of square units in their area. Can you find these dimensions? **4 units by 4 units and 6 units by 3 units**

Lesson 8-2 Overview

Broad Goals This lesson introduces the properties of area. These properties are applied in the remainder of the chapter to determine or estimate areas for any plane region and to deduce area formulas for the common plane figures.

Perspective To find the area of a region, we cover the region with a tessellation. One can think of the area as the number of copies of the fundamental region needed.

Although the fundamental region is almost always a square, it need not be a square. For example, suppose a wall is to be covered with a mosaic of congruent tiles. A measure of the area of a wall is the number of tiles required to cover the wall. A measure of the area of a floor can be the number of tiles needed to cover the floor. A measure of the area of a sports field can be the number of pieces of sod needed to cover it.

We also may measure with non-space-filling objects. For example, a measure (not area) of a piece of steel could be the number of bolts that can be made from it. If oranges are to be packed in a box, a measure of the bottom of the box is the number of oranges that can cover the bottom of the box.

(Overview continues on page 442.)

Notes on Reading

Since all students will have seen the area formula for a rectangle, it is clear that this lesson has other goals. The primary goal is to prepare students for the next few lessons. Emphasize that *all* area formulas are derived from the four properties of this lesson.

❶ Some parts of the Area Postulate may not be so obvious to students. Consider the Rectangle Formula. Suppose the dimensions of a rectangle are $\sqrt{2}$ by $\sqrt{3}$ units. Is it true that the area is $\sqrt{2} \cdot \sqrt{3}$, or $\sqrt{6}$ square units? How could this be verified? [Estimate by decimals.] Piaget has shown that the Additive Property of Area is not inherent from birth. Young children often think that altering the arrangement of the pieces alters the amount as well. The postulate is obvious to us because we have encountered these ideas before.

❷ Point out how the parts of the Area Postulate are used in **Example 1.** All the parts are mentioned except the Uniqueness Property, which is implicit in the phrase "... the area of the house." If there were more than one area, we could not speak of *the* area.

Most teachers of UCSMP *Geometry* like the emphasis put on units in student answers. Part of the purpose of using various units in problems (**Example 2** and **Question 15**, for example) is to alert students to the importance of paying attention to units. This is something students must be aware of outside of school as well.

Have students record the results of the **Activity** for use with **Question 5** on page 445.

2.5 km

1.5 km

Many plowed fields like these in the Midwest are rectangular.

Fundamental Properties of Area

Whenever the dimensions of the rectangle are integers, the unit squares will fit exactly. But suppose a farm is a rectangular region, 1.5 kilometers by 2.5 kilometers, as shown here.

One way to find the area of the farm is shown by the figures below. First, pick a unit. Here the natural unit is 1 square kilometer. Then split the farm region into square kilometers. There are two whole-square kilometers, three half-square kilometers, and one quarter-square kilometer. Think of putting them end to end. The result is 3.75 square kilometers. This is exactly what you get by multiplying 1.5 kilometers by 2.5 kilometers.

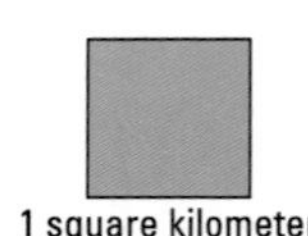

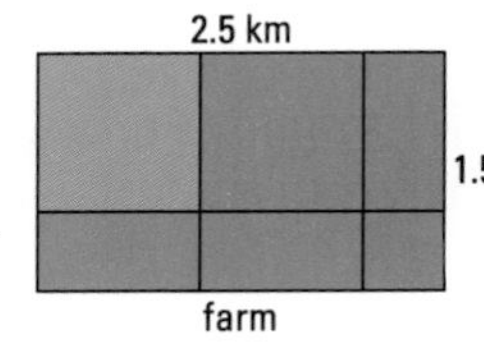

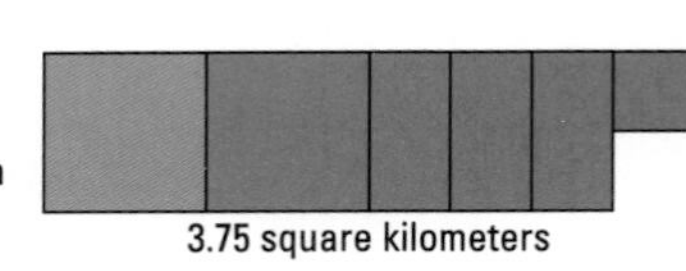

This one situation illustrates the four fundamental properties of area which we assume.

❶ **Area Postulate**

a. Uniqueness Property Given a unit region, every polygonal region has a unique area.

b. Rectangle Formula The area A of a rectangle with dimensions ℓ and w is ℓw. ($A = \ell w$)

c. Congruence Property Congruent figures have the same area.

d. Additive Property The area of the union of two nonoverlapping regions is the sum of the areas of the regions.

Activity

Measure to determine the area of rectangle $WXYZ$

a. in square centimeters. 10 cm²

b. in square millimeters. 1000 mm²

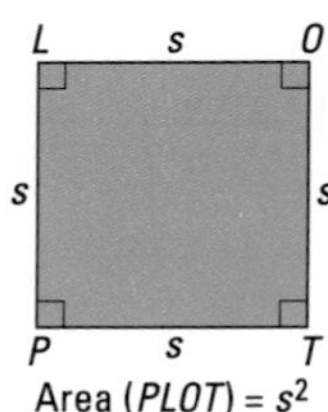

Area ($PLOT$) = s^2

From the Area Postulate, other properties of area can be deduced. For instance, a special case of the Rectangle Formula is that a formula for the area of any square with side s is $A = s^2$. This is pictured at the left.

Lesson 8-2 Overview, continued

The square region fulfills the need for an easy-to-use unit for area, one that does not overlap and which will fill or can be cut to fill many regions. Because a tessellation of square regions is customarily used to measure area, we say that area is measured in "square units."

Since we do not have to tessellate with squares to find area, we could ask, "How many rectangles of this size can fit in a region?" That question would be appropriate if there were a sheet of material out of which rectangles were to be made. It is related to the question, "How many scarfs can be made from this bolt of silk?"

The fundamental properties of area are similar to those for angle measure and distance that students have seen in earlier chapters. The Uniqueness Property guarantees that the answers will not be ambiguous. The Congruence Property essentially says that area remains uniform throughout the plane. The Rectangle Formula gives us a starting point for calculating the areas, just as the distance formula did for lengths and the number 180° did for angles. The Additive Property allows us to calculate the areas of unions of nonoverlapping figures, just as Angle Addition did for some angles and the Betweenness Property did for lengths.

The Uniqueness Property guarantees that a figure F can have only one area. Sometimes we write **Area(F)** for the area of the figure F. With this notation, the Congruence Property of Area becomes: If $F \cong G$, then Area(F) = Area(G). **Nonoverlapping** regions means regions that do not share interior points. They may share boundaries, as in the drawing below. The Additive Property of Area becomes: If F and G do not overlap, then Area $(F \cup G)$ = Area (F) + Area(G).

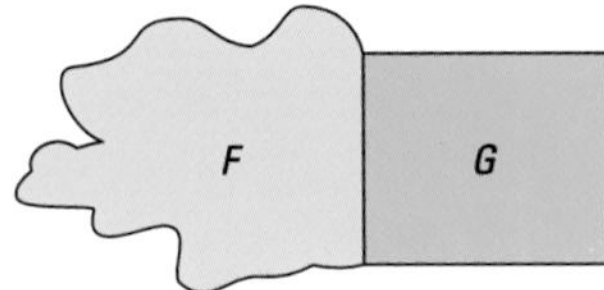

Area $(F \cup G)$ = Area (F) + Area (G)

Notice that the perimeter of $F \cup G$ does *not* equal the sum of the perimeters of F and G, where the common border is counted twice.

2 All the fundamental properties of area are used in Example 1.

Example 1

The floor plan of a ranch house is drawn on a coordinate system.
a. Find the dimensions of rooms I, II, and III if the unit is 1 foot.
b. Find the floor area of the house.

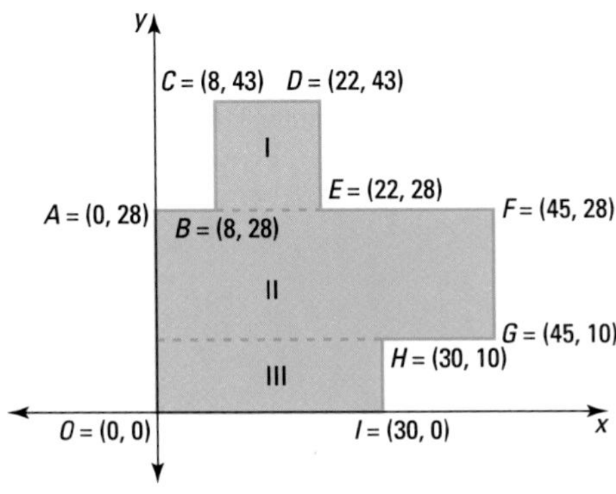

Solution

a. The Uniqueness and Congruence properties assure us that regions I, II, and III have areas that are unique and constant. I, II, and III are rectangles. The horizontal dimensions are found by subtracting appropriate pairs of the x-coordinates of the vertices. For example, $CD = |22 - 8| = 14$. The vertical dimensions are found by subtracting the y-coordinates of the vertices. For example,

$$BC = |28 - 43| = 15.$$

Dimensions of room I: CD = 14 ft and BC = 15 ft
Dimensions of room II: AF = 45 ft and FG = 18 ft
Dimensions of room III: OI = 30 ft and HI = 10 ft

▶

Art Connection Frank Lloyd Wright, one of America's most creative and influential architects, used stained glass in many of his buildings. He created the window pictured at the beginning of this lesson, *Window Triptych from the Avery Coonley Playhouse,* in 1912. The window is now displayed at the Art Institute of Chicago.

Additional Examples

These examples are also given on **Teaching Aid 106.**

1. Find the area of the region shown below. 1,089 square units

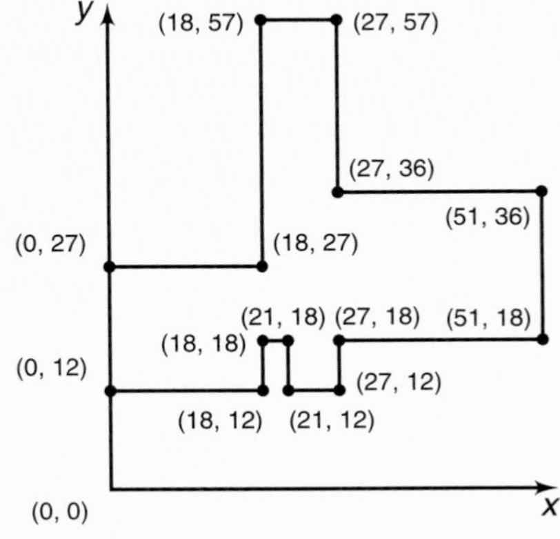

2. A playground is 50 yards by 100 yards. If a roll of sod that is 72 inches long and 18 inches wide costs $1.59, about how much will it cost to sod the field? $7,950

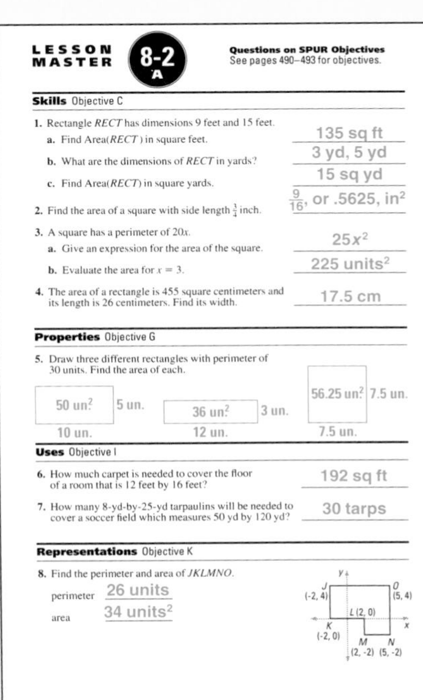

LESSON MASTER 8-2 A

Questions on SPUR Objectives
See pages 490–493 for objectives.

Skills Objective C

1. Rectangle *RECT* has dimensions 9 feet and 15 feet.
   a. Find Area(*RECT*) in square feet. 135 sq ft
   b. What are the dimensions of *RECT* in yards? 3 yd, 5 yd
   c. Find Area(*RECT*) in square yards. 15 sq yd
2. Find the area of a square with side length $\frac{3}{4}$ inch. $\frac{9}{16}$, or .5625, in^2
3. A square has a perimeter of $20x$.
   a. Give an expression for the area of the square. $25x^2$
   b. Evaluate the area for $x = 3$. 225 units^2
4. The area of a rectangle is 455 square centimeters and its length is 26 centimeters. Find its width. 17.5 cm

Properties Objective G

5. Draw three different rectangles with perimeter of 30 units. Find the area of each.

50 un^2 5 un. 10 un.
36 un^2 3 un. 12 un.
56.25 un^2 7.5 un. 7.5 un.

Uses Objective I

6. How much carpet is needed to cover the floor of a room that is 12 feet by 16 feet? 192 sq ft
7. How many 8-yd-by-25-yd tarpaulins will be needed to cover a soccer field which measures 50 yd by 120 yd? 30 tarps

Representations Objective K

8. Find the perimeter and area of *JKLMNO*.

perimeter 26 units
area 34 units^2

Optional Activities

Activity 1

Materials: Graph paper or **Teaching Aid 105**

As an extension of **Question 24**, have students make a scale drawing of the floor plan of their house and approximate its floor area. Suggest that they make their drawing on graph paper or use **Teaching Aid 105.**

Activity 2

You may want to use *Activity Kit, Activity 18,* as a follow-up to this lesson, or as a lead-in to Lessons 8-4 and 8-5. In this activity, students cut and rearrange pieces of polygons to derive area formulas.

Notes on Questions

Question 4 Allow various ways to find the area.

Question 6 You might want to survey the students. Ask: How many added to get the answer? How many subtracted?

Question 9 This question continues to develop the notion of building from the specific to the general.

Question 10 Some students may not see that the answer is the whole minus a part.

Question 12 Ask students to generalize these examples. [If the area of a square is A, then the square has sides of length $\sqrt{A}$.]

(Notes on Questions continue on page 446.)

b. By the Rectangle Formula:

$$\text{Area(I)} = 15 \text{ ft} \cdot 14 \text{ ft} = 210 \text{ sq ft}$$
$$\text{Area(II)} = 18 \text{ ft} \cdot 45 \text{ ft} = 810 \text{ sq ft}$$
$$\text{Area(III)} = 10 \text{ ft} \cdot 30 \text{ ft} = 300 \text{ sq ft}$$

By the Additive Property of Area, the area of the house is the sum of the areas of rooms I, II, and III.

$$\text{Area(floor)} = 210 + 810 + 300 \text{ sq ft} = 1320 \text{ sq ft}$$

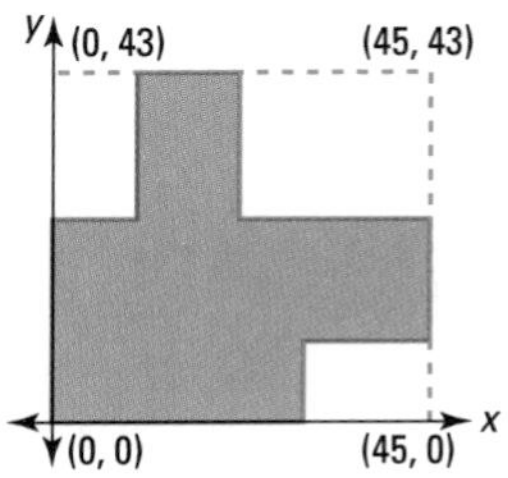

Check

One way to check is to consider the rectangle with vertices (0, 0), (45, 0), (45, 43), and (0, 43). This rectangle has area 43 · 45, or 1935 sq ft. It includes the entire floor plan plus rectangles in three corners. The sum of the areas of those corner rectangles subtracted from 1935 sq ft should give you the same answer as above.

y (0, 43) (45, 43) (0, 0) (45, 0) x

Example 2 describes a common problem involving area.

Example 2

A carpet dealer advertises a particular carpet for $18.95 a square yard. How much will it cost to carpet a rectangular room 9 feet wide and 12 feet long?

Solution

In doing calculations like these, it helps to keep track of the units. The unit "dollars per square yard" is written as $\frac{\$}{\text{yd}^2}$.

$$\begin{aligned}\text{Total cost} &= \text{total area} \cdot \text{cost per unit area}\\ &= (9 \text{ ft} \cdot 12 \text{ ft}) \cdot 18.95 \tfrac{\$}{\text{yd}^2}\\ &= (3 \text{ yd} \cdot 4 \text{ yd}) \cdot 18.95 \tfrac{\$}{\text{yd}^2}\\ &= 12 \text{ yd}^2 \cdot 18.95 \tfrac{\$}{\text{yd}^2}\\ &= \$227.40\end{aligned}$$

This cost does not include tax and any other charges such as padding or installation.

Example 2 could have been worked out in feet and square feet. Then you would need to realize that since 1 yard = 3 feet,

$$1 \text{ yard}^2 = (3 \text{ feet})^2 = 9 \text{ feet}^2.$$

That is, there are 9 square feet in 1 square yard, as pictured below.

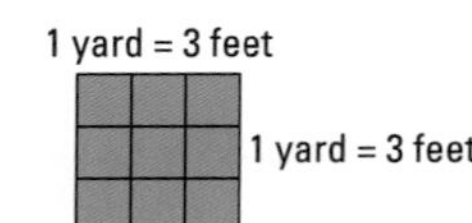

1 square yard = 9 square feet

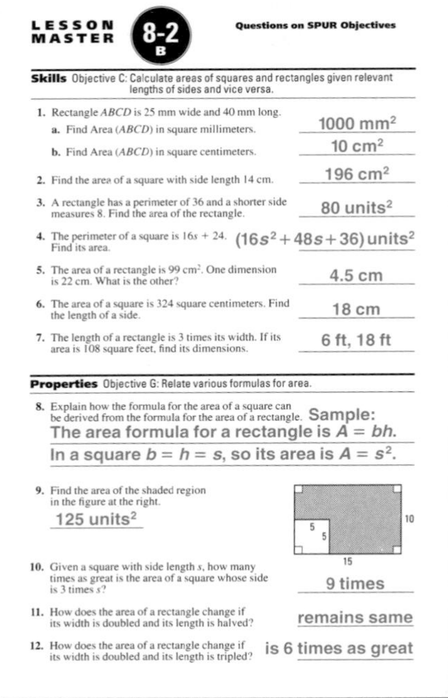

LESSON MASTER 8-2 B — Questions on SPUR Objectives

Skills Objective C: Calculate areas of squares and rectangles given relevant lengths of sides and vice versa.

1. Rectangle $ABCD$ is 25 mm wide and 40 mm long.
   a. Find Area ($ABCD$) in square millimeters. 1000 mm^2
   b. Find Area ($ABCD$) in square centimeters. 10 cm^2
2. Find the area of a square with side length 14 cm. 196 cm^2
3. A rectangle has a perimeter of 36 and a shorter side measures 8. Find the area of the rectangle. 80 units^2
4. The perimeter of a square is $16s + 24$. Find its area. $(16s^2 + 48s + 36) \text{ units}^2$
5. The area of a rectangle is 99 cm^2. One dimension is 22 cm. What is the other? 4.5 cm
6. The area of a square is 324 square centimeters. Find the length of a side. 18 cm
7. The length of a rectangle is 3 times its width. If its area is 108 square feet, find its dimensions. 6 ft, 18 ft

Properties Objective G: Relate various formulas for area.

8. Explain how the formula for the area of a square can be derived from the formula for the area of a rectangle. Sample: The area formula for a rectangle is $A = bh$. In a square $b = h = s$, so its area is $A = s^2$.
9. Find the area of the shaded region in the figure at the right. 125 units^2 (figure labels: 5, 5, 10, 15)
10. Given a square with side length s, how many times as great is the area of a square whose side is 3 times s? 9 times
11. How does the area of a rectangle change if its width is doubled and its length is halved? remains same
12. How does the area of a rectangle change if its width is doubled and its length is tripled? is 6 times as great

Adapting to Individual Needs

Extra Help

A very practical application of area is shown in **Example 2.** Nevertheless, many students do not obtain the correct area in such situations because they multiply the length and width in feet and then divide the product by 3 instead of by 9. You might draw a square that is 1 yard on each side on the chalkboard. Then show that, although 1 yard = 3 feet, 1 square yard = 9 square feet.

Challenge

Ask students to find 3 possible pairs of integers for the length and width of a rectangle with a perimeter of 64 cm. [Sample: 22 cm by 10 cm; 20 cm by 12 cm; 17 cm by 15 cm] Then ask students to determine the area of the rectangle using these 3 sets of dimensions. [Sample: 220 cm^2, 240 cm^2, 255 cm^2] Next have students find the dimensions which would maximize the area of the rectangle. [16 cm by 16 cm which gives an

4b) Answers may vary. Only two rectangular areas are subtracted from the whole area, while three or more areas have to be added.

QUESTIONS

Covering the Reading

1. Rectangle $ABCD$ has dimensions 8.3 cm and 11.4 cm.
   a. What is an appropriate unit of area in this situation? square centimeter
   b. Find Area($ABCD$). 94.62 cm^2

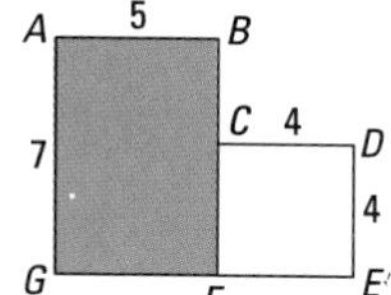

2. In the figure at the left, all of the angles are right angles. Find the area of each region.
   a. $ABFG$ 35 $units^2$
   b. $CDEF$ 16 $units^2$
   c. $ABCDEG$ 51 $units^2$
3. Which properties of area are used in answering Question 2? Uniqueness Property, Rectangle Formula, Additive Property
4. a. The outline of a floor plan of a large house is given at the right. The unit of length is one meter. Find the area of the floor. 315 m^2
   b. In part **a**, which method seems easier to you: breaking the floor into smaller rectangles and adding their areas, or surrounding the floor with one rectangle and subtracting the areas of the corner rectangles? Explain the reasons for your choice. See left.

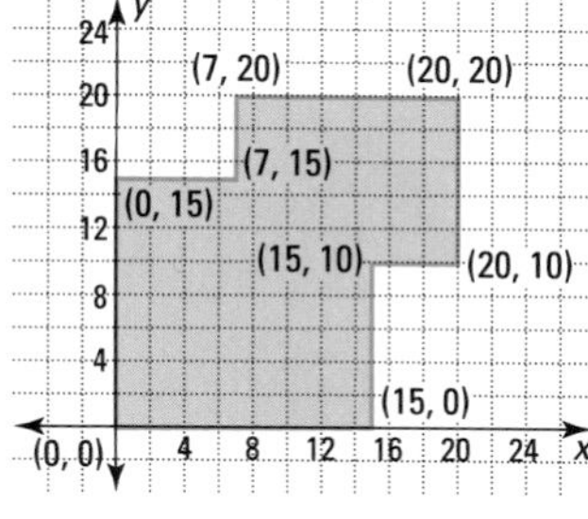

5. Give the answers to the Activity in this lesson. a) 10 cm^2; b) 1000 mm^2
6. Complete the Check in Example 1. $1935 - (15 \cdot 8 + 15 \cdot 23 + 10 \cdot 15) = 1320$; it checks.
7. A carpet store is selling a particular carpet for \$11.95 a square yard. How much will it cost to carpet a room that is 15 feet by 12 feet, before tax or any other charges? \$239
8. How many square feet are in a square yard? 9

Applying the Mathematics

9. Find the area of the polygon with the given vertices.
   a. (0, 0), (0, 10), (10, 10), (10, 0) 100 $units^2$
   b. (0, 0), (0, k), (k, k), (k, 0) k^2 $units^2$
10. At the left, $ABCD$ and $AMEN$ are squares, M is the midpoint of $\overline{AB}$, and $BC = 16$. Find Area($BCDNEM$). 192 $units^2$
11. The area of a rectangle is 50 square yards. The length of the rectangle is 100 yards. What is the width of the rectangle? $\frac{1}{2}$ yard
12. To the nearest whole unit, find the side of a square with the given area.
   a. 49 square units 7 units
   b. $\frac{3}{4}$ square unit ≈ 1 unit
   c. 200 square units ≈ 14 units
   d. 3141 square units ≈ 56 units

area of 256 cm^2] In general what type of retangle gives the greatest area for a given perimeter? [a square]

Follow-up for lesson 8-2

Practice

For more questions on SPUR Objectives, use **Lesson Master 8-2A** (shown on page 443) or **Lesson Master 8-2B** (shown on pages 444–445).

Assessment

Written Communication Have students write a paragraph describing the difference between perimeter and area. Have them include appropriate diagrams and formulas. [Students provide a clear explanation that shows they understand the difference between perimeter and area.]

Extension

A rectangular garden 40 ft by 24 ft is surrounded by a path 6 ft wide. What is the area of the path? [912 sq ft]

Project Update Project 5, *Floor Plans and Area*, on page 486, relates to the content of this lesson.

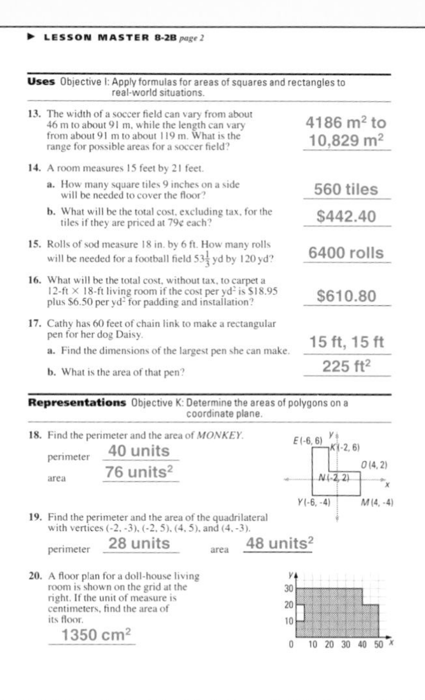

▶ **LESSON MASTER 8-2B** *page 2*

Uses Objective I: Apply formulas for areas of squares and rectangles to real-world situations.

13. The width of a soccer field can vary from about 46 m to about 91 m, while the length can vary from about 91 m to about 119 m. What is the range for possible areas for a soccer field? 4186 m^2 to 10,829 m^2
14. A room measures 15 feet by 21 feet.
    a. How many square tiles 9 inches on a side will be needed to cover the floor? 560 tiles
    b. What will be the total cost, excluding tax, for the tiles if they are priced at 79¢ each? \$442.40
15. Rolls of sod measure 18 in. by 6 ft. How many rolls will be needed for a football field $53\frac{1}{3}$ yd by 120 yd? 6400 rolls
16. What will be the total cost, without tax, to carpet a 12-ft × 18-ft living room if the cost per yd^2 is \$18.95 plus \$6.50 per yd^2 for padding and installation? \$610.80
17. Cathy has 60 feet of chain link to make a rectangular pen for her dog Daisy.
    a. Find the dimensions of the largest pen she can make. 15 ft, 15 ft
    b. What is the area of that pen? 225 ft^2

Representations Objective K: Determine the areas of polygons on a coordinate plane.

18. Find the perimeter and the area of *MONKEY*.
    perimeter 40 units
    area 76 $units^2$

    E (-6, 6) K (-2, 6) O (4, 2) N (-2, 2) Y (-6, -4) M (4, -4)
19. Find the perimeter and the area of the quadrilateral with vertices (-2, -3), (-2, 5), (4, 5), and (4, -3).
    perimeter 28 units area 48 $units^2$
20. A floor plan for a doll-house living room is shown on the grid at the right. If the unit of measure is centimeters, find the area of its floor.
    1350 cm^2

Notes on Questions

Question 13 The thinking in **parts a and b** of this question can be used by students to derive the conversion relationship in **part c** (if students have forgotten the conversion). But it is easier simply to square both sides of an equation: 12 inches = 1 foot implies that 144 square inches = 1 square foot.

Question 15 Sports Connection In the U.S., field hockey is played by more females than males, but in other countries both males and females participate.

Question 19 This is a difficult question for many students and is worth a detailed discussion.

Sports Connection The largest swimming pool in the world is the sea water Orthlieb Pool in Casablanca, Morocco. It is 1,574 feet long and 246 feet wide, and it covers an area of 8.9 acres.

Question 25 Be sure to assign this question because it illuminates the idea that numbers involved in areas are products of numbers involved in lengths and therefore can be much greater. Many students are surprised to learn that Alaska is so large. On maps it is often reduced in size so that it will fit neatly with a map of the contiguous 48 states.

13. **a.** A desk is 24″ by 12″. What is its area in square inches?
b. The same desk is 2′ by 1′. What is its area in square feet?
c. How many square inches are in a square foot?
a) 288 sq. in.; b) 2 sq ft; c) 144

14. The sides of a square are tripled.
a. What happens to its perimeter? Its perimeter is tripled.
b. What happens to its area? Its area is multiplied by 9.

15. In Olympic field hockey, the dimensions of the field are 100 yards by 60 yards. A piece of sod is 1.5 ft by 6 ft. Find the number of pieces of sod needed to cover an Olympic field-hockey field. 6000

Review

16. If a regular pentagon has perimeter 13, what is the length of a side? *(Lesson 8-1)* 2.6

17. A parallelogram has perimeter 462 cm. One side is 185 cm. Find the lengths of the other three sides. *(Lesson 8-1)* 46 cm, 46 cm, 185 cm

18. The length of one side of a rhombus is $3x$. Find its perimeter. *(Lesson 8-1)*
$12x$

19. A pool is 50 m long and 25 m wide.
a. A fence is built parallel to the sides of the pool and 10 m from each side. What is the perimeter of the fence? 230 m
b. If a park district has budgeted money for 200 meters of fencing, how far from the pool can they put the fence? *(Lesson 8-1)* 6.25 m

20. The longest side of the triangle at the right is twice as long as the shortest side. The third side is $1\frac{1}{2}$ times as long as the shortest side. If the perimeter of the triangle is 45, how long are its three sides? *(Lesson 8-1)* 10, 15, 20

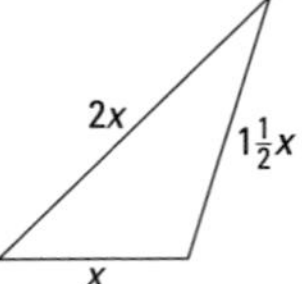

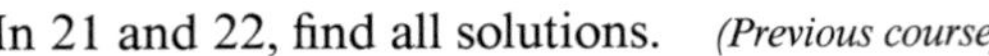

In 21 and 22, find all solutions. *(Previous course)*

21. $x^2 = 16$
$x = \pm 4$

22. $5y^2 = 240$
$y = \pm\sqrt{48} \approx \pm 6.93$

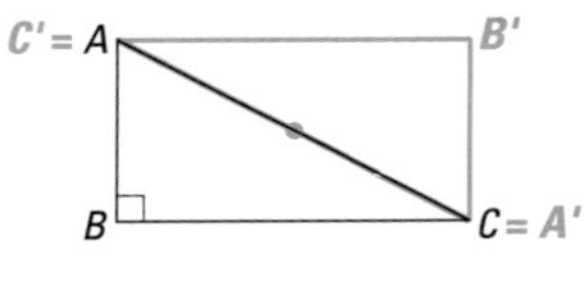

23. Trace right $\triangle ABC$ shown at the left. Draw $R(ABC) = A'B'C'$, where R is the rotation of 180° about the midpoint of the hypotenuse. What shape is $ABCB'$? *(Lesson 7-6)*
See left. $ABCB'$ is a rectangle.

Exploration

24. Find a rectangular room in your home. Calculate its area to the nearest square foot. Answers will vary.

25. In 1860, the total area of the United States was 3,021,295 square miles. By 1870, the total area had become 3,612,299 square miles. What caused such a large change?
Answers may vary. Sample: The territory purchased from Russia in 1867 later became the state of Alaska.

Setting Up Lesson 8-3

You will need a display map of the United States or **Teaching Aid 104** if you have students do *Warm-up* on page 447. You might want to have a world map if you have students discuss *English Language Development* on page 451.

LESSON

8-3

Areas of Irregular Regions

Can't top it! Can't knock it! *Not quite mile-high, Mt. Katahdin (5258 ft) is the tallest peak in Maine and clearly visible from Millinocket Lake.*

An almanac gives the total land area of the 48 contiguous states of the United States as about 2,962,000 square miles. (The other two states, Alaska and Hawaii, add about 577,000 square miles to the area.) The contiguous United States is an irregular region about 3000 miles from east to west and 1600 miles from north to south. In this lesson, you will see how areas of irregular regions can be estimated.

A Typical Example

Here is a scale drawing of Millinocket Lake in northern Maine.

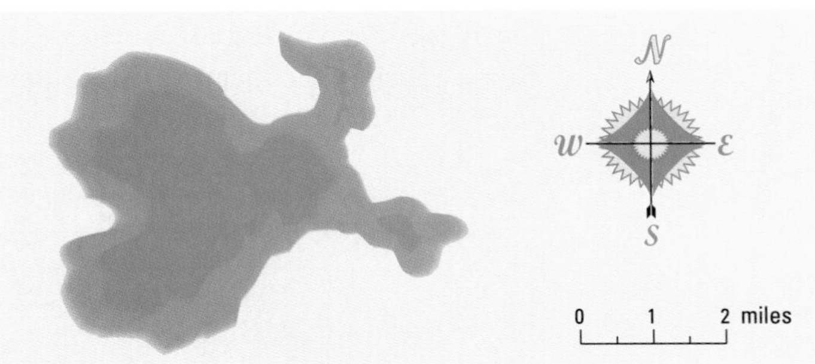

Like many shapes, the boundary of the lake is not the union of circular arcs and segments. Its shape is *irregular*. Still, it has an area; it takes up space. For all sorts of reasons, such as zoning, selling lakefront property, or tracking the fish in the lake, people might want to know its area.

Lesson 8-3

Objectives

B Describe or apply a method for determining the area of an irregularly shaped region.

Resources

From the ***Teacher's Resource File***

- Lesson Master 8-3A or 8-3B
- Answer Master 8-3
- Assessment Sourcebook: Quiz for Lessons 8-1 through 8-3
- Teaching Aids
  - 102 Warm-up
  - 104 Map of the United States
  - 105 Graph paper
  - 107 Area of Millinocket Lake and Additional Example
  - 108 Optional Activity 1 and Challenge

Additional Resources

- Visuals for Teaching Aids 102, 104–105, and 107–108

Teaching Lesson 8-3

Warm-up

A map of the United States is shown on **Teaching Aid 104.**

1. Refer to a map of the United States. Which states seem to be most nearly rectangular? Colorado and Wyoming
2. Why do most states have boundaries that are not straight lines? Often the boundaries are rivers or other bodies of water.

Lesson 8-3 Overview

Broad Goals This lesson shows students how to estimate areas of irregular regions by successive approximation with grids containing smaller and smaller squares.

Perspective One theme that permeates mathematics is the use of simple ideas to develop powerful techniques. This lesson may be simple in that it uses only counting, but its idea is basic to all considerations of area and is fundamental in calculus. In the language of limits, the area of an irregular region is the limit of $U \cdot (I + B/2)$ as U approaches 0. (We do not recommend using this as the first example with the language of limits; the idea of limits is enough here.)

The vast majority of students' experiences with areas will have been with polygons and circles. In real life, many figures do have these shapes, but many do not. This lesson is an eye-opener for many students; it shows them how to calculate areas of regions that they may never have thought possible to calculate. This lesson also points out and stresses that the concept of area is separate from its calculation.

Outside of mathematics, the word "area" sometimes means a number and sometimes it refers to a region, as in the question

(Overview continues on page 448.)

Notes on Reading

All the geographical regions mentioned in this and later lessons are actual entities. The diagram used to find the area of Millinocket Lake in the **Activity** is also shown on **Teaching Aid 107.**

It may seem unusual to study the area of irregular regions immediately after the introduction of the area concept, but in fact, this lesson provides a better context for the Area Postulate because formulas do not interfere with the ideas. Also, this approach supports the students' sense that many real-world shapes are not polygonal, but it is important to know their areas.

Students hear of the areas of geographical regions but they do not know how they are found. Point out that the process is easy and natural. Cover the region with smaller and smaller squares. Count the squares inside the region and half of those on the boundary. The reason for adding half of the boundary squares is the assumption that, on the average, about half of the boundary squares are inside the region.

Point out that the four parts of the Area Postulate are used in finding the area of a lake or other region: the region has a unique area; it is based on the areas of congruent rectangles (squares being rectangles); the area of the irregular region is estimated by adding the areas of the squares.

Many students will want exactness even when the situation does not call for it. They will argue whether a square is on the boundary, completely inside the figure, or completely outside the figure. Emphasize that what is being obtained is an estimate and that, in a practical situation, if one wanted more accuracy, one would use smaller squares. *Allow leeway in answers.*

To get a first approximation, you can draw a rectangle around the lake.

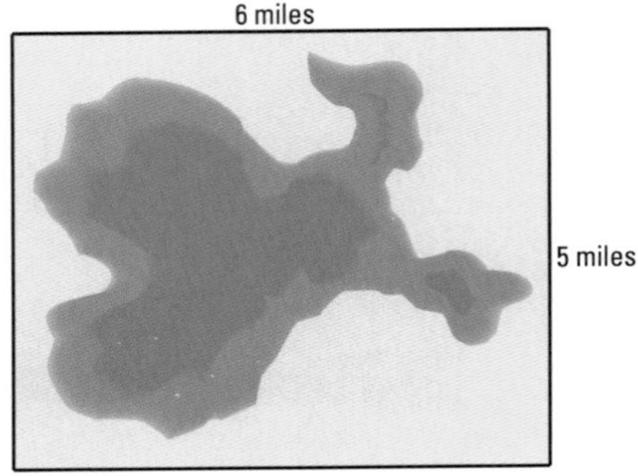

The area of the lake is less than the area of the rectangle, which is 6 miles · 5 miles. That is, the area of the lake is less than 30 square miles.

To get a better estimate, you might cover the lake with part of a tessellation of congruent squares. Here the squares are 1 mile on a side.

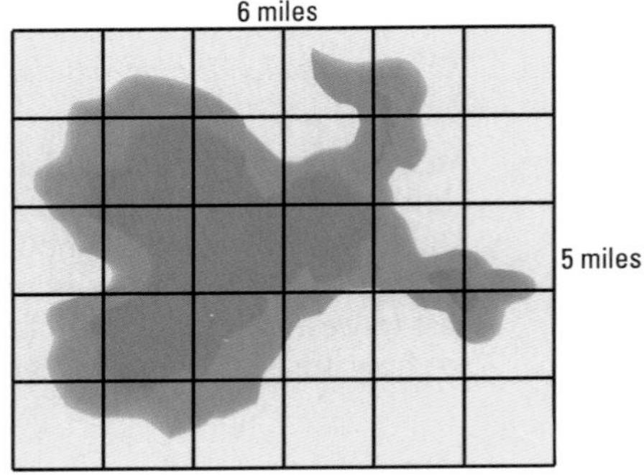

The squares above are too big to estimate the lake's area accurately. Within every square you would have to estimate how much of the square is covered by the lake. Smaller squares give a more accurate estimate. Below, the squares used are $\frac{1}{2}$ mile on a side.

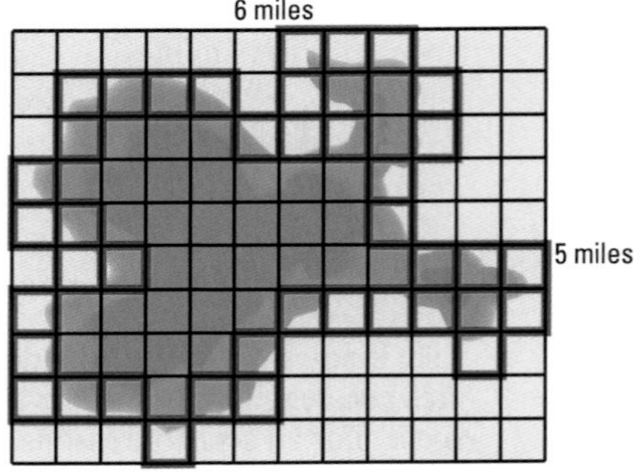

Lesson 8-3 Overview, continued

"What area do you live in?" We try in UCSMP materials to restrict the use of the word area to its numerical meaning, and we encourage teachers to practice the same restriction in the classroom so as to clarify when the number is being discussed. (Do not penalize students for using area in both ways, however, since using "area" for "region" is not incorrect outside the classroom.)

Optional Activities

Activity 1
Materials: **Teaching Aid 108**

After discussing **Question 23**, explain that Pick's Theorem gives the area of figures on a typical geoboard. Then you might give an outline of the proof of this theorem. The diagram in **Question 23** is on **Teaching Aid 108,** but the figure at the right has a unit square drawn around each point of the lattice with that point as the center.

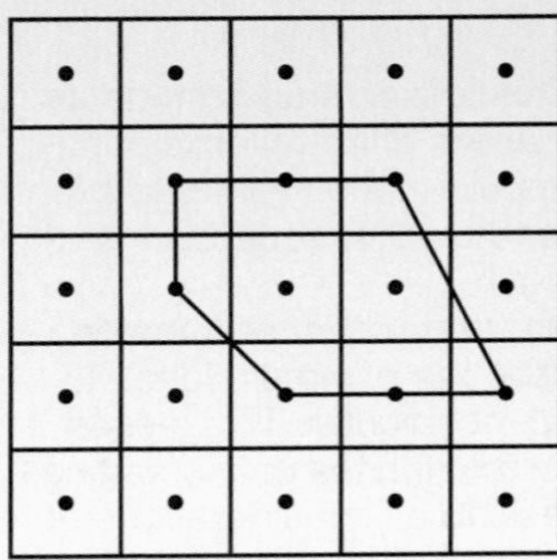

Computing the Area

The idea now is to count the number of small squares entirely inside the lake in the last figure on page 448. (There are 34.) Then count the number of squares partially covering the lake. (You should get 41). They are drawn with bold red edges. Instead of trying to estimate how much of each square is inside and then adding the fractions, it is easier to assume that, on average, half of each partly covered square is inside. So add *half* the second number to the first. $34 + \frac{41}{2} = 34 + 20.5 = 54.5$.

An estimate for the area of Millinocket Lake is 54.5 of these squares. Since each small square is $\frac{1}{2}$ mile on a side, the area of each small square is $\frac{1}{4}$ square mile, so an estimated area of the lake is $54.5 \cdot \frac{1}{4}$ square mile, or about 13.6 square miles.

In general, if I is the number of inside squares, B is the number of boundary squares, and U is the area of a single square, then an estimate for the total area is $(I + \frac{1}{2}B) \cdot U$.

Caution: When calculating area this way, do not spend too much time deciding whether a square is entirely inside or on the boundary. Your answer will always be an estimate, so do not search for an exact answer.

To get a closer estimate, use a grid with smaller squares. Then U is smaller. In the activity below, the sides of the squares are half the length of those above, so each side is $\frac{1}{4}$ mile and $U = \frac{1}{16}$ square mile. We have identified those squares that lie on the boundary.

Activity

Use this grid to estimate the area of the lake. Sample: $I = 170$, $B = 75$, so area is about 12.97 mi^2

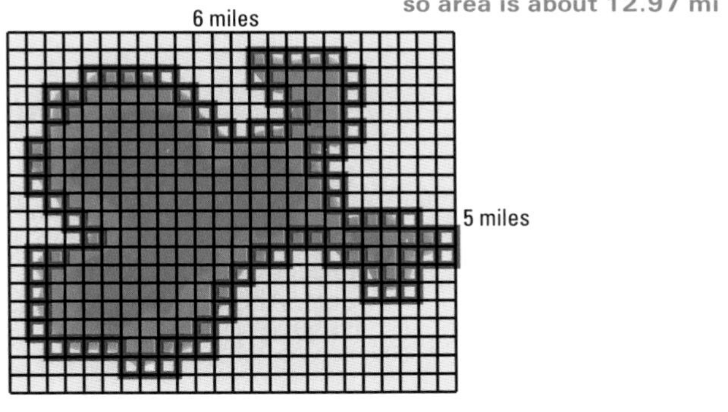

The above procedure can be continued using finer and finer grids. The estimates can be made to differ from the actual area by no more than 0.1 square mile, 0.01 square mile, or even less. When smaller and smaller squares are used, we say that the true area of the lake is the *limit* which the estimates approach. According to the Maine Department of Natural Resources, the official area of Millinocket Lake is 12.34 square miles.

Have students record the results of the **Activity** for use with **Question 4** on page 450.

Additional Examples

You might want to use this additional example when discussing the lesson. This example is also given on **Teaching Aid 107.**

Find the area of this lake by counting squares entirely inside and partially covering the lake. Assume each square is $\frac{1}{4}$ mi by $\frac{1}{4}$ mi.

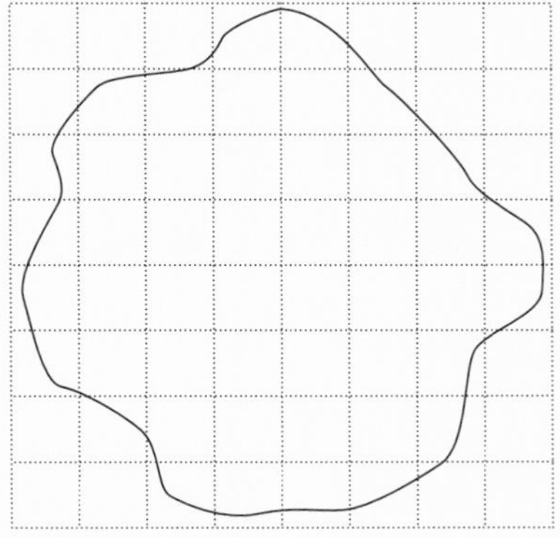

About 2.3 sq mi

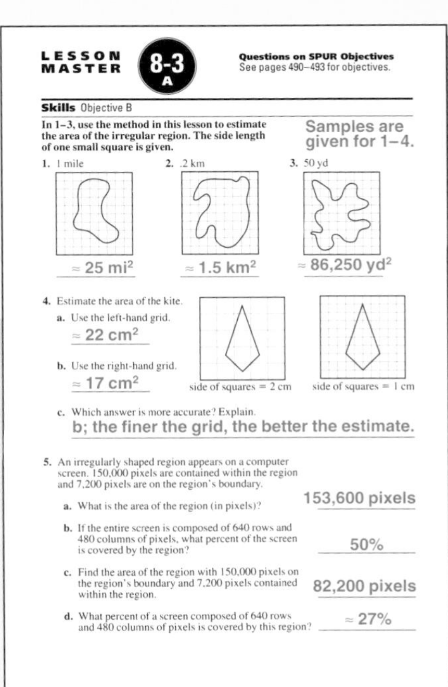

LESSON MASTER 8-3 A

Questions on SPUR Objectives
See pages 490–493 for objectives.

Skills Objective B

In 1–3, use the method in this lesson to estimate the area of the irregular region. The side length of one small square is given.

Samples are given for 1–4.

1. 1 mile — ≈ 25 mi²
2. .2 km — ≈ 1.5 km²
3. 50 yd — ≈ 86,250 yd²

4. Estimate the area of the kite.
a. Use the left-hand grid. ≈ 22 cm²
b. Use the right-hand grid. ≈ 17 cm²

side of squares = 2 cm   side of squares = 1 cm

c. Which answer is more accurate? Explain.
b; the finer the grid, the better the estimate.

5. An irregularly shaped region appears on a computer screen. 150,000 pixels are contained within the region and 7,200 pixels are on the region's boundary.
a. What is the area of the region (in pixels)? 153,600 pixels
b. If the entire screen is composed of 640 rows and 480 columns of pixels, what percent of the screen is covered by the region? 50%
c. Find the area of the region with 150,000 pixels on the region's boundary and 7,200 pixels contained within the region. 82,200 pixels
d. What percent of a screen composed of 640 rows and 480 columns of pixels is covered by this region? ≈ 27%

a. The interior points are one of two kinds: either the square lies entirely inside the figure or it overlaps an edge. It can be shown that for any region of the square outside the figure, there is a congruent region elsewhere along the same edge inside the figure but not part of any square. Hence, each interior point corresponds to one square region. That gives the I in the formula.

b. The points on the boundary are of two types: those at endpoints and those between endpoints. It can be shown that each point between endpoints separates the square around it in half; hence, for each of those points $\frac{1}{2}$ is added to the area. That gives the $\frac{1}{2}P$ in the formula.

(Optional Activities continue on page 450.)

Notes on Questions

Question 4 The change in the estimate from the grid on page 448 to the grid in the **Activity** on page 449 is from 13.6 square miles to 12.97 square miles. If the latter value is correct, then the previous estimate is off by about 5%. If the purpose of estimation is to determine how much water is available for migrating ducks, would the first estimate be adequate? [Yes]

Questions 8–9 These questions give students opportunities to use the approximation method to estimate areas. You might ask students to do these questions first individually and then compare their results with those of other students. In **Question 8,** you might also ask students which estimate is better.

Questions 10–12 The unit of area called the acre is confusing to many students, because they do not see the "square." In fact, unlike a square mile or square centimeter, an acre does not have a particular shape. It is defined purely by its conversion factor. The equivalent metric unit is the *hectare*, equal to 10,000 square meters. A hectare is 1000 *ares*, a unit whose singular is spelled exactly like the verb "are," and so is seldom used in English. One hectare ≈ 2.47 acres.

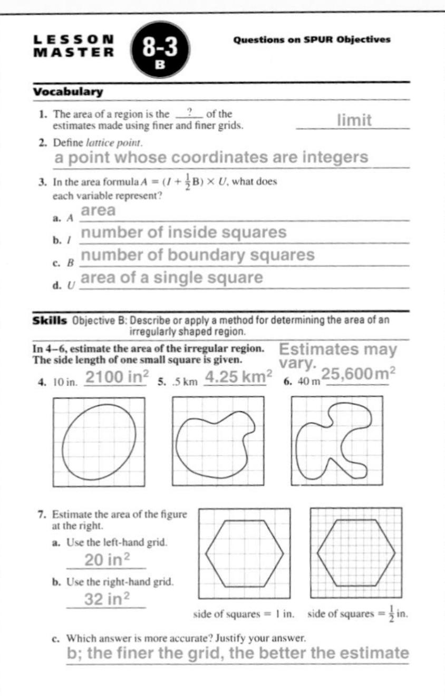

LESSON MASTER 8-3 B — Questions on SPUR Objectives

Vocabulary

1. The area of a region is the __?__ of the estimates made using finer and finer grids. limit
2. Define *lattice point*. a point whose coordinates are integers
3. In the area formula $A = (I + \frac{1}{2}B) \times U$, what does each variable represent?
   a. A area
   b. I number of inside squares
   c. B number of boundary squares
   d. U area of a single square

Skills Objective B: Describe or apply a method for determining the area of an irregularly shaped region.

In 4–6, estimate the area of the irregular region. The side length of one small square is given. Estimates may vary.

4. 10 in. 2100 in^2 5. .5 km 4.25 km^2 6. 40 m $25{,}600\text{m}^2$

7. Estimate the area of the figure at the right.
   a. Use the left-hand grid. 20 in^2
   b. Use the right-hand grid. 32 in^2
   side of squares = 1 in. side of squares = $\frac{1}{2}$ in.
   c. Which answer is more accurate? Justify your answer. b; the finer the grid, the better the estimate

The advantage of this method is that it works for any reasonably smooth curve. This same idea is used in calculus to calculate areas bounded by curves. Although it takes a long time to figure out areas in this way with pencil and paper, the method can be programmed on a computer. Also, when the curve can be described by an equation, there may exist a simple formula for its area.

QUESTIONS

Covering the Reading

1. Three tessellations of squares are used in this lesson to estimate the area of a lake. What is the area of an individual square
   a. in the first tessellation? 1 square mile
   b. in the second tessellation? $\frac{1}{4}$ square mile
   c. in the finest tessellation? $\frac{1}{16}$ square mile

2. Give three reasons people might have for estimating the area of a lake.
   Samples: for zoning, selling lakefront property, tracking fish

3. Suppose E is the number of squares entirely inside a region and P is the number of squares partially inside the region. If each square has area U square units, what formula gives an estimate, in square units, for the region's area? $\left(E + \frac{P}{2}\right)U = A$

4. **a.** Was your answer to the Activity greater than or less than the estimate of 13 square miles? less than
   b. Was it greater than or less than the official area of 12.34 square miles? greater than

5. **a.** What is an advantage of the method of using grids to estimate area?
   b. What is a disadvantage?
   See left.

5a) Sample: The method works for any reasonably smooth curve.
b) Sample: It takes a long time to figure out areas by counting.

6. The area of a region is the __?__ of the estimates made using finer and finer grids. limit

Applying the Mathematics

7. Recall that the resolution of TV screens or computer monitors of different sizes can be compared by calculating the number of dots (pixels) per square inch. Some Apple Macintosh™ computer screens measure about 10″ by 7.5″. There are 640 rows and 480 columns of dots. About how many dots per square inch is this?
   4096 dots/in^2

c. Lastly, consider the squares around the vertices. The angle of the figure at each vertex is less than 180, hence each interior region is less than $\frac{1}{2}$ of the square. To show that the sum of those regions is 1 less than $\frac{1}{2}$ the number of squares: It can be shown that the pieces of square in the interior of angles at the vertices "fit" together, using corresponding angles formed by the sides crossing horizontal and vertical lines. Thus, for an n-gon, the angles "sweep" $(n - 2) \cdot 180$ degrees. Since $n \cdot 180°$ would cover $\frac{n}{2}$ squares, $(n - 2) \cdot 180°$ covers 1 less square. This provides the -1 in the formula.

8. The two figures below are congruent. The grid squares on the left are $\frac{1}{4}$ inch on a side, and the grid squares on the right are $\frac{1}{8}$ inch on a side. Estimate the area of the figure, using the given grid.

a.

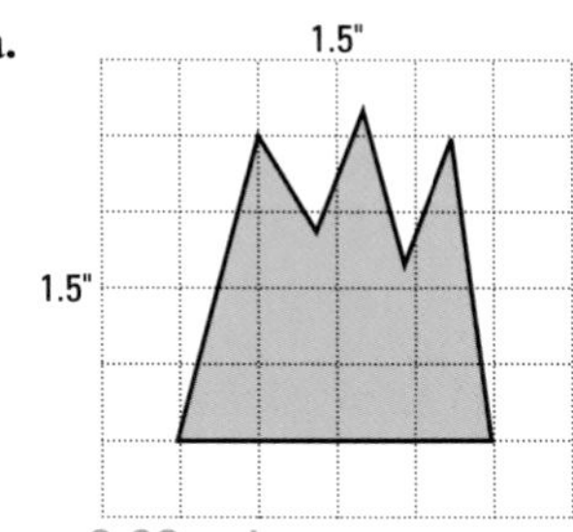

≈ 0.66 sq in.

b.

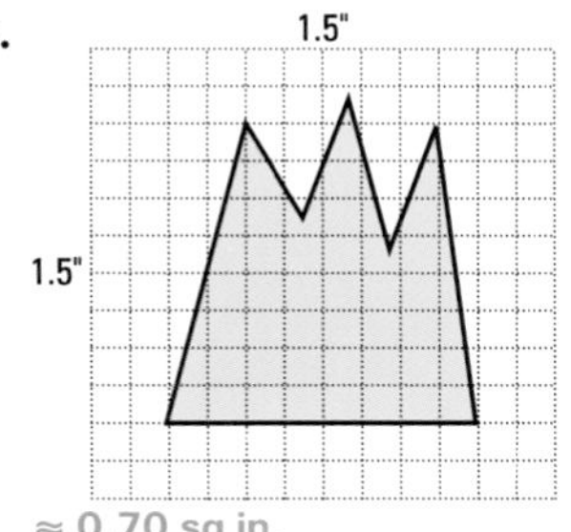

≈ 0.70 sq in.

9. At the right is a scale drawing of Wilson Reservoir in Kansas on a grid of squares each 1 km on a side. Estimate the area of the reservoir. $\approx 66.5 \text{ km}^2$

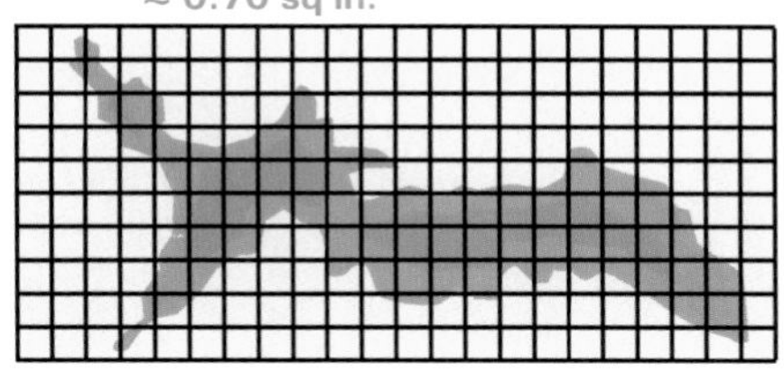

In 10–12, use this information. An *acre* is a unit of area commonly used to measure plots of land. Originally an acre was about the amount of land a farmer could plow in a day. Today an acre has an exact conversion equation: 640 acres = 1 square mile.

10. There are 5280 feet in a mile.
   a. How many square feet are in a square mile? $27{,}878{,}400 \text{ ft}^2$
   b. How many square feet are in an acre? $43{,}560 \text{ ft}^2$

11. Lake Dumont in the state of Michigan has an area of 215 acres. About what percent of a square mile is this? about 34%

12. A house is built on a rectangular half-acre lot. What might be the dimensions (in feet) of the rectangle? Sample: 242 ft by 90 ft

13. A farm in Europe has an area of 30 square kilometers. A farm in the United States has an area of 20 square miles. If 1 mile ≈ 1.6 km, which farm is bigger? the farm in the U.S.

Spanish spuds. *A farmer plows a potato field in Costa Blanca, Spain. In 1994, Spain produced 4.5 million tons of potatoes, their fourth largest crop.*

Review

14. At the right, a tilted square $EFGH$ is placed inside a square $ABCD$. *(Lessons 8-1, 8-2)*
   a. If $AB = 7$ and $HE = 5$, what is the area of the shaded region? 24 sq units
   b. If $AB = x$ and $HE = 5$, what is the area of the shaded region? $(x^2 - 25)$ sq units

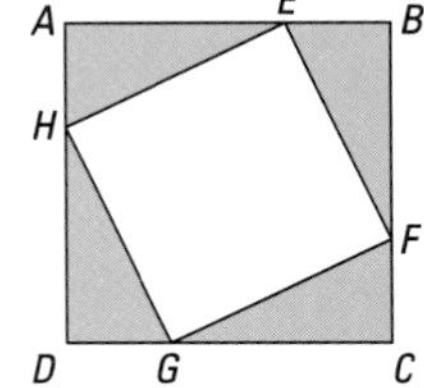

15. Suppose the sides of a rectangle are multiplied by 10. *(Lessons 8-1, 8-2)*
   a. What happens to its area? Its area is multiplied by 100.
   b. What happens to its perimeter? Its perimeter is multiplied by 10.

Multicultural Connection The term *acre* originally referred to how much land a farmer and his oxen could plow in a day. Eventually, this amount was standardized at 43,560 square feet. In other countries, however, different measures are used. In Japan it is the *cho* (≈ 2.45 acres). In Turkey, it is the *denum* (≈ 0.62 acre).

Question 12 This question has infinitely many answers; the ordered pairs of dimensions x and y lie on the hyperbola with equation $xy = 21{,}780$. You might graph these pairs; for any pair (a, b) the rectangle with vertices $(0, 0)$, $(a, 0)$, (a, b), and $(0, b)$ has the shape of the lot.

Question 14b You might want to ask students to factor $x^2 - 5^2$. $[(x + 5)(x - 5)]$

(Notes on Questions continue on page 452.)

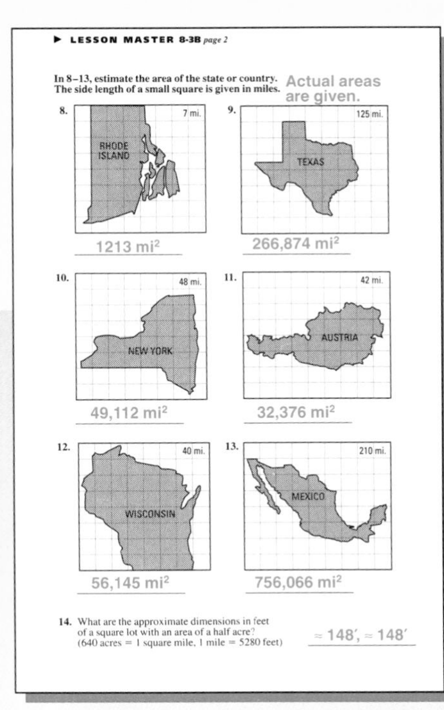

▸ **LESSON MASTER 8-3B** *page 2*

In 8–13, estimate the area of the state or country. The side length of a small square is given in miles. Actual areas are given.

8. (Rhode Island, 7 mi.) 1213 mi^2

9. (Texas, 125 mi.) $266{,}874 \text{ mi}^2$

10. (New York, 48 mi.) $49{,}112 \text{ mi}^2$

11. (Austria, 42 mi.) $32{,}376 \text{ mi}^2$

12. (Wisconsin, 40 mi.) $56{,}145 \text{ mi}^2$

13. (Mexico, 210 mi.) $756{,}066 \text{ mi}^2$

14. What are the approximate dimensions in feet of a square lot with an area of a half acre? (640 acres = 1 square mile, 1 mile = 5280 feet) ≈ 148′, ≈ 148′

Optional Activities

Activity 2

Materials: Graph paper or **Teaching Aid 105**

After discussing the lesson, you might have students estimate the area of their hand by placing it on a sheet of graph paper, outlining it, and counting squares inside and on the boundary. Determine who has the largest hand, and who has the smallest hand (in area).

Adapting to Individual Needs

English Language Development

Materials: Map of the U.S. **(Teaching Aid 104)** and/or map of the world

Explain that the word *contiguous* means adjoining. Then, on a map of the U.S. identify states that are contiguous to your state and states that are not contiguous.
If you have a world map, have non-English-speaking students identify countries, if any, that are contiguous to their native country.

Notes on Questions

Question 16 Cooperative Learning Encourage students to compare their solutions.

Question 23 A proof of Pick's Theorem is outlined in Activity 1 of *Optional Activities* on pages 448–450.

Follow-up for Lesson 8-3

Practice

For more questions on SPUR Objectives, use **Lesson Master 8-3A** (shown on page 449) or **Lesson Master 8-3B** (shown on pages 450–451).

Assessment

Quiz A quiz covering Lessons 8-1 through 8-3 is provided in the *Assessment Sourcebook.*

Written Communication Have students **work in pairs**. Have each student draw an irregular closed figure on grid paper. Then have students exchange papers and estimate the area of the figure and write an explanation of how they arrived at their answer. [Students provide a reasonable explanation to justify their answers.]

Extension

Have students find the dimensions of a square with an area of one acre. [= 209 ft on a side]

Projects Update Project 5, *Floor Plans and Area*, and Project 6, *Area of Puerto Rico*, on page 486, relate to the content of this lesson.

16. A person wishes to tile a kitchen floor with square tiles 8 inches on a side. If the kitchen measures 10 feet by 12 feet, how many tiles are needed? *(Lesson 8-2)* 270 tiles

17. A rectangle has area of 96 square units. If its width is 4 units, what is its perimeter? *(Lessons 8-1, 8-2)* 56 units

18. If the unit of the area of a figure is square kilometers, what is the natural unit for the perimeter of the figure? *(Lessons 8-1, 8-2)* kilometers

19. Use the figure at the right.

Given: $\angle PAQ \cong \angle DAR$,
$\angle PQA \cong \angle DRA$, and
$PQ = RD$.

To prove: $\triangle PAD$ is isosceles. *(Lesson 6-2)*
See margin.

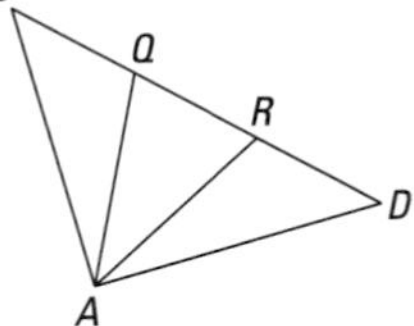

20. In $\odot O$ below, find the measures of $\overset{\frown}{AB}$, $\overset{\frown}{BC}$, and $\overset{\frown}{CA}$. *(Lesson 3-2)*
$m\overset{\frown}{AB} = 110°$, $m\overset{\frown}{BC} = 135°$, $m\overset{\frown}{CA} = 115°$

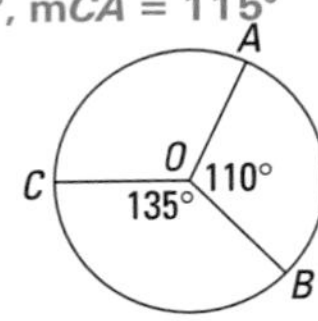

21. *True or false.* A solution to $2y^2 = 16$ is -2. *(Previous course)*
False

22. *Multiple choice.* If $\sqrt{48} = k\sqrt{3}$, what is k? *(Previous course)* a

(a) 4 (b) 16
(c) $\sqrt{45}$ (d) cannot be determined

Exploration

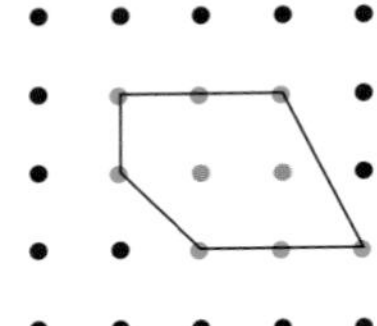

23. *Multiple choice.* A **lattice point** is a point whose coordinates are integers. When the vertices of a polygon are lattice points, there is a formula for its area. The formula is known as Pick's Theorem. Let P be the number of lattice points *on* the polygon. Let I be the number of lattice points *inside* the polygon. Use the polygon at the left and test with other polygons to answer this question: Which expression gives the polygon's area in square units? a

(a) $\frac{1}{2}P + I - 1$ (b) $\frac{1}{2}P + I$
(c) $\frac{1}{2}P + I + 1$ (d) $\frac{1}{2}(P + I)$

Adapting to Individual Needs

Challenge

Materials: **Teaching Aid 108**

Give students **Teaching Aid 108** or the figure shown at the right (without the dark segments). Have them try to find how it could be cut into exactly two pieces that can be rearranged to form a square. [See dark segments.]

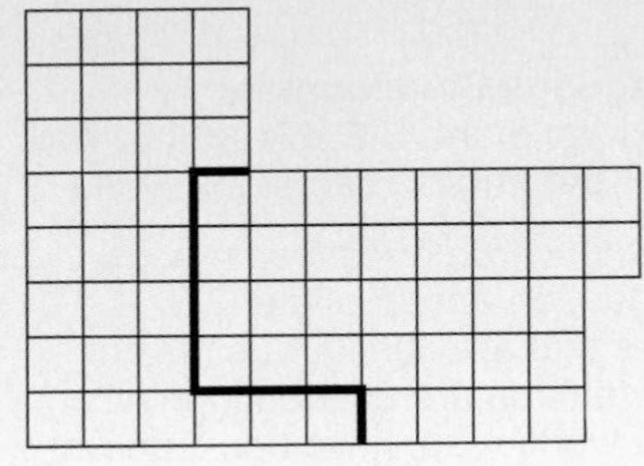

Additional Answers

19.

Conclusions	Justifications
1. $\triangle PQA \cong \triangle DRA$	AAS Congruence Thm. (given)
2. $\overline{PA} \cong \overline{DA}$	CPCF Thm
3. $\triangle PAD$ is isosceles	def. of isosceles △

LESSON

8-4

Areas of Triangles

Most of the shapes you have studied so far have been special types of polygons, not the irregular shapes considered in the last lesson. Some polygonal shapes are so common that formulas have been developed to give their areas. All of these formulas can be derived from the Rectangle Formula.

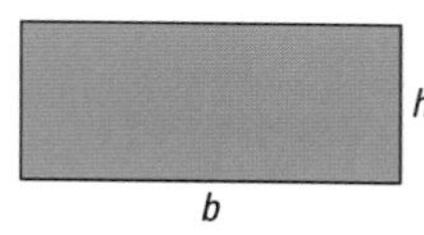

Area = *hb*

Area of a Right Triangle

It is easy to find the area of any right triangle ABC. Just rotate $\triangle ABC$ 180° about M, the midpoint of $\overline{AC}$, as you did in making a tessellation. The image is $\triangle CDA$. Since all four angles of $ABCD$ are 90° angles, $ABCD$ is a rectangle. By the Congruence and Additive Properties of the Area Postulate, the area of each triangle is half the rectangle. This argument proves the Right Triangle Area Formula.

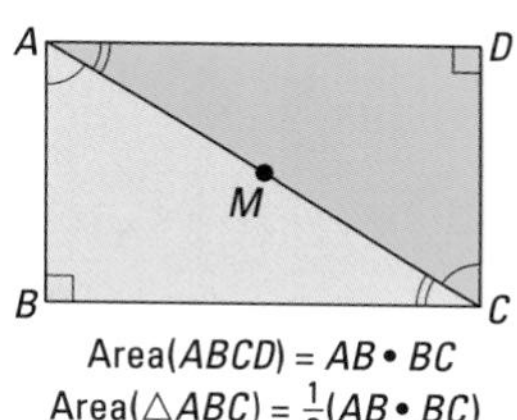

$\text{Area}(ABCD) = AB \cdot BC$
$\text{Area}(\triangle ABC) = \frac{1}{2}(AB \cdot BC)$

Right Triangle Area Formula
The area of a right triangle is half the product of the lengths of its legs.

$$A = \frac{1}{2}hb$$

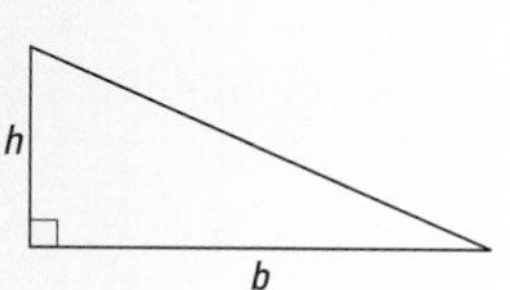

Lesson 8-4

Objectives

C Calculate areas of triangles given relevant lengths of sides, and vice versa.
G Relate various formulas for area.
I Apply formulas for areas of triangles to real-world situations.
K Determine the areas of triangles on a coordinate plane.

Resources

From the ***Teacher's Resource File***
- Lesson Master 8-4A or 8-4B
- Answer Master 8-4
- Teaching Aids
  102 Warm-up
  109 Extension

Additional Resources
- Visuals for Teaching Aids 102, 109
- GeoExplorer or other automatic drawers

Teaching Lesson 8-4

Warm-up

How many right triangles can you form by connecting different sets of three points on a 3-by-3 pegboard?
44 right triangles

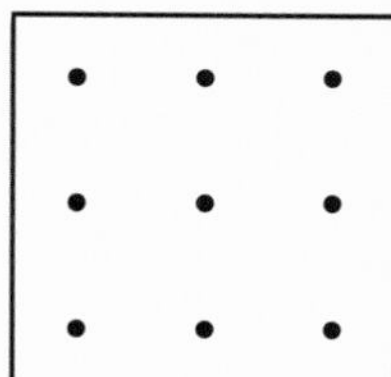

Lesson 8-4 Overview

Broad Goals From the formula for the area of a rectangle, we derive a formula for the right triangle; combining right triangles gives the formula for any triangle.

Perspective We assume that students have seen the formulas for the areas of right triangles and triangles previously. If they have not, this lesson may take more than one day.

This is a standard approach to the areas of right triangles and triangles. Students should see right triangles as halves of rectangles. They should realize that an oblique triangle can be split into two right triangles by the altitude to its longest side. They should also realize that any side of a triangle can be the base. We retain the customary b and h in the formulas because it fits well with area formulas for quadrilaterals.

Example 2 considers a triangle on a coordinate grid. This reinforces the notion of the tessellation of squares underlying the idea of area, and of the idea of square units in area. It also provides a nice algebraic setting for area.

Notes on Reading

You might emphasize that the general approach taken to the finding of the areas of triangles is quite similar to the approach taken to the solving of equations in algebra. In algebra, one reduces equations to those one can solve. In geometry, one splits up figures into those for which one knows the area.

Error Alert Although most students have seen a formula for the area of a triangle, they may make assumptions which hinder their application of it. Often the area formula is memorized as "one half the product of base and height." Tacitly, base becomes the "longest side" or "the bottom side." Students may have difficulty determining the area if the given data do not fit their idea of a base. Use the drawings in the lesson or your own drawing to show students that the base of a triangle is not necessarily the longest side or the bottom side.

For an alternate way to show that the area of a triangle is $\frac{1}{2}bh$, see Activity 1 in *Optional Activities* below.

Example 1

Find the area of $\triangle PQR$ at the right.

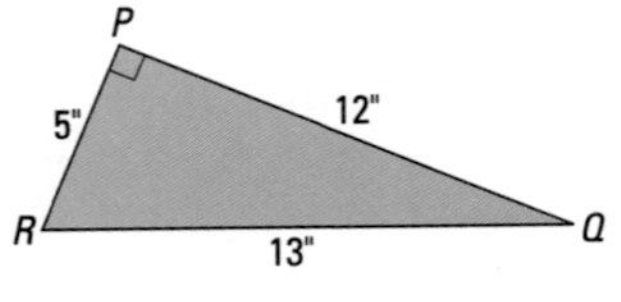

Solution

The legs of $\triangle PQR$ are 5" and 12".

So $\text{Area}(\triangle PQR) = \frac{1}{2} \cdot 5 \cdot 12 = 30 \text{ in}^2$.

Area of Any Triangle

From the area of a right triangle, a formula for the area of *any* triangle can be derived. The idea of *altitude* is needed. In a triangle, an **altitude** is the perpendicular segment from a vertex to the line containing the opposite side. In each drawing below, $\overline{AD}$ is the altitude to side $\overline{BC}$ of $\triangle ABC$. The length of an altitude is called the **height** or the **altitude** of the triangle with that base.

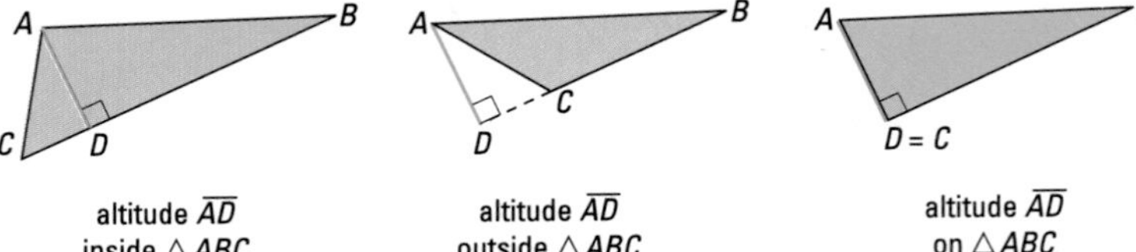

altitude $\overline{AD}$ inside $\triangle ABC$ | altitude $\overline{AD}$ outside $\triangle ABC$ | altitude $\overline{AD}$ on $\triangle ABC$

In all cases, the same simple formula for the area of the triangle can be deduced.

Triangle Area Formula

The area of a triangle is half the product of a side (the base) and the altitude (height) to that side.

$$A = \frac{1}{2}hb$$

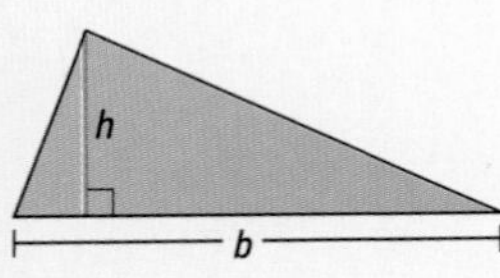

Proof:

Argument:

Case I: Altitude *inside* $\triangle ABC$

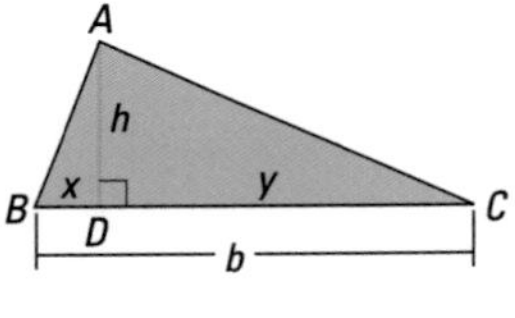

The altitude splits $\triangle ABC$ into two right triangles. Let $BD = x$ and $DC = y$. Then $b = x + y$.

$\text{Area}(\triangle ABC) = \text{Area}(\triangle ABD) + \text{Area}(\triangle ADC)$	Additive Property of Area
$= \frac{1}{2}hx + \frac{1}{2}hy$	Right Triangle Area Formula
$= \frac{1}{2}h(x + y)$	Distributive Property
$= \frac{1}{2}hb$	Substitution Property

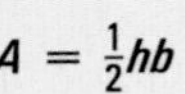

Optional Activities

Activity 1 Alternate Approach

You can use this activity as another way to show that the area of a triangle is $\frac{1}{2}bh$. Use a rectangle and triangle similar to those shown in the diagram. One dimension of the rectangle should be the base of the large triangle and the other dimension should be half the height of the large triangle. Each of the right triangles outside of the large triangle has a leg of length $\frac{h}{2}$. Each of these right triangles is congruent to a triangle in the top half of the large triangle by the AAS Congruence Theorem. Thus, the area of the rectangle is equal to the area of the triangle.

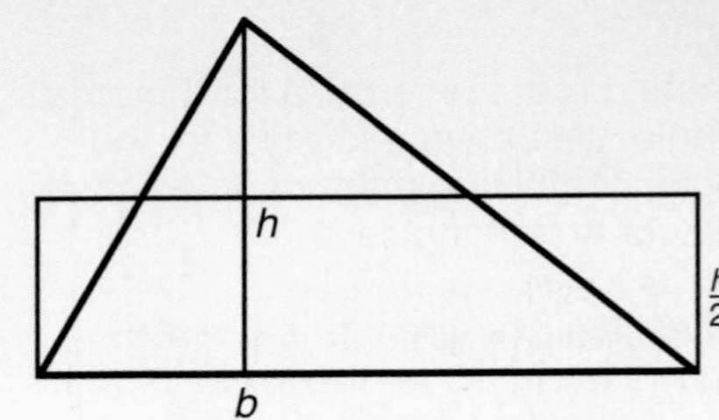

Case II: Altitude *outside* $\triangle ABC$
The area of $\triangle ABC$ can be found by subtracting the areas of two right triangles.

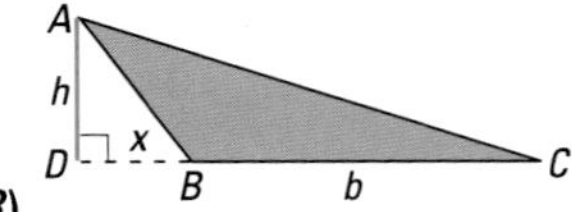

$$\begin{aligned}\text{Area}(\triangle ABC) &= \text{Area}(\triangle ADC) - \text{Area}(\triangle ADB)\\ &= \tfrac{1}{2}h(x+b) - \tfrac{1}{2}hx\\ &= \tfrac{1}{2}hx + \tfrac{1}{2}hb - \tfrac{1}{2}hx\\ &= \tfrac{1}{2}hb\end{aligned}$$

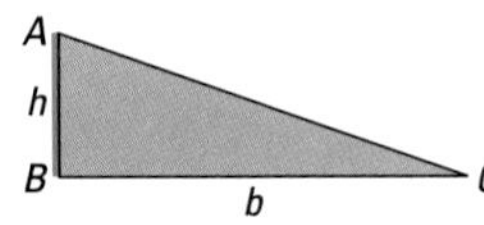

Case III: Altitude *on* $\triangle ABC$
In this case, the triangle is a right triangle, so the formula works.

When a figure is given on the coordinate plane, there is a natural unit square.

Example 2

Given coordinates as shown, find the area of
a. $\triangle ADE$...

a. $\triangle ABC$. **b.** $\triangle ADE$.
c. $\triangle ACE$. **d.** $\triangle ABE$.

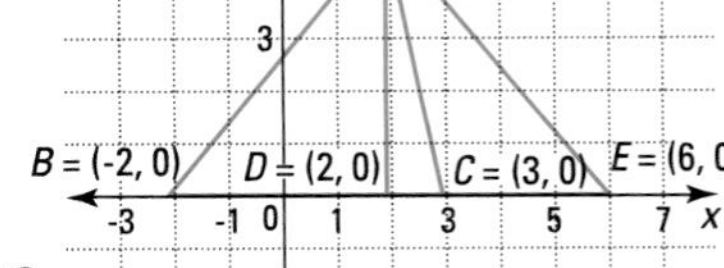

Solution

$\overline{AD}$ is the altitude of each triangle and $AD = 5$ units.

a. $\text{Area}(\triangle ABC) = \frac{1}{2} \cdot AD \cdot BC$
$= \frac{1}{2} \cdot 5 \cdot |3 - (-2)|$
$= \frac{1}{2} \cdot 5 \text{ units} \cdot 5 \text{ units}$
$= 12.5 \text{ units}^2$

b. $\text{Area}(\triangle ADE) = \frac{1}{2} \cdot AD \cdot DE$
$= \frac{1}{2} \cdot 5 \cdot |6 - 2|$
$= \frac{1}{2} \cdot 5 \text{ units} \cdot 4 \text{ units}$
$= 10 \text{ units}^2$

c. $\text{Area}(\triangle ACE) = \frac{1}{2} \cdot AD \cdot CE$
$= \frac{1}{2} \cdot 5 \cdot |6 - 3|$
$= \frac{1}{2} \cdot 5 \text{ units} \cdot 3 \text{ units}$
$= 7.5 \text{ units}^2$

d. $\text{Area}(\triangle ABE) = \frac{1}{2} \cdot AD \cdot BE$
$= \frac{1}{2} \cdot 5 \cdot |6 - (-2)|$
$= \frac{1}{2} \cdot 5 \text{ units} \cdot 8 \text{ units}$
$= 20 \text{ units}^2$

Additional Examples

1. A right triangle has legs with lengths 2.1 meters and 3.9 meters. What is its area? 4.095 square meters
2. Find the area of $\triangle ABC$ if $A = (7, 5)$, $B = (-2, 5)$, and $C = (-2, 11)$. 27 square units

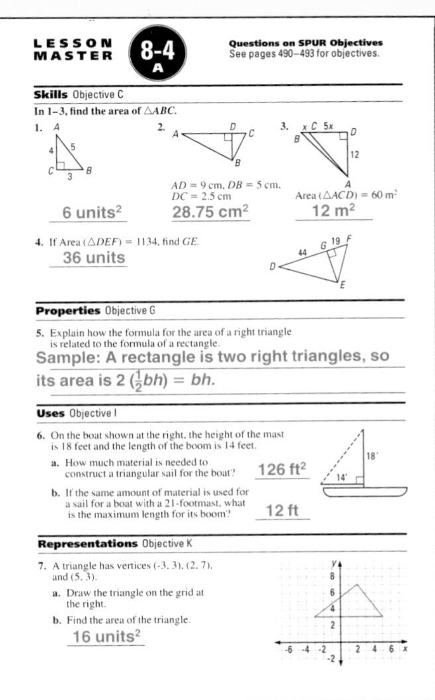

LESSON MASTER 8-4 A

Questions on SPUR Objectives
See pages 490–493 for objectives.

Skills Objective C

In 1–3, find the area of $\triangle ABC$.

2. $AD = 9$ cm, $DB = 5$ cm, $DC = 2.5$ cm
3. Area ($\triangle ACD$) = 60 m²

1. 6 units² 2. 28.75 cm² 3. 12 m²

4. If Area ($\triangle DEF$) = 1134, find GE. 36 units

Properties Objective G

5. Explain how the formula for the area of a right triangle is related to the formula of a rectangle.
Sample: A rectangle is two right triangles, so its area is $2\left(\frac{1}{2}bh\right) = bh$.

Uses Objective I

6. On the boat shown at the right, the height of the mast is 18 feet and the length of the boom is 14 feet.
   a. How much material is needed to construct a triangular sail for the boat? 126 ft²
   b. If the same amount of material is used for a sail for a boat with a 21-footmast, what is the maximum length for its boom? 12 ft

Representations Objective K

7. A triangle has vertices (-3, 3), (2, 7), and (5, 3).
   a. Draw the triangle on the grid at the right.
   b. Find the area of the triangle. 16 units²

Optional Activities

Activity 2 Technology Connection
Materials: GeoExplorer or other automatic drawers

You might use this activity after students complete the lesson. Have students use an automatic drawer to draw and measure the lengths of the three altitudes of a triangle. Then have them multiply these by half the lengths of the corresponding sides of the triangles to show that all these calculations give the same area. Students might also use the drawer to draw rectangles with the same base and height as the triangle and then give the area. Verify that the triangle has one half the area of the rectangles.

Notes on Questions

Questions 4–6, 11, and 15 These questions have more than enough information. This bothers some students, who view such problems as ones containing tricks. This is not the case at all. In the real world you can sometimes get any dimension you want by measuring. A basic task in calculating area is to determine which lengths are needed.

Questions 12–13, 15–16 Cooperative Learning Consider having students **work in small groups** to answer these questions. Have students (1) identify which number is the altitude and which is the base (any side can be a base); (2) give the area. Other members of the group should respond with questions or assistance.

Question 12 This is an important question, because students need the experience of actually measuring to determine area. Due to variation in skill of measurement, answers may vary slightly within each group. Students should learn to discern when an answer is acceptable.

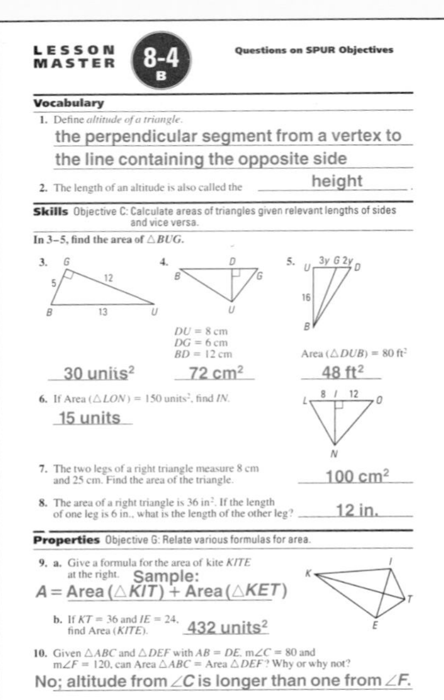

LESSON MASTER 8-4 B Questions on SPUR Objectives

Vocabulary

1. Define *altitude of a triangle*.
   the perpendicular segment from a vertex to the line containing the opposite side
2. The length of an altitude is also called the height.

Skills Objective C: Calculate areas of triangles given relevant lengths of sides and vice versa.

In 3–5, find the area of $\triangle BUG$.

3. 30 units²
4. $DU = 8$ cm, $DG = 6$ cm, $BD = 12$ cm. 72 cm²
5. Area$(\triangle DUB) = 80$ ft². 48 ft²
6. If Area$(\triangle LON) = 150$ units², find IN. 15 units
7. The two legs of a right triangle measure 8 cm and 25 cm. Find the area of the triangle. 100 cm²
8. The area of a right triangle is 36 in². If the length of one leg is 6 in., what is the length of the other leg? 12 in.

Properties Objective G: Relate various formulas for area.

9. a. Give a formula for the area of kite $KITE$ at the right. Sample: A = Area$(\triangle KIT)$ + Area$(\triangle KET)$
   b. If $KT = 36$ and $IE = 24$, find Area$(KITE)$. 432 units²
10. Given $\triangle ABC$ and $\triangle DEF$ with $AB = DE$, $m\angle C = 80$ and $m\angle F = 120$, can Area $\triangle ABC$ = Area $\triangle DEF$? Why or why not?
    No; altitude from $\angle C$ is longer than one from $\angle F$.

Questions

Covering the Reading

In 1 and 2, give a formula for the area of the figure.

1. right triangle $A = \frac{1}{2}hb$ **2.** triangle $A = \frac{1}{2}hb$

3. Sketch a triangle with a *vertical* base and an altitude to that base
a. with the altitude outside the triangle.
b. with the altitude coinciding with a side.
c. with the altitude interior to the triangle.
See left.

3) Samples: a) b) c)

In 4 and 5, find the area of the triangle.

4.

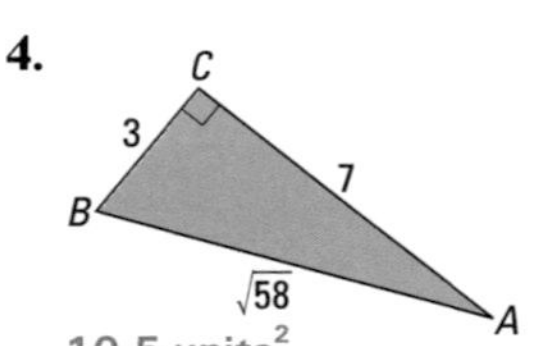

10.5 units²

5.

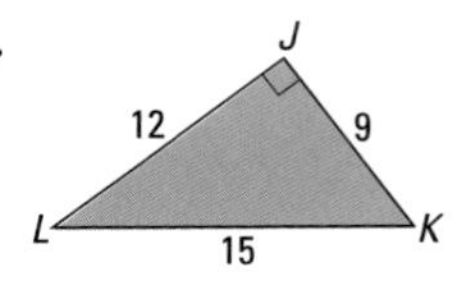

54 units²

6. In the figure at the right, give the area of
a. $\triangle EFH$. 24 units²
b. $\triangle FGH$. 60 units²
c. $\triangle EGH$. 84 units²

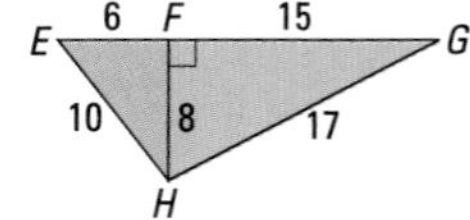

7. a. How is Area$(\triangle ABC)$ related to the areas of the two right triangles in the figure at the right?
b. If $BD = 7$ mm, $AC = 15$ mm, and $CD = 5$ mm, what is Area$(\triangle ABC)$?

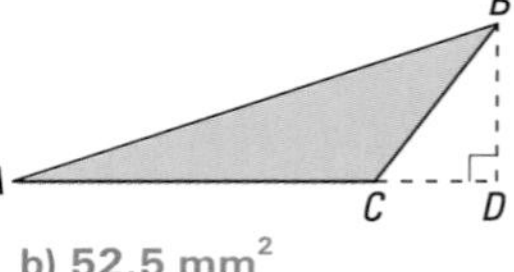

a) Area$(\triangle ABC)$ = Area$(\triangle ABD)$ − Area$(\triangle CBD)$; b) 52.5 mm²

In 8 and 9, find the area of $\triangle XYZ$.

8. **9.**

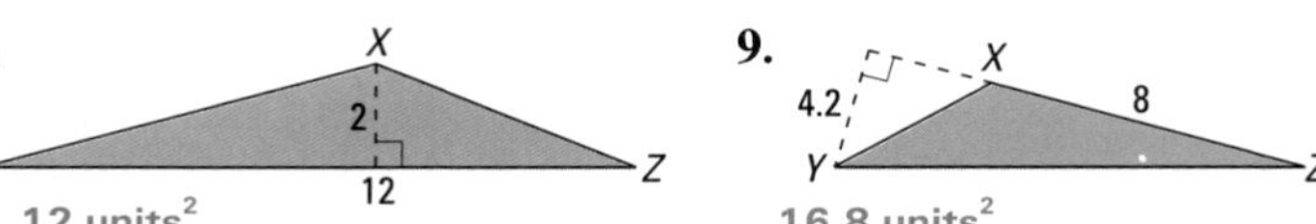

12 units² 16.8 units²

10. Refer to the figure below. Find the area of
a. $\triangle PQR$. 6 units²
b. $\triangle PRS$. 12 units²
c. $\triangle PQS$. 18 units²

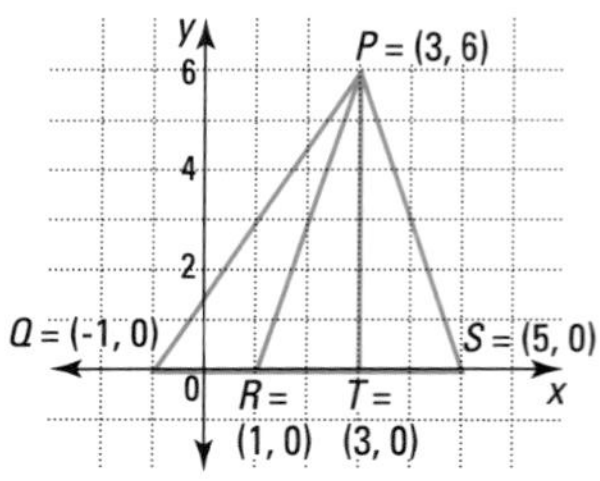

Adapting to Individual Needs

Extra Help

Refer students to the three diagrams of $\triangle ABC$ on page 454. Point out that $\overline{BC}$ is considered the base in each triangle, and $\overline{AD}$ is the altitude to the base in each case. Stress that either of the remaining sides in each triangle could be considered the base; however, new altitudes then would have to be determined. Have students draw several different triangles, with all three altitudes drawn in each triangle. Students should find the areas of all three triangles to check that they are equal.

Applying the Mathematics

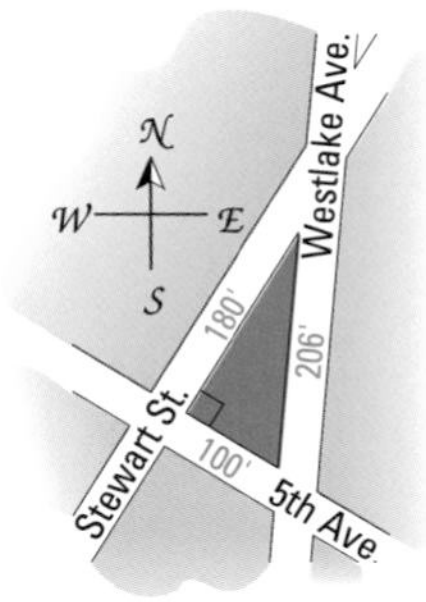

11. The Westlake Center in Seattle, Washington, is a casual place where you can get a meal, listen to a street band, and catch a ride on a monorail. It is next to some of the most exclusive shops in Seattle. It occupies a triangular lot, with approximate dimensions as shown at the left. What is the area of the lot? 9000 ft²

12. Trace $\triangle XYZ$ at the right.

a. Accurately draw one of its altitudes. See right.

b. Estimate its area in square millimeters by measuring a side, measuring the length of the altitude to that side, and using the Triangle Area Formula. See left.

c. Will you get the same area if you start with a different altitude? Why or why not?
Yes, because the base changes as well and all cases reduce to $A = \frac{1}{2}bh$.

13. Find the length of a side of a triangle with area 18 in² and altitude 12 in.
3 in.

14. Suppose the sides of a right triangle are doubled. What happens to

a. its perimeter? Its perimeter is doubled.

b. its area? Its area is multiplied by 4.

15. Approximate dimensions (in meters) of a part of a roof ABC with $AC = BC$ are given at the right.

a. What is the perimeter of this part of the roof? 32 m

b. What is its area? 48 m²

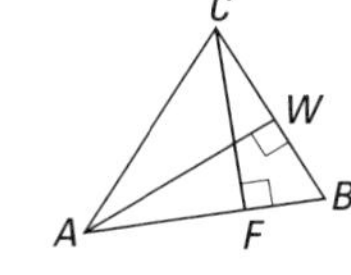

16. $\triangle ABC$ at the right has altitudes $\overline{AW}$ and $\overline{CF}$. If $AB = 8$, $CF = 6$, and $AW = 7$, find CB. (Hint: Compute Area($\triangle ABC$) in two different ways.)
$\frac{48}{7} \approx 6.86$ units

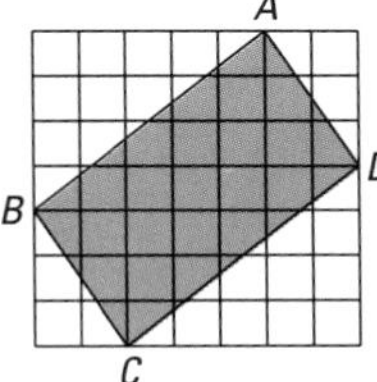

17. The grid at the right is a tessellation of unit squares. Find the exact area of quadrilateral $ABCD$. 23 units²

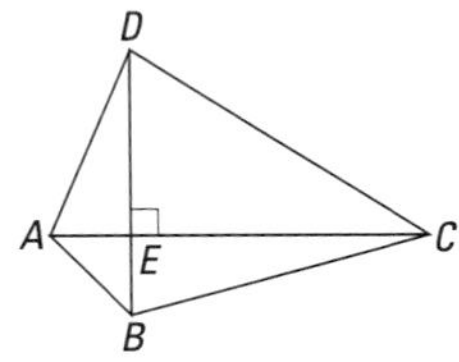

18. A quadrilateral $ABCD$ with perpendicular diagonals is drawn at the right.

a. Prove that its area is half the product of the lengths of its diagonals: Area $ABCD = \frac{1}{2}AC \cdot BD$. See left.

b. To which of the following types of quadrilaterals does the result in part **a** apply: isosceles trapezoids, kites, parallelograms, rectangles, rhombuses, squares, or trapezoids?
kites, rhombuses, squares

Westlake Center in Seattle, Washington.

12b) Sample: $XY \approx 35$ mm, $CZ \approx 10$ mm; area ≈ 175 mm²

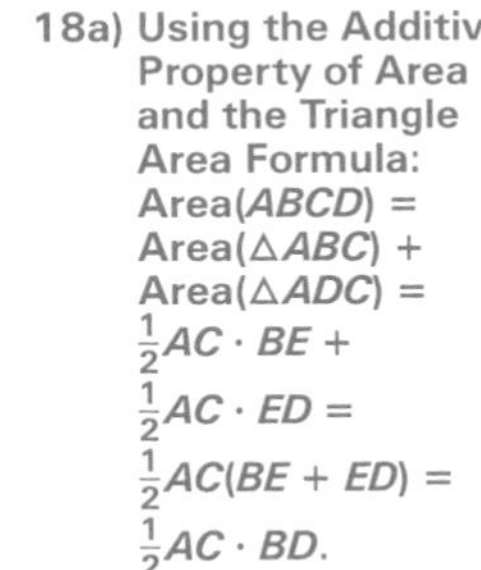

18a) Using the Additive Property of Area and the Triangle Area Formula: Area($ABCD$) = Area($\triangle ABC$) + Area($\triangle ADC$) = $\frac{1}{2}AC \cdot BE + \frac{1}{2}AC \cdot ED = \frac{1}{2}AC(BE + ED) = \frac{1}{2}AC \cdot BD$.

Question 13 The area formula has three variables: *A*, *b*, and *h*. Given any two, the third can be determined. So far, area has been calculated from the two lengths. However, in this question, the area and one length are known, from which the other length can be calculated.

Question 17 Some students may think *ABCD* is a rectangle and multiply the lengths of adjacent sides to get the area. This is not correct, as a calculation of slope would indicate. Still, there are at least five ways to approach this problem.
(i) Pick's Theorem;
(ii) interior squares plus one half of boundary squares;
(iii) squares pieced together from congruent triangles;
(iv) large square minus four triangular corners;
(v) triangles determined by horizontal and vertical lines through vertices.

Question 18 You might ask students to consider which approaches are relatively convenient, and which one they prefer most. This result is quite useful, although, in some books, it is applied only to rhombuses. Encourage students to remember the result in full generality, as applying to all quadrilaterals with perpendicular diagonals, and also as a kite area formula.

(Notes on Questions continue on page 458.)

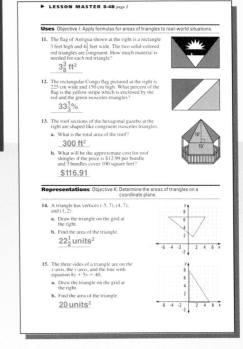

▶ **LESSON MASTER 8-4B** *page 2*

Uses Objective I: Apply formulas for areas of triangles to real-world situations.

11. The flag of Antigua shown at the right is a rectangle 3 feet high and $4\frac{1}{2}$ feet wide. The two solid-colored red triangles are congruent. How much material is needed for each red triangle?
$3\frac{3}{8}$ ft²

12. The rectangular Congo flag pictured at the right is 225 cm wide and 150 cm high. What percent of the flag is the yellow stripe which is enclosed by the red and the green isosceles triangles?
$33\frac{1}{3}$%

13. The roof sections of the hexagonal gazebo at the right are shaped like congruent isosceles triangles.
a. What is the total area of the roof?
300 ft²
b. What will be the approximate cost for roof shingles if the price is \$12.99 per bundle and 3 bundles cover 100 square feet?
\$116.91

Representations Objective K: Determine the areas of triangles on a coordinate plane.

14. A triangle has vertices (-5, 7), (4, 7), and (1, 2).
a. Draw the triangle on the grid at the right.
b. Find the area of the triangle.
$22\frac{1}{2}$ units²

15. The three sides of a triangle are on the x-axis, the y-axis, and the line with equation $8x + 5y = 40$.
a. Draw the triangle on the grid at the right.
b. Find the area of the triangle.
20 units²

Adapting to Individual Needs

Challenge

Notice that both of the following figures involve 12 toothpicks. The first has an area of 9 square units and the second has an area of 5 square units.

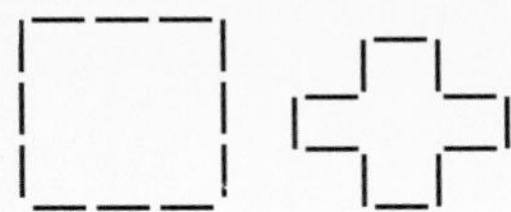

Have students use 12 toothpicks to form a polygon with an area of 4 square units. (The entire length of each toothpick must be used.) [Many solutions are possible. One is shown. Make a 3-4-5 right triangle, which has an area of 6 sq. units. Move 3 toothpicks to reduce the area by 2 square units.]

Notes on Questions

Question 26 Teachers have identified this question as one that students enjoy.

Follow-up for Lesson 8-4

Practice

For more questions on SPUR Objectives, use **Lesson Master 8-4A** (shown on page 455) or **Lesson Master 8-4B** (shown on pages 456–457).

Assessment

Oral/Written Communication Have students **work in groups.** Have students take turns drawing triangles on grid paper. Then have them work together to determine the area of each triangle. [Students correctly apply the Triangle Area Formula to determine areas.]

Extension

Show students the diagram below which is also on **Teaching Aid 109.** Have them determine the area of each shaded triangle. [5 square units] Then discuss the methods they used to find the areas. [Methods may vary. Some students may see that each triangle has an altitude of 5 units and a base of 2 units.] Now you might have students use this idea to draw other triangles that look different but have the same area.

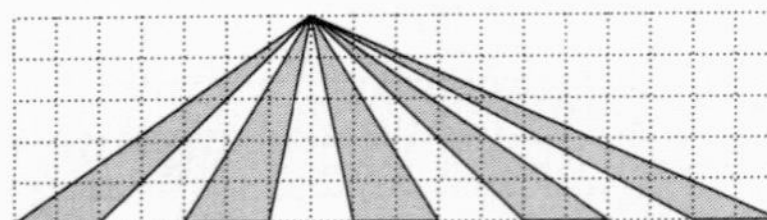

Project Update Project 2, *Hero's Formula,* on page 485, relates to the content of this lesson.

19a) 286,650 square miles; answers may vary by ±4900 square miles.
b) 266,400 square miles; answers may vary by ±1225 square miles.

Review

19. Each grid square below at the left is 70 miles on a side, and each grid square at the right is 35 miles on a side. Estimate the area of Texas using each grid. *(Lesson 8-3)* See left.

a.

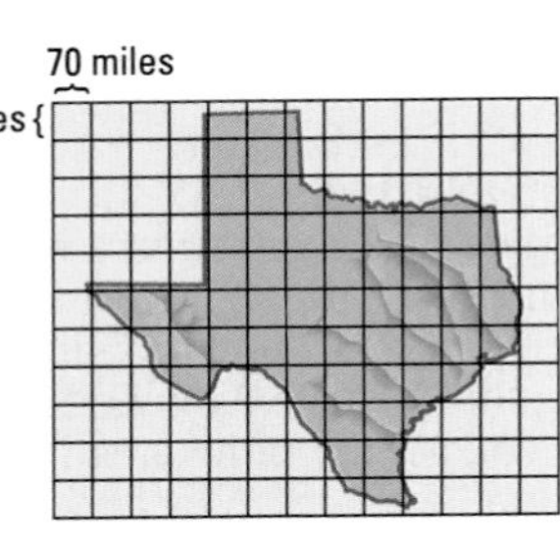

b.

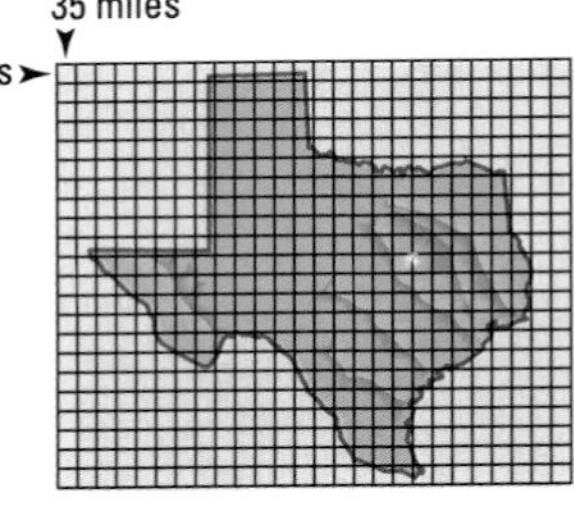

20. There are 1760 yards in a mile. How many square yards are in a square mile? *(Lesson 8-3)* 3,097,600 square yards

21. Hexagon $ABCDEF$ has vertices at points $A = (0, 12)$, $B = (11, 12)$, $C = (11, 4)$, $D = (9, 4)$, $E = (9, 0)$, and $F = (0, 0)$. Find Area($ABCDEF$). *(Lesson 8-3)* 124 units^2

22. At the right, $PRVW$ and $QRTS$ are squares. Q and T are the midpoints of $\overline{PR}$ and $\overline{RV}$, respectively, and $RT = x$. Find the area of the shaded region. *(Lesson 8-2)* $3x^2$ square units

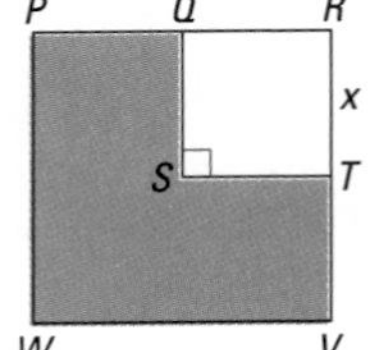

23. Write a proof argument.
Given: In the figure at the left, $AB = AD$ and $\angle ABD \cong \angle BDC$.
To prove: $ABCD$ is a trapezoid. *(Lesson 6-5)*
See margin.

24. Expand each expression. *(Previous course)*
a. $(x + y)(x + y)$ $x^2 + 2xy + y^2$
b. $(x + y)(x - y)$ $x^2 - y^2$
c. $(x + y)^2$ $x^2 + 2xy + y^2$

25. *Multiple choice.* $\sqrt{20} =$ a
(a) $2\sqrt{5}$ (b) $4\sqrt{5}$ (c) $2\sqrt{10}$ (d) $10\sqrt{2}$ *(Previous course)*

Exploration

26. At the right, the named points are equally spaced along the rectangle $AEHL$. Each point A, B, C, D, and E is connected to each point H, I, J, K, and L. How many triangles in the drawing have the same area as $\triangle CLH$? Name them.
There are nine besides $\triangle CLH$: $\triangle ALH$, $\triangle BLH$, $\triangle DLH$, $\triangle ELH$, $\triangle AEH$, $\triangle AEI$, $\triangle AEJ$, $\triangle AEK$, $\triangle AEL$

Adapting to Individual Needs

English Language Development
You might suggest that students with limited English proficiency write the formulas introduced in this lesson on index cards. Suggest that they draw and label a figure and then write the formulas in both words and symbols.

Additional Answers

23.

Conclusions	Justifications
0. $\angle ABD \cong \angle BDC$	Given
1. $\overline{DC} \parallel \overline{AB}$	AIA $\cong \Rightarrow \parallel$ lines
2. $ABCD$ is a trapezoid.	def. of trapezoid

LESSON

8-5

Areas of Trapezoids

Complex housing. *This modern housing development in the Ramat Polin section in Jerusalem utilizes pentagons and trapezoids in a most interesting way.*

Knowing a formula for the area of a triangle is useful because any polygon can be split into triangles. Recall that when this occurs, we say that the polygon has been *triangulated*. Pentagon *ABCDE* at the left below has been copied and triangulated at the right.

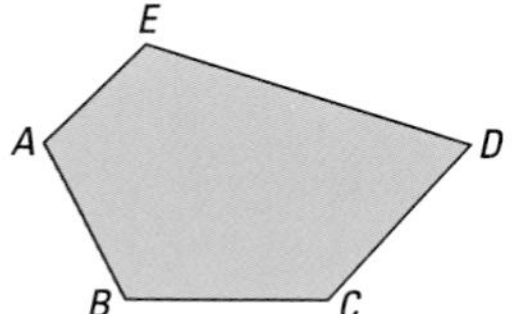

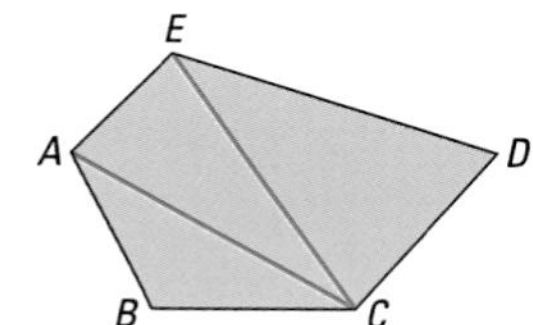

❶ This idea provides an algorithm for finding the area of *any* polygon. Step 1: Triangulate the polygon. Step 2: Find the area of each triangle (by measuring lengths of sides and altitudes). Step 3: Add these areas to find the area of the polygon.

But an algorithm is not the same as a formula. There is no known general formula for the area of a polygon, even if you know the lengths of all its sides and the measures of all its angles. But if a polygon can be split into triangles with sides and their altitudes known, then there can be a formula. One kind of polygon that can be split in this way is the trapezoid.

Lesson 8-5

Objectives

C Calculate areas of trapezoids and parallelograms given relevant lengths of sides, and vice versa.
G Relate various formulas for area.
I Apply formulas for areas of trapezoids and parallelograms to real-world situations.
K Determine the areas of trapezoids and parallelograms on a coordinate plane.

Resources

From the ***Teacher's Resource File***
- Lesson Master 8-5A or 8-5B
- Answer Master 8-5
- Teaching Aids
  - 102 Warm-up
  - 104 Map of the United States
  - 105 Graph Paper
  - 110 Additional Examples
  - 111 Challenge

Additional Resources
- Visuals for Teaching Aids 102, 104–105 and 110–111

Teaching Lesson 8-5

Warm-up

A builder has an unusual plot of land shaped as shown below. The builder wants to split the plot into four congruent lots. How could this be done?

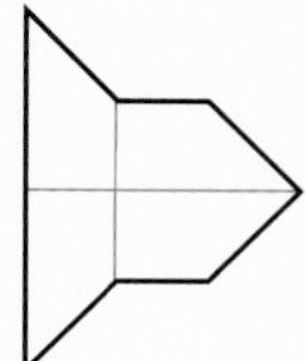

Notes on Reading

❶ The word *algorithm* was introduced in Lesson 3-8 and mentioned in previous UCSMP courses. Most students should be familiar with it by now; if not, provide some examples, such as the long-division algorithm, and the algorithm for approximating the area of an irregular region.

Lesson 8-5 Overview

Broad Goals In this lesson, the formula for the area of any trapezoid is derived and applied to all those figures that are trapezoids, including parallelograms.

Perspective If a polygon is constructed so that its triangles have the same altitudes (as in a trapezoid) or have bases of the same length (as in a regular polygon), then the distributive property can be used to derive a rather simple formula for the area of the polygon.

In this lesson, we first derive the formula $A = \frac{1}{2}h(b_1 + b_2)$ for a trapezoid. Then, by letting $b_1 = b_2$, we obtain the formula $A = bh$ for a parallelogram. An advantage of the hierarchy and our more general definition of trapezoid which includes parallelograms is now apparent: the formula for area of a parallelogram is a special case of that of a trapezoid.

Note that Step 2 of the algorithm for finding the area of any polygon (on page 459) is easier said than done. Students should see that much work is necessary to find the areas. If there are two measurements for each triangle, then there are $2(n - 2)$ measurements for an n-gon. Point out that to reduce the number of measurements, it is wise to use sides shared by triangles.

Students often have been asked to "show work" to get full credit or to use a particular procedure to arrive at an answer that they could obtain more easily some other way. For this reason, some students will not use the Trapezoid Area Formula, but will split up every trapezoid into two triangles (as is done in the specific example at the top of the page) to find the area. When asked why they don't use the formula, they will point to the specific example and say, "That's the way it was done in the book."

Point out that the book goes through one example this way for two reasons. First, the example is generalized to get the formula. Second, if students forget the formula, they can go through the process that was used to arrive at the formula.

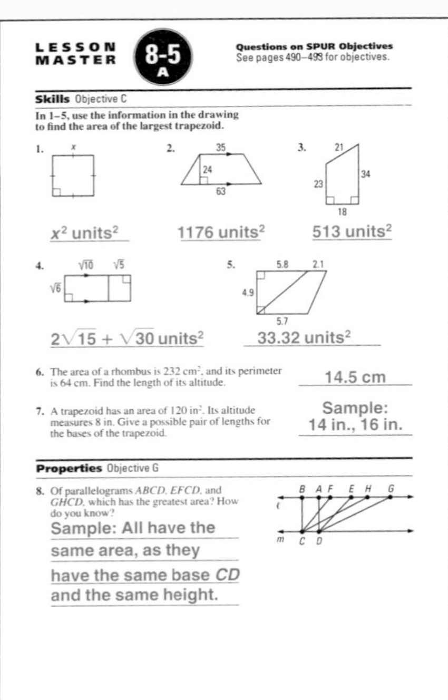

LESSON MASTER 8-5 A

Questions on SPUR Objectives
See pages 490–493 for objectives.

Skills Objective C

In 1–5, use the information in the drawing to find the area of the largest trapezoid.

1. x — x^2 units^2

2. 35, 24, 63 — 1176 units^2

3. 21, 34, 23, 18 — 513 units^2

4. $\sqrt{10}$, $\sqrt{5}$, $\sqrt{6}$ — $2\sqrt{15} + \sqrt{30}$ units^2

5. 5.8, 2.1, 4.9, 5.7 — 33.32 units^2

6. The area of a rhombus is 232 cm^2, and its perimeter is 64 cm. Find the length of its altitude. — 14.5 cm

7. A trapezoid has an area of 120 in^2. Its altitude measures 8 in. Give a possible pair of lengths for the bases of the trapezoid. — Sample: 14 in., 16 in.

Properties Objective G

8. Of parallelograms *ABCD*, *EFCD*, and *GHCD*, which has the greatest area? How do you know?
Sample: All have the same area, as they have the same base *CD* and the same height.

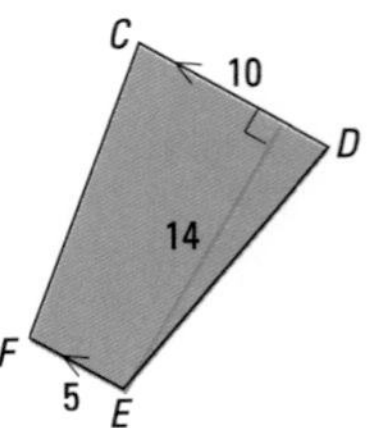

A Specific Example

The **height** or **altitude** of a trapezoid refers to any segment from one base perpendicular to the other, or to the length of that segment. This length is constant because the bases are parallel. In trapezoid *CDEF* at the left, the lengths of the bases (10 and 5) and its height (14) are given. This is enough to find the area.

First split the trapezoid into triangles *CEF* and *CDE*. The height of the trapezoid is the height of each triangle, and the bases of the trapezoid are the corresponding bases of the triangles. So the area of each triangle can be found.

$$\begin{aligned}\text{Area}(CDEF) &= \text{Area}(\triangle CEF) + \text{Area}(\triangle CDE)\\ &= \tfrac{1}{2}(5 \cdot 14) + \tfrac{1}{2}(10 \cdot 14)\\ &= 35 + 70\\ &= 105 \text{ square units}\end{aligned}$$

A General Formula

The ideas used in the specific instance above can be applied to deduce a formula for the area of a trapezoid. A bonus is that a trapezoid area formula applies to all of the special kinds of quadrilaterals which are below the trapezoid in the hierarchy of quadrilaterals.

Trapezoid Area Formula
The area of a trapezoid equals half the product of its altitude and the sum of the lengths of its bases.

$$A = \tfrac{1}{2}h(b_1 + b_2)$$

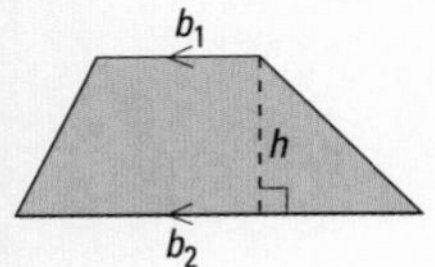

Proof:

Given: *ZOID* is a trapezoid with altitude h and bases b_1 and b_2.

To prove: $\text{Area}(ZOID) = \tfrac{1}{2}h(b_1 + b_2)$.

Drawing:

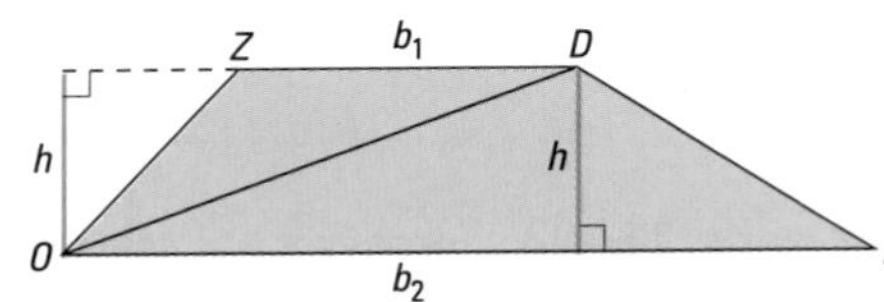

Argument:

$\text{Area}(ZOID)$	$= \text{Area}(\triangle ZOD) + \text{Area}(\triangle DOI)$	Additive Property of Area
	$= \tfrac{1}{2}h \cdot b_1 + \tfrac{1}{2}h \cdot b_2$	Triangle Area Formula
	$= \tfrac{1}{2}h(b_1 + b_2)$	Distributive Property

Optional Activities

Activity 1

Materials: Graph paper or **Teaching Aid 105**

You can use this activity to introduce the lesson. Have each student draw a polygon of his or her choice and actually triangulate that polygon. Then have students find the areas of their polygons by adding the areas of the triangles. Repeat the activity with a trapezoid.

Activity 2 Geography Connection

Materials: Map of the U.S. or **Teaching Aid 104**

As an extension of **Question 26** ask students to find states that have shapes which allow their areas to be rather easily approximated. [Samples: Think of Colorado and Wyoming as rectangles, Utah and New Mexico as the union of rectangles; North Dakota and Connecticut as trapezoids.]

Recall that $\frac{1}{2}(b_1 + b_2)$ is the mean or average of b_1 and b_2. So the area of a trapezoid equals the product of its altitude and the average of its bases.

Example 1

Compute the area of *ABCD* at the right.

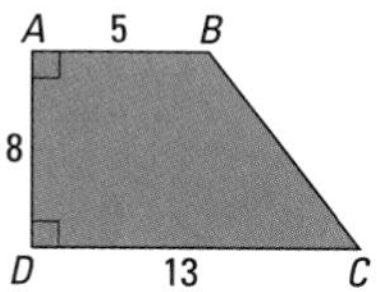

Solution

By the Two Perpendiculars Theorem, $\overline{AB} \parallel \overline{CD}$, so $\overline{AB}$ and $\overline{CD}$ are the bases of a trapezoid. Apply the Trapezoid Area Formula with $b_1 = 5$, $b_2 = 13$, and $h = 8$.

$$\begin{aligned} \text{Area}(ABCD) &= \frac{1}{2}h(b_1 + b_2) \\ &= \frac{1}{2} \cdot 8(5 + 13) \\ &= 4 \cdot 18 \\ &= 72 \text{ units}^2 \end{aligned}$$

Check

The area of a trapezoid is the product of its altitude and the average of the bases. The average of 5 and 13 is $\frac{5 + 13}{2} = 9$. Since $8 \cdot 9 = 72$, the answer checks.

Areas of Parallelograms

Since every parallelogram is a trapezoid, the trapezoid formula applies to parallelograms as well. For example, *SPOT* is a parallelogram with altitude h. In a parallelogram, opposite sides are equal, so $b_1 = b_2 = b$.

$$\begin{aligned} \text{Area}(SPOT) &= \tfrac{1}{2}h(b_1 + b_2) \\ &= \tfrac{1}{2}h(b + b) \\ &= \tfrac{1}{2}h(2b) \\ &= hb \end{aligned}$$

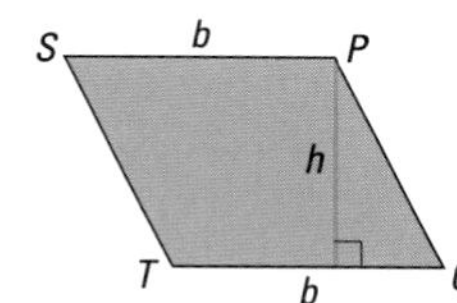

Parallelogram Area Formula
The area of a parallelogram is the product of one of its bases and the altitude to that base.
$A = hb$

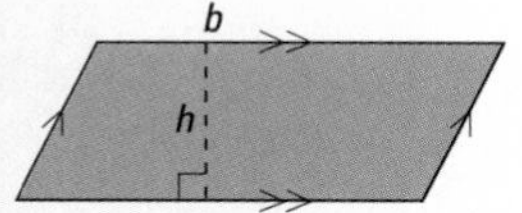

In Example 2, many lengths are given. You must be careful in selecting which lengths to use.

As an alternate approach, you might prefer the discussion of the Trapezoid Area Formula given in Activity 3 in *Optional Activities* below.

Error Alert To avoid the tacit assumption that an altitude of a trapezoid is "vertical," place a trapezoid on an overhead projector in a variety of positions. Recall the fact that parallel lines are equidistant was proved. Therefore, it is appropriate to speak of the altitude as the distance between the parallel lines.

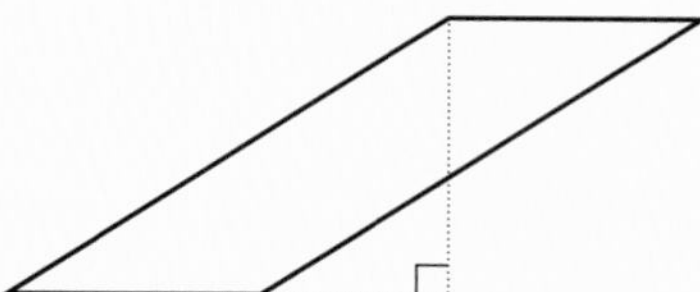

Now consider the fact that a parallelogram has two altitudes. To avoid the tacit assumption that an altitude of a parallelogram may always be drawn "inside" the parallelogram, consider parallelograms with bases that cannot be projected orthogonally one on the other, as shown above.

You might want to mention that the areas of trapezoids (and rectangles) are important in calculus to help approximate the area of a nonpolygonal region. The bases are usually vertical segments.

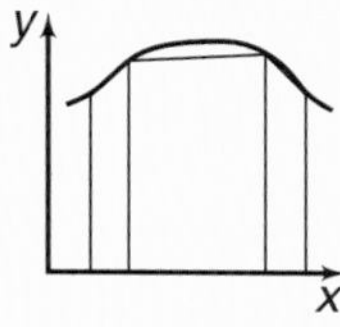

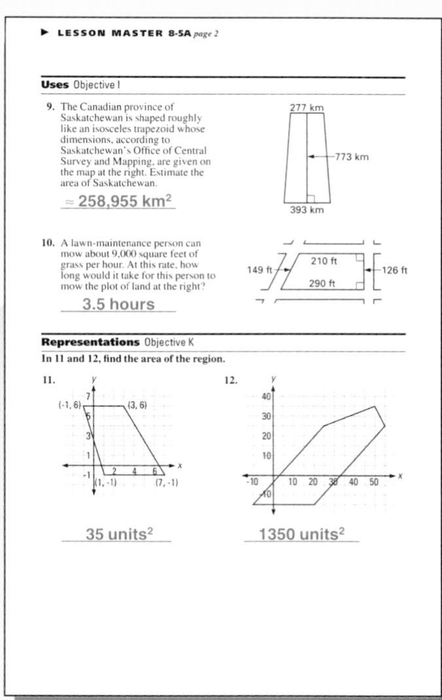

▶ **LESSON MASTER 8-5A** *page 2*

Uses Objective I

9. The Canadian province of Saskatchewan is shaped roughly like an isosceles trapezoid whose dimensions, according to Saskatchewan's Office of Central Survey and Mapping, are given on the map at the right. Estimate the area of Saskatchewan.

   ≈ 258,955 km²

10. A lawn-maintenance person can mow about 9,000 square feet of grass per hour. At this rate, how long would it take for this person to mow the plot of land at the right?

    3.5 hours

Representations Objective K

In 11 and 12, find the area of the region.

11.

   35 units²

12.

   1350 units²

Optional Activities

Activity 3 Alternate Approach You might prefer to present the Trapezoid Area Formula as follows: The area of a trapezoid equals the product of its altitude and the average of its bases. This can be visualized by drawing altitudes through the midpoints of the legs of the trapezoid. Then rotate the triangles (as shown) 180°. The resulting figure is a rectangle with height equal to the height of the trapezoid and base equal to the average of the two bases of the trapezoid.

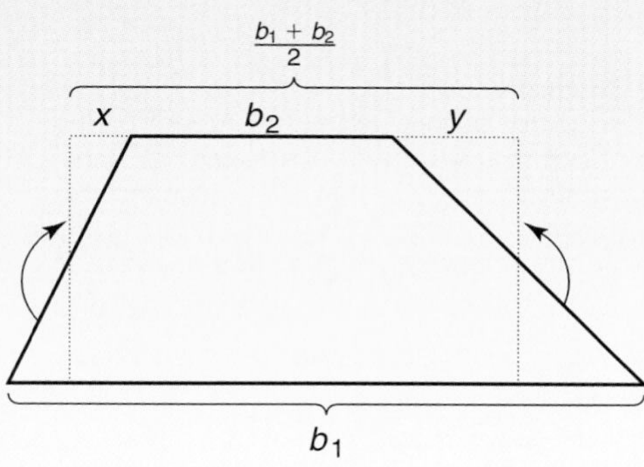

Additional Examples

These examples are also given on **Teaching Aid 110.**

1. Find the area of isosceles trapezoid *WXYZ.* **110 square units**

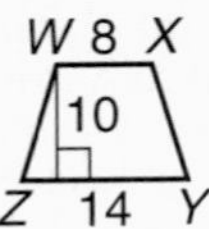

2. Find the area of parallelogram RSTV. **450 square units**

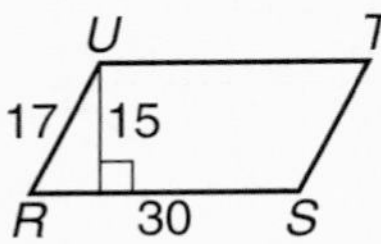

3. Find the area of quadrilateral *ABCD* if $A = (7, 3)$, $B = (7, 15)$, $C = (-2, 11)$, and $D = (-2, 5)$. **81 square units**
4. Show that the Trapezoid Area Formula can be used to find the area of a square with side *s*. **The square has two bases of length *s* and height *s*. By the Trapezoid Area Formula, its area is $\frac{1}{2}s(s + s) = \frac{1}{2}s \cdot 2s = s^2$.**

Notes on Questions

Question 2 The concept of triangulation of polygons has not been defined formally. For any convex polygon, the diagonals from any fixed vertex form a triangulation of the polygon. That could be considered a *minimal triangulation.* Convex quadrilaterals have two minimal triangulations.

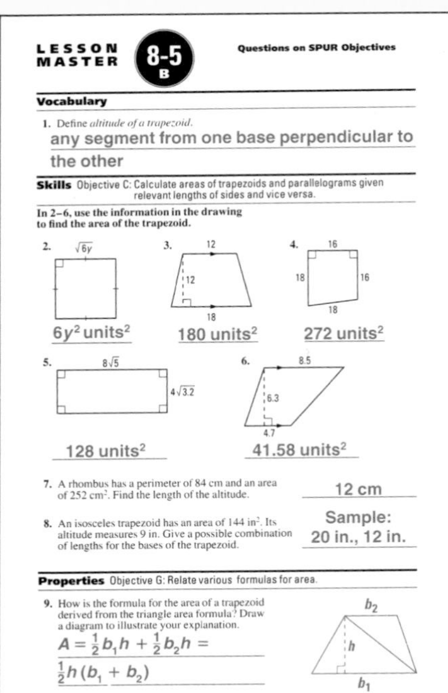

LESSON MASTER 8-5 B Questions on SPUR Objectives

Vocabulary

1. Define *altitude of a trapezoid.* any segment from one base perpendicular to the other

Skills Objective C: Calculate areas of trapezoids and parallelograms given relevant lengths of sides and vice versa.

In 2–6, use the information in the drawing to find the area of the trapezoid.

2. $\sqrt{6y}$ — $6y^2$ units²
3. 12, 12, 18 — 180 units²
4. 16, 18, 16, 18 — 272 units²
5. $8\sqrt{5}$, $4\sqrt{3.2}$ — 128 units²
6. 8.5, 6.3, 4.7 — 41.58 units²
7. A rhombus has a perimeter of 84 cm and an area of 252 cm². Find the length of the altitude. 12 cm
8. An isosceles trapezoid has an area of 144 in². Its altitude measures 9 in. Give a possible combination of lengths for the bases of the trapezoid. Sample: 20 in., 12 in.

Properties Objective G: Relate various formulas for area.

9. How is the formula for the area of a trapezoid derived from the triangle area formula? Draw a diagram to illustrate your explanation. $A = \frac{1}{2}b_1h + \frac{1}{2}b_2h = \frac{1}{2}h(b_1 + b_2)$

Example 2

Find the area of parallelogram *ABCD*.

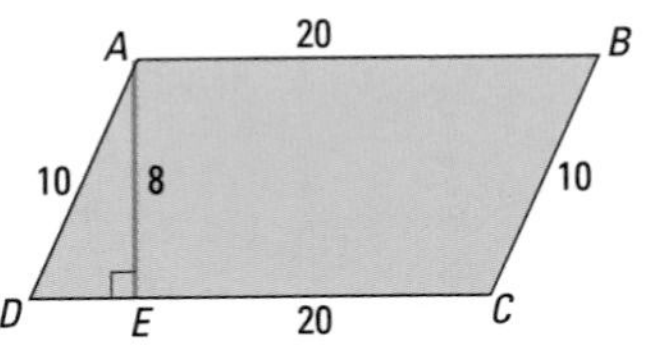

Solution

Area = hb
= 8 · 20
= 160 units²

Notice that the sides with length 10 are not used.

1) Triangulate the polygon; find the area of each triangle; add all the areas.

Sample:

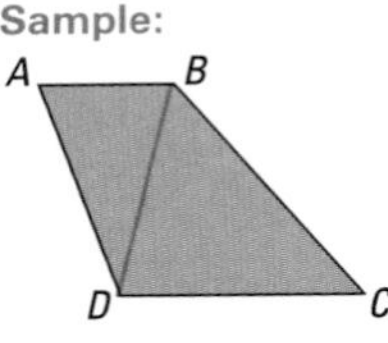

QUESTIONS

Covering the Reading

1. Describe an algorithm for obtaining the area of any polygon. See left.
2. Trace trapezoid *ABCD* at the left. Then triangulate it. See left.
3. Give the area formula for any trapezoid. $A = \frac{1}{2}h(b_1 + b_2)$
4. $\frac{1}{2}(b_1 + b_2)$ is the _?_ or _?_ of b_1 and b_2. mean, average

In 5 and 6, use the figure at the right.

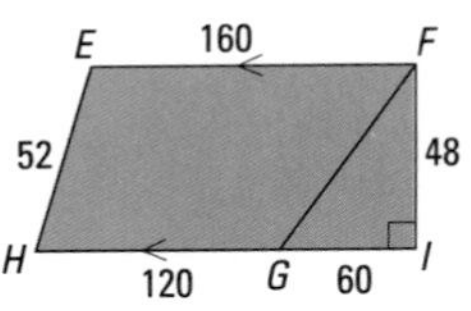

5. a. Name the bases and altitude of trapezoid *EFGH*. bases: $\overline{EF}$ and $\overline{GH}$; altitude: $\overline{IF}$
   b. Find Area(*EFGH*). 6720 units²
6. Find Area(*EFIH*). 8160 units²

In 7–9, find the area of the largest trapezoid in the drawing.

7.

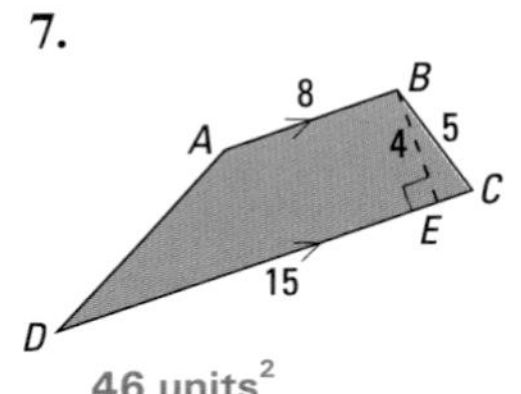

46 units²

8.

87.5 units²

9.

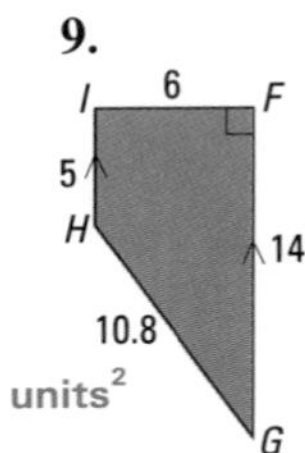

57 units²

10. Give an area formula for any parallelogram. $A = hb$

In 11 and 12, **a.** Find the area of the parallelogram. **b.** List all lengths in the figure you did not need to answer part **a.**

11.

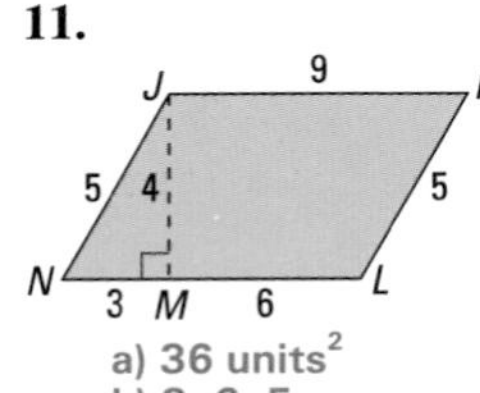

a) 36 units²
b) 3, 6, 5

12.

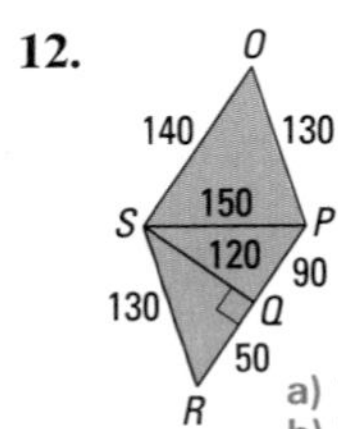

a) 16,800 units²
b) 130, 150, 50, 90

Adapting to Individual Needs

Extra Help

In the proof of the Trapezoid Area Formula, point out that the given trapezoid *ZOID* could also be triangulated by drawing the diagonal from *Z* to *I*. Then the two triangles would be △*ZDI* and △*ZOI*. But the proof would look the same because the area of △*ZDI* is $\frac{1}{2}h \cdot b_1$ and the area of △*ZOI* is $\frac{1}{2}h \cdot b_2$.

Additional Answers

17a. Sample Argument:

Conclusions	Justifications
1. $AF = BC$	Isosceles Trapezoid Thm.
2. $\angle F = \angle C$	def. of isosceles trapezoid
3. $m\angle AEF = 90$, $m\angle BDC = 90$	def. of perpendicular

Applying the Mathematics

13a, b)

A 20 B; 10, 8, 10; D E C E'

13. a. Trace the figure of Example 2. a, b) See left.
    b. Translate $\triangle ADE$ by the vector $\overrightarrow{DC}$. Call E' the image of E.
    c. What is the shape of figure $ABE'E$? rectangle
    d. What is the area of figure $ABE'E$? 160 units^2
    e. Will this idea work for all parallelograms? Yes

In 14 and 15, find the area of the trapezoid with the given vertices.

14.

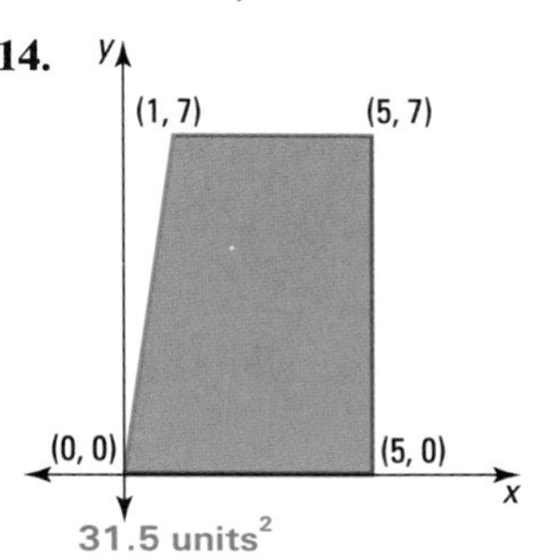

31.5 units^2

15.

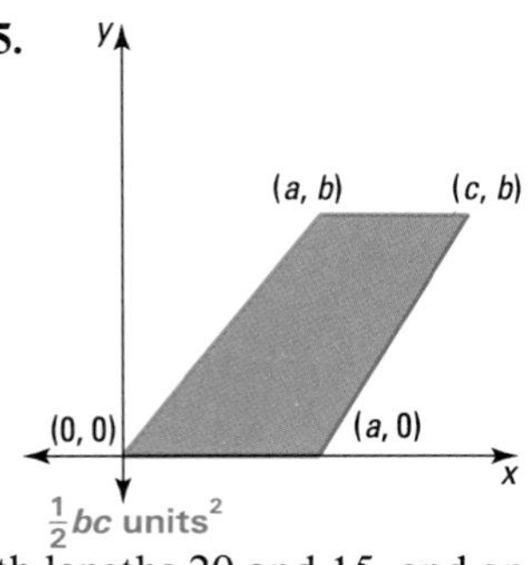

$\frac{1}{2}bc$ units^2

16. A trapezoid has a pair of bases with lengths 20 and 15, and an area of 60. What is the altitude of the trapezoid? $\frac{24}{7} \approx 3.43$ units

17. At the right, $ABCF$ is an isosceles trapezoid with bases $\overline{AB}$ and $\overline{FC}$. $\overline{AE} \perp \overline{FC}$ and $\overline{BD} \perp \overline{FC}$. $FE = 2.5$, $ED = 8$, and $AE = 5$.
    a. Prove that $FE = DC$. (Hint: Use congruent triangles.) See margin.
    b. Find the area of $ABCF$. 52.5 units^2

A B F E D C

Review

In 18 and 19, *multiple choice.* Use the figure below. *(Lesson 8-4)*

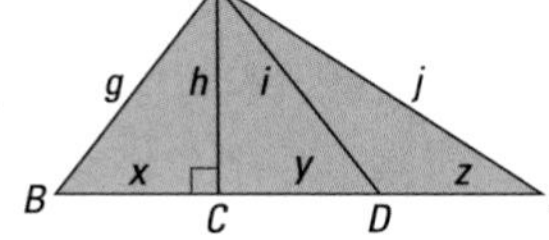

18. The area of $\triangle ABC$ is d
    (a) $h + x + g$ units^2
    (b) hx units^2.
    (c) $\frac{1}{2}hxg$ units^2.
    (d) $\frac{1}{2}hx$ units^2.

19. The area of $\triangle ABE$ is b
    (a) $h(x + y + z)$ units^2.
    (b) $\frac{1}{2}h(x + y + z)$ units^2.
    (c) $g + x + y + z + j$ units^2.
    (d) $\frac{1}{2}(g + j)(x + y + z)$ units^2.

20. Find, to the nearest tenth, the length of the altitude to $\overline{QR}$ in the figure at the right. *(Lesson 8-4)* 14.1 units

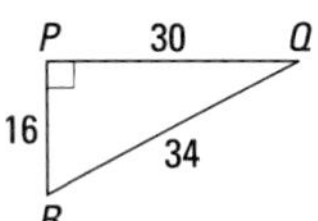

4. m∠AEF = m∠BDC — Substitution
5. $\triangle AEF \cong \triangle BDC$ — AAS Congruence Thm. (Steps 1, 2, 4)
6. $FE = DC$ — CPCF Thm.

Questions 5–6 Students should see multiple ways to find the area. Point out that in the real world, pertinent data must be selected from among all available data to solve problems. Here, the side of length 52 is not needed.

Question 10 This is a new formula students can add to their list of formulas, but they could always use the Trapezoid Area Formula.

Questions 11–12 Once the relevant information has been sorted out, encourage students to use the formula of **Question 10** to make these questions easy.

Question 14 Allow a variety of methods, but stress the ease of the Trapezoid Area Formula.

Question 15 You might ask if the answer to this question provides a general formula for any trapezoid [No, one diagonal here is an altitude.] and if it can be applied to the previous question. [No]

Question 16 The data given uniquely determine the altitude but not the shape of the trapezoid. Two segments of length 15 and 20 on parallel lines $\frac{24}{7}$ units apart determine a trapezoid with area 60 regardless of where the segments are placed. Students might **work in small groups** and draw various trapezoids that satisfy the given condition to verify this.

(Notes on Questions continue on page 464.)

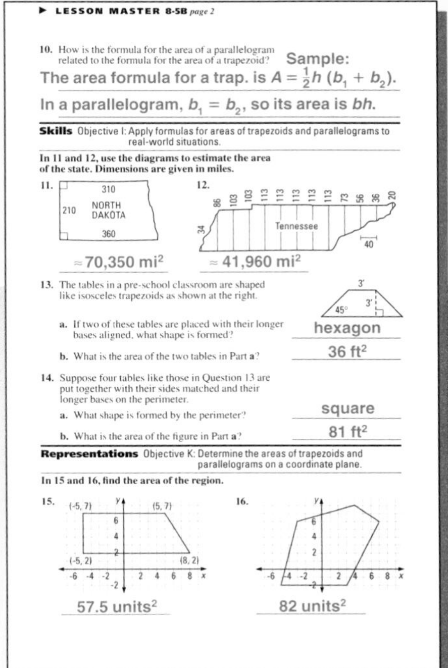

► LESSON MASTER 8-5B *page 2*

10. How is the formula for the area of a parallelogram related to the formula for the area of a trapezoid? Sample: The area formula for a trap. is $A = \frac{1}{2}h(b_1 + b_2)$. In a parallelogram, $b_1 = b_2$, so its area is bh.

Skills Objective I: Apply formulas for areas of trapezoids and parallelograms to real-world situations.

In 11 and 12, use the diagrams to estimate the area of the state. Dimensions are given in miles.

11. 310; 210; NORTH DAKOTA; 360 — ≈70,350 mi^2

12. 86, 103, 103, 113, 113, 113, 113, 113, 73, 56, 36, 20; 34; Tennessee; 40 — ≈41,960 mi^2

13. The tables in a pre-school classroom are shaped like isosceles trapezoids as shown at the right. (3′, 3′, 45°)
    a. If two of these tables are placed with their longer bases aligned, what shape is formed? hexagon
    b. What is the area of the two tables in Part **a**? 36 ft^2

14. Suppose four tables like those in Question 13 are put together with their sides matched and their longer bases on the perimeter.
    a. What shape is formed by the perimeter? square
    b. What is the area of the figure in Part **a**? 81 ft^2

Representations Objective K: Determine the areas of trapezoids and parallelograms on a coordinate plane.

In 15 and 16, find the area of the region.

15. (-5, 7), (5, 7), (-5, 2), (8, 2) — 57.5 units^2

16. 82 units^2

Notes on Questions

Question 26 Geography Connection Remind students that the two north-south borders of Nevada would intersect if extended even though they are perpendicular to the same line. The lines (great circles) containing these borders intersect at the North Pole. Even so, the calculations are very close to the actual area of the state.

Follow-up for Lesson 8-5

Practice

For more questions on SPUR Objectives, use **Lesson Master 8-5A** (shown on pages 460–461) or **Lesson Master 8-5B** (shown on pages 462–463).

Assessment

Oral/Written Communication Have students assume they have to justify the Trapezoid Area Formula to someone who has never seen the formula nor the proof given in the book. [Students recognize that any trapezoid can be split into two triangles and that the Trapezoid Area Formula evolves from using the Triangle Area Formula twice or the method used in Activity 3 of the *Optional Activities* could be used.]

Extension

Writing Have students write a paragraph explaining why the four triangles formed by intersecting diagonals in a parallelogram have the same area. [All four triangles have height *h* and base *b*.]

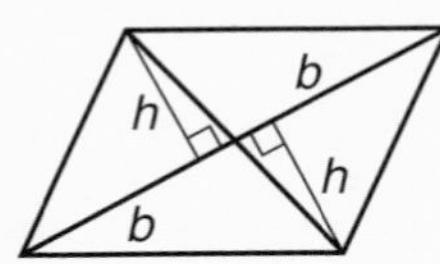

21. Paisley needs a piece of fabric cut in the shape at the right. Explain how she could estimate the amount of fabric needed for that piece. *(Lesson 8-3)* Place a grid on the shape. Add the number of squares entirely inside the figure to one-half the number of squares partially covering the figure. Multiply the result by the area of each square.

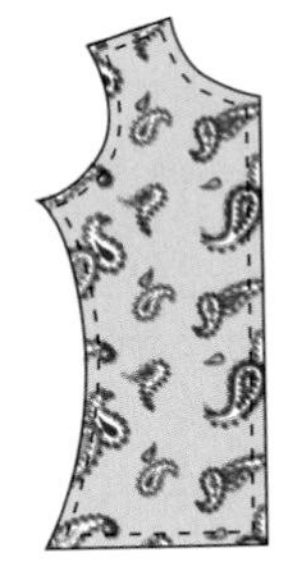

22. How many trapezoids are in the figure for Question 8? *(Lesson 6-5)* four

23. $\overline{AC}$ and $\overline{BD}$ are diameters of $\odot E$, as shown at the right. If $m\widehat{AB} = 72°$, what is $m\angle BEC$? *(Lesson 3-2)* 108

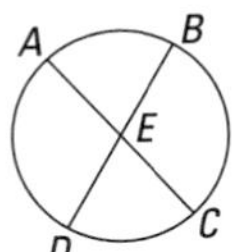

24. *Multiple choice.* $(a + 5)^2 =$ c
    (a) $a^2 + 25$
    (b) $a^2 + 5a + 25$
    (c) $a^2 + 10a + 25$
    (d) none of these
    (Previous course)

25. Simplify $\sqrt{27}$. *(Previous course)* $3\sqrt{3}$

Exploration

26. The state of Nevada is shaped roughly like a trapezoid. c, d) See left.
    a. Use the dimensions given below to estimate the area of the trapezoid that includes Nevada. 113,150 sq mi
    b. The Colorado River cuts off a region of southeast Nevada that is also roughly a trapezoid with north-south bases 80 and 120 miles long and an east-west length of 30 miles. Approximate the area of this region. 3000 sq mi
    c. From your calculations in parts **a** and **b**, estimate the area of Nevada.
    d. From a map or almanac, find the official area of Nevada in square miles. How close to the official area is your estimate from part **c**?

26c) 110,150 sq mi
d) From the *1995 World Almanac and Book of Facts*, the area is 109,806 mi^2. The estimate is off by 344 mi^2, or about 0.3%.

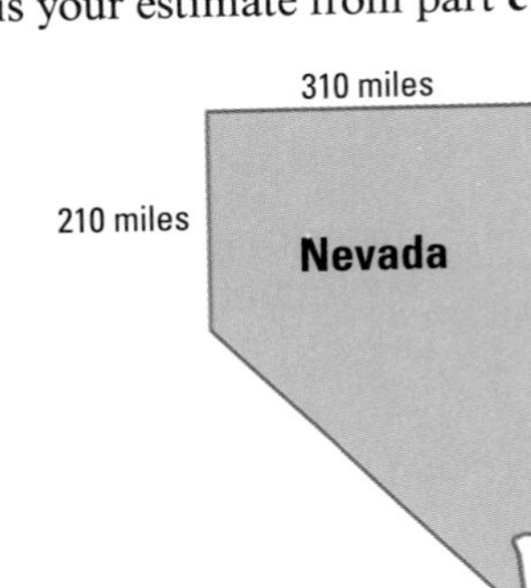

In the southeast region of Nevada is Lake Meade, which is formed by the Colorado River backing up at Hoover Dam shown here.

Adapting to Individual Needs

Challenge
Materials: **Teaching Aid 111**

Give students **Teaching Aid 111.** Note that the area of the square is 64 square units and is split into two triangles and two trapezoids. If these four pieces are rearranged, they form a rectangle that is 5 units by 13 units with an area of 65 square units. Have students try to explain this discrepancy. [Although the four pieces seem to form a rectangle, there is a slight gap along the diagonal that has an area of 1 square unit. If the pieces are drawn large enough, the gap becomes more obvious.]

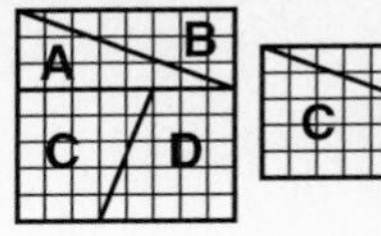

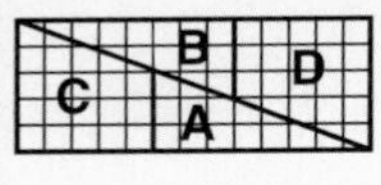

Setting Up Lesson 8-6

Use the In-class Activity on page 465 before assigning Lesson 8-6.

Materials Students will need scissors for *Warm-up* on page 467.

Introducing Lesson 8-6

Creating Squares from Right Triangles

IN-CLASS ACTIVITY

Work in a group of two or three. Your group will need a ruler, protractor, and scissors. You might want to use centimeter grid paper to draw your triangles.

This activity is preparation for a proof of the Pythagorean Theorem in Lesson 8-6.

1 Trace and cut out four copies of right triangle *ABC*.

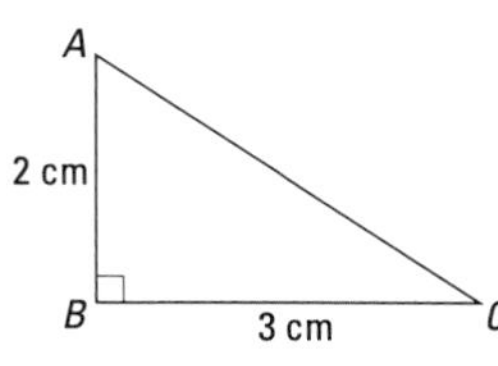

2 Put the copies together so that the legs of the triangles form the quadrilateral *BDFH*, as shown at the right.

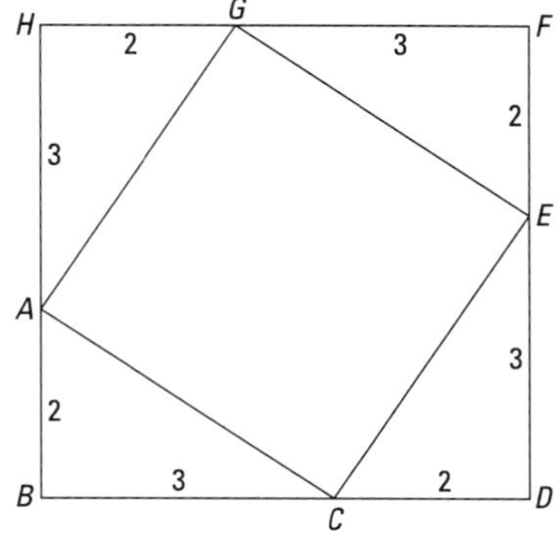

3 **a.** Measure the sides and angles of *BDFH*. See margin.
b. What type of figure is it? b. square
c. What is its area? 25cm^2

4 **a.** Measure the sides and angles of *ACEG*. See margin.
b. What type of figure is it? square

5 Compute the area of *ACEG* using the following relationship:
Area(*ACEG*) = Area(*BDFH*) − Area(△*ABC*) − Area(△*CDE*) − Area(△*EFG*) − Area(△*GHA*). See margin.

In-class Activity

Resources

From the ***Teacher's Resource File***
- Answer Master 8-6
- Teaching Aid 112: Creating Squares from Right Triangles

Additional Resources
- Visual for Teaching Aid 112
- Scissors

This In-class Activity runs students through a specific case of the general proof of the Pythagorean Theorem shown on page 468. We recommend that it be done in class with students **working in pairs.**

For Step 3a, students should know the side and angle measures without using a measuring tool.

For Step 4a, some students may wonder if the measure of each of the four angles should be precisely 90°. Ask them to consider, for example, the measure of $\angle ACE$. $m\angle ACE = 180° - (m\angle BCA + m\angle ECD) = 180° - 90° = 90°$.

You might wish to take the activity one step further. Note that since the middle figure is a square with area 13, its side has length $\sqrt{13}$. Thus, by area alone, we have obtained the length of the hypotenuse of a right triangle from the lengths of its legs. This is how the Pythagorean Theorem is proved in Lesson 8-6.

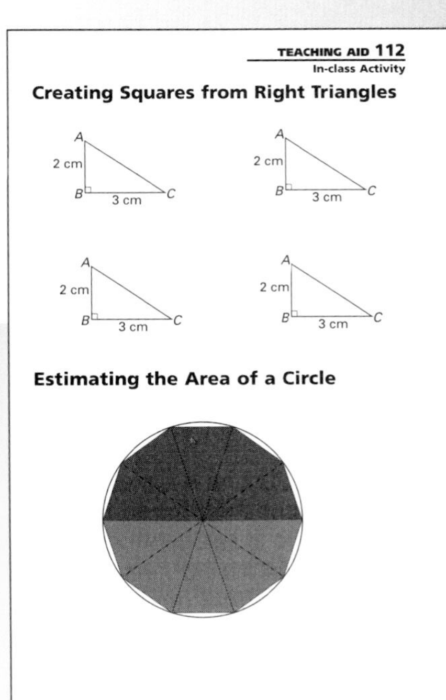

TEACHING AID 112
In-class Activity

Creating Squares from Right Triangles

A, 2 cm, B, 3 cm, C (four copies of the triangle)

Estimating the Area of a Circle

Additional Answers

Step 3.
a. $m\angle B = m\angle D = m\angle F = m\angle H = 90°$
$BD = DF = FH = HB = 5$ cm

Step 4.
a. $m\angle GAC = m\angle ACE = m\angle CEG = m\angle EGA = 90°$
$AC = CE = EG = GA \approx 3.6$ cm

Step 5.
$\text{Area}(ACEG) = 25 - \frac{1}{2}\cdot 2\cdot 3 - \frac{1}{2}\cdot 2\cdot 3 - \frac{1}{2}\cdot 2\cdot 3 - \frac{1}{2}\cdot 2\cdot 3 = 13\text{ cm}^2$

Lesson **8-6**

Objectives

D Apply the Pythagorean Theorem to calculate lengths and areas in right triangles and other figures.
E Apply the Pythagorean Converse Theorem.
H Apply the Pythagorean Theorem to real-world situations.
L Identify cultures in which the Pythagorean Theorem is known to have been studied.

Resources

From the ***Teacher's Resource File***

- Lesson Master 8-6A or 8-6B
- Answer Master 8-6
- Assessment Sourcebook: Quiz for Lessons 8-4 through 8-6
- Teaching Aids
  103 Warm-up
  113 Additional Examples
- Activity Kit, Activity 19
- Technology Sourcebook, Computer Master 16

Additional Resources

- Visuals for Teaching Aids 103, 113
- GeoExplorer or other automatic drawers
- Scissors
- Rope, chalk, and a yardstick
- **Geometry Template,** or a protractor and ruler

LESSON

8-6 The Pythagorean Theorem

Harvest scene. *Egyptians used a rope with knots tied at equal intervals for measuring. These ropes were also used for constructing right triangles.* *See page 469.*

Square Roots

From the area of a square you can determine the length of any of its sides. If the area is A, the length of the side is $\sqrt{A}$. That is why $\sqrt{A}$ is called the **square root** of A. From its definition, $\sqrt{A} \cdot \sqrt{A} = A$.

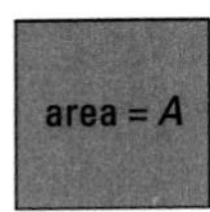

Example 1

The area of the square below is 400 cm^2. What is the length of a side?

400 cm^2

Solution

The length of a side is $\sqrt{400}$. Think: What number multiplied by itself is 400? That number is 20. **The length is 20 cm.**

Check

20 cm · 20 cm = 400 cm^2.

Lesson 8-6 Overview

Broad Goals This lesson reviews the Pythagorean Theorem, offers a proof utilizing area, and deduces its converse.

Perspective Students who have studied from UCSMP texts will have seen the Pythagorean Theorem at least twice before. Other students may also have seen this theorem once or twice. Thus, the purpose of this lesson is to discuss the proof of the theorem, not just to calculate lengths.

The Pythagorean Theorem, together with the SSS Congruence Theorem, enables us to deduce the converse of the Pythagorean Theorem, giving a condition that determines right triangles. Because a theorem is used in the proof of its own converse, many students wrongly think that the theorem has been used to prove itself.

Optional Activities

Activity 1 Technology Connection
If your students have not seen the Pythagorean Theorem before, consider having them explore it with an automatic drawer before reading this lesson. Students should be asked to draw a variety of triangles, including right triangles, measure the sides, add the squares of the two shorter sides, and compare the sum with the square of the longest side. Encourage students to make conjectures about their observations.

"The First Great Theorem"

The *Pythagorean Theorem* relates the lengths of the three sides of any right triangle.

Pythagorean Theorem
In any right triangle with legs of lengths a and b and hypotenuse of length c, $a^2 + b^2 = c^2$.

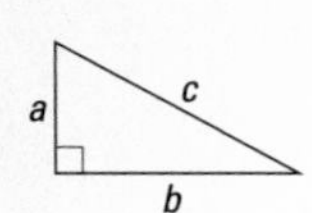

Ancient geometer. *Pythagoras had an acute interest in right triangles.*

❶ The Pythagorean Theorem received the name we give it because the Greek mathematician Pythagoras or one of his students proved it in the 6th century B.C. In the western world, this was the earliest proof known until recent times. Today we are aware of many proofs of this result from cultures throughout the world, and it is not clear where or when the first proof originated. The theorem which we call the "Pythagorean Theorem" was known to the Babylonians before 1650 B.C., and possibly known in India before 800 B.C. Howard Eves, a mathematical historian at the University of Maine, has appropriately called the Pythagorean Theorem "the first great theorem" in mathematics.

Area = c^2
Area = a^2
Area = b^2

The Pythagorean Theorem can also be interpreted as a theorem about areas. It is called "The Theorem of Three Squares" in Japan.

Pythagorean Theorem (alternate statement)
In any right triangle, the sum of the areas of the squares on its legs equals the area of the square on its hypotenuse.

A collection of 370 different proofs of the Pythagorean Theorem was compiled by Elisha Loomis in 1940. It includes proofs by the 12th-century Hindu mathematician Bhaskara, by the 15th-century Italian Leonardo Da Vinci (better known as a painter, sculptor, architect, and engineer), by the 19th-century American James A. Garfield (better known as the 20th president of the United States), and many others. These and most early proofs of the Pythagorean Theorem deduced the theorem from the areas of triangles and rectangles. The proof we give in this lesson is of this type. It dates back at least to the year 1733, but is similar to early Chinese proofs. Howard Eves thinks it may have been the proof Pythagoras actually used. Later in this book you will see a completely different proof based on similar triangles.

Teaching Lesson 8-6

Warm-up

Cut out the four pieces from squares *A* and *B* and rearrange them to cover square *C*. What conclusion can you make? $a^2 + b^2 = c^2$

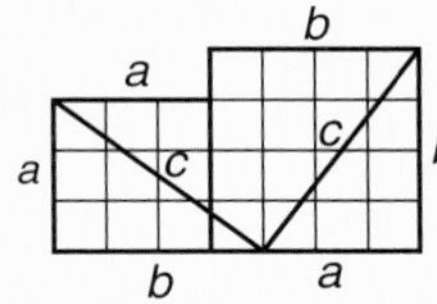

Square A Square B

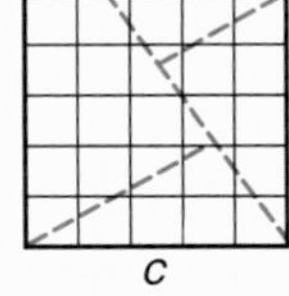

Square C

Notes on Reading

If your students have not studied the Pythagorean Theorem before, see Activity 1 in *Optional Activities* on page 466.

❶ **Multicultural Connection** The existence of the Pythagorean Theorem in so many diverse cultures provides evidence of the universality of geometry. We think it is especially important that students read the three paragraphs between the first statement of the theorem and its proof.

History Connection It may surprise some students (and adults) that James A. Garfield's name is included here. Garfield became the 20th president of the United States in 1881. He won the 1880 presidential election against Ulysses S. Grant by an electoral majority without a popular majority—the first president to be so elected. On July 2, 1881, however, after only four months in office, he was shot in Washington, D.C. He died 80 days later, on September 19, 1881.

Optional Activities

Activity 2 Using Physical Models
Materials: Rope, chalk, and a yardstick

Students are often intrigued by the Egyptian method for constructing a right triangle, as described on page 469, but they must actually do the technique for best effect. After discussing the method, have students **work in groups.** Give each group a rope, chalk, and a yardstick. Have them do the following: Mark off equal consecutive lengths from one end of the rope (12 lengths). Then bend the rope at the 3rd mark and the 7th mark; stretch to make a triangle. Students should note that the lengths 3, 4, and 5 satisfy the Pythagorean relationship and the triangle is a right triangle. Repeat by bending at other points as counterexamples, or splitting into other lengths, such as 5, 12, and 13.

Activity 3
Materials: **Geometry Template** or a protractor and ruler

You may want to use *Activity Kit, Activity 19,* as a follow-up to the lesson. In this activity, students investigate situations arising from drawing squares or triangles on the sides of parallelograms.

❷ A proof of the Pythagorean Theorem must be discussed. The only nontrivial part of the proof is deducing that the middle figure has four right angles—this comes from the fact that the measures of the acute angles are complementary, so two of the angles at the vertices of the quadrilateral have measures adding to 90. Since the three angles add to 180, the third angle must be a right angle.

As with the derivation of the area formulas, some students have trouble distinguishing the method from the result; they will want to set up a big square for every Pythagorean Theorem problem. Again emphasize the power of a theorem; it enables one to not have to go through the procedure of setting up a big square every time. To do that, the theorem must be proved in general, which is why variables are used in the proof. Also emphasize the power of algebra from which this wonderful result came. With algebraic representation of side lengths and algebraic manipulation came a result which holds for *all* right triangles. Many ancient peoples knew of certain triples of integers which were sides of a right triangle, for instance 3-4-5, but not all peoples discovered and proved the relationship among the squares of the sides of *all* right triangles.

Remind students that a calculator approximates square roots to the number of digits it can display, unless x is a perfect square.

Music Connection A song "The Square of the Hypotenuse," by Saul Chaplin and Johnny Mercer, was written for the film "Merry Andrew" in 1958 and sung by Danny Kaye. It is found in the book *The Mathematical Magpie,* by Clifton Fadiman.

❷ A Proof of the Pythagorean Theorem

Look back at the In-class Activity on page 465. You should have found that $ACEG$ is a square with area 13. This means that the length of its side is $\sqrt{13}$. The sides of the four right triangles are thus 2, 3, and $\sqrt{13}$. Notice that $2^2 + 3^2 = (\sqrt{13})^2$. The general proof involves the same kind of figure as the In-class Activity, except that it uses a and b instead of 2 and 3.

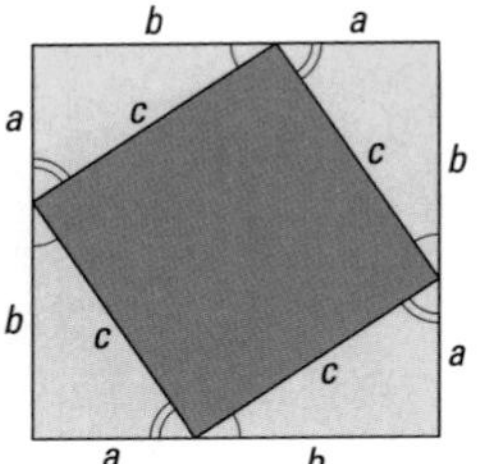

Proof:

Given: A right triangle with legs a and b and hypotenuse c.

To prove: $a^2 + b^2 = c^2$

Argument:

The right triangle and its congruent copies are shown at the left. The outer quadrilateral is a square because each side has length $(a + b)$ and it has four right angles. The purple quadrilateral also is a square because each side has length c and each angle is a right angle. (Do you see why?) Now we find the area of the purple square as you did in the Activity.

Area of purple square = Area(large square) − Area(4 right △s)

Since each side of the large square is $a + b$, its area is $(a + b)^2$.

Each of the four right triangles has area $\frac{1}{2}ab$.

So the purple square has area $(a + b)^2 - 4 \cdot \frac{1}{2}ab = (a^2 + 2ab + b^2) - 2ab$
$= a^2 + b^2$.

But the area of the purple square is c^2. So $c^2 = a^2 + b^2$.

The Pythagorean Theorem is useful in many kinds of problems.

Example 2

A conveyor belt carries bales of hay 35 feet up from ground level to a hayloft. The end of the belt is 42 feet from the barn. How far does a bale of hay travel on the conveyor belt?

Solution

The endpoints of the conveyor belt and the point directly below the hayloft determine a right triangle. Call x the length of the path.

$$x^2 = 35^2 + 42^2$$
$$= 1225 + 1764$$
$$= 2989$$

So $x = \sqrt{2989} \approx 54.7$ feet.

Given the lengths of the hypotenuse and a leg of a right triangle, you can use the Pythagorean Theorem to find the length of the other leg.

Optional Activities

Activity 4 After discussing the proof given in the text, you might show students the following proof, which is credited to James A. Garfield before he became president of the United States. The proof essentially uses the bottom half of the figure from the In-class Activity, on page 465. We begin with $\triangle WZV$ and form a congruent copy in the position of $\triangle VYX$ as shown here, so that $\overline{XY} \parallel \overline{WZ}$. Thus $WXYZ$ is a trapezoid.

Since the acute angles at V are complementary, $\angle WVX$ is a right angle. Now the total area can be found either by using the trapezoid formula, or by adding the areas of the three triangles.

Area(trapezoid)	Area (triangles)
$= \frac{1}{2}(a + b)(a + b)$	$\frac{1}{2}ab + \frac{1}{2}ab + \frac{1}{2}c^2$
$= \frac{1}{2}(a^2 + 2ab + b^2)$	$= \frac{1}{2}(ab + ab + c^2)$
	$= \frac{1}{2}(2ab + c^2)$

Equating the two expressions for the area and simplifying gives $a^2 + 2ab + b^2 = 2ab + c^2$, or $a^2 + b^2 = c^2$

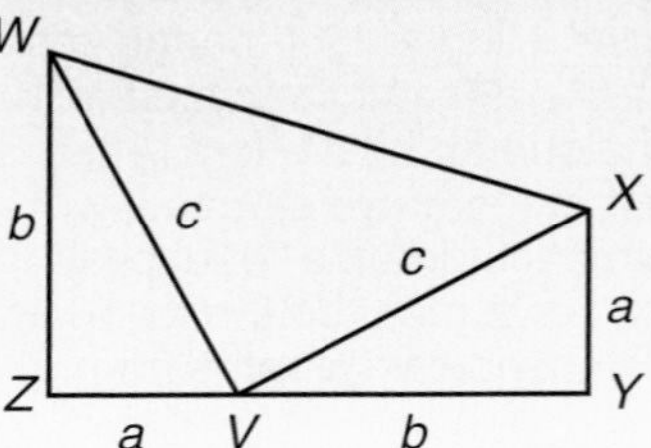

Example 3

A truck driver uses a portable conveyor belt 13 feet long to unload cartons to a loading dock 5 feet above the truck bed. How far does the conveyor belt extend into the truck?

Solution

From the Pythagorean Theorem,

$$5^2 + YZ^2 = 13^2.$$
$$25 + YZ^2 = 169$$
$$YZ^2 = 144$$
$$YZ = 12 \text{ feet}$$

Check

Does $5^2 + 12^2 = 13^2$? Yes, $25 + 144 = 169$.

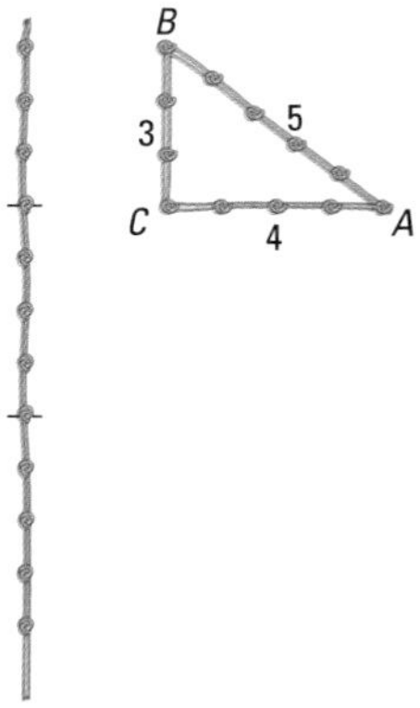

B 3 5 C 4 A

The Converse of the Pythagorean Theorem

To make a right triangle, the ancient Egyptians took a rope with 12 equally spaced knots in it, and then bent it in two places to form a triangle with sides of lengths 3, 4, and 5. The angle formed by the sides of lengths 3 and 4 was used as a right angle.

Is the angle at C exactly 90°? Here we know that $3^2 + 4^2 = 5^2$, and wonder if the triangle is a right triangle. The converse of a theorem is not necessarily true, but the converse of the Pythagorean Theorem is true.

Pythagorean Converse Theorem
If a triangle has sides of lengths a, b, and c, and $a^2 + b^2 = c^2$, then the triangle is a right triangle.

Proof

Given: Triangle ABC with sides of lengths a, b, and c and with $c^2 = a^2 + b^2$.

To prove: $\triangle ABC$ is a right triangle.

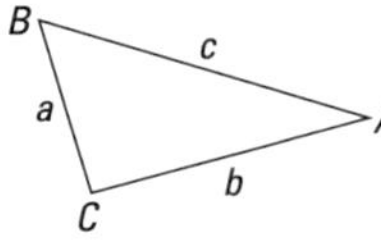

Drawing:

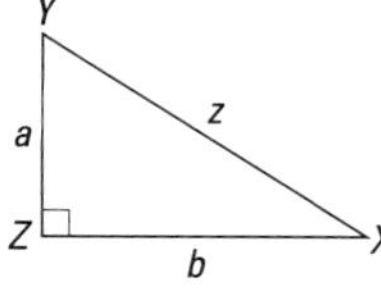

Argument:
Consider right $\triangle XYZ$ with legs of lengths a and b, the same as $\triangle ABC$, and hypotenuse z.

By the Pythagorean Theorem, in $\triangle XYZ$, $a^2 + b^2 = z^2$.
But it is given that $a^2 + b^2 = c^2$.
So, by substitution, $z^2 = c^2$.
Taking positive square roots of each side, $z = c$.

Thus the three sides of $\triangle ABC$ are congruent to the three sides of $\triangle XYZ$. So, by the SSS Congruence Theorem, $\triangle ABC \cong \triangle XYZ$. Since $\angle Z$ is a right angle, $\angle C$ is a right angle by the CPCF Theorem. Thus $\triangle ABC$ is a right triangle.

Additional Examples

These examples are also given on **Teaching Aid 113.**

1. What is the length of a side of a square whose area is 225 ft^2? **15 ft**
2. Two points A and B are 100 feet apart on the horizontal ground. A pole 5 feet tall is positioned between them perpendicular to the ground. A rope is tightly attached at points A and B, passing over the top of the pole. Does the length of the rope depend on the location of the pole? (Note: Diagram is not drawn to scale.)

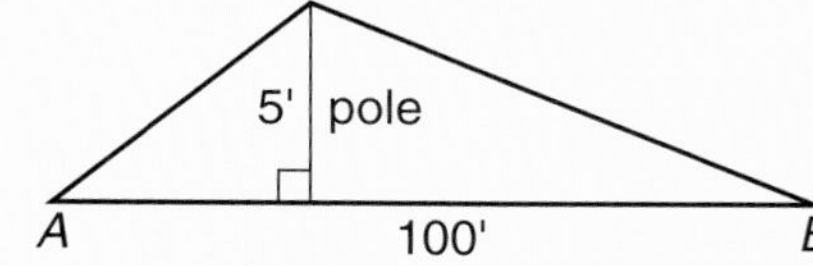

Yes. For instance, if the pole is 5 feet from one end, the rope would have to be about 102.2 feet long, but if it were in the center, the length would be about 100.5 feet. (Have students estimate before calculating. They may be surprised that the length of the rope is sometimes so close to 100 feet.)

3. Find RS in $\triangle RST$. **18 units**

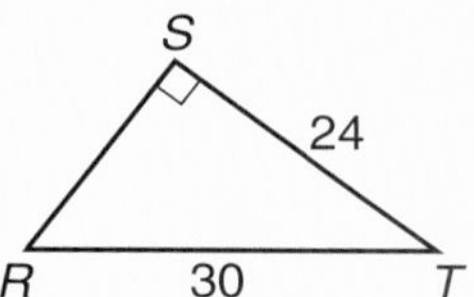

4. Determine if {39, 65, 52} is a Pythagorean triple. **Yes.** $39^2 + 52^2 = 65^2$.

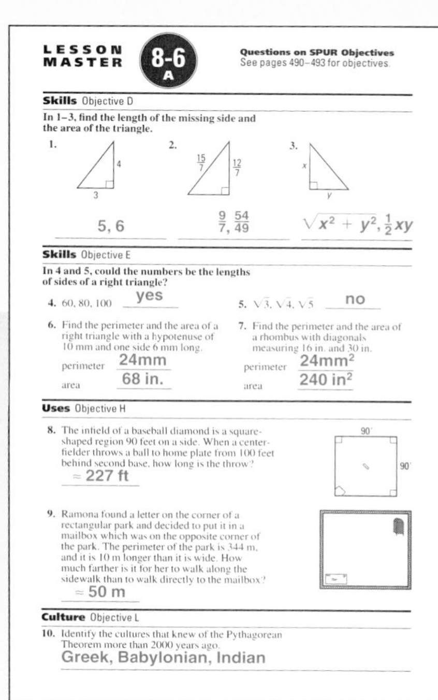

LESSON MASTER **8-6 A**

Questions on SPUR Objectives
See pages 490–493 for objectives.

Skills Objective D

In 1–3, find the length of the missing side and the area of the triangle.

1. (triangle with legs 3 and 4) 5, 6
2. (triangle with sides $\frac{15}{7}$ and $\frac{12}{7}$) $\frac{9}{7}, \frac{54}{49}$
3. (triangle with legs x and y) $\sqrt{x^2 + y^2}, \frac{1}{2}xy$

Skills Objective E

In 4 and 5, could the numbers be the lengths of sides of a right triangle?

4. 60, 80, 100 yes
5. $\sqrt{3}, \sqrt{4}, \sqrt{5}$ no
6. Find the perimeter and the area of a right triangle with a hypotenuse of 10 mm and one side 6 mm long.
   perimeter 24mm
   area 68 in.
7. Find the perimeter and the area of a rhombus with diagonals measuring 16 in. and 30 in.
   perimeter $24mm^2$
   area 240 in^2

Uses Objective H

8. The infield of a baseball diamond is a square-shaped region 90 feet on a side. When a centerfielder throws a ball to home plate from 100 feet behind second base, how long is the throw? ≈ 227 ft
   (90′, 90′)
9. Ramona found a letter on the corner of a rectangular park and decided to put it in a mailbox which was on the opposite corner of the park. The perimeter of the park is 344 m, and it is 10 m longer than it is wide. How much farther is it for her to walk along the sidewalk than to walk directly to the mailbox? ≈ 50 m

Culture Objective L

10. Identify the cultures that knew of the Pythagorean Theorem more than 2000 years ago.
    Greek, Babylonian, Indian

Optional Activities

Activity 5 Technology Connection
In *Technology Sourcebook, Computer Master 16,* students investigate two proofs of the Pythagorean Theorem, one credited to Leonardo da Vinci and the other to President James Garfield.

Notes on Questions

Question 5 This question should be discussed. It outlines the proof of the Pythagorean Theorem.

Questions 7–10, 12–17 On many standardized tests, it is useful to know common Pythagorean triples and their multiples, such as the following: 3, 4, 5; 5, 12, 13; 7, 24, 25; 8, 15, 17; 9, 40, 41. Encourage students to look for these triples and multiples of them.

Question 18 Students should learn to (1) find the area given the length of a side, and (2) find the length of a side given the area.

Question 24 This question helps to prepare students for similarity and trigonometry. If one leg is twice the other, the hypotenuse is always the same multiple of the shorter leg. The sides are in the same extended ratio $1 : 2 : \sqrt{5}$.

(Notes on Questions continue on page 472.)

It is also true that if $a^2 + b^2 \neq c^2$, then a, b, and c cannot be lengths of sides of a right triangle. A proof is given in Chapter 11.

Example 4

A set of three numbers that can be the lengths of sides of a right triangle is called a **Pythagorean triple.** Determine if {11, 20, 23} is a Pythagorean triple.

Solution

Take the two smallest numbers, 11 and 20, and see if the sum of their squares equals the square of the largest number, 23.

Does $11^2 + 20^2 = 23^2$?
No, because $11^2 + 20^2 = 521$
and $23^2 = 529$

The set {11, 20, 23} is not a Pythagorean triple.

QUESTIONS

Covering the Reading

1. If a square has area 225 square meters, how long is a side? 15 meters
2. Babylonian manuscripts indicate knowledge of the Pythagorean Theorem a thousand years before Pythagoras. About how many years ago were the Babylonian manuscripts created? about 3600 years
3. Explain why the name "Theorem of Three Squares" is an appropriate name for what we call the Pythagorean Theorem. See left.
4. Name two famous people who gave original proofs of the Pythagorean Theorem. Sample: Leonardo Da Vinci, James Garfield
5. Use the figure at the right.
   a. What is the area of each triangle? $\frac{1}{2}ab$
   b. What is the area of the large square? See left.
   c. What is the area of the tilted square in terms of a and b? $a^2 + b^2$
   d. What is c in terms of a and b? $\sqrt{a^2 + b^2}$

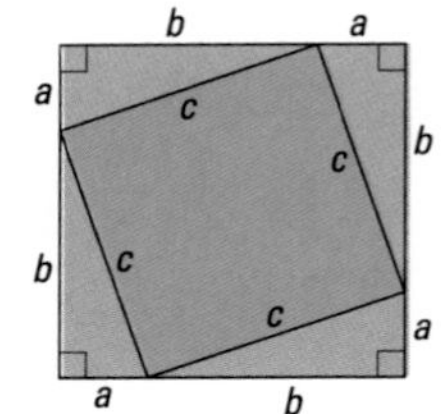

3) Sample: In $a^2 + b^2 = c^2$, each square term equals the area of a square on one side of the triangle.

5b) $(a + b)^2$ or $a^2 + 2ab + b^2$

6. To find the length of the hypotenuse of a right triangle, which is quicker for you, the method of Question 5 or the Pythagorean Theorem? Pythagorean Theorem

In 7 and 8, find the length of the hypotenuse.

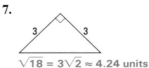

7. 3, 3
$\sqrt{18} = 3\sqrt{2} \approx 4.24$ units

8. 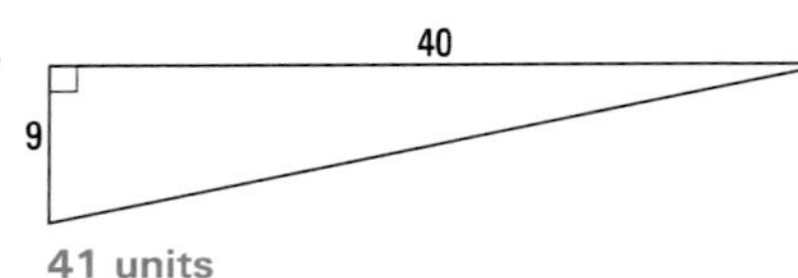

41 units

Adapting to Individual Needs

Extra Help

Because some triangles involve lengths that are Pythagorean triples, students sometimes think they have made a mistake when they solve for an unknown length in a right triangle and obtain a non-integer or decimal solution. Point out that *most* right triangles do not involve Pythagorean triples, so students should not be surprised when they obtain such non-integer answers.

LESSON MASTER 8-6 B Questions on SPUR Objectives

Vocabulary

1. State the *Pythagorean Theorem.* In any right triangle with legs of lengths a and b and hypotenuse of length c, $a^2 + b^2 = c^2$.

2. State the *Pythagorean Converse Theorem.* If a triangle has sides of lengths a, b, and c and $a^2 + b^2 = c^2$, then the triangle is a right triangle.

Skills Objective D: Apply the Pythagorean Theorem to calculate lengths and areas in right triangles and other figures.

In 3–5, a triangle is given. a. Find the length of the missing side. b. Find the area.

3. (5, 13) a. 12 units b. 30 units²
4. (24, 7) a. 25 units b. 84 units²
5. (6n, 5m) a. $\sqrt{25m^2 + 36n^2}$ un. b. 15 mn un.²

6. Find the perimeter and the area of a rhombus with diagonals measuring 20 in. and 32 in.
perimeter $8\sqrt{89} \approx 75.47$ in. area 320 in²

Skills Objective E: Apply the Pythagorean Converse Theorem.

In 7–9, could the numbers be the lengths of sides of a right triangle?

7. 4, 5, 7 no 8. 9, 40, 41 yes 9. 20, 21, 29 yes

10. Find the perimeter and the area of a right triangle with a hypotenuse of 25 mm and one side 7 mm long.
perimeter 56 mm area 84 mm²

11. Given $A = (5, 2)$ and $B = (8, 2)$, give possible integer coordinates for C such that $BC = \sqrt{34}$. Samples: (5, 7), (5, -3), (8, 7), (8, -3)

470

In 9 and 10, find the length of the missing leg.

9. **10.**

9. 12 units

10. $\sqrt{1599} \approx$ 39.99 units

11. Suppose that the hayloft in Example 2 was 20 feet high instead of 35 feet. To the nearest tenth of a foot, how far would the bale travel? 46.5 ft

In 12–17, determine if the set is a Pythagorean triple.

12. {3, 4, 5} Yes **13.** {14, 8, 17} No **14.** {25, 24, 7} Yes

15. {40, 9, 41} Yes **16.** {1.67, 2.76, 3.33} No **17.** $\{2, 2\frac{2}{3}, 3\frac{1}{3}\}$ Yes

Applying the Mathematics

18. If a square room has an area of 20 square feet, what is the length of a side of the room, to the nearest inch? 54″

In 19–21, give answers to the nearest tenth. It helps to draw a picture.

19. Felicia walked from her home due north 10 miles, then due east 3 miles. How far was she from home? $\sqrt{109} \approx 10.4$ miles

20. Find the length of a diagonal of a rectangular field with sides 24 meters and 70 meters. 74 meters

21. The base of an 8-foot ladder is placed 2 feet away from a wall. How high up the wall will the ladder reach? $\sqrt{60} \approx 7.75$ feet

22. How long would it take a person to walk around the trapezoidal field pictured here, at a rate of 90 meters per minute? (Hint: Draw a perpendicular line from Q to $\overline{TS}$.) $\frac{1400}{90} \approx 15.56$ minutes

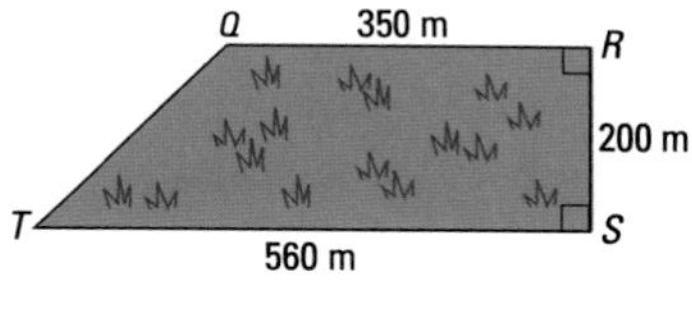

23. Find the perimeter of the rhombus shown at the right if $RO = 48$ and $MH = 14$. 100

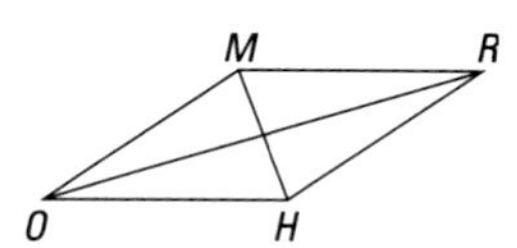

24. One leg of a right triangle is twice the length of the other. How many times as long as the smaller leg is the hypotenuse? (That is, find the value of k below.) $k = \sqrt{5} \approx 2.24$

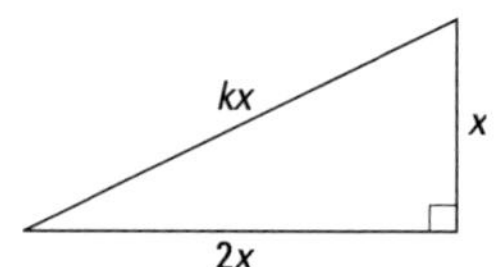

Follow-up for Lesson 8-6

Practice

For more questions on SPUR Objectives, use **Lesson Master 8-6A** (shown on page 469) or **Lesson Master 8-6B** (shown on pages 470–471).

Assessment

Quiz A quiz covering Lessons 8-4 through 8-6 is provided in the *Assessment Sourcebook.*

Oral/Written Communication Have students **work in groups** to make up real-life situations where the Pythagorean Theorem could be used . [Students provide meaningful situations where the Pythagorean Theorem is useful.]

(Follow-up continues on page 472.)

Adapting to Individual Needs

Challenge

The figure at the right is composed of a series of adjacent right triangles. Find h. [$\sqrt{7}$]. Find the length of the hypotenuse of the nth triangle in the pattern in terms of n. [$\sqrt{n+1}$]

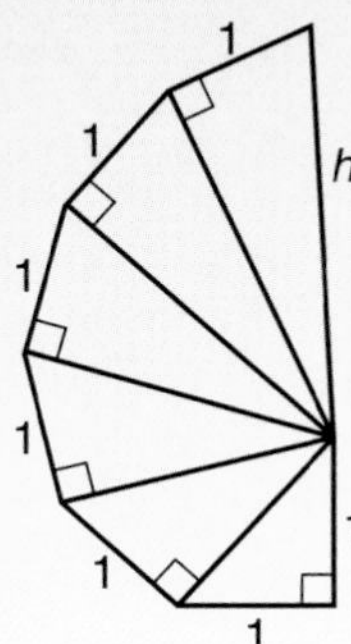

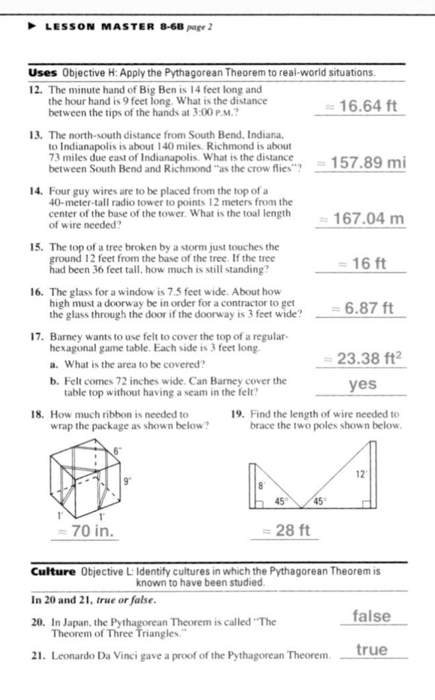

▶ **LESSON MASTER 8-6B** *page 2*

Uses Objective H: Apply the Pythagorean Theorem to real-world situations.

12. The minute hand of Big Ben is 14 feet long and the hour hand is 9 feet long. What is the distance between the tips of the hands at 3:00 P.M.? ≈ 16.64 ft

13. The north-south distance from South Bend, Indiana, to Indianapolis is about 140 miles. Richmond is about 73 miles due east of Indianapolis. What is the distance between South Bend and Richmond "as the crow flies"? ≈ 157.89 mi

14. Four guy wires are to be placed from the top of a 40-meter-tall radio tower to points 12 meters from the center of the base of the tower. What is the toal length of wire needed? ≈ 167.04 m

15. The top of a tree broken by a storm just touches the ground 12 feet from the base of the tree. If the tree had been 36 feet tall, how much is still standing? ≈ 16 ft

16. The glass for a window is 7.5 feet wide. About how high must a doorway be in order for a contractor to get the glass through the door if the doorway is 3 feet wide? ≈ 6.87 ft

17. Barney wants to use felt to cover the top of a regular-hexagonal game table. Each side is 3 feet long.

a. What is the area to be covered? ≈ 23.38 ft²

b. Felt comes 72 inches wide. Can Barney cover the table top without having a seam in the felt? yes

18. How much ribbon is needed to wrap the package as shown below? ≈ 70 in.

19. Find the length of wire needed to brace the two poles shown below. ≈ 28 ft

Culture Objective L: Identify cultures in which the Pythagorean Theorem is known to have been studied.

In 20 and 21, *true or false.*

20. In Japan, the Pythagorean Theorem is called "The Theorem of Three Triangles." false

21. Leonardo Da Vinci gave a proof of the Pythagorean Theorem. true

Extension

Table 1		
a	*b*	*c*
3	4	5
5	12	13
7	24	25
9	40	41
11	60	61
13	84	85
[15]	[112]	[113]

Table 2		
a	*b*	*c*
4	3	5
8	15	17
12	35	37
16	63	65
20	99	101
24	143	145
[28]	[195]	[197]

Some Pythagorean triples are shown in Table 1. Ask students how they can determine the next row. Ask them to give formulas for *b* and *c* in terms of *a*. [Sample: The first column increases by 2; the second column increases by 4 more than the last increase; the third column is 1 more than the second column. General formulas are: a, $b = \frac{a^2 - 1}{2}$, $c = \frac{a^2 + 1}{2}$.] Another sequence of triples is shown in Table 2. Ask students to give general formulas for *b* and *c* in terms of *a*. [Sample: a, $b = (\frac{a}{2})^2 - 1$, $c = (\frac{a}{2})^2 + 1$.]

Project Update Project 2, *Hero's Formula,* on page 485, relates to the content of this lesson.

Notes on Questions

Question 26 Career Connection A process is outlined in this question which is actually used by surveyors. Point out the importance of trapezoids. Discuss the cleverness of the surveyors. Although it would be easy to measure the length of one side of the triangle, assuming their tools to be a tape measure and compass, what advantage is there in working from north-south or east-west lines? [These can be found with a compass.] What problems would there be in finding an altitude of $\triangle FND$? [It would be difficult to determine the direction perpendicular to any of the sides.]

Question 28 The drawing is very rough; in 1995 *Information Please Almanac,* the area of Lake Michigan is given as 22,400 square miles.

Review

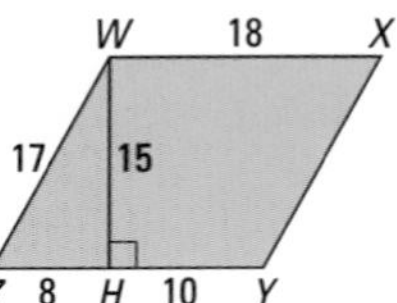

25. Find the area of the parallelogram at the left. *(Lesson 8-5)* 270 units²

26. Surveyors were hired to find the area of the empty lot $\triangle DNF$ below. First, they marked off an east-west line $\overleftrightarrow{EW}$ through *A*. Then they measured the north-south lines and recorded:

segment	$\overline{DC}$	$\overline{NB}$	$\overline{FG}$	$\overline{CB}$	$\overline{BG}$
length (in feet)	80	200	160	66	250

What is the area of the lot? (Hint: Consider the areas of trapezoids in the figure.) *(Lesson 8-5)* 16,320 sq ft

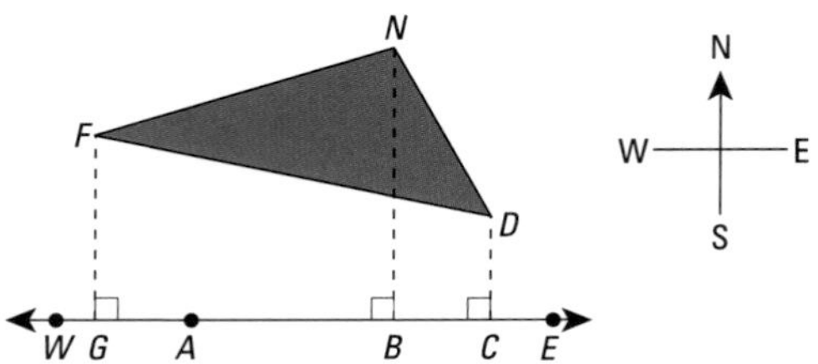

27. Find the area of the triangle of Question 7. *(Lesson 8-4)* 4.5 units²

28. Estimate the area of Lake Michigan using the given grid. *(Lesson 8-3)*
a. See left. **b.**

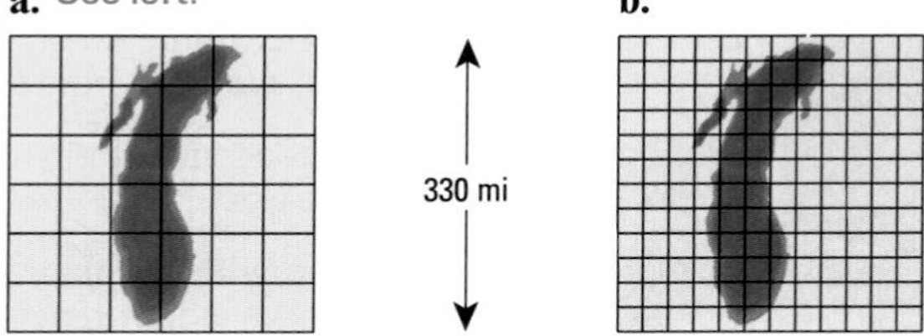

28a) 24,200 miles²; answers may vary by ±3000 miles².
b) 23,066 miles²; answers may vary by ±800 miles².

29. Draw a circle. On the circle, identify an arc with each measure. *(Lesson 3-2)* See left.
a. 90° **b.** 80° **c.** 220°

29a, b, c) Sample:

B, C, A, D; 80°, 90°

m $\widehat{BCD}$ = 220°

Exploration

30. For any positive numbers *x* and *y* with $x > y$, the set of three numbers $\{x^2 - y^2, 2xy, x^2 + y^2\}$ is a Pythagorean triple. For instance, if $x = 3$ and $y = 2$, then $x^2 - y^2 = 5$, $2xy = 12$, and $x^2 + y^2 = 13$. Since $5^2 + 12^2 = 13^2$, {5, 12, 13} is a Pythagorean triple. Some Pythagorean triples appear in Questions 12–17. By substituting other values for *x* and *y*, find four other Pythagorean triples not listed there. Sample:
$x = 3, y = 1$: {6, 8, 10}; $x = 10, y = 1$: {20, 99, 101};
$x = 4, y = 2$: {12, 16, 20}; $x = 5, y = 3$: {16, 30, 34}

Setting Up Lesson 8-7

Use the In-class Activity on page 473 before assigning Lesson 8-7.

Introducing Lesson 8-7

Estimating the Circumference of a Circle

IN-CLASS ACTIVITY

Work with another student. You will need a ruler, a compass, and some string. You can use an automatic drawer if one is available.

In the figures below, regular polygons are inscribed in congruent circles with radii of 1.5 cm. Steps 1–6) See margin for samples.

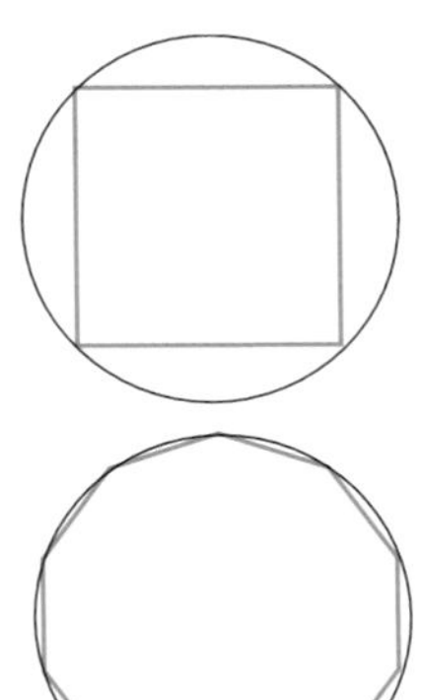

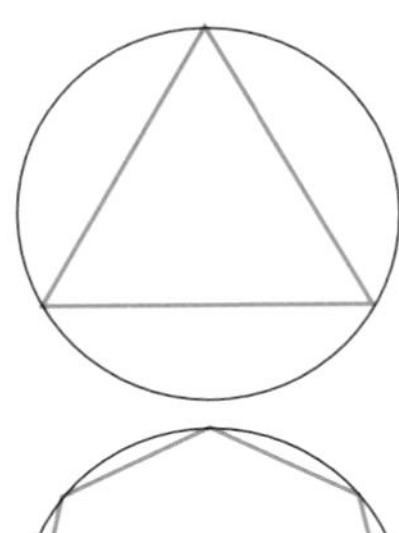

1 Measure the side of each polygon. (An automatic drawer can also be used to create and measure the figures above.)

2 Use the information from Step 1 to calculate the perimeter of each polygon.

3 The perimeter of a circle is called its *circumference.* Which of the four perimeters is the best approximation to the circumference of the circle? Why do you think so?

4 Draw a polygon whose perimeter would give you a better approximation of the circumference than these four polygons.

5 Below right is a circle congruent to the ones above. Use a string to estimate the circumference of the circle (in centimeters) by placing the string on the circle and then measuring its length.

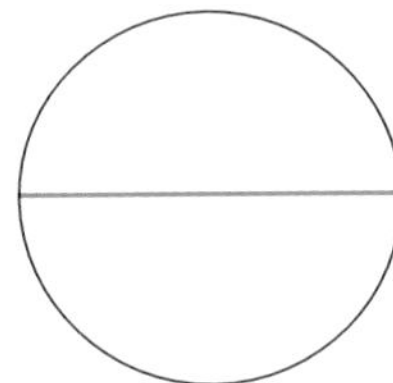

6 Compute $\frac{\text{circumference}}{\text{length of diameter}}$.

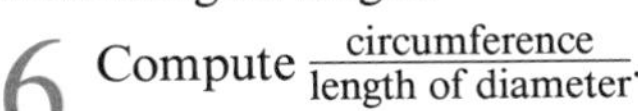

In-class Activity

Resources

From the ***Teacher's Resource File***

- Answer Master 8-7

This In-class Activity shows the method of approximating the circumference of a circle by using inscribed regular polygons of greater and greater numbers of sides.

This activity is best done before students read Lesson 8-7, but could also be done afterwards. Because the radius of the circle is 1.5 cm, the measurements should be taken in centimeters, as accurately as possible—to the nearest tenth of a centimeter.

Have students record the results of the In-class Activity for use with **Question 2** on page 476.

Additional Answers

Step 1.
A. 2.1 cm B. 2.6 cm
C. 0.9 cm D. 1.3 cm

Step 2.
A. 8.4 cm B. 7.8 cm
C. 9 cm D. 9.1 cm

Step 3.
The 10-gon; it has the most sides; thus, it is closer to the circle itself.

Step 4. Sample:

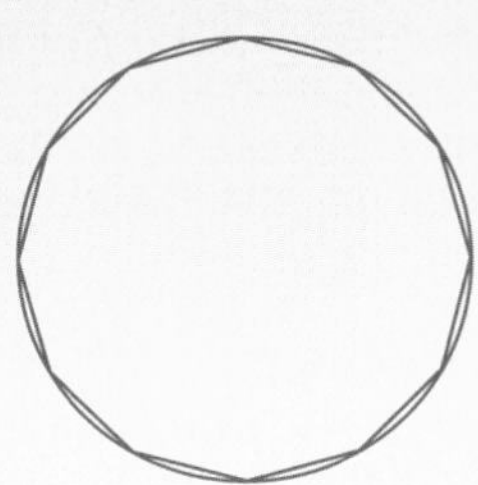

Step 5. About 9.5 cm
Step 6. About 3.14

Lesson 8-7

Objectives

F Calculate lengths and measures of arcs and the circumference of a circle given measures of relevant lengths and angles, and vice versa.

J Apply formulas for the circumference of a circle to real situations.

Resources

From the ***Teacher's Resource File***

- Lesson Master 8-7A or 8-7B
- Answer Master 8-7
- Teaching Aid 103: Warm-up
- Technology Sourcebook, Computer Master 17

Additional Resources

- Visual for Teaching Aid 103
- GeoExplorer or other automatic drawers

Teaching Lesson 8-7

Warm-up

Refer to the diagram below. Find each measure.

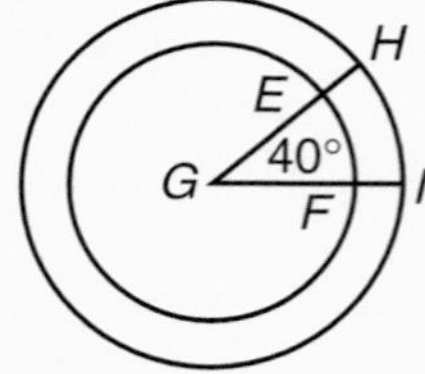

1. m$\widehat{EF}$ 40°
2. m$\widehat{HI}$ 40°
3. m∠EGF 40
4. m∠HGI 40
5. Which is longer, $\widehat{EF}$ or $\widehat{HI}$? $\widehat{HI}$

LESSON

8-7 *Arc Length and Circumference*

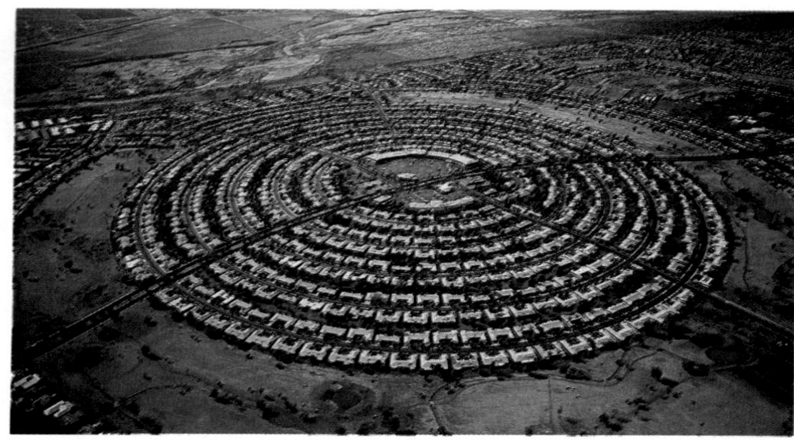

Driving on an arc. *The streets in Sun City, Arizona, are arranged in concentric circles.*

The word **circumference** is a synonym for *perimeter. Circumference* is used with closed curves like circles and ellipses, while *perimeter* is used for polygons and other figures.

When designing a ring for an individual client, a jeweler may measure the circumference of the client's ring finger just above a knuckle. This circumference helps the jeweler to determine the diameter of the finger. Then the jeweler can design and make a ring that will fit.

Relating the Circumference to the Diameter

A procedure like that in the first 4 steps of the In-class Activity on page 473 can be used to estimate the length of any arc of a circle. Recall that a chord is a segment whose endpoints are on a given circle.

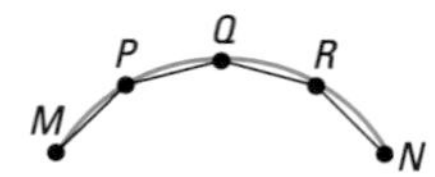

At the right, the length of $\widehat{MN}$ is approximated by $MP + PQ + QR + RN$. By drawing more and more chords of increasingly shorter lengths, the total length of the chords approaches the length of the arc as a limit.

If this is done with an entire circle, the limit is the circumference of the circle. The ratio of the circumference C to the diameter d is equal in all circles. It is denoted by the famous number π, the Greek letter pi. You estimated pi in Step 6 of the In-class Activity.

Lesson 8-7 Overview

Broad Goals This lesson reviews the formula for circumference of a circle, which we assume students have seen before.

Perspective The term *circumference* is used to denote the perimeter of any simple closed curve, but it is not used for other figures. Thus, one speaks of the *circumference* of an ellipse, but the *perimeter* of a regular 32-gon. Pi (π) is defined as the ratio of the circumference of a circle to its diameter. This definition carries the tacit assumption that there is a single ratio, and that assumption is not obvious. To prove it requires notions of limits and similar triangles. Thus, we do not attempt a proof in this course.

Students have seen approximation of area by finer and finer grids of squares superimposed on the region in question. To find arc length, the lengths of segments are added together. The smaller the lengths, the more accurate the approximation. These two geometric examples help to provide a foundation for the notion of limit.

These examples of limits have counterparts in the real world. "Circular" objects are often made with short segments. Farm silos and barrels are made of flat staves; the Susan B. Anthony dollar has a circular edge but the face shows a nonagon; a computer

Definition

$\pi = \frac{C}{d}$, where C is the circumference and d is the diameter of a circle.

The number π is irrational; π cannot be written either as a finite decimal or as a simple fraction. The decimal for π is infinite. Here are the first 50 decimal places.

3.14159 26535 89793 23846 26433 83279 50288 41971 69399 37510 . . .

Most scientific calculators have a key for π which gives the first 6 or 8 places in its decimal approximation. π is about 3.14159 or about $\frac{22}{7}$.

Solving the defining equation $\pi = \frac{C}{d}$ for C gives a formula for the circumference of any circle. Substituting $2r$ for d gives a formula for the circumference in terms of the circle's radius.

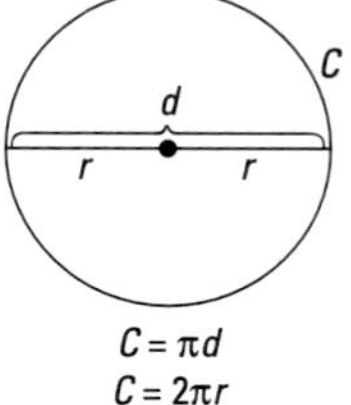

$C = \pi d$
$C = 2\pi r$

Circle Circumference Formula
If a circle has circumference C, diameter d, and radius r, then $C = \pi d$, or $C = 2\pi r$.

Substituting 3.14 for π in the circumference formula gives an estimate for C.

$$C \approx 3.14d$$

Exact and Approximate Answers

When you are asked to give an exact circumference, you should leave π in the answer; for example, in the circle below, $C = 7\pi$. If you are not asked for an exact answer, then you can use an approximation for π, such as 3.14 or the approximation given by your calculator. For the circle below, $C = 7\pi \approx 7 \cdot 3.14 = 21.98$.

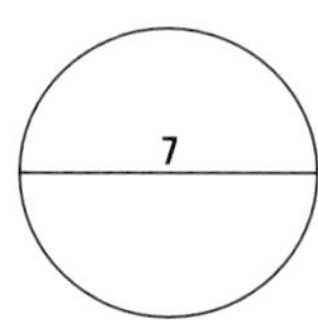

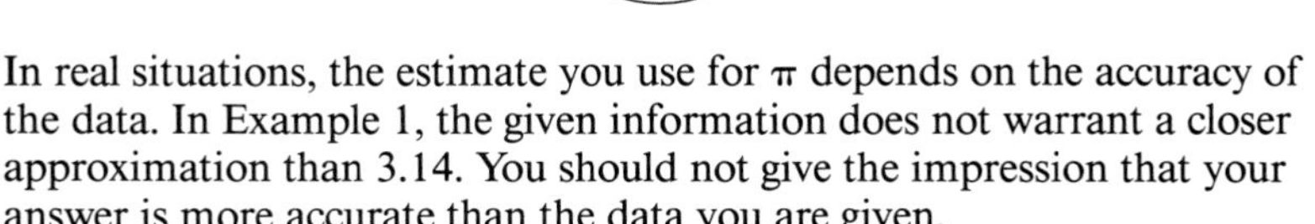

In real situations, the estimate you use for π depends on the accuracy of the data. In Example 1, the given information does not warrant a closer approximation than 3.14. You should not give the impression that your answer is more accurate than the data you are given.

Example 1

The larger bicycle wheel pictured at the left has a diameter of 22 inches. If a rider can get it to go 300 revolutions in a minute, how far will the bike have traveled in that time?

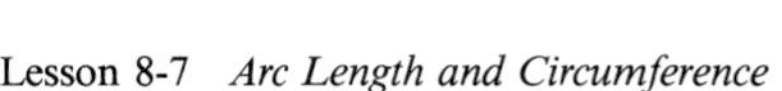

Notes on Reading

Multicultural Connection The finger-ring is an extremely ancient piece of jewelry. Several different types exist (or have existed) around the world. The signet ring, used as a seal or official stamp, dates to Western Asia about 7,000 years ago. It was used commonly in ancient Egypt, Greece, Rome, and Europe, up to about the 18th century. The archer's thumb ring was worn in China, India, Medieval Europe, and elsewhere before the development of the crossbow made its use for archers obsolete. Commemorative and mourning rings came into fashion in England in about the 14th century. Marriage, betrothal, and engagement rings appeared in Roman times, and have since come into widespread use.

Arc *measure* was introduced in Chapter 3 and some students may confuse it with arc *length.* **Example 2** involves both. To emphasize the distinction between arc measure and arc length, we always use the degree symbol for the measure of arcs. Emphasize that arc measure involves the amount of rotation, whereas circumference is associated with arc length. Every circle contains 360° of arc, but circles may have different circumferences. A bicycle race track with several lanes and turns of different degrees may be useful in creating a sense of need for two different types of measure for arcs. Students easily agree that all 90° turns are the same and draws a circle by selecting a series of points an equal distance from a center point and drawing short segments connecting them.

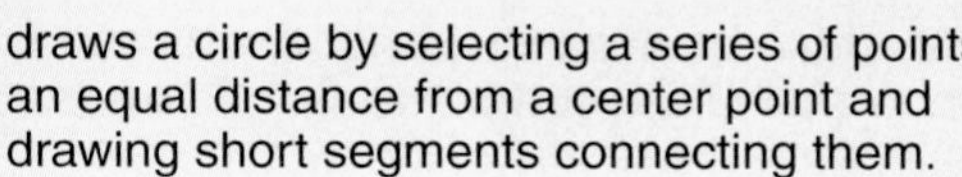

The circumference of a circle with diameter d is πd, which is about $3.14d$, or $6.28r$. That is, the circumference is more than 6 times the radius. This can be verified by the common design made with a compass—inscribing a regular hexagon in circle O. The sides of the hexagon all have lengths equal to the radius (Connecting the vertices to the center of the circle forms six equilateral triangles.) So the perimeter of polygon $ABCDEF$ is 6 times the radius. But clearly the circumference of the circle is greater than that, so a circumference of $6.28 \cdot OA$ seems reasonable.

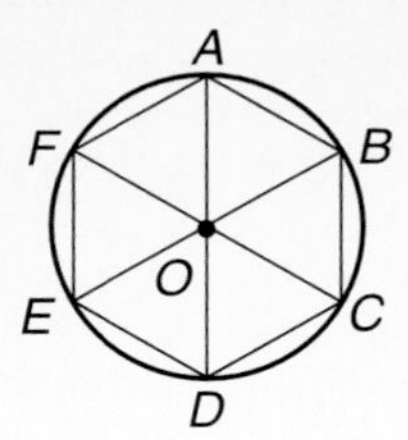

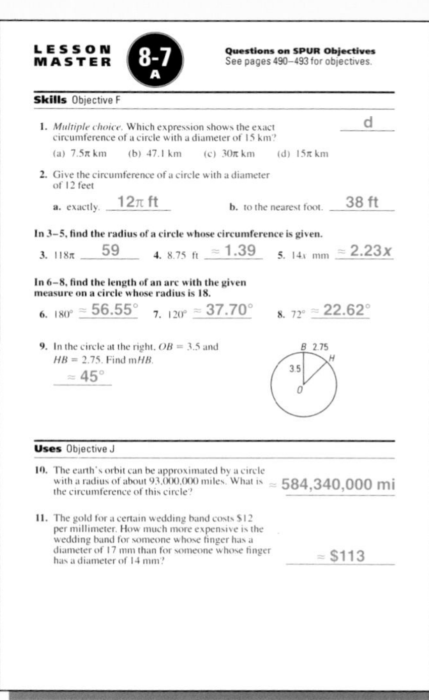

LESSON MASTER 8-7 A

Questions on SPUR Objectives
See pages 490–493 for objectives.

Skills Objective F

1. *Multiple choice.* Which expression shows the exact circumference of a circle with a diameter of 15 km? ___d___
(a) 7.5π km (b) 47.1 km (c) 30π km (d) 15π km

2. Give the circumference of a circle with a diameter of 12 feet
a. exactly. ___12π ft___ b. to the nearest foot. ___38 ft___

In 3–5, find the radius of a circle whose circumference is given.

3. 118π ___59___ 4. 8.75 ft ___≈ 1.39___ 5. 14x mm ___≈ 2.23x___

In 6–8, find the length of an arc with the given measure on a circle whose radius is 18.

6. 180° ___≈ 56.55°___ 7. 120° ___≈ 37.70°___ 8. 72° ___≈ 22.62°___

9. In the circle at the right, $OB = 3.5$ and $HB = 2.75$. Find m$\overset{\frown}{HB}$.
___≈ 45°___

Uses Objective J

10. The earth's orbit can be approximated by a circle with a radius of about 93,000,000 miles. What is the circumference of this circle? ___≈ 584,340,000 mi___

11. The gold for a certain wedding band costs $12 per millimeter. How much more expensive is the wedding band for someone whose finger has a diameter of 17 mm than for someone whose finger has a diameter of 14 mm? ___≈ $113___

are different from a sharper 60° turn. Yet, any bike in an outer lane on the 90° turn travels farther than a bike on the inner lane.

Discuss when 3.14 or $3\frac{1}{7}$ are adequate approximations (buying fencing for a circular flower garden) and when they would be woefully inadequate (designing a die to drill a car-engine cylinder).

Only a few students these days know their hat sizes. Boys are in the range from $6\frac{1}{2}$ to $7\frac{1}{2}$. Girls are in a range from 20 to 24. What is the basis for the measurements? [One is the diameter of the head in inches, the other the circumference in inches.]

Additional Examples

1. A new truck tire has a radius of about 24 inches. A worn tire has a radius of about 23 inches. How many more times will a worn tire have to turn in a mile than a new tire does? About 18 times more, since a 24-in. tire turns about 420 times in a mile while a 23-in. tire turns about 438 times.
2. The minute hand on a clock is 20 cm long. A fly has been sitting on the tip of the minute hand. How far has it traveled between 11 P.M. and 3:45 A.M.? The arc traveled is $4.75 \times 360° = 1710°$. The distance $= \frac{1710}{360} \times 2 \times 20 \times \pi \approx 597$ cm.

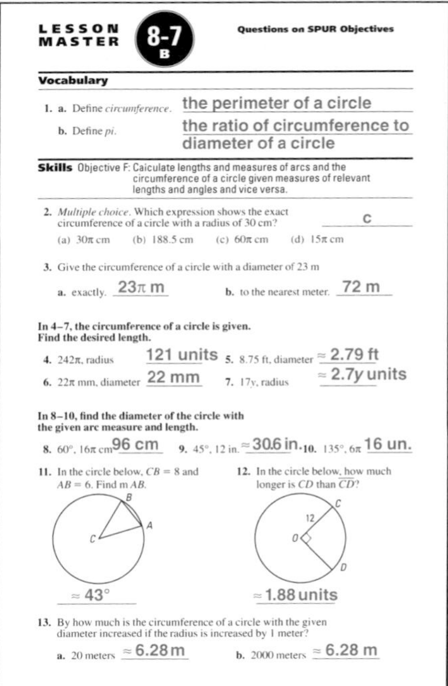

LESSON MASTER 8-7 B Questions on SPUR Objectives

Vocabulary

1. a. Define *circumference*. the perimeter of a circle
   b. Define *pi*. the ratio of circumference to diameter of a circle

Skills Objective F: Calculate lengths and measures of arcs and the circumference of a circle given measures of relevant lengths and angles and vice versa.

2. *Multiple choice*. Which expression shows the exact circumference of a circle with a radius of 30 cm? c
   (a) 30π cm (b) 188.5 cm (c) 60π cm (d) 15π cm
3. Give the circumference of a circle with a diameter of 23 m
   a. exactly. 23π m b. to the nearest meter. 72 m

In 4–7, the circumference of a circle is given. Find the desired length.

4. 242π, radius 121 units
5. 8.75 ft, diameter ≈ 2.79 ft
6. 22π mm, diameter 22 mm
7. $17y$, radius ≈ $2.7y$ units

In 8–10, find the diameter of the circle with the given arc measure and length.

8. 60°, 16π cm 96 cm
9. 45°, 12 in. ≈ 30.6 in.
10. 135°, 6π 16 un.
11. In the circle below, $CB = 8$ and $AB = 6$. Find mAB. ≈ 43°
12. In the circle below, how much longer is CD than $\overline{CD}$? ≈ 1.88 units
13. By how much is the circumference of a circle with the given diameter increased if the radius is increased by 1 meter?
    a. 20 meters ≈ 6.28 m b. 2000 meters ≈ 6.28 m

Solution

One revolution moves the bike the length of the circumference of the wheel.

$$C \approx 3.14 \cdot 22 = 69.08 \text{ inches each revolution}$$

The value 69.08 is too accurate for the given information. It has four meaningful digits but the given information has at most two meaningful digits. So round to 69.
In 300 revolutions, the distance traveled is

$$300 \cdot 69 = 20{,}700 \text{ inches.}$$

Dividing by 12 gives the answer in feet. It travels about 1700 ft.

Check

We check by estimating. Since 22″ is a little less than 2 feet and π is a little more than 3, the circumference of the wheel is about 6 feet. In 300 revolutions, the bike should go about 1800 feet. The answer seems reasonable.

Computing Arc Length

The circumference of a circle can be thought of as the arc length of a 360° arc of the circle. Recall that the degree measure of the arc tells you how much of the circumference the arc covers. You can compute the length of an arc if you know the radius of its circle and the degree measure of the arc.

Example 2

In $\odot O$, $OB = 1.3$ cm and $m\angle AOB = 80$. Find the length of $\widehat{AB}$.

Solution

$m\angle AOB = 80$, so $m\widehat{AB} = 80°$. Thus $\widehat{AB}$ covers $\frac{80}{360}$ of the entire circumference of $\odot O$. So:

$$\begin{aligned} \text{length of } \widehat{AB} &= \frac{80}{360} \cdot C \\ &= \frac{80}{360} \cdot (2\pi r) \\ &= \frac{80}{360} \cdot 2 \cdot \pi \cdot 1.3 \\ &= \frac{208\pi}{360} \text{ cm} \\ &\approx 1.8 \text{ cm.} \end{aligned}$$

QUESTIONS

Covering the Reading

1. *Circumference* is a synonym for __?__. perimeter
2. Refer to the In-class Activity. a) The 10-gon; it had the most sides; thus it was closer to the circle.
   a. What was your answer in Step 3?
   b. What was your approximation for π in Step 6? 3.14

Optional Activities

Activity 1 Here are two activities to support the idea that the circumference of a circle is a number between the perimeters of an inscribed and a circumscribed polygon.

(1) Have students **work in pairs.** Have each student draw a circle of radius ≈ 4 in. Have one student in each pair inscribe a polygon with sides of 1 inch (except for the last one) by starting at a point and carefully drawing chords 1 inch long. Have the other student in the pair circumscribe the circle with the same type of polygon with sides of 1 inch. Compare the average of the two perimeters with the number 8π.

(2) Have students draw a 20-cm-diameter circle which is circumscribed and inscribed with squares. Have them find the perimeter of both squares, and the average of the perimeters. Ask if the average is less than, equal to, or greater than the circumference

3. Define π. π is $\frac{C}{d}$, where C is the circumference and d is the diameter of a circle.

4. π is often approximated by the fraction __?__ or the decimal __?__. 22/7, 3.14

5. *Multiple choice.* The diameter of a circle is 15″. Which is the exact measure of its circumference? b
   (a) 30π″ (b) 15π″ (c) 94.2″ (d) 47.1″

In 6 and 7, use $\odot F$ at the right.

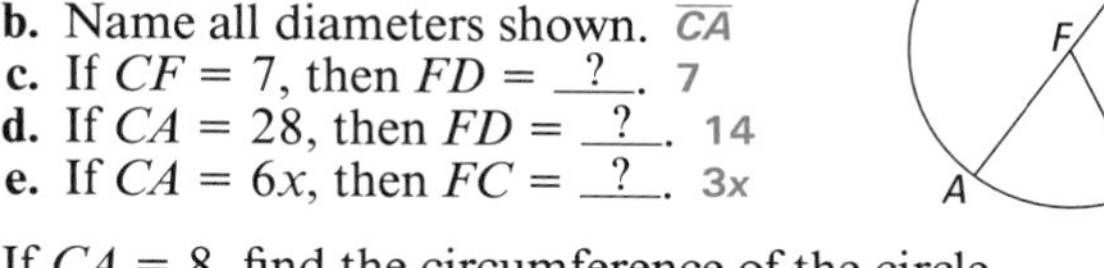

6. a. Name all radii shown. $\overline{FA}, \overline{FC}, \overline{FD}$
   b. Name all diameters shown. $\overline{CA}$
   c. If $CF = 7$, then FD = __?__. 7
   d. If $CA = 28$, then FD = __?__. 14
   e. If $CA = 6x$, then FC = __?__. 3x

7. If $CA = 8$, find the circumference of the circle
   a. exactly. 8π units b. to the nearest tenth. 25.1 units

8. In Example 1, about how far will the bike travel in five minutes if each wheel makes 210 revolutions per minute? about 72,450 inches = 6037.5 ft ≈ 1.14 miles

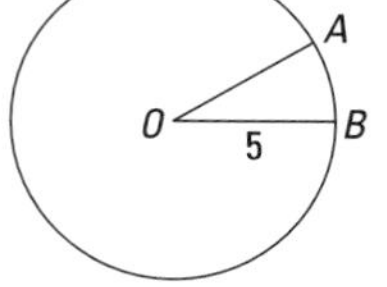

9. In $\odot O$ at the left, $m\widehat{AB} = 30°$. Find the length of $\widehat{AB}$
   a. exactly. $\frac{5\pi}{6}$ units b. to the nearest hundredth. 2.62 units

Applying the Mathematics

10. Write how you would explain the difference between arc length and arc measure to a younger person. Arc length is a distance, while arc measure shows the amount of a turn.

11. A circular pond is enclosed by a square wall ten meters on a side. What is the maximum possible distance around the edge of the pond? $10\pi \approx 31.4$ m

12. On the Allen-Bradley Company building in Milwaukee, four clocks face in four different directions. The minute hand on each clock is 20′ long. How far does the tip of each minute hand travel in a day
    a. measured in degrees? 8640°
    b. measured in feet? 960π or about 3016 feet

Allen-Bradley clock, Milwaukee, Wisconsin

13. Suppose it takes you 110 seconds to walk around a circular garden. At this rate, about how long would it take you to walk straight through the garden along a diameter? $\frac{110}{\pi}$ or about 35 seconds

14. Gail Ant is crawling along the crust of a large piece of 16″-diameter pizza. The piece has central angle 45°. How much further (to the nearest tenth of an inch) does she crawl than her cousin Kerr Ant who is on a medium piece of 12″-diameter pizza, central angle 45°? 1.6″

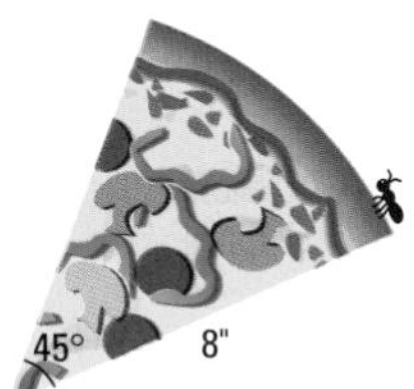

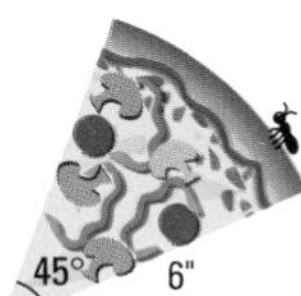

Notes on Questions

Question 3 Students may find defining a number as a ratio of lengths unusual. However, they have seen it before. The number "half" can be thought of as a ratio of lengths, as can any fraction.

Question 4 Another ratio of integers which approximates π is $\frac{355}{113}$, which was used by the Chinese. It differs from π by less than .00000027.

Question 12 You might ask which answer would be the same for a wristwatch (if it has hands). [Part a]

Question 13 Again, there is a reversal of the formula; given the circumference, find the diameter.

(Notes on Questions continue on page 478.)

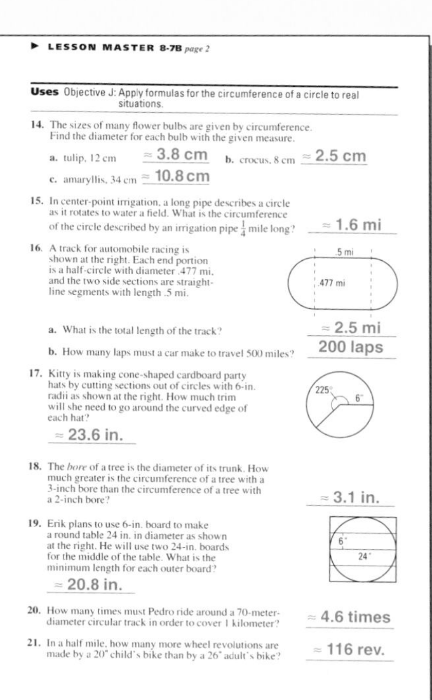

▶ **LESSON MASTER 8-7B** *page 2*

Uses Objective J: Apply formulas for the circumference of a circle to real situations.

14. The sizes of many flower bulbs are given by circumference. Find the diameter for each bulb with the given measure.
    a. tulip, 12 cm ≈ 3.8 cm b. crocus, 8 cm ≈ 2.5 cm
    c. amaryllis, 34 cm ≈ 10.8 cm

15. In center-point irrigation, a long pipe describes a circle as it rotates to water a field. What is the circumference of the circle described by an irrigation pipe $\frac{1}{4}$ mile long? ≈ 1.6 mi

16. A track for automobile racing is shown at the right. Each end portion is a half-circle with diameter .477 mi, and the two side sections are straight-line segments with length .5 mi.
    a. What is the total length of the track? ≈ 2.5 mi
    b. How many laps must a car make to travel 500 miles? 200 laps

17. Kitty is making cone-shaped cardboard party hats by cutting sections out of circles with 6-in. radii as shown at the right. How much trim will she need to go around the curved edge of each hat? ≈ 23.6 in.

18. The *bore* of a tree is the diameter of its trunk. How much greater is the circumference of a tree with a 3-inch bore than the circumference of a tree with a 2-inch bore? ≈ 3.1 in.

19. Erik plans to use 6-in. board to make a round table 24 in. in diameter as shown at the right. He will use two 24-in. boards for the middle of the table. What is the minimum length for each outer board? ≈ 20.8 in.

20. How many times must Pedro ride around a 70-meter-diameter circular track in order to cover 1 kilometer? ≈ 4.6 times

21. In a half mile, how many more wheel revolutions are made by a 20" child's bike than by a 26" adult's bike? ≈ 116 rev.

of the circle. [Outside square perimeter = 80 cm; inside square perimeter ≈ 56.6 cm; average ≈ 68.3 cm; circumference ≈ 62.8 cm; average is greater.]

Activity 2 Technology Connection In *Technology Sourcebook, Computer Master 17,* students draw concentric circles and determine the relationship between central angles and the measures of corresponding arcs, between circumference and arc length, and between arc length and chord length.

Notes on Questions

Questions 17–20 Students need practice in remembering formulas. Remind them of the list of formulas at the end of the chapter and at the back of the book. You may want to point out how many of the formulas of this chapter they have studied so far—all but one.

Questions 24–25 It is important that students have practice at answering questions giving comparisons. They often appear on standardized tests.

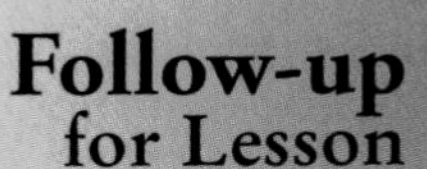

Follow-up for Lesson 8-7

Practice

For more questions on SPUR Objectives, use **Lesson Master 8-7A** (shown on page 475) or **Lesson Master 8-7B** (shown on pages 476–477).

Assessment

Oral/Written Communication Have students **work in pairs.** First have each student draw a circle showing a sector with radius and central angle labeled. Then have them exchange circles and find the length of the arc subtended by the sector. [Students correctly determine arc length when they know the radius and the degree measure of the arc.]

Extension

Ask students to calculate the distance around a pie with an 8-inch diameter. [≈ 25.13 in.] Then have the students find the distance around the remaining crust of the pie if it is missing one slice with a 60° central angle. [≈ 20.94 in.]

Review

15. Below, E, F, G, and H are midpoints of the sides of rectangle $ABCD$. If $AB = 8$ and $BC = 6$, find the perimeter of $EFGH$. *(Lessons 8-1, 8-6)* 20 units

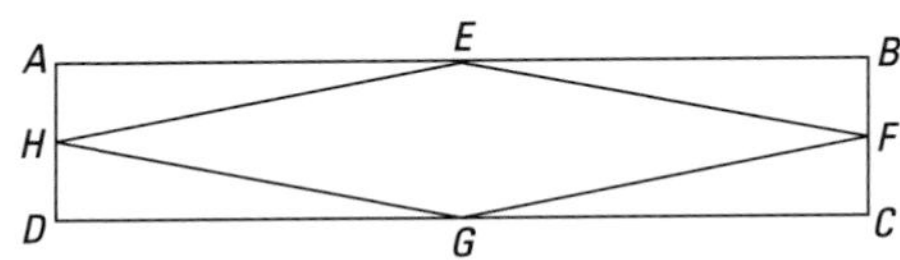

16. $\triangle PON$ is equilateral. M is the midpoint of $\overline{NO}$. *(Lessons 8-4, 8-6)*
a. Find OM. 1 unit
b. Find PM. $\sqrt{3} \approx 1.7$ units
c. Give the area of $\triangle PON$. $\sqrt{3} \approx 1.7$ square units

In 17–20, give a formula for the indicated quantity. *(Lessons 8-1, 8-5)* See left.

17. area of a trapezoid
18. area of a parallelogram
19. perimeter of a square
20. perimeter of a kite

17) $A = \frac{1}{2}h(b_1 + b_2)$
18) $A = bh$
19) $p = 4s$
20) $p = 2a + 2b$

21. Find the area of parallelogram $PARL$. *(Lessons 8-5, 8-6)* 2000 units^2

22. Find the area of a parallelogram $ABCD$ with vertices $A = (0, 0)$, $B = (7, 0)$, $C = (12, 4)$, and $D = (5, 4)$. *(Lesson 8-5)* 28 units^2

23. The sides of a triangle are multiplied by 6.
a. What happens to its perimeter? Its perimeter is multiplied by 6.
b. What happens to its area? *(Lessons 8-1, 8-4)* Its area is multiplied by 36.

In 24 and 25, refer to the figure below.

24. *Multiple choice.* Which of the following is true? *(Lesson 8-4)* b
(a) Area($\triangle XYZ$) > Area($\triangle XYW$)
(b) Area($\triangle XYZ$) = Area($\triangle XYW$)
(c) Area($\triangle XYZ$) < Area($\triangle XYW$)

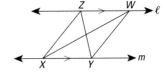

25. *Multiple choice.* If q is the perimeter of $\triangle XYZ$ and r is the perimeter of $\triangle XYW$, then d
(a) $q > r$.
(b) $q = r$.
(c) $q < r$.
(d) the relationship between q and r cannot be determined.
(Lesson 8-1)

26. Refer to Example 1. How fast is the bicycle going in miles per hour? *(Previous course)* ≈ 20 mph

Exploration

27. a. Using a tape measure or string, measure the circumference of your neck to the nearest half inch or centimeter. Sample: $14\frac{1}{2}$ in.
b. Assuming your neck is circular, use your measurement to estimate your neck's radius. Sample: $14.5/2\pi \approx 2.3$ inches
c. What would be another way to determine its radius? Estimate the diameter by measuring the distance between straightedges on either side of your neck. Half the diameter is the radius.

Adapting to Individual Needs

Extra Help
For students who confuse arc measure with arc length, you might use the example of a second hand on a clock. Have students suppose that two flies are sitting on the second hand, one at 1 inch from the center and the other at 2 inches from the center. Point out that both flies travel through the same arc measure, but not the same arc length, as the second hand revolves.

Challenge
Have students look up radian measure.
1. What is the formula for converting between degrees and radians? [180° = π radians]
2. What is the formula for arc length in terms of radians? [If the measure of the central angle is q radians and the radius is r, then the length of the arc is rq.]

Setting Up Lesson 8–8

Use the In-class Activity on page 479 before discussing Lesson 8-8.

Materials If you have students do *Optional Activities* on page 481, they will need scissors.

Introducing Lesson 8-8

Estimating the Area of a Circle

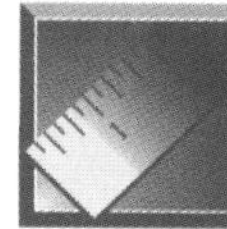

IN-CLASS ACTIVITY

Work on this Activity with a partner. You will need a ruler, compass, protractor, and scissors.

1 Trace the circle containing the decagon from the In-class Activity on page 473. Draw in the five symmetry lines that connect opposite vertices. Cut out the 10 wedges and rearrange them horizontally, as started below at the right.

1–4) See margin.

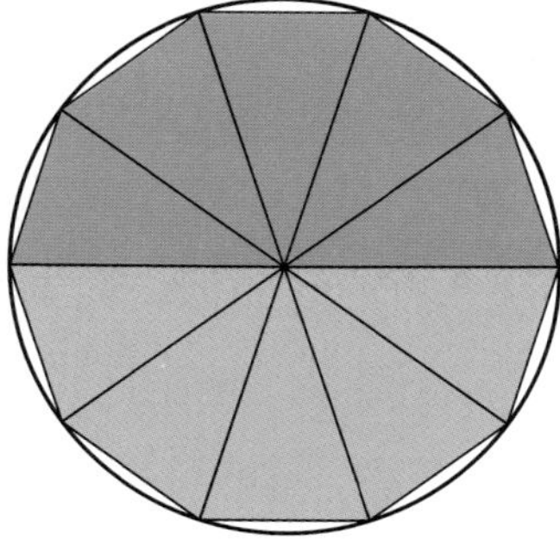

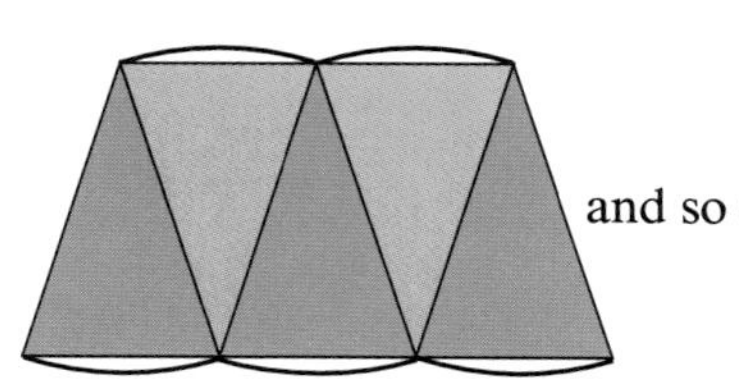

and so on

2 Trace a quadrilateral that approximates the shape you formed in Step 1. What type of quadrilateral is it?

3 Find the area of the quadrilateral you drew in Step 2. How did you calculate this area?

4 How does the area you found in Step 3 compare to the areas found by other students? If there are differences in your answers, what accounts for these differences? Do you think the actual area of the circle is greater than, equal to, or less than the area you calculated?

Additional Answers

Step 1:

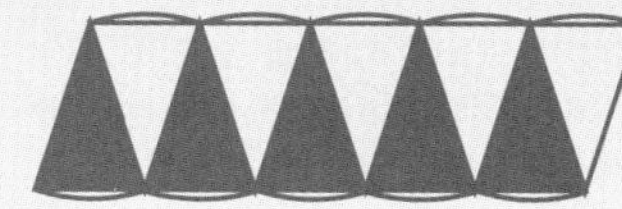

Step 2:

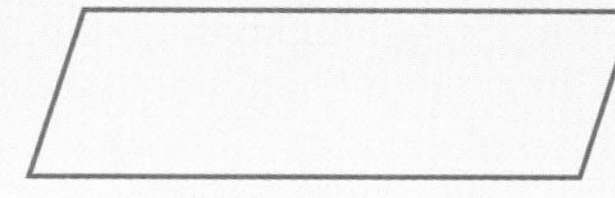

parallelogram

Step 3: Each base ≈ 1.6 cm from previous Activity measures; each altitude ≈ 2.4 cm; area of each triangle ≈ 1.92 cm^2; so area of the parallelogram ≈ 10(1.92) = 19.2 cm^2.

Step 4: In theory, there should be no difference. However, measurement errors and estimates will cause differences. The actual area of the circle is larger than the area calculated.

In-class Activity

Resources

From the ***Teacher's Resource File***

- Answer Master 8-8
- Teaching Aid 112: Estimating the Area of a Circle

Additional Resources

- Visual for Teaching Aid 112

This In-class Activity introduces the use of triangles to estimate the area of a circle.

In the activity, students rearrange sectors of a circle into a figure resembling a parallelogram, and add the areas of congruent triangles to find the area of that figure. You might have students color half of the circle in one color, and the other half in a second color, and then use one half for the sectors that point down, the other half for the sectors that point up. This makes it possible to see that the top side of the "parallelogram" is half the circumference. The argument is generalized at the beginning of Lesson 8-8.

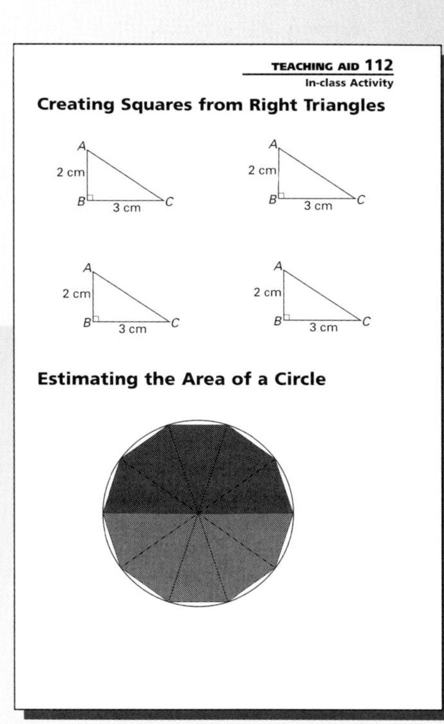

Lesson 8-8

Objectives

F Calculate the area of a circle given measures of relevant lengths and angles, and vice versa.
G Relate various formulas for area.
J Apply formulas for the area of a circle to real situations.

Resources

From the ***Teacher's Resource File***
- Lesson Master 8-8A or 8-8B
- Answer Master 8-8
- Teaching Aids
  103 Warm-up
  114 Additional Examples
  115 Extension
  116 Optional Activities
- Technology Sourcebook, Computer Master 18

Additional Resources
- Visuals for Teaching Aids 103, 114–116
- GeoExplorer or other automatic drawers
- Scissors
- Videodisc

Teaching Lesson 8-8

Warm-up

Writing Alice has a large circular table that she plans to edge with a metal band and then cover with glass. She was surprised to discover that the number of units in the perimeter was the same as the number of square units in the area. Ask students to write an explanation.
The radius is 2 ft, so the perimeter is 4π ft and the area is 4π ft^2.

LESSON

8-8 *The Area of a Circle*

Dome de dome dome. *Shown is one of the domes of Rowes Wharf, a shopping mall in Boston, as viewed from directly underneath its center.*

A circle is not a polygon. But it can be approximated as closely as you want by a polygon. We could try to get its area by finer and finer grids, using the method in Lesson 8-3. However, it is easier to use sectors, as in the In-class Activity on page 479. A **sector** is a region bounded by two radii and an arc of a circle. Dividing a circle into sectors is similar to triangulating a polygon.

The circle at the left below has radius r. It is split into 16 congruent sectors. Each sector resembles an isosceles triangle with altitude r, but with a curved base. At the right the sectors are rearranged as in the In-class Activity. Together they form a figure that is like a parallelogram with height r. Each base is a union of 8 arcs. So each base of the "parallelogram" has length half the circumference of the circle, or $\frac{1}{2}C$. Since $C = 2\pi r$, $\frac{1}{2}C = \pi r$.

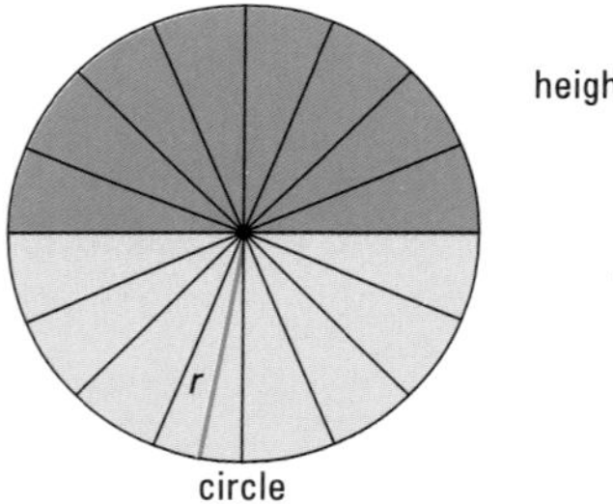

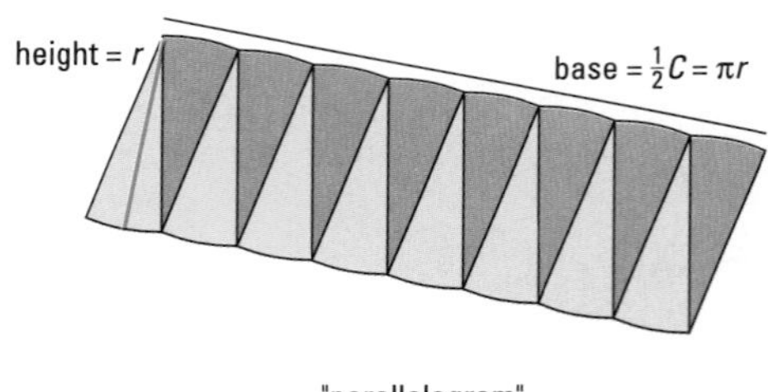

Lesson 8-8 Overview

Broad Goals In this lesson, the formula $A = \pi r^2$ for the area of a circle is derived from the formula for circumference, and its application with probability is introduced.

Perspective This is a relatively easy and short lesson. We assume that students have seen the formula $A = \pi r^2$ in previous courses, so there is ample time to spend on the derivation of the formula and its applications. This may also be an opportune time to start the review of the chapter.

Notice the sequence that took place in the chapter. Area of a rectangle → area of a right triangle → area of a triangle → area of a trapezoid → area of a parallelogram → area of a circle. Reviewing this sequence constitutes a review of all of the area formulas of this chapter.

Video

Wide World of Mathematics The segment, *Warp Speed at the Arena,* shows a sped-up transformation of the Madison Square Garden arena from a circus to a hockey rink to a rock concert. For each of the arena layouts, students may compute floor areas and seating space. Related questions and an investigation are provided in videodisc stills and in the Video Guide. A related CD-ROM activity is also available.

As the number of sectors increases, the figure they form closely resembles a parallelogram with base πr and height r. That parallelogram would have area $bh = \pi r \cdot r = \pi r^2$. The areas of the "parallelograms" become better and better approximations to the area of the circle. *We say that the limit of the areas of the parallelograms is the area of the circle.* This gives a famous formula.

Circle Area Formula
The area A of a circle with radius r is πr^2.

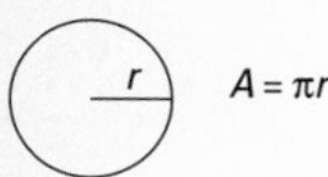

Example 1

Find the area (to the nearest square inch) of the top of a manhole cover with diameter 22″.

Solution

Since $d = 22''$, $r = 11''$.

$$\begin{aligned} \text{Area(circle)} &= \pi r^2 \\ &= 121\pi \\ &\approx 121 \cdot 3.14 \\ &\approx 380 \text{ square inches} \end{aligned}$$

Areas and Probability

The center of a target is called a *bull's-eye.* If an object randomly hits the target, then the probability that it will hit the bull's-eye is

$$\frac{\text{area of bull's-eye}}{\text{area of the target}}.$$

Example 2

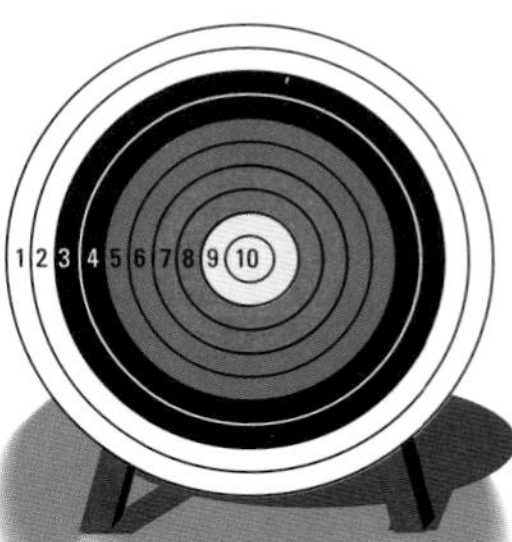

In Olympic archery, the target's bull's-eye has a radius of 4 cm and the radius of the outside circle is 80 cm. What is the probability that an arrow shot hitting the target randomly hits the bull's-eye?

Solution

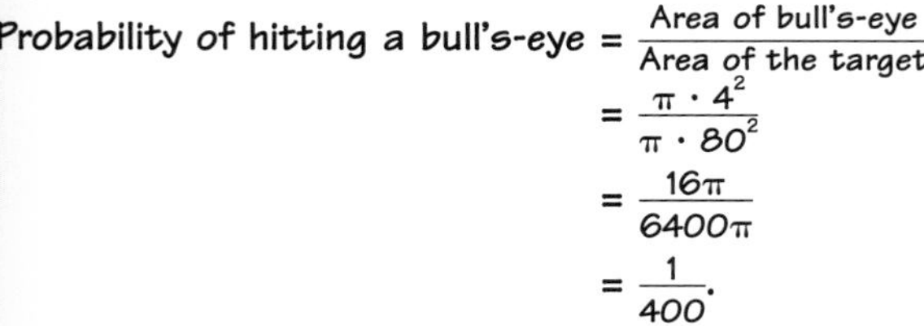

$$\begin{aligned} \text{Probability of hitting a bull's-eye} &= \frac{\text{Area of bull's-eye}}{\text{Area of the target}} \\ &= \frac{\pi \cdot 4^2}{\pi \cdot 80^2} \\ &= \frac{16\pi}{6400\pi} \\ &= \frac{1}{400}. \end{aligned}$$

Notes on Reading

The derivation of the area formula for a circle uses the idea of a limit for the third time in this chapter. In explaining the derivation of the Circle Area Formula, stress the idea that increasing the number of sectors yields a region that more closely approximates a parallelogram. These experiences build the notion of limit. Limits are unavoidable since the area of a curved region is found by using properties based on rectangles.

To give students a concrete view of the area formula for a circle, you might want to use Activity 1 in *Optional Activities* below.

It is important that students be able to go from radius to diameter to circumference to area. It might be worth class time to show students how to calculate the other three quantities, given any one of them. Stress that if the circumference is given, the radius should be calculated first because it is the quantity needed for substituting into the area formula.

The use of area formulas to calculate geometric probabilities, as in **Example 2,** is discussed in UCSMP *Algebra.* However, it may be new for some students. Many students do not have a natural sense for guessing the amount of shaded area outside an inscribed square, so their guess is too low.

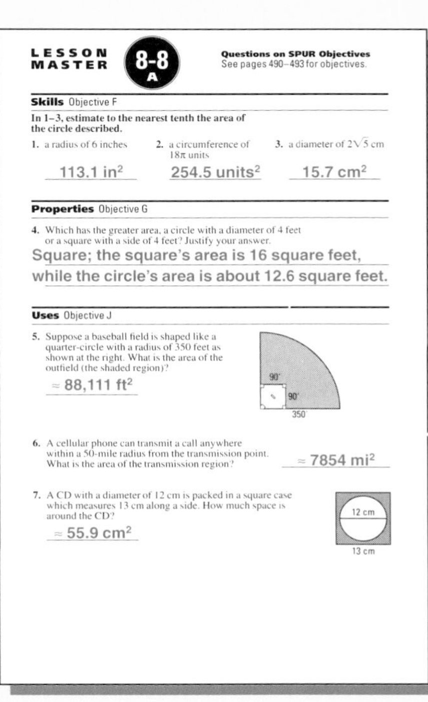

LESSON MASTER 8-8 A

Questions on SPUR Objectives
See pages 490–493 for objectives.

Skills Objective F

In 1–3, estimate to the nearest tenth the area of the circle described.

1. a radius of 6 inches — 113.1 in^2
2. a circumference of 18π units — 254.5 units^2
3. a diameter of $2\sqrt{5}$ cm — 15.7 cm^2

Properties Objective G

4. Which has the greater area, a circle with a diameter of 4 feet or a square with a side of 4 feet? Justify your answer.
Square; the square's area is 16 square feet, while the circle's area is about 12.6 square feet.

Uses Objective J

5. Suppose a baseball field is shaped like a quarter-circle with a radius of 350 feet as shown at the right. What is the area of the outfield (the shaded region)?
$\approx 88{,}111 \text{ ft}^2$

6. A cellular phone can transmit a call anywhere within a 50-mile radius from the transmission point. What is the area of the transmission region?
$\approx 7854 \text{ mi}^2$

7. A CD with a diameter of 12 cm is packed in a square case which measures 13 cm along a side. How much space is around the CD?
$\approx 55.9 \text{ cm}^2$

Videodisc Bar Codes

Search Chapter 39

Play

Optional Activities

Activity 1
Materials: **Teaching Aid 116,** scissors

To begin this lesson and to give students a concrete view of the area formula for a circle, give each of them a circle and several squares with sides equal to the radius of the circle **(Teaching Aid 116).** Have them cut the squares to cover the circle without overlapping as best they can.

(Optional Activities continue on page 482.)

Additional Examples

These examples are also given on **Teaching Aid 114.**

1. A rotating lawn sprinkler shoots water a distance of 10 meters. What is the area of the region where it waters? $100\pi \approx 314 \text{ m}^2$
2. The radii of circles in the dart board shown below are 10 cm, 20 cm, and 35 cm. If a dart falls randomly within the largest circle, what is the probability that it will score 30 points or more?

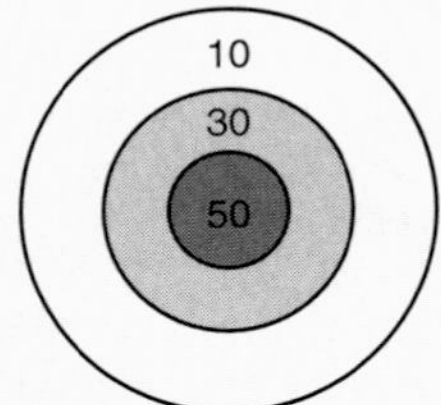

$\frac{400\pi}{1225\pi} \approx 32.7\%$

3. Which is larger, one of 8 congruent wedges of a 14" pizza or one of 6 congruent wedges of a 12" pizza? The wedge from the 14" pizza.

Notes on Questions

Question 3 Use this question to point out the necessity of using more than several decimal places of π.

If $\frac{22}{7}$ is used as an approximation for π, then an answer of 15,400 square inches will be found. If 3.14 is used as an approximation to π, an answer of 15,386 square inches will be found.

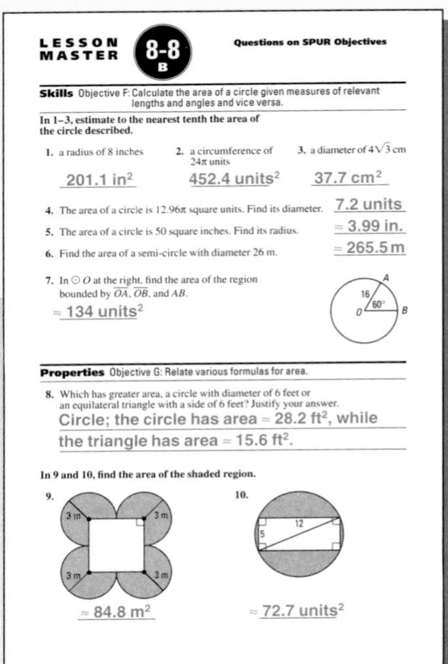

LESSON MASTER 8-8 B Questions on SPUR Objectives

Skills Objective F: Calculate the area of a circle given measures of relevant lengths and angles and vice versa.

In 1–3, estimate to the nearest tenth the area of the circle described.

1. a radius of 8 inches — 201.1 in^2
2. a circumference of 24π units — 452.4 units^2
3. a diameter of $4\sqrt{3}$ cm — 37.7 cm^2
4. The area of a circle is 12.96π square units. Find its diameter. 7.2 units
5. The area of a circle is 50 square inches. Find its radius. ≈ 3.99 in.
6. Find the area of a semi-circle with diameter 26 m. ≈ 265.5 m
7. In $\odot O$ at the right, find the area of the region bounded by $\overline{OA}$, $\overline{OB}$, and AB. $\approx 134 \text{ units}^2$

Properties Objective G: Relate various formulas for area.

8. Which has greater area, a circle with diameter of 6 feet or an equilateral triangle with a side of 6 feet? Justify your answer. Circle; the circle has area $\approx 28.2 \text{ ft}^2$, while the triangle has area $\approx 15.6 \text{ ft}^2$.

In 9 and 10, find the area of the shaded region.

9. $\approx 84.8 \text{ m}^2$
10. $\approx 72.7 \text{ units}^2$

Areas of Sectors

Just as arc length is part of the circumference of a circle, the area of a sector is part of the area of a circle.

Example 3

In $\odot O$ at the right, the radius is 15. Find the area of the shaded sector.

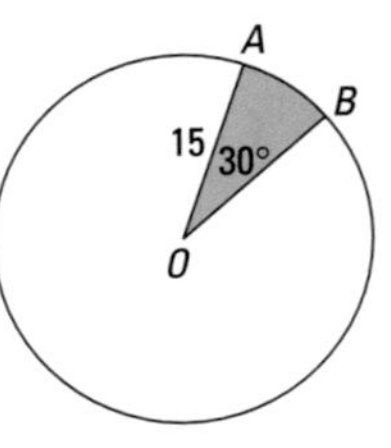

Solution

$m\angle AOB = 30$, so the shaded sector is $\frac{30}{360}$ of the area of $\odot O$.

$$\begin{aligned}\text{Area of shaded sector} &= \frac{30}{360} \cdot (\text{Area of } \odot O)\\ &= \frac{1}{12} \cdot \pi(15)^2\\ &= \frac{225}{12}\pi\\ &\approx 58.90 \text{ square units.}\end{aligned}$$

Check

The area of the circle is $\pi \cdot 15^2$, or 225π. $225\pi \approx 706.86$, which is about 12 times 58.90.

QUESTIONS

Covering the Reading

1. At the right, a circle with radius 10 is split into 16 congruent sectors. The 16 sectors can be put together (as in the lesson) into a "parallelogram."
   a. What is the height of the parallelogram? 10 units
   b. What is the base of the parallelogram?
   c. What is the area of the parallelogram?
   b) $10\pi \approx 31.42$ units c) $100\pi \approx 314.2 \text{ units}^2$
2. Give the exact area of a circle with radius r. πr^2
3. Estimate the area to the nearest square inch of a circle with radius 70″. $15{,}394 \text{ in}^2$
4. A penny has a diameter of approximately 18 mm. Find its area to the nearest square millimeter. 254 mm^2
5. A dart board is shown at the right. If a dart randomly hits the target, what is the probability that it lands in the bull's-eye? $\frac{1}{1296}$

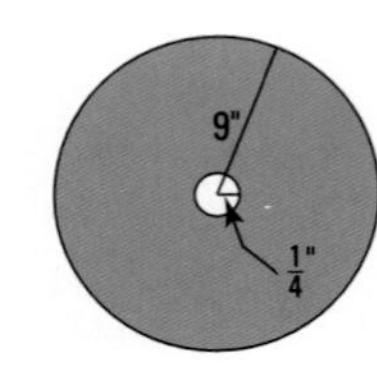

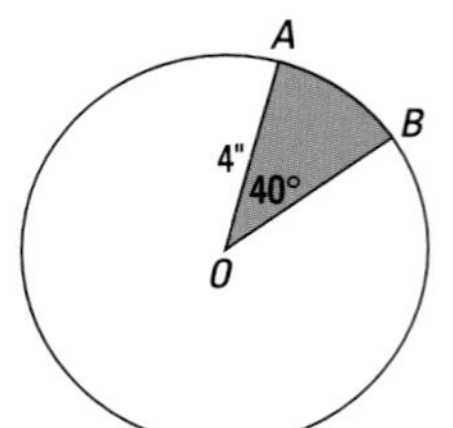

6. Find the area of the shaded sector at the left. $\frac{16}{9}\pi$ or about 5.6 in^2

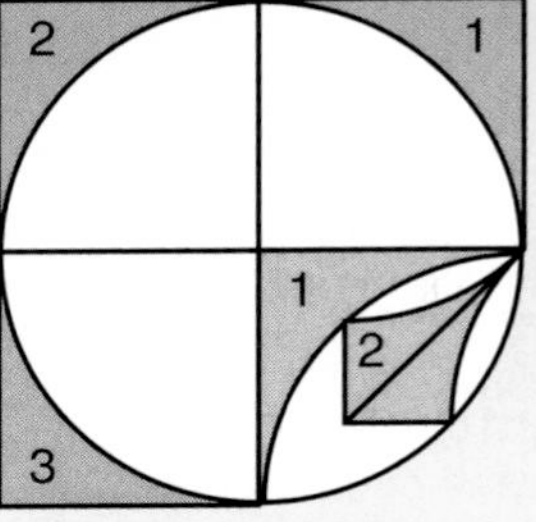

The illustration shows three squares in which 90° sectors were cut out. One of the three cutouts fits in the fourth quadrant of the circle. Students will have to decide if the football-shaped region remaining can be covered with the two remaining cutoffs. One of them fits easily as shown. By cutting and placing the pieces of the third cutout, students will see that the circle has an area a little more than three squares with side lengths equal to the radius. This gives meaning to the fact that 3.14... squares are approximately enough.

Applying the Mathematics

7. a. Give, to the nearest hundred square meters, the area that can be irrigated by a circular sprinkler 60 meters long rotating around a fixed point. 11,300 square meters

b. Give the circumference of the irrigated region, to the nearest meter.
377 m

8. A circle has area 144π. Find

a. its radius. 12 units **b.** its diameter. 24 units **c.** its circumference. 24π units

9a) What is the area of Farmer Bob's field?

9. Refer to the cartoon.

a. What question do you think is in the Geometry book? See left.

b. Answer that question. $90{,}000\pi\ m^2 \approx 282{,}600\ m^2$

TROT

10. a. On a 10″ pizza, which measures 10″, the radius, diameter, or circumference? diameter

b. How many times as much of each ingredient is needed for an 18″ pizza than for a 10″ pizza with the same thickness? 3.24

c. If an 18″ pizza is sliced into 8 congruent sectors, what is the area of a slice? about 31.8 in^2

11. Use the concentric circles at the right. The radius of the larger circle is four times the radius of the smaller circle. If a dart lands randomly in the large circle, find the probability it will land

a. in the inner circle. $\frac{1}{16}$

b. in the shaded region. $\frac{15}{16}$

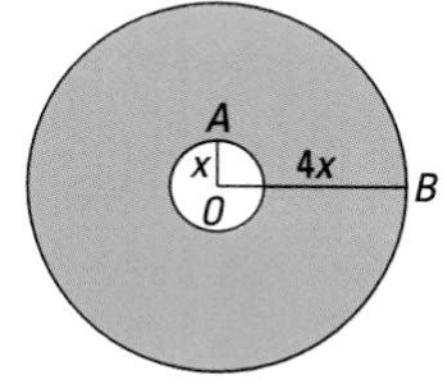

12. In the figure at the left, eight circular metal disks are to be cut out of a 12-cm by 24-cm piece of metal. The rest is not used.

a. What is the area of the metal that is not used? $288 - 72\pi \approx 61.8\ cm^2$

b. What percent of the metal is not used? about 21.5%

Question 8 To express the area of a circle in terms of π is common. However, students should not expect that an expression for the exact area must always be in terms of π. For instance, if we ask for a circle with the same area as a square 10 cm on a side, then the area of the circle is 100 cm^2.

Question 10 Students may have seen this example in previous UCSMP courses. The general principle is that if the ratio of diameters is a to b, then the ratio of ingredients is a^2 to b^2.

Question 11 Some students may not see that the shaded region is formed by removing a smaller circle from a larger one. With an overhead projector, show that the results are the same no matter where the smaller circle is removed from the larger, that is, even if the bull's-eye is not in the center.

Question 12 Suggest that students use the problem-solving strategy of solving a simpler equivalent problem: Split the piece into the 8 squares circumscribing the given circles. The ratio of metal wasted is the same for a single part as for the entire piece. You might ask students to conjecture whether more or less space is wasted if the diameter of metal disks is doubled, and only two can be cut out. [The same amount is wasted.]

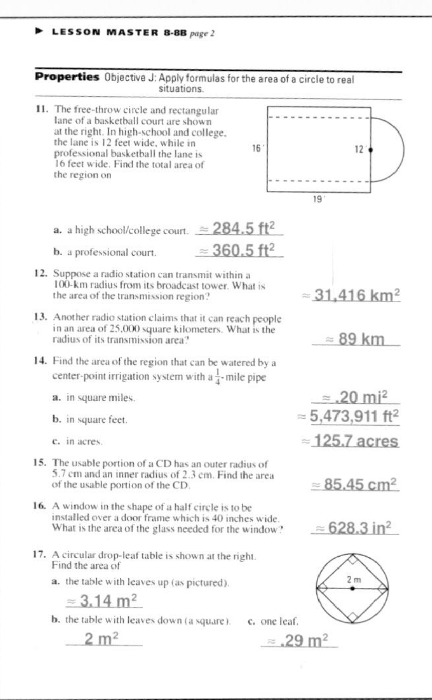

► **LESSON MASTER 8-8B** *page 2*

Properties Objective J: Apply formulas for the area of a circle to real situations.

11. The free-throw circle and rectangular lane of a basketball court are shown at the right. In high-school and college, the lane is 12 feet wide, while in professional basketball the lane is 16 feet wide. Find the total area of the region on

a. a high school/college court. $\approx 284.5\ ft^2$

b. a professional court. $\approx 360.5\ ft^2$

12. Suppose a radio station can transmit within a 100-km radius from its broadcast tower. What is the area of the transmission region? $\approx 31{,}416\ km^2$

13. Another radio station claims that it can reach people in an area of 25,000 square kilometers. What is the radius of its transmission area? ≈ 89 km

14. Find the area of the region that can be watered by a center-point irrigation system with a $\frac{1}{4}$-mile pipe

a. in square miles. $\approx .20\ mi^2$

b. in square feet. $\approx 5{,}473{,}911\ ft^2$

c. in acres. ≈ 125.7 acres

15. The usable portion of a CD has an outer radius of 5.7 cm and an inner radius of 2.3 cm. Find the area of the usable portion of the CD. $\approx 85.45\ cm^2$

16. A window in the shape of a half circle is to be installed over a door frame which is 40 inches wide. What is the area of the glass needed for the window? $\approx 628.3\ in^2$

17. A circular drop-leaf table is shown at the right. Find the area of

a. the table with leaves up (as pictured). $\approx 3.14\ m^2$

b. the table with leaves down (a square). $2\ m^2$ **c.** one leaf. $\approx .29\ m^2$

Optional Activities

Activity 2 Technology Connection
In *Technology Sourcebook, Computer Master 18,* students construct polygons and inscribed circles and derive the constant relationship of the area of a circle to the area of a square in terms of π. Students also investigate the relationship between the area of a circle and the area of a regular n-gon as n increases.

Adapting to Individual Needs

Extra Help
When some students apply the Circle Area Formula, they double the radius instead of squaring it. As a result, they find the circumference instead of the area. Remind them that r^2 means $r \cdot r$.

Follow-up for Lesson 8-8

Practice

For more questions on SPUR Objectives, use **Lesson Master 8-8A** (shown on page 481) or **Lesson Master 8-8B** (shown on pages 482–483).

Assessment

Written Communication Have students write a paragraph explaining why it is so difficult to hit the bull's-eye of a dartboard. [Students explain that the probability of hitting the bull's-eye is determined by the ratio of the area of the bull's-eye to the area of the dartboard. The area of the bull's-eye is small in relation to the area of the dartboard.]

Extension

These figures are shown on **Teaching Aid 115.** If each square has side 10, find the area of the following shapes bounded by circular arcs.

1.

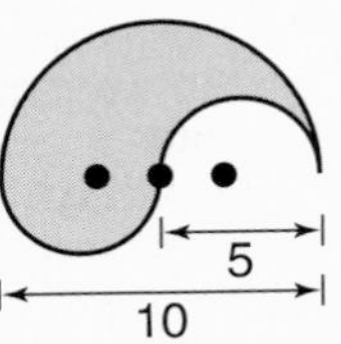

[$\frac{25\pi}{2}$ units^2]

2.

[$100 - \frac{75}{4}\pi$ units^2]

3.

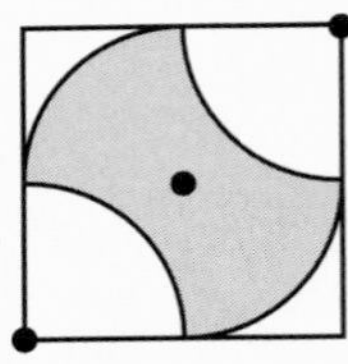

[50 units^2]

Projects Update Project 3, *Broadcast Areas,* and Project 4, *Quadrature of the Lune,* on pages 485–486, relate to the content of this lesson.

These windmills in Zaanse Schans, Holland, near Amsterdam, are more decorative than functional.

Review

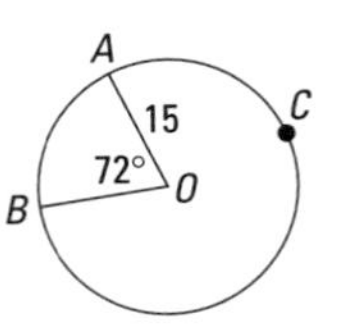

13. In $\odot O$ at the right, $OA = 15$ and $m\angle AOB = 72$.
  a. Find m $\widehat{AB}$. 72°
  b. Find the length of $\widehat{AB}$. *(Lessons 3-2, 8-7)* $6\pi \approx 18.8$ units

14. A windmill is turning in the wind. If the length of a blade is 12 meters and it makes 6 revolutions in a minute, how far will the tip of each blade travel in an hour? *(Lesson 8-7)* $8640\pi \approx 27{,}143$ meters ≈ 27 kilometers

15. A car has tires with a diameter of 205 mm. How many revolutions does each tire make in traveling 300 meters? *(Lesson 8-7)* about 466

16. A rectangle is 16″ by 22″.
  a. Find the lengths of its diagonals. $\sqrt{740} \approx 27.2''$
  b. Find its perimeter. *(Lessons 8-1, 8-6)* 76″

17. The two legs of a right triangle have lengths $4x$ and $9x$.
  a. What is the area of the triangle? $18x^2$ units^2
  b. What is the perimeter of the triangle? *(Lessons 8-1, 8-4, 8-6)* $(13 + \sqrt{97})x \approx 22.8x$ units

18. Can 13, 84, and 85 be the lengths of sides of a right triangle? *(Lesson 8-6)* Yes

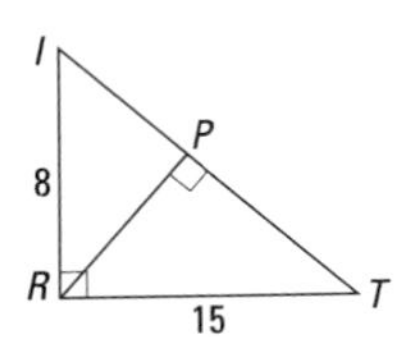

19. In the triangle at the left, find RP to the nearest tenth. *(Lessons 8-4, 8-6)* 7.1 units

20. Find the area of a kite with diagonals 42′ and 12′. *(Lesson 8-4)* 252 ft^2

21. Find the area of the polygon with vertices (4, 3), (4, -3), (-4, -3), and (-4, 3). *(Lesson 8-2)* 48 units^2

22. Fill in the blanks in the following conversion formulas. *(Previous course)*
  a. 1 centimeter = __?__ meter .01
  b. 1 cm^2 = __?__ m^2 0.0001
  c. 1 yard = __?__ in. 36
  d. 1 yd^2 = __?__ in^2 1296
  e. 1 mile = __?__ yards 1760
  f. 1 mi^2 = __?__ yd^2 3,097,600

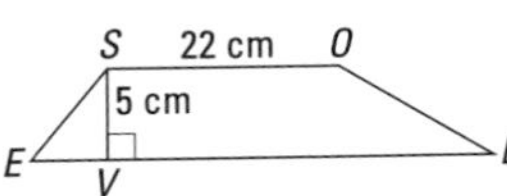

23. $SOLE$ is a trapezoid with bases $\overline{SO}$ and $\overline{EL}$. $\overline{SV} \perp \overline{EL}$. If $SO = 22$ cm, $SV = 5$ cm, and Area($SOLE$) = 150 cm^2, find EL. *(Lesson 8-5)* 38 cm

Exploration

Sample answers are given.

24. Find a soft drink can or other can with a circular base.
  a. What is the capacity of the can (measured in ounces or milliliters)? 12 ounces
  b. Measure the diameter d as accurately as you can with a ruler or tape measure. $\approx 2\frac{9}{16}$ inches
  c. Measure the circumference C with a tape measure or by rolling it on a ruler, again as accurately as you can. $\approx 8\frac{1}{4}$ inches
  d. Calculate $\frac{C}{d}$ to the nearest hundredth. 3.22
  e. What number should $\frac{C}{d}$ approximate? π
  f. Why isn't $\frac{C}{d}$ exactly that number? errors in measurements

Adapting to Individual Needs

Challenge

1. Have students derive a formula for the area of a sector of a circle, whose central angle is $x°$. [$A = \frac{x}{360}\pi r^2$]
2. Refer students back to *Challenge* in Lesson 8–7. Have them derive a formula for the area of a sector of a circle, whose central angle is θ radians. [$A = \frac{1}{2}r^2\theta$]

Setting Up Lesson 9-1

Materials To demonstrate the "Unique Plane Assumptions" in Lesson 9-1, you can use a piece of plywood and three dowel rods of equal length.

A project presents an opportunity for you to extend your knowledge of a topic related to the material of this chapter. You should allow more time for a project than you do for typical homework questions.

1 Perimeter of Your School

Measure the perimeter of your school. Write a report which includes:

a. a description of how you found the perimeter;
b. your actual measurements and calculations;
c. the perimeter of the school calculated from an actual floor plan; and
d. the actual error, percent of error, and the reasons for any differences between the answers in parts **b** and **c.**

2 Hero's Formula

Let s be half the perimeter of the triangle of sides a, b, and c. Then Area$(\triangle ABC) = \sqrt{s(s-a)(s-b)(s-c)}$. This formula was discovered by Archimedes, but it is known as **Hero's** or **Heron's Formula,** after the Greek mathematician and physicist Hero (or Heron) of Alexandria, who lived about 50 A.D.

a. Use Heron's formula to find the area of a triangle with sides 9, 12, and 15. Check by using an alternate method.
b. Find the area of a triangle with sides 10, 17, and 21.
c. Using an automatic drawer, draw three triangles, at least two of them scalene, and verify that the formula holds for these triangles.

3 Broadcast Areas

Radio stations have maps of the areas in which their signals are received. Contact four radio stations with various tower locations, broadcast frequencies, and transmission powers to find out their signal areas. Use the formulas and techniques of this chapter to calculate their broadcast areas. Do research to discover what affects the size and shape of these areas. Which factors are permanent? Which factors change as conditions change? Which other factors affect the size of a region in which a station can be received?

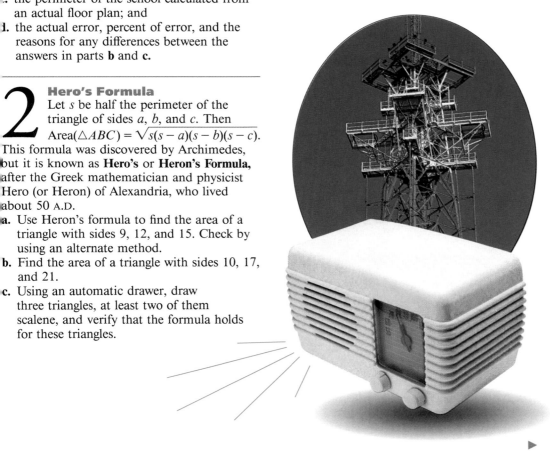

Chapter 8 Projects

The projects relate chiefly to the content of the lessons of this chapter as follows:

Project	Lesson(s)
1	8-1
2	8-4, 8-6
3	8-8
4	8-8
5	8-2, 8-3
6	8-3

1 Perimeter of Your School For **parts a and b,** the perimeter can be computed by measuring lengths and widths of classrooms, the halls, and special areas like the cafeteria, gymnasium, auditorium, and offices. These measures can be used to give the total length of each exterior wall of the school. Instruments which can be used include rulers, yardsticks and meter sticks, and measuring wheels. For **part c,** the perimeter of the school can be found by converting the measurements on the scale drawing to actual measurements, and then computing the perimeter based on the converted measurements. For **part d,** actual error is found by subtracting the answer in **part b** from the answer in **part c.** The percent of error is found by dividing this number by the answer in **part c.**

2 Hero's Formula Since the triangle in **part a** is a right triangle, its area can be found easily without Hero's formula. For **part b,** substitution is all that is needed. For **part c** students should have the automatic drawer find the area. Then they should record the lengths of the sides and do the calculations themselves, by writing out the formula and showing their work.

3 Broadcast Areas You might suggest that students use a map of the region covered by the broadcast areas of the stations they select and then have them mark the location of each tower and shade each area covered. Make sure they use the same scale as shown on the map they use.

Possible responses

1a–c. Responses will vary.

d. Sample: Measurements may differ due to: not measuring along a straight line, not placing the measuring device at the exact location, thickness of walls, precision of the measuring device, and rounding error.

2a. Here, let $a = 9$, $b = 12$, $c = 15$, and so $s = 18$.
$A = \sqrt{18 \cdot 3 \cdot 6 \cdot 9} = 54$
The triangle is a right triangle with legs 9 and 12, so has area $\frac{1}{2} \cdot 9 \cdot 12 = 54$.

b. Here, let $a = 10$, $b = 17$, and $c = 21$, and so $s = 24$.
$A = \sqrt{24 \cdot 3 \cdot 7 \cdot 14} = 84$

c. Responses will vary.

(Responses continue on page 486.)

4 Quadrature of the Lune This diagram can be constructed using an automatic drawer: Construct a circle O; then construct two radii $\overline{OP}$ and $\overline{OR}$ which are perpendicular. Construct $\overline{PR}$, and mark the midpoint S of $\overline{PR}$. Use $\overline{PS}$ as a radius for circle S. The area of triangle $OPR = .5 \cdot PR \cdot OS$. The area of the lune is the difference between the area of the semicircle and the region that is not the lune: $.5\pi \cdot (PS)^2 - [\frac{90}{360}\pi \cdot (OP)^2 - (.5 \cdot PR \cdot OS)]$. When circle O is enlarged or shrunk, these two areas remain equal to each other. The proof is given in the project responses.

5 Floor Plans and Area A variation of this project is to ask students to design their own floor plan for a house or apartment with multiple rooms, for example, bedrooms, kitchen, closets, hallways, staircase wells, living and dining rooms, bathrooms, and so on. The floor plan should be drawn to scale, for example, using the scale 1 inch to 1 foot. On the floor plan, students should label each room. Then the project can be completed as indicated, using the student's own plan.

6 Area of Puerto Rico Students need to be able to convert from centimeters and inches to miles and kilometers. 1.5 cm on the map corresponds to about 20 actual kilometers (2.5 mi). One inch, or 2.54 cm, on the map corresponds to about 33 actual kilometers (≈ 21 mi).

(continued)

4 Quadrature of the Lune

In Question 18 of Lesson 2-8, you were asked to make a conjecture about the area of a figure like the one below, called a *lune*. The lune below is a region bounded by arcs $\widehat{PQR}$ and $\widehat{PR}$. In about 460 B.C., Hippocrates of Chios proved that the area of $\triangle POR$ was equal to the area of this lune.

a. Use a 90° central angle and form circles

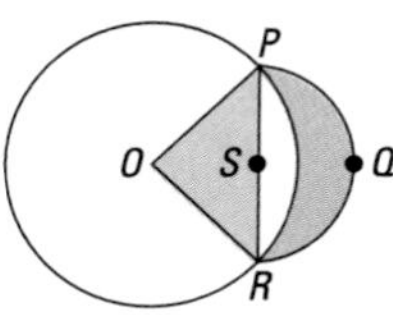

with different radii to calculate the area of the triangle and the corresponding lune. (You will need to find the area of $\triangle POR$ and of sector POR and subtract them to find the area X of the region bounded by $\overline{PR}$ and $\widehat{PR}$. Then find the area of the semicircle with diameter $\overline{PR}$ and subtract X from it to obtain the area of the lune.)

b. Generalize your findings for a circle of any radius.

c. Will the conjecture hold for angles of other sizes? Why or why not? Write a report with your drawings, calculations, and conclusions.

5 Floor Plans and Area

Find at least four advertisements that show a floor plan for apartments or houses. Calculate the area of the floor(s) and the area of each interior space, including hallways, closets, staircase wells, and so on. For each floor plan, show your calculations and write a brief description of how much *living space* (space which is used for sitting, eating, cooking, sleeping) the floor plan provides. Write an introductory paragraph explaining the source of your floor plans and how you determined living space and non-living space. What kind of space is most important in a home? Why do you think so? What percent of the space is used for non-living areas? What advantages and disadvantages do you see in the amount of living space in each floor plan?

6 Area of Puerto Rico

Make three copies of the map of Puerto Rico. Use the method of Lesson 8-3 to estimate its area by using finer and finer grids. Notice the scale in the lower left-hand corner in miles and kilometers.* Compare your answer to the area given in an atlas or almanac. (If a map of your city or town is available with scale of distance given, you may use that instead of the map below.) *You will need to calculate the area of the square of each grid in terms of the scale on the map.

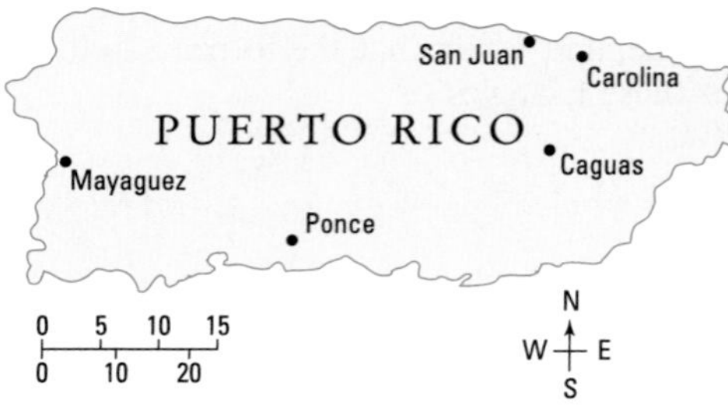

Additional responses, page 485

3. Permanent factors which affect the size and shape of the broadcast areas include the frequency of the wave and the wavelength (AM stations are measured in kilohertz and FM stations are in megahertz), the height of the tower, the base input current, the length and configuration of the antenna—all of these affect the power transmitted by a radio station antenna. Other permanent factors include the location of the antenna. If it is on a hill, the waves will travel farther without interference; if it is atop a tall building, the same is true. If the antenna is near other antennas outputting radio waves of the same (or nearly the same) frequencies, the signals may overlap, and the result is static. The angle at which the wave is broadcast also affects the area. Nonpermanent factors include the weather conditions. Moving vehicles and airplanes temporarily block or interfere with the broadcasting wave. Additionally, sunspot activity can affect the atmospheric conditions on Earth, and thus will affect the broadcasting ability.

SUMMARY

This chapter is devoted to deriving and applying formulas for area, perimeter, and circumference. Perimeter, or circumference, measures the boundary of a figure. An equilateral n-gon with sides of length s has perimeter ns. A circle with diameter d has circumference πd. The length of an arc is a fraction of that circumference.

In contrast to perimeter, area measures the region enclosed by a figure. This region can be estimated by using congruent squares. With finer and finer grids, even the areas of irregular shapes can be estimated.

Mathematics captivates the imagination of many people because so many things can be derived from just a few simple statements. In this chapter, that idea is exemplified by the derivation of many area formulas from just a few basic properties.

A rectangle with dimensions h and b has area hb. Splitting it with a diagonal, two congruent right triangles are formed. Each has area $\frac{1}{2}hb$. By splitting it into right triangles, the area of *any* triangle can be shown to be $\frac{1}{2}hb$. Putting two triangles together, the area of any trapezoid is $\frac{1}{2}h(b_1 + b_2)$. A special case of a trapezoid is a parallelogram, whose area is hb. (See the List of Formulas at the back of the book for a summary of these and other formulas.)

This chapter contains some of the most important formulas in geometry. Areas of right triangles and squares help to develop the Pythagorean Theorem: In a right triangle with legs a and b and hypotenuse c, $c^2 = a^2 + b^2$. The areas of triangles can be put together to derive the formula $A = \pi r^2$ for the area of a circle.

VOCABULARY

Below are the most important terms and phrases for this chapter. For the starred (*) terms you should be able to give a definition of the term. For the other terms you should be able to give a general description and specific example of each.

Lesson 8-1
*perimeter of a polygon
dimensions of a rectangle
length and width of a rectangle
Equilateral Polygon Perimeter Formula

Lesson 8-2
square units
Area Postulate:
Uniqueness Property
Rectangle Formula
Congruence Property
Additive Property
Area(F)
nonoverlapping regions

Lesson 8-3
lattice point

Lesson 8-4
Right Triangle Area Formula
*altitude of a triangle
height of a triangle
Triangle Area Formula

Lesson 8-5
height or altitude of a trapezoid
Trapezoid Area Formula
Parallelogram Area Formula

Lesson 8-6
square root
Pythagorean Theorem
Pythagorean Converse Theorem
Pythagorean triple

Lesson 8-7
circumference
*π (pi)
Circle Circumference Formula
arc length

Lesson 8-8
sector
Circle Area Formula

Summary

The Summary gives an overview of the entire chapter and provides an opportunity for students to consider the material as a whole. Thus, the Summary can be used to help students relate and unify the concepts presented in the chapter.

Vocabulary

Terms, symbols, and properties are listed by lesson to provide a checklist of concepts a student must know. Emphasize to students that they should read the vocabulary list carefully before starting the Progress Self-Test. If students do not understand the meaning of a term, they should refer back to the indicated lesson.

4a–b. Let $OP = r$. When $m\angle POR = 90$, $OS = PS = \frac{1}{2}r\sqrt{2}$. Area($\triangle POR$) = $\frac{r^2}{2}$. Area(Lune) = $\frac{1}{2}\pi \cdot (PS)^2 - [\frac{90}{360}\pi \cdot (OP)^2 - (\frac{1}{2}PR \cdot OS)] = \frac{1}{4}\pi r^2 - (\frac{1}{4}\pi r^2 - \frac{r^2}{2}) = \frac{r^2}{2}$.

c. In general, when $\angle POR$ is acute, Area(Lune) < Area($\triangle OPR$). When $\angle POR$ is obtuse, Area(Lune) > Area($\triangle OPR$).

5. Responses will vary.

6. The actual land area of Puerto Rico according to the 1995 *World Almanac* is 3,339 square miles, or 8,650 square kilometers; this includes the area of several smaller islands not pictured in this book. Sample: First estimate: Use one rectangle. 13.5 cm (112.5 mi or 180 km) × 4.5 cm (37.5 mi or 60 km) = 4219 mi², or 10800 km². Second estimate: Use squares with side 1.5 cm (12.5 mi, or 20 km). These have area 156.25 mi², or 400 km². 5 squares completely inside and 21 squares on boundary = 5 + 10.5 = 15.5 squares. Total area ≈ 2421 mi², or 6200 km². Third estimate: Use squares with side 0.5 cm per side (4.17 mi, or 6.67 km). These have area 17.36 mi² or 44.44 km². Then there are about

(Responses continue on page 488.)

Progress Self-Test

For the development of mathematical competence, feedback and correction, along with the opportunity to practice, are necessary. The Progress Self-Test provides the opportunity for feedback and correction; the Chapter Review provides additional opportunities and practice. We cannot overemphasize the importance of these end-of-chapter materials. It is at this point that the material "gels" for many students, allowing them to solidify skills and understanding. In general, student performance should be markedly improved after these pages.

Assign the Progress Self-Test as a one-night assignment. Answers to all questions are in the Selected Answers section of the student book. Encourage students to take the Progress Self-Test honestly, grade themselves, and then be prepared to discuss the test in class.

Advise students to pay special attention to those Chapter Review questions (pages 490–493) which correspond to questions missed on the Progress Self-Test.

Additonal Answers

11b. Because $121 + 3600 = 3721 = 61^2$, meeting the condition of Pythagorean Converse Theorem.

Additional responses, page 486

128 squares completely inside and 56 squares on boundary = 128 + 28 = 156 squares. Total area ≈ 2708 mi^2, or 6933 km^2.

Fourth estimate: Use squares with sides .125 in. (2.67 mi, or 4.17 km). These have area 7.11 mi^2, or 17.36 km^2. There are about 322 squares completely inside and 129 squares on boundary = 322 + 64.5 = 386.5 squares. Total area ≈ 2748 mi^2, or 6710 km^2.

PROGRESS SELF-TEST

Directions: Take this test as you would take a test in class. Then check your work with the solutions in the Selected Answers section in the back of this book. You will need graph paper and a calculator in addition to pencil and paper.

1. Give the perimeter of the parallelogram below. 110 units

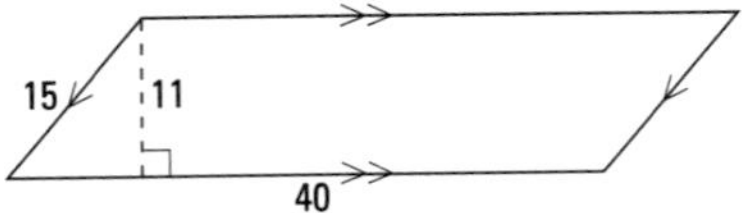

In 2 and 3, give the area of the figure.

2.

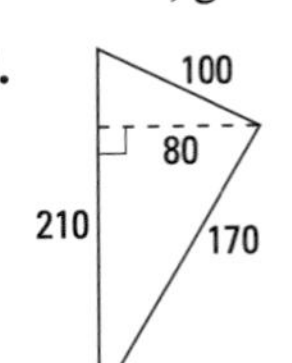

8400 $units^2$

3.

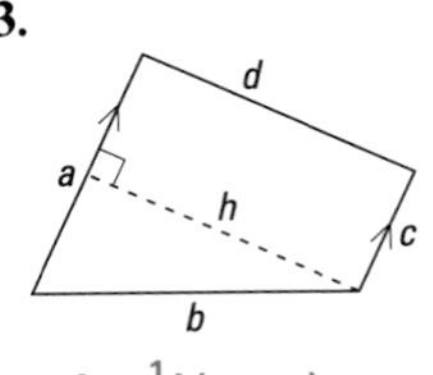

$A = \frac{1}{2}h(a + c)$

4. If the perimeter of a regular hexagon is q, what is the length of a side? $\frac{q}{6}$

5. A rectangle has area of 200 m^2 and length 25 m. What is its width? 8 m

6. A trapezoid has an area of 48 square units. Its height is 6 units and one base is 9 units. Find the length of the other base. 7 units

7. Give the circumference and area of a circle with diameter 12″

a. exactly. $12\pi''$; 36π in^2

b. estimated to the nearest inch and square inch. 38″; 113 in^2

8. In ⊙O at the right, $\overrightarrow{OC}$ bisects right angle DOB and $OB = 20$.

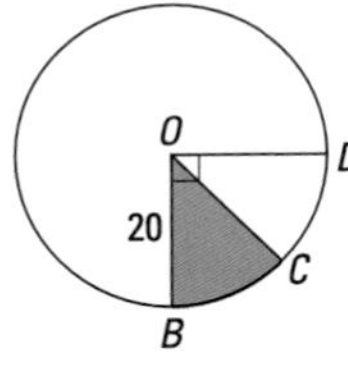

a. What is the length of arc $\widehat{CD}$? ≈ 15.7 units

b. What is the area of the shaded sector? ≈ 157 $units^2$

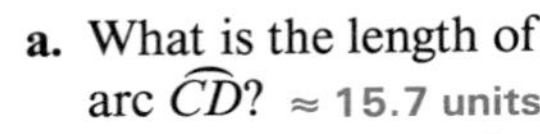

9. Find the length of $\overline{WX}$ in $\triangle WXY$ below. 40 units

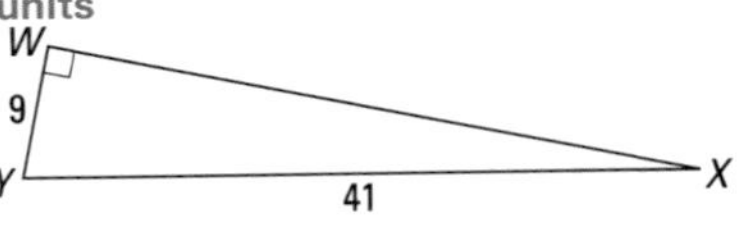

10. The two legs of a right triangle have lengths 20 and 21. What is the perimeter of the triangle? 70 units

11. a. Could 11, 60, and 61 be lengths of sides of a right triangle? Yes

b. Why or why not? See margin.

12. In the map and grid of the state of Rhode Island shown below, each small square has side length 5 miles. Use the method of this chapter to approximate the area of the land portion. Do not include the areas of the five small islands. Sample: 937.5 sq mi

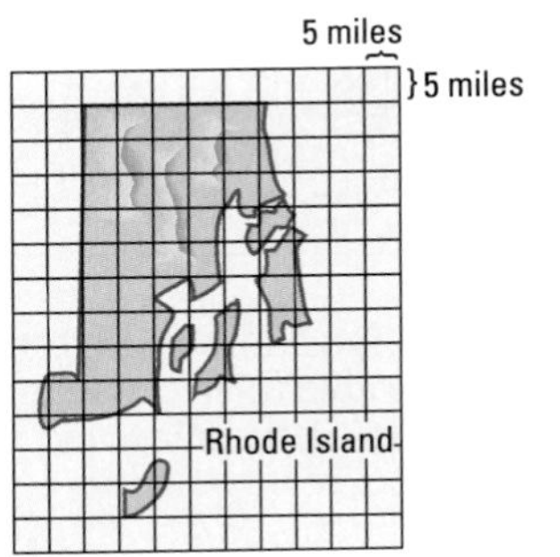

13. ⊙A with diameter 12 is contained in square $EFGH$ shown at the right. What is the area of the shaded region? ≈ 30.96 $units^2$

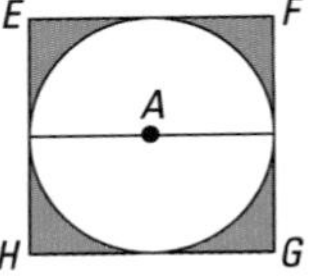

14. The sides of a rectangle are all multiplied by 4. a) It is multiplied by 4.

a. What happens to its perimeter?

b. What happens to its area? It is multiplied by 16.

PROGRESS SELF-TEST

15. Below, a frame 2″ wide is put around a rectangular painting that is 12″ by 17″. What is the outside perimeter of the frame? 74″

16. A 5-meter ladder is resting on level ground against a wall. If its base is 1.8 meters away from the wall, how high up the wall will it reach? Answer to the nearest tenth of a meter. 4.7 m

17. In October, 1989, an earthquake measuring 6.9 on the Richter scale caused substantial damage in San Francisco, 80 miles from the epicenter of the quake in Santa Cruz, California. To the nearest hundred square miles, how much area was within 80 miles of the epicenter? 20,100 square miles

Quake's Cost. *The earthquake in San Francisco in October, 1989, caused billions of dollars of damage and destroyed over 100,000 buildings.*

18. A room measures 9 ft by 15 ft. How many square yards of carpeting are needed to cover the floor? 15 sq yd

19. A park with perimeter 2640 ft is shaped like a square. What is its area? 435,600 sq ft

20. A Japanese "star" archery target is pictured below. If an arrow hits the target at random, what is the probability it hits the bull's-eye? $\frac{1}{9}$

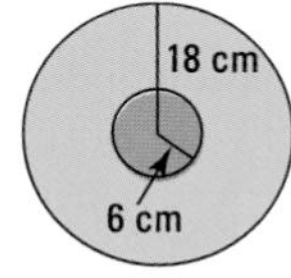

21. A triangle on a coordinate grid has vertices (8, 0), (-1, 0), and (0, 1). Find its area. 4.5 units^2

22. Find the area of the octagon below. 78 units^2

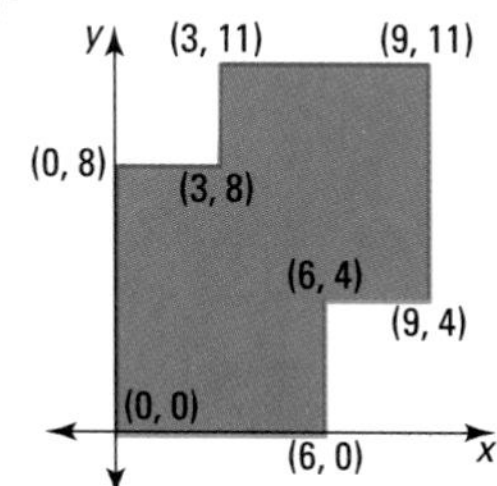

23. Name the cultures in which the Pythagorean Theorem was discovered. Sample: Greek, Chinese, Babylonian

Chapter 8 Review

Resources

From the ***Teacher's Resource File***

- Answer Master for Chapter 8 Review
- Assessment Sourcebook: Chapter 8 Test, Forms A–D Chapter 8 Test, Cumulative Form

Additional Resources

- Quiz and Test Writer

The main objectives for the chapter are organized in the Chapter Review under the four types of understanding this book promotes—Skills, Properties, Uses, and Representations.

Whereas end-of-chapter material may be considered optional in some texts, in UCSMP *Geometry* we have selected these objectives and questions with the expectation that they will be covered. Students should be able to answer these questions with about 85% accuracy after studying the chapter.

You may assign these questions over a single night to help students prepare for a test the next day, or you may assign the questions over a two-day period. If you work the questions over two days, then we recommend assigning the *evens* for homework the first night so that students get feedback in class the next day, then assigning the odds the night before the test, because answers are provided to the odd-numbered questions.

It is effective to ask students which questions they still do not understand and use the day or days as a total class discussion of the material which the class finds most difficult.

CHAPTER REVIEW

Questions on SPUR Objectives

SPUR stands for **S**kills, **P**roperties, **U**ses, and **R**epresentations. The Chapter Review questions are grouped according to the SPUR Objectives for this chapter.

SKILLS DEAL WITH THE PROCEDURES USED TO GET ANSWERS.

Objective A: *Calculate perimeters of parallelograms, kites, and equilateral polygons given appropriate lengths, and vice versa.* *(Lesson 8-1)* 2, 7) See below.

In 1–4, give the perimeter of the figure.

1. a kite in which one side has length 10 and another side has length 6 32 units

2. a rhombus in which one side has length t

3. a regular pentagon in which one side has length 47 meters 235 meters

4. a square whose area is 324 square feet 72 ft

5. The perimeter of a rectangle is 28 cm. One side has length 4 cm. What is the length of the other side? 10 cm

6. If the perimeter of an equilateral triangle is P, what is the length of a side of the triangle? $\frac{1}{3}P$

7. $ABCD$ is a parallelogram pictured at the right. If its perimeter is 75, what are the lengths of its sides?

A, B, C, D; $2x$; x

8. An equilateral hexagon has perimeter 1. What is the length of each side? $\frac{1}{6}$ unit

2) $4t$ units 7) 12.5 units, 25 units

Objective B: *Describe or apply a method for determining the area of an irregularly shaped region.* *(Lesson 8-3)* 9–12) Samples are given.

In 9 and 10, each small square is 30 m on a side. Estimate the area of the island (in square meters).

9. 13,950 m^2 **10.** 13,500 m^2

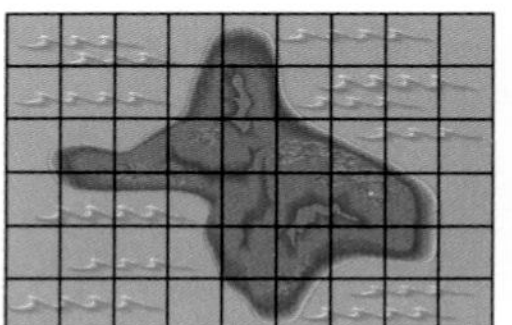

In 11 and 12, estimate the area of the mainland of South Carolina using the given grid.

11. 37,500 sq mi **12.** 33,750 sq mi

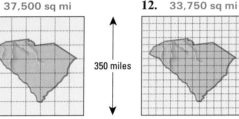

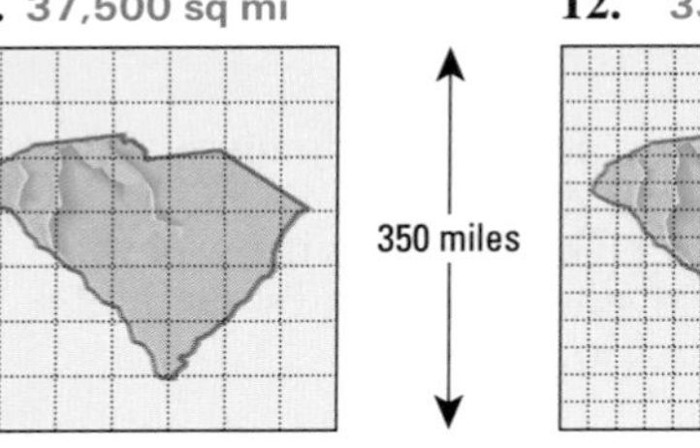

Objective C: *Calculate areas of squares, rectangles, parallelograms, trapezoids, and triangles given relevant length of sides, and vice versa.* *(Lessons 8-2, 8-4, 8-5)*

In 13–16, calculate the area of the figure.

13. rectangle $MOST$ 4.55 cm^2

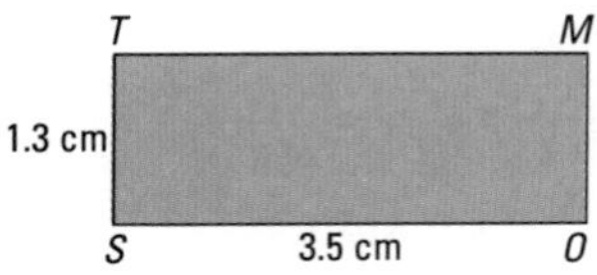

14. $\triangle EFG$ at the right in which $GE = 36x$ $288x^2$ $units^2$

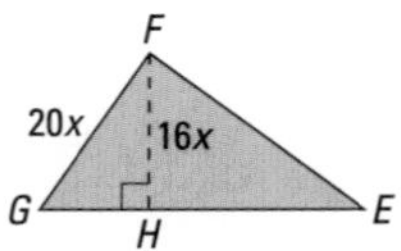

15. a trapezoid with bases 11 and 13 and altitude 6 72 $units^2$

16. the triangle with sides of lengths 13, 14, and 15 at the right 84 $units^2$

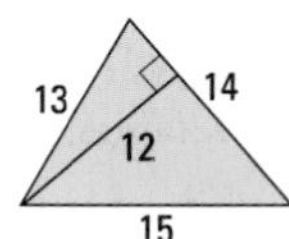

490

17. Find the area of the isosceles trapezoid below.

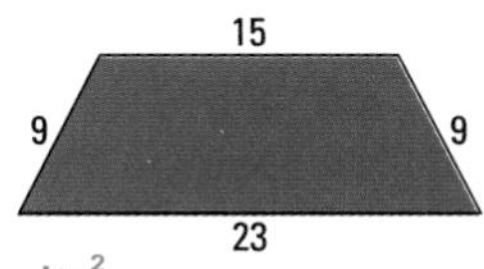

≈ 153.2 units²

18. Find the area of a square with perimeter 100 feet. 625 sq ft

19. A square has area 12.25. What is the length of a side of this square? 3.5 units

20. The bases of a trapezoid have lengths 20 feet and 30 feet and the trapezoid has area 800 square feet. What is the length of the altitude of the trapezoid? 32 ft

21. $\triangle PQR$ at the right is a right triangle. $\overline{QA}$ is the altitude to $\overline{PR}$. Find QA. 12 units

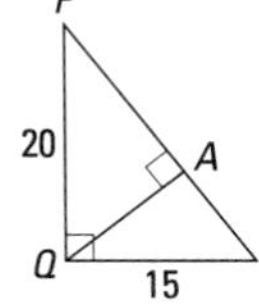

22. Give dimensions of a rectangle with perimeter 200 ft and area less than 100 ft^2.
Sample: 99 ft by 1 ft

Objective D: *Apply the Pythagorean Theorem to calculate lengths and areas in right triangles and other figures.* *(Lesson 8-6)*

In 23 and 24, find the length of the missing side.

23.

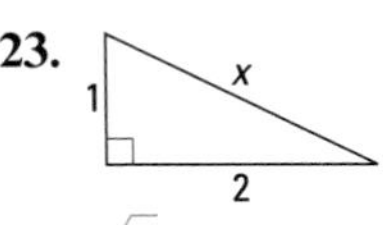

$\sqrt{5} \approx 2.24$ units

24.

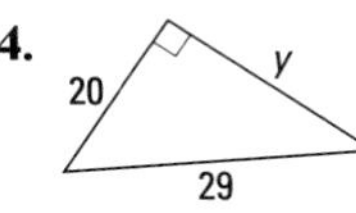

21 units

25. The two legs of a right triangle have lengths $6x$ and $7x$. What is its perimeter? ≈ 22.2x units

26. The hypotenuse of a right triangle is 50 and one leg is 40. What is the area of the triangle?
600 units²

27. A rectangle has dimensions 60 cm and 45 cm. What is the length of a diagonal? 75 cm

28. A square has area 16 square miles. What is the length of a diagonal? $4\sqrt{2} \approx 5.66$ units

Objective E: *Apply the Pythagorean Converse Theorem.* *(Lesson 8-6)*

In 29–32, could the numbers be the lengths of sides of a right triangle?

29. 8, 31, 32 No

30. 16, 30, 34 Yes

31. 1, 2, $\sqrt{3}$ Yes

32. $\sqrt{7}$, $\sqrt{11}$, 4 No

Objective F: *Calculate lengths and measures of arcs, the circumference, and the area of a circle given measures of relevant lengths and angles, and vice versa.* *(Lessons 8-7, 8-8)* 34) 24 units

33. Give the circumference and area of a circle with radius 10 b) 62.83 units, 314.16 units²

a. exactly. 20π units, 100π units²

b. estimated to the nearest hundredth.

34. A circle has area 144π. What is its diameter?

35. A circle has circumference $40x$ meters. What is its radius? ≈ 6.4x meters

36. In $\odot Q$ at the right, $QY =$ 11 cm and $m\angle YQZ = 50$.

a. Find the length of $\overset{\frown}{YZ}$.

b. Find the area of the shaded sector.
See margin.

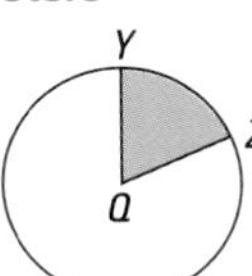

37. In $\odot O$ at the right, $\overline{BD}$ is a diameter, $OD = 15$, and $m\angle AOD = 20$.

a. Find the length of $\overset{\frown}{AB}$ to the nearest tenth. 41.9 units

b. Find the area of the sector bounded by A, O, and D.
≈ 39.27 units²

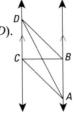

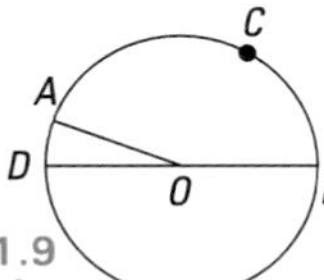

PROPERTIES DEAL WITH THE PRINCIPLES BEHIND THE MATHEMATICS.

Objective G: *Relate various formulas for area.* *(Lessons 8-2, 8-4, 8-5, 8-8)* 38, 39) See margin.

38. Explain how the area formula for a trapezoid is derived from the formula for the area of a triangle.

39. Explain how the area formula for a parallelogram is derived from the formula for the area of a trapezoid.

40. *Multiple choice.* In the figure at the right, Area($\triangle ABC$) __?__ Area($\triangle ABD$).
(a) < (b) = (c) > b

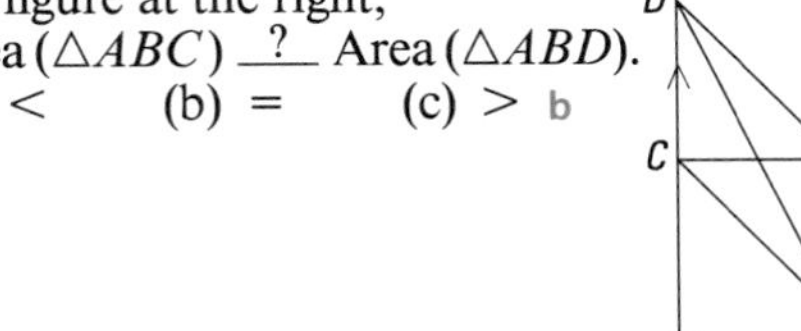

Assessment

Evaluation The *Assessment Sourcebook* provides five forms of the Chapter 8 Test. Forms A and B present parallel versions in a short-answer format. Forms C and D offer performance assessment. The fifth test is Chapter 8 Test, Cumulative Form. About 50% of this test covers Chapter 8; 25% of it covers Chapter 7, and 25% covers earlier chapters.

For information on grading, see *General Teaching Suggestions; Grading* in the *Professional Sourcebook,* which begins on page T20 in this Teacher's Edition.

Additional Answers

36a. ≈ 9.60 cm

b. ≈ 52.80 cm^2

38. Area of triangle: $A = \frac{1}{2}hb$.
A trapezoid can be divided into two triangles with the same height but different bases, so $A = \frac{1}{2}hb_1 + \frac{1}{2}hb_2 = \frac{1}{2}h(b_1 + b_2)$.

39. Area of trapezoid:
$A = \frac{1}{2}h(b_1 + b_2)$, but in a parallelogram, $b_1 = b_2 = b$, so $A = \frac{1}{2}h(b + b) = \frac{1}{2} \cdot h \cdot 2b = bh$.

Feedback After students have taken the test for Chapter 8 and you have scored the results, return the tests to students for discussion. Class discussion of the questions that caused trouble for the most students can be very effective in identifying and clarifying misunderstandings. You might want to have them write down the items they missed and work, either in groups or at home, to correct them. It is important for students to receive feedback on every chapter test, and we recommend that students see and correct their mistakes before proceeding too far into the next chapter.

41. In the figure at the right, square $ABCD$ has vertices on $\odot O$. Find an exact value for the area of the shaded region. $49\pi - 98$

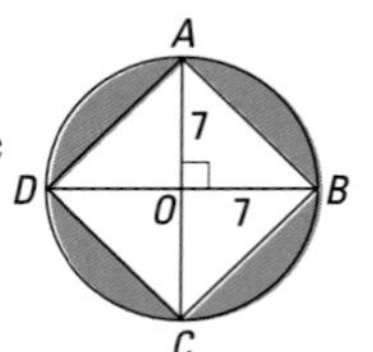

42. Refer to the figure below. Two metal disks are cut out of a 10-m by 20-m rectangle of metal. The leftover metal is recycled. What is the area of the metal that is recycled? about 43 m^2

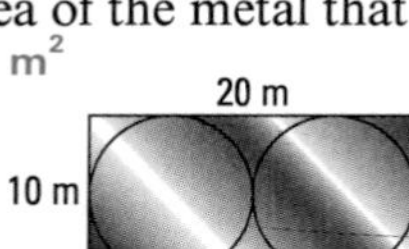

43. In the figure below, $\overline{AB}$ is a diameter of $\odot O$ and $\overline{AO}$ is a diameter of $\odot P$. If $AP = x$, find an exact value for the area of the shaded region. $3\pi x^2$ units^2

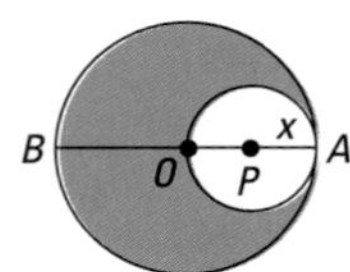

44. $WXYZ$ below is a square with segments as marked. Find the area of the shaded region. $8s^2$ units^2

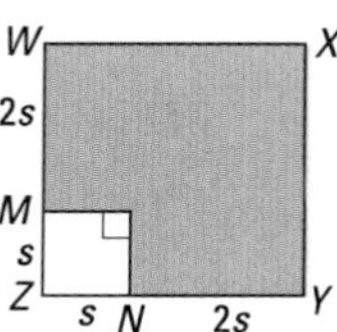

Objective H: *Apply the Pythagorean Theorem and perimeter formulas for parallelograms, kites, and equilateral polygons to real-world situations.* *(Lessons 8-1, 8-6)*

45. If a 20 foot ladder reaches $19\frac{1}{2}$ feet high on a wall, how far away from the wall is the bottom of the ladder? ≈ 4.4 ft

46. A frame 3 cm wide is put around a rectangular-shaped painting that is 8 cm by 20 cm. What is the perimeter of the outside of the frame? 80 cm

47. A stop sign is a regular octagon. For safety reasons, the manufacturer of the sign wishes to dull the edges by wrapping them with tape. If one edge of the sign has length k, what is the total length of tape needed? $8k$ units

48. A rectangular room is 9′ by 11′. Baseboard is to be put around the room in all places except the 3′ wide door. How many feet of baseboard are needed? 37′

49. How long would it take for a person to walk around the trapezoidal field shown at the right at a rate of 300 feet per minute? 14 min.

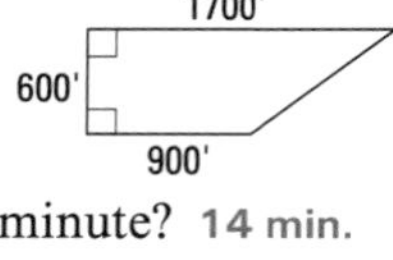

50. A school bus drops off Dennis and his little sister, Nati, at a corner near their house. To get to their house, Dennis walks north 68 yards along the sidewalk and then west 49 yards along their driveway. Nati cuts directly across the yard to get to the same place. How much farther does Dennis walk? about 33 yd

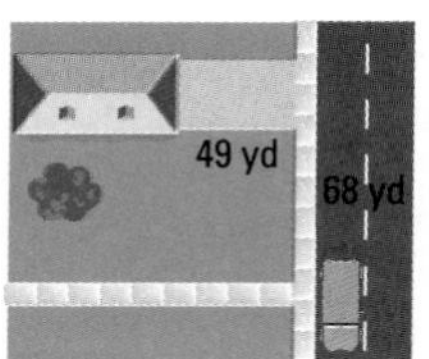

USES DEAL WITH APPLICATIONS OF MATHEMATICS IN REAL SITUATIONS.

Objective I: *Apply formulas for areas of squares, rectangles, parallelograms, trapezoids, and triangles to real-world situations.* *(Lessons 8-2, 8-4, 8-5)*

51. What is the area of a square park that is 210 meters on a side? 44,100 m^2

52. A person wishes to tile part of a bathroom floor with 1-inch-square tiles. How many tiles will be needed if the floor is a rectangular region 6′ long and 4′ wide? 3456

53. What is the area of the field shown in Question 49? 780,000 sq ft

54. A triangular piece of fabric is needed for a sail. If the sail is to be 14′ high and is 15′ long at the base, about how much fabric will be used? 105 sq ft

Objective J: *Apply formulas for the area and circumference of a circle to real situations. (Lessons 8-7, 8-8)*

55. Due to a chemical spill, authorities evacuated all people within 3 km of the spill. To the nearest tenth of a square kilometer, what was the area of the evacuated region? 28.3 km^2

56. A car's tire has a radius of 1 foot. How many revolutions will the tire make if the car goes 1 mile? (1 mile = 5280 feet) ≈ 840

57. For his dog, Eugene wants to make a circular play area surrounded by a fence. He has 100 feet of fencing. What is the diameter of the largest play area he can make? $\frac{100}{\pi} \approx 31.8$ ft

58. In the Olympic free pistol event, a target is 50 meters from the shooter. If a bullet lands at random in the target shown below, what is the probability it lands in the bull's-eye? $\frac{1}{400}$

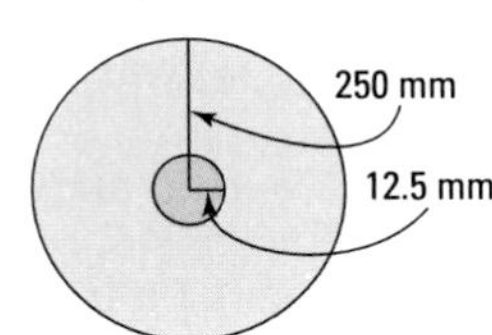

REPRESENTATIONS DEAL WITH PICTURES, GRAPHS OR OBJECTS THAT ILLUSTRATE CONCEPTS.

Objective K: *Determine the areas of polygons on a coordinate plane. (Lessons 8-2, 8-4, 8-5)*

59. Find the area of the decagon below.

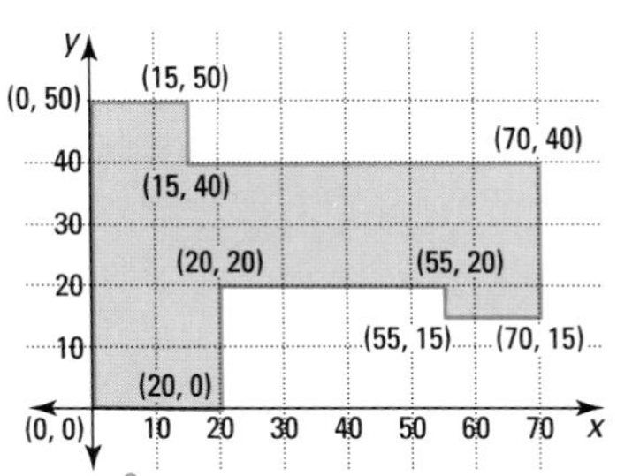

2025 $units^2$

60. A triangle has vertices (7, -4), (-3, -4), and (-1, 11). Find its area. 75 $units^2$

61. The grid at the right is in unit squares. Find the area of quadrilateral $ABCD$. 32 $units^2$

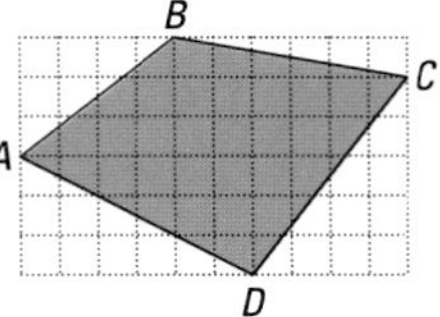

62. Find the area of the quadrilateral with the given vertices at the right. Assume a, b, and c are positive, with $b > c$. $ab - \frac{1}{2}ac$

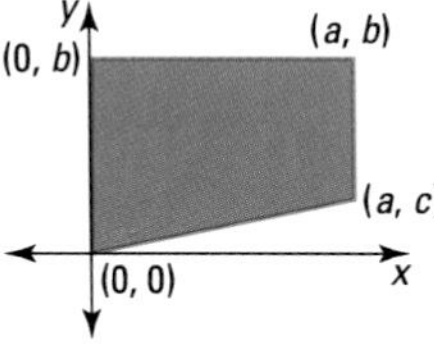

CULTURE DEALS WITH THE PEOPLES AND THE HISTORY RELATED TO THE DEVELOPMENT OF MATHEMATICS IDEALS.

Objective L: *Identify cultures in which the Pythagorean Theorem is known to have been studied. (Lesson 8-6)*

63. *Multiple choice.* In which of these cultures did the mathematician Pythagoras live? a
(a) Greek (b) Chinese
(c) Indian (d) Babylonian

64. *True or false.* Over 200 different proofs of the Pythagorean Theorem are known. True

65. *True or false.* In some cultures, the Pythagorean Theorem has a different name. True

66. *Multiple choice.* When was the first known proof of the Pythagorean Theorem? a
(a) over 2500 years ago
(b) 1500–2000 years ago
(c) about 1000 years ago
(d) less than 500 years ago

Chapter 9 Planner

Adapting to Individual Needs

The student text is written for the vast majority of students. The chart at the right suggests two pacing plans to accommodate the needs of your students. Students in the Full Course should complete the entire text by the end of the year. Students in the Minimal Course will spend more time when there are quizzes and more time on the Chapter Review. Therefore, these students may not complete all of the chapters in the text.

Options are also presented to meet the needs of a variety of teaching and learning styles. For each lesson, the Teacher's Edition provides a section entitled *Adapting to Individual Needs.* This section regularly includes **Optional Activities, Challenge** problems, **English Language Development** suggestions, and suggestions for providing **Extra Help.** The Teacher's Edition also frequently includes an **Error Alert,** an **Extension,** and an **Assessment** alternative. The options available in Chapter 9 are summarized in the chart below.

Chapter 9 Pacing Chart

Day	Full Course	Minimal Course
1	9-1	9-1
2	9-2	9-2
3	9-3	9-3
4	9-4	9-4
5	Quiz*; 9-5	Quiz*; begin 9-5.
6	9-6	Finish 9-5.
7	9-7	9-6
8	Quiz*; 9-8	9-7
9	9-9	Quiz*; begin 9-8.
10	Self-Test	Finish 9-8.
11	Review	9-9
12	Test*	Self-Test
13	Comprehensive	Review
14	Test*	Review
15		Test*
16		Comprehensive
17		Test*

*in the Teacher's Resource File

In the Teacher's Edition...

Lesson	Optional Activities	Extra Help	Challenge	English Language Development	Error Alert	Extension	Cooperative Learning	Ongoing Assessment
9-1	●		●	●	●	●	●	Oral
9-2	●		●			●		Written
9-3	●	●	●	●		●	●	Written
9-4	●	●	●	●		●	●	Diagnostic
9-5	●	●	●	●		●	●	Oral
9-6	●	●	●		●	●	●	Oral
9-7	●					●	●	Oral
9-8	●	●	●	●	●	●	●	Oral/Written
9-9	●	●	●			●	●	Written

Chapter 9 Block Schedule

Day	Recommended Pacing
1	Lessons 9-1, 9-2
2	Lesson 9-3
3	Lessons 9-4, 9-5
4	Lessons 9-6, 9-7
5	Lesson 9-8
6	Lesson 9-9, Self-Test, Chapter Review
7	Chapter Review, Chapter Test or Comprehensive Test

In the Additional Resources...

	In the Teacher's Resource File								
Lesson	Lesson Masters, A and B	Teaching Aids*	Activity Kit*	Answer Masters	Technology Sourcebook	Assessment Sourcebook	Visual Aids**	Technology	Video Segments
Opener		117					117		
9-1	9-1	118		9-1			118, AM		
9-2	9-2	118		9-2			118, AM		
9-3	9-3	118	20	9-3			118, AM		
9-4	9-4	119, 121		9-4		Quiz	119, 121, AM		
9-5	9-5	119, 122, 123, 124		9-5			119, 122, 123, 124, AM		
9-6	9-6	119		9-6			119, AM		
9-7	9-7	120, 125, 126		9-7		Quiz	120, 125, 126 AM		
In-class Activity		127		9-8			127 AM		
9-8	9-8	120, 128	21	9-8	19		120, 128, AM	GeoExplorer	
In-class Activity		129		9-9			129, AM		
9-9	9-9	104, 120, 130		9-9			104, 120, 130, AM		9-9
End of Chapter				Review		Tests			

*Teaching Aids are pictured on pages 494C and 494D. The activities in the Activity Kit are pictured on page 494C. Teaching Aid 127 which accompanies the In-class Activity preceding Lesson 9-8 is pictured with the lesson notes on page 536. Teaching Aid 129 which accompanies the In-class Activity preceding Lesson 9-9 is pictured with the lesson notes on page 543.

**Visual Aids provide transparencies for all Teaching Aids and all Answer Masters.

Also available is the Study Skills Handbook which includes study-skill tips related to reading, note-taking, and comprehension.

Integrating Strands and Applications

	9-1	9-2	9-3	9-4	9-5	9-6	9-7	9-8	9-9
Mathematical Connections									
Number Sense			●		●				
Algebra	●		●	●				●	
Geometry	●	●	●	●	●	●	●	●	●
Measurement	●	●	●	●	●	●	●	●	●
Logic and Reasoning	●	●	●	●	●	●	●	●	●
Patterns and Functions	●	●		●	●	●		●	●
Discrete Mathematics				●				●	●
Interdisciplinary and Other Connections									
Art					●			●	
Science			●		●	●	●		●
Social Studies		●	●	●	●	●	●	●	●
Multicultural	●			●	●	●		●	●
Technology								●	
Career							●		
Sports			●						

Teaching and Assessing the Chapter Objectives

Chapter 9 Objectives (Organized into the SPUR categories—Skills, Properties, Uses, and Representations)	Lessons	Progress Self-Test Questions	Chapter Review Questions	In the Teacher's Resource File: Chapter Test, Forms A and B	Chapter Test, Forms	
					C	D
Skills						
A: Draw common 3-dimensional shapes.	9-2, 9-3, 9-4, 9-5	1, 2, 3	1–8	1, 2	3	
B: Draw plane sections of common 3-dimensional shapes.	9-5	5, 7	9–12	4, 5, 12		
C: Give views of a figure from the top, sides, or front.	9-7	8, 9	13–16	8, 13	3	✓
D: Given appropriate lengths, calculate areas and lengths in 3-dimensional figures.	9-3, 9-4, 9-5	11, 12, 13	17–24	11, 12, 14	5	
E: From 2-dimensional views of a figure, determine the 3-dimensional figure.	9-7	16, 17	25–28	16, 20	6	✓
Properties						
F: Apply the properties of planes.	9-1, 9-2	4	29–33	3	1	
G: Determine symmetry planes in 3-dimensional figures.	9-6	6, 10	34–37	6	3	
Uses						
H: Recognize 3-dimensional figures in the real world.	9-3, 9-4, 9-5	14, 15	38–41	18, 19	2	✓
I: Apply the Four-Color Theorem to maps.	9-9	21	42–45	17	4	
Representations						
J: Make a surface from a net, and vice versa.	9-8	18, 19	46–51	9, 10, 15	3	
K: Interpret maps of the world.	9-9	20	52–55	7		

Assessment Sourcebook
Quiz for Lessons 9-1 through 9-4
Quiz for Lessons 9-5 through 9-7
Chapter 9 Test, Forms A–D
Chapter 9 Test, Cumulative Form
Comprehensive Test, Chapters 1–9

Quiz and Test Writer

Activity Kit

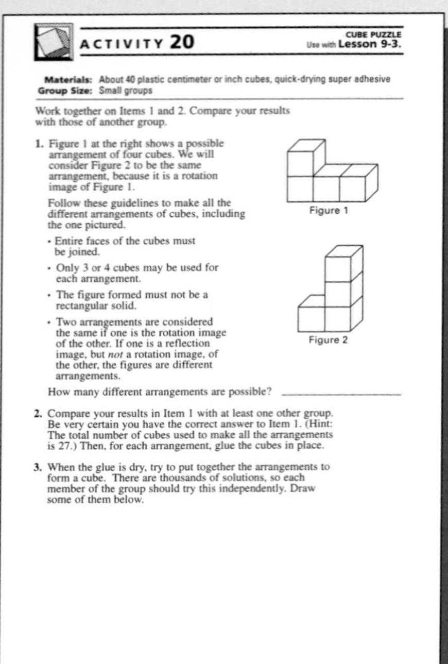

ACTIVITY 20

CUBE PUZZLE
Use with **Lesson 9-3.**

Materials: About 40 plastic centimeter or inch cubes, quick-drying super adhesive
Group Size: Small groups

Work together on Items 1 and 2. Compare your results with those of another group.

1. Figure 1 at the right shows a possible arrangement of four cubes. We will consider Figure 2 to be the same arrangement, because it is a rotation image of Figure 1.

   Follow these guidelines to make all the different arrangements of cubes, including the one pictured.

   - Entire faces of the cubes must be joined.
   - Only 3 or 4 cubes may be used for each arrangement.
   - The figure formed must not be a rectangular solid.
   - Two arrangements are considered the same if one is the rotation image of the other. If one is a reflection image, but *not* a rotation image, of the other, the figures are different arrangements.

   How many different arrangements are possible? ____________

2. Compare your results in Item 1 with at least one other group. Be very certain you have the correct answer to Item 1. (Hint: The total number of cubes used to make all the arrangements is 27.) Then, for each arrangement, glue the cubes in place.
3. When the glue is dry, try to put together the arrangements to form a cube. There are thousands of solutions, so each member of the group should try this independently. Draw some of them below.

Figure 1

Figure 2

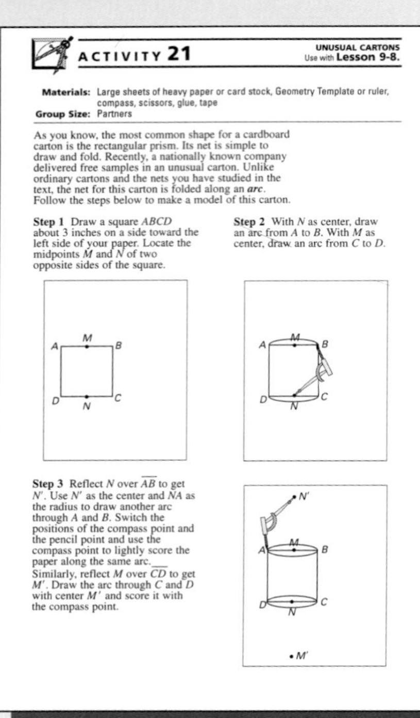

ACTIVITY 21

UNUSUAL CARTONS
Use with **Lesson 9-8.**

Materials: Large sheets of heavy paper or card stock, Geometry Template or ruler, compass, scissors, glue, tape
Group Size: Partners

As you know, the most common shape for a cardboard carton is the rectangular prism. Its net is simple to draw and fold. Recently, a nationally known company delivered free samples in an unusual carton. Unlike ordinary cartons and the nets you have studied in the text, the net for this carton is folded along an ***arc***. Follow the steps below to make a model of this carton.

Step 1 Draw a square *ABCD* about 3 inches on a side toward the left side of your paper. Locate the midpoints *M* and *N* of two opposite sides of the square.

Step 2 With *N* as center, draw an arc from *A* to *B*. With *M* as center, draw an arc from *C* to *D*.

Step 3 Reflect *N* over $\overline{AB}$ to get *N′*. Use *N′* as the center and *NA* as the radius to draw another arc through *A* and *B*. Switch the positions of the compass point and the pencil point and use the compass point to lightly score the paper along the same arc. Similarly, reflect *M* over $\overline{CD}$ to get *M′*. Draw the arc through *C* and *D* with center *M′* and score it with the compass point.

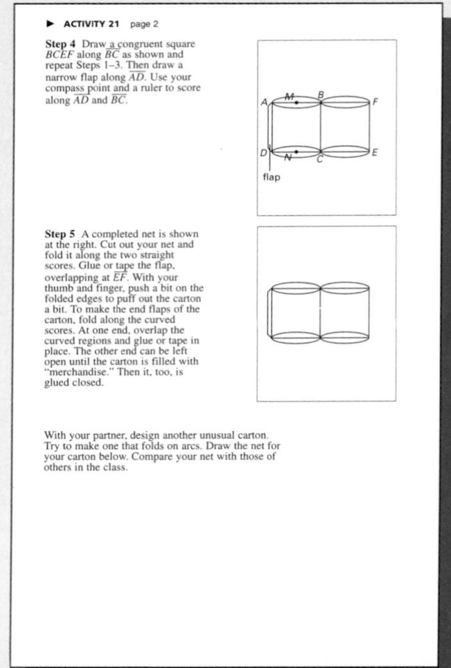

▶ **ACTIVITY 21** page 2

Step 4 Draw a congruent square *BCEF* along $\overline{BC}$ as shown and repeat Steps 1–3. Then draw a narrow flap along $\overline{AD}$. Use your compass point and a ruler to score along $\overline{AD}$ and $\overline{BC}$.

Step 5 A completed net is shown at the right. Cut out your net and fold it along the two straight scores. Glue or tape the flap, overlapping at $\overline{EF}$. With your thumb and finger, push a bit on the folded edges to puff out the carton a bit. To make the end flaps of the carton, fold along the curved scores. At one end, overlap the curved regions and glue or tape in place. The other end can be left open until the carton is filled with "merchandise." Then it, too, is glued closed.

With your partner, design another unusual carton. Try to make one that folds on arcs. Draw the net for your carton below. Compare your net with those of others in the class.

Teaching Aids

Teaching Aid 104, Map of the United States (shown on page 434C), can be used with **Lesson 9-9.**

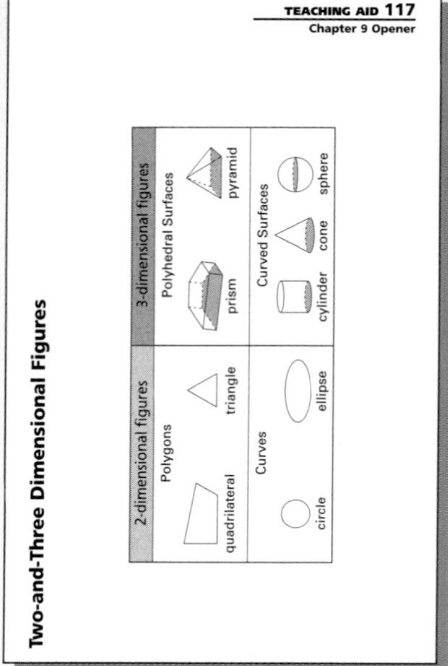

TEACHING AID 117
Chapter 9 Opener

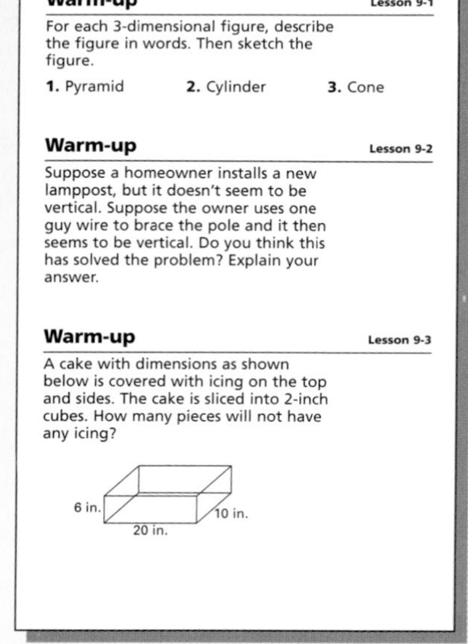

TEACHING AID 118

Warm-up Lesson 9-1

For each 3-dimensional figure, describe the figure in words. Then sketch the figure.

1. Pyramid **2.** Cylinder **3.** Cone

Warm-up Lesson 9-2

Suppose a homeowner installs a new lamppost, but it doesn't seem to be vertical. Suppose the owner uses one guy wire to brace the pole and it then seems to be vertical. Do you think this has solved the problem? Explain your answer.

Warm-up Lesson 9-3

A cake with dimensions as shown below is covered with icing on the top and sides. The cake is sliced into 2-inch cubes. How many pieces will not have any icing?

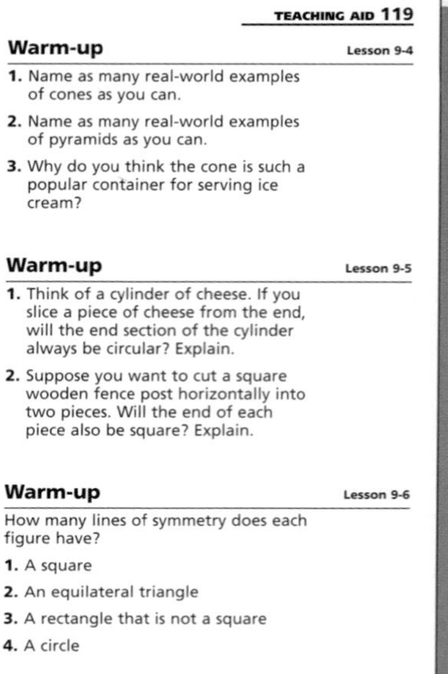

TEACHING AID 119

Warm-up Lesson 9-4

1. Name as many real-world examples of cones as you can.

2. Name as many real-world examples of pyramids as you can.

3. Why do you think the cone is such a popular container for serving ice cream?

Warm-up Lesson 9-5

1. Think of a cylinder of cheese. If you slice a piece of cheese from the end, will the end section of the cylinder always be circular? Explain.

2. Suppose you want to cut a square wooden fence post horizontally into two pieces. Will the end of each piece also be square? Explain.

Warm-up Lesson 9-6

How many lines of symmetry does each figure have?

1. A square

2. An equilateral triangle

3. A rectangle that is not a square

4. A circle

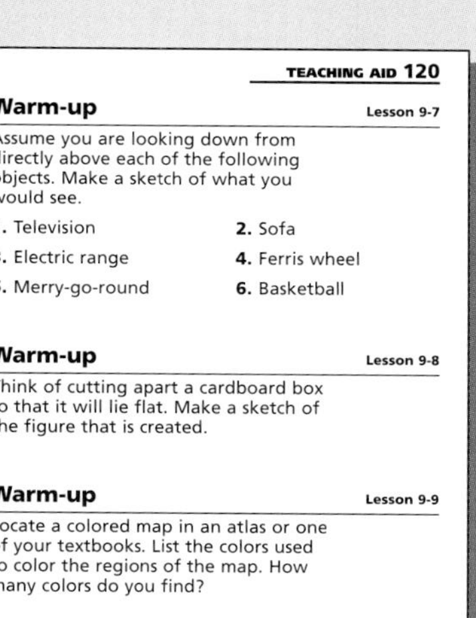

TEACHING AID 120

Warm-up
Lesson 9-7

Assume you are looking down from directly above each of the following objects. Make a sketch of what you would see.

1. Television **2.** Sofa
3. Electric range **4.** Ferris wheel
5. Merry-go-round **6.** Basketball

Warm-up
Lesson 9-8

Think of cutting apart a cardboard box so that it will lie flat. Make a sketch of the figure that is created.

Warm-up
Lesson 9-9

Locate a colored map in an atlas or one of your textbooks. List the colors used to color the regions of the map. How many colors do you find?

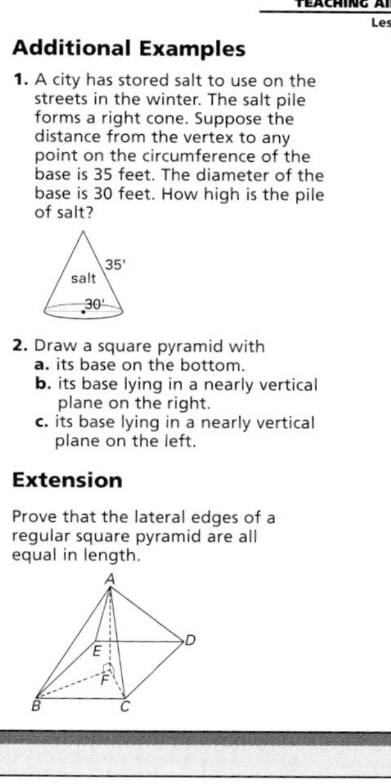

TEACHING AID 121
Lesson 9-4

Additional Examples

1. A city has stored salt to use on the streets in the winter. The salt pile forms a right cone. Suppose the distance from the vertex to any point on the circumference of the base is 35 feet. The diameter of the base is 30 feet. How high is the pile of salt?

2. Draw a square pyramid with
a. its base on the bottom.
b. its base lying in a nearly vertical plane on the right.
c. its base lying in a nearly vertical plane on the left.

Extension

Prove that the lateral edges of a regular square pyramid are all equal in length.

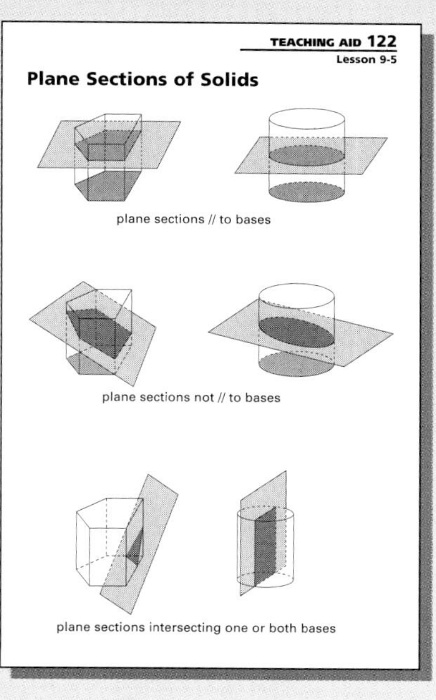

TEACHING AID 122
Lesson 9-5

Plane Sections of Solids

plane sections // to bases

plane sections not // to bases

plane sections intersecting one or both bases

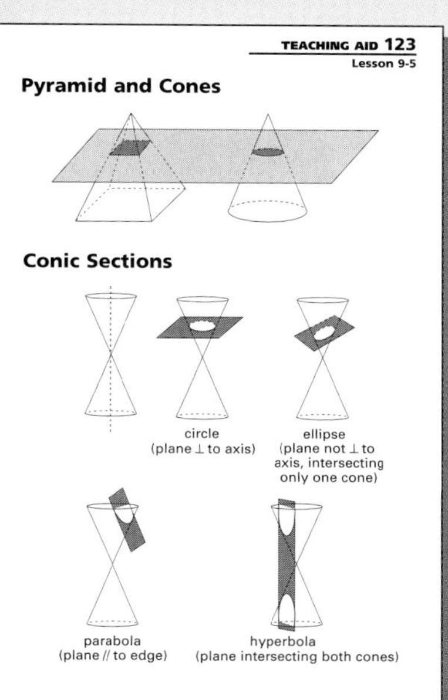

TEACHING AID 123
Lesson 9-5

Pyramid and Cones

Conic Sections

circle (plane ⊥ to axis)

ellipse (plane not ⊥ to axis, intersecting only one cone)

parabola (plane // to edge)

hyperbola (plane intersecting both cones)

TEACHING AID 124
Lesson 9-5

Optional Activities

Surface	Possible Section
Sphere	
Cylinder	
Pyramid	
Prism	
Cone	

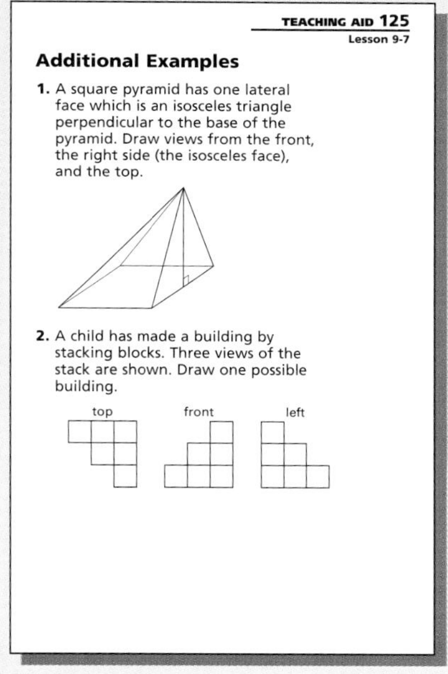

TEACHING AID 125
Lesson 9-7

Additional Examples

1. A square pyramid has one lateral face which is an isosceles triangle perpendicular to the base of the pyramid. Draw views from the front, the right side (the isosceles face), and the top.

2. A child has made a building by stacking blocks. Three views of the stack are shown. Draw one possible building.

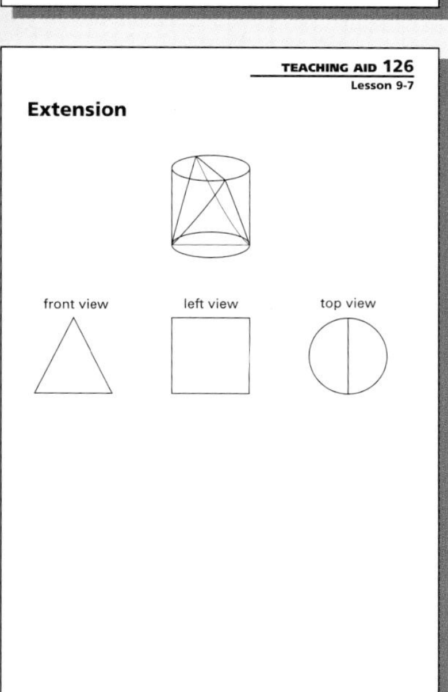

TEACHING AID 126
Lesson 9-7

Extension

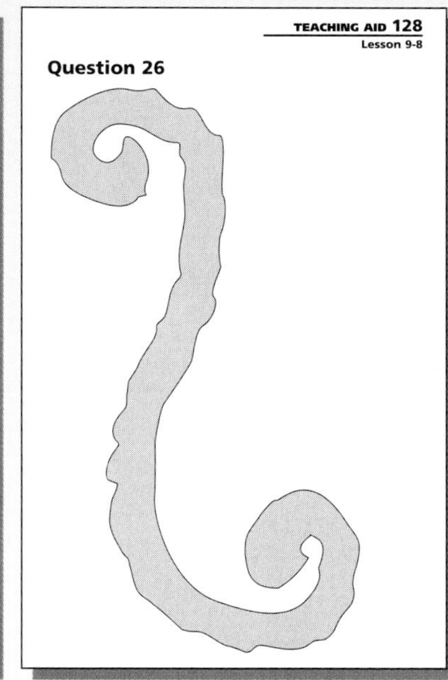

TEACHING AID 128
Lesson 9-8

Question 26

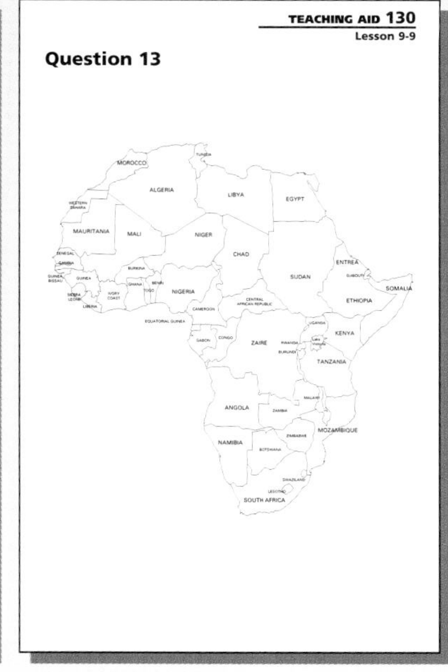

TEACHING AID 130
Lesson 9-9

Question 13

Chapter Opener

Pacing

All lessons in this chapter are designed to be covered in one day. At the end of the chapter, you should plan to spend 1 day to review the Progress Self-Test, 1–2 days for the Chapter Review, and 1 day for a test. You may wish to spend a day on projects, and possibly a day is needed for quizzes. Therefore, this chapter should take 12–15 days. We strongly advise you not to spend more than 15 days on this chapter; the ideas are reviewed, particularly in the next chapter.

Using Pages 494–495

Teaching Aid 117, which shows the figures identified in the chapter opener, can be used when discussing these pages.

Analogy is a powerful tool for helping us to understand the different dimensions. However, analogies are not always unique. For instance, most people view a *sphere* as the 3-dimensional analogue of a circle. But one could argue that a *cylinder* is a 3-dimensional analogue of a circle, because just as a circle is the set of points at a given distance from a given *point* in a *plane,* so a cylinder is the set of points at a given distance from a given *line* in *space.*

One could also argue that the dihedral angle is a 3-dimensional analogue of an angle. An angle is the union of two rays that have the same endpoint; a dihedral angle is the union of two half planes with the same edge.

CHAPTER 9

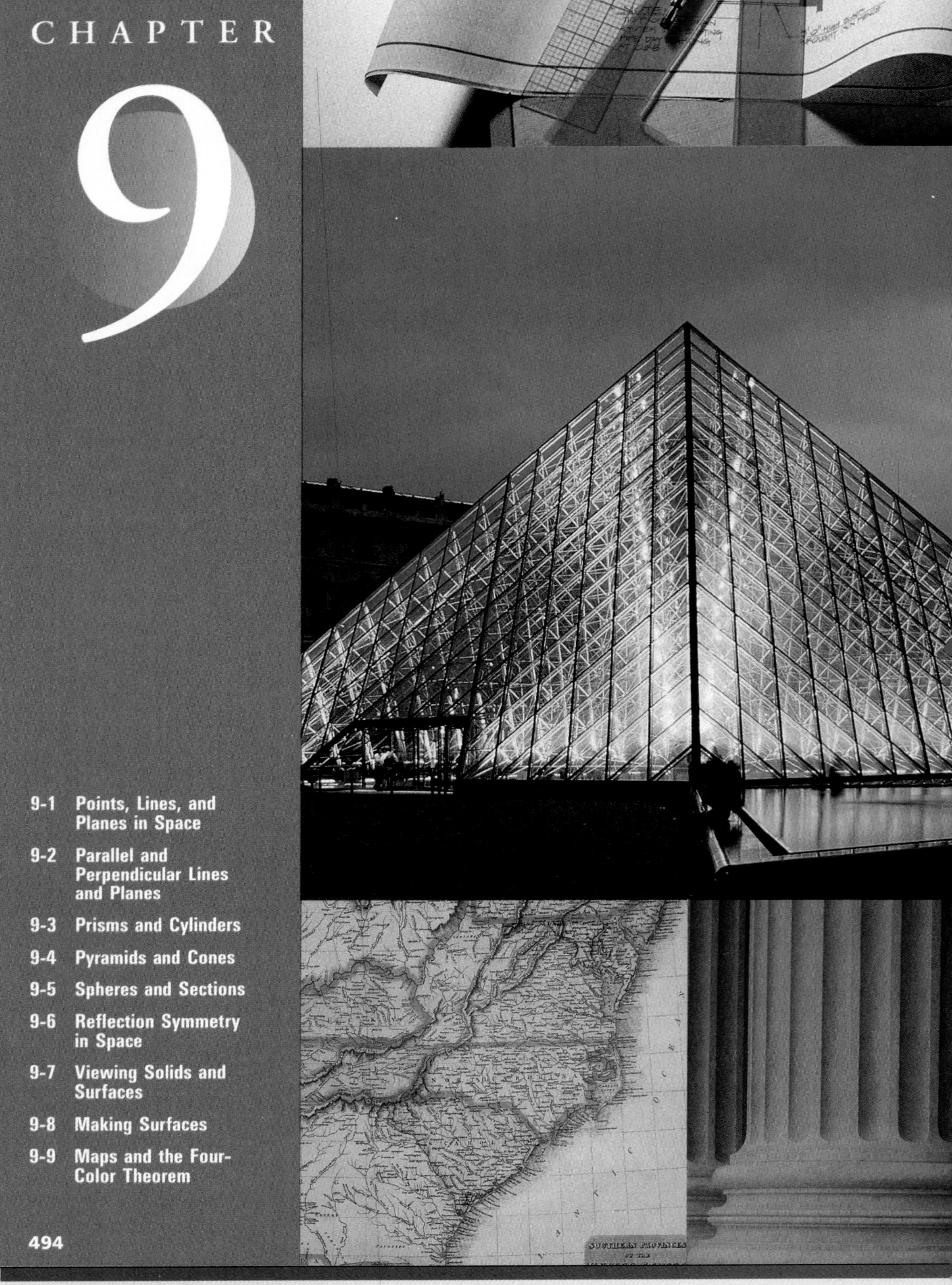

9-1 Points, Lines, and Planes in Space
9-2 Parallel and Perpendicular Lines and Planes
9-3 Prisms and Cylinders
9-4 Pyramids and Cones
9-5 Spheres and Sections
9-6 Reflection Symmetry in Space
9-7 Viewing Solids and Surfaces
9-8 Making Surfaces
9-9 Maps and the Four-Color Theorem

494

Chapter 9 Overview

This chapter is a noncomputational chapter dealing with the common 3-dimensional shapes: prisms, cylinders, pyramids, cones, and spheres. It grew out of an awareness that many students are asked to learn formulas for the surface areas and volumes of 3-dimensional figures without having much familiarity with these figures. So, they are forced to memorize the formulas without understanding, and their performance suffers.

The absence of algebra and formulas in this chapter contrasts with the computational chapters that precede and follow it. For most students, this is an easy chapter.

The main goals of this chapter are drawing and visualizing the common figures, and learning vocabulary and basic properties. A hierarchy relating the major types of surfaces studied in this chapter is in the Chapter Summary on page 554.

In the real world, most students can visualize well enough to drive a car and recognize details in drawing. Visualization in life, however, is not the same as visualization in geometry; there are many special skills associated with geometric visualization. Many students need instruction and practice in determining the cues that help them to distinguish one figure from another.

THREE-DIMENSIONAL FIGURES

Everything you touch or see, from paper to pencil, from house to car, from city to planet, does not lie in a single plane. All objects are 3-dimensional. The study of 3-dimensional figures is called *solid geometry*. However, mathematicians often analyze 3-dimensional shapes by looking at their parts in lower dimensions.

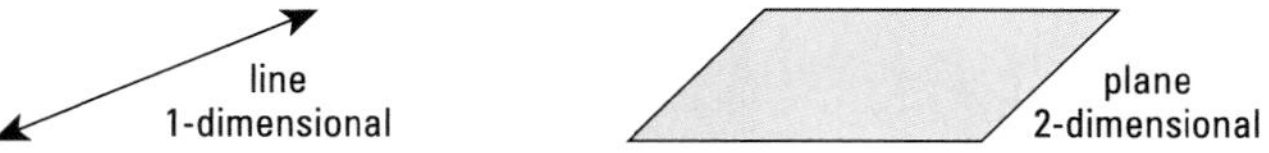

Just as the 1-dimensional line has the plane as its 2-dimensional counterpart, every 2-dimensional figure has its counterpart in three dimensions.

2-dimensional figures	3-dimensional figures
Polygons: quadrilateral, triangle	Polyhedral Surfaces: prism, pyramid
Curves: circle, ellipse	Curved Surfaces: cylinder, cone, sphere

In this chapter, you will learn the important properties of the above basic 3-dimensional figures, how to draw them, and how they are used. You will also see how they are related to the 2-dimensional figures you already know.

Literature Connection The classic book *Flatland,* by Edwin A. Abbott, is highly recommended as a study in understanding different dimensions.

Photo Connections

The photo collage makes real-world connections to the content of the chapter: 3-dimensional figures.

Plans: Architectural plans for buildings give accurate scale model measurements, or *elevations,* of the sides of the buildings. Examples of such elevations are shown in Lesson 9-7.

Pyramid: Visitors enter the Louvre Museum in Paris through a glass-and-steel pyramid designed by an American architect, I. M. Pei. Although parts of the Louvre date to the 1500s, the pyramid was completed in 1989.

Staircase: Staircases show wonderful examples of parallel and perpendicular lines and planes.

Map: Many people are surprised to learn that any map can be colored with four or fewer colors. The Four-Color Theorem is the topic of Lesson 9-9.

Columns: Architects have used free standing and structural columns in buildings since ancient times. The Greeks developed three classic types of columns—Doric, Ionic, and Corinthian. The columns shown here are Roman Doric; they are similar to the older Greek Doric style, but they also include molded bases.

Chapter 9 Projects

At this time you might want to have students look over the projects on pages 552–553.

Drawing is much more a learned skill than is visualization, and you may have students with learning disabilities that prevent them from copying your drawings, even with practice. However, the authors strongly believe that drawing skills can be learned. Students usually improve their drawing skills with instruction and practice.

Many visual aids are provided to support the teaching of this chapter. Still, it is recommended that physical models of 3-dimensional shapes be used whenever possible, both in this chapter and in Chapter 10.

Lesson 9-1

Objectives

F Apply the properties of planes.

Resources

From the ***Teacher's Resource File***
- Lesson Master 9-1A or 9-1B
- Answer Master 9-1
- Teaching Aid 118: Warm-up

Additional Resources
- Visual for Teaching Aid 118
- Two tacks and string
- Plywood and three dowels

Teaching Lesson 9-1

Warm-up

For each 3-dimensional figure, describe the figure in words. Then sketch the figure. **Descriptions and drawings will vary.**

1. Pyramid **2.** Cylinder **3.** Cone

Notes on Reading

❶ Only **parts d, e, and f** of the Point-Line-Plane postulate are new in this lesson. You can motivate **part d** by presenting an example and counterexample: place two tacks on a flat surface and tie a taut string around them. The string, representing a line, lies flat on the surface. For the same two tacks on a bent flexible surface that is no longer planar, the taut string will not lie on the surface (at least not if you are on the "concave side" of the surface).Thus **part d** of the postulate determines the property we refer to as *flatness.*

LESSON

9-1 *Points, Lines, and Planes in Space*

One good turn deserves another. *When pushing a panel in a revolving door, you move parts of planes in space about their line of intersection.*

Just as you had ideas about what points and lines should be before we stated postulates about them, you may have ideas about planes. Most of the figures you have seen in the previous chapters lie in a single plane. Their points are coplanar. You can think of a plane as being flat and having no thickness, like a table top that goes on forever. In fact, mathematicians draw a plane on a page the same way as they would draw a tabletop. We name planes with a single capital letter, like X. We use a dashed line to represent parts of a figure "behind" the drawn plane.

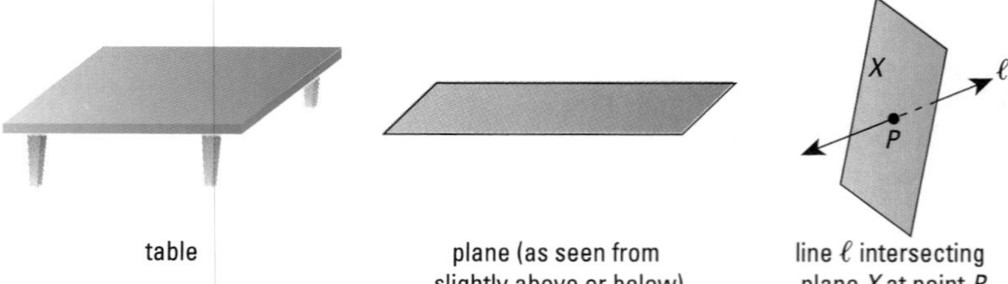

Point-Line-Plane Postulate

Recall from Chapter 1 that the three terms *point*, *line*, and *plane* are undefined because we cannot define every word and because, in different geometries, they have different meanings. Our assumptions about points and lines were summarized in Lesson 1-7 in the Point-Line-Plane Postulate, which is repeated here.

Lesson 9-1 Overview

Broad Goals This lesson introduces three additional parts of the Point-Line-Plane Postulate. These three parts complete the constraints on the undefined terms, and form the basis for making deductions in Euclidean geometry of three dimensions.

Perspective The major ideas of this lesson are: (1) planes are customarily drawn as parallelograms, and (2) certain combinations of points or lines determine a plane.

Until now in the text, all deductions have involved coplanar figures, so only the parts of the Point-Line-Plane Postulate that apply to points and lines have been needed. In the statement of this postulate on page 497, only **part c** involves planes in space. It tells us that space contains more points than a single plane—that is, it ensures that there is another dimension. **Parts d, e, and f** of the Point-Line-Plane Postulate tell us how lines and planes relate to each other in that space. **Part d** says that a line is parallel to a plane, intersects a plane in one point, or is in the plane. **Part e** says that three non-collinear points determine a plane, just as two points determine a line. **Part f** says that two planes either are parallel or intersect in a line.

Point-Line-Plane Postulate

a. Unique Line Assumption
Through any two points, there is exactly one line.

b. Number Line Assumption
Every line is a set of points that can be put into a one-to-one correspondence with the real numbers, with any point on it corresponding to 0 and any other point corresponding to 1.

c. Dimension Assumption
(1) Given a line in a plane, there is at least one point in the plane that is not on the line.
(2) Given a plane in space, there is at least one point in space that is not in the plane.

To convey the ideas about planes precisely, three new assumptions are added to the Point-Line-Plane Postulate. The remainder of this lesson discusses these assumptions and presents other information about planes.

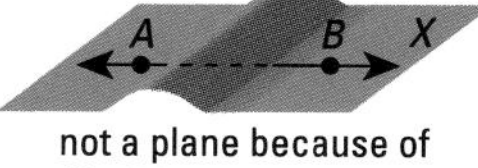

not a plane because of Flat Plane Assumption

The Flat Plane Assumption conveys the idea that planes have no bumps and go on forever. It implies that segments connecting points do not jump out of planes.

❶ **d. Flat Plane Assumption**
If two points lie in a plane, the line containing them lies in the plane.

Determining a Plane

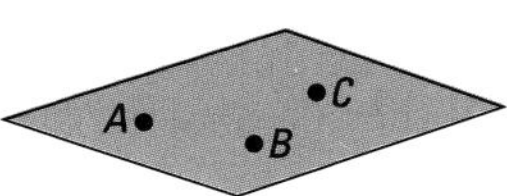

The Unique Plane Assumption is sometimes stated: Three noncollinear points determine a plane.

❷ **e. Unique Plane Assumption**
Through three noncollinear points, there is exactly one plane.

A three-legged stool works on the principle of the Unique Plane Assumption. It is stable on the plane containing the tips of its three legs. A chair with four legs, however, is often unstable. It is wobbly when the tips of its legs are not coplanar.

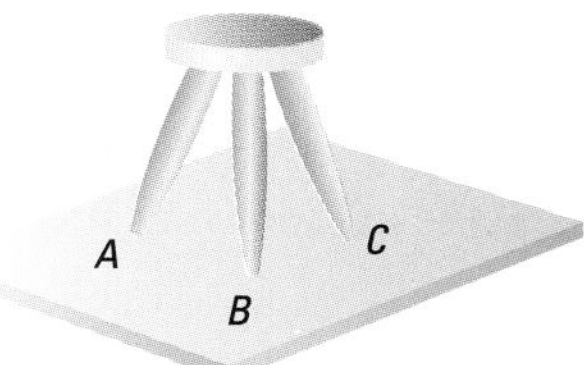

The stool is stable on the plane containing *A*, *B*, and *C*.

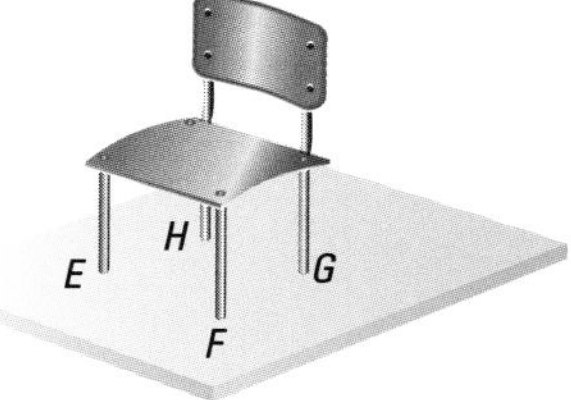

The chair will wobble unless *G* lies in the plane determined by *E*, *F*, and *H*.

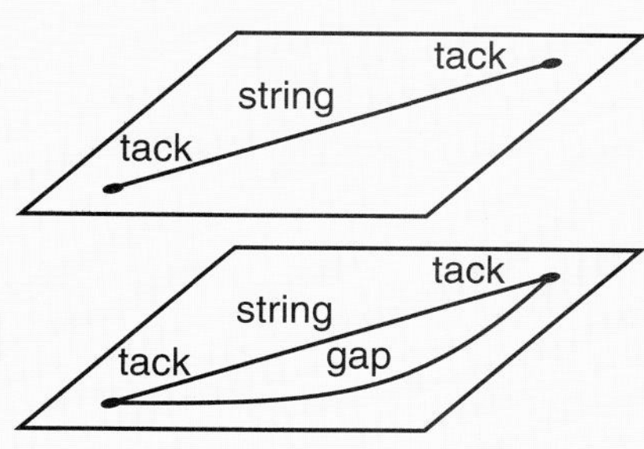

❷ To motivate **part e,** you might hand a student a piece of plywood and three dowels of the same length. Ask what can be done to assure that the plywood is in a plane parallel to the desk top. Is one dowel sufficient, excluding the idea of finding the center of gravity of the piece of plywood? Are two sufficient to determine the tilt of the plane? If three dowels are placed in a line, will that determine the tilt of the plane? [Three noncollinear positions are sufficient to determine the tilt of the plane.]

Because of the models used to demonstrate planes, students may tacitly assume properties for planes that are not true. For example, one sheet of paper may be positioned to touch another in only one point.

Part f ensures that planes *do not have edges.* Another misconception gleaned from models is that planes have thickness. If that were the case, two intersecting planes, like two pieces of cardboard, would have a long rectangular solid in common. **Part f** also ensures that the planes *do not have thickness.*

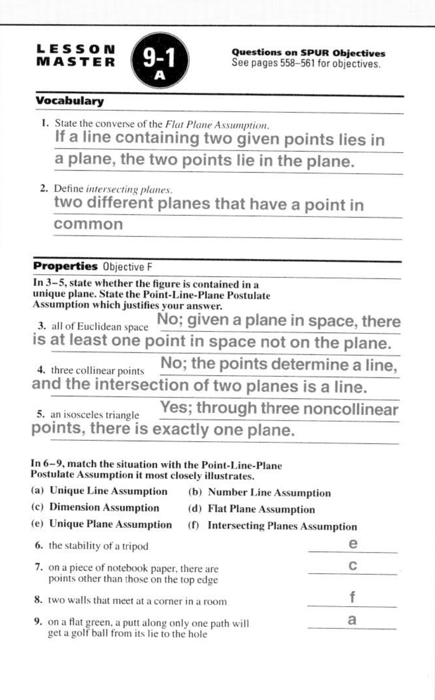
LESSON MASTER 9-1 A
Questions on SPUR Objectives
See pages 558–561 for objectives.

Vocabulary

1. State the converse of the *Flat Plane Assumption.*
If a line containing two given points lies in a plane, the two points lie in the plane.

2. Define *intersecting planes.*
two different planes that have a point in common

Properties Objective F

In 3–5, state whether the figure is contained in a unique plane. State the Point-Line-Plane Postulate Assumption which justifies your answer.

3. all of Euclidean space No; given a plane in space, there is at least one point in space not on the plane.
4. three collinear points No; the points determine a line, and the intersection of two planes is a line.
5. an isosceles triangle Yes; through three noncollinear points, there is exactly one plane.

In 6–9, match the situation with the Point-Line-Plane Postulate Assumption it most closely illustrates.

(a) Unique Line Assumption **(b) Number Line Assumption**
(c) Dimension Assumption **(d) Flat Plane Assumption**
(e) Unique Plane Assumption **(f) Intersecting Planes Assumption**

6. the stability of a tripod e
7. on a piece of notebook paper, there are points other than those on the top edge c
8. two walls that meet at a corner in a room f
9. on a flat green, a putt along only one path will get a golf ball from its lie to the hole a

Optional Activities

Cooperative Learning You might use this activity after students have completed the lesson. Have them **work in pairs** and make a list of as many items they can see that model points, lines, and planes in space. When they have completed their lists, have each group report to the class. List all items on the board, noting duplications.

Adapting to Individual Needs

English Language Development
Before beginning the lesson you might review the meaning of the following terms with students who have limited English proficiency: *flat, thickness, unique, dimensions, coplanar, and noncollinear.*

Additional Examples

You might want to use this additional example when discussing the lesson.

Writing Can a line which is not perpendicular to a plane be perpendicular to a line in the plane? If so, draw a picture and explain. If not, explain why not.

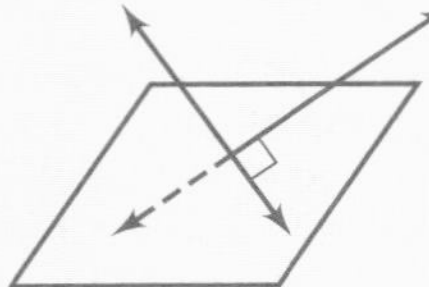

Yes, every line oblique to a plane forms a right angle with exactly one line in the plane.

Notes on Questions

Question 6 Error Alert Drawing two intersecting planes is difficult for many students. The following steps may be helpful: (1) Draw a parallelogram with two horizontal and two oblique sides. (2) Above the parallelogram, draw an oblique segment parallel and congruent to the oblique sides of the parallelogram. (3) Draw segments of equal length down from the endpoints of the segment just drawn, each passing through a horizontal side of the parallelogram. (4) Draw a segment to connect the bottom ends of the segments drawn in step 3. The new segments determine a parallelogram. (5) Draw the line of intersection determined by the points of intersection in step 3. It should be

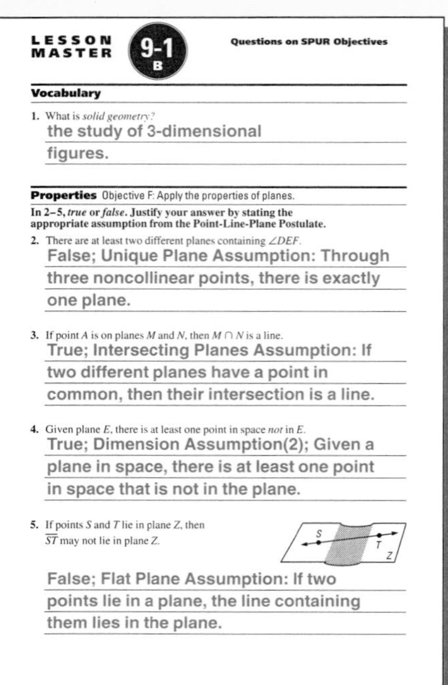

LESSON MASTER 9-1 B — Questions on SPUR Objectives

Vocabulary

1. What is *solid geometry*? the study of 3-dimensional figures.

Properties Objective F: Apply the properties of planes.

In 2–5, *true* or *false*. Justify your answer by stating the appropriate assumption from the Point-Line-Plane Postulate.

2. There are at least two different planes containing $\angle DEF$. False; Unique Plane Assumption: Through three noncollinear points, there is exactly one plane.
3. If point A is on planes M and N, then $M \cap N$ is a line. True; Intersecting Planes Assumption: If two different planes have a point in common, then their intersection is a line.
4. Given plane E, there is at least one point in space *not* in E. True; Dimension Assumption(2); Given a plane in space, there is at least one point in space that is not in the plane.
5. If points S and T lie in plane Z, then $\overline{ST}$ may not lie in plane Z. False; Flat Plane Assumption: If two points lie in a plane, the line containing them lies in the plane.

Three noncollinear points A, B, and C also determine other figures. For example, they can determine a triangle ABC or $\angle ABC$; a line $\overleftrightarrow{AB}$ and a point C not on it; two intersecting lines $\overleftrightarrow{AC}$ and $\overleftrightarrow{BC}$; and so on. Through any of these figures, there is exactly one plane.

Intersecting Planes

There are, however, infinitely many planes through a single line. Think of an open door in various positions. At each position, a broad side of the door determines a plane through an imaginary line determined by the hinges. Two different planes that have a point in common are called intersecting planes.

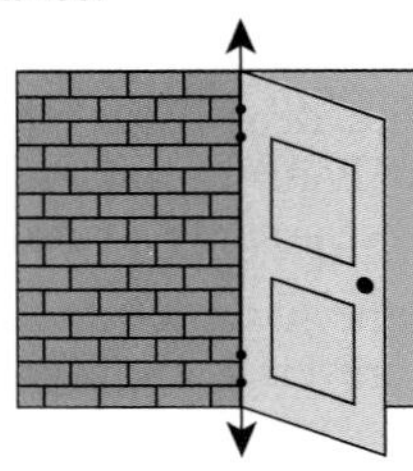

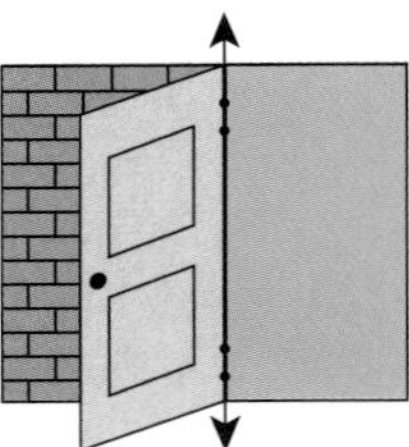

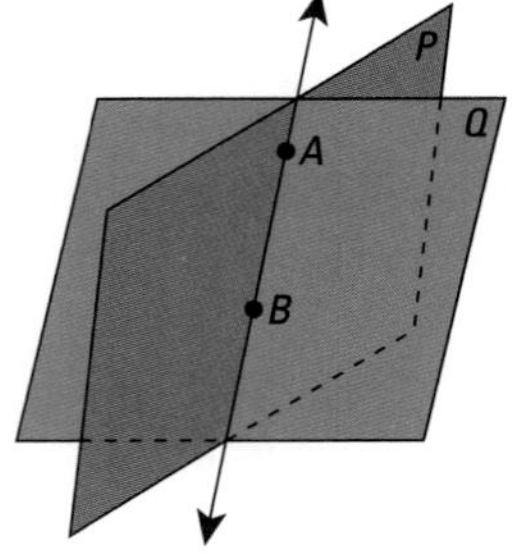

Intersecting planes P and Q
$P \cap Q = \overleftrightarrow{AB}$

f. Intersecting Planes Assumption
If two different planes have a point in common, then their intersection is a line.

Because lines have no thickness, the Intersecting Planes Assumption implies that planes have no thickness. It also implies that planes go on forever. Even though planes cannot be drawn as if they go on forever, they do.

QUESTIONS

Covering the Reading

In 1–4, name a 2- or 3-dimensional counterpart for the 1- or 2-dimensional idea.

1. line plane
2. polygon polyhedral surface
3. collinear coplanar
4. perpendicular lines perpendicular planes, line ⊥ to a plane
5. Draw a plane as seen from slightly above. See left.
6. Draw two intersecting planes. See left.
7. a. When will a three-legged stool rest stably on a floor? always
   b. When will a four-legged chair rest stably? See left.
   c. To what part of the Point-Line-Plane Postulate are the answers to parts **a** and **b** related? part e: through three noncollinear points, there is exactly one plane.

5) Sample:

6) Sample:

7) when the ends of the legs are coplanar

Adapting to Individual Needs

Challenge

Consider a system in which the surfaces of the four walls, floor, and ceiling of a typical rectangular room are called "planes", and they are the only planes. Line segments would be referred to as "lines." Which of the postulates from this lesson are true in this system? [Only c, d, and f]

Additional Answers

16. A plane figure F is a reflection-symmetric figure if and only if there is a line m such that $r_m(F) = F$.
17. A circle is the set of all points in a plane at a certain distance (its radius) from a certain point (its center).
18. A regular polygon is a convex polygon whose angles are all congruent and whose sides are all congruent.

Applying the Mathematics

In 8–11, state whether the figure can be contained by exactly one plane.

8. a line and a point not on the line Yes

9. two intersecting lines Yes

10. three noncollinear points Yes

11. a triangle Yes

12. In pioneer days, homes often had dirt floors which were uneven. Would four-legged chairs have been practical? Why or why not? See below.

13. Why is the surface of a table a better model for a plane than the entire tabletop? Because a plane has no thickness.

12) No. Four-legged chairs whose tips are in the same plane will not lie level on uneven floors.

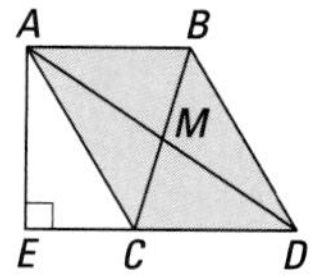

Review

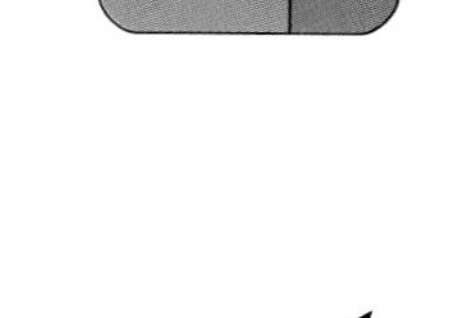

14. In parallelogram $ABDC$ at the left, $AC = 8$, $ED = 10$, and $CD = 6$. Find Area($ABDC$) to the nearest tenth. *(Lessons 8-5, 8-6)* 41.6 units^2

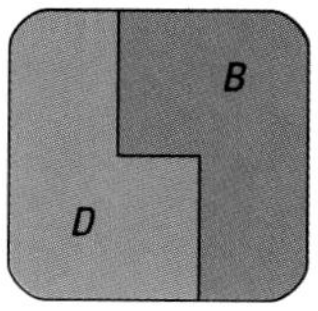

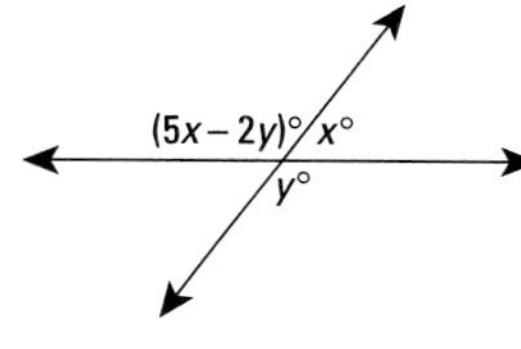

15. In the figure at the left, D and B are nonoverlapping figures. *(Lesson 8-2)*

a. *True or false.* Area($D \cup B$) $=$ Area(D) $+$ Area(B) True

b. *True or false.* The perimeter of $D \cup B$ $=$ the perimeter of D $+$ the perimeter of B. False

16. Define *reflection-symmetric figure.* *(Lesson 6-1)* See margin.

In 17 and 18, give a precise definition. *(Lessons 2-4, 6-7)* See margin.

17. circle

18. regular polygon

19. Two lines intersect with angle measures as given in the figure at the left. Find x and y. *(Lesson 3-3)* 67.5, $y = 112.5$

$(5x - 2y)°$ $x°$ $y°$

20. Three identical cubes used in the British game Crown and Anchor are pictured below. What symbol is on the face opposite the crown? *(Previous course)* anchor

Exploration

21. Tripods are based on the Unique Plane Assumption. But tripods can tip over. When will this happen, and why? Sample: It will happen when the center of gravity of the tripod is not above the triangular region determined by the tips of the legs.

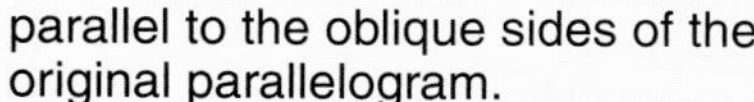

parallel to the oblique sides of the original parallelogram.

Question 8–11 Ask students to suggest physical models of planes determined by each of these four conditions.

Follow-up for Lesson 9-1

Practice

For more questions on SPUR Objectives, use **Lesson Master 9-1A** (shown on page 497) or **Lesson Master 9-1B** (shown on pages 498–499).

Assessment

Oral Communication Ask students for examples from the real world that illustrate the postulates in this lesson. [Students demonstrate an understanding of the postulates by providing appropriate examples from their surroundings.]

Extension

Ask students to find the radius of a circle whose area equals the area of a square whose side is 10 in. [$\sqrt{\frac{100}{\pi}}$, or $\approx$ 5.64 in.]

Projects Update Project 4, *Geometry on a Sphere,* on page 552, relates to the content of this lesson.

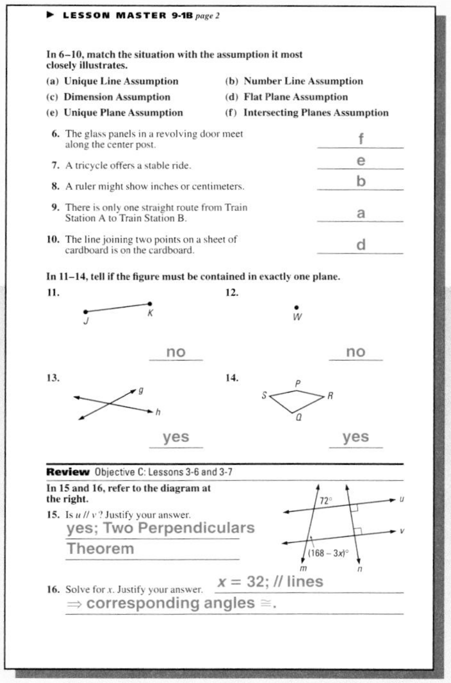

▶ **LESSON MASTER 9-1B** *page 2*

In 6–10, match the situation with the assumption it most closely illustrates.

(a) Unique Line Assumption (b) Number Line Assumption
(c) Dimension Assumption (d) Flat Plane Assumption
(e) Unique Plane Assumption (f) Intersecting Planes Assumption

6. The glass panels in a revolving door meet along the center post. f

7. A tricycle offers a stable ride. e

8. A ruler might show inches or centimeters. b

9. There is only one straight route from Train Station A to Train Station B. a

10. The line joining two points on a sheet of cardboard is on the cardboard. d

In 11–14, tell if the figure must be contained in exactly one plane.

11. J K — no

12. W — no

13. g h — yes

14. P S R Q — yes

Review Objective C: Lessons 3-6 and 3-7

In 15 and 16, refer to the diagram at the right.

15. Is $u \parallel v$? Justify your answer. yes; Two Perpendiculars Theorem

16. Solve for x. Justify your answer. $x = 32$; // lines ⇒ corresponding angles ≅.

72° u v $(168 - 3x)°$ m n

Setting Up Lesson 9-2

Be sure to discuss **Questions 16–18** in this lesson. These questions are important for the lessons that follow, in which analogous definitions are given for 3-dimensional figures.

Lesson 9-2

Objectives

A Draw common 3-dimensional shapes.

F Apply the properties of planes.

Resources

From the ***Teacher's Resource File***

- Lesson Master 9-2A or 9-2B
- Answer Master 9-2
- Teaching Aid 118: Warm-up

Additional Resources

- Visual for Teaching Aid 118

Teaching Lesson 9-2

Warm-up

Writing Suppose a homeowner installs a new lamppost, but it doesn't seem to be vertical. Suppose the owner uses one guy wire to brace the pole and it then seems to be vertical. Do you think this has solved the problem? Explain your answer. **Answers will vary.**

Notes on Reading

Students should feel comfortable with most (if not all) concepts introduced in this lesson, because these concepts are similar to those in the plane geometry students have already learned. Also, because students have already learned many similar or related concepts, it will help them to see the different meanings that concepts such as angle, distance, parallelism, and perpendicularity have in a 3-dimensional setting.

LESSON

9-2

Parallel and Perpendicular Lines and Planes

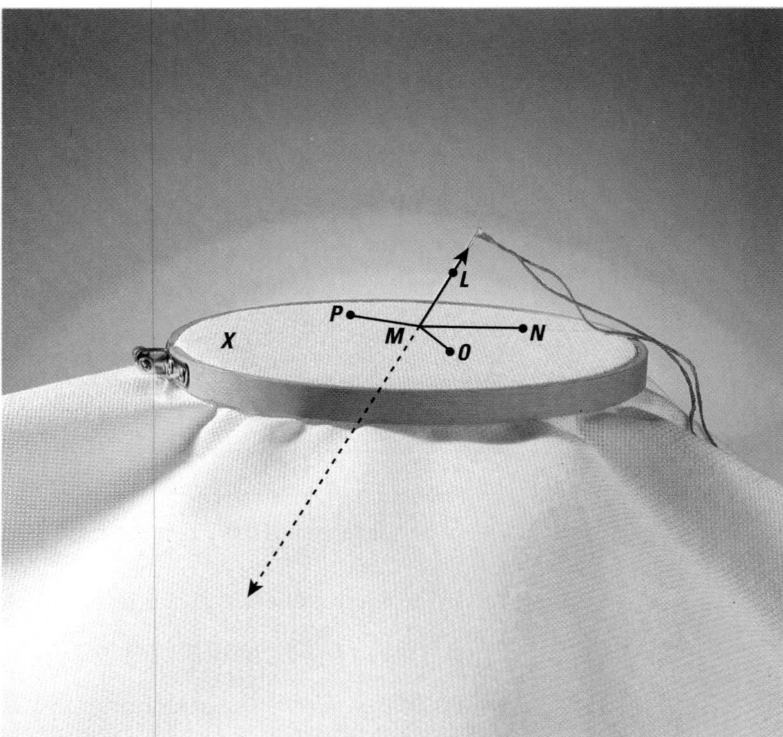

It's a stitch. *A sewing needle piercing a fabric is like a line intersecting a plane. Get the point?*

As stated earlier, virtually all ideas in two dimensions have counterparts in three dimensions. In this lesson, you will examine some ideas in three dimensions related to parallelism and perpendicularity. As in two dimensions, these ideas are related to measures of angles.

Angles Formed by a Line and a Plane

A line that is not in a plane can intersect the plane in at most one point. (If it intersects in two points, then by the Flat Plane Assumption, it lies in the plane.)

When a line intersects a plane, many angles can be formed with lines in the plane. In the picture above, $\overleftrightarrow{LM}$ intersects plane X at M. Three of the angles formed are $\angle LMO$, $\angle LMN$, and $\angle LMP$. The measure of the smallest of all the possible angles defines the angle measure between the line and the plane. This cannot be greater than 90°. When we represent a three-dimensional situation in a picture like the one above, it is difficult to tell if the smallest angle has been drawn.

Lesson 9-2 Overview

Broad Goals This lesson examines the relationships between a line and a plane as well as the relationships between planes. The measures of angles formed by a line and a plane, the concept of dihedral angles, and parallelism and perpendicularity of lines and planes are introduced and discussed.

Perspective In plane geometry, we study the relationships between points and lines. Angles, distance, parallelism, and perpendicularity are a few of the most important concepts in that study.

This lesson introduces students to some basic concepts regarding the relationships between lines and planes in solid geometry, including the relationships between a line and a plane and between two planes. The lesson consists mainly of two parts. The first part begins with measures of angles formed by a line and a plane, the definition of perpendicularity for a line and a plane, and the proof of a theorem which is often used as a justification in deducing that a line is perpendicular to a plane. The second part deals with the relationships between two planes. Dihedral angles, parallel and perpendicular planes, and the distances between parallel planes are introduced. Also, the concepts of parallelism of a line and a plane and of the distances from a

Recall from Lesson 3-3 that the Leaning Tower of Pisa makes a smallest angle of 85° with the plane of the ground. But, as you could tell by walking around it, it is also possible to find angles from 85° to 95° between the ground and the edge of the tower. There are even lines on the ground that form a 90° angle with the tower, as shown at the left. But the Leaning Tower of Pisa is *not* perpendicular to the ground. We say that it makes an angle of 85° with the ground.

> **Definition:**
> If a line ℓ intersects a plane X at point P, then **line ℓ is perpendicular to plane X** ($\ell \perp X$) if and only if ℓ is perpendicular to every line in X that contains P.

Most flagpoles are perpendicular to the ground. This means that the pole is perpendicular to any line on the ground drawn through its base.

Based on the definition, it is very difficult to prove that a line is perpendicular to a plane. Infinitely many lines in the plane through the point of intersection would have to be considered! Fortunately, because of the following theorem, you only need to find two lines in the plane through the point of intersection that are perpendicular to the given line.

The proof shows that if two lines in a plane are perpendicular to a line t through their intersection P, then any other line in that plane through P is perpendicular to t. It involves an ingenious use of congruent triangles.

> **Line-Plane Perpendicularity Theorem**
> If a line is perpendicular to two different lines at their point of intersection, then it is perpendicular to the plane that contains those lines.

❶ **Proof**

Given: Lines ℓ and m are in plane X and intersect at P; $t \perp \ell$; $t \perp m$.

To prove: $t \perp X$.

Drawing:

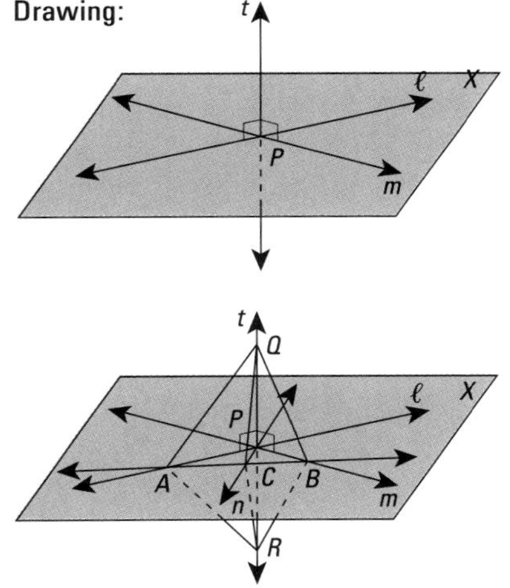

Argument:
Draw n as a line in X containing P. Draw an auxiliary line in plane X intersecting ℓ, m, and n in points A, B, and C, respectively. Choose points Q and R on line t so that they are on opposite sides of X and $PQ = PR$. Connect Q and R to A, B, and C.

▶

A vertical line is a line perpendicular to a horizontal plane. The notion of a line perpendicular to a plane is a generalization. Note that if a line forms 90° angles with only two lines in the plane through its point of intersection with the plane, then the line is perpendicular to all lines in the plane through this point.

❶ The proof of the Line-Plane Perpendicularity Theorem is formidable. It is presented not because we expect students to be able to reconstruct it, but to illustrate that ideas involving two dimensions discussed earlier apply also to three dimensions. You might wish to ask students to give some practical examples (such as in the structure of a building) of the applications of the theorem.

Even though copying a simple figure is difficult for some students, almost everyone can benefit from some practice. If students have difficulty drawing planes and 3-dimensional figures, a transparent plastic ruler with lines on it can assist them in drawing parallel lines. Emphasize that to draw a horizontal plane, one should draw a parallelogram with a pair of horizontal sides; to draw a vertical plane, one should use a pair of vertical sides.

point to a plane and from a line to a parallel plane are introduced.

In the proof of the theorem in this lesson, we make the assumption that the theorems that have been proved for the plane also apply in space. In particular, triangles that lie in two different planes are proved congruent using the standard triangle congruence theorems.

Optional Activities

After students have completed **Questions 1–3,** you might have them practice making drawings like those in the **Questions,** but with planes at different angles.

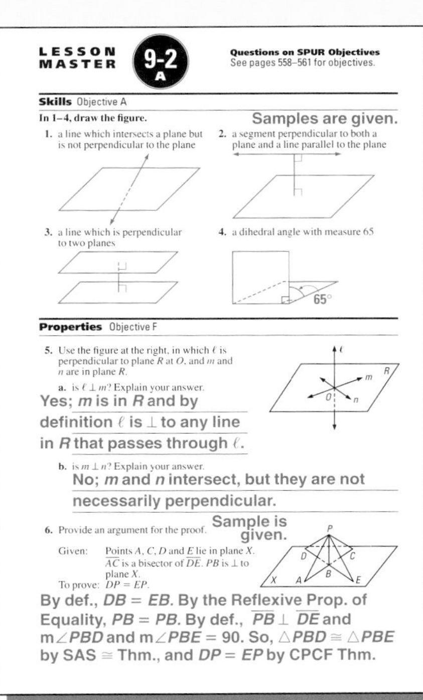

LESSON MASTER 9-2 A

Questions on SPUR Objectives
See pages 558–561 for objectives.

Skills Objective A

In 1–4, draw the figure. Samples are given.

1. a line which intersects a plane but is not perpendicular to the plane
2. a segment perpendicular to both a plane and a line parallel to the plane
3. a line which is perpendicular to two planes
4. a dihedral angle with measure 65

65°

Properties Objective F

5. Use the figure at the right, in which ℓ is perpendicular to plane R at O, and m and n are in plane R.
   a. is $\ell \perp m$? Explain your answer.
   Yes; m is in R and by definition ℓ is $\perp$ to any line in R that passes through ℓ.
   b. is $m \perp n$? Explain your answer.
   No; m and n intersect, but they are not necessarily perpendicular.

6. Provide an argument for the proof. Sample is given.
   Given: Points A, C, D and E lie in plane X. $\overline{AC}$ is a bisector of $\overline{DE}$. PB is $\perp$ to plane X.
   To prove: $DP = EP$.
   By def., $DB = EB$. By the Reflexive Prop. of Equality, $PB = PB$. By def., $\overline{PB} \perp \overline{DE}$ and $m\angle PBD$ and $m\angle PBE = 90$. So, $\triangle PBD \cong \triangle PBE$ by SAS $\cong$ Thm., and $DP = EP$ by CPCF Thm.

Additional Examples

You might want to use this additional example when discussing the lesson.

Draw a dihedral angle that seems to have a measure of 30°. **Sample:**

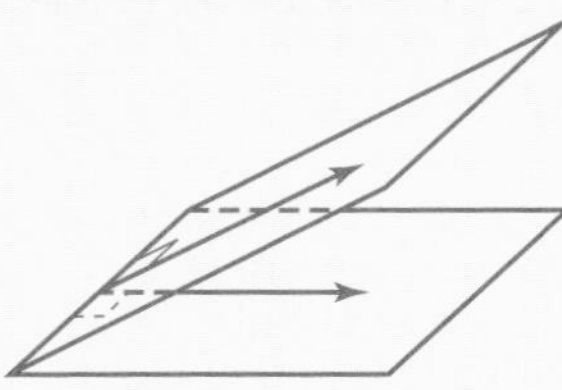

Notes on Questions

Question 13 There can be more than one correct answer. The usual analogy replaces *line* with *plane* in both places, resulting in a false statement. A valid analogy can be formed by replacing only the first *line* with *plane,* resulting in: "If two planes are perpendicular to the same line, then they are parallel."

(Notes on Questions continue on page 504.)

Follow-up for Lesson 9-2

Practice

For more questions on SPUR Objectives, use **Lesson Master 9-2A** (shown on page 501) or **Lesson Master 9-2B** (shown on pages 502–503).

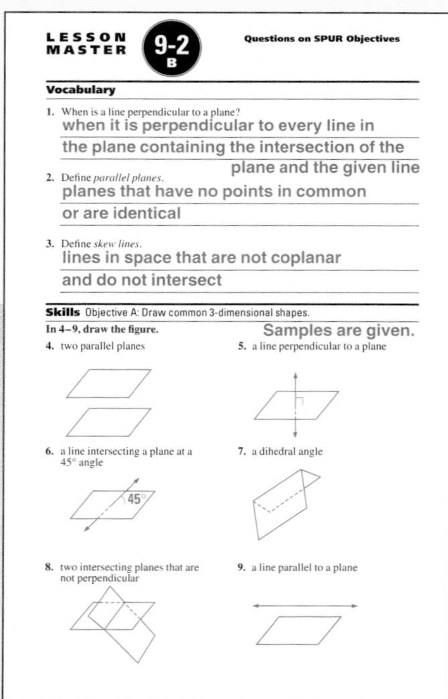

LESSON MASTER 9-2 B — Questions on SPUR Objectives

Vocabulary

1. When is a line perpendicular to a plane?
when it is perpendicular to every line in the plane containing the intersection of the plane and the given line
2. Define *parallel planes.*
planes that have no points in common or are identical
3. Define *skew lines.*
lines in space that are not coplanar and do not intersect

Skills Objective A: Draw common 3-dimensional shapes.

In 4–9, draw the figure. Samples are given.

4. two parallel planes
5. a line perpendicular to a plane
6. a line intersecting a plane at a 45° angle
7. a dihedral angle
8. two intersecting planes that are not perpendicular
9. a line parallel to a plane

Now we proceed to prove four pairs of triangles congruent, one after the other. (You are asked in Question 6 to explain why the triangles are congruent.) Each pair of congruent triangles enables us to deduce that two segments or angles are congruent. Then applying the definitions of $\perp$ bisector and of a line $\perp$ to a plane finishes the proof.

Conclusions	Justifications
1. $\triangle PQA \cong \triangle PRA$	a.
2. $\overline{QA} \cong \overline{RA}$	b.
3. $\triangle PQB \cong \triangle PRB$	c.
4. $\overline{QB} \cong \overline{RB}$	d.
5. $\triangle QAB \cong \triangle RAB$	e.
6. $\angle QBA \cong \angle RBA$	f.
7. $\triangle QBC \cong \triangle RBC$	g.
8. $QC = RC$	h.

Since C is equidistant from the endpoints of $\overline{QR}$, it lies on the $\perp$ bisector of $\overline{QR}$. P also lies on the $\perp$ bisector of $\overline{QR}$. Thus $\overleftrightarrow{PC}$, which is line n, is the $\perp$ bisector of $\overline{QR}$, which is on line t. Thus $t \perp n$. Since n can be any line through P in plane X, t is $\perp$ to plane X.

In the above proof, we used theorems about figures in a plane to deduce theorems about figures in space. Because the proofs are sometimes quite long, we do not prove every property that we state for 3-dimensional figures. But every property could be proved from the postulates in this book.

One application of the Line-Plane Perpendicularity theorem is as follows. Suppose you wish to make certain that a post is perpendicular to the ground. Then you only have to draw two lines on the ground to the post and make certain that the post is perpendicular to each of those lines.

Parallel and Perpendicular Planes

The ideas of parallel and perpendicular lines have counterparts with planes. Two planes are **parallel planes** if and only if they have no points in common or they are identical. As with parallel lines, the **distance between parallel planes** is the length of a segment perpendicular to the planes with an endpoint in each plane. The **distance to a plane from a point** not on it is measured along the perpendicular segment to the plane from the point. A line is parallel to a plane if they do not intersect in a single point.

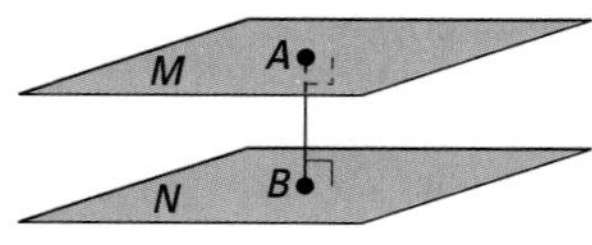

Planes M and N are parallel. The distance between them is AB.

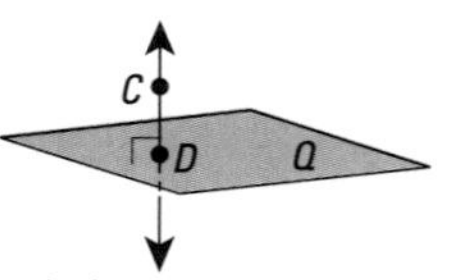

$\overleftrightarrow{CD}$ is $\perp$ to plane Q. The distance from point C to plane Q is CD.

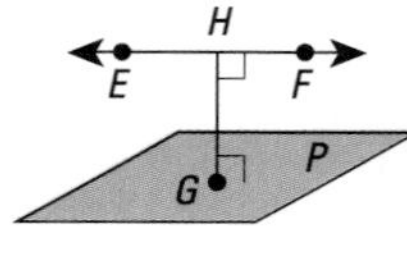

$\overleftrightarrow{EF}$ is // to plane P. The distance from $\overleftrightarrow{EF}$ to plane P is HG.

Adapting to Individual Needs

Challenge

1. Suppose a line m intersects a plane Y at an angle of x°. Let z be the measure of the angle formed by m and any line in Y that intersects m. What is the range of values possible for z? [$x \le z \le 180 - x$]
2. Suppose two parallel planes are intersected by a third plane. Formulate 3-dimensional analogues to the Corresponding Angles Postulate.

[If two planes are cut by a third plane so that two corresponding dihedral angles have the same measure, then the planes are parallel. If two parallel planes are cut by a third plane, then corresponding dihedral angles have the same measure.]

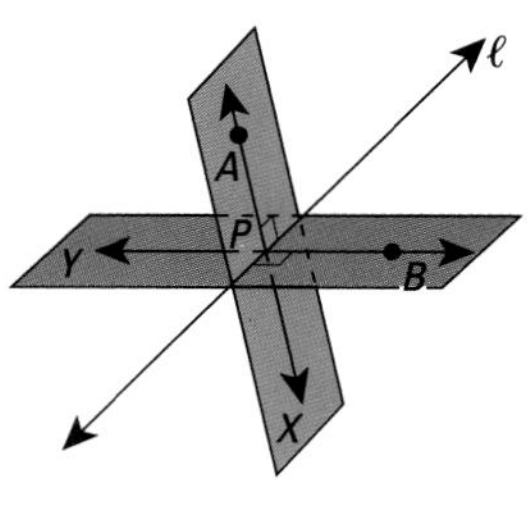

Dihedral Angles and Perpendicular Planes

When two planes intersect, four **dihedral angles** are formed. These dihedral angles are measured in the following way. Suppose the planes X and Y intersect at ℓ. Pick a point P on ℓ. Draw $\overleftrightarrow{PA} \perp \ell$ in X and $\overleftrightarrow{PB} \perp \ell$ in Y. The measures of the dihedral angles are the measures of the four angles formed by $\overleftrightarrow{PA}$ and $\overleftrightarrow{PB}$.

If $\overleftrightarrow{PA} \perp \overleftrightarrow{PB}$, then the planes are perpendicular.

3) Sample:

5) A line ℓ is perpendicular to a plane X if and only if it is perpendicular to every line in X through their intersection.

QUESTIONS

Covering the Reading

In 1–3, draw the figure.

2) Sample:

1. a line intersecting a plane at a 30° angle See margin.
2. a line perpendicular to a plane See right.
3. two perpendicular planes See left.
4. **a.** *True or false.* An edge of the Leaning Tower of Pisa is perpendicular to the plane of the ground. False
   b. Why or why not? The Tower of Pisa forms an 85° angle with the ground.
5. When, by definition, is a line perpendicular to a plane? See left.
6. Give the justifications for steps 1–8 in the proof on page 502. See margin.
7. The front and back walls of most classrooms are like parts of parallel planes. How is the distance between them measured? by measuring the length of a segment ⊥ to both walls with one endpoint on each wall
8. Draw a dihedral angle with a measure of 120°. See margin.
9. How would you measure the distance from the upper right-hand corner of this page to a wall in front of you? by measuring the length of the segment ⊥ to the wall with one endpoint in the wall and the other at the corner of the page

Applying the Mathematics

In 10–12, think of a classroom having west, east, north, and south walls; a floor; and a ceiling. What in the classroom illustrates each idea?

10. two perpendicular planes Sample: the floor and a wall
11. three planes each perpendicular to the other two Sample: the floor, north wall, and east wall
12. a line perpendicular to a plane Sample: the ceiling and the line of intersection of the south and west walls
13. **Theorem:** If two lines in a plane are perpendicular to the same line, then they are parallel. What is a three-dimensional counterpart to this theorem? Is it true? Sample: If two planes are perpendicular to the same plane, they are parallel. No.
14. A utility pole is knocked down in a storm. What is the approximate measure of the angle through which the pole falls? 90°

Cast a different light. *Dramatic lighting emphasizes the dihedral angles formed by the ceilings and the walls.*

Assessment

Written Communication Have students pick at least two new terms or definitions introduced in this lesson and then write a description, including diagrams if necessary, that would clarify the meanings to someone who was not familiar with the terms. [Students provide clear descriptions of two terms presented in the lesson.]

Extension

Ask students to determine and draw pictures of the possible intersections of *three* different planes. [If all three planes are parallel, there are no points in common. If exactly two planes are parallel, then there are no points in common to all three; however, the third plane intersects both parallel planes and the lines of intersection are parallel. If no two are parallel, then the intersection is either (a) a single point (think of the corners of a room), or (b) a line (think of three consecutive pages of a book).]

Project Update Project 4, *Geometry on a Sphere,* on page 552, relates to the content of this lesson.

Additional Answers

1. Sample:

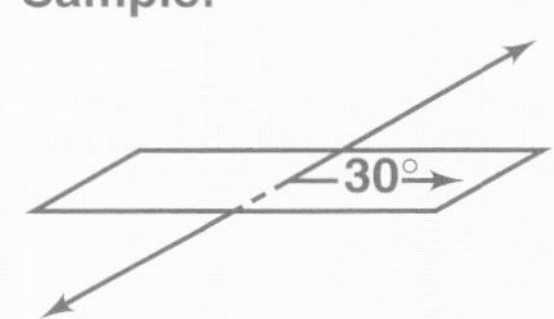

▶ **LESSON MASTER 9-2B** *page 2*

Properties Objective F: Apply the properties of planes.

10. a. At the right, m and n are in plane D. $a \perp m$ and $a \perp n$. Is $a \perp D$? Explain your answer.
Yes; if a line is ⊥ to two different lines in space at the same point, it is ⊥ to the plane containing the lines.

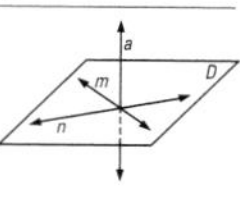

b. Is a perpendicular to any other lines in D? Explain your answer. Yes; since a is ⊥ to the plane, it is ⊥ to every line in the plane that intersects a by def. of line ⊥ to a plane.

c. Is $m \perp n$? Explain your answer. No; m and n intersect but are not necessarily perpendicular.

d. Why can't you apply the Two Perpendiculars Theorem from Chapter 3 to conclude that $m \parallel n$? The Two Perpendiculars Theorem applies to lines in the same plane.

11. Provide the argument for the proof.

Given: $\overline{GE} \perp$ plane S at E; E is the midpoint of $\overline{XY}$; X, E, and Y are in plane S.
To prove: $\triangle GXE \cong \triangle GYE$.

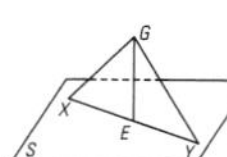

Sample: Since $\overline{GE} \perp S$, $\overline{GE} \perp \overline{XY}$ by definition of a line ⊥ to a plane. Since E is the midpoint of $\overline{XY}$, $\overline{GE}$ is the ⊥ bisector of $\overline{XY}$. So, $\overline{EX} \cong \overline{EY}$ and $\overline{GX} \cong \overline{GY}$ by the ⊥ Bisector Thm. $\overline{GE} \cong \overline{GE}$ by the Reflexive Prop. of Congruence. Thus, $\triangle GXE \cong \triangle GYE$ by the SSS Congruence Thm.

Additional Answers, continued

6. Justifications
   a. SAS Congruence Theorem
   b. CPCF Theorem
   c. SAS Congruence Theorem
   d. CPCF Theorem
   e. SSS Congruence Theorem
   f. CPCF Theorem
   g. SAS Congruence Theorem
   h. CPCF Theorem

8.

Notes on Questions

Question 16 Of course, the assumption here is that the tree is perpendicular to the ground. To underscore the concept of an angle formed by a line and a plane, consider the angle through which a tree (or pole) would fall if it were oblique to the ground.

Question 17 The angle of inclination of an object is an important idea both in mathematics and in its applications; it leads to many problems in trigonometry, surveying, astronomy, and navigation. You might ask: As a person walks toward a tall building, will the angle of inclination of the top of the building increase, decrease, or remain the same? [Increase] As a person rides up a glass elevator and looks to the top of the atrium, does the angle of inclination increase, decrease, or remain the same? [Decrease] If a person is looking at the top of a pole perpendicular to the ground and is walking, but the angle of inclination remains unchanged, what is the path the person is walking? [Circle]

Question 24 You might demonstrate this situation using chairs in your classroom. Many students will have been taught to draw chairs as if their legs were perpendicular to the floor and will never have examined actual chairs. Usually, unless they are braced, legs of chairs form an angle of about 75° or less with the floor.

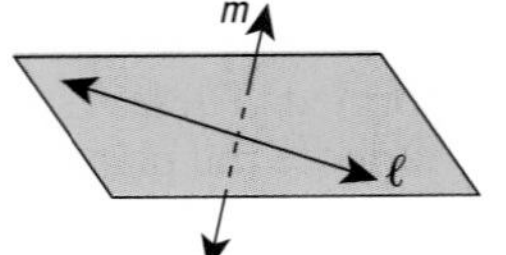

15. Lines in space that are not coplanar and do not intersect, like ℓ and m at the left, are called **skew lines.** Draw a cube and identify two skew lines on it. See margin.

16. You are replanting a young tree and you want to be sure its trunk is perpendicular to the ground. From at least how many locations do you need to look to check it? Explain how you will know it is perpendicular. See margin.

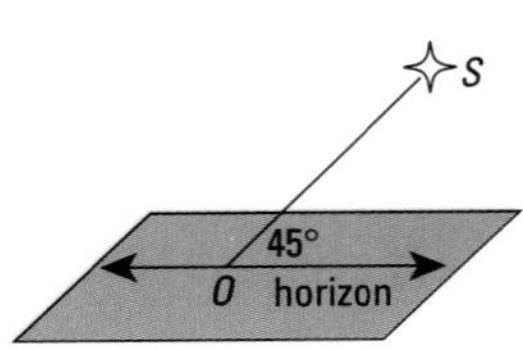

17. The *angle of inclination* of an object S in the sky is the measure of the angle formed by S, the observer O, and the plane of Earth. For instance, a star halfway to overhead has an angle of inclination of 45°.

a. What is the largest possible angle of inclination? 90°

b. What is the angle of inclination of a star that is $\frac{1}{3}$ the way from the horizon to directly overhead? 30°

Review

18. What assumed property of points, lines, and planes guarantees that a plane has no bumps? *(Lesson 9-1)* Flat Plane Assumption

19. Can two planes intersect in a segment? Why or why not? *(Lesson 9-1)* See margin.

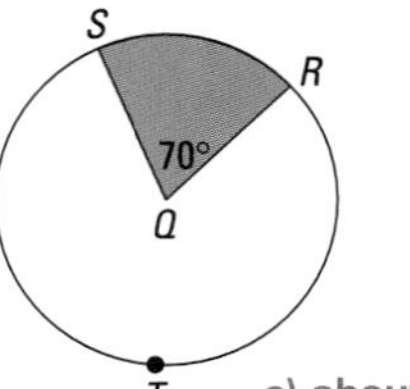

20. Given $\odot Q$ at the right with $m\angle Q = 70$ and $QR = 30$ cm. *(Lessons 8-7, 8-8)*

a. Find the length of $\widehat{RTS}$.

b. Find the area of the circle.

c. To the nearest percent, how much of the interior of the circle lies in the shaded sector?

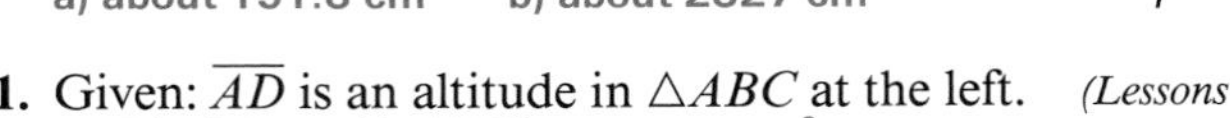

a) about 151.8 cm b) about 2827 cm^2 c) about 19%

65, 52, 30, A, B, C, D

21. Given: $\overline{AD}$ is an altitude in $\triangle ABC$ at the left. *(Lessons 8-4, 8-6)*

a. Find Area ($\triangle ABC$). 1599 units^2

b. Find AC. about 49.2 units

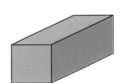

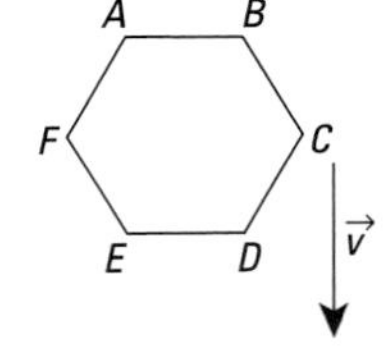

22. Trace the regular hexagon at the right. Find the image of $ABCDEF$ under translation by vector $\vec{v}$. *(Lesson 4-6)* See margin.

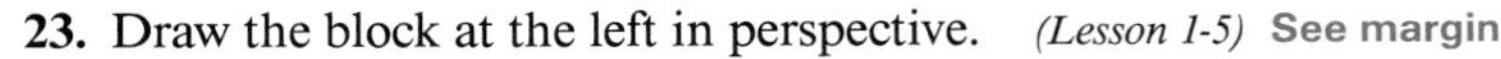

23. Draw the block at the left in perspective. *(Lesson 1-5)* See margin.

Exploration

24. Examine the legs of a chair at home or in school.

a. Measure the angle between each leg and the plane of the floor.

b. Are most of the chair legs you see perpendicular to the floor?

a) Answers may vary. b) Most are not exactly perpendicular to the floor.

Additional Answers

15. Sample: ℓ and m are skew lines

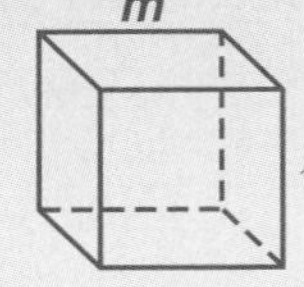

16. 2; if its trunk is perpendicular to two lines in the ground, then it is perpendicular to the ground.

19. No; by the Intersecting Planes Assumption, their intersection is a line.

22.

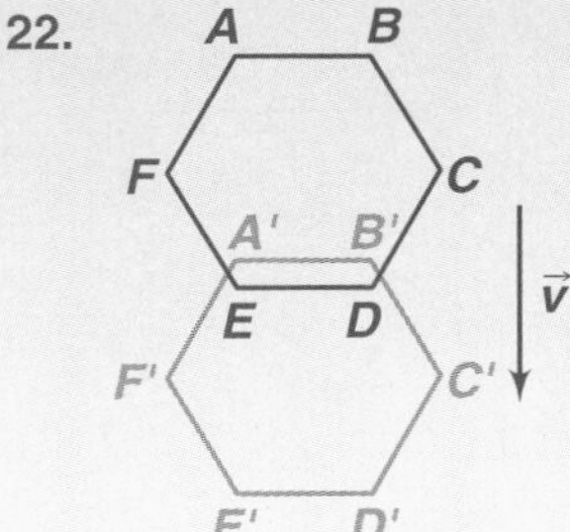

23. Sample:

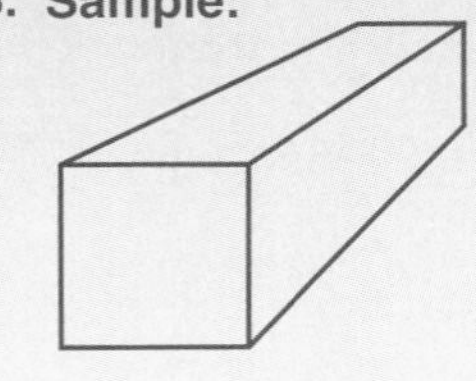

504

LESSON

9-3

Prisms and Cylinders

Recall that polygons and polygonal regions are different. A polygon is the boundary of a polygonal region. The region is the union of the boundary and its interior.

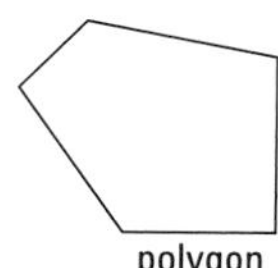
polygon

polygonal region

A similar distinction is made with 3-dimensional figures. In rough language—these are not good definitions—a **surface** is the boundary of a 3-dimensional figure. A **solid** is the union of the boundary and the region of space enclosed by the surface. Earth is a solid; a soap bubble is a surface. A brick is a solid; a carton is a surface. When drawing, you can distinguish a solid from a surface by shading and showing none of the hidden edges.

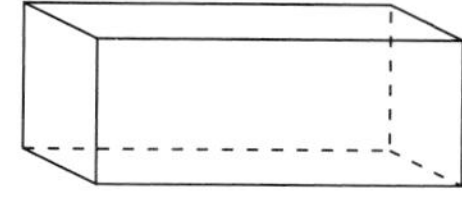
A carton or box is a surface.

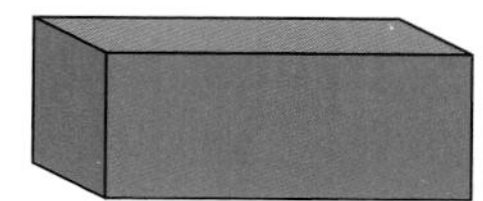
A brick is a rectangular solid.

Boxes

The carton pictured above exemplifies the surface called a *box*. The union of a box and its interior is called a **rectangular solid.** A brick is usually a rectangular solid. Boxes are as important in three dimensions as rectangles are in two, so it is useful to have names for their parts. In the next two paragraphs, refer to the box drawn below.

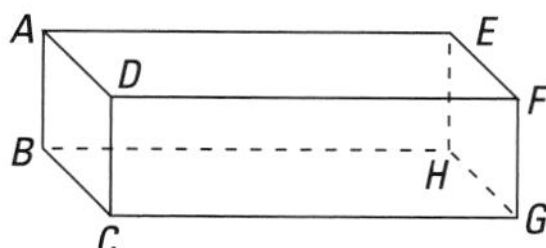

A **box** has six **faces,** each of which is a rectangular region. Some of the faces are drawn as parallelograms to give the appearance of three dimensions. When two of the faces are horizontal, all six faces can be identified by their locations: top ($AEFD$), bottom ($BHGC$), right ($EFGH$), left ($ABCD$), front ($DFGC$), and back ($AEHB$). The **opposite faces** lie in parallel planes. The plane of the front face is perpendicular to the planes

Lesson 9-3

Objectives

A Draw prisms and cylinders.
D Given appropriate lengths, calculate areas and lengths in prisms and cylinders.
H Recognize prisms and cylinders in the real world.

Resources

From the ***Teacher's Resource File***
- Lesson Master 9-3A or 9-3B
- Answer Master 9-3
- Teaching Aid 118: Warm-up
- Activity Kit, Activity 20

Additional Resources
- Visual for Teaching Aid 118

Teaching Lesson 9-3

Warm-up

A cake with dimensions as shown below is covered with icing on the top and sides. The cake is sliced into 2-inch cubes. How many pieces will not have any icing? **48 pieces**

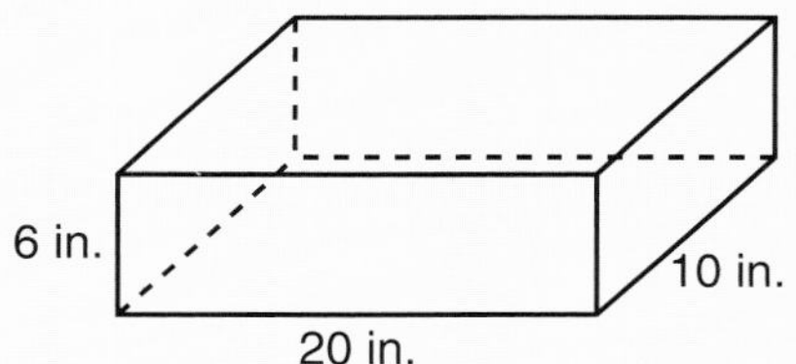

Lesson 9-3 Overview

Broad Goals This lesson covers drawings and vocabulary related to prisms and cylinders, the most common types of cylindric surfaces.

Perspective With 3-dimensional figures, major types of surfaces include both curved and rectilinear (straight-edged) surfaces. This does not happen in two dimensions; polygons are separated, in most classifications, from circles or ellipses. In three dimensions, however, prisms and cylinders are classified as cylindric surfaces, and pyramids and cones are classified together as conic surfaces.

The definitions of prisms and cylinders are analogous. A cylinder and prism are surfaces, not solids, yet the common use of these terms often refers to solids; for example, a roller for a conveyor belt and glass which reflects light are solid. The definitions of surfaces given here are traditional, and analogous to those of polygons and curves by including the boundaries but not the interior points.

Students need practice in drawing and should be expected to make drawings that are good enough to be used for reasoning.

Notes on Reading

As you discuss the lesson, you might want to have students copy and label the drawings in this lesson into notebooks. They can then refer to their drawings to ensure that the terminology is clear. Throughout this chapter we suggest that students put drawings of additional 3-dimensional figures in their notes.

❶ It is important for students to understand the definition of cylindric solids so that the volume formulas given in Chapter 10 will become more intuitive. A cylindric solid is made up of the set of points between the translation image and the preimage of the 2-dimensional region together with the image and preimage, and its volume is the product of the area of the preimage region and the distance between the planes of the preimage and image regions (the bases).

Recall that the concept of triangle was presented in general, and special triangles were derived from the general definition. Likewise, the concept of cylindric solid is presented in general and the specific cylinder and prism follow as special cases. Point out that the region being translated may be of any shape. Many tall buildings are cylindric solids in which the cross-sectional regions are nonpolygonal, noncircular figures. Lake Point Towers in Chicago, the tallest purely residential building in the world, for example, has the following geometric shape.

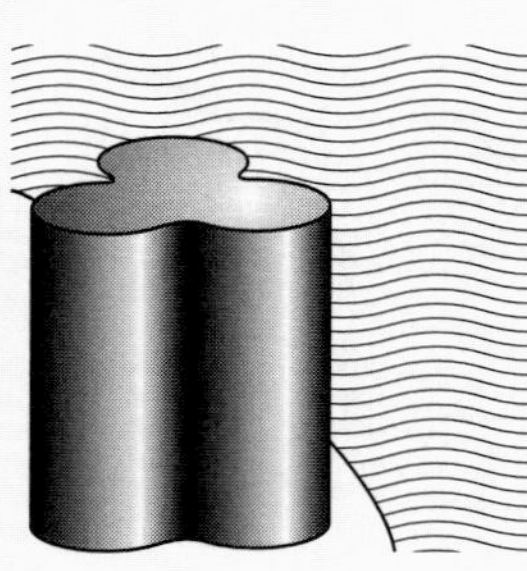

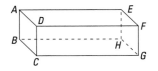

of the top, bottom, and sides. At each corner of the box, three planes meet and each of these planes is perpendicular to the other two. A **cube** is a box whose faces are all square.

The 12 segments, $\overline{AB}$, $\overline{AE}$, $\overline{AD}$, $\overline{BH}$, and so on, are the **edges** of the box. Each edge is perpendicular to two faces. For example, edge $\overline{CG}$ is perpendicular to the left face $ABCD$ and the right face $EFGH$. The endpoints of the edges—A, B, C, D, E, F, G, and H—are the 8 **vertices** of the box.

Most classrooms are like big boxes. The floor and two adjacent walls meet in a bottom corner of the room just as the bottom, front, and left sides of a box meet. The plane of the floor is perpendicular to the plane of each wall.

Classrooms and cartons exemplify the same kind of geometric figure. Even a piece of notebook paper can be thought of as a three-dimensional figure, for it has thickness (about 0.002 inch or 0.05 mm). Thus, the geometric figure that best describes notebook paper is a rectangular solid. Part of the power of geometry is that the same ideas can apply to things as small as parts of atoms or as large as galaxies, as wide as classrooms or as thin as paper.

Cylindric Solids and Surfaces

A rectangular solid is a special type of *cylindric solid.* In general, to form a cylindric solid, begin with a 2-dimensional region. Think of translating the region out of its plane into space in a fixed direction.

❶ **Definition**
A **cylindric solid** is the set of points between a region and its translation image in space, including the region and its image.

Below, a circular region and a pentagonal region have been translated by the vector $\vec{v}$. Their translation images lie in a plane parallel to the original plane. Note that to appear three dimensional, circles are represented by ovals and the pentagons have also been distorted.

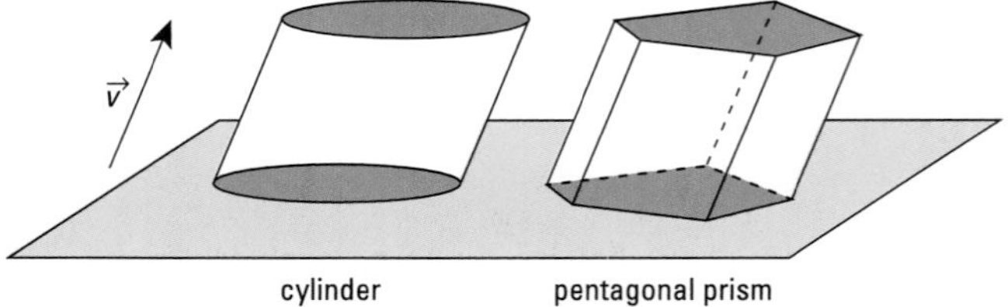

The original region and its translation image are the **bases** of the cylindric solid. Bases are always congruent and always in parallel planes. The rest of the surface of the solid is the **lateral surface.** The union of the bases and the lateral surface is the **cylindric surface.** The height or **altitude** of the solid is the distance between the planes of the bases.

Optional Activities

Activity 1
In the **Activity** on pages 507–508, students are directed to draw a pentagonal prism after being shown how to draw a hexagonal prism. After students have completed the lesson, you may wish to have them use this method to draw other prisms. A bulletin board could be created using the drawings. Other students could make models of the hierarchy of cylindric surfaces and make mobiles to hang in the classroom. The visual display will help them to remember the hierarchy.

Activity 2
You may use *Activity Kit, Activity 20,* as a follow-up to the lesson. In this activity, students explore a popular puzzle involving pieces that form a cube.

Two cylindric surfaces have special names.

Definitions
A **cylinder** is the surface of a cylindric solid whose base is a circle.
A **prism** is the surface of a cylindric solid whose base is a polygon.

When the vector determining the translation is perpendicular to the planes of the bases, a **right cylinder** or **right prism** is formed. A nonright cylinder or prism is called **oblique.** The cylinder pictured on page 506 is oblique; a can is a right cylinder, like the one pictured below.

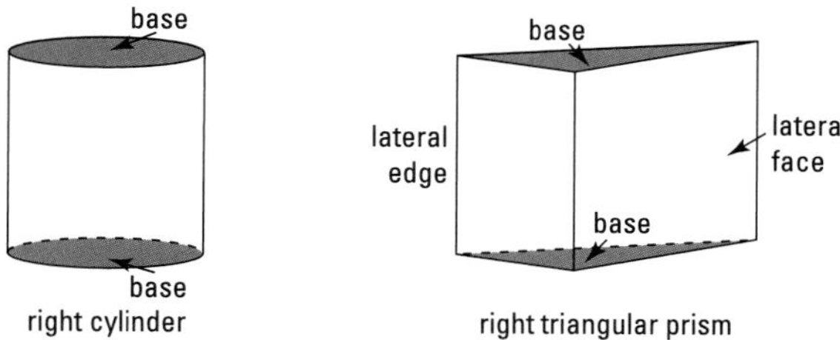

Prisms are also named by their bases. On page 506, an oblique pentagonal prism is shown. A triangular prism has triangles for its bases. The faces of the lateral surface of a prism are called **lateral faces** and they are always parallelograms. The intersection of two lateral faces is called a **lateral edge.**

Tin cans, ceramic tiles, hockey pucks, and new pencils (without erasers) are a few of the physical objects that illustrate cylindrical surfaces. You should be able to sketch any type of cylindric surface.

Activity
Sample: Algorithm 1:

❷ **Activity**

Sketch a right pentagonal prism using each of the following two algorithms, shown here for a hexagonal prism. See left and page 508.

Algorithm 1

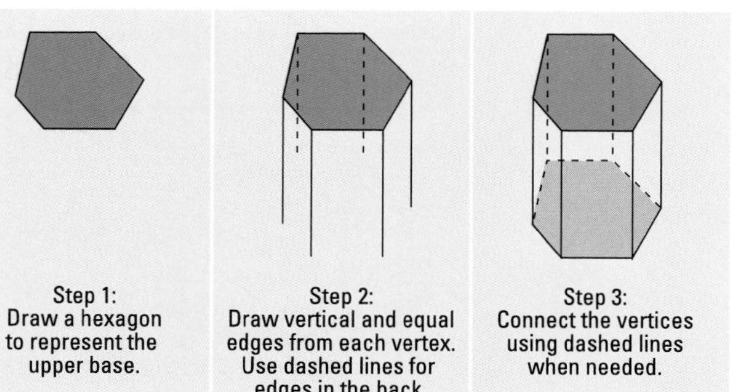

Step 1: Draw a hexagon to represent the upper base.

Step 2: Draw vertical and equal edges from each vertex. Use dashed lines for edges in the back.

Step 3: Connect the vertices using dashed lines when needed.

▶

❷ The sketch in the **Activity** is done without using perspective. The method used models the definition; that is, a plane figure is given, translating segments are drawn from its defining points, and the images of those points determine the image of the given plane figure.

Have students record the results of the **Activity** for use with **Question 2** on page 508.

You might ask students how the drawing in the **Activity** would be changed if perspective were used. [The corresponding non-horizontal edges on the two bases would not be drawn parallel, but would be drawn as if they intersected at the horizon, an imaginary horizontal line behind the drawing. The placement of the horizon indicates the viewer's position.] You might point out that dotting the nearer edges in the prism of the **Activity** and making the back edges dark gives the impression that one is looking at the prism from the bottom rather than from the top.

Discuss the hierarchy on page 508 making certain that students can give examples of figures that do not fit at each level of the hierarchy (for example, a surface that is not a cylindric surface; a right prism that is not a box, and so on).

Adapting to Individual Needs

Extra Help

Since students are familiar with common examples of cylinders and prisms, such as tin cans and cardboard boxes, they sometimes assume that all prisms and cylinders are right prisms or right cylinders. Stress that the definition for both cylinder and prism allows both oblique and right figures.

English Language Development

A great number of different solids and surfaces are identified in this lesson. You might pair English-speaking students with students with limited English proficiency so they can talk to each other about the figures while they copy and label drawings into their notebooks.

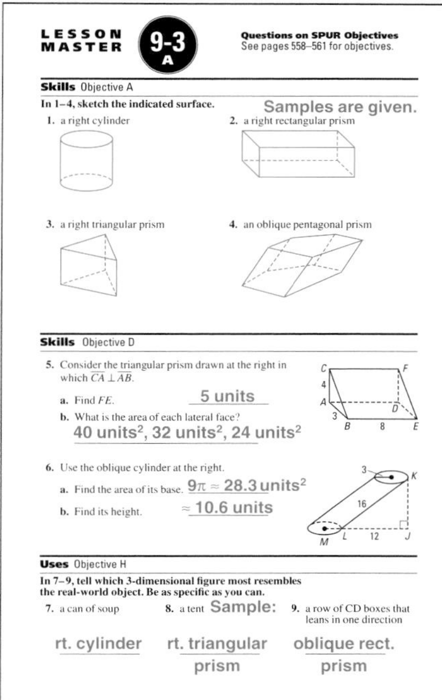

LESSON MASTER 9-3 A

Questions on SPUR Objectives
See pages 558–561 for objectives.

Skills Objective A

In 1–4, sketch the indicated surface. Samples are given.

1. a right cylinder
2. a right rectangular prism
3. a right triangular prism
4. an oblique pentagonal prism

Skills Objective D

5. Consider the triangular prism drawn at the right in which $\overline{CA} \perp \overline{AB}$.
   a. Find FE. 5 units
   b. What is the area of each lateral face? 40 units^2, 32 units^2, 24 units^2

6. Use the oblique cylinder at the right.
   a. Find the area of its base. $9\pi \approx 28.3$ units^2
   b. Find its height. ≈ 10.6 units

Uses Objective H

In 7–9, tell which 3-dimensional figure most resembles the real-world object. Be as specific as you can.

7. a can of soup — rt. cylinder
8. a tent — Sample: rt. triangular prism
9. a row of CD boxes that leans in one direction — oblique rect. prism

Additional Examples

You might want to use these additional examples when discussing the lesson.

1. Why are the lateral faces of any prism parallelograms? **Each face is a quadrilateral in which two edges have the same length and are parallel. Thus, by the Sufficient Conditions for a Parallelogram Theorem, the quadrilateral is a parallelogram.**
2. How many diagonals does a box have? **There are 16 diagonals. Of these, 12 are face diagonals and 4 are interior diagonals.**
3. Refer to the box in **Question 4** on page 509.
   a. Name an edge which is neither parallel nor perpendicular to $\overline{AD}$. $\overline{HB}$ **or** $\overline{CE}$ **or** $\overline{GH}$ **or** $\overline{EF}$
   b. Name four points that are coplanar but not in the same face. **Sample: *A*, *B*, *E*, and *F***
   c. Is there a plane which contains $\overline{AD}$ and $\overline{FG}$? **Yes, plane *ADFG***
   d. Is there a plane which contains $\overline{AD}$ and $\overline{GH}$? **No; these lines are skew lines.**
   e. Is there a plane which contains *B*, *D* and *G*? **Yes; the points are noncollinear.**

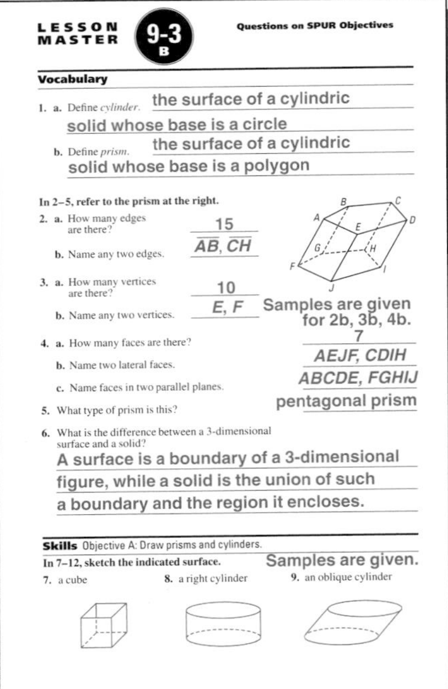
LESSON MASTER 9-3 B

Questions on SPUR Objectives

Vocabulary

1. a. Define *cylinder*. the surface of a cylindric solid whose base is a circle
   b. Define *prism*. the surface of a cylindric solid whose base is a polygon

In 2–5, refer to the prism at the right.

2. a. How many edges are there? 15
   b. Name any two edges. $\overline{AB}$, $\overline{CH}$
3. a. How many vertices are there? 10
   b. Name any two vertices. *E*, *F*

Samples are given for 2b, 3b, 4b.

4. a. How many faces are there? 7
   b. Name two lateral faces. *AEJF*, *CDIH*
   c. Name faces in two parallel planes. *ABCDE*, *FGHIJ*
5. What type of prism is this? pentagonal prism
6. What is the difference between a 3-dimensional surface and a solid? A surface is a boundary of a 3-dimensional figure, while a solid is the union of such a boundary and the region it encloses.

Skills Objective A: Draw prisms and cylinders.

In 7–12, sketch the indicated surface. Samples are given.

7. a cube
8. a right cylinder
9. an oblique cylinder

Activity
Sample: Algorithm 2:

Algorithm 2

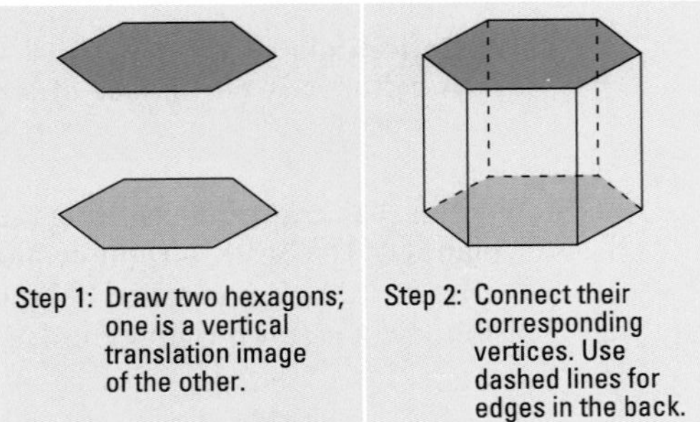

Step 1: Draw two hexagons; one is a vertical translation image of the other.
Step 2: Connect their corresponding vertices. Use dashed lines for edges in the back.

To use Algorithm 1 to sketch an oblique prism, you would draw parallel, equal, but nonvertical edges in Step 2. To use Algorithm 2, you would draw the second hexagon using a nonvertical translation vector.

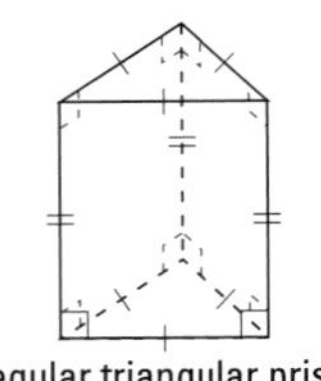
regular triangular prism

A **regular prism** is a right prism whose base is a regular polygon. At the left is a sketch of a regular triangular prism. Notice that the bases are equilateral triangles, and all the lateral faces are congruent rectangles.

Hierarchy of Cylindric Surfaces

From their definitions, the various special types of cylindric surfaces fit nicely into a hierarchy.

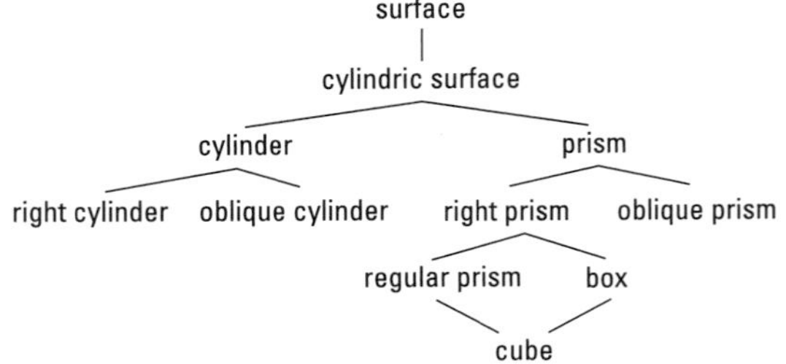

QUESTIONS

Covering the Reading

1a) Sample:

b) Sample:

1. a. Sketch the surface of a brick. **See left.**
   b. Sketch a solid brick. **See left.**
2. Show your sketches for the Activity in this lesson. **See page 507 and above.**
3. Consider a box.
   a. A segment connecting two adjacent vertices is called a(n) __?__ of the box. **edge**
   b. How many lateral faces does the box have? **4**
   c. How many faces does the box have? **6**
   d. How many lateral edges does the box have? **4**
   e. How many edges does the box have? **12**

4a) *ABCD* and *GHEF*, or *ABHG* and *DCEF*, or *ADFG* and *BCEH*

4. Refer to the box drawn at the right.
   a. Name faces in two parallel planes. See left.
   b. If $AB = 7$, name all other edges that measure 7. $\overline{CD}$, $\overline{GH}$, $\overline{EF}$
5. Give the special name for the cylindric surface 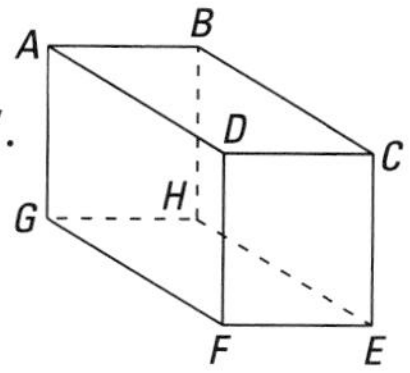
   a. whose base is a hexagon. hexagonal prism
   b. whose base is a circle. cylinder

In 6–9, sketch a figure of the given type. 6–9) See left.

6. right triangular prism
7. regular octagonal prism
8. right cylinder
9. oblique cylindric solid
10. Refer to the hierarchy in this lesson. What types of figures is a tin can? right cylinder, cylinder, cylindric surface, and surface
11. What type of figure is both a regular prism and a box? cube

Tottering twin towers. *The condemned Lindheimer Observatory at Northwestern University leaned dangerously during demolition.*

Applying the Mathematics

In 12 and 13, tell which 3-dimensional figure most resembles the real-world object. Give as specific a name as you can, distinguishing solids from surfaces.

12. a CD (ignoring the hole in the middle) solid right cylinder
13. an unsharpened pencil without an eraser Sample: solid right (often hexagonal) prism or solid right circular cylinder

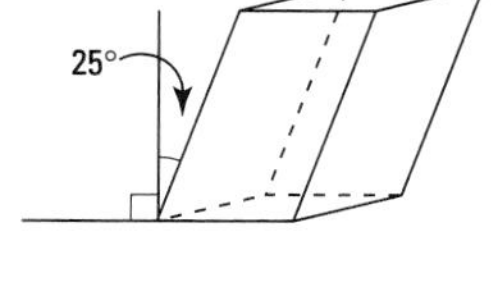

In 14 and 15, use the fact that the edges of an oblique prism are not perpendicular to the planes of the bases. Such prisms seem to lean. The amount of lean is measured from the perpendicular, as shown at the left.

14. Sketch a triangular prism with a 30° lean. See margin.
15. Sketch a pentagonal prism with a 45° lean. See margin.

6) 7)

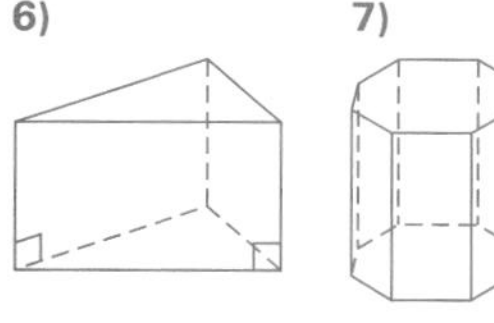

8) 9)

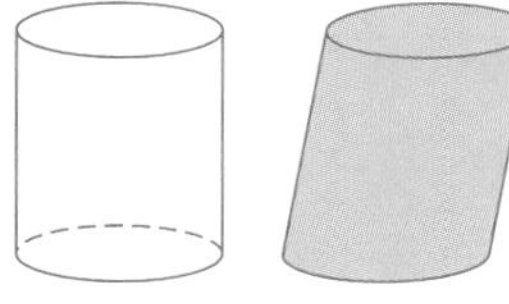

In 16 and 17, use the box drawn at the right. $BC = 4$, $AB = 12$, and $CG = 3$.

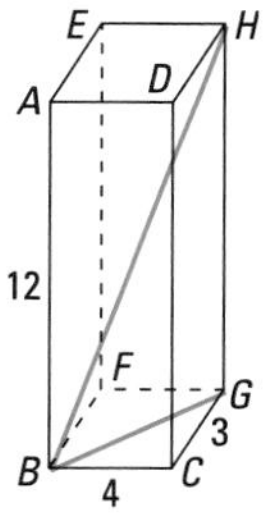

16. Find the area of
    a. $ABCD$. 48 units^2
    b. $AEHD$. 12 units^2
    c. $AEFB$. 36 units^2
17. a. Find the length of $\overline{BG}$. 5 units (Hint: There are right triangles in this drawing.)
    b. Find the length of $\overline{BH}$. 13 units
    c. Find the area of $\triangle BGH$. 30 units^2
18. Refer to the oblique cylinder at the right.
    a. What is the height of the cylinder? 15 units
    b. What is the area of a base? $36\pi \approx 113.1$ units^2

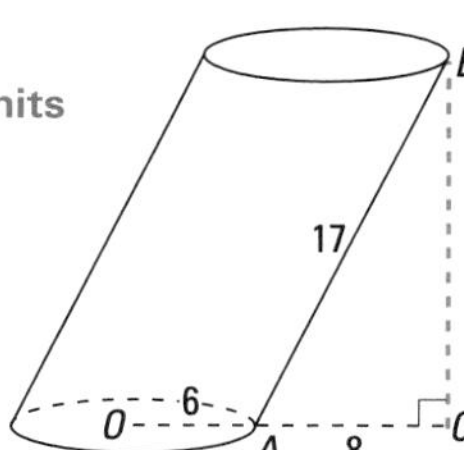

Notes on Questions

Questions 6–9 Many students have difficulty drawing sketches. Refer them to the algorithm given in the lesson's **Activity.** You might have students **work in pairs.**

Question 13 Some pencil surfaces are cylinders, many others are hexagonal prisms.

Question 17 In a later lesson, it will be proved that if d is the length of the longest diagonal in a box with sides of a, b, and c, then $d^2 = a^2 + b^2 + c^2$.

Question 18 You might want to point out that throughout the chapter these area calculations are done because these areas become one ingredient in the calculation of volume in the next chapter.

(Notes on Questions continue on page 510.)

Follow-up for Lesson 9-3

Practice

For more questions on SPUR Objectives, use **Lesson Master 9-3A** (shown on page 507) or **Lesson Master 9-3B** (shown on pages 508–509).

(Follow-up continues on page 510.)

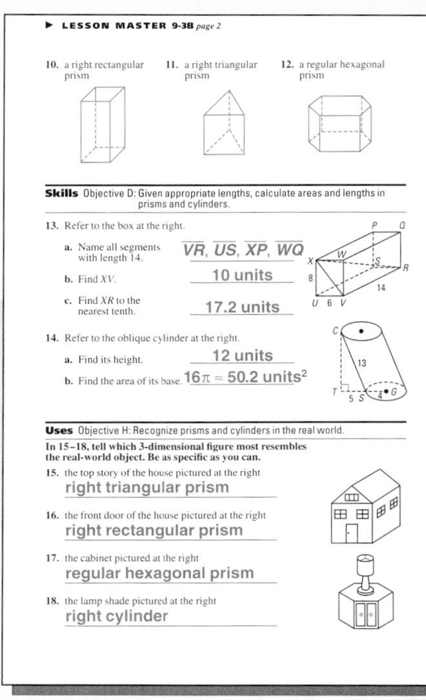

▸ **LESSON MASTER 9-3B** *page 2*

10. a right rectangular prism
11. a right triangular prism
12. a regular hexagonal prism

Skills Objective D: Given appropriate lengths, calculate areas and lengths in prisms and cylinders.

13. Refer to the box at the right.
    a. Name all segments with length 14. $\overline{VR}$, $\overline{US}$, $\overline{XP}$, $\overline{WQ}$
    b. Find XV. 10 units
    c. Find XR to the nearest tenth. 17.2 units
14. Refer to the oblique cylinder at the right.
    a. Find its height. 12 units
    b. Find the area of its base. $16\pi \approx 50.2$ units^2

Uses Objective H: Recognize prisms and cylinders in the real world.

In 15–18, tell which 3-dimensional figure most resembles the real-world object. Be as specific as you can.

15. the top story of the house pictured at the right right triangular prism
16. the front door of the house pictured at the right right rectangular prism
17. the cabinet pictured at the right regular hexagonal prism
18. the lamp shade pictured at the right right cylinder

Additional Answers

14. Sample:

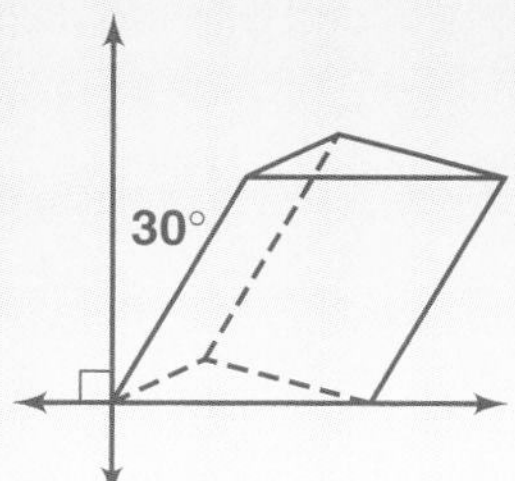

15. Sample:

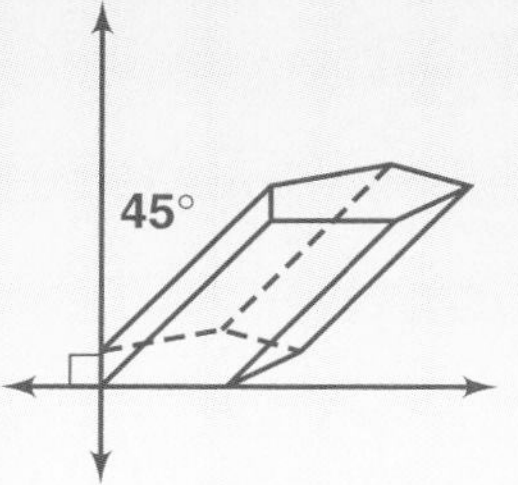

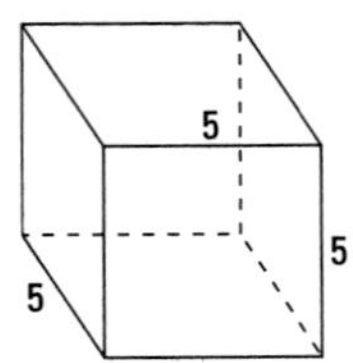

19. A cube is made of sticks, so it is hollow and you can stick your hand through it.
    a. If one edge has length 5, what is the total length of the sticks needed to make the cube? 60 units
    b. Generalize part **a** for a cube with edges of length *s*. If one edge has length *s*, then the length of all edges is 12*s*.
20. A computer artist wants to show a box on a computer screen. To do this, the artist has to think of the drawing as 2-dimensional even though it looks 3-dimensional. Given the coordinates of *A*, *B*, *C*, and *D* as shown below, what are the coordinates of *E*, *F*, *G*, and *H*? $E = (25, 70)$, $F = (85, 70)$, $G = (60, 50)$, $H = (25, 20)$

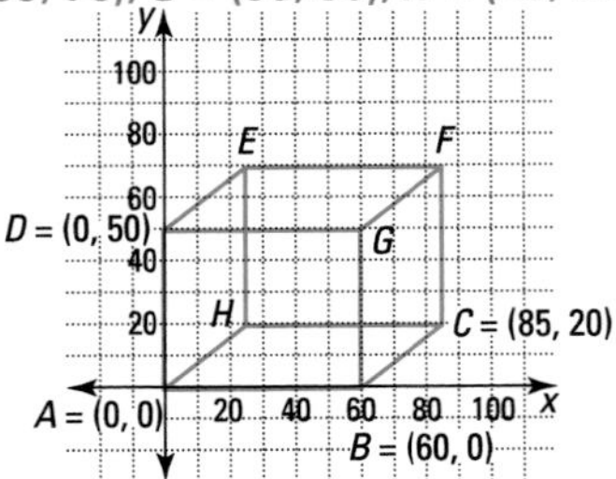

21) Sample:

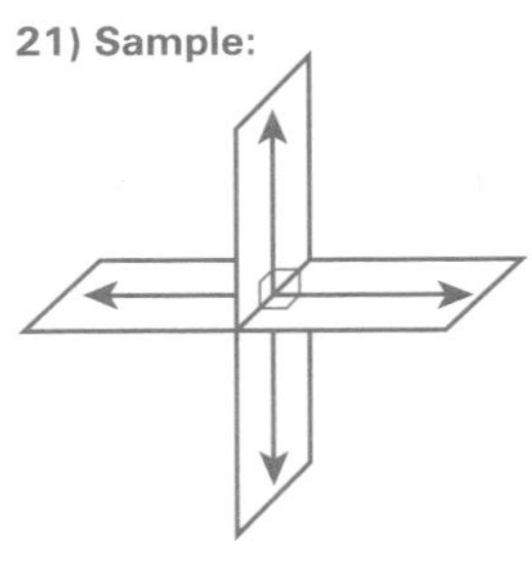

29) Sample: a pass to the side, as a lateral in football, or extending from side to side, as the lateral axis of an airplane. Lateral faces of a prism are faces on the side.

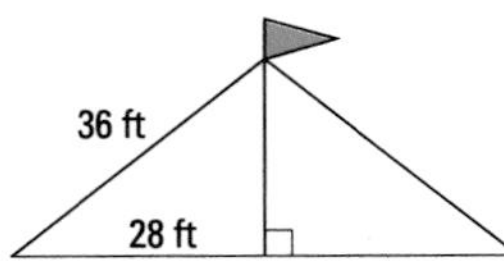

Lateral lateral. *In rugby, a player can pass the ball to a teammate on his or her side.*

Review

21. Draw two perpendicular planes. *(Lesson 9-2)* See left.
22. Name a 3-dimensional counterpart of intersecting lines. *(Lesson 9-1)* intersecting planes
23. How many planes contain two distinct points *A* and *B*? *(Lesson 9-1)* infinitely many
24. Ropes are needed to stake a tent pole so that it remains perpendicular to the ground. Each of the ropes is staked into the ground 28 feet from the base of the pole and is 36 feet in length from the ground to where they meet the pole, one foot from the top. In the figure at the left, how tall is the tent pole? *(Lesson 8-6)* $\sqrt{512} + 1 \approx 23.6$ ft
25. Draw a tessellation of the plane using equilateral triangles. *(Lesson 7-6)* See margin.
26. Define each term. *(Lesson 1-6)*
    a. *coplanar* two or more figures that lie in the same plane
    b. *collinear* points that are part of the same line

Exploration

27. Some prisms have special properties relative to light. What are these properties? A prism separates a beam of white light into a spectrum of colors.
28. The cells in honeycombs of bees are in the shapes of right hexagonal prisms. Why do bees use this shape? Hexagons tessellate, so a strong structure can be built in a small space.
29. Find two nonmathematical meanings of the word *lateral* in a dictionary. How is the mathematical meaning related to these meanings? See left.

Assessment

Written Communication Have students use either Algorithm 1 on page 507 or Algorithm 2 on page 508 to draw at least two other prisms with each having a different polygonal base. [Students provide two acceptable (not necessarily perfect) drawings of a prism. Encourage students' efforts.]

Extension

Have students make a classroom collection of as many 3-dimensional surfaces as possible. They should name each geometric figure represented and identify its properties. [Answers will vary.]

Project Update Project 2, *Structures,* on page 552, relates to the content of this lesson.

Notes on Questions

Question 21 Cooperative Learning You might divide the class into groups and have the different groups draw perpendicular planes with the line of intersection vertical, horizontal, and/or oblique.

Question 27 Science Connection In the science of optics, a prism is a piece of transparent material which refracts light. It is cut with precise angles and faces. Ordinary triangular prisms separate white light into its constituent colors, forming a full or partial rainbow spectrum for observers. Some prisms reverse the direction of light by internal reflection, thus creating a reversed image. Prisms are used in spectroscopes (instruments for analyzing light), and other optical instruments.

Adapting to Individual Needs

Challenge Writing Have students find shapes listed in this lesson and write a paragraph about what shapes seem to be used most frequently for packaging and why. [Sample: Boxes and cylinders are most common, because they fill space and stack easily. Unusual shapes, such as cones, pyramids, and non-rectangular prisms may be used to attract attention.]

Additional Answers
25. Sample:

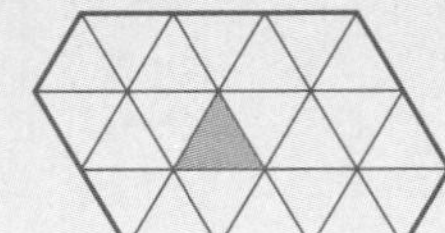

Setting Up Lesson 9-4

Materials If possible, have models of conic sections for students to use with the next lesson.

LESSON

9-4

Pyramids and Cones

Timeless shapes. *Pyramids have been prominent in architecture throughout time, from the pyramids at Giza, Egypt, to the Transamerica Building in San Francisco.*

Pyramids

Pyramids were built in many places in the ancient world as temples and burial sites. One of the wonders of the world is the collection of pyramids constructed by ancient Egyptians. The oldest of the Egyptian pyramids seems to have been designed by Imhotep for the Pharaoh Zoser around 2600 or 2800 B.C. The Transamerica Building in San Francisco, a more recently constructed building shaped like a pyramid, was built in 1972.

These structures are examples of *conic solids*. The boundary of a conic solid is a **conic surface.**

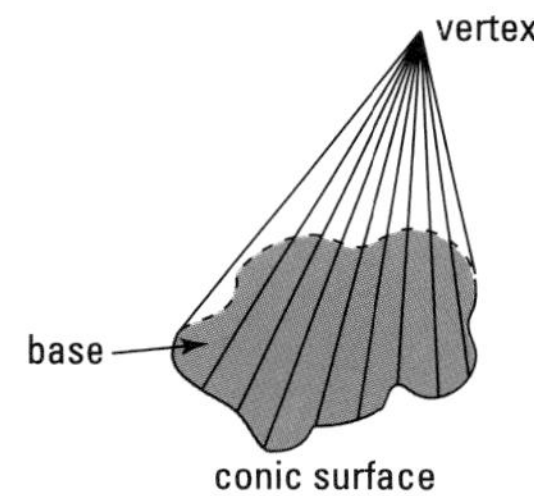

Definitions
Given a region (the **base**) and a point (the **vertex**) not in the plane of the base, a **conic solid** is the set of all points on segments joining the vertex and any point of the base.

A **pyramid** is the surface of a conic solid whose base is a polygon.

A **cone** is the surface of a conic solid whose base is a circle.

For example, a solid pyramid like the pyramids in Egypt is the set of points on segments joining a polygonal region (its base) and a point (its vertex) not in the plane of the region.

Lesson 9-4

Objectives

A Draw pyramids and cones.
D Given appropriate lengths, calculate areas and lengths in pyramids and cones.
H Recognize pyramids and cones in the real world.

Resources

From the ***Teacher's Resource File***

- Lesson Master 9-4A or 9-4B
- Answer Master 9-4
- Teaching Aids
  119 Warm-up
  121 Additional Examples and Extension
- Assessment Sourcebook: Quiz for Lessons 9-1 through 9-4

Additional Resources

- Visuals for Teaching Aids 119, 121
- Models of Conic Sections

Teaching Lesson 9-4

Warm-up

1. Name as many real-world examples of cones as you can. **Samples: ice-cream holder, drinking cup, party hat**
2. Name as many real-world examples of pyramids as you can. **Samples: Egyptian pyramids, tent**
3. Why do you think the cone is such a popular container for serving ice cream? **Sample: A cone is easy to hold.**

Lesson 9-4 Overview

Broad Goals The goal of this lesson is to continue the development of vocabulary and drawing skills, and to apply them to pyramids and cones.

Perspective In Lesson 9-3, the general concept of cylindric solid was defined. Under this definition, cylinders and prisms are special cases of cylindric surfaces. In this lesson, a general definition of conic solid is given, of which cones and pyramids are special cases of conic surfaces. As with the cylinder and prism, the definitions of cone and pyramid include the base as part of the surface.

A cone is sometimes defined as the locus of points on all lines which form an angle of a given measure at a point of a given line. Then a cone has two parts (its *nappes*) and extends forever. The definition chosen in this lesson is more appropriate for the calculations of surface area and volume that occur in the next chapter.

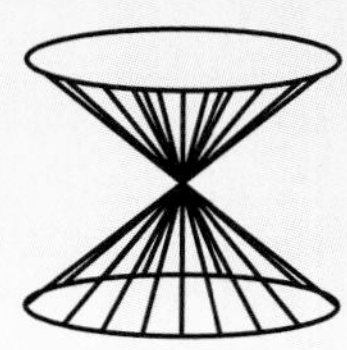

(Overview continues on page 512.)

Notes on Reading

As suggested in the previous lesson, students should redraw and label the figures in this lesson in their notebooks. Then they can refer to them as needed.

Multicultural Connection Most people have heard of the great pyramids of Egypt, but there are also a number of pyramids in Mexico and Central America. Many ancient Mesoamerican cultures built them, including the Mayas, the Toltecs, and the Aztecs. Most were built in the "classic" period (250 A.D.–950 A.D.), and were used as sacred temples. One of the largest and most famous of such pyramids is the Pyramid of the Sun at Teotihuacán. Built in the 2nd century A.D., it stands 66 meters high and is cut with hundreds of broad steps that ascend to its summit.

Cooperative Learning If you have models of conic solids available, you may have students **work in small groups** to learn the terminology in this lesson. Give each group models and have them identify each of the following: faces, edges, vertices, the base, lateral face, lateral edge, and the vertex. Also have them determine where the axis would be, the lateral surface, and how they would find the slant height. Group members should be responsible for correcting any errors. Each student should be responsible for identifying his or her solid according to the hierarchy on page 513, using all classifications that fit.

❶ The adjective "regular," when applied to geometric figures, usually means "possessing the most symmetry." Thus a "regular polygon" possesses the most symmetry of any polygon. Analogously, a "regular pyramid" has the most symmetry of any pyramid. A regular pyramid whose base is a regular n-gon has n planes of symmetry and n-fold rotational symmetry about its axis (the line through its vertex perpendicular to its base). Symmetry is discussed in Lesson 9-6.

Have students record the results of the **Activity** for use with **Question 3a** on page 514.

The parts of a pyramid are named in the figure at the right. The segments connecting the vertex of the pyramid to the vertices of the base are **lateral edges.** The other edges are called **base edges.** The polygonal regions formed by the edges are the **faces** of the pyramid. All faces other than the base are triangular regions. These triangular regions are the **lateral faces** of the pyramid.

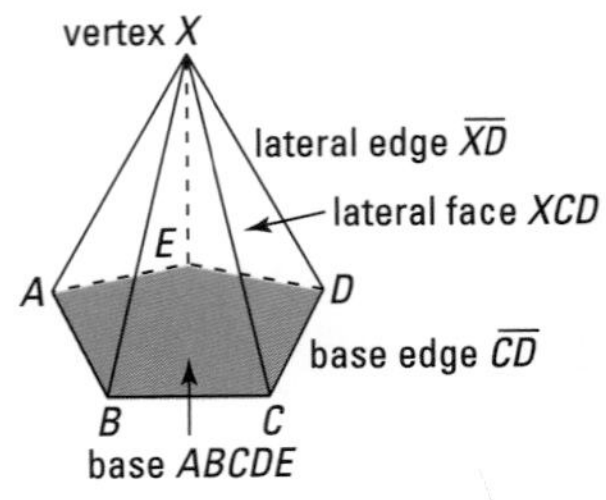

❶ Pyramids are classified by their bases, just as prisms are. There are triangular pyramids, square pyramids, pentagonal pyramids, and so on. If the base of a pyramid is rotation-symmetric and the segment connecting the vertex to the center of symmetry of the polygonal base is perpendicular to the plane of the base, then the pyramid is a **right pyramid.** If a pyramid is not right, it is an **oblique pyramid.** A **regular pyramid** is a right pyramid whose base is a regular polygon. The Egyptian pyramids are regular square pyramids.

Activity

Sketch a right rectangular pyramid using the algorithm below, shown for a regular square pyramid. See page 514.

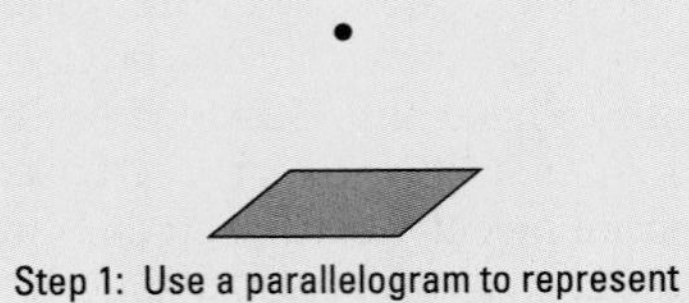

Step 1: Use a parallelogram to represent a square not in the plane of the paper, and put a point above its center of symmetry.

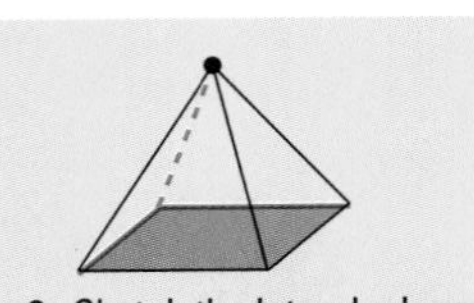

Step 2: Sketch the lateral edges, using dashed lines for the unseen edges.

Cones

From its definition, a cone is like a pyramid in that it has one base and a vertex. But the base of a cone is a circle. The line through the vertex and the center of the circle is the **axis** of the cone. When the axis is perpendicular to the plane of the circle, the cone is called a **right cone.** Otherwise the cone is an **oblique cone.** The surface of a cone other than the base is the **lateral surface** of the cone. A **lateral edge** of a cone is any segment whose endpoints are the vertex and a point on the circle.

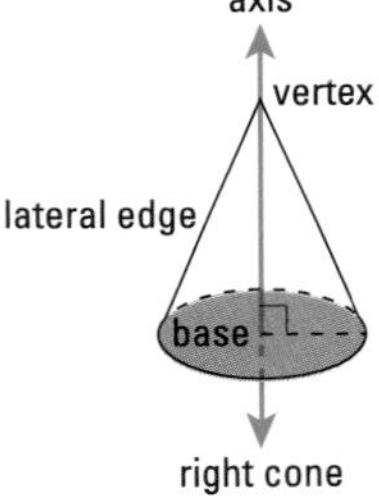

right cone

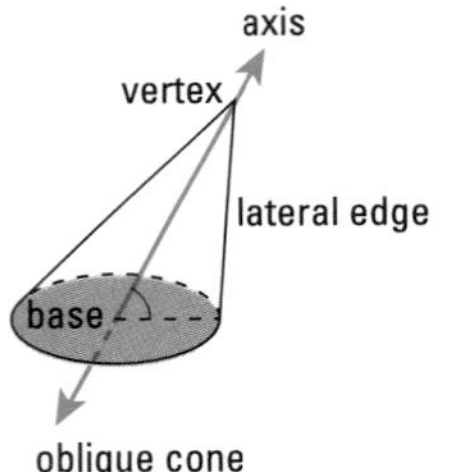

oblique cone

Lesson 9-4 Overview, continued

In this book, all cones and cylinders have circular bases. In some books, the right cone on page 512 would be called a right *circular* cone, but our definition of a cone makes this terminology redundant.

Buildings of the Muttart Conservatory in Edmonton, Alberta, Canada.

Heights of Pyramids and Cones

The **height** or **altitude** of a pyramid or cone is the distance from the vertex to the plane of the base. The height of a right pyramid or right cone is the length of the segment connecting the vertex to the base's center of symmetry.

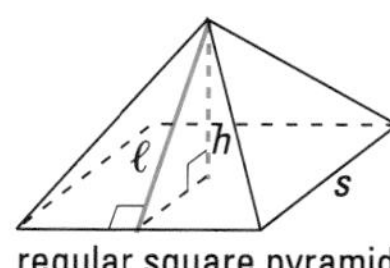

height h;
slant height ℓ

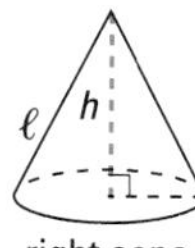

Each lateral face of a regular pyramid is an isosceles triangle congruent to all the other lateral faces. The altitude of any of the triangles forming one of the lateral faces of a regular pyramid, measured from the pyramid's vertex, is called the **slant height** of the pyramid (ℓ in the pyramid above). In a pyramid, the slant height is greater than the height but less than the length of a lateral edge. A right cone also has a **slant height;** it is the length of a lateral edge.

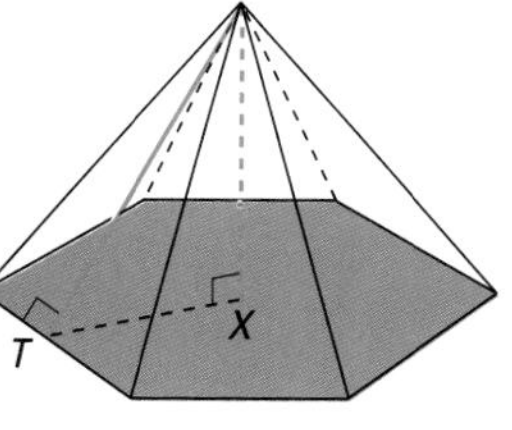

Example

The regular hexagonal pyramid shown at the left has height $VX = 12$. If $TX = 7$, find its slant height to the nearest tenth.

Solution

By the Pythagorean Theorem,

$$VT^2 = TX^2 + VX^2$$
$$VT^2 = 7^2 + 12^2$$
$$VT^2 = 193.$$
$$VT = \sqrt{193}$$
$$VT \approx 13.9 \text{ units}$$

Hierarchy of Conic Surfaces

Below is a hierarchy of conic surfaces. Compare this hierarchy with the hierarchy of cylindrical surfaces. They are very much alike.

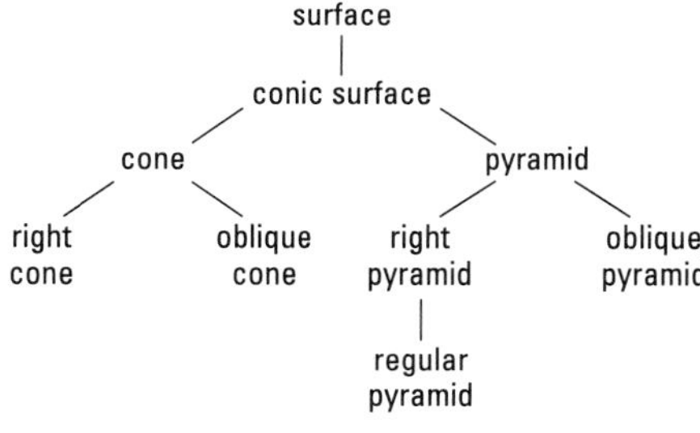

Notice the similarities between cones and pyramids, and between cylinders and prisms. In the next chapter, you will see similarities in the formulas for the volumes and surface areas of these figures.

Additional Examples

These examples are also given on **Teaching Aid 121.**

1. A city has stored salt to use on the streets in the winter. The salt pile forms a right cone. Suppose the distance from the vertex to any point on the circumference of the base is 35 feet. The diameter of the base is 30 feet. How high is the pile of salt?
   $\sqrt{1000} \approx 32$ feet

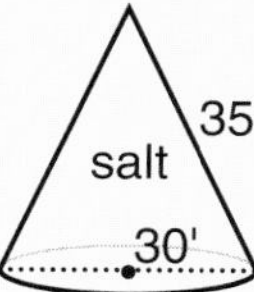

2. Draw a square pyramid with
   a. its base on the bottom.
   b. its base lying in a nearly vertical plane on the right.
   c. its base lying in a nearly vertical plane on the left.
   Samples:
   a. 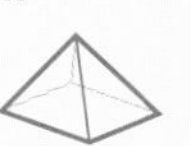 b.  c. 

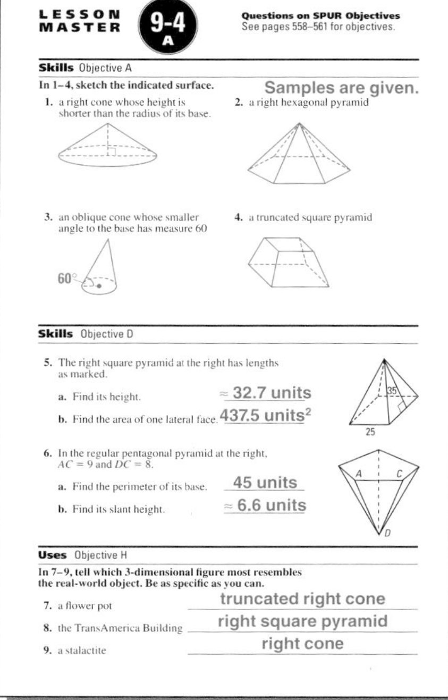

LESSON MASTER 9-4 A — Questions on SPUR Objectives. See pages 558–561 for objectives.

Skills Objective A

In 1–4, sketch the indicated surface. Samples are given.

1. a right cone whose height is shorter than the radius of its base.
2. a right hexagonal pyramid
3. an oblique cone whose smaller angle to the base has measure 60
4. a truncated square pyramid

Skills Objective D

5. The right square pyramid at the right has lengths as marked.
   a. Find its height. $\approx$ 32.7 units
   b. Find the area of one lateral face. 437.5 units²
6. In the regular pentagonal pyramid at the right, $AC = 9$ and $DC = 8$.
   a. Find the perimeter of its base. 45 units
   b. Find its slant height. $\approx$ 6.6 units

Uses Objective H

In 7–9, tell which 3-dimensional figure most resembles the real-world object. Be as specific as you can.

7. a flower pot — truncated right cone
8. the TransAmerica Building — right square pyramid
9. a stalactite — right cone

Optional Activities

After completing the lesson, interested students might enjoy making a mobile showing the hierarchy of conic surfaces given in this section. Students should build the models using the directions given in the text. Hang the mobiles in the classroom.

Adapting to Individual Needs

Extra Help

In the preceding lesson, students learned that a rectangular solid has 8 vertices (plural of *vertex*). In this lesson, we talk about *the* vertex of a cone or of a pyramid. Point out to students that a pyramid can have other vertices (either endpoint of any edge), but there is only one vertex that is called *the* vertex—the one which is not a vertex of the base.

Notes on Questions

Question 2 You might ask if it can be determined from the drawing alone whether the pyramid drawn is a *regular* square pyramid. [No]

Questions 15–16 A truncated conic solid is also called a *frustum* of the solid. To draw the truncated surface, suggest to students that they first draw the entire cone or pyramid, next draw a cross-section, and then erase the top part.

Question 18 A square pyramid made of wire or straws and placed on the overhead projector and then rotated may demonstrate these images.

(Notes on Questions continue on page 516.)

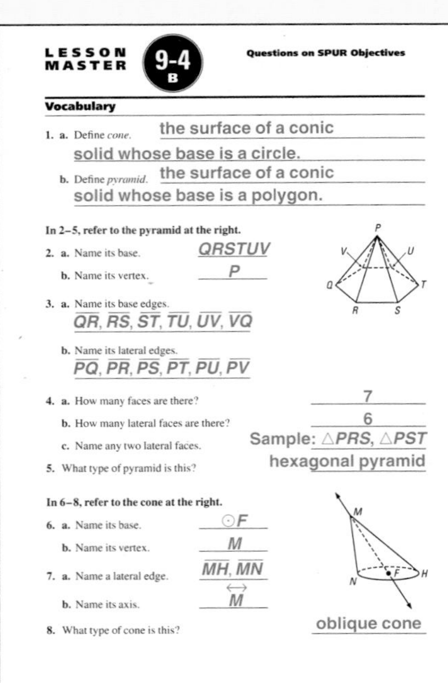

LESSON MASTER 9-4 B — Questions on SPUR Objectives

Vocabulary

1. a. Define *cone.* the surface of a conic solid whose base is a circle.
   b. Define *pyramid.* the surface of a conic solid whose base is a polygon.

In 2–5, refer to the pyramid at the right.

2. a. Name its base. QRSTUV
   b. Name its vertex. P
3. a. Name its base edges. $\overline{QR}, \overline{RS}, \overline{ST}, \overline{TU}, \overline{UV}, \overline{VQ}$
   b. Name its lateral edges. $\overline{PQ}, \overline{PR}, \overline{PS}, \overline{PT}, \overline{PU}, \overline{PV}$
4. a. How many faces are there? 7
   b. How many lateral faces are there? 6
   c. Name any two lateral faces. Sample: $\triangle PRS$, $\triangle PST$
5. What type of pyramid is this? hexagonal pyramid

In 6–8, refer to the cone at the right.

6. a. Name its base. $\odot F$
   b. Name its vertex. M
7. a. Name a lateral edge. $\overline{MH}, \overline{MN}$
   b. Name its axis. $\overleftrightarrow{M}$
8. What type of cone is this? oblique cone

3a)

b)

8) Sample:

2 cm

9a, b)

height

slant height

QUESTIONS

Covering the Reading

1. Approximately how many centuries elapsed between the building of the oldest known Egyptian pyramid and construction of the Transamerica Building? 47

2. A regular square pyramid is sketched at the right. Identify
   a. its base. *ABDE*
   b. its vertex. *C*
   c. a lateral edge. $\overline{BC}$ or $\overline{AC}$ or $\overline{EC}$ or $\overline{DC}$
   d. a lateral face. See below.
   e. an edge of the base. $\overline{AB}$ or $\overline{BD}$ or $\overline{DE}$ or $\overline{EA}$

   d) $\triangle ACB$ or $\triangle BCD$ or $\triangle DCE$ or $\triangle ACE$.

A B C E D

3. a. Show your answer to the Activity in this lesson. See left.
   b. Draw an oblique triangular pyramid. See left.

4. *O* is the center of the circle drawn at the right, and $\overline{MO}$ is perpendicular to the plane of the circle.
   a. What type of surface is shown? right cone
   b. Name its axis. $\overleftrightarrow{MO}$
   c. Name a lateral edge. $\overline{MN}$ or $\overline{ML}$
   d. Name its vertex. *M*
   e. Name the base. $\odot O$
   f. What is its height? *MO*
   g. What is its slant height? *ML* or *MN*

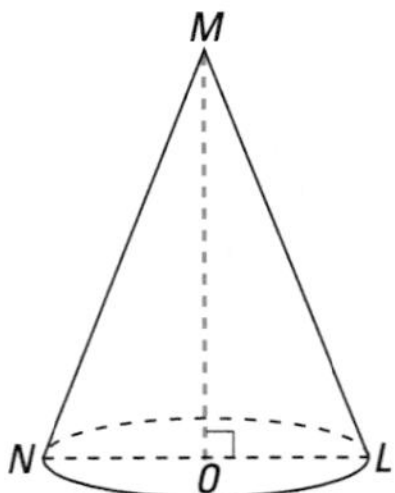

In 5–7, what type of surface is drawn?

5.
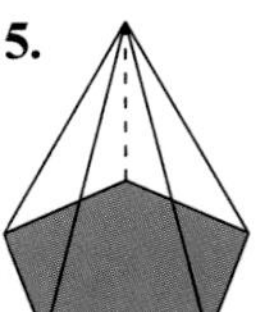
pentagonal pyramid

6.
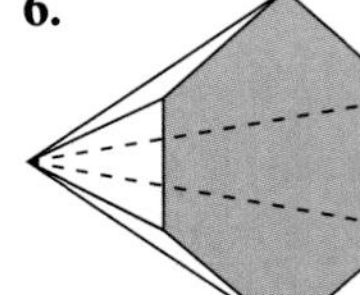
hexagonal pyramid

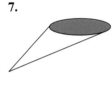

7.
oblique cone

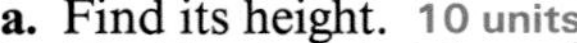
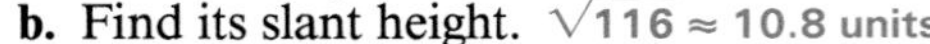

8. Sketch a cone with a base having radius 2 cm. See left.

9. a. Sketch a regular octagonal pyramid. See left.
   b. On your sketch, identify the height and the slant height.

10. In the regular pentagonal pyramid at the left, $RQ = 4$ and $PQ = 10$.
    a. Find its height. 10 units
    b. Find its slant height. $\sqrt{116} \approx 10.8$ units

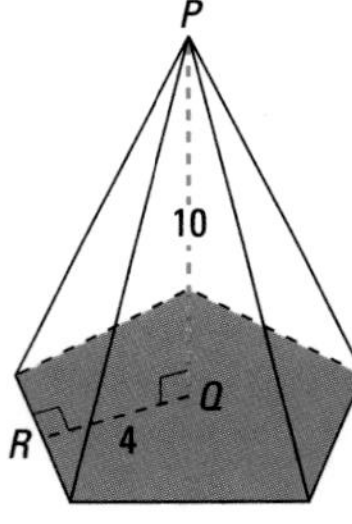

Adapting to Individual Needs

English Language Development

Continuing the suggestions in the previous lesson, you might again have students with limited English proficiency discuss their work with English-speaking students as they draw the figures in their notebooks.

Applying the Mathematics

11. Given a right square pyramid, arrange each part in order from smallest to largest: the length of a lateral edge, the height of the pyramid, the slant height.
the height of the pyramid, slant height, length of a lateral edge

12. Suppose the base of a pyramid is a hexagon.
a. How many lateral faces does the pyramid have? 6
b. How many faces does the pyramid have? 7
c. How many lateral edges does the pyramid have? 6
d. How many edges does the pyramid have? 12

13. Repeat Question 12, but suppose the base is an n-gon.
a) n b) $n + 1$ c) n d) $2n$

14. In the early 20th century, Chinese officials wore conical hats as part of their summer uniform. Suppose the height of a conical hat is 17 cm and the radius of the base is 33 cm.
a. Find the slant height. $\sqrt{1378} \approx 37.1$ cm
b. Find the circumference of its base. $66\pi \approx 207.35$ cm^2

In 15 and 16, a conic surface or conic solid has been cut by a plane parallel to its base. The part of the conic surface between and including the two parallel planes is called a **truncated surface.**

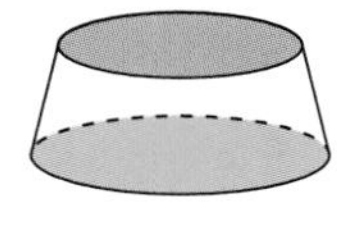
truncated cone

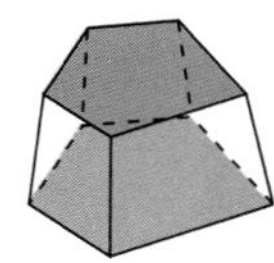
truncated pentagonal pyramid

15. Where in a circus might you find a truncated cone?
Sample: a platform that elephants stand on

16. Draw a truncated hexagonal pyramid. (Hint: Think of the original vertex as a vanishing point.)
See left.

17. Cut a quarter disk out of a piece of paper with dimensions as shown at the left. Roll the paper so that $\overline{AB}$ and $\overline{AC}$ coincide and a cone is formed.
a. What is the circumference of the base of this cone? $2\pi \approx 6.28''$
b. What is the radius of the base of the cone (to the nearest tenth of an inch)? 1.0″ exactly

A, 90°, 4", 4", B, C

16) Sample:

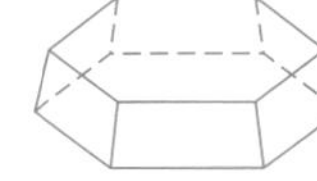

18. Suppose you can see only the edges of a right square pyramid and they glow in the dark. Where are you in relation to the pyramid if you see it as shown?

a.

above the vertex

b.
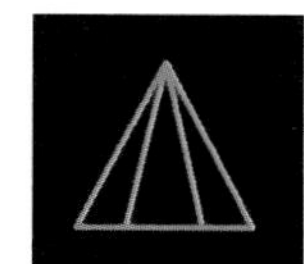
left of front in plane of vertex

c.
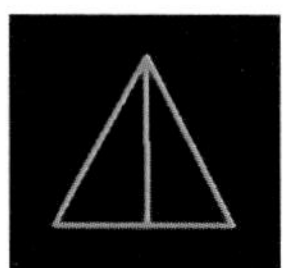
in front of a vertex of the base in plane of base

Follow-up for Lesson 9-4

Practice

For more questions on SPUR Objectives, use **Lesson Master 9-4A** (shown on page 513) or **Lesson Master 9-4B** (shown on pages 514–515).

Assessment

Quiz A quiz covering Lessons 9-1 through 9-4 is provided in the *Assessment Sourcebook.*

Diagnostic Write the names of several figures on the chalkboard. Choose students to come to the board, make a reasonable drawing of one of the figures, and identify the various parts of the figure. Have all other students make suggestions for improving or clarifying the drawing. Repeat this process until all students have had a chance to draw a figure. [Check accuracy of students' drawings.]

(Folow-up continues on page 516.)

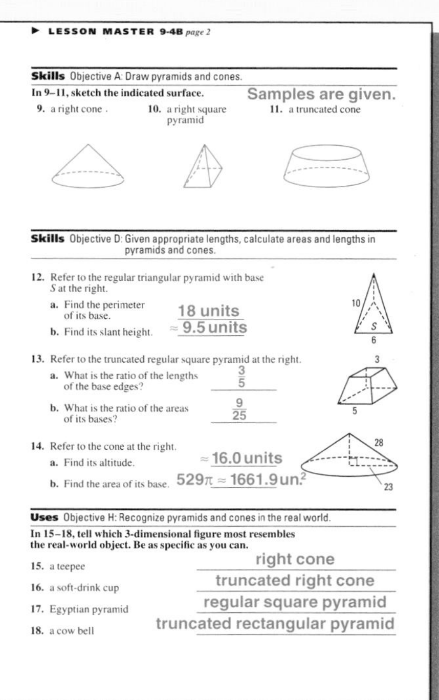
▶ LESSON MASTER 9-4B *page 2*

Skills Objective A: Draw pyramids and cones.

In 9–11, sketch the indicated surface. Samples are given.
9. a right cone 10. a right square pyramid 11. a truncated cone

Skills Objective D: Given appropriate lengths, calculate areas and lengths in pyramids and cones.

12. Refer to the regular triangular pyramid with base S at the right.
a. Find the perimeter of its base. 18 units
b. Find its slant height. ≈ 9.5 units

13. Refer to the truncated regular square pyramid at the right.
a. What is the ratio of the lengths of the base edges? $\frac{3}{5}$
b. What is the ratio of the areas of its bases? $\frac{9}{25}$

14. Refer to the cone at the right.
a. Find its altitude. ≈ 16.0 units
b. Find the area of its base. $529\pi \approx 1661.9$ un.^{2}

Uses Objective H: Recognize pyramids and cones in the real world.

In 15–18, tell which 3-dimensional figure most resembles the real-world object. Be as specific as you can.
15. a teepee — right cone
16. a soft-drink cup — truncated right cone
17. Egyptian pyramid — regular square pyramid
18. a cow bell — truncated rectangular pyramid

Adapting to Individual Needs

Challenge
Suppose the base of a pyramid is an n-gon. How many faces does the pyramid have? [$n + 1$] How many edges does it have? [$2n$] Euler's general formula for solids with polygonal faces may be demonstrated here: the number of faces plus the number of vertices equals the number of edges plus two; that is, $F + V = E + 2$. How many vertices does this n-gon have? [$V = n + 1$]

Extension

Teaching Aid 121 contains the diagram below. Have students prove that the lateral edges of a regular square pyramid are all equal in length.

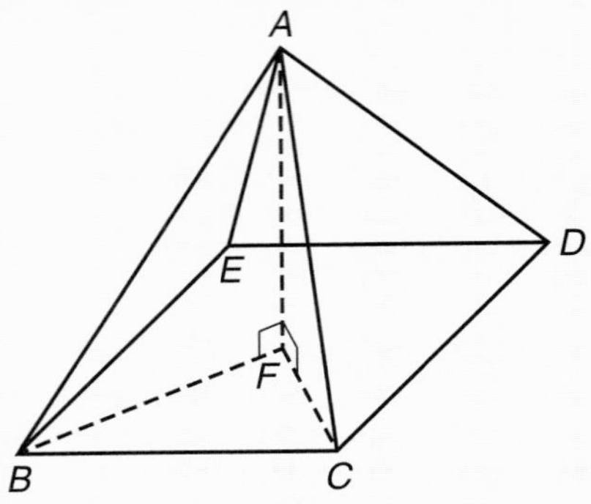

[Given: *ABCDE* is a regular square pyramid with base *BCDE*. *F* is the intersection of the diagonals of the base. We need to prove that $AB = AC$.

Argument: $\overline{FB}$ and $\overline{FC}$ are halves of diagonals of equal length, so $FB = FC$. Since the altitude is perpendicular to the plane of the base, $\overline{AF} \perp \overline{FB}$ and $\overline{AF} \perp \overline{FC}$. Thus, $m\angle AFB = m\angle AFC = 90$ by the definition of perpendicular. Since $AF = AF$, $\triangle AFB \cong \triangle AFC$ by the SAS Congruence Theorem. Since $\overline{AB}$ and $\overline{AC}$ are corresponding parts, they are congruent by the *CPCF* Theorem. $AC = AD = AE$ can be shown using a similar argument.]

Project Update Project 2, *Structures,* on page 552, relates to the content of this lesson.

Notes on Questions

Question 27 History Connection Of the seven wonders of the ancient world, so named by the Greeks, only the pyramids still stand. The Greeks were not familiar with wonders outside the Greek empire, such as the Great Wall of China. It is our experience that students come up with interesting answers to **part b.**

Review

19. Draw an oblique rectangular prism. *(Lesson 9-3)* See left.

20. Pictured at the left is a prism. Explain why *ABED* is a parallelogram. *(Lesson 9-3)* See margin.

21. What is the difference between a right cylinder and an oblique cylinder? *(Lesson 9-3)* In a right cylinder, the direction of the translation is $\perp$ to the base. In an oblique cylinder, it is not.

In 22 and 23, refer to the cube at the right. $AT = 5$. *(Lessons 8-2, 8-6, 9-3)*

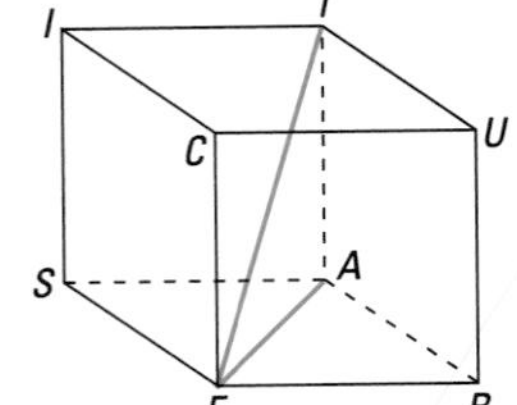

22. Find the indicated length. See left.
a. AB **b.** EA **c.** ET

23. What is the sum of the areas of all six faces? 150 units^2

24. How many different planes contain the indicated figure?
a. three given noncollinear points one
b. a given $\triangle ABC$ one
c. a given line *(Lesson 9-1)* infinitely many

25. Refer to $\triangle ABC$ at the right.
a. Find the area of $\triangle ABC$. 240 units^2
b. Find the length of the altitude to $\overline{AC}$. *(Lesson 8-4)* about 18.5 units

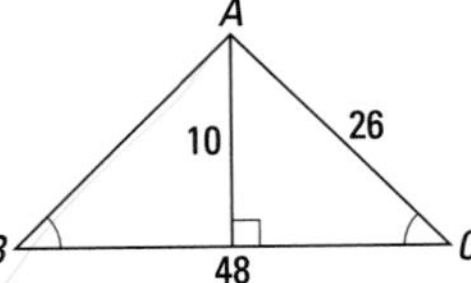

26. Rectangle *F* has double the length and one-third the width of rectangle *G*. How do their areas compare? *(Lesson 8-2)* Rectangle *F* has $\frac{2}{3}$ of the area of rectangle *G*.

A triangular prism by Firth of Lorne near Oban, Argyll, Scotland.

Exploration

27. The pyramids of Egypt were called by ancient Greek writers one of the "seven wonders of the world."
a. What were the other wonders of the world for those Greek writers?
b. Identify a structure that has been called one of the wonders of today's world. Samples: the Brooklyn Bridge, Hoover Dam, Angkor Wat (Angkor temple) in Cambodia

a) Hanging Gardens of Babylon, statue of Zeus at Olympia, Temple of Artemis at Ephesus, Mausoleum at Halicarnassus, Colossus at Rhodes, Pharos or lighthouse of Alexandria

19) Sample:

22a) 5 units
b) $\sqrt{50} \approx 7.1$ units
c) $\sqrt{75} \approx 8.7$ units

Additional Answers

20. $\overline{AD}$ and $\overline{BE}$ are parallel and equal in length by the definition of prism. Therefore, by the Sufficient Conditions for a Parallelogram Theorem, *ABED* is a parallelogram.

Setting Up Lesson 9-5

Materials You may want to have a globe available when you discuss the section of Lesson 9-5, *Earth as a Sphere.* If you do Activity 2 in *Optional Activities* on page 519, students may find it helpful to have clear models of 3-dimensional figures and sand to fill them.

LESSON

9-5

Spheres and Sections

Planet Earth. *This famous photograph of Earth taken from the moon is dramatic confirmation that Earth is nearly spherical in shape.*

Ancient Greek astronomers deduced that Earth was a sphere based on the fact that Earth casts a consistent round shadow on the moon during eclipses of the moon. Nevertheless, many Europeans in the Middle Ages and Renaissance believed the world was flat. That belief persisted until 1522, when the voyage begun by Ferdinand Magellan, a Portuguese navigator, was completed, heralding the first circumnavigation of Earth.

The Sphere

A 3-dimensional counterpart of the circle is the *sphere.*

Definition
A **sphere** is the set of points in space at a certain distance (its radius) from a point (its center).

To draw a solid sphere (such as an orange or a baseball), shade the drawing as shown below at the left. To draw the surface (such as a beach ball or a bubble), draw only an outline, as shown below at the right, with arcs added to give the illusion of depth.

solid sphere

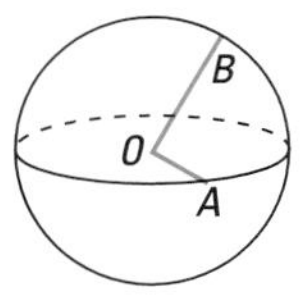

sphere

Lesson 9-5 Overview

Broad Goals This lesson discusses terminology relating to a wide range of figures, beginning with the definition of a sphere and then the sections of spheres (great circles and small circles), continuing with the sections of prisms, cylinders, and pyramids, and ending with the famous conic sections.

Perspective This is an exceedingly important lesson for visualization. Students need to be able to conceptualize plane sections in order to deal with many calculations of surface area and volume. However, drawing plane sections is quite difficult for many students. Though drawing should be covered, it should not be overemphasized.

Lesson 9-5

Objectives

A Draw spheres.
B Draw plane sections of common 3-dimensional shapes.
D Given appropriate lengths, calculate areas and lengths in spheres.
H Recognize 3-dimensional figures in the real world.

Resources

From the ***Teacher's Resource File***
- Lesson Master 9-5A or 9-5B
- Answer Master 9-5
- Teaching Aids
  119 Warm-up
  122 Plane Sections of Solids
  123 Plane Sections of Pyramids and Cones; Conic Sections
  124 Optional Activities

Additional Resources
- Visuals for Teaching Aids 119, 122–124
- Globe
- Clear models of 3-dimensional figures, sand

Teaching Lesson 9-5

Warm-up

1. Think of a cylinder of cheese. If you slice a piece of cheese from the end, will the end section of the cylinder always be circular? Explain. **Not necessarily; the angle of the slice will determine whether the end section is circular or not.**
2. Suppose you want to cut a square wooden fence post horizontally into two pieces. Will the ends of each piece also be square? Explain. **Not necessarily; it depends upon what angle is used for making the cut.**

Notes on Reading

As you discuss the lesson, students should draw figures from the lesson in their notes.

Teaching Aids 122–123 contain the diagrams on pages 520–521. You may wish to use **Teaching Aids 122–123** during your classroom discussions.

Science Connection Students may be studying biology concurrently with this course or may have already studied biology; if so, they may have seen cross sections of leaves or of animals. The drawings in this lesson and the drawings they may have made in biology complement each other.

❶ **Geography Connection** This is an appropriate time to bring in a globe and talk about the great circles of longitude and the small circles of latitude, and to discuss the latitude and longitude of various places. Many students are surprised to learn that Europe is quite a bit north of the United States. For example, Chicago is at the same latitude as Rome; Anchorage, Alaska, is on about the same latitude as Stockholm, Sweden. But to fly from Anchorage to Stockholm you wouldn't fly due east (or due west) even though they are on the same circle of latitude. The shortest path from Anchorage to Stockholm is along the great-circle route almost over the North Pole.

The terminology of circles extends to spheres. On page 517 the sphere at the right has center O and radius OA. The segments $\overline{OA}$ and $\overline{OB}$ are also called **radii.** Similarly, the **diameter** of a sphere is a number that is twice the radius, while any segment connecting two points of the sphere and containing the center of the sphere is a diameter.

Marble I *by Charles Bell is computer-generated art.*

❶ Small Circles and Great Circles

Two types of intersections can occur with the intersection of a sphere and a plane (see the figures below). The intersection is a point if the plane just touches the sphere; otherwise it is a circle. (You are asked to prove that the intersection is a circle in Question 18.) If the plane contains the center of the sphere, the intersection is called a **great circle** of the sphere. Otherwise, the intersection is called a **small circle.**

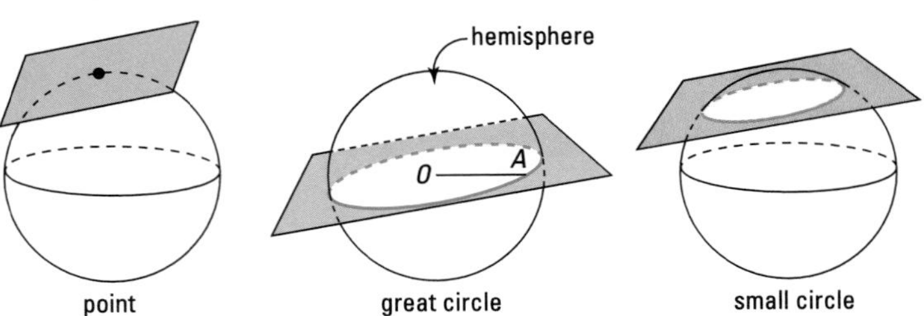

A great circle separates the sphere into two **hemispheres** which may or may not contain the great circle itself.

Earth as a Sphere

Earth is almost a solid sphere. One of its great circles is the equator, which separates the Northern Hemisphere from the Southern Hemisphere. Points on the equator are about 6378 km (or 3963 miles) from the center of Earth. However, Earth has been slightly flattened by its rotation. The North and South poles are about 6357 km (or 3950 miles) from the center of Earth.

Below are two sketches of Earth. The sketch at the left is of Earth as seen from slightly north of the equator. Notice how the oval representing the circle of the equator is widened to give the illusion of looking at it from above. In this sketch the South Pole cannot be seen. The sketch at the right shows Earth as seen from the plane of the equator.

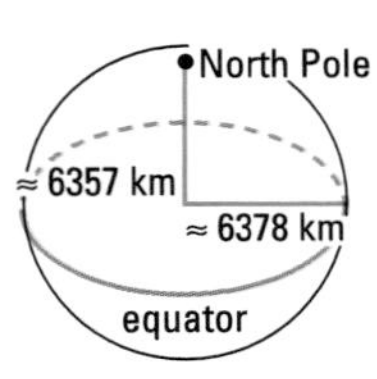

Earth as seen from above the equator and North Pole

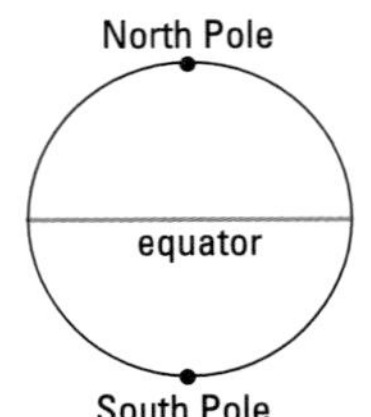

Earth as seen from plane of the equator

Optional Activities

Activity 1 Cooperative Learning
Materials: **Teaching Aid 124**

As a summary for the lesson, you might discuss the possible sections of surfaces students have studied. Have students **work in groups** to complete the chart on **Teaching Aid 124** by identifying the possible sections of spheres, cylinders, pyramids, prisms, and cones.

Surface	Possible Section
Sphere	[small circle, great circle]
Cylinder	[ellipse (includes circle), rectangle, "cut off ellipse"]
Pyramid	[polygons with as many as one more side than the base has edges]
Prism	[polygons with no more than 2 sides more than the number of edges of the base]
Cone	[parabola, hyperbola, ellipse (includes circle)]

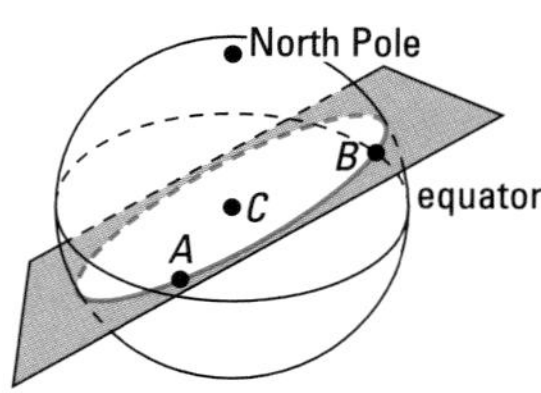

Consider two points A and B on Earth. Since there is exactly one plane that contains three noncollinear points, if A and B are not endpoints of a diameter, there is a single plane containing A, B, and the sphere's center C. The intersection of that plane with the sphere is a great circle. Aircraft and ocean liners often travel along an arc of a great circle because it is the shortest route from A to B. The path they take is called a **great circle route** from A to B.

In 1995, Alexandria, Egypt was a city of over 3.4 million people.

❷ In about 230 B.C., the Greek mathematician Eratosthenes estimated the circumference of Earth in the following way. He noticed that at noon on the summer solstice (around June 21st), the Sun was directly overhead at Syene. He knew that Alexandria was about 5000 stades due north of Syene. (The stade was a Greek unit of length.) In another year, he calculated that at noon on the summer solstice at Alexandria, the Sun was 7.2° away from overhead.

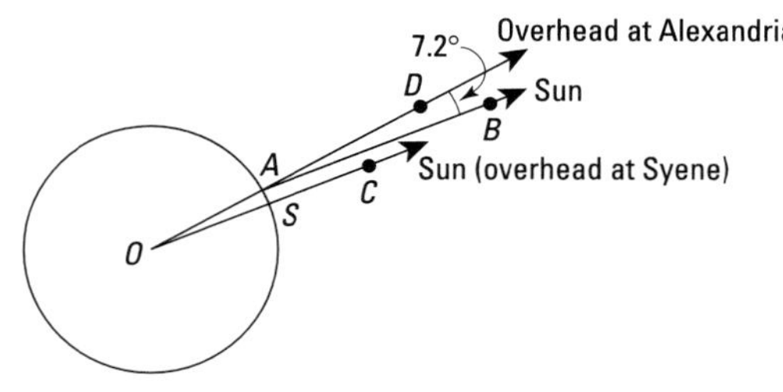
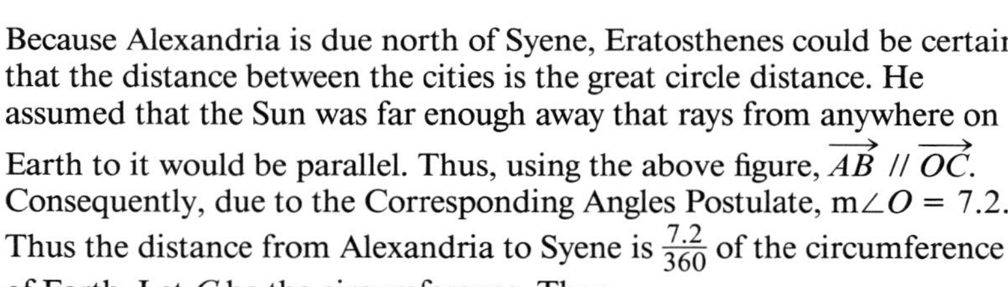

Because Alexandria is due north of Syene, Eratosthenes could be certain that the distance between the cities is the great circle distance. He assumed that the Sun was far enough away that rays from anywhere on Earth to it would be parallel. Thus, using the above figure, $\overrightarrow{AB} \parallel \overrightarrow{OC}$. Consequently, due to the Corresponding Angles Postulate, $m\angle O = 7.2$. Thus the distance from Alexandria to Syene is $\frac{7.2}{360}$ of the circumference of Earth. Let C be the circumference. Then

$$\frac{7.2}{360}C = 5000.$$
$$C = 250{,}000 \text{ stades}$$

We think one stade was equal to about 517 feet. This means that 250,000 stades equals about 24,500 miles. Today, with accurate readings taken from space, we know that the circumference of a north-south great circle is about 24,860 miles. The circumference at the equator is about 24,900 miles. The value obtained by Eratosthenes was within 2% of the actual value.

❷ **History Connection** Your students may recall the "Sieve of Eratosthenes," from their elementary school mathematics, named for this 3rd-century-B.C. mathematician.The "sieve" is a surprisingly simple procedure for identifying prime numbers. With a list of the whole numbers in order in front of the students, cross out the number 1, and then proceed to cross out every second number following the number 2, every third number following the number 3, every fourth number following the number 4, and so on, crossing out every nth number after n. The integers that remain after this process, beginning with 2, are prime.

When students try to apply to spheres terminology they have learned earlier in this chapter, explain that a sphere is *not* a cylindric or conic shape. The terminology of circles more properly applies. Students often say "large circle" instead of *great circle,* not realizing that *great circle* is a technical term.

Have students record the results of **Activities 1 and 2** for use with **Questions 9 and 10** on page 522.

As a summary of the lesson, you might use Activity 1 in *Optional Activities* on page 518.

Optional Activities

Activity 2 Using Physical Models
Materials: Clear models of 3-dimensional shapes, sand

A good way to demonstrate plane sections of 3-dimensional figures is to put sand into clear models of cones, pyramids, boxes, and cylinders. Give such models to groups of students. Tilt the models so that the sand forms the plane section. It is not difficult to see what shape is formed. Then students should try to draw the figure and its section.

Additional Examples

You might want to use these additional examples when discussing the lesson.

1. If points A and B are the endpoints of a diameter of a sphere, why is there more than one great circle through them? **The great circle must contain A, B, and the center of the sphere, but these points are collinear, and there are many planes which contain a given line.**

2a. Can two different great circles of a sphere lie in parallel noncoincident planes? **No; each plane must contain the center of the sphere.**

b. Can two different small circles of a sphere be in parallel planes? **Yes; examples are the circles of latitude on Earth.**

Plane Sections

A great circle is an example of a *plane section* of a figure.

> **Definition**
> A **plane section** of a three-dimensional figure is the intersection of that figure with a plane.

Biologists use plane sections of body tissue to study organs and blood. These sections are thin enough so that light from a microscope can shine through them. Doctors use special scanners to take x-rays of plane sections of the human body for diagnostic purposes. In geometry, two questions about plane sections arise naturally: What are the plane sections of a figure? How can plane sections be sketched?

We have already answered these questions for a sphere. For a solid prism or cylinder, there are different plane sections, depending on whether the intersecting plane

1. is parallel to the bases,
2. is not parallel to and does not intersect a base or bases, or
3. intersects one or both bases.

If the intersecting plane is parallel to the bases, then the section is a region congruent to the bases.

plane sections // to bases

Suppose the intersecting plane is not parallel to and does not intersect the bases. For a prism, the section will be a polygonal region of the same number of sides but not congruent to the base. For a cylinder, the section will be an *ellipse* and its interior.

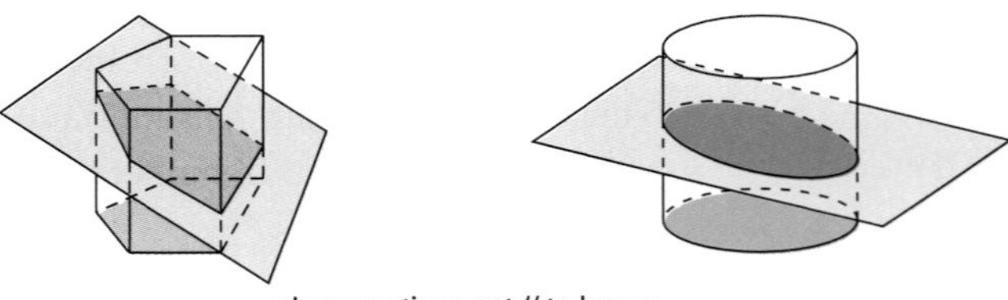

plane sections not // to bases

Adapting to Individual Needs

Extra Help

Be sure students understand the distinction between *a* diameter and *the* diameter of a sphere. Stress that any given sphere has only one *number* that is called *the diameter.* But there are an infinite number of segments having length equal to this number. Each of these segments is a diameter.

English Language Development

Before students with limited English proficiency read this lesson, you might want to discuss the meaning of each of the following terms: *ellipse, parabola,* and *hyperbola.*

When a plane intersects a base as well as lateral faces, a variety of sections are possible. An example of a plane intersecting a solid pentagonal prism is shown below at the left. The section is a triangle. An example of a plane intersecting a solid cylinder is shown at the right. The section is a rectangle.

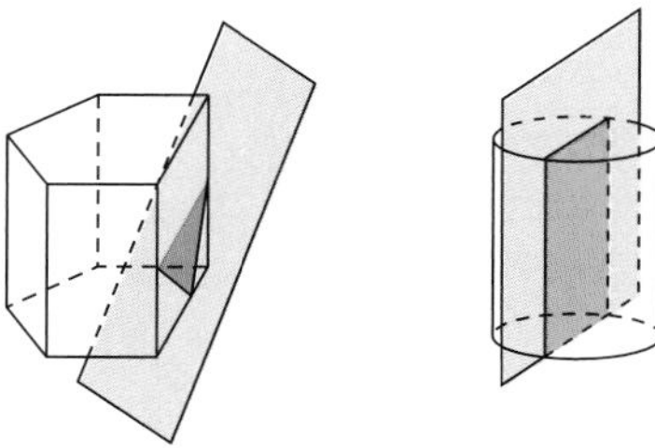

plane sections intersecting one or both bases

(Act. 1)

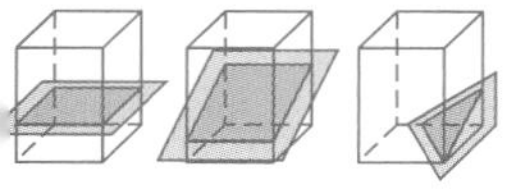

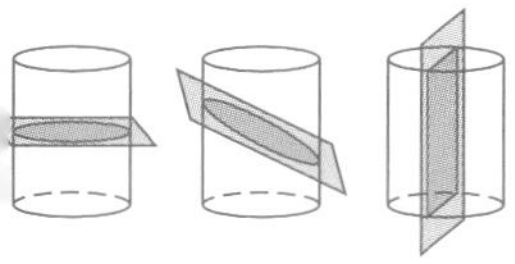

Activity 1

Without tracing, make drawings like the three plane sections of prisms shown above and on page 520, but with a *solid right quadrangular prism* (one with a quadrilateral base). See left.

(Act. 2)

Activity 2

Without tracing, make drawings like the three plane sections of cylinders shown above and on page 520. See left.

Plane Sections of Pyramids and Cones

For pyramids and cones, sections parallel to the base have shapes similar to the base, but they are smaller. You can sketch them by drawing segments or arcs parallel to the base.

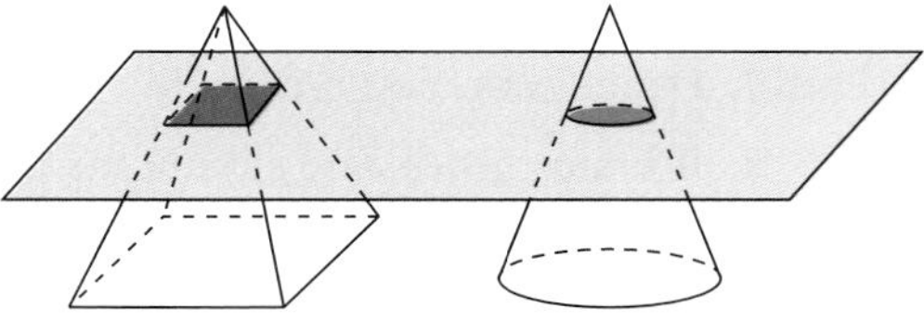

Conic Sections

Notice the figures at the top of page 522. At the far left are two right cones with the same axis, formed by rotating a line intersecting the axis about that axis. The plane sections formed are called the **conic sections.** The conic sections describe orbits of planets and paths of balls and rockets. Lenses and reflectors with these shapes have focusing properties used for long-range navigation (LORAN), telescopes, headlights, satellite dishes, flashlights, and whispering chambers. You are certain to study them in other mathematics courses.

Adapting to Individual Needs

Challenge

Two spheres have radii 20 cm and 12 cm. The spheres intersect so that the distance between their centers is 24 cm.

1. What figure represents the intersection of the two spheres? [circle]
2. What is the length of the intersection of the two spheres? [62.69 cm]

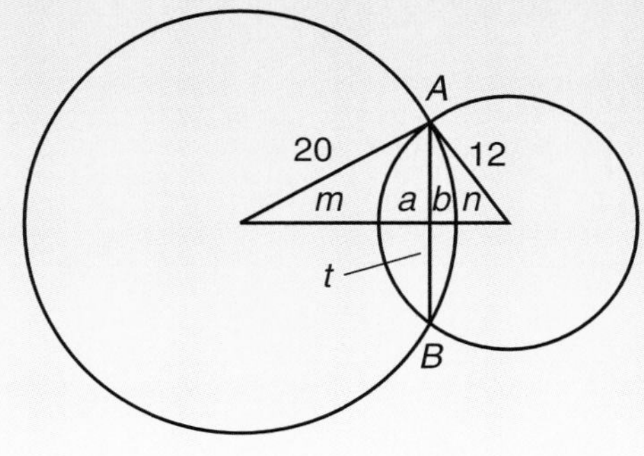

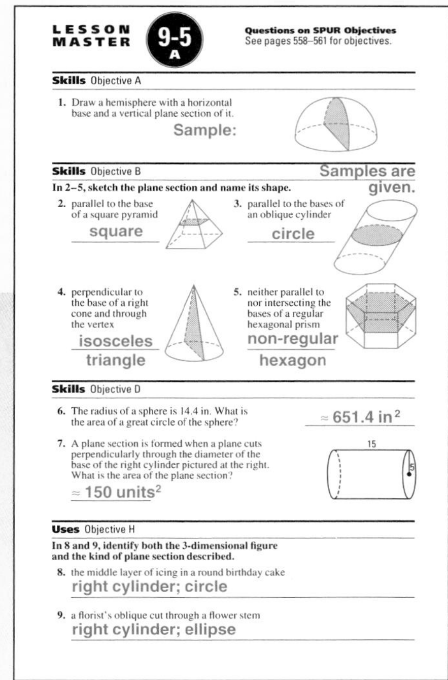

LESSON MASTER 9-5 A

Questions on SPUR Objectives
See pages 558–561 for objectives.

Skills Objective A

1. Draw a hemisphere with a horizontal base and a vertical plane section of it.
Sample:

Skills Objective B — Samples are given.

In 2–5, sketch the plane section and name its shape.

2. parallel to the base of a square pyramid — square
3. parallel to the bases of an oblique cylinder — circle
4. perpendicular to the base of a right cone and through the vertex — isosceles triangle
5. neither parallel to nor intersecting the bases of a regular hexagonal prism — non-regular hexagon

Skills Objective D

6. The radius of a sphere is 14.4 in. What is the area of a great circle of the sphere? ≈ 651.4 in^2
7. A plane section is formed when a plane cuts perpendicularly through the diameter of the base of the right cylinder pictured at the right. What is the area of the plane section? ≈ 150 units^2

15
5

Uses Objective H

In 8 and 9, identify both the 3-dimensional figure and the kind of plane section described.

8. the middle layer of icing in a round birthday cake — right cylinder; circle
9. a florist's oblique cut through a flower stem — right cylinder; ellipse

Notes on Questions

Questions 11, 13–15, 20 Drawing 3-dimensional figures can be quite difficult for some students. Suggest that they review the drawing algorithms in Lessons 9-3 and 9-4.

Question 19 The proof is for planes whose distance from the center is greater than zero but less than the radius of the sphere. Emphasize that points O, P, and A are constants; point X is a variable which may be replaced by any point in the intersection of the plane and the sphere.

(Notes on Questions continue on page 524.)

Additional Answers

13a. Sample:

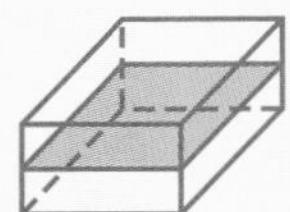

b. Sample:

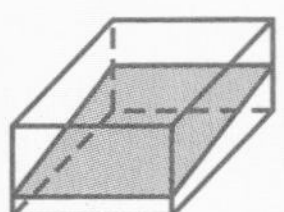

c. Part a is a rectangle, part b is a rectangle.

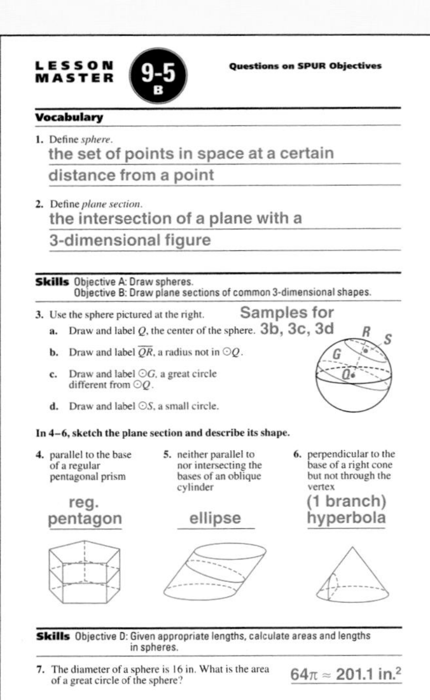

LESSON MASTER 9-5 B Questions on SPUR Objectives

Vocabulary

1. Define *sphere*. the set of points in space at a certain distance from a point

2. Define *plane section*. the intersection of a plane with a 3-dimensional figure

Skills Objective A: Draw spheres. Objective B: Draw plane sections of common 3-dimensional shapes.

3. Use the sphere pictured at the right. Samples for 3b, 3c, 3d
   a. Draw and label Q, the center of the sphere.
   b. Draw and label $\overline{QR}$, a radius not in $\odot Q$.
   c. Draw and label $\odot G$, a great circle different from $\odot Q$.
   d. Draw and label $\odot S$, a small circle.

In 4–6, sketch the plane section and describe its shape.

4. parallel to the base of a regular pentagonal prism — reg. pentagon
5. neither parallel to nor intersecting the bases of an oblique cylinder — ellipse
6. perpendicular to the base of a right cone but not through the vertex — (1 branch) hyperbola

Skills Objective D: Given appropriate lengths, calculate areas and lengths in spheres.

7. The diameter of a sphere is 16 in. What is the area of a great circle of the sphere? $64\pi \approx 201.1$ in.^{2}

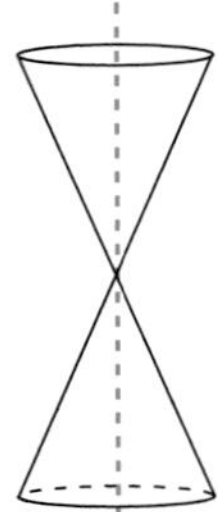

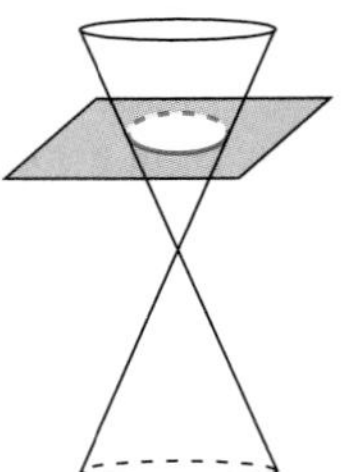

circle (plane ⊥ to axis)

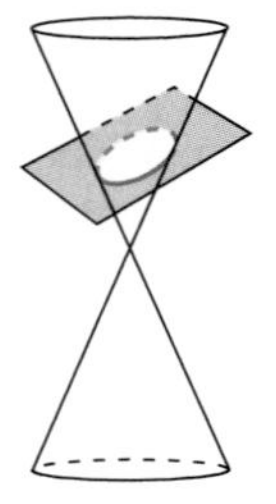

ellipse (plane not ⊥ to axis, intersecting only one cone)

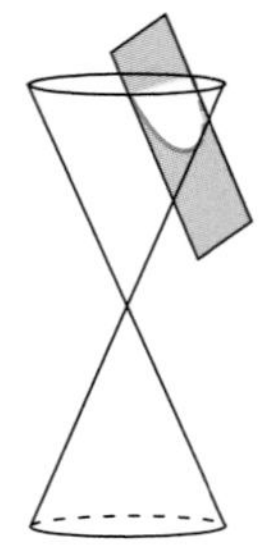

parabola (plane // to edge)

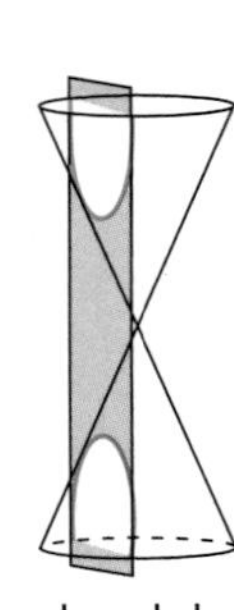

hyperbola (plane intersectin both cones)

QUESTIONS

Covering the Reading

1. Define *sphere*.
   A sphere is the set of all points in space at a fixed distance from a point.
2. How does the definition of sphere differ from the definition of circle? See left.
3. The intersection of a plane and a sphere is either a single point or a(n) __?__. circle
4. *Multiple choice.* If you think of Earth as a sphere, then the equator is c
   (a) a diameter. (b) a small circle.
   (c) a great circle. (d) a chord.
5. a. What is the length of a diameter of Earth at the equator?
   b. What is the length of a diameter of Earth connecting the poles?
   c. Why are these different numbers? See left.
   a) 12,756 km or 7926 mi b) 12,714 km or 7900 mi
6. What is meant by a *great circle route*? A route between two points on Earth's surface along one of its great circles.
7. Define *plane section*. See left.
8. If Eratosthenes were alive in the United States today, he could repeat his calculation of the circumference of Earth. Wichita, Kansas, is 345 miles due north of Fort Worth, Texas. At a given moment, the sun is 5° lower in the sky in Wichita than Fort Worth. From this information, what estimate would Eratosthenes obtain for the Earth's circumference?
   24,840 miles
9. Show your drawings from Activity 1. See page 521.
10. Show your drawings from Activity 2. See page 521.
11. a. Draw a right square pyramid and a plane section parallel to its base. See left.
    b. How do the section and the base compare?
    The plane section is also a square, but smaller.
12. a. Name the four types of conic sections. a, b) See left.
    b. Name three situations where conic sections are used.

2) A circle is the set of all points in a plane (not space) at a fixed distance from a point.

5c) The Earth has been flattened slightly at its poles because of its rotation.

7) A plane section of a three-dimensional figure is the intersection of that figure with a plane.

11a)

12a) circle, ellipse, parabola, hyperbola
b) Sample: orbits of planets, telescopes, headlights

Applying the Mathematics

In 13–15, copy the figure shown. See margin.
a. Sketch a plane section parallel to the base(s).
b. Sketch a plane section not parallel to and not intersecting the base(s).
c. Name the shape of each plane section.

13.
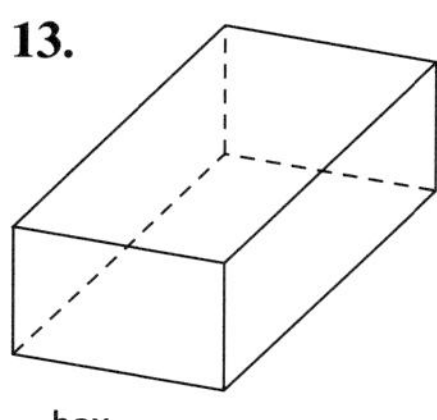

14.
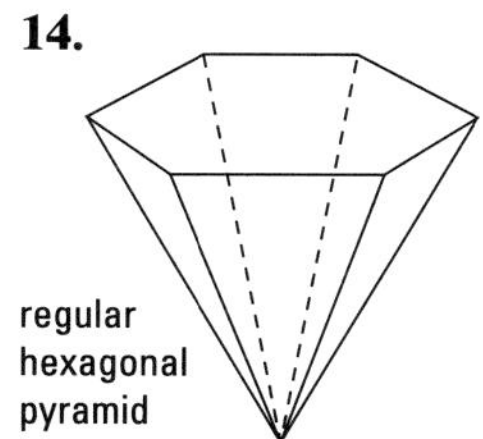

15.
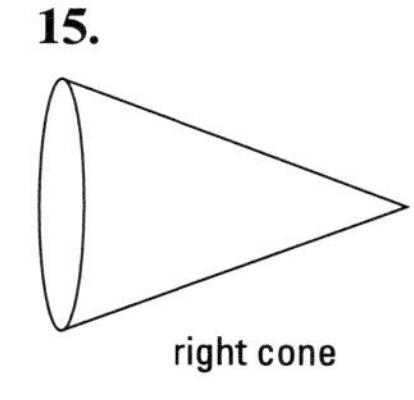

16. Slicing a grapefruit with a knife is a model for a plane intersecting a solid sphere. Describe the possible plane sections. circular region

In 17 and 18, tell which 3-dimensional geometric figure most resembles each real-world object. Distinguish solids from surfaces.

17. table tennis ball sphere

18. peach solid sphere

19. Here is a proof that the intersection of a sphere and a plane not through its center is a circle. It is given that sphere O and plane M intersect in the curve as shown below. Fill in the missing justifications. See left.

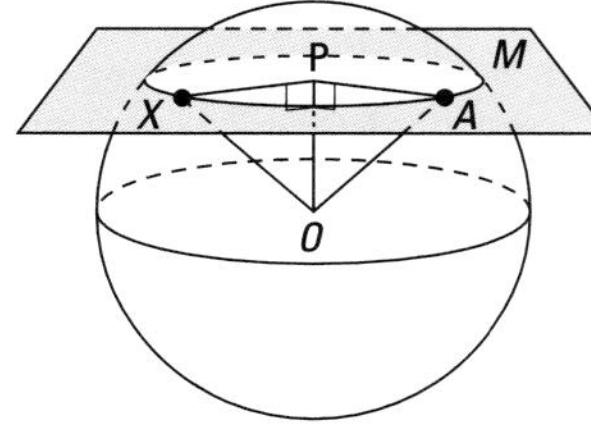

Argument:
Let P be the foot of the $\perp$ from point O to plane M. Let A and X be two points on the intersection. Then, by definition of a line perpendicular to a plane, $\overline{OP} \perp \overline{PA}$ and $\overline{OP} \perp \overline{PX}$. $\overline{OP} \cong \overline{OP}$ because of the __a.__ and $\overline{OA} \cong \overline{OX}$ because __b.__. So $\triangle OPX \cong \triangle OPA$ by __c.__.

Thus, due to __d.__, $PX = PA$. Thus any point X on the intersection lies at the same distance from P as A does. So by the definition of circle, the intersection of sphere O and plane M is the circle with center P and radius PA.

9a) Reflexive Property of Congruence
b) definition of sphere
c) HL Congruence Theorem
d) CPCF Theorem

Follow-up for Lesson 9-5

Practice

For more questions on SPUR Objectives, use **Lesson Master 9-5A** (shown on page 521) or **Lesson Master 9-5B** (shown on pages 522–523).

Assessment

Oral Communication Choose one type of solid figure discussed in this chapter. Have students find as many different cross sections of the figure as possible. Repeat this process until all students have had a chance to respond. [Allow any reasonable drawings, even if all possibilities are not discovered.]

(Follow-up continues on page 524.)

Additional Answers
14a. Sample:

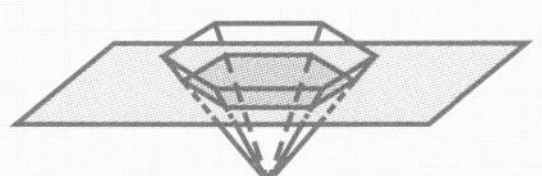

b. Sample:

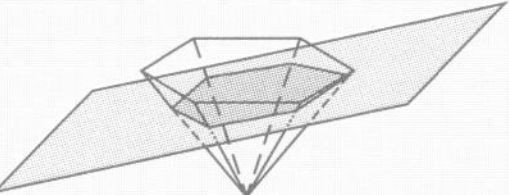

c. Part a is a regular hexagon, and part b is a nonregular hexagon.

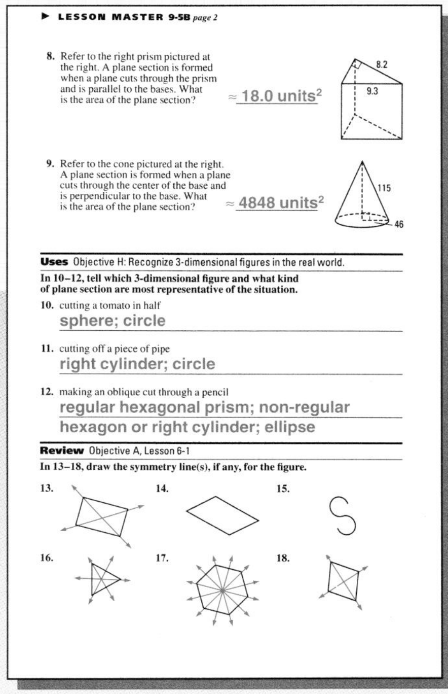

▶ **LESSON MASTER 9-5B** *page 2*

8. Refer to the right prism pictured at the right. A plane section is formed when a plane cuts through the prism and is parallel to the bases. What is the area of the plane section? ≈ 18.0 units²

8.2
9.3

9. Refer to the cone pictured at the right. A plane section is formed when a plane cuts through the center of the base and is perpendicular to the base. What is the area of the plane section? ≈ 4848 units²

115
46

Uses Objective H: Recognize 3-dimensional figures in the real world.

In 10–12, tell which 3-dimensional figure and what kind of plane section are most representative of the situation.

10. cutting a tomato in half
sphere; circle

11. cutting off a piece of pipe
right cylinder; circle

12. making an oblique cut through a pencil
regular hexagonal prism; non-regular hexagon or right cylinder; ellipse

Review Objective A, Lesson 6-1

In 13–18, draw the symmetry line(s), if any, for the figure.

13. **14.** **15.** S

16. **17.** **18.**

Additional Answers, continued
15a. Sample:

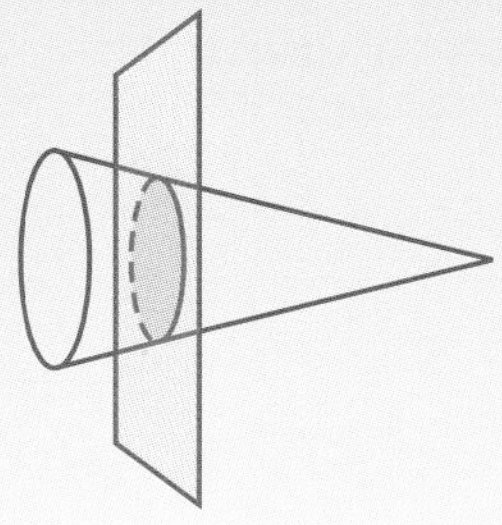

b. Sample:

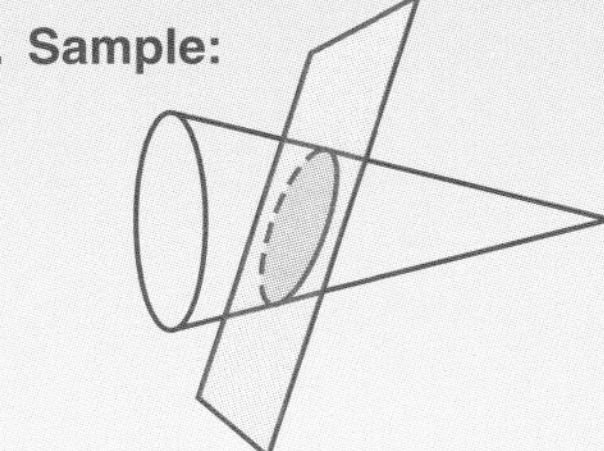

c. Part a is a circle and part b is a non-circular ellipse.

Extension

Here is a famous puzzle problem. The equator of the earth is approximately 6378 kilometers long. Imagine a snug belt around the equator of the earth. Its length is 6378 kilometers. Suppose it is cut and a piece 5 meters long is added. The new belt is 6378.005 kilometers long. It is no longer snug. Suppose it is the same distance away from the earth everywhere. Is it loose enough to slip a piece of paper under it? Could you put your hand under it? Could you crawl under it? [The circumference of the original circle is immaterial. If 5 meters is added to any circumference, then $\frac{5}{\pi}$ meters is added to the diameter; that is, almost 80 cm (≈ 31.5 inches) will be added to the radius, enough for a person to crawl under.]

Projects Update Project 2, *Structures,* Project 4, *Geometry on a Sphere,* and Project 7, *Plane Sections of a Cube,* on pages 552–553, relate to the content of this lesson.

Notes on Questions

Question 25 This question should be discussed in preparation for the next lesson.

Question 28 You might ask the following question: In what direction should you travel to get to South America from North America? [Southeast; South America lies almost entirely east of the east coast of the United States.]

20) Sample:

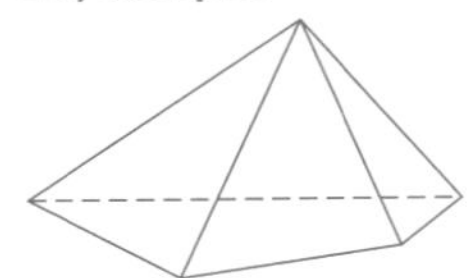

26a) Sample:

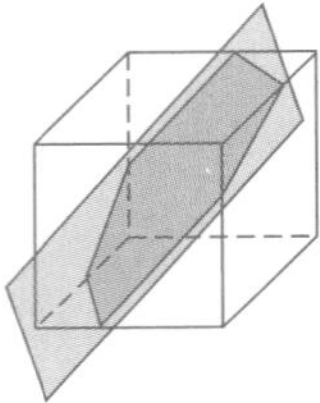

27a) Sample: England
b) Pacific
c) Eastern and Western hemispheres
d) It divides Earth into east and west hemispheres for purposes of time and dates.

Review

20. A quadrangular pyramid has a quadrilateral as its base. Draw a quadrangular pyramid. *(Lesson 9-4)* See left.

21. In the regular square pyramid at the right, $\overline{AX}$ is the height and F is the midpoint of $\overline{BC}$. If $AX = 15$ and $CD = 16$, find

a. XF. 8 units

b. Area($\triangle ABC$). *(Lessons 8-4, 9-4)* 136 units²

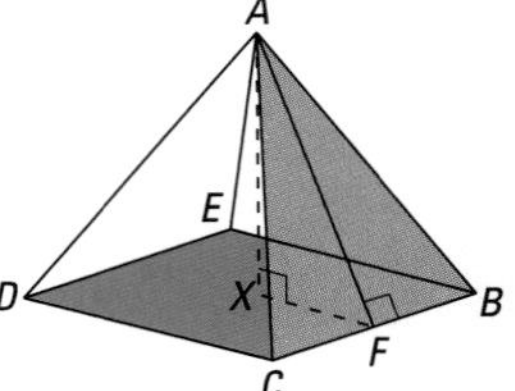

In 22 and 23, use the box at the right. $AB = 10$, $AE = 6$, and $AD = 8$. *(Lessons 8-2, 9-3)*

22. Find each value. (Some segments are not drawn.)

a. CD 10 units b. DE 10 units c. CE $\sqrt{200} \approx 14.14$ units

23. Find the sum of the areas of the six faces. 376 units²

24. Use the information in this lesson to give the circumference of the equator: **a.** to the nearest 100 miles **b.** to the nearest 100 kilometers. *(Lesson 8-7)* a) 24,900 mi b) 40,100 km

25. Describe the location of the reflection image of a point P over a line ℓ when P is not on ℓ. *(Lesson 4-1)* The point Q is the reflection image of P over a line ℓ when P is not on ℓ if and only if ℓ is the perpendicular bisector of $\overline{PQ}$.

Exploration

26. a. It is possible for a plane section of a cube to be a hexagon. Draw a cube or make a model to demonstrate how this is possible. See left.

b. Is it possible for a plane section of a cube to be a pentagon? Yes

c. Is it possible for a plane section of a cube to be a triangle? Yes

d. Is it possible for a plane section of a cube to be a quadrilateral that is not a parallelogram? Yes

27. On Earth, the union of the prime meridian and International Date Line approximates a great circle containing the North and South Poles. See left.

a. Name a country through which the prime meridian passes.

b. Name the ocean that contains the International Date Line.

c. Into what hemispheres does this great circle separate Earth?

d. What is the purpose of this circle?

28. What point on Earth is opposite where you live? Answers may vary.

Setting Up Lesson 9-6

Go over **Question 25** in this lesson. It reviews the concept of reflection that will be extended to three dimensions in the next lesson.

LESSON

9-6

Reflection Symmetry in Space

El Castillo de la Maya. *This great pyramid is part of the ruins of the ancient Mayan city Chichén Itzá located in present-day Yucatan, Mexico. This pyramid has four symmetry planes.*

Reflections in Space

The properties of reflections in two dimensions carry over to three dimensions. For example, when you look in a mirror, the mirror appears to lie halfway between you and your image. Also, an imaginary line from the tip of your nose to its image will always be perpendicular to the mirror. So, as with 2-dimensional figures, reflection symmetry in 3-dimensional figures is a powerful way of developing their properties.

In general, a plane M is the **perpendicular bisector** of a segment $\overline{AB}$ if and only if $M \perp \overline{AB}$ and M contains the midpoint of $\overline{AB}$. This enables 3-dimensional reflections (over planes) to have the same defining condition as their 2-dimensional counterparts (over lines).

Definition:
For a point P which is not on a plane M, the **reflection image of P over M** is the point Q if and only if M is the perpendicular bisector of $\overline{PQ}$. For a point P on a plane M, the **reflection image of P over M** is P itself.

Lesson 9-6

Objectives

G Determine symmetry planes in 3-dimensional figures.

Resources

From the ***Teacher's Resource File***
- Lesson Master 9-6A or 9-6B
- Answer Master 9-6
- Teaching Aid 119: Warm-up

Additional Resources
- Visual for Teaching Aid 119

Teaching Lesson 9-6

Warm-up

How many lines of symmetry does each figure have?

1. A square 4
2. An equilateral triangle 3
3. A rectangle that is not a square 2
4. A circle Infinitely many

Lesson 9-6 Overview

Broad Goals This lesson introduces the idea of reflections in space and the related idea of reflection symmetry in space.

Perspective In this book, the 3-dimensional idea of reflection in space is an extension of the 2-dimensional idea discussed in detail earlier. Intuitively, the order is the reverse. The 2-dimensional reflection gets its name from the 3-dimensional situations with which we are all familiar, namely, looking at images in a plane mirror. So there is a sense in which this lesson brings the idea back to where it began. It is important for students to realize that the reflection images they see in actual mirrors can be described mathematically.

The same can be said for the idea of symmetry. We think of symmetry in houses, bodies, animals, and many other animate and inanimate objects. Three-dimensional symmetry is thus more familiar than its 2-dimensional counterpart.

In this chapter, many definitions of 3-dimensional ideas are analogous to those in two dimensions. It is not surprising, therefore, that 3-dimensional reflections and congruence in three dimensions possess many of the same properties as their

(Overview continues on page 526.)

Notes on Reading

❶ This lesson can be used to review all the space figures studied so far. They are listed below with the minimum number of symmetry planes in parentheses: prism (0), right prism (1), regular prism whose base is an n-gon ($n + 1$), cylinder (1), right cylinder (1 parallel to bases, infinitely many perpendicular), pyramid (0), regular pyramid whose base is an n-gon (n), cone (0), right cone (infinitely many, all containing the axis), sphere (infinitely many, all containing the center).

Because so many of the properties in two dimensions carry over into three dimensions, this is an appropriate time to review the properties of reflections and the definition of congruent figures. Suggest that students think of the properties in two dimensions along with their analogues in three dimensions as they are reading the lesson.

❷ **Science Connection** Crystals usually form when a supersaturated solution, one which can no longer retain dissolved material, "throws" a precipitate. The precipitate consists of millions of cells that cluster in a geometric pattern, thus forming the unique, symmetrical solid known as a crystal. Salt, for instance, is made up of millions of cubic cells which, when bonded together form visible crystals of roughly cubic shape. Gemstones and ice also display this natural growth from a tiny "seed" to visible versions of the same shape. Crystals are rarely perfect, however. Defects caused by impurities, internal mutations, or other irregularities make all sorts of crystal variants possible. Crystallography is the science of describing, classifying, and measuring the geometric forms of crystals.

Reflections over planes preserve the same properties as their 2-dimensional relatives: angle measure, betweenness, collinearity, and distance. So the definition of congruence in the plane can be extended to three dimensions.

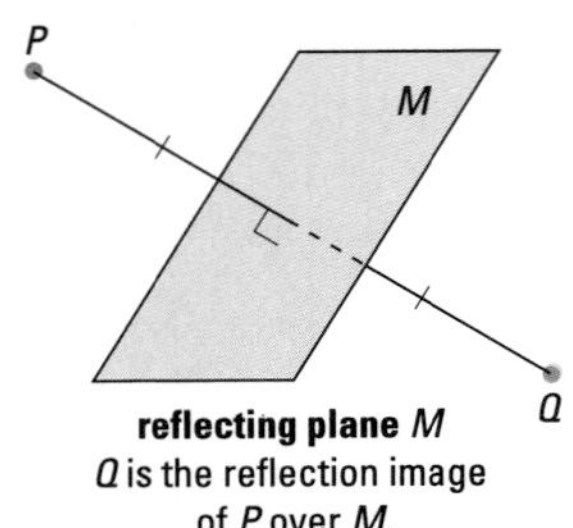

reflecting plane M
Q is the reflection image of P over M.

> **Definition**
> Two three-dimensional figures F and G are **congruent figures** if and only if G is the image of F under a reflection or composite of reflections.

As in two dimensions, reflections switch orientation. Figures with the same orientation are **directly congruent.** Figures with different orientation are **oppositely congruent.** You are oppositely congruent to your image in a mirror.

❶ Symmetry Planes

A 2-dimensional figure is reflection-symmetric if and only if it coincides with its image under some reflection. There is a corresponding definition for three dimensions.

> **Definition**
> A three-dimensional figure F is a **reflection-symmetric figure** if and only if there is a plane M (the **symmetry plane**) such that $r_M(F) = F$.

❷ Both nonliving and living natural objects possess reflection symmetry. Symmetry allows rock collectors, chemists, and geologists to identify types of crystals. In animals, reflection symmetry is sometimes called **bilateral symmetry.**

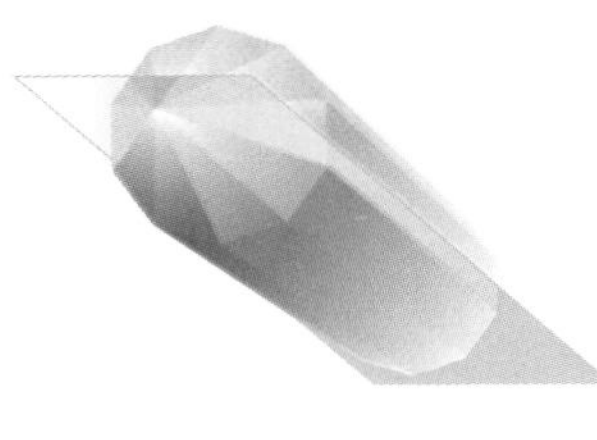

crystal

beetle

Lesson 9-6 Overview, continued

2-dimensional counterparts. For instance, reflections in space have the A-B-C-D properties, the Flip-Flop Theorem holds, congruence is transitive, and the CPCF Theorem is true.

Other properties have analogues also. For instance, if M is a plane and F is a figure such that $r_M(F) = F$, then the points of F which are their own images are exactly the points of intersection of F with the plane M.

Optional Activities

After discussing this lesson, you might have students examine models and/or drawings from the previous lessons and describe the symmetry of each.

Adapting to Individual Needs

Extra Help

Students may need to be reminded that the drawings of planes, including symmetry planes, represent planes that extend infinitely. Point out that the shaded portions of the planes represent the part of the plane that is within the interior of the given figure. Sometimes an additional external portion of the plane is drawn, and sometimes only the interior (shaded) portion is shown.

The body surfaces of most people have approximate bilateral symmetry. The right side and left side are reflection images of each other over the plane that goes through the middle of the body from head to toe. Note that you cannot slide or turn a right hand onto a left hand, because they have different orientation.

Space figures may have any number of symmetry planes, from zero to infinitely many. The right cylinder below at the left has infinitely many vertical symmetry planes (any plane containing $\overline{PQ}$) and one horizontal symmetry plane. The regular triangular pyramid at the right has exactly three symmetry planes, one of which is drawn.

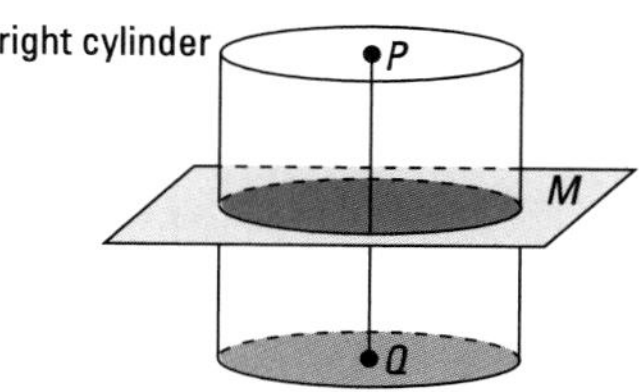

M is the ⊥ bisector of $\overline{PQ}$.

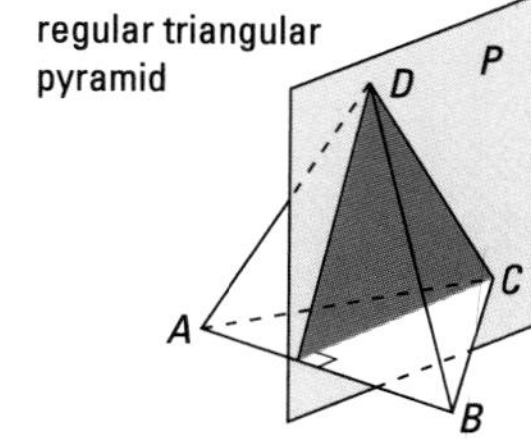

P is the ⊥ bisector of $\overline{AB}$.

Any right prism will have as many symmetry planes as the base has symmetry lines, plus an additional symmetry plane parallel to the bases. A right pyramid has as many symmetry planes as the base has symmetry lines. Regular prisms and regular pyramids have the most symmetry planes for their shapes.

Example

Determine the number of symmetry planes for a common cardboard box, like that shown here. Sketch one of the symmetry planes.

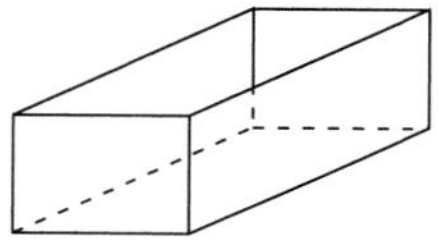

Solution

A box is a right rectangular prism, so the box has one symmetry plane for each symmetry line of its base, plus an additional plane parallel to the bases.

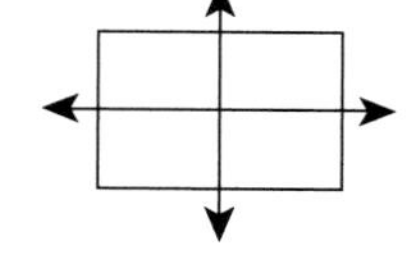

One symmetry plane is shown below.

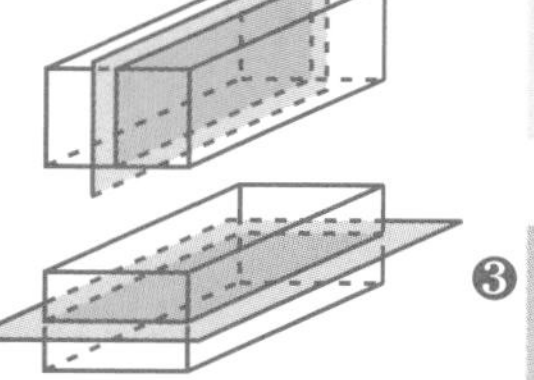

❸ **Activity**

Trace the box above. Sketch the other two symmetry planes. See left.

❸ Drawing symmetry planes is difficult for students. Many of them have never drawn geometric figures as complicated as these. Give plaudits for good efforts.

Have students record the results of the **Activity** for use with **Question 8** on page 528.

Additional Examples

1. Suppose two congruent regular square pyramids are placed so their square bases coincide. The result is an octahedron. Determine the number of symmetry planes for the octahedron. 5, the planes perpendicular to the base through the symmetry lines of the square and the plane containing the coinciding bases

2a. How many symmetry planes does a typical circular cake have? Infinitely many

b. Describe their locations. Any vertical plane through the center of the base and one horizontal plane halfway between its bases

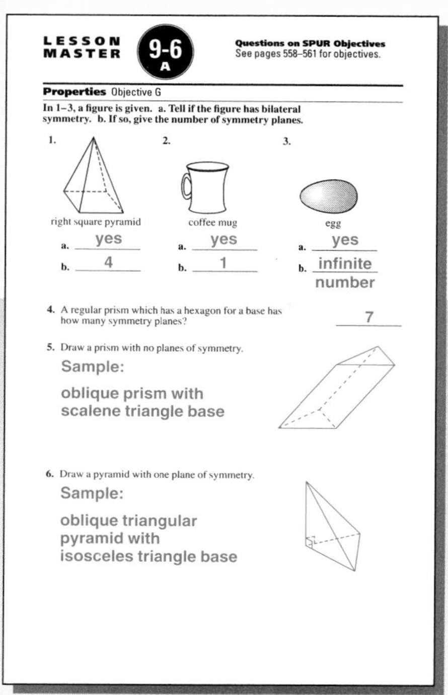
LESSON MASTER 9-6 A Questions on SPUR Objectives See pages 558–561 for objectives.

Properties Objective G

In 1–3, a figure is given. a. Tell if the figure has bilateral symmetry. b. If so, give the number of symmetry planes.

1. right square pyramid	2. coffee mug	3. egg
a. yes	a. yes	a. yes
b. 4	b. 1	b. infinite number

4. A regular prism which has a hexagon for a base has how many symmetry planes? 7

5. Draw a prism with no planes of symmetry. Sample: oblique prism with scalene triangle base

6. Draw a pyramid with one plane of symmetry. Sample: oblique triangular pyramid with isosceles triangle base

Adapting to Individual Needs

Challenge

Have students identify a geometric figure with the given property.

1. No planes of symmetry [Sample: An oblique scalene triangular prism]
2. Exactly one plane of symmetry [Sample: A right prism whose base has no line of symmetry]
3. Exactly two planes of symmetry [Sample: A right prism whose base is a kite (but not a rhombus)]
4. Exactly three planes of symmetry [Sample: A right cylindric solid whose base is an ellipse]
5. Exactly four planes of symmetry [Sample: A right prism whose base is an equilateral triangle]
6. More than four, but not an infinite number of, planes of symmetry [Sample: A right prism whose base is a regular hexagon]

Notes on Questions

Question 3 Error Alert Students may think there are nine symmetry planes, but that is true only if the box has all faces congruent, namely, if it is a cube. See **Question 9.**

Questions 4–7 Point out to students that if a figure has no symmetry lines in two dimensions, then solids with plane sections of those shapes will not have symmetry planes, except for right cylindric shapes which will have one symmetry plane. For instance, the parallelepiped seems to students to be symmetric, but just as with the parallelogram, it has point symmetry, not reflection symmetry. These are good questions to discuss in small groups.

Question 9 The difference between the cube and the box of the **Example** in the lesson is that the cube has symmetry planes through the parallel diagonals of opposite faces. With two diagonals each, there are six additional symmetry planes.

Question 12 If a prism has more than one symmetry plane, then its base must have reflection symmetry.

(Notes on Questions continue on page 530.)

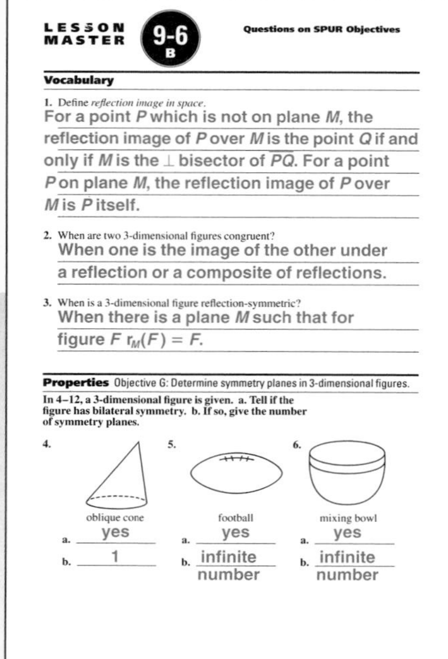
LESSON MASTER 9-6 B Questions on SPUR Objectives

Vocabulary

1. Define *reflection image in space.*
For a point P which is not on plane M, the reflection image of P over M is the point Q if and only if M is the ⊥ bisector of $\overline{PQ}$. For a point P on plane M, the reflection image of P over M is P itself.

2. When are two 3-dimensional figures congruent?
When one is the image of the other under a reflection or a composite of reflections.

3. When is a 3-dimensional figure reflection-symmetric?
When there is a plane M such that for figure F $r_M(F) = F$.

Properties Objective G: Determine symmetry planes in 3-dimensional figures.

In 4–12, a 3-dimensional figure is given. a. Tell if the figure has bilateral symmetry. b. If so, give the number of symmetry planes.

4. oblique cone a. yes b. 1
5. football a. yes b. infinite number
6. mixing bowl a. yes b. infinite number

4a) Yes
b) infinitely many

5a) Yes
b) 4

6a) Yes
b) infinitely many

7a) Yes
b) 1

10a) Sample:

A, D, C, E, B

b) a triangular region with vertices A, D, and E, the midpoint of $\overline{BC}$.

12) Yes. Any right prism with a base that is not reflection-symmetric has exactly one plane of symmetry. Sample:

QUESTIONS

Covering the Reading

1. What properties of a figure are preserved by reflections in space? angle measure, betweenness, collinearity, and distance

2. *Multiple choice.* If a human stands upright, the symmetry plane is:
(a) // to the ground about waist high.
(b) ⊥ to the ground, halfway between the front and back.
(c) ⊥ to the ground, halfway between right and left sides. c

3. How many symmetry planes does a box have? three

In 4–7, a figure is given. **a.** Tell if the figure has reflection symmetry. **b.** Indicate the number of symmetry planes. See left.

4. 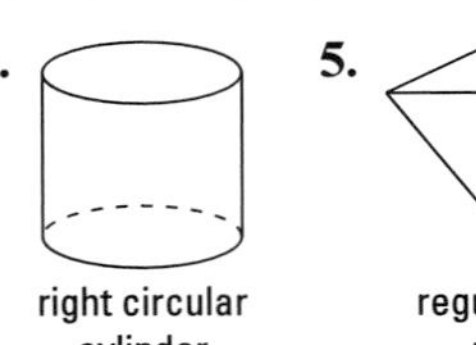
right circular cylinder

5. 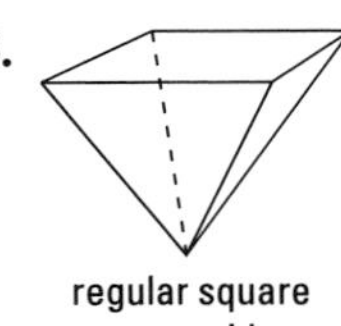
regular square pyramid

6. 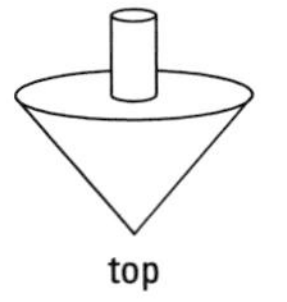
top

7. 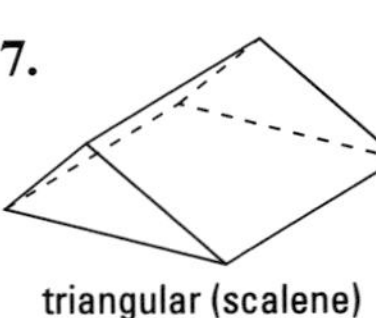
triangular (scalene) prism

8. Display your drawings from the Activity in this lesson. See page 527.

9. How many symmetry planes does a cube have? nine

Applying the Mathematics

10. A symmetry plane of a regular triangular pyramid is drawn in this lesson. See left.
a. Draw this pyramid with another of its symmetry planes.
b. Describe the plane section formed by your symmetry plane.

11. Draw the symmetry plane(s) of this oblique cylinder. See below.

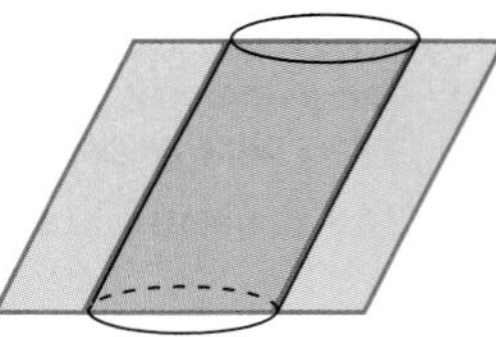

12. Is it possible for a prism to have only one plane of symmetry? Explain why or why not, and sketch one if it is possible. See left.

13. *True or false.* The cross section formed by any symmetry plane of a regular prism is a parallelogram. Explain your answer. False. A symmetry plane parallel to the bases will have a cross section congruent to the bases.

Review

In 14 and 15, copy the figure shown. b, c) See margin.
a. Sketch a plane section parallel to the base.
b. Sketch a plane section not parallel to and not intersecting the base(s).
c. Name the shape of each section. *(Lesson 9-5)*

The cat's meow. *This pet carrier in the shape of a hexagonal prism provides creature comforts for the cat that loves to travel. How many symmetry planes does it have?* 2

14.

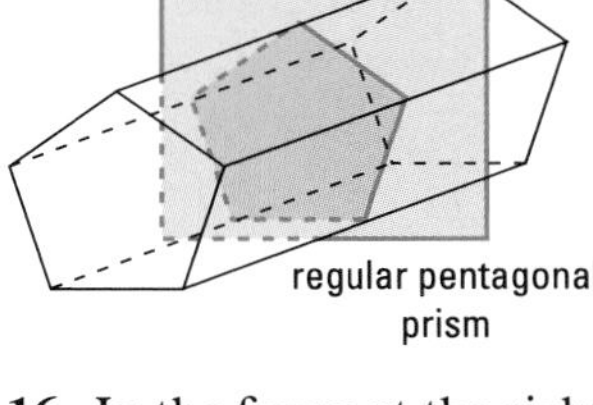

15.

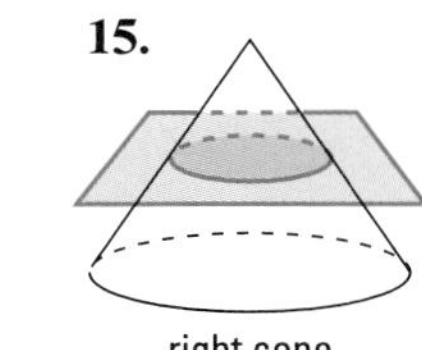

16. In the figure at the right, *FOUR* is a square. *Z* is not in the plane of *FOUR*.
a. Identify the figure. square pyramid
b. Name its base. *FOUR*
c. Name its vertex. *Z*
d. Name all the lateral edges. See left.
e. Name all of its faces. *(Lesson 9-4)* See left.

Z R U F O

17. A regular square pyramid has a slant height of 13 and a base with side length 10.

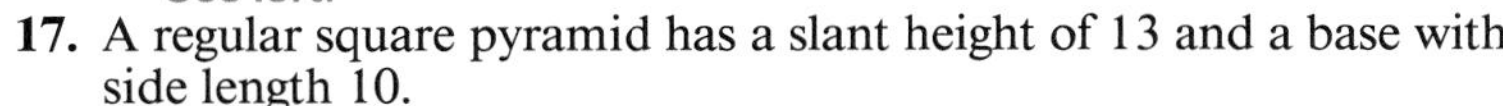

a. Draw and label a diagram of the pyramid. See left.
b. What is the height of the pyramid? *(Lesson 9-4)* 12 units

16d) $\overline{ZF}, \overline{ZO}, \overline{ZU}, \overline{ZR}$
e) $\triangle ZRF$, $\triangle ZRU$, $\triangle ZUO$, $\triangle ZOF$, *FOUR*

17a) Sample:

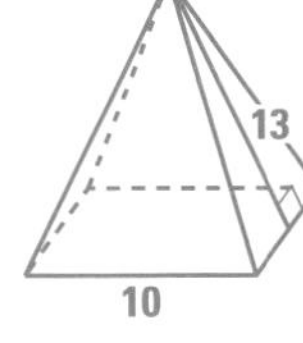

In 18 and 19, tell which figure studied in this chapter most resembles the real-world object. Give as specific a name as you can, distinguishing solids from surfaces. *(Lesson 9-3)*

18. a penny
solid right cylinder

19. a desk drawer
box without its top

20. A cylinder has a base with area of 20.25π. Find the circumference of the base. *(Lessons 8-7, 9-3)* 9π units

21. Find the area of $\triangle PQR$. *(Lessons 8-4, 8-6)* 240 units^2

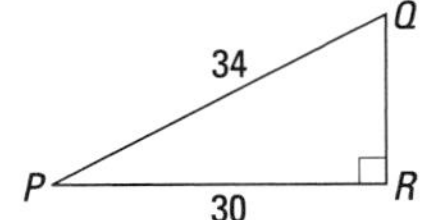

Follow-up for Lesson 9-6

Practice

For more questions on SPUR Objectives, use **Lesson Master 9-6A** (shown on page 527) or **Lesson Master 9-6B** (shown on pages 528–529).

Assessment

Oral Communication Have students **work in groups.** First have them find at least two different solid objects in the classroom that have one or more symmetry planes. Then have them use a sheet of paper to represent the symmetry plane and hold it in the correct position (or positions) to illustrate the symmetry plane(s). [Students correctly identify symmetry planes for solid figures.]

Extension

Have students make nine copies of the same cube and draw the nine symmetry planes for the cube. [Check students' drawings.]

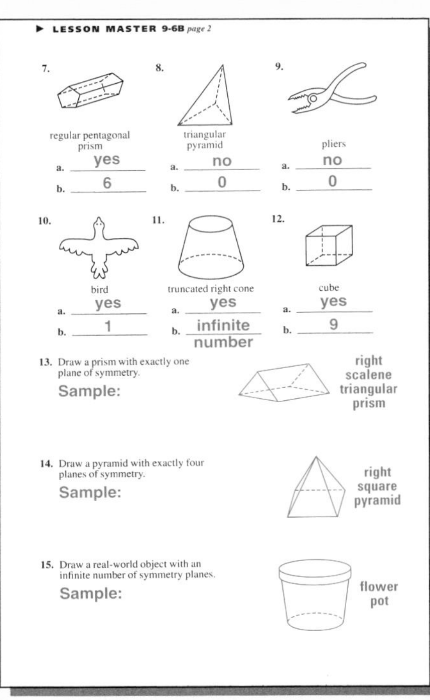

► LESSON MASTER 9-6B *page 2*

7. regular pentagonal prism — a. yes b. 6

8. triangular pyramid — a. no b. 0

9. pliers — a. no b. 0

10. bird — a. yes b. 1

11. truncated right cone — a. yes b. infinite number

12. cube — a. yes b. 9

13. Draw a prism with exactly one plane of symmetry.
Sample: right scalene triangular prism

14. Draw a pyramid with exactly four planes of symmetry.
Sample: right square pyramid

15. Draw a real-world object with an infinite number of symmetry planes.
Sample: flower pot

Additional Answers

14b. Sample:

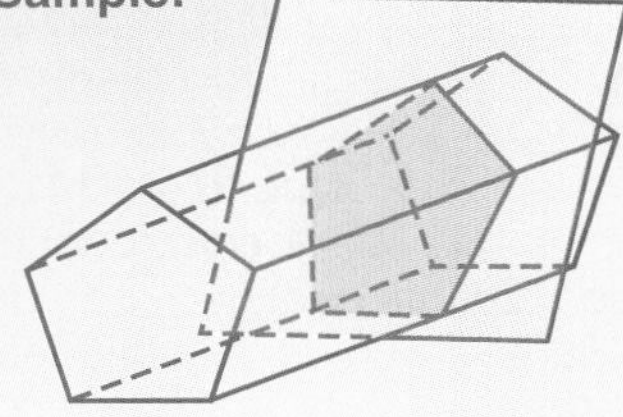

15b. Sample:

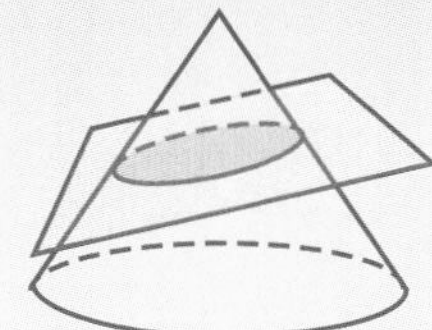

14c. Part a is a pentagon congruent to the base; part b is a pentagon.

15c. Part a is a circle; part b is an ellipse.

Notes on Questions

Question 22 Point out that there are several ways to prove the statements. Encourage students to find more than one way or to compare their proofs with others'.

Question 24 Almost everyone is surprised by this result. Most people have the misconception that if they cannot see their feet in a mirror, that by moving farther away they will be able to see their feet because the image is smaller. On the contrary, the mirror always allows you to see the same amount of your body, exactly twice the vertical height of the mirror (unless you bend your head forward or backward).

Question 25 Students may find it interesting that many people have facial expressions which are not symmetric. For example, some faces seem to be smiling on the left and somber on the right. Have students examine their own faces.

Additional Answers

22. Sample arguments:
    a. $BCGF$ and $EFGH$ are squares. Therefore, $BF = CG$, $EF = HG$. $\angle BFE$ and $\angle CGH$ are right angles. By the SAS Congruence Theorem, $\triangle BFE \cong \triangle CGH$. By the CPCF Theorem, $BE = CH$.
    b. $BCGF$ and $EFGH$ are squares. Therefore, $BC = FG$ and $FG = EH$. By the Transitive Property of Equality, $BC = EH$. From part a, $BE = CH$. Thus $BCHE$ is a parallelogram by the Sufficient Conditions for Parallelogram Theorem.
    c. $EFGH$ is a square. Therefore, the 4 sides are congruent, and the 4 angles are right angles. By the SAS Congruence Theorem, $\triangle EHG \cong \triangle HEF$. Therefore, $EG = HF$ by CPCF Theorem.
    d. $\overline{CG}$ and $\overline{BF}$ are perpendicular to the plane $EFGH$. Therefore, $\overline{CG} \perp \overline{EG}$, $\overline{BF} \perp \overline{HF}$. $BCGF$ is a square, so $CG = BF$. From part c, $\triangle CEG \cong \triangle BHF$ by SAS Congruence Theorem. Therefore, $CE = BH$ by CPCF Theorem.
    e. $\overline{BC}$ and $\overline{EH}$ are perpendicular to both plane $DCGH$ and plane $ABFE$. Therefore, $\overline{BC} \perp \overline{CH}$, $\overline{BC} \perp \overline{BE}$, $\overline{EH} \perp \overline{CH}$, $\overline{EH} \perp \overline{EB}$. BCHE is a rectangle by the definition of rectangle.

22. Given that the figure at the right is a cube, write an argument that proves the following statements in order. *(Lessons 6-3, 7-8, 9-3)*
a. $BE = CH$ See margin.
b. $BCHE$ is a parallelogram.
c. $EG = HF$
d. $BH = CE$
e. $BCHE$ is a rectangle.

23. What qualities of a good definition are violated by the following definition of *Equator* from *Webster's II New Riverside Dictionary*?

Equator: The great circle circumscribing the Earth's surface, the reckoning datum of latitudes and dividing boundary of Northern and Southern Hemispheres, formed by the intersection of a plane passing through the Earth's center perpendicular to its axis of rotation. *(Lesson 2-4)*
This has more information than is necessary.

Exploration

24. Standing upright and still, you want to see the front of your entire body, head to toe, in a mirror. How far up and down the wall does the mirror have to go? (Hint: Try with an actual mirror. Block out the parts of the mirror that are not needed.) See left.

24) The top of the mirror has to be at half the distance between your eyes and the top of your head; the bottom of the mirror has to be at half the distance between your eyes and the bottoms of your feet.

25. Find a picture of your face, taken from the front. Except for scars, is the surface of your face *exactly* symmetric to a vertical plane down the middle? No

26. a. What is *radial symmetry*? a biological term for rotation symmetry
b. Name some living things that possess it.
Sample: starfish, sand dollar, daisy, sunflower

Setting Up Lesson 9-7

Materials For Lesson 9-7, you may want to use various 3-dimensional objects from the classroom, or have students bring in various objects from home to use in drawing different views. Also have congruent cubes available so students can stack and draw them from various angles. It is suggested that the students use clay for *Extension* on page 534.

530

LESSON

9-7 Viewing Solids and Surfaces

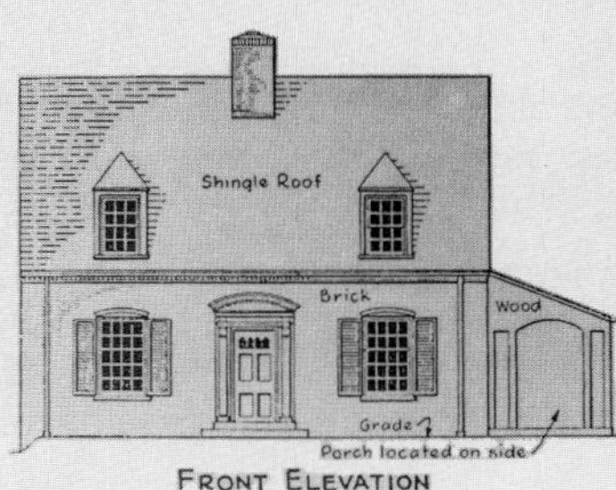

FRONT ELEVATION

RIGHT SIDE ELEVATION

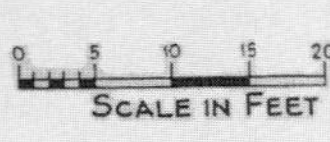

Views and Elevations

The house shown above was built in Highland, Indiana. Like many houses today, it was designed by an architect. Underneath the picture of the house are **views** or **elevations** from the front and right side. Architects draw views of a planned building from the top, sides, and other positions to help a client visualize the finished product. Computer-assisted design programs (CADs) also can provide many views or elevations of buildings. These elevations give accurate scale-model measurements; most photographs and perspective-type drawings do not.

In geometry, views of 3-dimensional figures are usually drawn without perspective as if the figures are solid but with all visible edges shown. (You were shown two views of Earth in Lesson 9-5.) From the views you can determine a possible shape of the original figure. The abbreviations L (left), R (right), F (front), and B (back) give guidance.

Lesson 9-7

Objectives

C Give views of a figure from the top, sides, or front.

E From 2-dimensional views of a figure, determine the 3-dimensional figure.

Resources

From the ***Teacher's Resource File***

- Lesson Master 9-7A or 9-7B
- Answer Master 9-7
- Teaching Aids
  120 Warm-up
  125 Additional Examples
  126 Extension
- Assessment Sourcebook: Quiz for Lessons 9-5 through 9-7

Additional Resources

- Visuals for Teaching Aids 120, 125–126
- 3-Dimensional objects, congruent cubes
- Clay

Teaching Lesson 9-7

Warm-up

Assume you are looking down from directly above each of the following objects. Make a sketch of what you would see. **Sketches will vary.**

1. Television **2.** Sofa
3. Electric range **4.** Ferris wheel
5. Merry-go-round **6.** Basketball

Notes on Reading

This lesson should help students visualize 3-dimensional figures. Drawing a figure may seem easier than it is.

Lesson 9-7 Overview

Broad Goals The primary goal of this lesson is to teach visualization and drawing skills. Students are asked to draw what a solid might be given various views of it, and to draw various views given the solid.

Perspective The content of this lesson is not usually found in geometry courses, but is taught in drafting or mechanical drawing courses. Because we feel the content is important, involves significant geometry, and is often not seen by students, we have included it here.

For many students even the simplest questions involving viewing from different positions are quite difficult. This is not because the questions are intrinsically difficult, but because many students have never been asked to do this sort of thing.

Yet in reading architect's plans, directions for building models, directions for assembling things bought for the home, maps, blueprints, and so on, the ability to visualize from various locations is very important.

The content of this lesson enhances skills important to the consumer. Most students will encounter situations in their lives in which diagrams of projected views are used, for example, in houses and furnishings.

Have students record the results of the **Activity** for use with **Question 7** on page 534.

You might use various objects in the classroom, or have students bring in various objects for use in drawing different views. Bring in some congruent cubes, stack them in various ways, and have students draw views from the top, front, and one side. Students could **work in groups** to make the drawings of the top, side, or front view. The reverse process, determining the figure from its views, as in **Example 2,** is more difficult and provides practice in deduction.

Reading Mathematics You might read this lesson aloud with students, especially **Examples 1 and 2.** Make sure students understand how to interpret the solutions given, and encourage them to make sketches. It may help to have individual models that students can observe at eye level. Students can create "buildings" from congruent cubes.

Additional Examples

These examples are also given on **Teaching Aid 125.**

1. A square pyramid has one lateral face which is an isosceles triangle perpendicular to the base of the pyramid. Draw views from the front, the right side (the isosceles face), and the top.

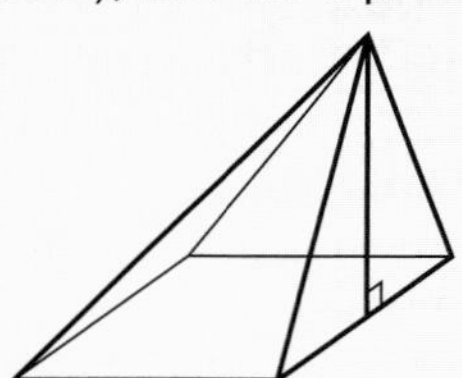

Views (not full size)

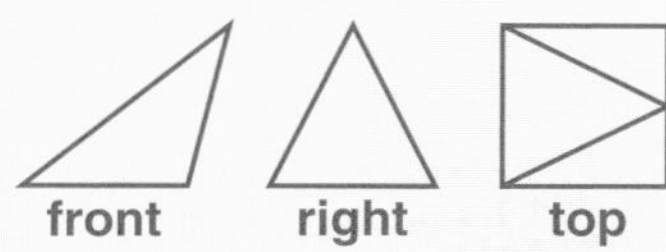

2. A child has made a building by stacking blocks. Three views of the stack are shown. Draw one possible building.

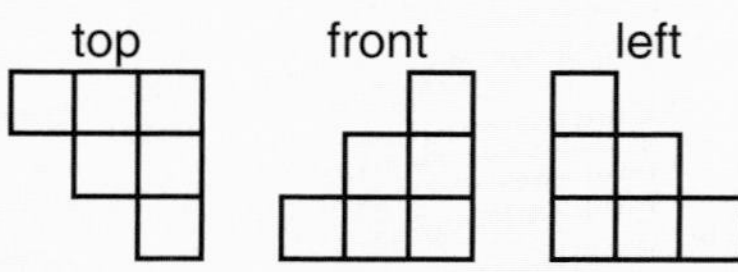

Example 1

Given the regular square pyramid at the right, draw views from the front, right side, and top.

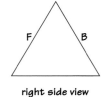

front

Solution

The bottoms of the front and side views are the same length as a side of the square base. The views are triangles, the same height as the height of the pyramid. The top view shows the base as a square and the vertex at the center of the square.

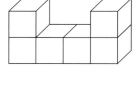

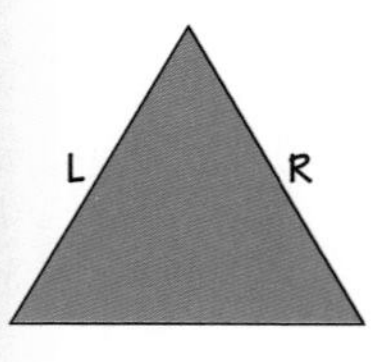

front view

F B

right side view

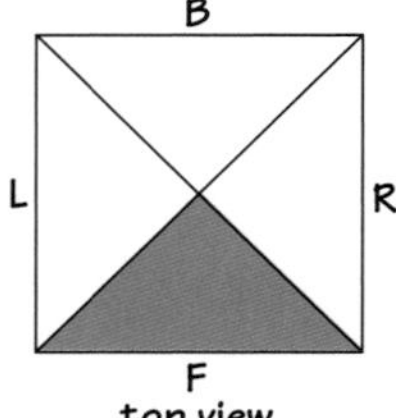

top view

Activity

Make a shape out of six congruent cubes different from the one shown at the left. Draw views from the front, right side, and top.
See left for sample.

front

right

top

Without experience, few people can visualize the shape of a structure by just looking at views. In this book, unless told otherwise, you should assume that the solids viewed are those we have already discussed—prisms, cylinders, pyramids, or cones—or combinations of them, as in Example 2.

Example 2

Here are three views of a prefabricated storage building made up of sections in the shape of congruent boxes.

Solution

a. How many stories tall is the building?
b. How many sections long is the building from front to back?
c. Where is the tallest part of the building located?

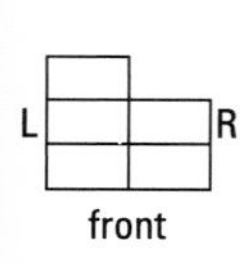

front

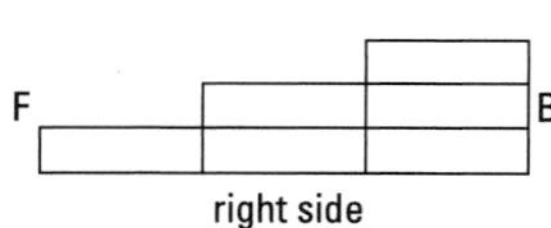

right side

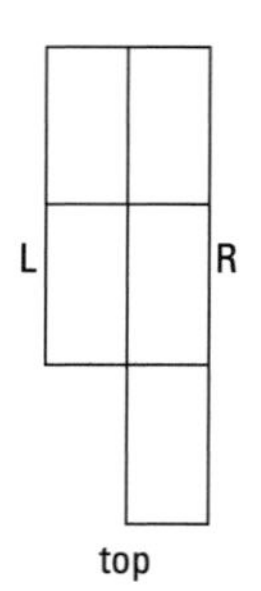

top

Optional Activities

After students have worked through **Example 1,** have them **work in groups** of three and draw the front view, the right side view, and the top view of any object of their choice in the classroom.

Additional Answers

3a-c.

4a-c.

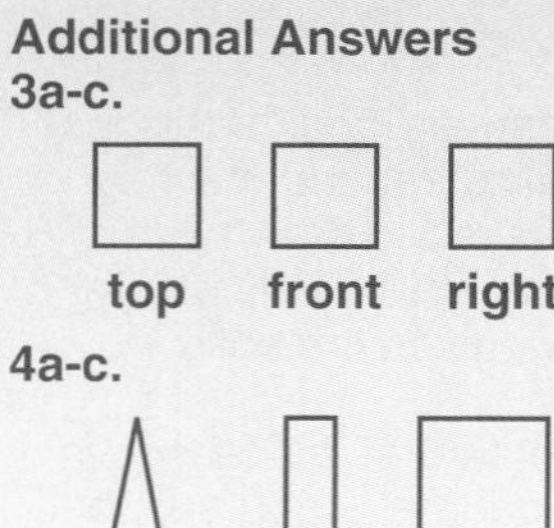

Solution

a. The top view tells you nothing about the height of the building. The front or side view tells you *it is 3 stories high.*

b. The top view tells you *it is 3 sections long;* the right side view confirms this.

c. The front view tells you that the tallest part is somewhere on the left side. The right side view tells you that the tallest part is at the back. Combining these conclusions, you can conclude that *The tallest part of the building is at the back left.*

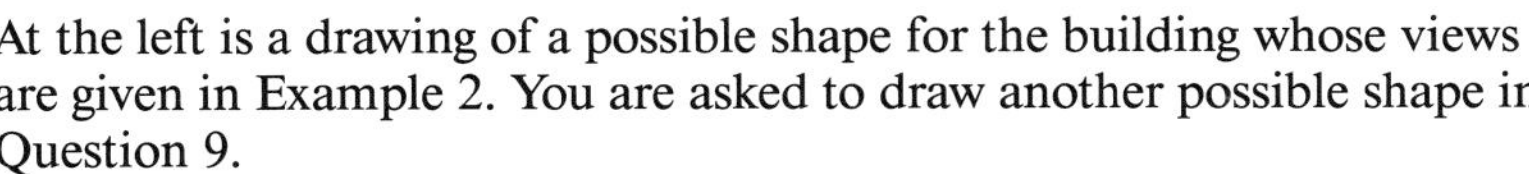

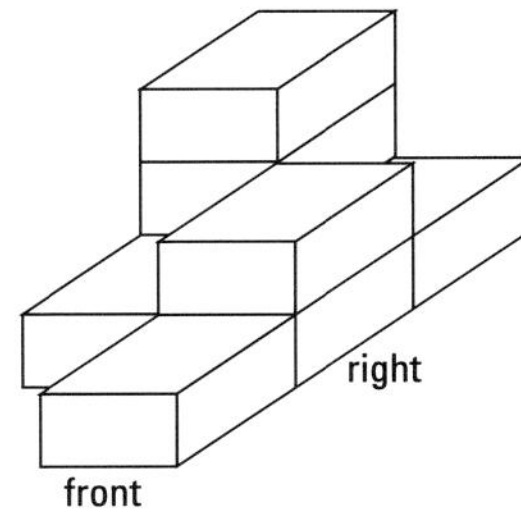

At the left is a drawing of a possible shape for the building whose views are given in Example 2. You are asked to draw another possible shape in Question 9.

It helps to make sketches to understand views. In making your sketches, you may want to put the hidden lines in at first and erase them as your sketch nears completion. Sometimes, in picturing these solids, the hidden lines are omitted so that the final shape is more easily viewed.

QUESTIONS

Covering the Reading

1. To an architect, what are *elevations*? different views of a building
2. A building is sketched at the left. See left.
   a. Draw a top view.
   b. Draw a view from the right side.
   c. Draw a front view.

2a) L R
b) F B
c) L R

In 3–6, sketch each shape as seen from each of the following positions: **a.** top, **b.** front, and **c.** right side.

3. a cube

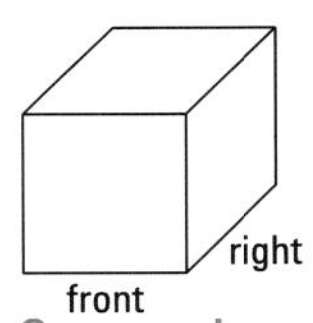

See margin.

4. a right prism with an isosceles triangular base

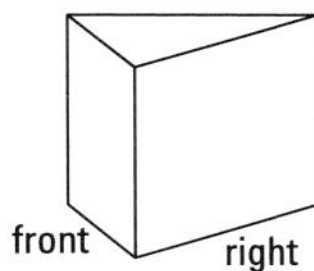

See margin.

5. a table

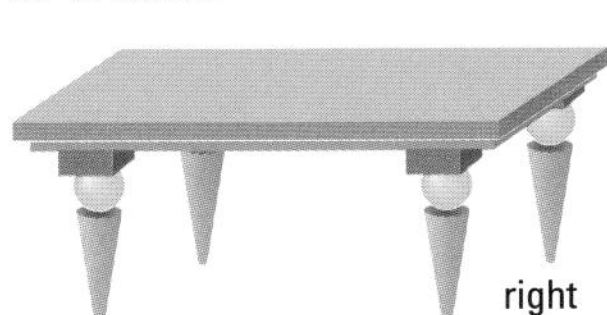

See margin.

6. a block of buildings

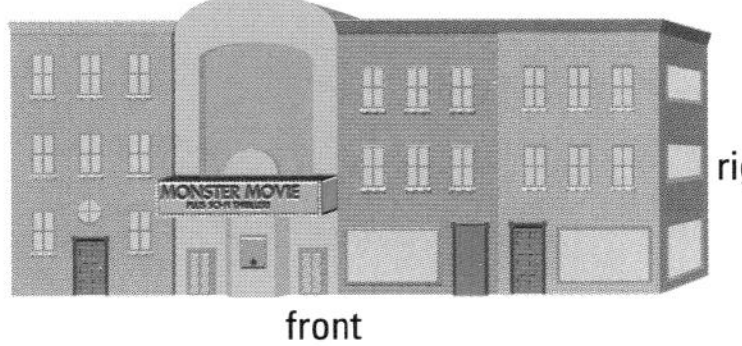

See margin.

Sample (from the front right):

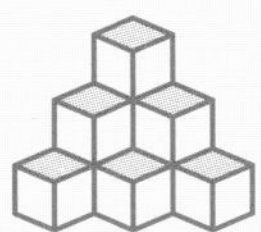

Notes on Questions

Questions 5 – 6 Many students have not done this kind of drawing before and may have difficulty.

(Notes on Questions continue on page 535.)

Follow-up for Lesson 9-7

Practice

For more questions on SPUR Objectives, use **Lesson Master 9-7A** (shown on page 533) or **Lesson Master 9-7B** (shown on pages 534 – 535).

Assessment

Quiz A quiz covering Lessons 9-5 through 9-7 is provided in the *Assessment Sourcebook.*

Oral Communication Hold an object in front of the class. Choose students to draw different views of the object on the chalkboard. Have the other students in the class make

(Follow-up continues on page 534.)

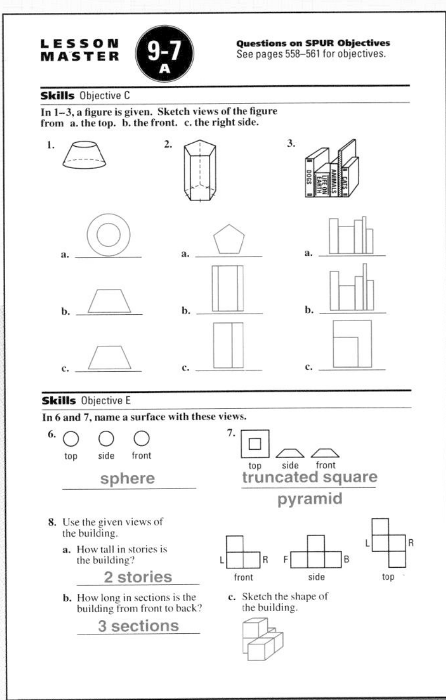
LESSON MASTER 9-7 A

Questions on SPUR Objectives
See pages 558–561 for objectives.

Skills Objective C

In 1–3, a figure is given. Sketch views of the figure from a. the top. b. the front. c. the right side.

1. 2. 3.

a. b. c.

Skills Objective E

In 6 and 7, name a surface with these views.

6. top side front — sphere

7. top side front — truncated square pyramid

8. Use the given views of the building.
   a. How tall in stories is the building? 2 stories
   b. How long in sections is the building from front to back? 3 sections
   c. Sketch the shape of the building.

front side top

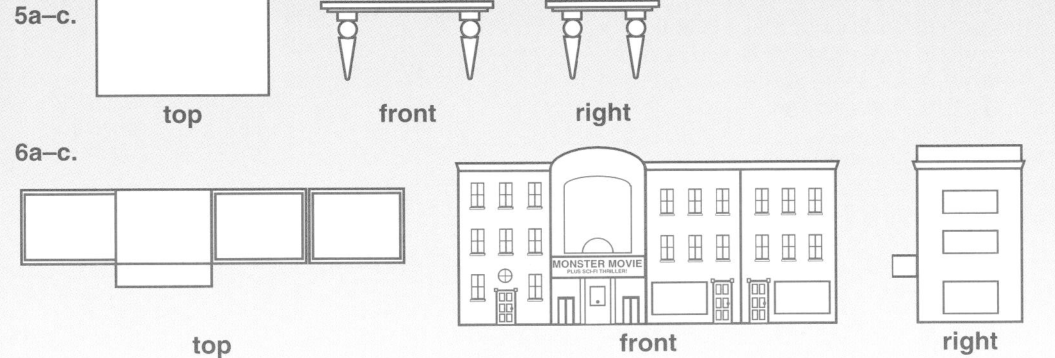

suggestions for improving or clarifying the drawings. Repeat this process. [Students correctly draw specific view.]

Extension

Have students make a clay model of the solid shown below (also on **Teaching Aid 126**). Its shadows are: from the left, a rectangle; from a little to the right of the front, a triangle; from the top, a circle.

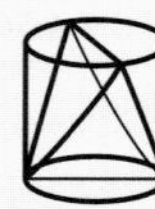

front view left view top view

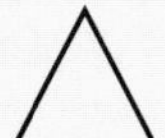

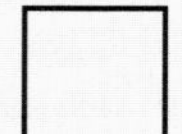

[To make the model, begin with clay in the shape of a cylindric solid. Draw a diameter of the top base; draw the diameter of the bottom base in a plane which is the perpendicular bisector of the top diameter. With a sharp knife, make cuts representing the two planes determined by the top diameter and the ends of the bottom diameter.]

Project Update Project 2, *Structures,* and Project 3, *Architectural Views,* on page 552, relate to the content of this lesson.

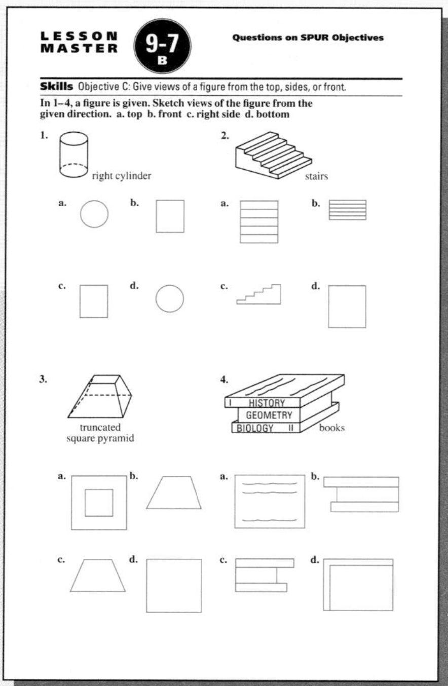

LESSON MASTER 9-7 B

Questions on SPUR Objectives

Skills Objective C: Give views of a figure from the top, sides, or front.

In 1–4, a figure is given. Sketch views of the figure from the given direction. a. top b. front c. right side d. bottom

1. right cylinder

2. stairs

3. truncated square pyramid

4. books

9) Sample:

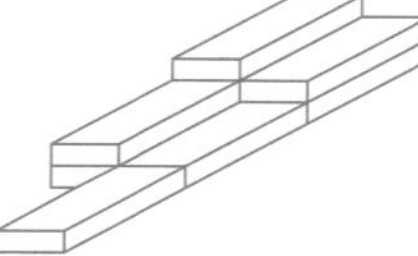

12b)

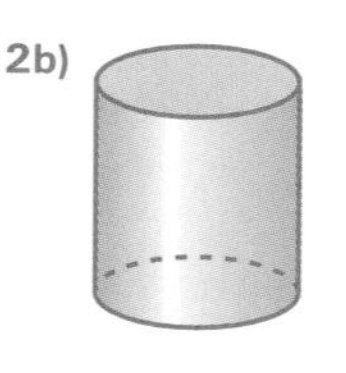

13)

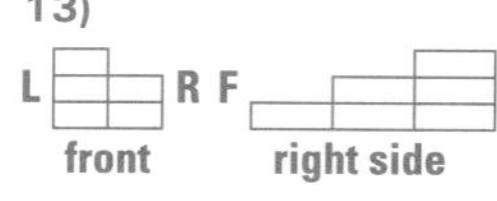

14)

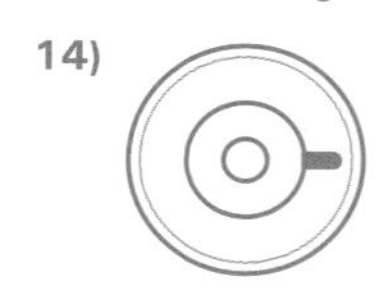

7. Give the three views you drew in the Activity of this lesson. See page 532.

8. A building has the views shown below.

a. How many stories tall is the building? 2

b. How many sections long is the building from front to back? 3

c. Where is the tallest part of the building located? on the left side, the two back sections

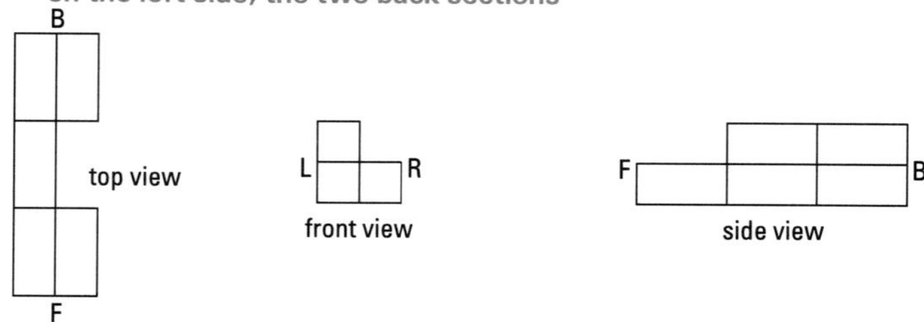

9. Sketch a possible shape, different from the solution given, for the building with the views given in Example 2. See left.

Applying the Mathematics

In 10 and 11, refer to the elevations and scale at the beginning of this lesson.

10. About how wide (in feet) is the house? about 34 ft by 22 ft

11. About how high is it (in feet) from the ground to the highest point on the roof? ≈ 25 ft

12. a. Which solid studied in this chapter has these views?

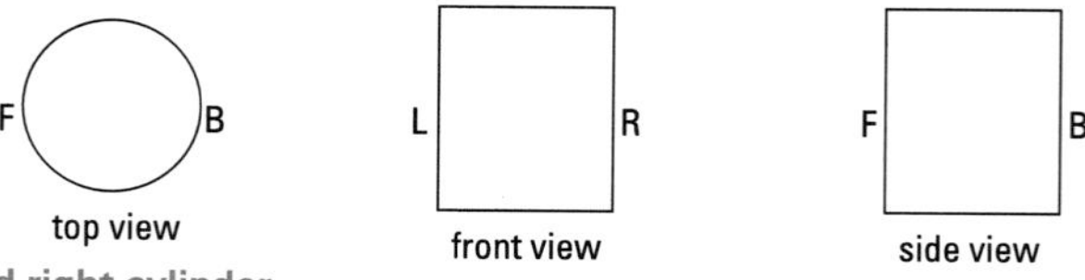

a solid right cylinder

b. Draw the solid. See left.

13. At the right is a top view of a building (like the one in Example 2) made up of sections in the shape of congruent boxes. The number in each box tells how many are stacked in that space. Draw the building as seen from the front and from the right side. See left.

14. Draw the cup and saucer at the right as seen from overhead. See left.

534

Setting Up Lesson 9-8

The In-class Activity on page 536 is designed to give students the idea of Lesson 9-8. It should be completed before students read the lesson.

Materials You might want to have students bring cereal boxes that can be cut and unfolded into their nets.

Additional Answers

22. Sample argument:

Conclusions	Justifications
1. $\overline{AB} \cong \overline{CD}$	Properties of a Parallelogram Thm.
2. $\overline{AB} \parallel \overline{CD}$	def. parallelogram
3. $\angle ABQ \cong \angle CDQ$, $\angle QAB \cong \angle QCD$	// Lines ⇒ AIA ≅ Thm.
4. $\triangle AQB \cong \triangle CQD$	ASA Congruence Thm. (steps 1 and 3)

15b)

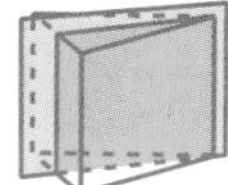

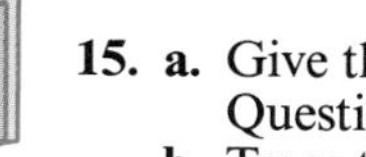

Review

15. a. Give the number of symmetry planes of the prism shown in Question 4. 2

b. Trace the drawing. Draw all symmetry planes and the cross sections they form. *(Lessons 9-5, 9-6)* See left.

In 16 and 17, use the right cone shown on the left. *(Lessons 8-6, 9-4, 9-6)*

16. a. How many symmetry planes does the figure have? infinitely many

b. Sketch a plane section parallel to an edge not containing the vertex. See left.

c. Name the shape of the section in part **b.** parabola

17. If the base of the cone has radius 8 and its slant height is 10, what is its height? 6 units

L R

18. At the left is a view of the moon and its equator as seen from Earth. The distance from L to R (through the center of the moon) is approximately 2160 miles. (Assume that the moon is a solid sphere.) *(Lesson 9-5)*

a. What is the approximate radius of the moon? 1080 miles

b. How far is it from L to R along the surface of the moon? $1080\pi \approx 3390$ miles

19. How many great circles on Earth contain a given point in Baltimore and a given point in Tokyo? *(Lesson 9-4)* one

20. A regular heptagonal region is translated into a congruent region in a parallel plane. What solid figure is formed by all points on segments connecting the original region and its image? *(Lesson 9-3)* solid heptagonal prism

21. The area of Wyoming, the least populous state in the United States, is about 97,105 square miles. It is shaped like a trapezoid with east-west bases of length 350 miles and 370 miles. Estimate the north-south altitude of this trapezoidal state. about 270 mi

A B Q D C

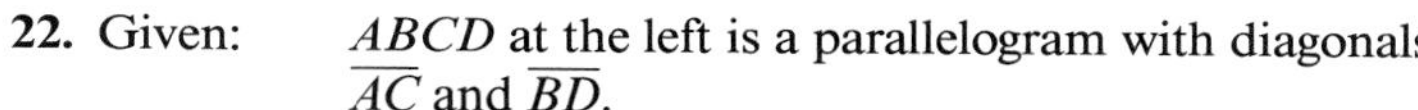

22. Given: $ABCD$ at the left is a parallelogram with diagonals $\overline{AC}$ and $\overline{BD}$.

To prove: $\triangle AQB \cong \triangle CQD$. *(Lessons 7-2, 7-7)* See margin.

23. What is a transformation? *(Lesson 4-1)* See left.

23) A correspondence between two sets of points such that (1) each point in the preimage set has a unique image, and (2) each point in the image set has exactly one preimage.

Exploration

24. Choose an object in your home or classroom and draw it from four viewpoints: top, front, right, and left. For what kind of object will all the views differ? Answers will vary.

25. a. Using a globe, draw Earth, including all visible land masses, as seen from below the South Pole. See margin.

b. Is this view the same as a *bottom* view? See margin.

25a.

b. Sample: To us, it might seem like a bottom view. However, to an Australian, the South Pole might be the top, and the North Pole the bottom. Then this view will be the top view. In theory, either the North or the South Pole could be considered as the bottom.

Notes on Questions

Questions 8 – 9 Cooperative Learning These questions are appropriate for small-group work.

Question 10 –11 These questions depend on the scale given below the elevations. Students may need to use proportions to answer the questions.

Question 12 Students may argue that a cylinder doesn't have a "front" or "side," since it looks the same from any viewing position. Point out that these words refer to fixed viewing positions, not to attributes of the figure itself.

Question 18 Science Connection Students may not realize that a back view of Earth's moon had not been seen until the Soviet Union sent a space probe around the moon in 1959.

Question 19 Geography Connection You might wish to mention that there is a formula for finding the distance between two places on Earth, given their latitudes and longitudes. The formula requires trigonometry, as it involves sines and cosines, and is found in UCSMP *Functions, Statistics, and Trigonometry.*

Question 24 Have students put their drawings for this question in their notebooks. Ask volunteers to show what they drew.

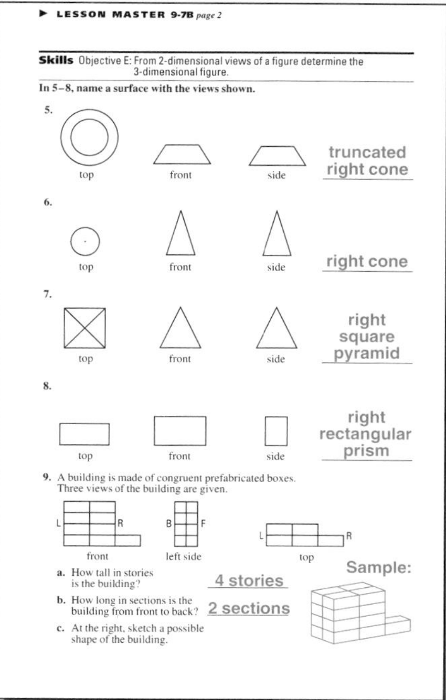

▶ LESSON MASTER 9-7B *page 2*

Skills Objective E: From 2-dimensional views of a figure determine the 3-dimensional figure.

In 5–8, name a surface with the views shown.

5. top front side truncated right cone

6. top front side right cone

7. top front side right square pyramid

8. top front side right rectangular prism

9. A building is made of congruent prefabricated boxes. Three views of the building are given.

L R front B F left side L R top

a. How tall in stories is the building? 4 stories

b. How long in sections is the building from front to back? 2 sections

c. At the right, sketch a possible shape of the building. Sample:

In-class Activity

Resources

From the ***Teacher's Resource File***

- Answer Master 9-8
- Teaching Aid 127: Nets

Additional Resources

- Visual for Teaching Aid 127

This In-class Activity is designed to give students the idea of folding a net into a cube, which will be introduced in the next lesson.

Students may use construction paper or other heavy paper for this In-class Activity. Or, students can cut out the figures, which appear on **Teaching Aid 127.**

Note that in a net for a polyhedron, the sum of angle measures around each vertex must be less than 360. This is one reason why figure C will not fold to a polyhedron.

TEACHING AID 127
Lesson 9-8

Nets

G
F E D H
I

U
L F R X
D

Introducing Lesson 9-8

Building Cubes

IN-CLASS ACTIVITY

Work with a partner. You will need a ruler, scissors, and tape.

1 Trace the three figures below. Then cut out each of your drawings.

A.

G
F E D H
I

B.

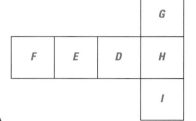

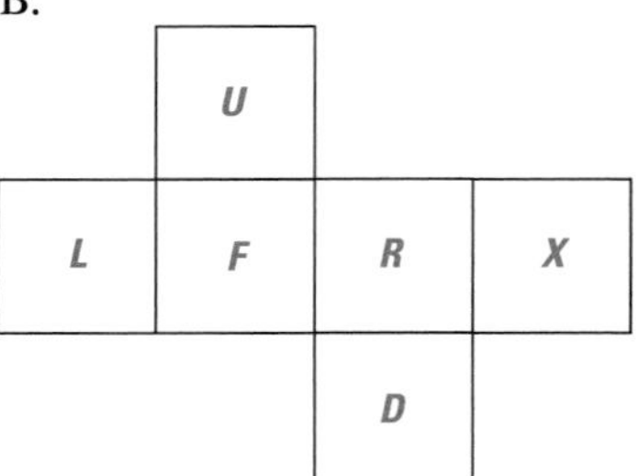

C.

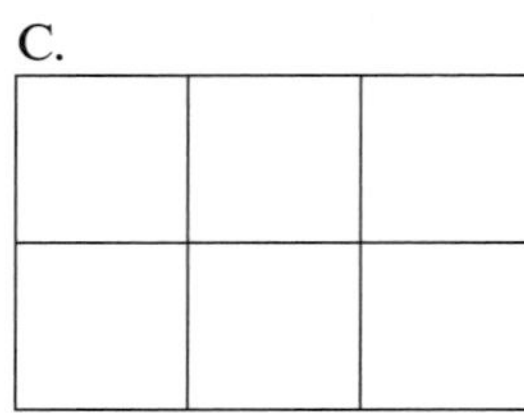

2 Folding along the edges, try to make each one into a cube. See margin.

3 **a.** Which figure(s) do not form a cube? Figure C
b. Why not? See margin.

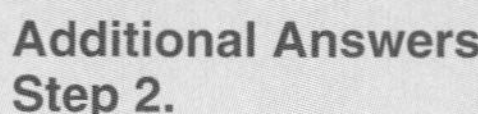

Additional Answers
Step 2.

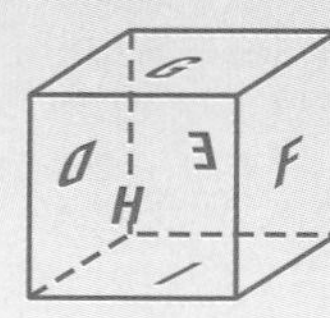

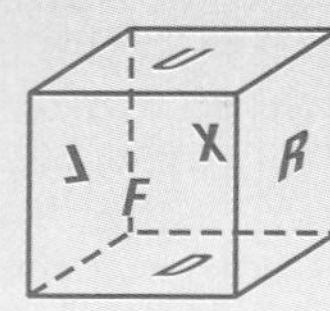

Step 3b. Sample: No more than three faces can come together at a vertex to form a cube. Figure C has 4 faces at one vertex.

LESSON

9-8

Making Surfaces

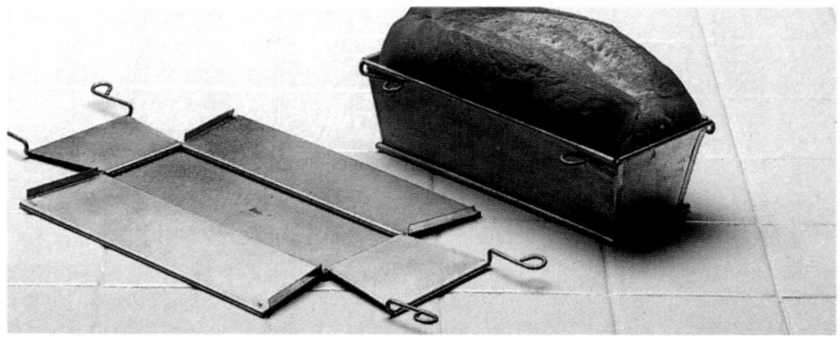

Dough net. *What advantages do you see in a baking pan which can be disassembled into a net?*

Polyhedra

Prisms and pyramids are special kinds of *polyhedra*. In general, a 3-dimensional surface which is the union of polygonal regions and which has no holes is called a **polyhedron.** The plural of *polyhedron* is either **polyhedrons** or **polyhedra.** Polyhedra can be classified by the number of their faces. Pictured below are a *tetrahedron* (4 faces) and a *hexahedron* (6 faces). The tetrahedron has 4 vertices and 6 edges. Both a box and a cube are special types of hexahedra.

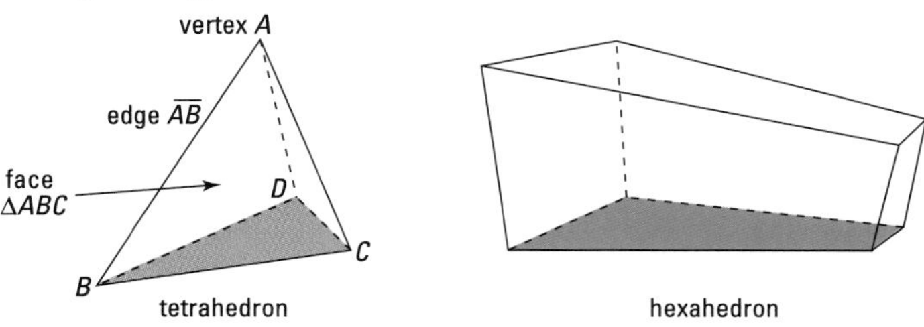

Regular polyhedra are the three-dimensional counterparts to regular polygons.

Definition
A regular polyhedron is a convex polyhedron in which all faces are congruent regular polygons and the same number of edges intersect at each of its vertices.

There are only five regular polyhedra; they are pictured here.

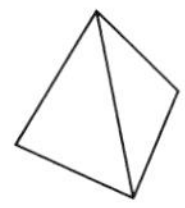

regular tetrahedron (4 faces)

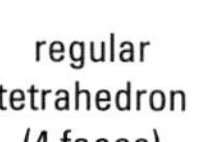

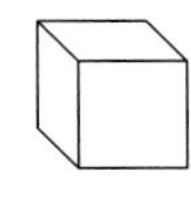

cube (6 faces)

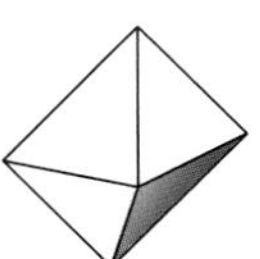

regular octahedron (8 faces)

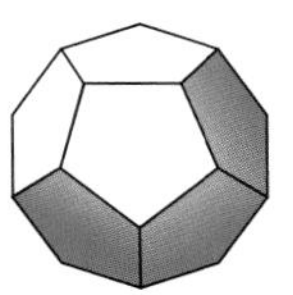

regular dodecahedron (12 faces)

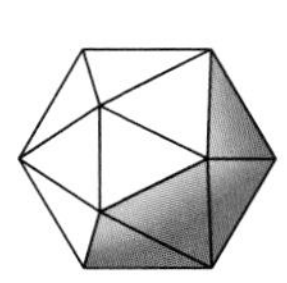

regular icosahedron (20 faces)

Lesson 9-8

Objectives

J Make a surface from a net, and vice versa.

Resources

From the ***Teacher's Resource File***
- Lesson Master 9-8A or 9-8B
- Answer Master 9-8
- Teaching Aids
  120 Warm-up
  128 Question 26
- Activity Kit, Activity 21
- Technology Sourcebook, Computer Master 19

Additional Resources
- Visuals for Teaching Aids 120, 128
- Cereal boxes
- GeoExplorer or other automatic drawers

Teaching Lesson 9-8

Warm-up

Think of cutting apart a cardboard box so that it will lie flat. Make a sketch of the figure that is created.
Sketches will vary.

Notes on Reading

You might wish to have students bring in cereal boxes that can be unfolded and cut into their nets. A display may be made of different nets of rectangular prisms and other figures.

Pacing Some teachers like to have classes spend a day making models of the regular polyhedra. This is an appropriate activity.

Lesson 9-8 Overview

Broad Goals In this lesson, students use the concept of a net to construct a surface.

Perspective The ideas of this lesson are applied to the concept of surface area in the next chapter. If a net exists for a surface (as it does for any conic or cylindric surface), then the surface area of the surface equals the area of the net. So, the word *net,* though not found in all geometry books, has an important application that is found in all books.

To construct a real surface with any nets here, students will need tape. Some people put flaps or tabs on the nets in appropriate places. Then, you may use glue rather than tape.

Posters of the regular polyhedra and models of polyhedra are available commercially. They make attractive displays and excellent teaching tools. Two sources are Creative Publications and Dale Seymour Publications.

Of all materials the authors have seen for making models, the easiest and most instructive are found in construction sets called "Polydrons," a British product available at most large toy stores and some exhibits at mathematics conferences in the United States. One set consists of a number of equilateral triangles and squares with sides of the same length that interlock and hinge to form either tessellations in two dimensions or surfaces in three dimensions. One of the authors obtained a set with 75 triangles and 15 squares, enough for four of the regular polyhedra at once, with some pieces left over. Stellated polyhedra are also possible. You can also buy 12 regular pentagons to make a dodecahedron. The idea is ingenious and won the 1985 Design Award for the outstanding British product of that year.

You might remind students that a *polygon* was defined as a union of three or more coplanar segments such that each intersected exactly two others, one at each endpoint. By analogy, we could define a *polyhedron* as a union of four or more polygonal regions such that each edge is the intersection of two of the regions. However, that definition would allow for polyhedra with holes.

This lesson presents another opportunity for extending ideas by analogy: In 1-dimensional space (a line), "regions" are bounded by 0-dimensional figures, that is, by points, and the minimum number of points needed to bound a region of the space is 2 (the endpoints of a segment). In 2-dimensional space, regions may be bounded by 1-dimensional figures, that is, by segments, and the minimum number of segments needed to bound a region of the space is 3 (a triangle). In 3-dimensional space, regions may be bound by 2-dimensional figures,

This piece of jewelry is in the shape of a regular icosahedron.

Nets for Polyhedra

In this book you have used perspective and nonperspective drawings, plane sections, and views to describe 3-dimensional figures in 2-dimensional drawings. You also can go the other way and use 2-dimensional drawings to make polyhedra and other 3-dimensional surfaces.

A **net** is a 2-dimensional figure that can be folded on its segments or curved on its boundaries into a 3-dimensional surface. To find the net for a particular surface, you can cut along the edges of the surface until it is flat. For instance, when cuts are made along some of the edges of a cube, then the cube can be flattened out.

Shown below is a net for a cube. In the In-class Activity, you folded a net like this into a cube. We have named the six faces by the first letters of the words up, down, left, right, back, and front. When you cut around the outside boundary, and folded along the common edges as shown, you formed a cube.

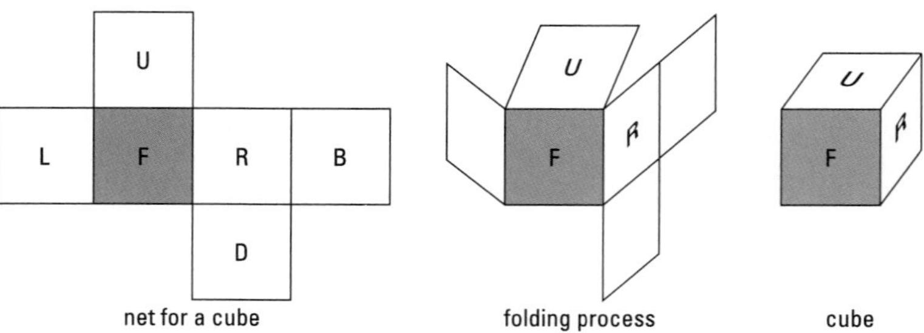

Not all networks of six squares fold to make a cube. In the In-class Activity, you found that the 2-by-3 network of squares pictured below is not a net for a cube. It can be folded into the lateral surface of a prism, as shown at the right, but this is not a polyhedron since it has holes.

Prisms and pyramids often have relatively simple nets.

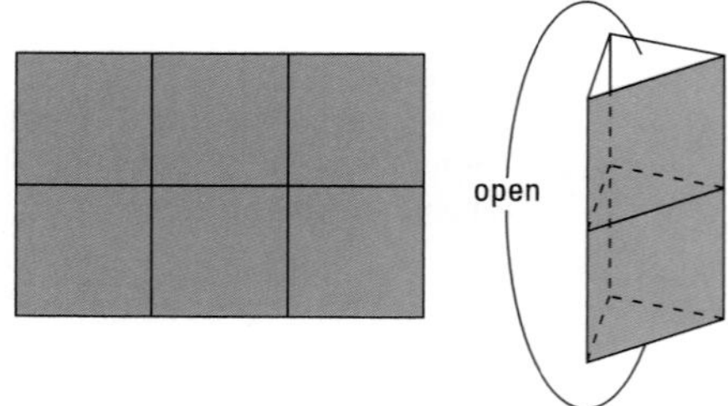

Optional Activities

Activity 1
Using Physical Models The In-class Activity on page 536 can be expanded to create blow-ups of the nets of the two examples which students can assemble. Also, as an extension of **Question 4,** ask students to make a net of each of the shapes named. It is good for students to familiarize themselves with both the making of surfaces from nets and the making of nets for surfaces.

Activity 2
You may use *Activity Kit, Activity 21,* as a follow-up to the lesson. In this activity, students draw a net that folds into an unusual carton.

Activity 3 Technology Connection
In *Technology Sourcebook, Computer Master 19,* students draw nets for prisms and pyramids. Then they print their nets and assemble the polyhedrons.

Cornered. *Many shapes have a function and purpose. This triangular prism is a practical space-saver.*

Example 1

Draw a net for the right triangular prism shown at the right.

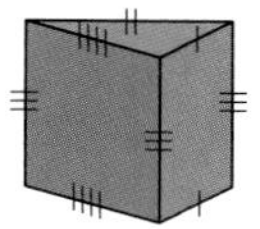

Solution

The bases are congruent triangles. The lateral faces are rectangles with one pair of sides the same length as the corresponding sides of the base. A net is shown at the right. Notice how the tick marks would match up if this net were cut out and folded into a prism.

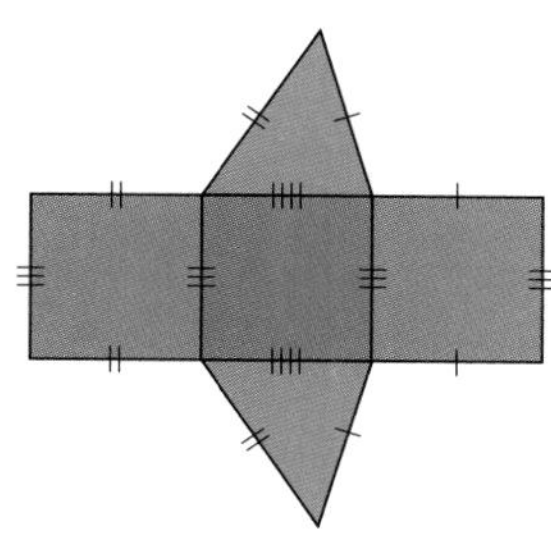

Activity

Consider a regular square pyramid like the one at the right. The base is a square, and the faces are isosceles triangles with their bases along the square's sides.

Step 1: To draw a net, first draw the square base.

Step 2: Draw four congruent isosceles triangles with each triangle having its base on an edge of the square.

The altitude of each triangular face must be greater than one-half the length of the side of the square. Why?

See left.

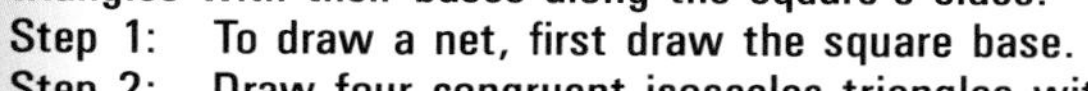

Steps 1 and 2

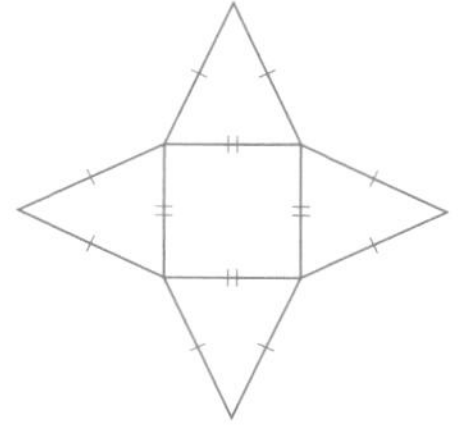

The vertices have to meet at a point above the base of the pyramid.

Nets for Cones and Cylinders

Cones and cylinders have simple nets.

Example 2

Draw a net for a cylinder h units high with base diameter d.

Solution

First, draw the circle that will be one base. The lateral surface of a cylinder is a rectangle. Since the diameter of the circle is d, the side of the rectangle that touches the circle has length πd, to match the circumference of the bases. The other side of the rectangle is the height h of the cylinder. Finally, draw a second circle, congruent to and across the lateral surface from the first. That will be the other base.

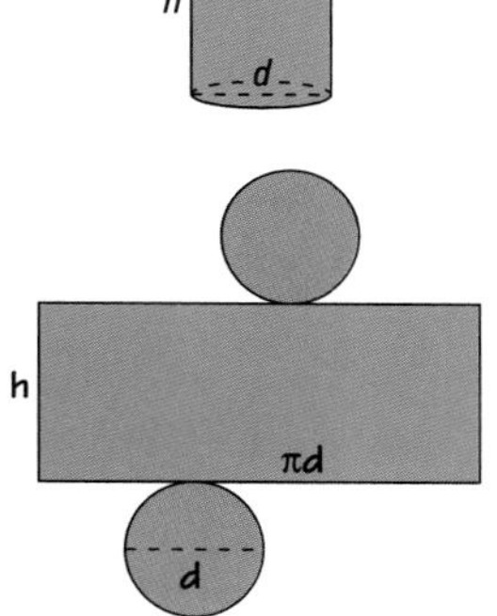

that is, by polygonal regions, and the minimum number of polygonal regions needed to bound a region is 4 (a tetrahedron). In general, in dimension n, the minimum number of bounding figures is $n + 1$.

Have students record the results of the **Activity** for use with **Question 6** on page 540.

Additional Examples

1. Draw a net for an octahedron of which all faces are congruent triangles. Sample with equilateral triangles.

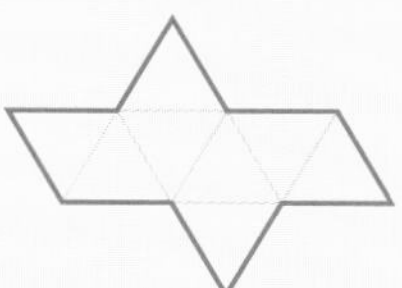

2. Design a net to be handed to spectators at a football game which they may bend into a megaphone. Sample:

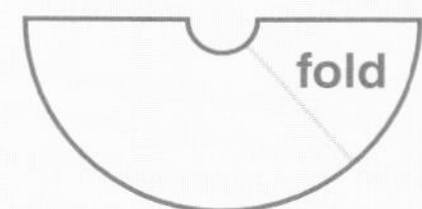

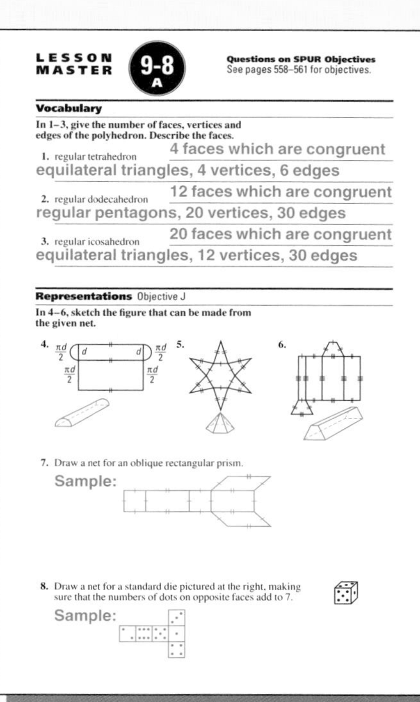

LESSON MASTER 9-8 A

Questions on SPUR Objectives
See pages 558–561 for objectives.

Vocabulary

In 1–3, give the number of faces, vertices and edges of the polyhedron. Describe the faces.

1. regular tetrahedron 4 faces which are congruent equilateral triangles, 4 vertices, 6 edges
2. regular dodecahedron 12 faces which are congruent regular pentagons, 20 vertices, 30 edges
3. regular icosahedron 20 faces which are congruent equilateral triangles, 12 vertices, 30 edges

Representations Objective J

In 4–6, sketch the figure that can be made from the given net.

4. $\frac{\pi d}{2}$ d d $\frac{\pi d}{2}$ $\frac{\pi d}{2}$ $\frac{\pi d}{2}$
5.
6.

7. Draw a net for an oblique rectangular prism.
Sample:

8. Draw a net for a standard die pictured at the right, making sure that the numbers of dots on opposite faces add to 7.
Sample:

Adapting to Individual Needs

Extra Help

Some students do not realize that a figure can have more than one net. Remind them of the In-class Activity preceding this lesson where two different nets form a cube.

English Language Development

To help students remember the terms *polyhedron, tetrahedron, hexahedron, octahedron, dodecahedron,* and *icosahedron,* call attention to how the prefixes relate to the number of faces of the figure: tetra (four), hexa (six), octa (eight), dodeca (twelve), icosa (twenty), and poly (many).

Notes on Questions

Question 2 This is an excellent exercise for viewing the relative positions of the faces of a cube. We like to call them *Up, Down, Right, Left, Front,* and *Back.* There is a software product called *SuperFactory,* produced by Sunburst Communications, which challenges a student to create a net to generate a cube. It requires determining the correct sequencing as well as the transformations necessary to create the cube.

Question 11 Ask students to state conditions for which a net can be made into a cube. Then ask these questions: Must there be a row of 4? [No] If there is a row of four, what must be true of the other two faces? [They must be on opposite sides of the row.]

Question 16 Error Alert This is not an easy question. Students may not be able to draw the correct net the first time they try. Compliment students for good attempts.

(Notes on Questions continue on page 542.)

LESSON MASTER 9-8 B Questions on SPUR Objectives

Vocabulary

1. Define *polyhedron.* a 3-dimensional surface which is the union of polygonal regions and has no holes
2. Define *regular polyhedron.* a convex polyhedron in which all faces are congruent regular polygons and the same number of edges intersect at each vertex
3. List the regular polyhedra. For each one describe the faces and tell how many faces it has.
tetrahedron, equilateral triangles, 4 faces
cube, squares, 6 faces
octahedron, equilateral triangles, 8 faces
dodecahedron, regular pentagons, 12 faces
icosahedron, equilateral triangles, 20 faces

Representations Objective J: Make a surface from a net and vice versa.

In 4–7, sketch the surface that can be made from each net.

4. 5.

A net for the lateral surface of a cone is given in Question 10.

For greatest accuracy, you need to construct the bases and faces of a net using a straightedge and compass, or you should trace very carefully and measure the original and your copy with ruler and protractor. Printouts from an automatic drawer also can be useful.

QUESTIONS

Covering the Reading

1) A net is a 2-dimensional figure that can be folded on its segments or curved on its boundaries into a 3-dimensional surface.

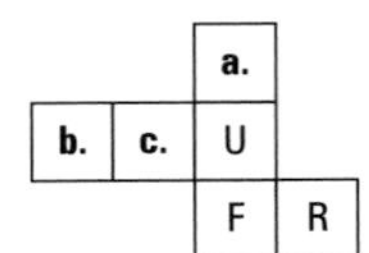

1. What is a *net*? See left.
2. At the left is a net for a cube. Identified are the locations of three faces. Where will the other squares of the net end up on the cube?
a) back b) down c) left
3. Is a cone a polyhedron? Why or why not?
No; its surface is not a union of polygonal regions.
4. Match the name of each regular polyhedron with the shape of its faces.
   a. tetrahedron i — (i) equilateral triangle
   b. cube ii — (ii) square
   c. regular octahedron i — (iii) regular pentagon
   d. regular dodecahedron iii — (iv) regular hexagon
   e. regular icosahedron i

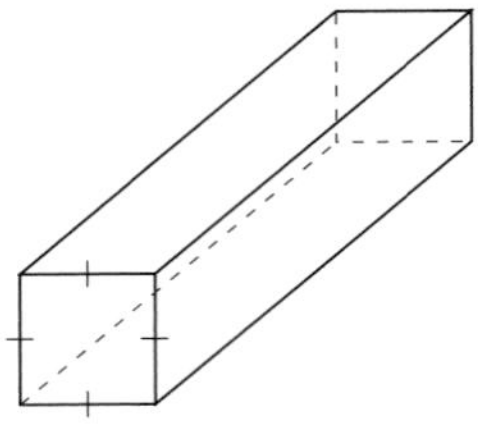

5. Draw a net for the box shown at the left. See left.

5)

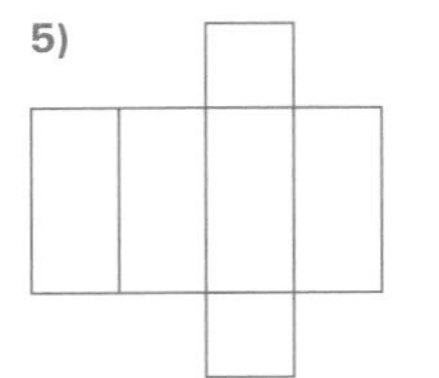

6. **a.** Show your net for the regular pyramid in this lesson's Activity.
   b. Trace your net in part **a,** cut it out, and fold it to make a pyramid.
   c. Why must the altitude of each triangular face be greater than half the length of a side of the square base?
   See page 539.
7. Suppose you wanted to make the cylinder pictured at the right. Draw a net you could use. Make the net actual size. Trace your net and cut it out to make the cylinder. See margin.

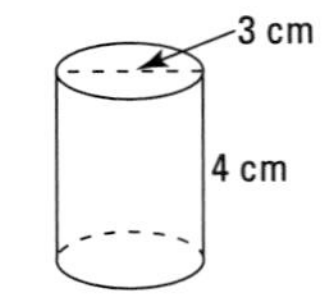

8. Draw a net for a regular triangular prism with a base edge of 3″ and a height of 2″.
See margin.

Applying the Mathematics

9. Connect the centers of the six faces of a cube. What polyhedron is formed? regular octahedron
10. **a.** A is the center of the partial disk at the right. If the shape is cut out and $\overline{AB}$ is moved to coincide with $\overline{AC}$, what 3-dimensional figure will be formed? cone without a base
    b. Make an accurate partial disk with AB = 4 in. and $m\angle BAC = 100$. Cut out the shape and make the surface. Answers may vary slightly.

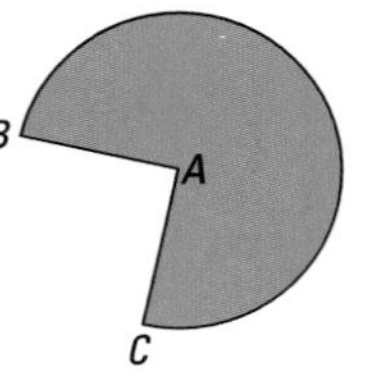

540

Additional Answers

7. (Art is reduced in size.)

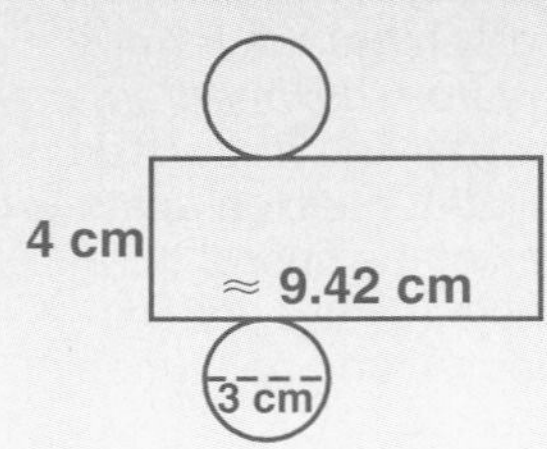

8. Sample: (Art is reduced in size.)

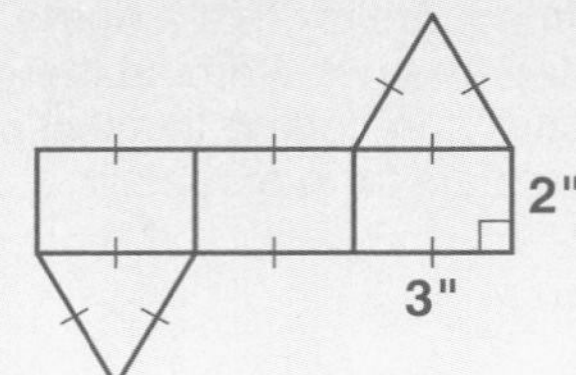

11. *Multiple choice.* Which cannot be a net for a cube? d

(a) 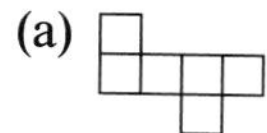 (b) 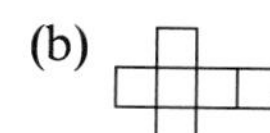 (c) 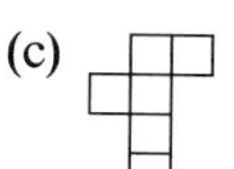 (d) 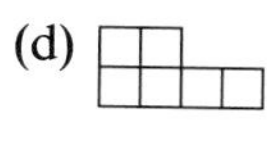

12) Sample, shown in reduced size:

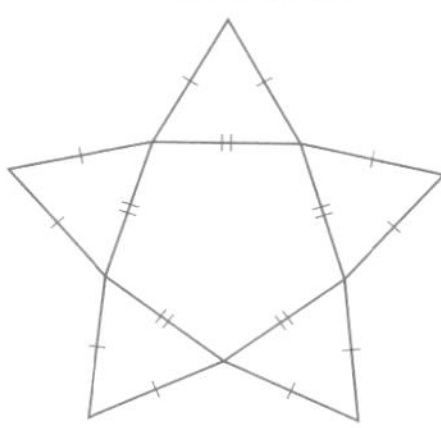

In 12 and 13, draw a net for the figure.

12. 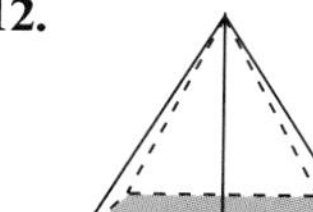

regular pentagonal pyramid
See left.

13. 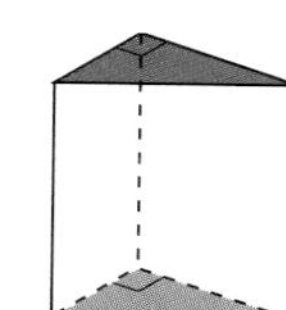

right prism whose bases are right triangles
See left.

14. The net at the left is for what figure? regular hexagonal prism

15. The can at the right has a paper label that exactly covers its lateral surface. What is the area of the label? about 56.5 square inches

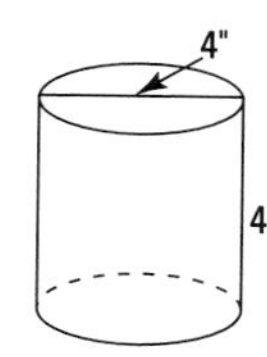

13) Sample, shown in reduced size:

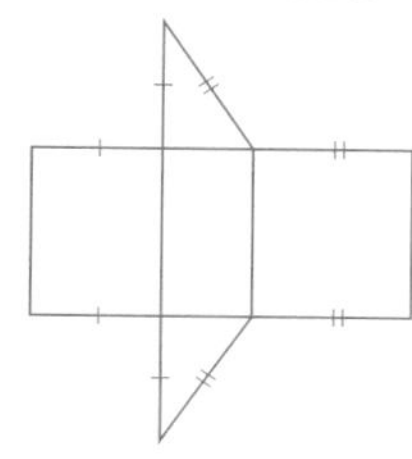

16. Pictured below are top, front, and left views of a solid. Draw a net for the surface of this solid. See margin.

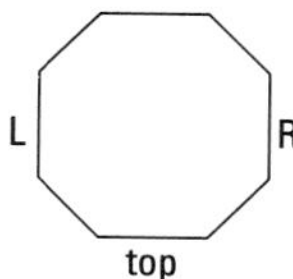

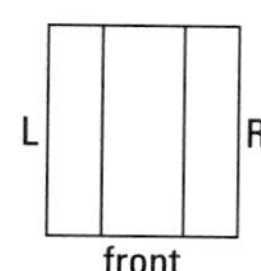

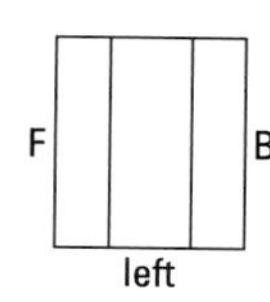

17. Draw a net for a cereal box. See margin.

Review

18. Here are three views of a building. *(Lesson 9-7)*
a. How many stories tall is the building? 3
b. How many sections long is the building from front to back? 3
c. Where is the tallest part of the building? middle, left section

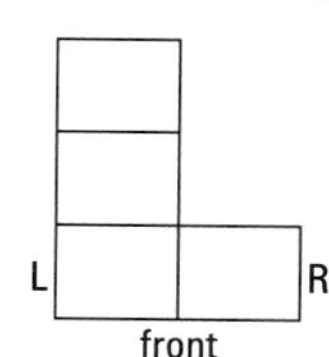

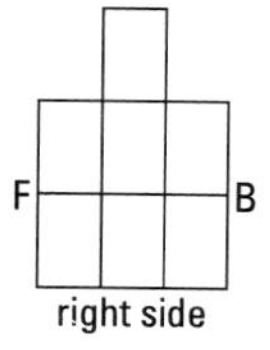

19. Draw top, front, and side views of the chair pictured at the left. (Assume the seat is horizontal.) *(Lesson 9-7)* See margin.

Additional Answers

16. Sample:

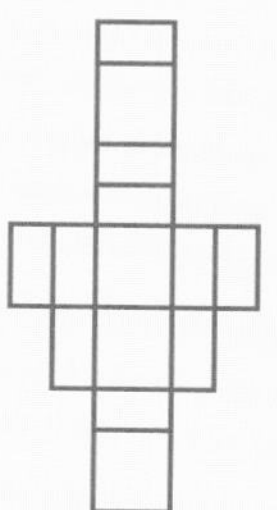

17. Sample:

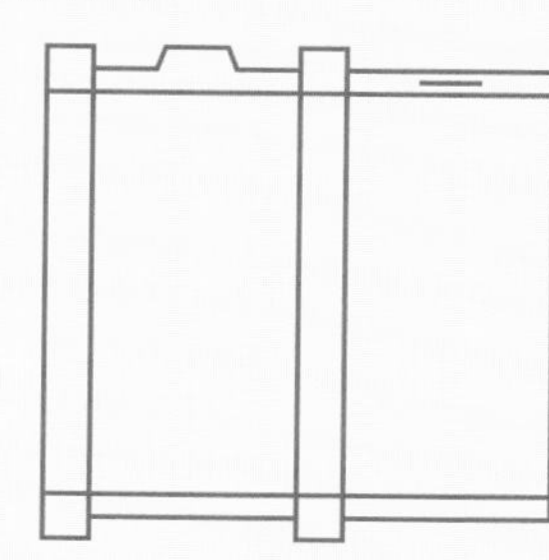

19.

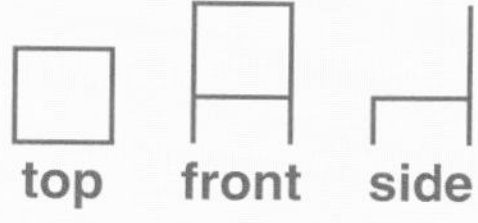

Adapting to Individual Needs

Challenge Writing

This lesson makes the statement that there are only five regular polyhedra. Some students might be interested in writing a paper which discusses how the regular polyhedra received their alternate name *(Platonic solids);* why there are only five regular polyhedra; the duality of pairs of shapes; and the verification of Euler's theorem for each regular polyhedral solid.

[One resource is UCSMP *Precalculus and Discrete Mathematics.*]

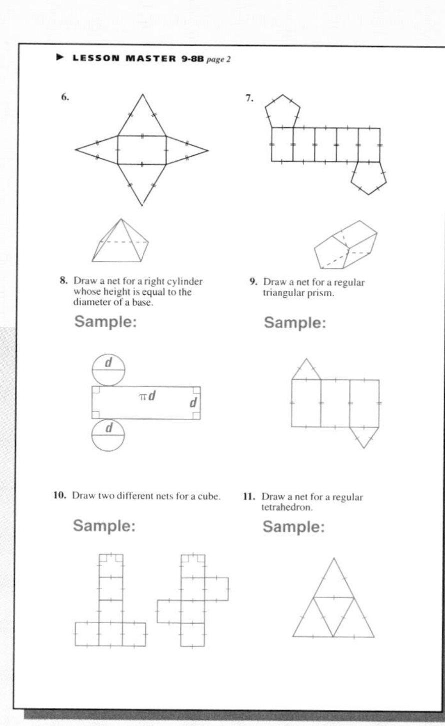

► LESSON MASTER 9-8B *page 2*

6.

7.

8. Draw a net for a right cylinder whose height is equal to the diameter of a base.
Sample:

9. Draw a net for a regular triangular prism.
Sample:

10. Draw two different nets for a cube.
Sample:

11. Draw a net for a regular tetrahedron.
Sample:

Notes on Questions

Question 21 History Connection The relationship $F + V - E = 2$ is sometimes known as Euler's Theorem. Descartes was the first to realize that there might be a formula that applies to all polyhedra; Euler deduced it. The theorem can be proved for all prisms by beginning with the results of **part d** ($n + 2$ faces, $2n$ vertices, $3n$ edges). The theorem can be proved for all pyramids by using the results of **part c** ($n + 1$ faces, $n + 1$ vertices, and $2n$ edges).

Question 26 Encourage students to try to peel an orange at home in one cut to see what curve they get. This net is on **Teaching Aid 128.**

Follow-up for Lesson 9-8

Practice

For more questions on SPUR Objectives, use **Lesson Master 9-8A** (shown on page 539) or **Lesson Master 9-8B** (shown on pages 540–541).

Assessment

Oral/Written Communication Have students **work in groups.** First have students locate a 3-dimensional object in their classroom that can be represented by a net. Have them determine the appropriate measurements and then draw a net to represent the figure with all necessary measurements shown. You may also have students make the model. [Students draw a correct net for an object.]

Extension

Writing Interested students might research *Archimedean polyhedra* and write about them. [Answers will vary.]

Project Update Project 1, *Nets for Packages,* and Project 5, *Regular Polyhedra,* on pages 552–553, relate to the content of this lesson.

21f) pyramid:
$(n + 1) + (n + 1) - 2n = 2n + 2 - 2n = 2$;
prism:
$(2n) + (n + 2) - (3n) = 3n + 2 - 3n = 2$

20. What surface studied in this chapter has the following views? *(Lesson 9-7)*

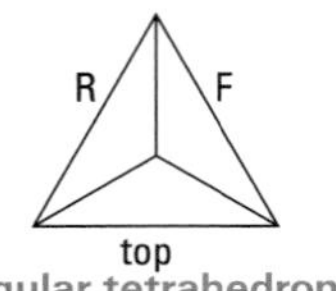

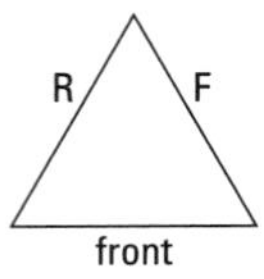

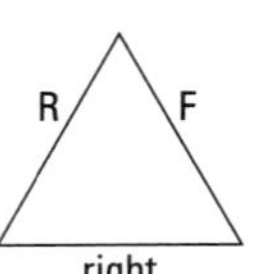

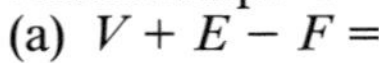
regular tetrahedron

21. In parts **a–d,** give the number of vertices V, edges E, and faces F for each type of figure. *(Lessons 9-3, 9-4, 9-6)*

a. any pyramid whose base is an octagon $V = 9, E = 16, F = 9$

b. any prism whose bases are octagons $V = 16, E = 24, F = 10$

c. any pyramid whose base is an n-gon $V = n + 1, E = 2n, F = n + 1$

d. any prism whose base is an n-gon $V = 2n, E = 3n, F = n + 2$

e. *Multiple choice.* Descartes discovered and Euler proved a simple relationship between the numbers of vertices V, edges E, and faces F of any polyhedron. Which of the following is the relationship? c

(a) $V + E - F = 2$ (b) $F + E - V = 2$

(c) $F + V - E = 2$ (d) $E + F - V = 2$

f. Use algebra and your results in parts **c** and **d** to verify your choice in part **e.** (You will need to use two equations, one for pyramids and one for prisms.) See left.

22. Refer to the right triangular prism in Example 1 in this lesson.

a. Is the figure reflection-symmetric? Yes

b. If so, give the number of symmetry planes. *(Lesson 9-6)* 1

23. In the late fifteenth century, women's steeple caps were popular in France. It was customary for all hair to be concealed by this conical headdress. Find the slant height of a right conical steeple cap with height 24 inches and base area 16π square inches. *(Lessons 8-6, 9-4)* about 24.3 inches

24. Suppose, in a quadrilateral $ABCD$, that $AB = BC = CD = DA$. Why can you conclude that $ABCD$ is a rhombus? *(Lesson 6-3)* by definition of a rhombus

25. Angles 1 and 2 are supplementary. Find t if $m\angle 1 = t$ and $m\angle 2 = t - 10$. *(Lesson 3-3)* $t = 95$

Exploration

26. At the left is a net for a sphere made by peeling an orange in a single cut. Your teacher has a larger copy of this net which you should use for this question.

a. Cut out the net and make a sphere from it.

b. Find the radius of the sphere (in centimeters). Answers will vary.

Setting Up Lesson 9-9

Materials Students will need a colored map in an atlas or a textbook for the *Warm-up* on page 544. You may want a globe and an atlas that has maps with Mercator projections to use when discussing Lesson 9-9.

Introducing Lesson 9-9

Coloring Map

IN-CLASS ACTIVITY

You will need colored pencils for this Activity. If colored pencils are not available, use a variety of patterns.

Below are maps of all the counties in the states of Vermont and Wyoming. 2) See below.

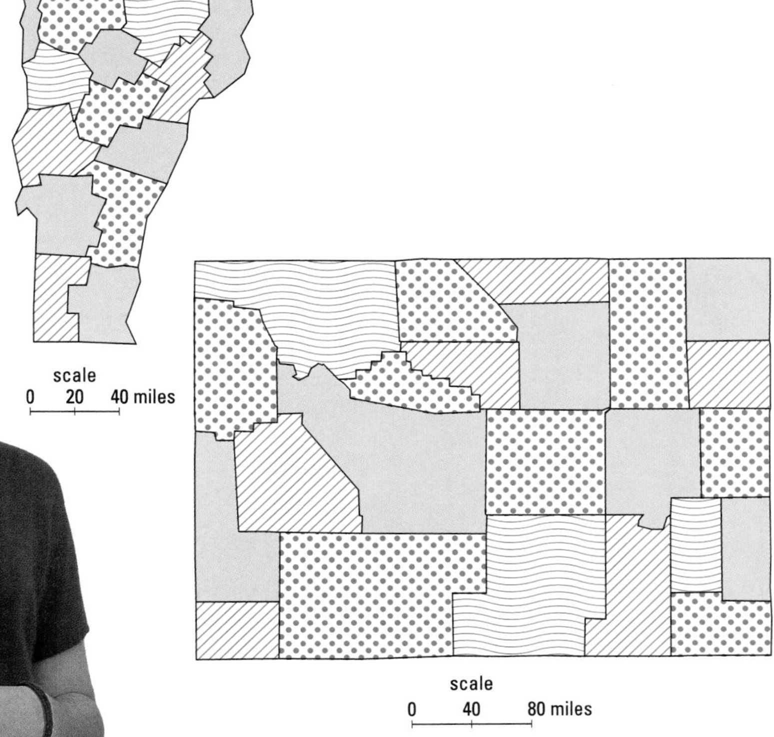

1 Trace or copy one of the maps (or both).

2 Color the counties using the following guidelines:
(1) Each county has the same color throughout.
(2) If two counties share a border, they must be different colors.
(3) If two counties share only a corner, they can have the same color.
(4) Try to use as few colors as possible.

In-class Activity

Resources

From the ***Teacher's Resource File***
- Answer Master 9-9
- Teaching Aid 129: Coloring Map

Additional Resources
- Visual for Teaching Aid 129

Any state's counties could be used for this exercise. We have chosen Vermont and Wyoming because they have fewer counties than most other states. Thus, the activity takes a little less time.

Teaching Aid 129 contains the maps on page 543.

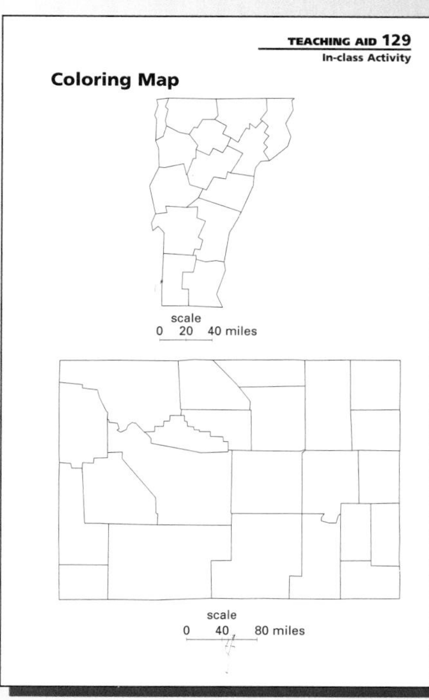

Lesson 9-9

Objectives

I Apply the Four-Color Theorem to maps.
K Interpret maps of the world.

Resources

From the ***Teacher's Resource File***
- Lesson Master 9-9A or 9-9B
- Answer Master 9-9
- Teaching Aids
  104 Map of the United States
  120 Warm-up
  130 Question 13

Additional Resources
- Visuals for Teaching Aids 104, 120, 130
- Globe and atlas that has Mercator projections
- Videodisc

Teaching Lesson 9-9

Warm-up

Locate a colored map in an atlas or one of your textbooks. List the colors used to color the regions of the map. How many colors do you find?
Answers will vary.

Notes on Reading

❶ Students may not realize that a net for even a part of a sphere is technically impossible, since even small sections are curved. So *every* 2-dimensional map of anything beyond tiny parts of the earth—parts that are groomed to be flat—is an approximation.

LESSON

9-9 *Maps and the Four-Color Theorem*

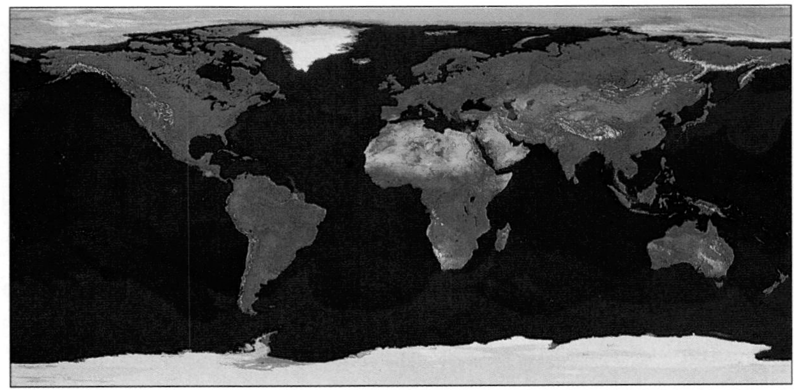

View from Tiros. *This picture of a cloudless world is a composite of the best images of each region as taken by the meteorological satellites. To see the distortion at the poles, compare Greenland (840,004 sq mi) to Australia (2,966,200 sq mi).*

Nets for a Sphere

❶ A map of the world is a 2-dimensional approximation for 3-dimensional Earth. In Lesson 9-8, you learned how to make nets of prisms, cylinders, pyramids, and cones. The challenge that map makers have had to face is that it is not possible to make a flat net for a sphere. To create a globe, globe manufacturers take a net of the surface of Earth and attach it to a sphere. This net consists of a set of tapered sections in shapes called **gores.** The diagram below shows some of the gores in the net.

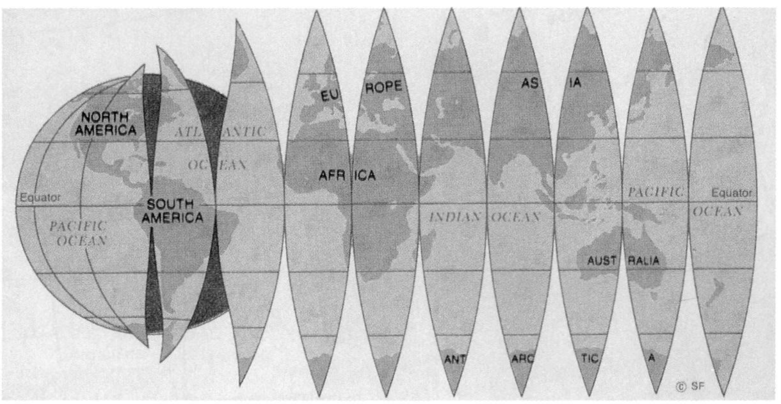

Lesson 9-9 Overview

Broad Goals There are two broad, major goals in this lesson. The first to introduce the problem of drawing a 2-dimensional map of an entire sphere, and to describe several solutions to this problem (one with gores, a second by the Mercator projection). The second is to point out a relatively recent development in mathematics through the discussion of the history of what is now the Four-Color Theorem.

Perspective This lesson consists of two major parts. The first part begins with relating nets to maps, and then introduces a little history of cartography and talks about transformations which are not isometries. The second part initiates a discussion of the problem of coloring neighboring regions on 2- and 3-dimensional surfaces, called the four-color problem. Also, a brief history about the Four-Color Theorem is introduced.

Mathematically, the problem of drawing a map of the world is that of creating a planar net for a sphere. This net is impossible, since (unlike a cylinder or a cone) a sphere has no lines or line segments that lie entirely on it.

Though even part of an exact map is impossible, maps are nevertheless important for travel and for knowing the boundaries of cities, states, and countries. It is therefore

While gores give a fairly accurate view of the surface of Earth, they are very difficult to use as a map. One problem is that different parts of the same country, such as the United States, are on different gores, making it hard to see the country's actual shape. A second problem is more practical. The nonconvex shape of this map makes it easy to tear and inconvenient to use.

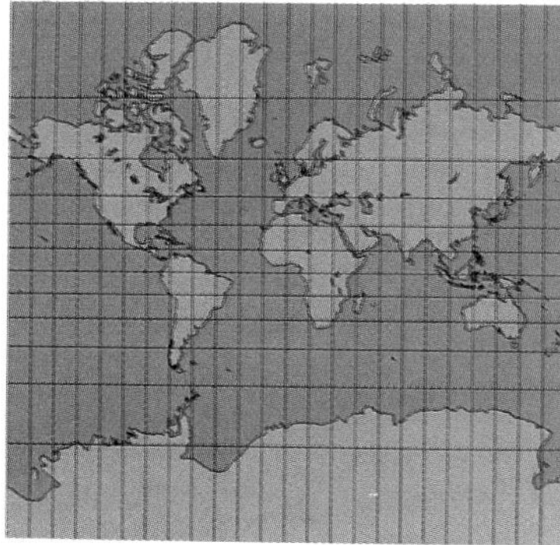

❷ Above is a map of the world like those you see most often reproduced in newspapers and books. It is called a **Mercator projection,** named for Gerhardus Mercator, the Flemish cartographer who created it in 1569. While commonly used, this map is *not* an accurate picture of the world. Greenland looks almost as large as the continent of Africa. But the land area of Greenland is about 840,000 square miles, while the land area of Africa is about 11,700,000 square miles. Africa actually has about 14 times the area of Greenland.

A Mercator-projection map is made by projecting the surface of Earth onto the lateral face of a cylinder. The ray with endpoint at the center of Earth containing a point P on the surface of Earth also contains its image point P' on the cylinder. This is done with all the points on the surface of Earth for which rays containing them intersect the cylinder. The cylinder is then unrolled to give the map. So a Mercator projection is a net for a cylinder, not for a sphere.

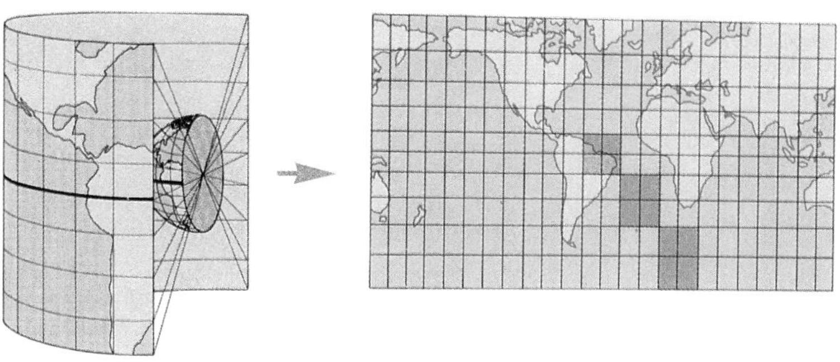

❷ We recommend using a globe and an atlas with Mercator projections. (Your school library probably has a number of atlases.) You can see that on a globe, Australia is many times larger in area than Greenland, and you can compare that with a Mercator projection which shows Greenland to be larger. Similarly, you can compare the areas of Africa and North America.

The Four-Color Theorem can be stated as a theorem involving networks. If the regions are states, as on page 546, to see the network, represent the capital of each state by a point. Connect two capitals if the states are adjacent. Color the capitals with the color you give the states. Then the four-color problem essentially says that, in certain networks, the nodes can be colored with four colors such that no arc connects two nodes of the same color. This idea is used in *Extension* on page 549.

Though the partial map on page 548 can be colored with three colors, if you add Oregon and California to the map, a fourth color is needed.

Geography Connection The only place in the U.S. where four states meet at one spot is the Four Corners Monument, an inlaid slab of concrete on a high plain near U.S. Highway 160. If you stand on the right spot, you can be in Arizona, New Mexico, Utah, and Colorado simultaneously.

A nice pattern is to surround a circle by 2 regions, 3 regions, 4 regions, and so on. When a circle is surrounded by an even number of regions, 3 colors are required; when surrounded by an odd number, 4 colors are required.

interesting to examine the various solutions that have been put forth. The Mercator projection has the advantage of being *conformal*—it preserves angles. Its outline is a rectangle, so it is easily duplicated. It is the most popular projection in books.

However, the Mercator projection has a serious problem that affects the world view of many in the United States. Because it enlarges (and distorts) regions near the poles, regions near the equator appear relatively small. Thus South America and Africa appear smaller than they are. On the Mercator-projection map, Africa looks smaller than North America; it is about 25% larger. Canada looks almost twice the size of the United States; it is actually about 6% larger.

The ease of the first part of this lesson may be dependent on the students' previous knowledge of geography. The point should be made that the meaning of the word *map* comes from the transformations of mapping a sphere onto a flat surface. In addition, it is useful to have maps of the earth with different projections, and a globe. You might be able to get these materials from your school's Social Studies department.

(Overview continues on page 546.)

You may wish to give students a copy of the map on **Teaching Aid 104** to color under the guidelines of the In-class Activity on page 543.

❸ Most students are intrigued by the four-color problem. The fact that it is a theorem will not deter students from attempting to draw a configuration that contradicts the theorem. This provides a good opportunity to explain once again the finality of proof in mathematics.

History Connection Many technological advances have evolved from attempts to solve difficult problems. It would take hours to place a telephone call today if mathematicians had not developed graph theory while attempting to solve the four-color problem. Also, while attempting to solve problems associated with space flight, scientists have produced other results (Tang, Teflon, and so on). The computer has opened the door to many mathematical investigations not possible before, in particular, to the mathematics associated with algorithms that are repeated many times.

This lesson helps students to become aware of the fact that mathematics is dynamic, not static. Since much of their study has been of geometry which was known to the ancient Greeks, they incorrectly assume that most mathematics was known to those people. Remind them that even the fourth-grade arithmetic of today is less than 500 years old, algebra is about 400 years old, calculus is about 300 years old, statistics is less than 200 years old (with much of it developed in this century), and computer science is less than 50 years old. More geometry theorems were discovered in the 19th century than in any previous century.

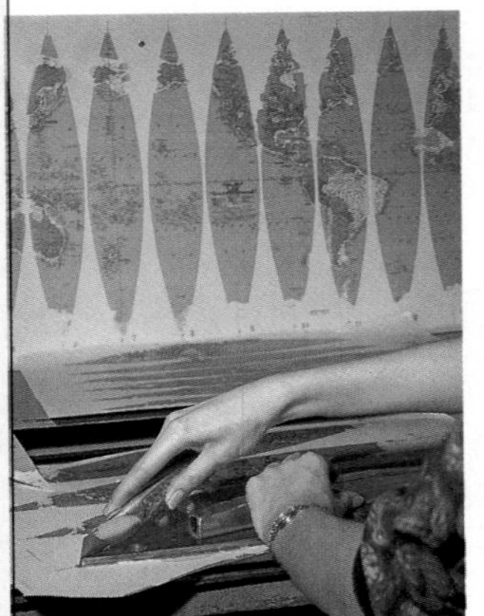

The process of creating a Mercator projection describes a transformation. Each point in the preimage (the surface of Earth) has a unique image point on the map. The preimage is not the entire surface of Earth, since the size of the cylinder will always prevent some points near the North and South poles from appearing on the map.

This transformation, however, is not an isometry because distance is not preserved. Thus distances near the poles are smaller than they appear on the map. Because area is based on distance, Greenland, near the North Pole, appears unusually large. However, the Mercator projection preserves betweenness and collinearity on the meridians (these great circles through the poles are projected onto vertical lines on the map) and on the curves of equal latitude (small circles on Earth are projected onto horizontal lines on the map). So the four directions—north, south, east, and west—are on perpendicular lines.

Coloring a Map

Here is a map of the 48 contiguous states of the United States (all but Alaska and Hawaii). To distinguish the states, each state has been colored under the guidelines of the In-class Activity on page 543. If two states share only a corner, as is the case with Colorado and Arizona, then they can have the same color. Notice that only four colors are needed for this map. Both of the maps in the In-class Activity required only four colors.

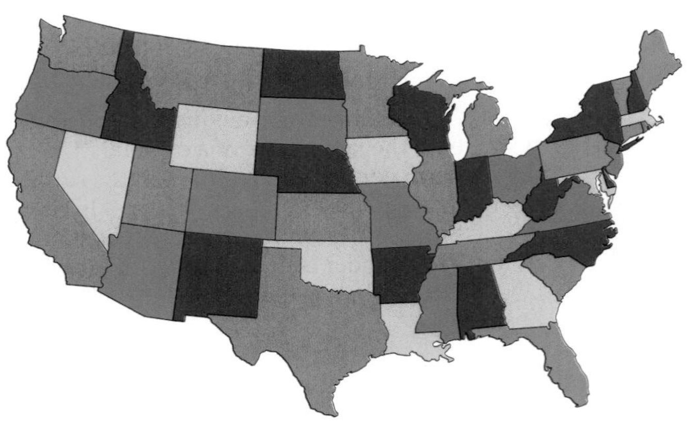

Four-Color Conjecture

In 1852, after studying many maps, Francis Guthrie, a British-born mathematician who later taught in South Africa, conjectured that *any* regions of a map on a sphere or a plane could be distinguished if four colors were used. For Guthrie, a region could have any shape as long as it remained connected. (The two unconnected parts of the state of Michigan were, for Guthrie, two separate regions.)

Lesson 9-9 Overview, continued

The four-color conjecture became famous because Guthrie knew Augustus DeMorgan, an eminent mathematician in England, and DeMorgan spoke about it to William Rowan Hamilton, Arthur Cayley, and Charles S. Peirce. These major figures in mathematics tried in vain to find a proof. In 1931, Hassler Whitney reconfigured the problem as one involving networks by associating each region on the map with a point as Euler had done with the Königsberg Bridge Problem. But there was a difference: two regions were connected by an arc if and only if they had a common boundary curve. The color of the region became the color of its point, so no arc could have two endpoints with the same color. This embedded the four-color problem into graph theory.

The proof of the Four-Color Theorem demonstrated the power of computers in proving theorems. Haken and Appel first proved a number of reduction theorems, relying heavily on the earlier work of others. A key step in their work was to correct some arguments in an earlier, flawed proof. They then reduced the problem to 1,952 different types of configurations in maps. Each configuration type had as many as 500,000 different cases. The computer was then employed to go through all the cases of each type and show that the maps could be colored with four colors.

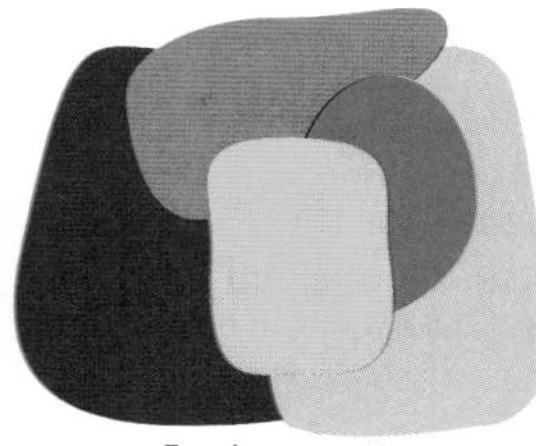
5 colors used

4 colors used

Guthrie's four-color conjecture states that every map *can* be colored using 4 colors or fewer. It does not say that a map *must* use four colors. For instance, the map at the top left has been colored using five different colors. However, it could have been colored using only four colors.

Example

Color this map using as few colors as possible.

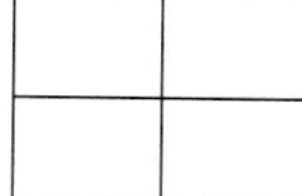

Solution

This map could be colored with 4 colors, but since these regions share a corner, only 2 colors are needed.

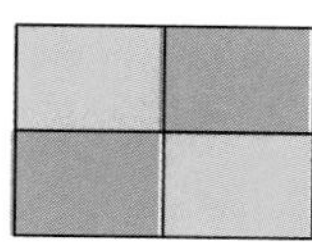

3 Guthrie was not able to prove his conjecture. In fact, many mathematicians tried to prove the conjecture but failed. For almost 125 years, this conjecture, the "four-color problem", was one of the most famous undecided questions in mathematics. By 1975, mathematicians had proved that any map with fewer than 40 regions could be colored with four colors or fewer, but they had not proved that *any* map could be so colored.

By working on this problem, mathematicians discovered some new mathematics. Much of the mathematics of graph theory was discovered in the search for a proof to the four-color conjecture.

The Four-Color Theorem

In 1976, two mathematicians at the University of Illinois, Wolfgang Haken and Kenneth Appel, *proved* that Guthrie's four-color conjecture was correct. They could not prove this just by drawing maps and coloring, for there are infinitely many maps. First they showed that any map they needed to consider was one of 1,952 types of maps. Then they used a computer to help prove that for each type, no more than four colors would be needed to color it. Because of their proof, the four-color conjecture became the *Four-Color Theorem.*

The Four-Color Theorem
Suppose regions which share a border of some length must have different colors. Then any map of regions on a plane or a sphere can be colored in such a way that only four colors are needed.

Additional Examples

Use the method of Lesson 8-3 with "squares" on the Mercator-projection map of page 545 to estimate the area of each continent. Assume that each square has an area of about 900,000 square miles.

1. Africa
   7 inside squares and 13 boundary squares give an estimate of 13.5 · 900,000, or 12,150,000, square miles. Actual area is about 11,700,000 square miles.
2. South America
   2 inside squares and 11 boundary squares give an estimate of 7.5 • 900,000, or 6,750,000, square miles. Actual area is about 6,900,000 square miles.

The entire proof of the Four-Color Theorem has never been written on paper. The proof is partially a usual paper-and-pencil demonstration and partially a computer program. To write the steps the computer has taken would take hundreds of thousands of pages. For this reason, there are still some mathematicians who would say that the conjecture has not been proved; however, most mathematicians today accept the computer-assisted proof.

Notes on Questions

Question 1 Students will need to refer to Lesson 9-5, on page 517, to answer this question.

Question 8 You might use transparencies to show that the coloring is not unique, that is one coloring cannot be derived from another coloring just by exchanging colors.

Question 11 If distance were preserved, then the map of North America would be congruent to the actual land mass. Students can check for the other properties by picking points on the Mercator projection and seeing if the points are also collinear on the Gall-Peters projection.

Question 12 Obviously there is some distortion in the locations of the four points because the four points do not all lie on one plane.

(Notes on Questions continue on page 550.)

Follow-up for Lesson 9-9

Practice

For more questions on SPUR Objectives, use **Lesson Master 9-9A** (shown on page 549) or **Lesson Master 9-9B** (shown on pages 550–551).

Assessment

Written Communication Have students write a paragraph explaining the advantages and disadvantages of the Mercator-projection method. [Students recognize that a Mercator projection enlarges and distorts regions near the poles and gives an unclear view of the world.]

Three-Color Maps

Work is still being done on this topic. In 1987, Elizabeth Wilmer, a student at Stuyvesant High School in New York City, won second prize in the nation in the Westinghouse Science Talent Search for her work on a three-color problem. She analyzed maps which could be colored with three colors. Here is an example of such a map with 19 regions.

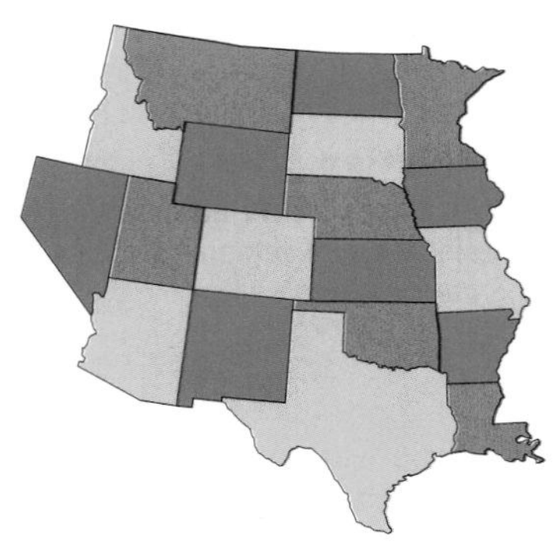

QUESTIONS

Covering the Reading

1. How many years after Magellan's ships circumnavigated Earth did Mercator create his map of the world? 47 years
2. Globe makers use tapered plane sections called __?__. gores
3. A Mercator projection is a net for a __?__. cylinder
4. Of the gores, the globe, and the Mercator projection, which have the following flaws?
   a. The countries are disconnected. gores
   b. The areas of land masses are distorted. Mercator projection
   c. Only half the world is visible. globe
5. Why is the Mercator projection a transformation? Each preimage point has a unique image, and vice versa.
6. a. The total area of the contiguous United States is approximately 3,120,000 sq mi. The area of the U.S. is about how many times that of Greenland? 3.7 times as large
   b. In the Mercator projection, does Greenland look larger than, smaller than, or about equal to the mainland United States? larger than
7. Who first stated the four-color conjecture? Francis Guthrie
8. Color the map at the left in as few colors as possible. See left.
9. How many years elapsed between the statement and the proof of the four-color conjecture? 124
10. Who is Elizabeth Wilmer? a student at Stuyvesant High School who worked on a three-color problem

Sample:

Video

Wide World of Mathematics The segment, *Coloring the Globe,* discusses the need to redesign globes to keep up with changes to world political boundaries. The segment may be used to introduce or extend a lesson on exploring the Four-Color Theorem. Related questions and an investigation are provided in videodisc stills and in the Video Guide. A related CD-ROM activity is also available.

Videodisc Bar Codes

Search Chapter 44

Play

Optional Activities

You might use this activity after students complete the lesson. Have students **work in pairs.** Tell each student to draw an elaborate "map," and give it to his or her partner. The partner should color the map using the map coloring steps that are given in the In-class Activity. Have students make conjectures about the number of colors that are necessary.

Applying the Mathematics

11.

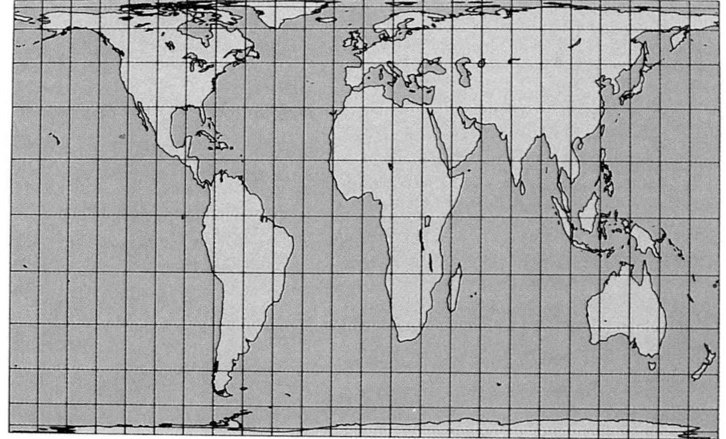

The Gall-Peters equal-area projection is a transformation that preserves relative areas of land masses. For instance, the ratio of the map area of Greenland to the map area of the United States equals the ratio of their actual areas, respectively. Examine the Gall-Peters projection shown above. Which of the A-B-C-D properties are *not* preserved by this transformation?
all of them

12. Oslo, Norway is due west of St. Petersburg, Russia. Also, Bi'r'Allāq, Libya is due west of Alexandria, Egypt.

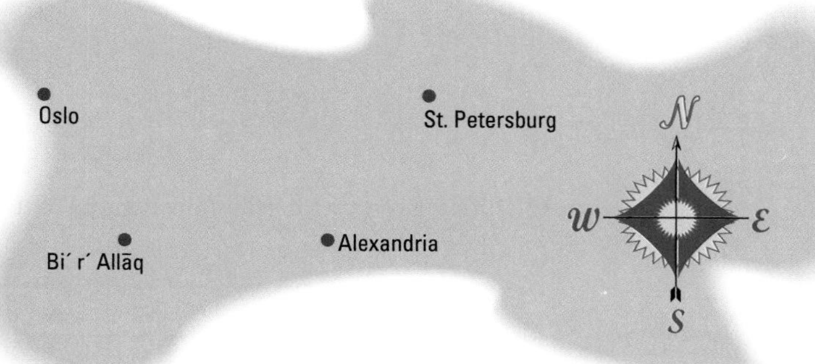

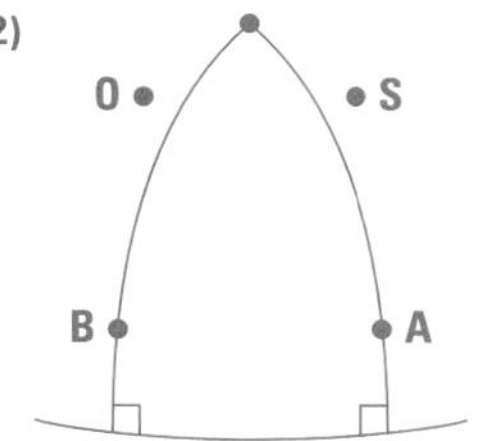

Oslo is west of a north-south line passing through Bi'r'Allāq, and St. Petersburg is east of a north-south line through Alexandria. Yet the distance from Oslo to St. Petersburg is less than the distance from Bi'r'Allāq to Alexandria. How can this be?
The north-south lines, or longitude, are not parallel. They get closer together as you go north from the equator.
See left.

Extension

A method for finding a coloring of a graph is to represent each of the regions as a vertex of a network. Regions that are connected or share a border with the region are vertices that are connected by an edge. Any vertices that are connected would have to be colored different colors since they share a border. An example is given:

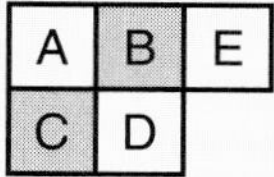

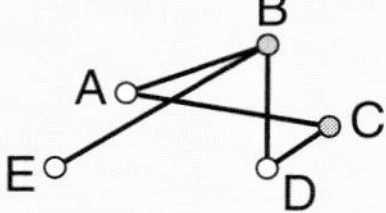

This figure could be colored in two colors *R* (red) and *B* (blue). For example, *B* and *C* could be colored red and *A*, *D*, and *E* could be colored blue. The graph's *chromatic number* is 2 because it can be colored in two colors. Have students draw a graph to represent the map below, color it, and find its chromatic number. [Chromatic number = 3; Sample graph given]

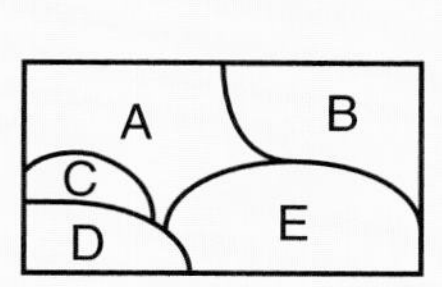

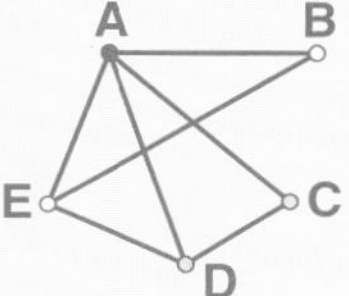

Project Update Project 6, *Continents and Their Countries,* on page 553, relates to the content of this lesson.

Adapting to Individual Needs

Challenge Writing

Have students research and write a report about the Four-Color Theorem and the mathematicians involved. [The reports could include information about Guthrie, how his conjecture was reported, some of the failed attempts at proving the conjecture, some of the areas of mathematics the conjecture has involved, and how the successful proof was obtained. The reports could also focus on how computers are used in proofs. The information can be found in encyclopedias and books on history of mathematics. One detailed resource is *The Four-Color Problem, Assaults and Conquest,* by Saary and Kainen.]

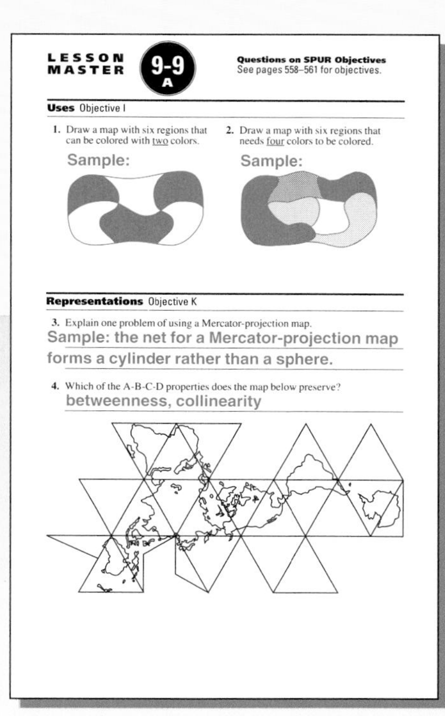

LESSON MASTER 9-9 A

Questions on SPUR Objectives
See pages 558–561 for objectives.

Uses Objective I

1. Draw a map with six regions that can be colored with two colors.
Sample:

2. Draw a map with six regions that needs four colors to be colored.
Sample:

Representations Objective K

3. Explain one problem of using a Mercator-projection map.
Sample: the net for a Mercator-projection map forms a cylinder rather than a sphere.

4. Which of the A-B-C-D properties does the map below preserve?
betweenness, collinearity

Notes on Questions

Question 13 This map is on **Teaching Aid 130.**

Question 14 That this map requires only two colors will surprise many students.

Question 15 Point out that a map does not have to contain many regions to require four colors.

Questions 27–28 Geography Connection These questions could add to students' knowledge of geography. You may wish to have students work in groups. You may be surprised at how much some students know, and disappointed at how little others know.

Additional Answers

17. Sample:

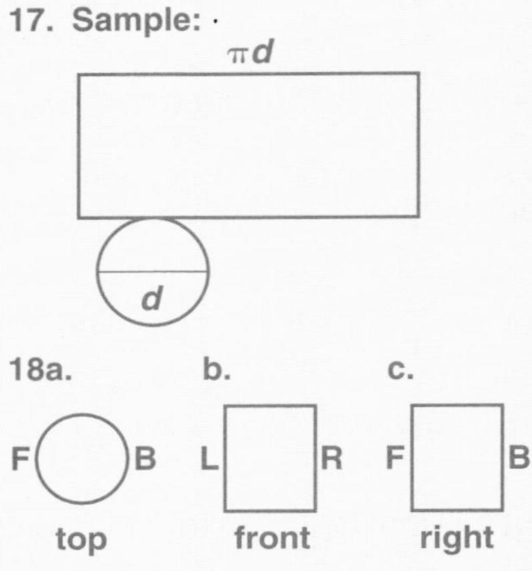

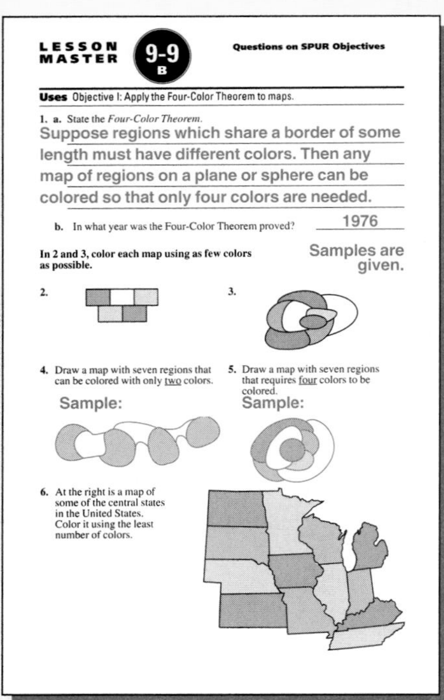

LESSON MASTER 9-9 B

Questions on SPUR Objectives

Uses Objective I: Apply the Four-Color Theorem to maps.

1. a. State the *Four-Color Theorem.* Suppose regions which share a border of some length must have different colors. Then any map of regions on a plane or sphere can be colored so that only four colors are needed.

b. In what year was the Four-Color Theorem proved? 1976

In 2 and 3, color each map using as few colors as possible. Samples are given.

2.

3.

4. Draw a map with seven regions that can be colored with only two colors. Sample:

5. Draw a map with seven regions that requires four colors to be colored. Sample:

6. At the right is a map of some of the central states in the United States. Color it using the least number of colors.

13. Below is a map of Africa. Borders of countries are drawn. Trace the map and color the mainland countries using the least number of colors. (Hint: Start where the countries are most densely packed, and finish with the outside countries.)

14. In the map below, the borders of countries are circular arcs. What is the least number of colors needed to color this map? 2

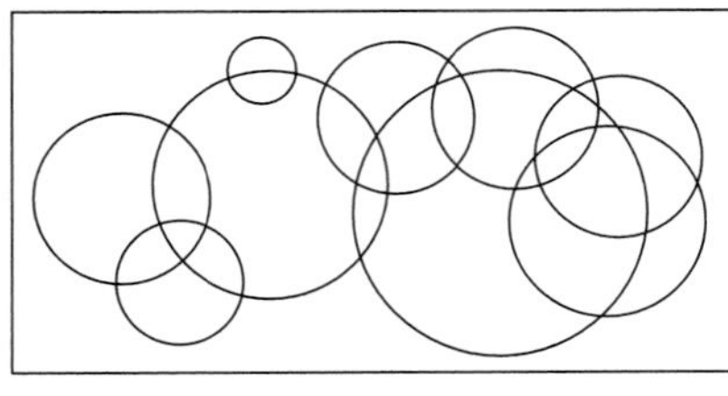

15) Sample:

15. Draw a map with only four regions that needs four colors to color it. See left.

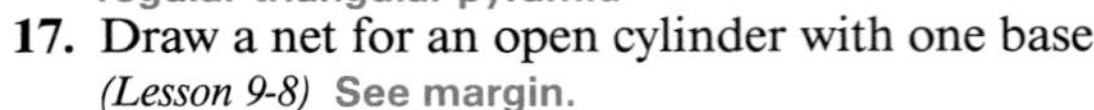

Review

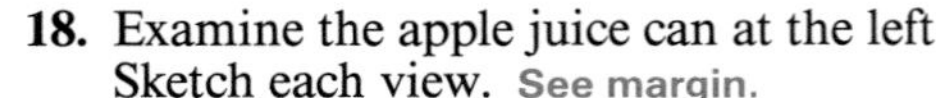

16. What shape can the net at the right form? *(Lesson 9-8)* regular triangular pyramid

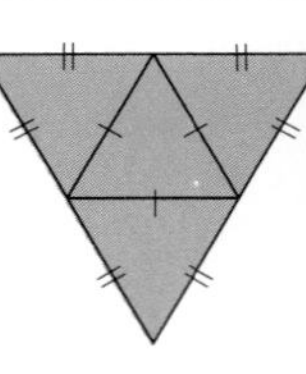

17. Draw a net for an open cylinder with one base. *(Lesson 9-8)* See margin.

18. Examine the apple juice can at the left. Sketch each view. See margin.
a. top **b.** front **c.** right *(Lesson 9-7)*

Adapting to Individual Needs

Extra Help

Point out that the Four-Color Theorem states that any map can be colored in such a way that only four colors are needed. It does not say that a map has to have exactly four colors. In fact, some map makers might use more than four colors simply for aesthetic reasons, but if they wanted to use as few colors as possible, they could use just four colors.

19)

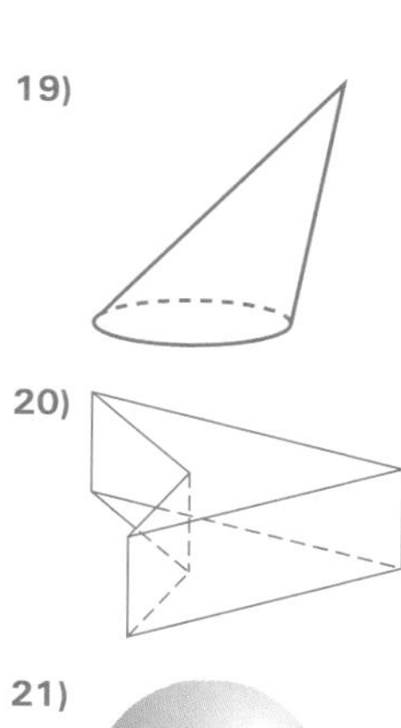

20)

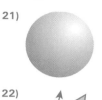

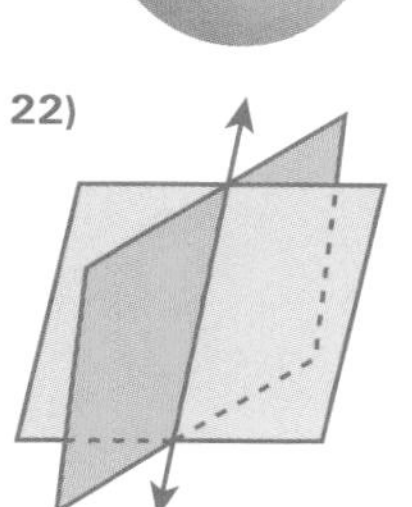

21)

22)

26a) Sample: Some globes use six colors.
b) Sample: Areas are colored according to elevation, mountains, bodies of water.

28a) One is the North Pole. Another is near the South Pole where, after walking a mile south, the explorer ends up on the small circle of latitude with circumference 1 mile. He or she could also start 1 mile north of the small circle with radius $\frac{1}{2}$ mi, $\frac{1}{3}$ mi, $\frac{1}{4}$ mi, and so on.

In 19–22, draw an example of each figure. *(Lessons 9-2, 9-3, 9-4, 9-5)*

19. an oblique cone **20.** a right prism with a nonconvex kite as a base

21. a solid sphere **22.** two intersecting planes

19–22) See left for samples.

In 23 and 24, tell which geometric three-dimensional figure most resembles the real-world object. Give as specific a name as you can, distinguishing solids from surfaces. *(Lessons 9-3, 9-5)*

23. straw
lateral surface of cylinder

24. cantaloupe
solid sphere

25. $ABCDE$ at the right is a regular pyramid. AO is the height. If $DE = 12$ and $AO = 10$, find each measure to the nearest tenth.

a. slant height $\sqrt{136} \approx 11.7$ units

b. BD $12\sqrt{2} \approx 17.0$ units

c. length of a lateral edge $\sqrt{172} \approx 13.1$ units

d. area of $\triangle AOD$ *(Lessons 8-4, 8-6, 9-4)*
$30\sqrt{2} \approx 42.4$ units^2

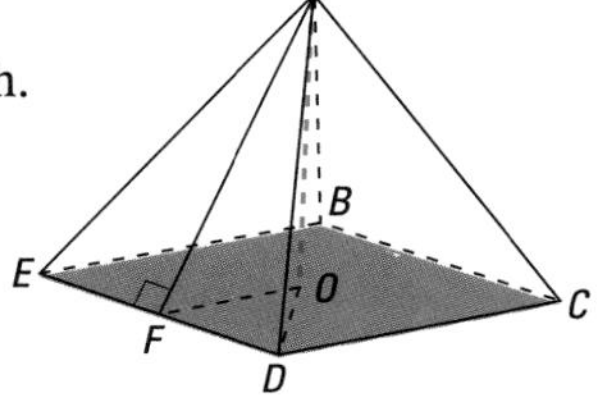

Exploration

26. Find a globe in a library, study, or store. See left.

a. How many colors are used to color the countries and the oceans?

b. What conventions are used in coloring the regions?

27. Using the United States map in this lesson, name all the states that

a. are shaded yellow.

b. are green.

c. are purple.

d. are red.

e. are not pictured.
See margin.

28. An old riddle is thus: "An explorer walks one mile due south, turns and walks one mile due east, turns again and walks one mile due north. The explorer is now at the original starting point. The explorer sees a bear. What color is the bear?"

a. Find all the points on Earth where an explorer could walk 1 mile south, 1 mile east and 1 mile north and end up at the original starting point. See left.

b. What kind of bears live near your answer to part **a**?
Polar bears live around the North Pole only.

27a. Nevada, Wyoming, Oklahoma, Louisiana, Iowa, Kentucky, Georgia, Maryland, Massachusetts
b. Oregon, Arizona, Colorado, South Dakota, Missouri, Mississippi, Ohio, Virginia, New Jersey, Rhode Island
c. Idaho, New Mexico, Nebraska, North Dakota, Arkansas, Wisconsin, Indiana, Alabama, North Carolina, West Virginia, New York, New Hampshire, Delaware
d. Washington, California, Utah, Montana, Kansas, Texas, Minnesota, Illinois, Michigan, Tennessee, Pennsylvania, Florida, South Carolina, Connecticut, Vermont, Maine
e. Hawaii, Alaska

Setting Up Lesson 10-1

Materials Students using Activity 1 in *Optional Activities* on page 566 will need empty boxes that can be flattened and food cans.

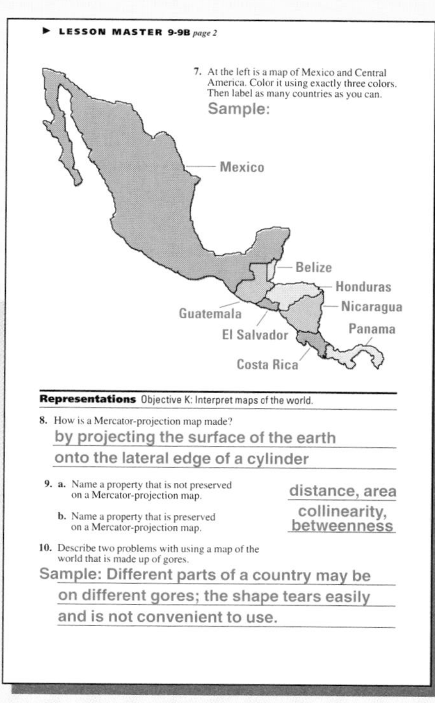
► LESSON MASTER 9-9B *page 2*

7. At the left is a map of Mexico and Central America. Color it using exactly three colors. Then label as many countries as you can.
Sample:

Representations Objective K: Interpret maps of the world.

8. How is a Mercator-projection map made?
by projecting the surface of the earth onto the lateral edge of a cylinder

9. a. Name a property that is not preserved on a Mercator-projection map. distance, area

b. Name a property that is preserved on a Mercator-projection map. collinearity, betweenness

10. Describe two problems with using a map of the world that is made up of gores.
Sample: Different parts of a country may be on different gores; the shape tears easily and is not convenient to use.

Chapter 9 Projects

The projects relate chiefly to the content of the lessons of this chapter as follows:

Project	Lesson(s)
1	9-8
2	9-3, 9-4, 9-5, 9-7
3	9-7
4	9-1, 9-2, 9-5
5	9-8
6	9-9
7	9-5

1 **Nets for Packages** Encourage students to look for packages other than rectangular boxes. For example, some chocolate bars are packaged in boxes shaped like triangular prisms.

2 **Structures** Samples of structures with different shapes include the Pentagon—a pentagonal prism, domes on many capitol buildings—hemispheres, many skylights—the shape of square pyramids, elevators—the shape of rectangular prisms, the spires on churches—hexagonal or octagonal pyramids, or cones. Columns on buildings are typically cylindrical in shape or may resemble prisms with various regular polygons as bases. Many high-rise buildings look like rectangular prisms, although some look like truncated surfaces, such as the John Hancock Tower in Chicago (a truncated rectangular pyramid). The geodesic dome in Walt Disney World approximates a sphere.

3 **Architectural Views** It is important to note that most designers do make drawings from various views for the people whose job it is to execute the designs. Multiple drawings of this type are essential for irregular roofs, recessed walls, and structures which are not basically rectangular prisms in shape. Often

PROJECTS 9 CHAPTER NINE

A project presents an opportunity for you to extend your knowledge of a topic related to the material of this chapter. You should allow more time for a project than you do for typical homework questions.

1 Nets for Packages

Many nets include flaps for adhesive. Undo three packages to determine the net from which the package was made. At least one package should be of a shape other than a box. Make a scale drawing of each net and package. Then design a net that would produce an appropriate package for a product of your choice.

2 Structures

Copy pictures or take photographs of buildings, dwellings, or other structures with a shape approximating each of the types of surfaces studied in this chapter: cylinders, prisms, cones, pyramids, other polyhedra, and spheres. (Do not use examples shown in this chapter.) Estimate the important dimensions of each structure. Arrange this information nicely on a poster or in a small booklet.

3 Architectural Views

Make a series of accurate drawings of the front, left side, right side, back, and top of the building in which you live. Include the scale you used. Then, do the same for a dream house of your design.

4 Geometry on a Sphere

Consider the following postulates and theorems from this book.

Point-Line-Plane Postulate
Corresponding Angles Postulate
Transitivity of Parallelism Theorem
Two Perpendiculars Theorem
Perpendicular to Parallels Theorem

a. Do these hold true if "points" are locations on a sphere, "lines" are great circles on the sphere, and a "plane" is the surface of the sphere? For each, explain why or why not using diagrams and words.

b. Do the five statements above hold true if great circles and small circles are considered to be the only lines in the "plane" of the sphere? Explain.

552

Possible responses

1. Responses will vary.
2. Responses will vary.
3. Responses will vary.

4a. Point-Line-Plane Postulate: The Unique Line Assumption does not hold—two great circles which intersect at the "poles" have two points in common. The Number Line Assumption does not hold, because the lines are closed. The Dimension Assumption holds because there are points on the sphere which do not lie on a given great circle. The part of the Dimension Assumption concerning planes holds vacuously since this condition limits us to one plane. The Flat Plane and Unique Plane Assumptions hold because all points in the geometry are in the plane. The Intersecting Planes Assumption holds vacuously because this space contains only one plane. With the restriction of lines being only great circles, there are no parallel lines in this space. Thus, the Corresponding Angles Postulate and the Two Perpendiculars Theorem do not hold. The Transitivity of Parallelism Theorem and the Perpendicular to Parallels Theorem can never have their hypotheses satisfied, so they hold vacuously.

5 Regular Polyhedra

Use cardboard and tape to construct models of the regular polyhedra from the nets provided. The patterns shown below should be enlarged. Cut along solid lines, fold along dotted lines.

tetrahedron

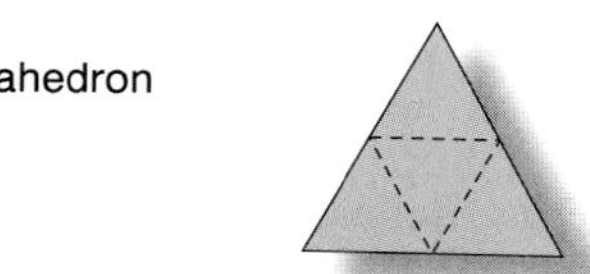

cube

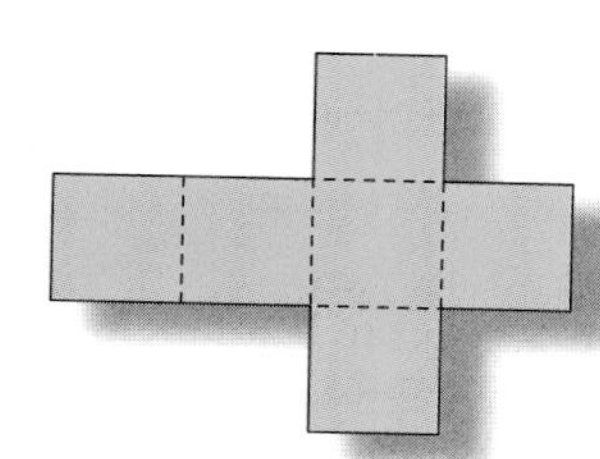

octahedron

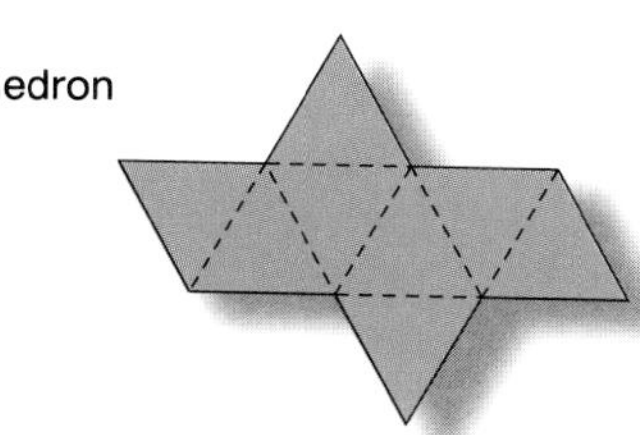

dodecahedron

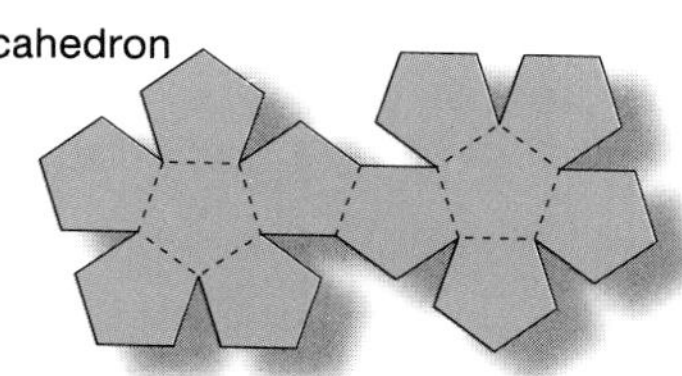

icosahedron

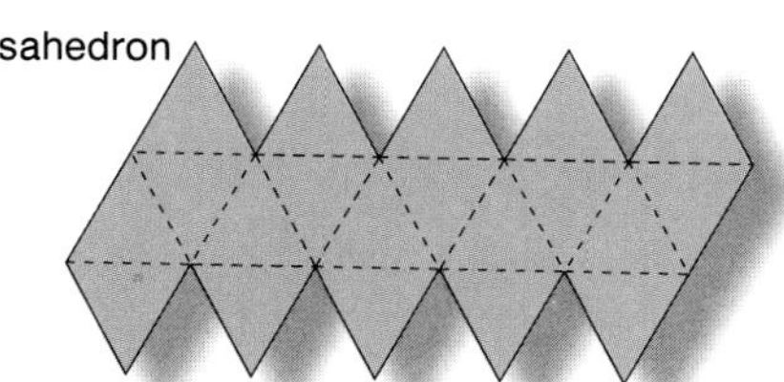

6 Continents and Their Countries

Create a map of the countries of South America and a map of the countries of Asia. Place the names of the countries on the maps. What is the least number of colors necessary to color each map? Color them, using that number of colors.

7 Plane Sections of a Cube

Make a series of large drawings of all the possible plane sections of a cube. How many are there? What are the minimum and maximum number of possible sides of a plane section of a cube? Make a conjecture about the minimum and maximum number of sides of the plane section of any regular prism with bases that are n-gons.

for very irregular-shaped structures, the designer will include drawings of a particular part from multiple views.

The scale used should be indicated, as well as the label of the view, on each drawing. If the residence is not a house, the actual drawings may be accessible through a building manager. The drawings of the two structures will vary by person.

4 Geometry on a Sphere A great deal of information can be found in advanced mathematics books that deal with non-Euclidean geometries. While students should be encouraged to explore these books, urge them to postpone their research until they have worked through the ideas in this project on their own.

5 Regular Polyhedra Some students might be interested in writing a paper about regular polyhedra. Such a paper might discuss how regular polyhedra received their alternate name, Platonic solids; why there are only five; the duality of pairs of shapes; and the verification of Euler's theorem for each solid.

6 Continents and Their Countries Students will find that coloring a map of South America is much easier than coloring a map of Asia because there are fewer countries. Be sure they use a current map of Asia, as recently several new countries have been added.

7 Plane Sections of a Cube Students may wish to cut clay models of cubes if they have trouble visualizing all the different kinds of plane sections. They can also make paper models of cubes and dip them in colored water.

b. The Point-Line-Plane Postulate has the same properties as in part a. Without the limitation of lines being only great circles, there now exist parallel lines, namely great circles and small circles formed by parallel planes intersecting the sphere. Corresponding Angles Postulate: Because the curvature of the sphere is constant, two parallel lines cut by a transversal will have corresponding angles which are congruent. The converse is not true. Consider the intersection of three great circles.

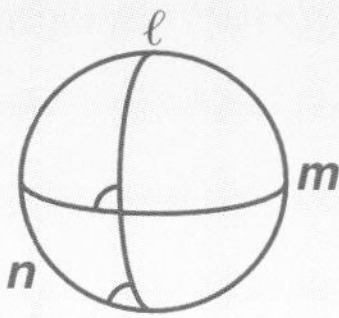

If $\ell \perp m$ and $\ell \perp n$ then the corresponding angles are congruent even though the lines are not parallel. The Transitivity of Parallelism Theorem does hold because the parallel great and small circles are formed by parallel planes, and the Transitivity of Parallelism Theorem holds for planes in three dimensions. By the

(Responses continue on page 554.)

Summary

The Summary gives an overview of the entire chapter and provides an opportunity for students to consider the material as a whole. Thus, the Summary can be used to help students relate and unify the concepts presented in the chapter.

SUMMARY

The purpose of this chapter is to familiarize you with the common 3-dimensional figures, the surfaces and solids that are the figures of solid geometry. You should know their definitions and how they are related, be able to sketch them, identify plane sections, draw views from different positions, and be able to build the simpler surfaces from 2-dimensional nets. Below is a hierarchy relating many of these surfaces.

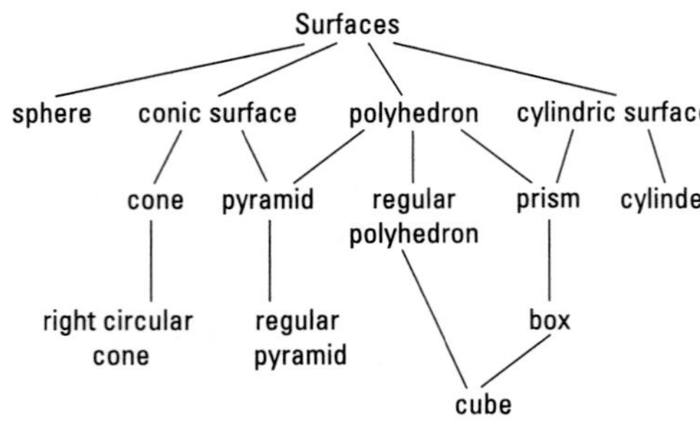

Many ideas from two dimensions extend to three. The basic properties of planes are given in the Point-Line-Plane Postulate. Intersecting planes form dihedral angles. If the measure of the dihedral angle is 90°, then the planes are perpendicular. Like lines, planes may be perpendicular or parallel. Spheres and circles have the same defining property except spheres are in three dimensions. Reflections and reflection symmetry are defined the same way in three dimensions as in two, except that the reflecting line is replaced by a reflecting plane.

Architects use views to describe 3-dimensional figures in two dimensions. Map makers have dealt differently with the impossibility of presenting the spherical Earth on a 2-dimensional map. Certain distortions have to be made in order for other properties to be preserved. The Four-Color Theorem applies to maps drawn on planes and spheres, whether or not shapes on the map are distorted.

Addtional responses, page 553

preceding drawing, we can see that the Two Perpendiculars Theorem does not hold. However, the Perpendicular to Parallels Theorem does not hold, because if circles meet at "90°" angles, the planes determining those circles are perpendicular. So, since this theorem holds for planes in three dimensions, it holds here as well.

5. See students' models.

6. By the Four-Color Theorem, both of these regions can be colored using four colors.

VOCABULARY

Below are the most important terms and phrases for this chapter. For the starred (*) terms you should be able to give a definition of the term. For the other terms you should be able to give a general description and a specific example of each.

Lesson 9-1
Point-Line-Plane Postulate:
Flat Plane Assumption
Unique Plane Assumption
Intersecting Planes Assumption
intersecting planes

Lesson 9-2
*line perpendicular to a plane
Line-Plane Perpendicularity Theorem
parallel planes
distance between parallel planes
distance to a plane from a point
dihedral angle
skew lines

Lesson 9-3
surface, solid
rectangular solid, box
faces of a box, opposite faces, cube
edges of a box
vertices of a box
*cylindric solid
base of a cylindric solid
lateral surface of a cylindric solid
cylindric surface
height or altitude of a cylindric solid
*cylinder
*prism
right prism, right cylinder
oblique prism, oblique cylinder
lateral faces of a prism
lateral edges of a prism
regular prism

Lesson 9-4
conic surface
*base of a conic solid
*vertex of a conic solid
*conic solid
*cone, *pyramid
lateral edges of a pyramid
base edges of a pyramid
faces of a pyramid
lateral faces of a pyramid
right pyramid, oblique pyramid
regular pyramid
axis of a cone
right cone, oblique cone
lateral surface of a cone
lateral edge of a cone
height or altitude of a pyramid
height or altitude of a cone
slant height of a pyramid
slant height of a cone
truncated surface

Lesson 9-5
*sphere
*the radius of a sphere
*center of a sphere
radii of a sphere
the diameter of a sphere
great circle
small circle
hemisphere
great circle route
*plane section
conic sections

Lesson 9-6
perpendicular bisector of a segment (in space)
*reflection image of a point over a plane
reflecting plane
*congruent figures (three-dimensional)
directly congruent figures in space
oppositely congruent figures in space
*reflection-symmetric figure in space
symmetry plane
bilateral symmetry

Lesson 9-7
views, elevations

Lesson 9-8
polyhedron, polyhedrons, polyhedra
tetrahedron, hexahedron
*regular polyhedron
octahedron, dodecahedron, icosohedron
net

Lesson 9-9
gores
Mercator projection
the Four-Color Theorem

Vocabulary

Terms, symbols, and properties are listed by lesson to provide a checklist of concepts a student must know. Emphasize to students that they should read the vocabulary list carefully before starting the Progress Self-Test. If students do not understand the meaning of a term, they should refer back to the indicated lesson.

7.

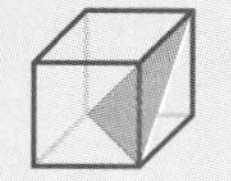
triangle

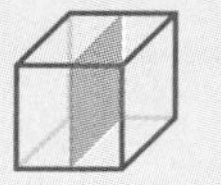
square

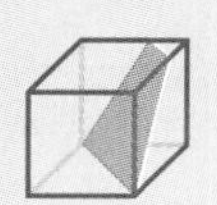
isosceles trapezoid

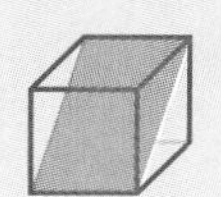
rectangle

hexagon

pentagon

rhombus

With a cube, it is not possible to have a plane section that is a kite, non-isosceles trapezoid, or non-rectangular parallelogram. For the plane section of any regular prism with bases that are n-gons, the minimum number of sides is 3, and the maximum number is $n + 2$.

Progress Self-Test

For the development of mathematical competence, feedback and correction, along with the opportunity to practice, are necessary. The Progress Self-Test provides the opportunity for feedback and correction; the Chapter Review provides additional opportunities and practice. We cannot overemphasize the importance of these end-of-chapter materials. It is at this point that the material "gels" for many students, allowing them to solidify skills and understanding. In general, student performance should be markedly improved after these pages.

Assign the Progress Self-Test as a one-night assignment. Worked-out *solutions* for all questions are in the Selected Answers section of the student book. Encourage students to take the Progress Self-Test honestly, grade themselves, and then be prepared to discuss the test in class.

Advise students to pay special attention to those Chapter Review questions (pages 558–561) which correspond to questions missed on the Progress Self-Test.

Additional Answers

1. Sample:

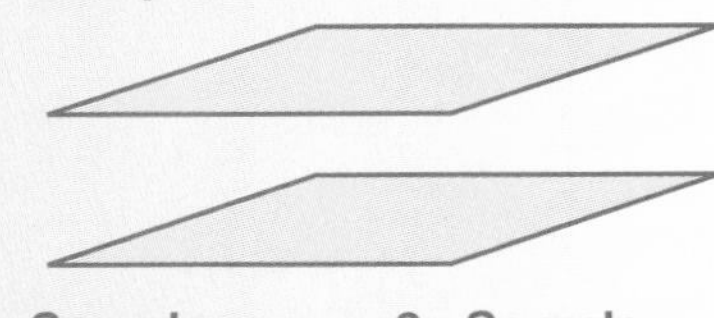

2. Sample:

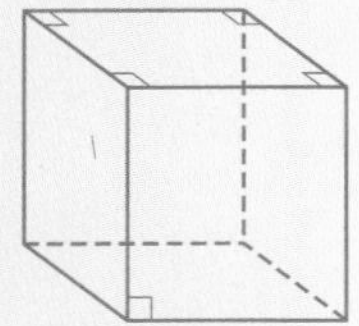

3. Sample:

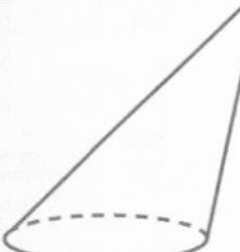

CHAPTER NINE

PROGRESS SELF-TEST

Directions: Take this test as you would take a test in class. Then check your work with the solutions in the Selected Answers section in the back of the book. You will need graph paper and a calculator.

1–5b, 7a, 9) See margin.

In 1–3, draw each figure.

1. two parallel planes
2. regular square prism
3. an oblique cone
4. Explain why a four-legged chair sometimes wobbles.

In 5–7, use the regular square pyramid below.

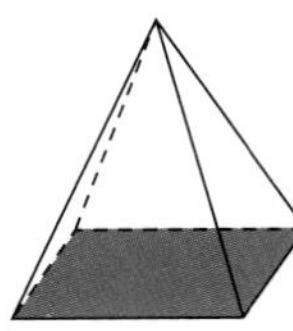

5. a. Trace the figure and sketch a plane section parallel to the base. square
   b. Trace the figure and sketch a plane section not parallel to and not intersecting the base. quadrilateral
   c. Name the shape of each section.
6. How many symmetry planes does this figure have? 4
7. a. Draw a sphere and a plane section containing the center.
   b. Name the plane section. Be as specific as possible. great circle
8. Sketch the top, front, and left views of this toy train car.

In 9 and 10, refer to the right cone below.

9. Draw each view.
   a. top
   b. front
   c. right

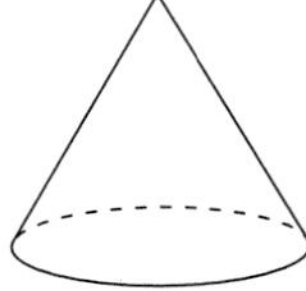

10. How many symmetry planes does it have? infinitely many
11. If a great circle on a sphere has circumference 28π cm, what is the radius of the sphere? 14 cm
12. Refer to the oblique cone with base $\odot O$, $OB = 10$ cm, $AO = 34$ cm, and $BD = 6$ cm.

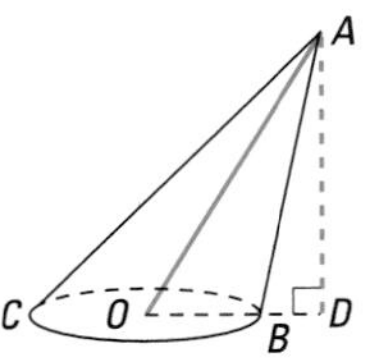

   a. What is the height of the cone? 30 cm
   b. Find the area of the base of the cone. ≈ 314.16 cm
13. In the right triangular prism below, $\overline{EF} \perp \overline{FG}$, $EF = 4''$, and $EG = 9''$. If the height of the prism is $22''$,
   a. find Area($EGHJ$). 198 in^2
   b. find Area($\triangle EFG$). 16.12 in^2

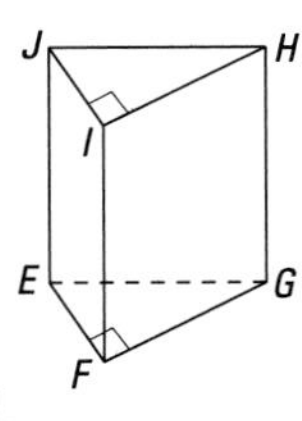

556

CHAPTER NINE

In 14 and 15, tell which three-dimensional figure most resembles the real-world object. Give as specific a name as you can, distinguishing whether it is a solid or a surface.

14. a stick of margarine rectangular solid

15. a blown-up balloon sphere (surface)

16. Here are front, right, and top views of a building.

a. How many stories tall is the building? 2

b. How many sections long is the building from front to back? 4

c. Where is the tallest part of the building located?
all sections of the left side

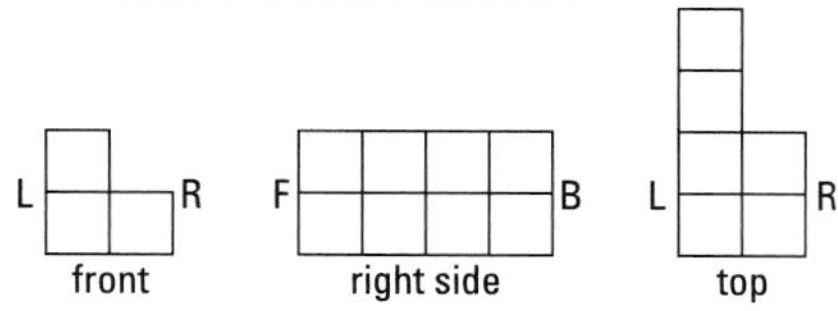

17. Give as specific a name as possible to the surface studied in this chapter with these views.

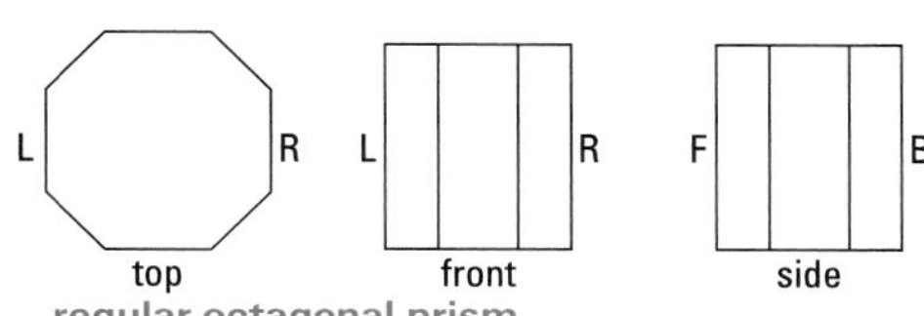

regular octagonal prism

18. Draw a net for a regular pentagonal pyramid.

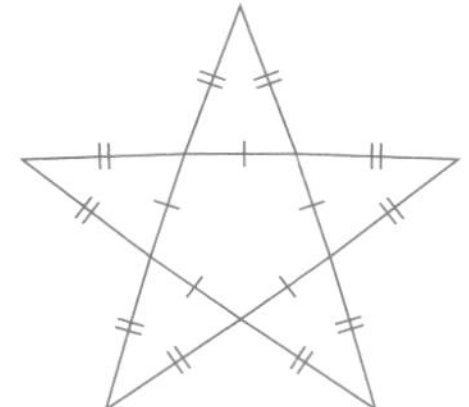

19. Name the figure that can be made from the net below. right prism with bases shaped like a parallelogram

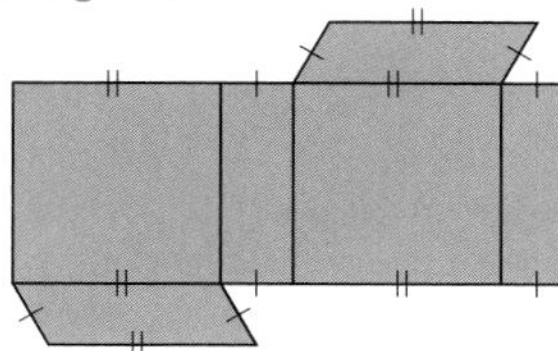

20. *Multiple choice.* In a Mercator projection, which of the following is preserved?
(a) relative distance
(b) relative areas of land mass
(c) connectedness of land mass
(d) betweenness c, d

21. Draw a map with five regions that requires four colors to be colored.

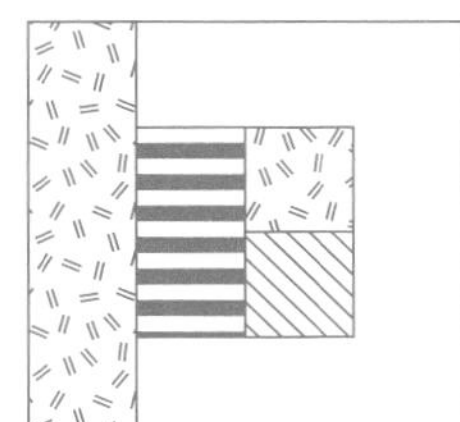

4. Sample: The endpoint of one leg does not lie in the plane determined by the endpoints of the other three legs.

5a. Sample:

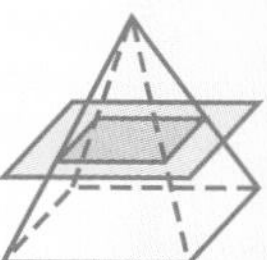

b. Sample:

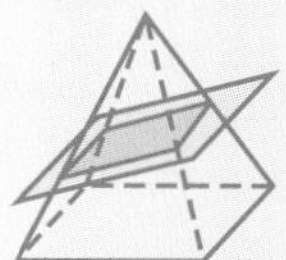

7a.

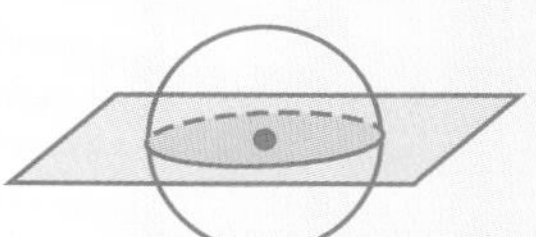

9a.

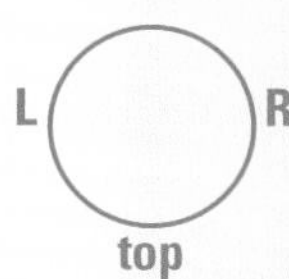

b.

c.

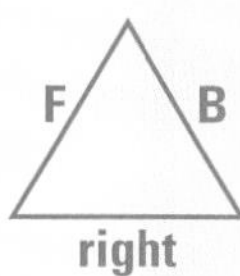

Chapter 9 Review

Resources

From the ***Teacher's Resource File***
- Answer Master for Chapter 9 Review
- Assessment Sourcebook: Chapter 9 Test, Forms A–D Chapter 9 Test, Cumulative Form Comprehensive Test, Chapters 1–9

Additional Resources
- Quiz and Test Writer

The main objectives for the chapter are organized in the Chapter Review under the four types of understanding this book promotes—Skills, Properties, Uses, and Representations.

(Review notes continue on page 560.)

Additional Answers

1. Sample:

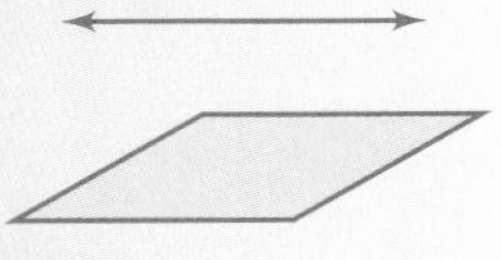

2. Sample:

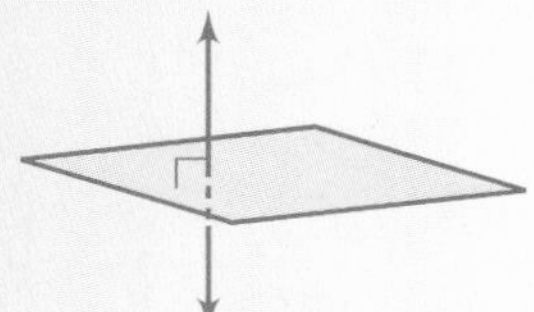

3. Sample:

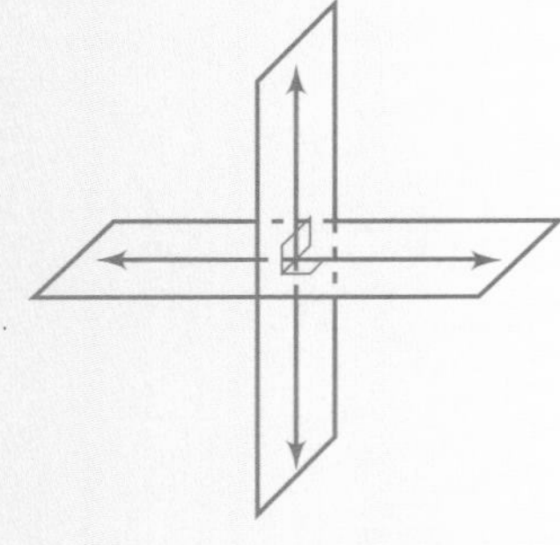

CHAPTER REVIEW

Questions on SPUR Objectives

SPUR stands for **S**kills, **P**roperties, **U**ses, and **R**epresentations. The Chapter Review questions are grouped according to the SPUR Objectives for this chapter.

SKILLS DEAL WITH THE PROCEDURES USED TO GET ANSWERS.

Objective A: *Draw common 3-dimensional shapes.* *(Lessons 9-2, 9-3, 9-4, 9-5)* **See margin.**

In 1–8, draw each figure.

1. a line parallel to a plane
2. a line perpendicular to a plane
3. two perpendicular planes
4. a right cone
5. a right hexagonal prism
6. a sphere
7. a regular square pyramid
8. an oblique cylinder

Objective B: *Draw plane sections of common 3-dimensional shapes.* *(Lesson 9-5)* **See margin.**

In 9–11, use the figures below.

a. Trace the figure and sketch a plane section parallel to the base(s).

b. Trace the figure and sketch a plane section not parallel to and not intersecting the base(s).

c. Name the shape of each section.

9. 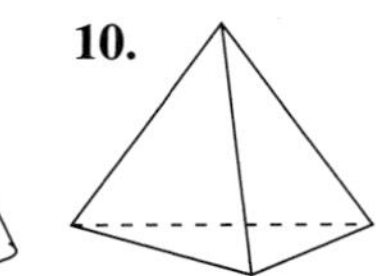 **10.** 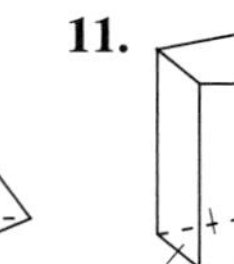 **11.**

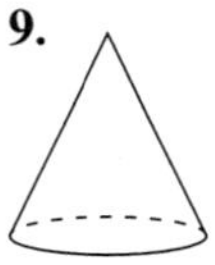

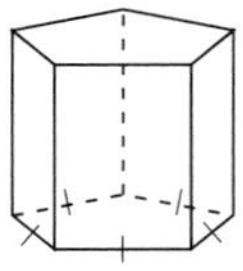

12. a. Draw a sphere and a plane section not containing the center.

b. Name the plane section. Be as specific as possible.

c. How does this plane section differ from a great circle of the sphere?

Objective C: *Give views of a figure from the top, sides, or front.* *(Lesson 9-7)* **See margin.**

13. Give each view of the right circular cylinder at the right.

a. top
b. front
c. right

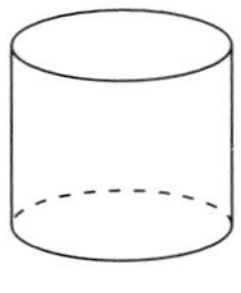

14. Give each view of the regular square pyramid at the right.

a. top
b. front
c. right

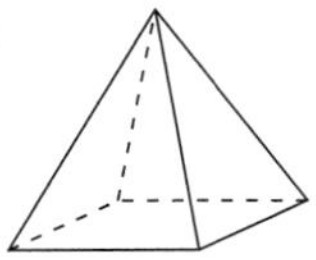

In 15 and 16, for each object sketch views of the **a.** top, **b.** front, and **c.** right.

15. a house

front

16. a cup

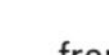

front

Objective D: *Given appropriate lengths, calculate areas and lengths in 3-dimensional figures.* *(Lessons 9-3, 9-4, 9-5)*

17. In the regular triangular pyramid shown at the right, $AC = 12$ and $AD = 10$.

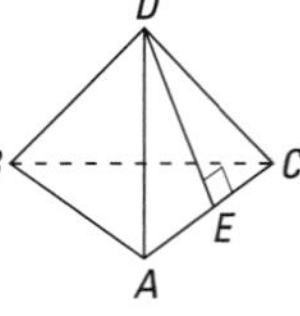

a. Find the perimeter of the base. **36 units**

b. Find the area of $\triangle ABD$. **48 units^2**

Additional Answers, continued

4. Sample:

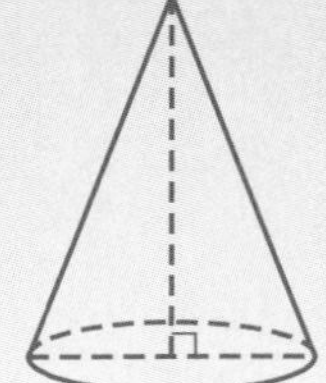

5. Sample:

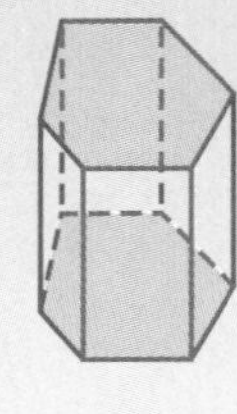

6. Sample:

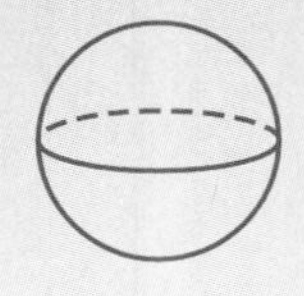

7. Sample:

8. Sample:

9a. Sample:

b. Sample:

c. Part a is a circle and part b is a an ellipse

18. Consider the oblique square prism shown below.

a. Which segment's length is the height of the prism? $\overline{LN}$

b. If $GN = 15$ and $LN = 40$, what is the length of $\overline{KF}$? ≈ 42.7 units

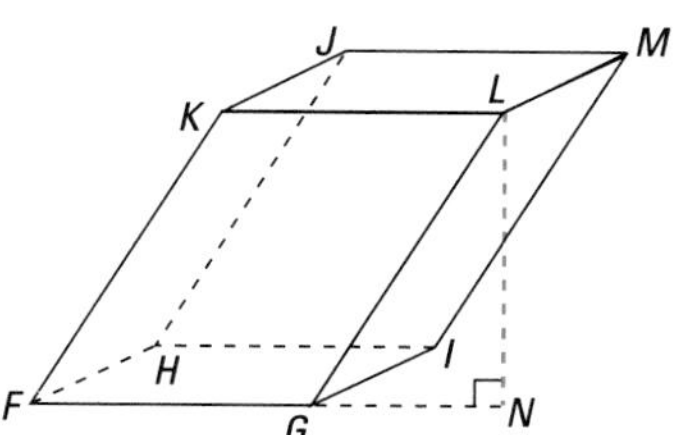

19. In the oblique cylinder at the right with base $\odot D$, $AC = 9$ cm, $BD = 10$ cm, and $CD = 3$ cm. a) $9\pi \approx 28.3$ cm^2

a. Find the area of the base of the cylinder.

b. Find the height of the cylinder. $\sqrt{32} \approx$ 5.7 cm

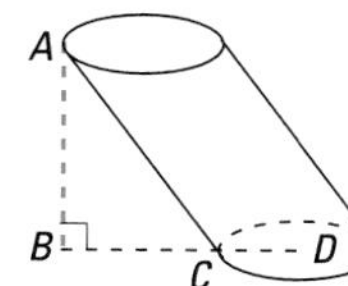

20. a. A sphere has radius 12″. What is the area of a great circle of the sphere? ≈ 452.4 in^2

b. Find the circumference of a great circle of the sphere. ≈ 75.4 in.

21. A right cone has a height of 24 mm and a slant height of 25 mm.

a. Draw such a cone. See margin.

b. Find the area of its base. $49\pi \approx 153.9$ mm^2

22. In the regular pentagonal pyramid shown at the right, $HO = 7$ and $HT = 16$. Find

a. OT. $\sqrt{207} \approx 14.4$ units

b. Area($\triangle HOT$). ≈ 50.4 units^2

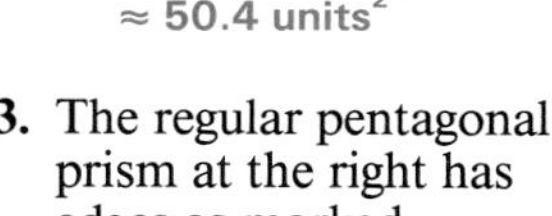

23. The regular pentagonal prism at the right has edges as marked.

a. Find the perimeter of one lateral face. 34 units

b. Find the sum of the areas of the five lateral faces. 350 units^2

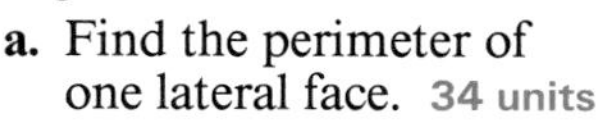

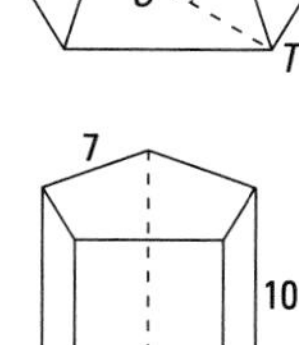

24. At the right is a right cylinder with parts marked. b) $240\pi \approx$ 754.0 units^2

a. Find the area of a base. $64\pi \approx$ 201.1 units^2

b. Find the area of the lateral surface.

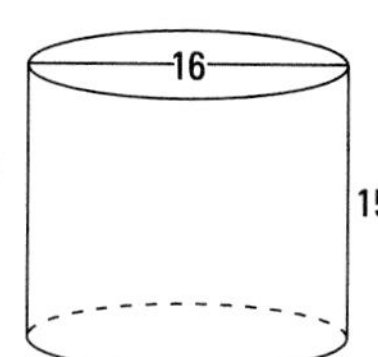

Objective E: *From 2-dimensional views of a figure, determine the 3-dimensional figure. (Lesson 9-7)*

In 25 and 26, use the given views of the buildings.

a. How many stories tall is the building?

b. How many sections long is the building from front to back?

c. Where is the tallest part of the building located?

25.

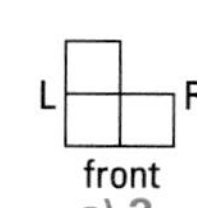

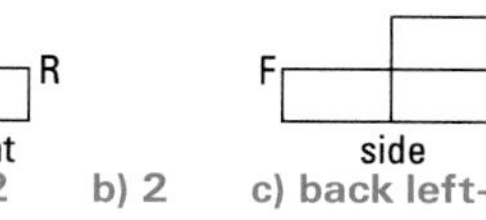

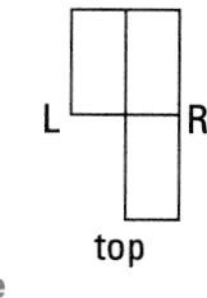

a) 2 b) 2 c) back left-hand side

26.

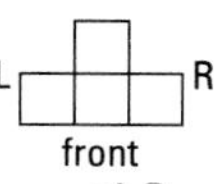

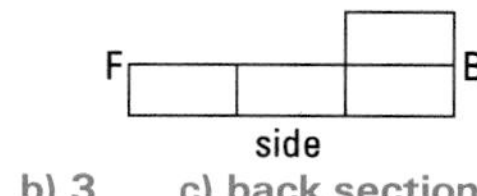

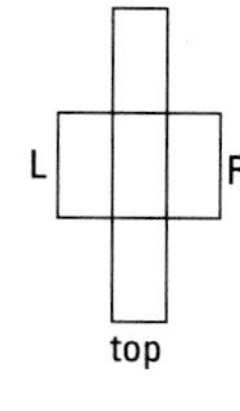

a) 2 b) 3 c) back section

27. Which cylindric solid studied in this chapter has these views? solid right cone

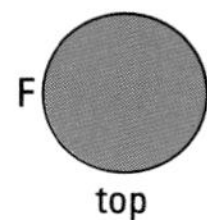

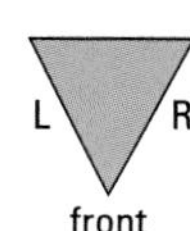

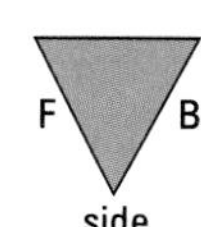

28. Give as specific a name as possible to the surface studied in this chapter with these views.

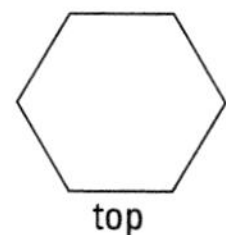

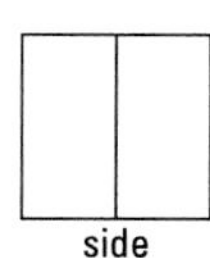

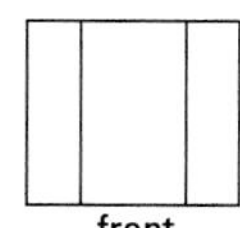

regular hexagonal prism

10a. Sample:

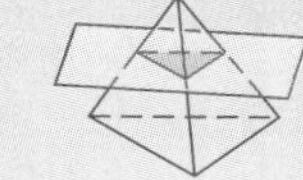

b. Sample:

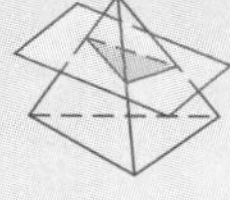

c. Part a is a triangle and part b is a triangle.

11a. Sample:

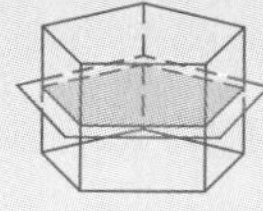

b. Sample:

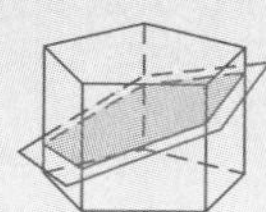

c. Part a is a regular pentagon, and part b is a nonregular pentagon.

12a.

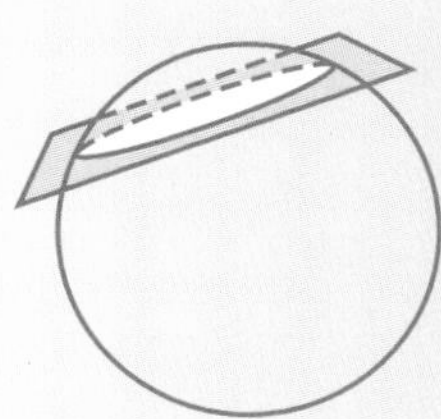

b. a small circle

c. Its center is not the center of the sphere.

13a–c.

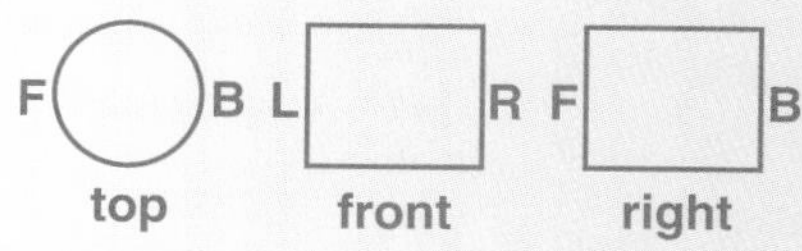

14a–c.

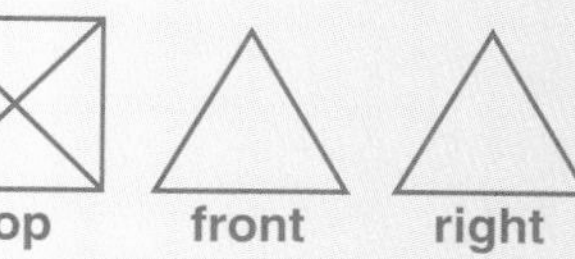

15a–c.

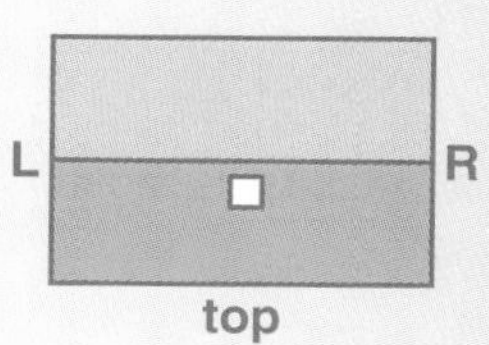

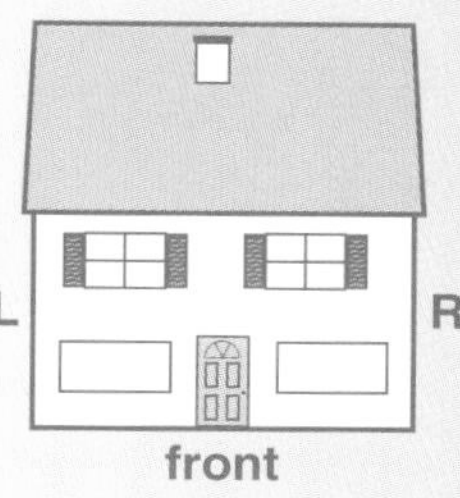

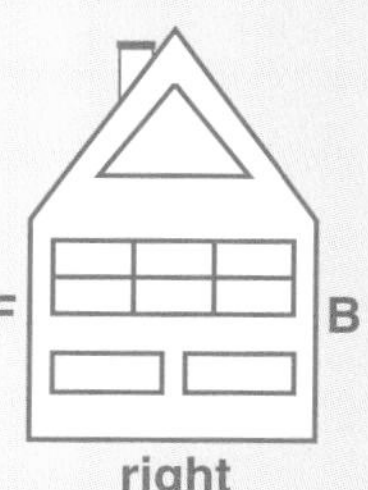

16a–c.

21a.

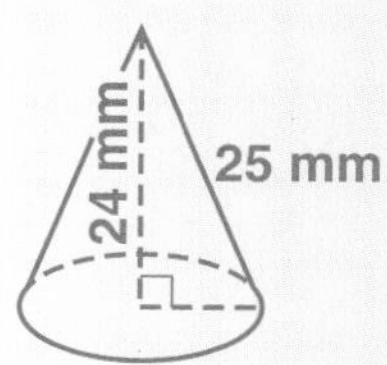

Whereas end-of-chapter material may be considered optional in some texts, in UCSMP *Geometry* we have selected these objectives and questions with the expectation that they will be covered. Students should be able to answer these questions with about 85% accuracy after studying the chapter.

You may assign these questions over a single night to help students prepare for a test the next day, or you may assign the questions over a two-day period. If you work the questions over two days, we recommend assigning the *evens* for homework the first night so that students get feedback in class the next day, then assigning the *odds* the night before the test because answers are provided to the odd-numbered questions.

It is effective to ask students which questions they still do not understand and use the day or days as a total class discussion of the material that the class finds most difficult.

CHAPTER NINE

PROPERTIES DEAL WITH THE PRINCIPLES BEHIND THE MATHEMATICS.

Objective F: *Apply the properties of planes.* *(Lessons 9-1, 9-2)*

29. Identify the figure that is the intersection of two planes. a line

30. Explain how the distance between parallel planes is determined. See margin.

In 31–33, use the figure below in which $\ell \perp m$ and $\ell \perp n$. 31) See margin.

31. Is $\ell \perp R$? Explain your answer.

32. Is $\ell \perp p$? Explain your answer.

33. Is $m \perp n$? Explain your answer. not necessarily

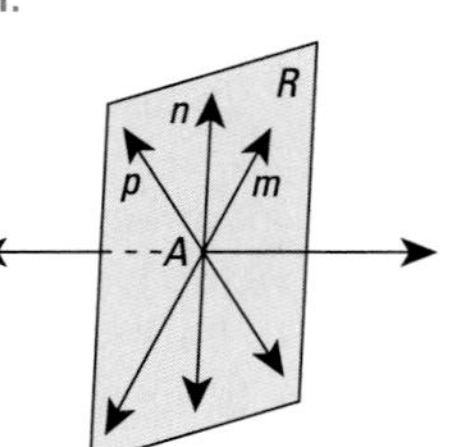

32) yes; by the definition of a line ⊥ to a plane

Objective G: *Determine symmetry planes in 3-dimensional figures.* *(Lesson 9-6)*

In 34 and 35, a figure is given.

a. Tell if the figure has bilateral symmetry.

b. Give the number of symmetry planes.

34.

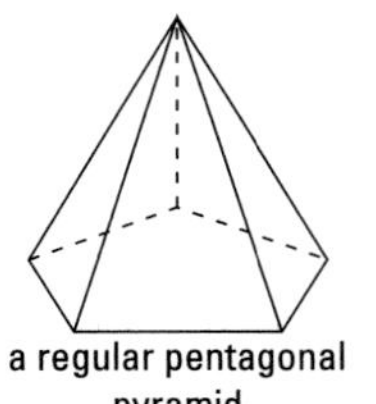

a regular pentagonal pyramid

a) Yes b) 5

35.

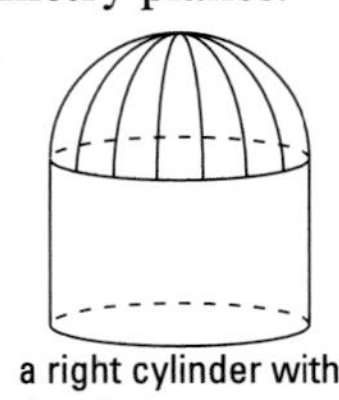

a right cylinder with hemisphere on top

a) Yes b) inf. many

36. At least how many symmetry planes does a box have? 3

37. A regular prism which has an octagon for a base has __?__ symmetry planes. 9

USES DEAL WITH APPLICATIONS OF MATHEMATICS IN REAL SITUATIONS.

Objective H: *Recognize 3-dimensional figures in the real world.* *(Lessons 9-3, 9-4, 9-5)*

In 38–41, tell which three-dimensional figure most resembles the real-world object. Give as specific a name as you can, distinguishing solids from surfaces. 38–41) See below.

38. a birthday cake **39.** the planet Mars

40. a bubble **41.** a paperback book

Objective I: *Apply the Four-Color Theorem to maps.* *(Lesson 9-9)* 42–44) See margin.

42. What is the Four-Color Theorem?

38) solid right cylinder

39) solid sphere

40) sphere

41) rectangular solid

43. Draw a map with four regions that needs four colors in order to be colored.

44. Draw a map with nine regions that needs three colors in order to be colored.

45. Trace this map and color it with at most 4 colors. See below for sample.

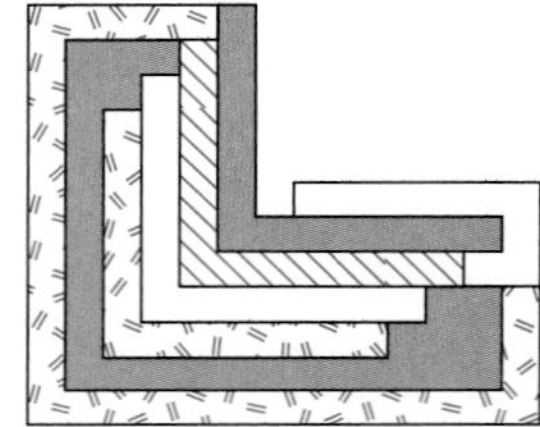

Additional Answers

30. The distance between parallel planes is the length of a segment perpendicular to the planes with an endpoint in each plane.

31. Yes; if a line is ⊥ to two different lines in space at the same point, then it is ⊥ to the plane containing those lines.

42. Suppose regions which share a border of some length must have different colors. Then any map of regions on a plane or a sphere can be colored in such a way that only four colors are needed.

43. Sample:

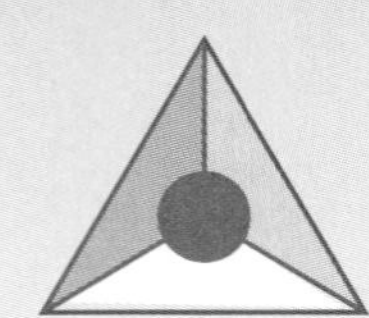

44. Sample:

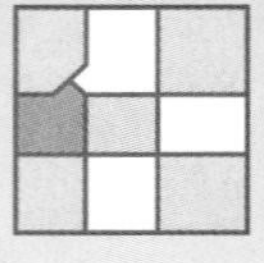

REPRESENTATIONS DEAL WITH PICTURES, GRAPHS, OR OBJECTS THAT ILLUSTRATE CONCEPTS.

Objective J: *Make a surface from a net, and vice versa.* *(Lesson 9-8)*

46. Tell whether each figure could be a net for a cube.

a. 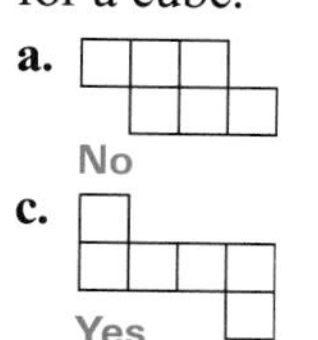
No

b. 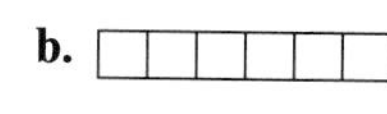
No

c. Yes

d. 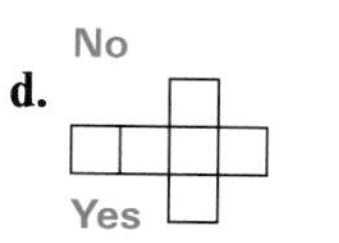
Yes

47–49) See below.

47. Draw a net for a square pyramid.

48. Draw a net for the lateral surface of a box with dimensions 4, 6, and 8.

49. Draw a net for a regular hexagonal prism with height 10 and a base with edge 7.

50. Name the figure that would be made from the net below. regular triangular prism

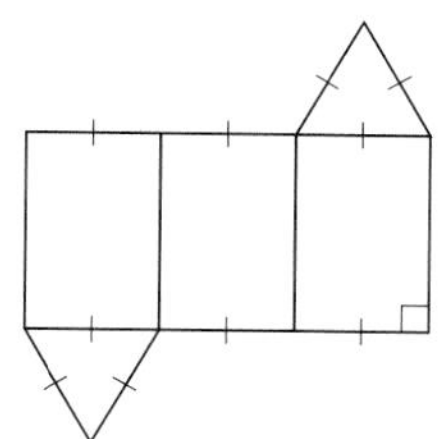

47)

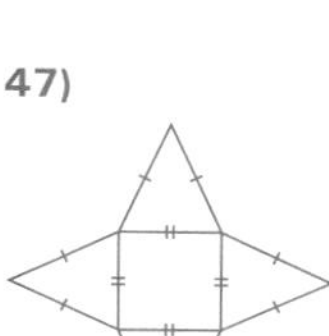

48)

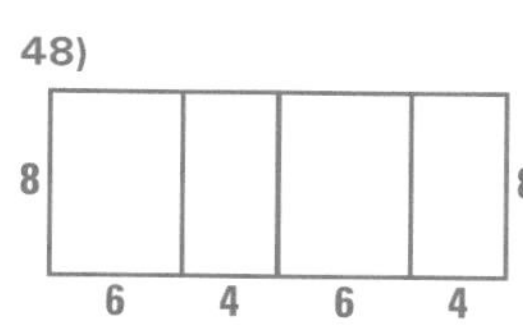

49)

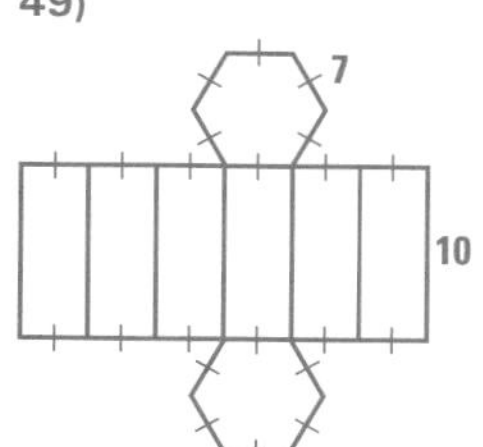

51. A cylinder has a height of 12 and a radius of 10. A net for this cylinder is given below.

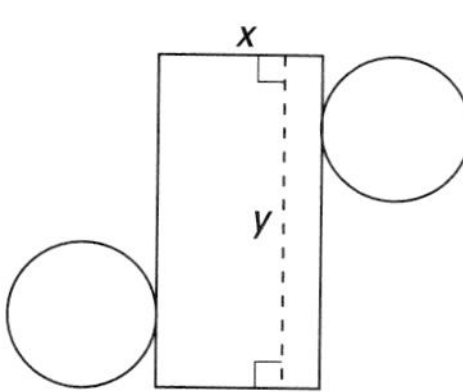

a. What is the value of x? 12 units

b. What is the value of y? $20\pi \approx 62.8$ units

Objective K: *Interpret maps of the world.* *(Lesson 9-9)* See below.

In 52–54, each type of view of Earth has a flaw. Describe the problem with each.

52. globe

53. gores

54. Mercator projection

55. What preservation properties of isometries do not hold for a Mercator projection map?

52) Sample: Only half the world can be seen at a time.

53) Sample: Connected parts of countries may appear disconnected on different gores.

54) Sample: Areas are distorted.

55) Distances are not preserved.

Assessment

Evaluation The *Assessment Sourcebook* provides six forms of the Chapter 9 Test. Forms A and B present parallel versions in a short-answer format. Forms C and D offer performance assessment. The fifth test is Chapter 9 Test, Cumulative Form. About 50% of this test covers Chapter 9, 25% of it covers Chapter 8, and 25% of it covers earlier chapters. In addition to these tests, Comprehensive Test Chapters 1–9 gives roughly equal attention to all chapters covered thus far.

For information on grading, see *General Teaching Suggestions; Grading* in the *Professional Sourcebook,* which begins on page T20 in this Teacher's Edition.

Feedback After students have taken the test for Chapter 9 and you have scored the results, return the tests to students for discussion. Class discussion of the questions that caused trouble for the most students can be very effective in identifying and clarifying misunderstandings. You might want to have them write down the items they missed and work, either in groups or at home, to correct them. It is important for students to receive feedback on every chapter test, and we recommend that students see and correct their mistakes before proceeding too far into the next chapter.

Chapter 10 Planner

Adapting to Individual Needs

The student text is written for the vast majority of students. The chart at the right suggests two pacing plans to accommodate the needs of your students. Students in the Full Course should complete the entire text by the end of the year. Students in the Minimal Course will spend more time when there are quizzes and more time on the Chapter Review. Therefore, these students may not complete all of the chapters in the text.

Options are also presented to meet the needs of a variety of teaching and learning styles. For each lesson, the Teacher's Edition provides a section entitled *Adapting to Individual Needs.* This section regularly includes **Optional Activities, Challenge** problems, **English Language Development** suggestions, and suggestions for providing **Extra Help.** The Teacher's Edition also frequently includes an **Error Alert,** an **Extension,** and an **Assessment** alternative. The options available in Chapter 10 are summarized in the chart below.

Chapter 10 Pacing Chart

Day	Full Course	Minimal Course
1	10-1	10-1
2	10-2	10-2
3	10-3	10-3
4	Quiz*; 10-4	Quiz*; begin 10-4.
5	10-5	Finish 10-4.
6	10-6	10-5
7	Quiz*; 10-7	10-6
8	10-8	Quiz*; begin 10-7.
9	10-9	Finish 10-7.
10	Self-Test	10-8
11	Review	10-9
12	Test*	Self-Test
13		Review
14		Review
15		Test*

*in the Teacher's Resource File

In the Teacher's Edition...

Lesson	Optional Activities	Extra Help	Challenge	English Language Development	Error Alert	Extension	Cooperative Learning	Ongoing Assessment
10-1	●		●		●	●	●	Oral/Written
10-2	●	●	●	●		●	●	Written
10-3	●	●	●	●		●	●	Oral/Written
10-4	●	●	●		●	●	●	Oral/Written
10-5	●	●	●	●		●	●	Oral/Written
10-6	●	●	●	●		●	●	Oral
10-7	●	●	●			●	●	Oral/Written
10-8	●			●	●	●		Written
10-9	●		●			●		Written

Chapter 10 Block Schedule

Day	Recommended Pacing
1	Lessons 10-1, 10-2
2	Lesson 10-3
3	Lessons 10-4, 10-5
4	Lesson 10-6
5	Lessons 10-7, 10-8
6	Lesson 10-9, Self-Test, Chapter Review
7	Chapter Review, Chapter Test

In the Additional Resources...

	In the Teacher's Resource File								
Lesson	**Lesson Masters, A and B**	**Teaching Aids***	**Activity Kit***	**Answer Masters**	**Technology Sourcebook**	**Assessment Sourcebook**	**Visual Aids****	**Technology**	**Video Segments**
10-1	10-1	131, 134, 135		10-1	20		131, 134, 135, AM	GeoExplorer	10-1
In-class Activity		136		10-2			136, AM		
10-2	10-2	131, 137		10-2	21		131, 137, AM	Spreadsheet	
10-3	10-3	131		10-3		Quiz	131, AM		
10-4	10-4	132	22	10-4	20, 21		132, AM	GeoExplorer Spreadsheet	
10-5	10-5	132, 138		10-5			132, 138, AM		
10-6	10-6	132, 139		10-6		Quiz	132, 139, AM		
In-class Activity		140		10-7			140, AM		
10-7	10-7	133, 141		10-7			133, 141 AM		
10-8	10-8	133, 142		10-8			133, 142, AM		
10-9	10-9	133		10-9			133, AM		
End of Chapter				Review		Tests			

*Teaching Aids are pictured on pages 562C and 562D. The activities in the Activity Kit are pictured on page 562C. Teaching Aid 136 which accompanies the In-class Activity preceding Lesson 10-2 is pictured with the lesson notes on page 569. Teaching Aid 140 which accompanies the In-class Activity preceding Lesson 10-7 is pictured with the lesson notes on page 598.

**Visual Aids provide transparencies for all Teaching Aids and all Answer Masters.

Also available is the Study Skills Handbook which includes study-skill tips related to reading, note-taking, and comprehension.

Integrating Strands and Applications

	10-1	10-2	10-3	10-4	10-5	10-6	10-7	10-8	10-9
Mathematical Connections									
Number Sense	●	●	●	●	●		●		
Algebra	●	●	●	●	●	●	●	●	●
Geometry	●	●	●	●	●	●	●	●	●
Measurement	●	●	●	●	●	●	●	●	●
Logic and Reasoning	●	●	●	●	●	●	●	●	●
Patterns and Functions	●	●	●	●	●	●	●	●	
Interdisciplinary and Other Connections									
Art			●				●		
Health				●					
Science		●			●	●		●	●
Social Studies		●			●	●		●	●
Multicultural			●	●		●	●		
Technology	●			●			●	●	
Consumer	●	●	●	●			●		●
Sports	●	●						●	●

Teaching and Assessing the Chapter Objectives

Chapter 10 Objectives (Organized into the SPUR categories—Skills, Properties, Uses, and Representations)	Lessons	Progress Self-Test Questions	Chapter Review Questions	In the Teacher's Resource File: Chapter Test, Forms A and B	In the Teacher's Resource File: Chapter Test, Forms C	In the Teacher's Resource File: Chapter Test, Forms D
Skills						
A: Calculate lateral areas, surface areas, and volumes of cylinders and prisms from appropriate lengths, and vice versa.	10-1, 10-3, 10-5	1, 2, 3	1–8	1, 2, 6	1	✓
B: Calculate lateral areas, surface areas, and volumes of pyramids and cones from appropriate lengths, and vice versa.	10-2, 10-7	4, 5, 6	9–16	3, 4, 9	1	
C: Calculate cube roots.	10-3	9	17–20	11		
D: Calculate the surface area and volume of a sphere from appropriate lengths, and vice versa.	10-8, 10-9	7, 8	21–24	7, 12	5	
Properties						
E: Determine what happens to the surface area and volume of a figure when its dimensions are multiplied by some number(s).	10-4, 10-8, 10-9	12, 13	25–28	16	2	
F: Develop formulas for specific figures from more general formulas.	10-6	10, 11, 15	29–32	10, 19	3	
G: Know the conditions under which Cavalieri's Principle can be applied.	10-5	14	33–36	8	6	
Uses						
H: Apply formulas for lateral and surface area to real situations.	10-1, 10-2, 10-9	16, 17	37–42	5, 14, 17, 18	5	✓
I: Apply formulas for volume to real situations.	10-3, 10-5, 10-7, 10-8	18, 19	43–50	15, 18		✓
Representations						
J: Represent products of two (or three) numbers or expressions as areas of rectangles (or volumes of boxes), and vice versa.	10-4	20, 21	51–56	13	4	

Assessment Sourcebook
Quiz for Lessons 10-1 through 10-3
Quiz for Lessons 10-4 through 10-6
Chapter 10 Test, Forms A–D
Chapter 10 Test, Cumulative Form

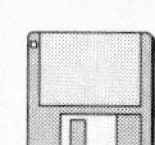
Quiz and Test Writer

Activity Kit

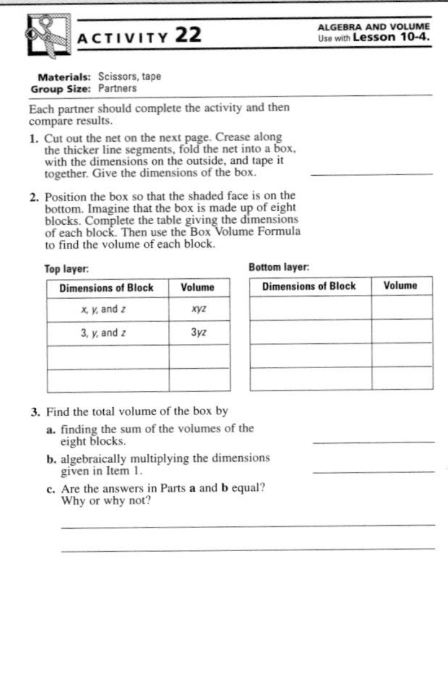

ACTIVITY 22 — ALGEBRA AND VOLUME Use with Lesson 10-4.

Materials: Scissors, tape
Group Size: Partners

Each partner should complete the activity and then compare results.

1. Cut out the net on the next page. Crease along the thicker line segments, fold the net into a box, with the dimensions on the outside, and tape it together. Give the dimensions of the box. ______

2. Position the box so that the shaded face is on the bottom. Imagine that the box is made up of eight blocks. Complete the table giving the dimensions of each block. Then use the Box Volume Formula to find the volume of each block.

Top layer:

Dimensions of Block	Volume
x, y, and z	xyz
3, y, and z	$3yz$

Bottom layer:

Dimensions of Block	Volume

3. Find the total volume of the box by
   a. finding the sum of the volumes of the eight blocks. ______
   b. algebraically multiplying the dimensions given in Item 1. ______
   c. Are the answers in Parts **a** and **b** equal? Why or why not?

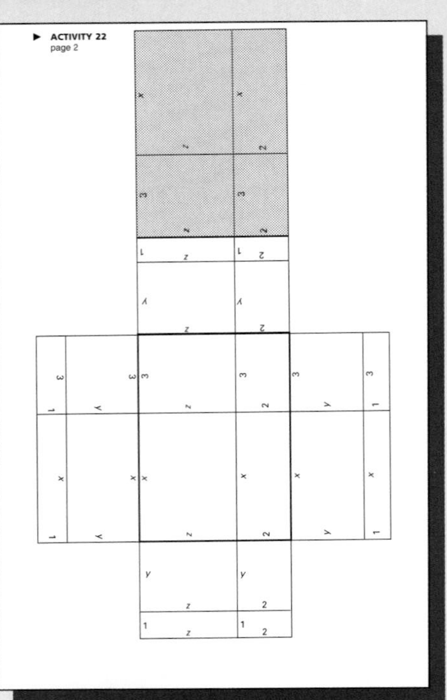

Teaching Aids

TEACHING AID 131

Warm-up
Lesson 10-1

For each situation, which measure is needed, surface area or volume?

1. The cushions of an old sofa are to be restuffed with material.
2. The old sofa is to be recovered.
3. A manufacturer of paper bags must determine the cost of the paper to make the bags.
4. A cement manufacturer is determining how much cement a bag holds.
5. You want to determine the size of an air conditioner needed for a room.
6. You want to know how much wallpaper is needed in a room.

Warm-up
Lesson 10-2

Find ℓ in each figure.

1. 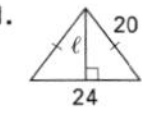

2. 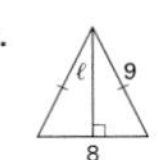

Warm-up
Lesson 10-3

A child has a set of 12 alphabet blocks, all the same size. If all the blocks are arranged to form a rectangular solid, what are the possible heights for the solid?

TEACHING AID 132

Warm-up
Lesson 10-4

A gardener pointed to a rectangular flower bed and said, "If I had made that bed 2 feet wider and 3 feet longer, it would have been 64 square feet larger; but if I had made it 3 feet wider and 2 feet longer, it would then have been 68 square feet larger." Find the length and the width of the flower bed.

Warm-up
Lesson 10-5

Your teacher will show you a large rectangular box and will give you the dimensions of the box.

1. Estimate how many gallons of water the box will hold.
2. Determine the volume of the box in gallons. Use the fact that a cubic foot of liquid contains about 7.48 gallons to find how much water the box will hold.
3. As a class, check your estimates using water and a gallon jug.

Warm-up
Lesson 10-6

1. How is a cone like a pyramid?
2. How is a prism like a cylinder?
3. What is the formula for the surface area of a prism or cylinder?
4. What is the formula for the surface area of a cone or pyramid?

TEACHING AID 133

Warm-up
Lesson 10-7

1. A triangle has the same area as a circle with a radius of 6 inches. If the base of the triangle is 3 inches, what is its height?
2. Another circle has the same area as a triangle whose base is 12 cm and whose height is 10 cm. What is the radius of the circle?

Warm-up
Lesson 10-8

Find the area of the shaded region between the circles.

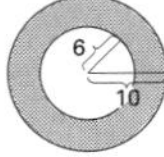

Warm-up
Lesson 10-9

Explain why it is difficult to wrap a basketball with paper.

TEACHING AID 134
Lesson 10-1

Net for Right Prism

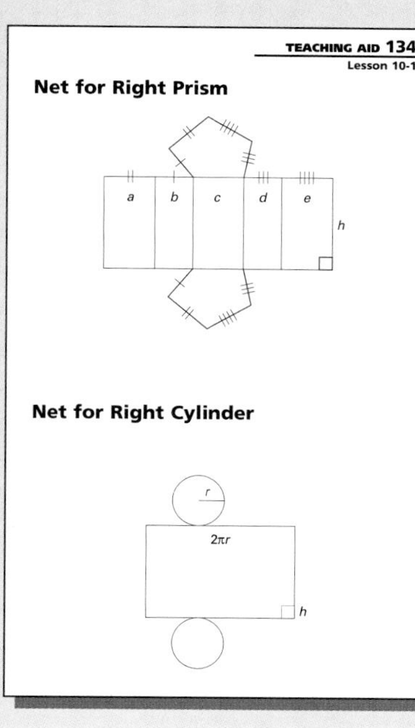

Net for Right Cylinder

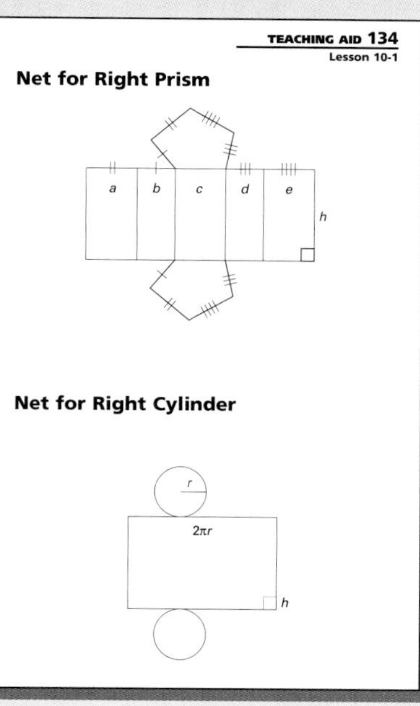

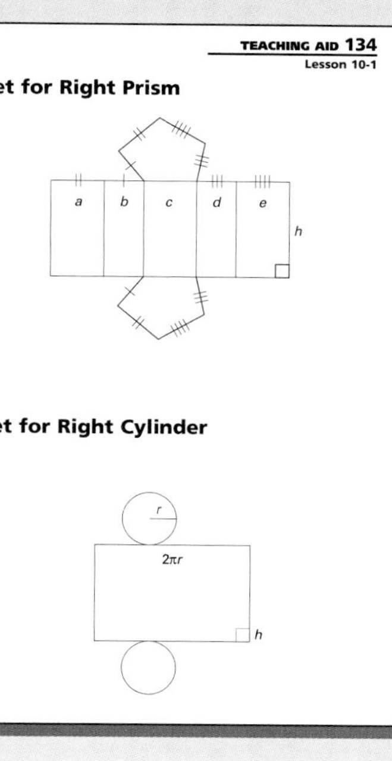

TEACHING AID 135
Lesson 10-1

Additional Examples

1. Is the surface area of an open box, with the base 12″ × 17″ and height 7″, the same as the surface area of the bag in Example 1 on page 564 of the Student Edition.
2. Find the lateral area and the surface area of the right cylinder above. (radius 7, height 15)

TEACHING AID 137
Lesson 10-2

Additional Examples

1. A small pyramid discovered recently at an Inca ceremonial site on the top of a mountain in the Andes has a square base with vertices pointed in the four directions—north, south, east, and west. The ratio of the height of the pyramid to the edges of the base are near the golden ratio—about 1.6 to 1. If the height of the pyramid is 2 meters, what are the lengths of an edge of its base, its slant height, and its lateral surface area?
2. A pile of sand has been stored in the shape of a cone. The yard-keeper knows that the pile is 20 feet tall and 102 feet in circumference at the base. What is the area of the conical tarpaulin needed to cover the pile?
3. A rubber sheet is fastened in a circular hoop 1 meter in diameter. A stick is positioned in the center and pushed up as shown, stretching the rubber sheet in the shape of a cone. How far up does the rubber sheet need to be pushed before the area of the rubber has doubled?

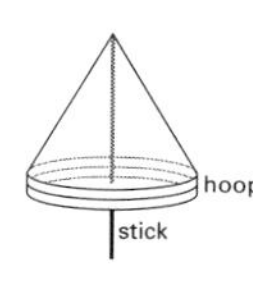

TEACHING AID 138
Lesson 10-5

Cavalieri's Principle

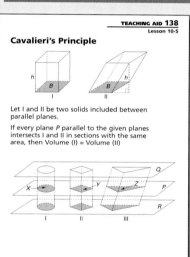

Let I and II be two solids included between parallel planes.

If every plane P parallel to the given planes intersects I and II in sections with the same area, then Volume (I) = Volume (II)

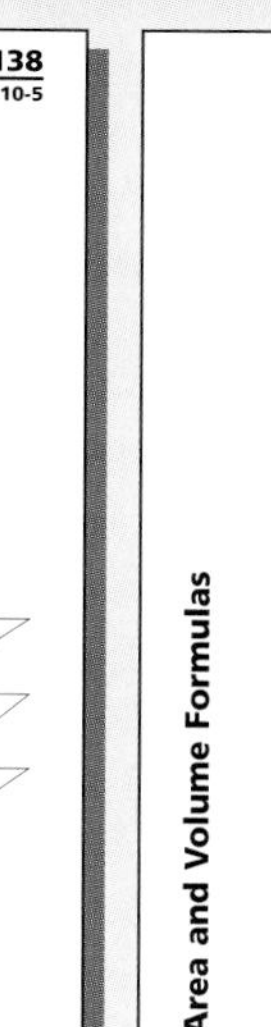

TEACHING AID 139
Lesson 10-6

Surface Area and Volume Formulas

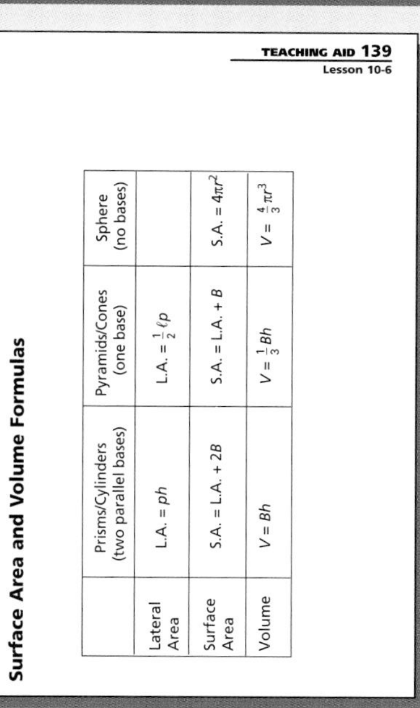

	Prisms/Cylinders (two parallel bases)	Pyramids/Cones (one base)	Sphere (no bases)
Lateral Area	L.A. = ph	L.A. = $\frac{1}{2}\ell p$	
Surface Area	S.A. = L.A. + $2B$	S.A. = L.A. + B	S.A. = $4\pi r^2$
Volume	$V = Bh$	$V = \frac{1}{3}Bh$	$V = \frac{4}{3}\pi r^3$

TEACHING AID 141
Lesson 10-7

Three pyramids Forming a Prism

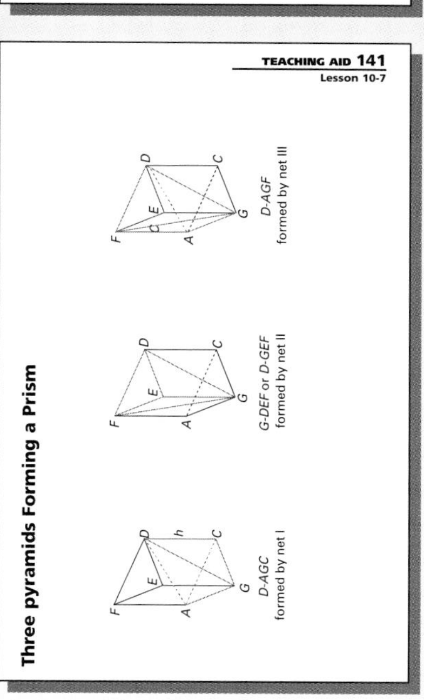

TEACHING AID 142
Lesson 10-8

Sphere and Cylinder

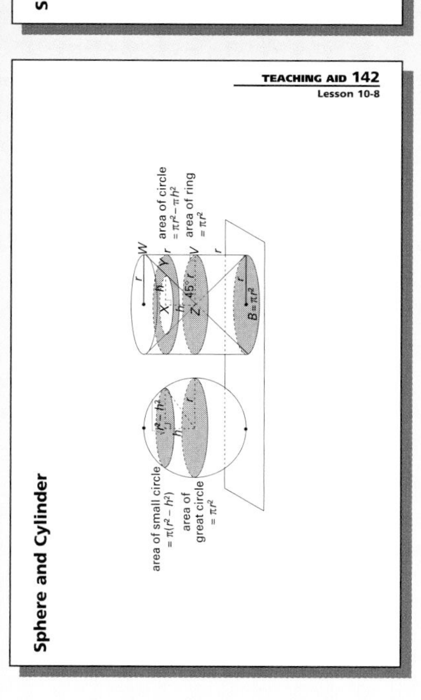

Chapter Opener 10

Pacing

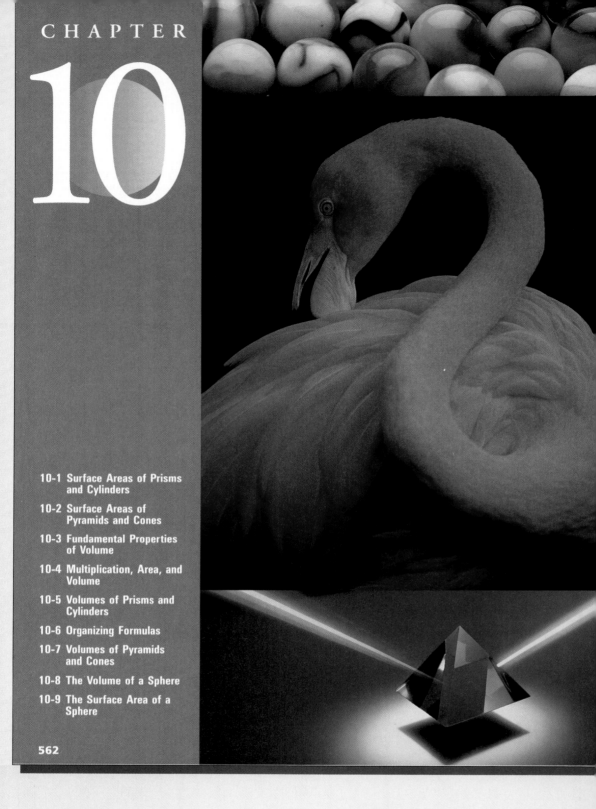

All lessons in this chapter are designed to be covered in one day. At the end of the chapter, you should plan to spend 1 day to review the Progress Self-Test, 1–2 days for the Chapter Review, and 1 day for a test. You may wish to spend a day on projects, and possibly a day is needed for quizzes. Therefore, this chapter should take 12–15 days. We advise you not to spend more than 17 days on this chapter; there is opportunity to review ideas in later chapters.

Using Pages 562–563

The examples on this page are designed to show the difference between surface area and volume. This is a difficult distinction for some students when applications are not discussed, but not as difficult when applications are present.

Emphasize the analogous relationship between the measures of boundary and of enclosed space of 2- and 3-dimensional figures; that is, area is to perimeter as volume is to surface area.

Students will need calculators every day in this chapter. You might also point out that the formulas for surface area and volume are summarized in two places—in Lesson 10-6 and in the Chapter Summary on page 615.

CHAPTER 10

Chapter 10 Overview

This chapter develops and discusses the formulas for the surface area and the volume of common 3-dimensional shapes: prisms, cylinders, pyramids, cones, and spheres. The goals of the chapter are for students to know and to be able to apply these formulas in both theoretical and real situations.

Lessons 10-1 and 10-2 look at surface area using the concept of a net. Lesson 10-3 introduces the basic properties of volume. Lesson 10-4 reminds students of the algebraic relationships among multiplication of polynomials, area, and volume. Lessons 10-5 and 10-7 discuss the volume formulas for prisms and cylinders and for pyramids and cones, treating these as pairs of related figures. Lessons 10-8 and 10-9 discuss the volume and surface area of a sphere. The content of this chapter is difficult for some students. Unlike formulas for area, which they have seen before, many of the formulas in this chapter may be new. Also, the formulas for the volume or surface area of one figure do not lead as easily into the formulas for another. Thus it is important that connections are made between formulas whenever possible and that their derivations be discussed. Lesson 10-6 points out how the hierarchies of 3-dimensional figures can help students remember the formulas.

SURFACE AREAS AND VOLUMES

The two most important measures of 3-dimensional figures are *surface area* and *volume*. They are the counterparts of perimeter and area in 2-dimensional figures. Surface area, like perimeter, is a measure of a boundary, the surface of a 3-dimensional figure. Volume, like area, is a measure of the space enclosed by the figure.

Surface Area helps in determining:		**Volume** helps in determining:
how much paper is needed to make a box,		how much the box can hold,
how much land there is to explore on the moon,		how much material makes up the moon,
how much heat a bird loses through its skin,		how much the bird weighs,
how much fabric is needed to cover a toy.		how much stuffing is needed to make the toy.

Surface area and volume are quite different, as the above examples show. In this chapter, you will learn how to calculate the surface area and volume of many of the 3-dimensional figures introduced in the last chapter. You also will learn how surface area and volume are related to each other, and you will explore the general properties underlying these measures.

Photo Connections

The photo collage makes real-world connections to the content of the chapter: surface area and volume.

Marbles: Marble games have been popular since ancient times. In the beginning, children played the games using such things as pebbles, nuts, knucklebones, and rounded pieces of baked clay. During the 18th century the balls for these games acquired the name "marbles" because they were made from chips of marble. Today marbles are made from clay, glass, steel, and plastic, as well as from semi-precious stones.

Flamingo: Flamingos are known for their long thin legs, long curved necks, and beautiful feathers which range in color from bright red to pale pink, depending on the species. Flamingos live in marshy areas in many parts of the world.

Storage Tanks: Storage tanks for grain, milk, oil, gasoline, and a variety of other materials, are often cylindrical. It takes less material to construct a cylindrical tank than it does to make a prism-shaped container with the same capacity.

Pyramid: When light hits geometric shapes cut from transparent materials, colorful light patterns may form.

Ice Cream Cones: During a hot summer day at the 1904 St. Louis World Fair, an ice cream vendor ran out of dishes. A nearby vendor, selling a Persian dessert waffle called *zalabia,* rolled the waffles into cones that could hold the ice cream. "Ice cream cones" immediately became popular.

Chapter 10 Projects

At this time you might want to have students look over the projects on pages 613–614.

The key points of Lesson 10-6 shown on pages 593 and 594 are important for students to keep in mind throughout the entire chapter. The points are: (1) Remember formulas which apply to the most figures. (2) To use a formula, you must know what each variable in the formula represents. (3) For special formulas for cones and cylinders, substitute the circle formulas $B = \pi r^2$ and $p = 2\pi r$ in the corresponding formulas for pyramids and prisms. (4) If you cannot remember a formula, try to derive it from some simpler formulas you know to be true. (5) Use general formulas to get formulas for special types of figures. Only the third of these hints does not apply in all of mathematics.

The following are some helpful teaching hints for this chapter: (1) Use concrete materials when possible. For instance, unroll a cylinder to find its lateral surface area. Use sand or water and an open prism and pyramid with the same base and height and show that the prism has three times the volume of the pyramid. (2) Focus students' attention on units. Surface area is area, so it is measured in square units. Thus, surface-area formulas always multiply two variables. Volume is measured in cubic units, so in volume formulas, three variables are multiplied. (3) Formulas must be memorized. Students should begin to memorize new formulas the day they are presented.

Lesson 10-1

Objectives

A Calculate lateral areas and surface areas of cylinders and prisms from appropriate lengths, and vice versa.

H Apply formulas for lateral and surface area of prisms and cylinders to real situations.

Resources

From the ***Teacher's Resource File***

- Lesson Master 10-1A or 10-1B
- Answer Master 10-1
- Teaching Aids
  - 131 Warm-up
  - 134 Nets for Right Prism and Right Cylinder
  - 135 Additional Examples
- Technology Sourcebook, Calculator Master 1

Additional Resources

- Visuals for Teaching Aids 131, 134–135
- Paper bags, boxes, food cans
- GeoExplorer or other automatic drawers
- Videodisc

Teaching Lesson 10-1

Warm-up

For each situation, which measure is needed, surface area or volume?

1. The cushions of an old sofa are to be restuffed with material.
2. The old sofa is to be recovered.
3. A manufacturer of paper bags must determine the cost of the paper to make the bags.

1. Vol. 2. S.A. 3. S.A.

LESSON

10-1 Surface Areas of Prisms and Cylinders

It's all "hot air." *The amount of material used in a balloon is found by measuring the balloon's surface area when inflated. Plastic, nylon, or polyethylene are the materials used to make hot-air balloons.*

The cost of any container, from a suitcase to a new house, from a paper bag to a hot-air balloon, depends on the amount of material used to make it. The amount of material covering the container is its **surface area,** which we abbreviate **S.A.**

Consider a paper bag. It is approximately a box, a type of prism, with the upper base missing. Since each face of a box is a rectangular region, the surface area of the bag is the sum of the areas of five rectangles. The areas are easily seen by examining the net for the bag.

Example 1

A grocery bag has a base 7″ by 12″ and a height of 17″. What is its total surface area?

Solution

Draw the bag and a net for it.

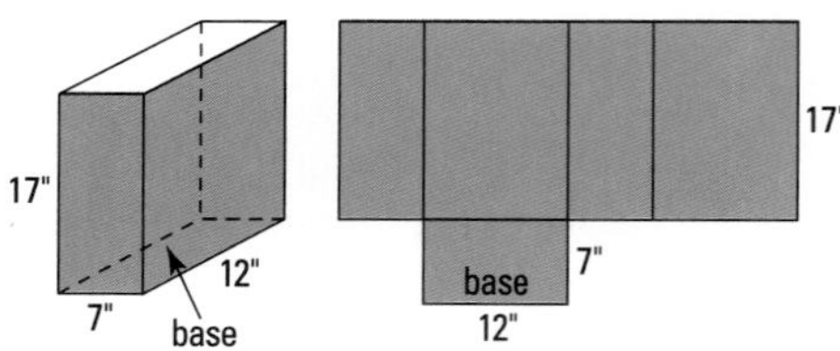

Surface area = area of base + sum of areas of lateral faces
= 7 · 12 + (7 · 17 + 12 · 17 + 7 · 17 + 12 · 17)
= 730 square inches

Lesson 10-1 Overview

Broad Goals This lesson discusses the general formula for the lateral surface area of a right cylindric surface, specializes the formula for prisms and cylinders, and extends the formula to include the total surface area.

Perspective There are formulas for the surface area and volume of many solids. The formulas selected are based on the fact that the solids discussed in Chapter 9 are the building blocks for more complicated figures.

This lesson illustrates the way formulas are presented in this book. Formulas are not given for all figures. Rather, we give formulas that apply to most figures, and students are expected to derive more specific formulas. The basic formula derived in this lesson is L.A. $= ph$ for the lateral area of a right prism or cylinder. Though it is a simple formula, together with the formulas for the perimeter (or circumference) of a figure, it enables students to calculate lateral area.

Thus, the formula for the lateral area of a cylinder, L.A. $= 2\pi rh$, is a special case of L.A. $= ph$; the formula for the surface area of a cylinder is found by adding the lateral area to the areas of the bases. These special formulas need not be memorized.

Stress that students should follow the procedure in **Example 2**—to write the formula first, and then substitute the values for the variables.

Lateral Area

The total area of the lateral surface of a solid is its **lateral area,** or **L.A.** In Example 1, the lateral area can be calculated by finding the sum of the areas of the four lateral faces.

$$\begin{aligned} \text{L.A.} &= 7 \cdot 17 + 12 \cdot 17 + 7 \cdot 17 + 12 \cdot 17 \\ &= (7 + 12 + 7 + 12) \cdot 17 \quad \text{Distributive Property} \\ &= 38 \cdot 17 \\ &= 646 \text{ in.}^2 \end{aligned}$$

Since the base rectangle has perimeter 7″ + 12″ + 7″ + 12″ = 38″ and the height of the bag is 17″, the calculation can be written as

$$\text{L.A.} = 38 \cdot 17 = \text{perimeter of base} \cdot \text{height of prism.}$$

This idea works with any right prism (or cylinder) because the length of any lateral edge equals the height of the prism (or cylinder). It does not hold for oblique prisms and cylinders.

Right Prism-Cylinder Lateral Area Formula
The lateral area, L.A., of a right prism (or right cylinder) is the product of its height h and the perimeter (circumference) p of its base.

$$\text{L.A.} = ph$$

Proof
Here are a representative right prism and right cylinder, each with height h. For the prism, the perimeter of either base is $a + b + c + d + e$. For the cylinder, the perimeter of either base is the circumference of the base, $2\pi r$.

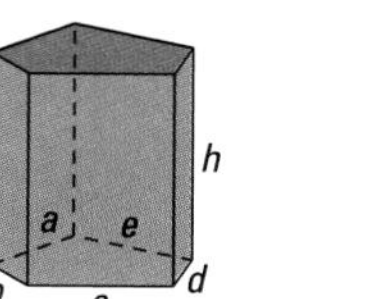

$p = a + b + c + d + e$

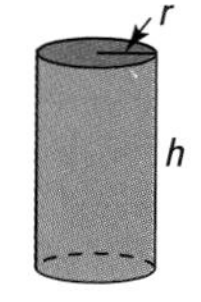

$p = 2\pi r$

Here are their nets.

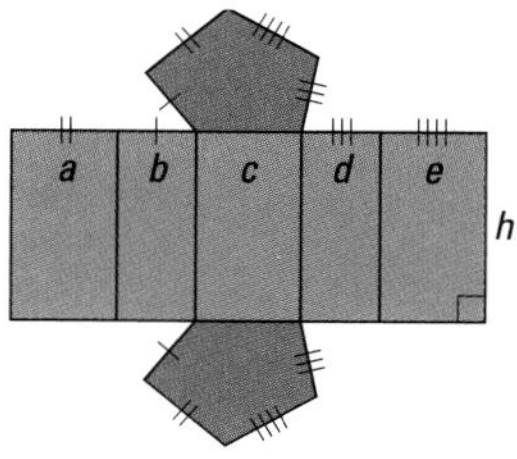

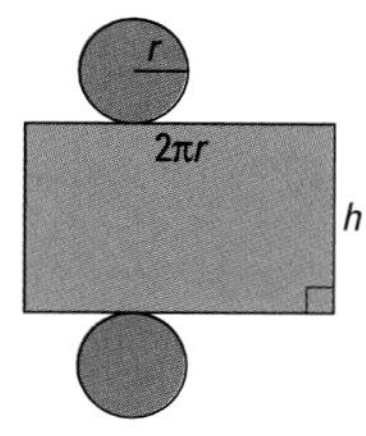

Now we compute the lateral areas. The lateral area is the area of the entire surface except the bases. The net for the lateral surface is a rectangle, and we use the formula for the area of a rectangle: base · height.

For the prism,
$\text{L.A.} = (a + b + c + d + e)h$
$= ph.$

For the cylinder,
$\text{L.A.} = 2\pi r \cdot h$
$= ph.$

4. A cement manufacturer is determining how much cement a bag holds. Volume
5. You want to determine the size of an air conditioner needed for a room. Volume
6. You want to know how much wallpaper is needed in a room. Surface area

Notes on Reading

You might want to use Activity 1 in *Optional Activities* on page 566 as you teach this lesson.

As your students read this lesson, they should notice that the formulas for the surface areas of prisms and cylinders (both cylindric solids) are derived simultaneously because the mathematics applies to both of them. Explain to students that although the main purpose of deducing a formula is to show that it is true, another purpose is to provide a way to retrieve the formula if they forget it.

Explain how formulas are organized in the chapter. The first formula given in this lesson is a general Right Prism-Cylinder Lateral Area Formula; from this, if a formula for the circumference of a circle is known, a specific formula for a right cylinder can be found.

We cannot emphasize enough the value of using actual objects. A paper bag or an empty cereal box is a good model for a right prism. Labels on cans sometimes unroll easily to enable you to show the

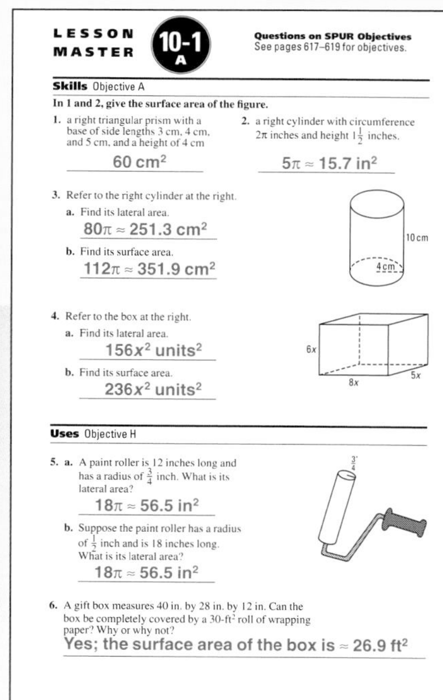
LESSON MASTER 10-1 A
Questions on SPUR Objectives
See pages 617–619 for objectives.

Skills Objective A

In 1 and 2, give the surface area of the figure.

1. a right triangular prism with a base of side lengths 3 cm, 4 cm, and 5 cm, and a height of 4 cm
60 cm^2
2. a right cylinder with circumference 2π inches and height $1\frac{1}{2}$ inches.
$5\pi \approx 15.7$ in^2
3. Refer to the right cylinder at the right.
a. Find its lateral area. $80\pi \approx 251.3$ cm^2
b. Find its surface area. $112\pi \approx 351.9$ cm^2
4. Refer to the box at the right.
a. Find its lateral area. $156x^2$ $units^2$
b. Find its surface area. $236x^2$ $units^2$

Uses Objective H

5. a. A paint roller is 12 inches long and has a radius of $\frac{3}{4}$ inch. What is its lateral area?
$18\pi \approx 56.5$ in^2
b. Suppose the paint roller has a radius of $\frac{1}{2}$ inch and is 18 inches long. What is its lateral area?
$18\pi \approx 56.5$ in^2
6. A gift box measures 40 in. by 28 in. by 12 in. Can the box be completely covered by a 30-ft^2 roll of wrapping paper? Why or why not?
Yes; the surface area of the box is ≈ 26.9 ft^2

Video

Wide World of Mathematics The segment, *Gateway Arch*, focuses on the St. Louis arch which is constructed of triangular-prism shaped sections covered by steel. The segment may be used to introduce or extend this lesson on calculating the surface area of prisms and cylinders. Related questions and an investigation are provided in videodisc stills and in the Video Guide. A related CD-ROM activity is also available.

Videodisc Bar Codes

Search Chapter 49

Play

lateral area of a right cylinder. If students have difficulty visualizing the relationship between the 3-dimensional drawing and the flat net in **Example 1**, have them actually cut a paper bag to spread out flat.

You may want to use **Teaching Aid 134** as you discuss the nets for a right prism and right cylinder.

Some students may wonder if they have to determine the net for a 3-dimensional figure in order to determine its surface area. Explain that a net is an aid in calculating and understanding surface area. Formulas exist so that the derivation is not necessary each time.

The formula S.A. = L.A. + 2*B*, for the surface area of a prism or a cylinder, requires an understanding of only the meanings of the terms *surface area* and *lateral area* and what figures are being discussed. (In the next lesson, students encounter the formula S.A. = L.A. + *B* for the pyramid and cone.)

Additional Examples

These examples are also given on **Teaching Aid 135.**

1. Is the surface area of an open box, with the base 12" × 17" and height 7", the same as the surface area of the bag in **Example 1**?
   No. The surface area of the open box is 610 square inches. The surface areas would be the same only if the top face of each were not removed.

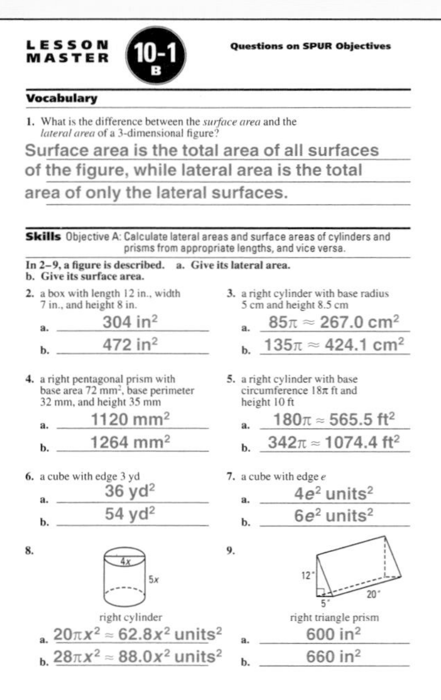

LESSON MASTER 10-1 B **Questions on SPUR Objectives**

Vocabulary

1. What is the difference between the *surface area* and the *lateral area* of a 3-dimensional figure?
   Surface area is the total area of all surfaces of the figure, while lateral area is the total area of only the lateral surfaces.

Skills Objective A: Calculate lateral areas and surface areas of cylinders and prisms from appropriate lengths, and vice versa.

In 2–9, a figure is described. a. Give its lateral area. b. Give its surface area.

2. a box with length 12 in., width 7 in., and height 8 in.
   a. 304 in²
   b. 472 in²
3. a right cylinder with base radius 5 cm and height 8.5 cm
   a. $85\pi \approx 267.0$ cm²
   b. $135\pi \approx 424.1$ cm²
4. a right pentagonal prism with base area 72 mm², base perimeter 32 mm, and height 35 mm
   a. 1120 mm²
   b. 1264 mm²
5. a right cylinder with base circumference 18π ft and height 10 ft
   a. $180\pi \approx 565.5$ ft²
   b. $342\pi \approx 1074.4$ ft²
6. a cube with edge 3 yd
   a. 36 yd²
   b. 54 yd²
7. a cube with edge *e*
   a. $4e^2$ units²
   b. $6e^2$ units²
8. right cylinder (4x, 5x)
   a. $20\pi x^2 \approx 62.8x^2$ units²
   b. $28\pi x^2 \approx 88.0x^2$ units²
9. right triangle prism (12", 5", 20")
   a. 600 in²
   b. 660 in²

Rolling a rectangular poster to fit into a cylinder allows it to be mailed without crushing.

Total Surface Area

The two congruent bases of every prism or cylinder have the same area. So the next theorem holds even for oblique prisms and cylinders.

Prism-Cylinder Surface Area Formula
The surface area, S.A., of any prism or cylinder is the sum of its lateral area L.A. and twice the area *B* of a base.

S.A. = L.A. + 2*B*

In this chapter, the important formulas to learn are highlighted in boxes. Of course, you must know what each letter in the formula represents. As shown in Example 2, it is usually wise to begin a problem by writing an appropriate formula. Then substitute given values for the variables. Substitute for the area and perimeter only when needed.

Example 2

Consider the right cylinder shown.

a. Find its lateral area.
b. Find its surface area.

Solution

a. Begin by writing a formula for the lateral area of a right cylinder.

L.A. = ph

Since the base is a circle and *r* = 3,

p = $2\pi r = 2\pi \cdot 3$.

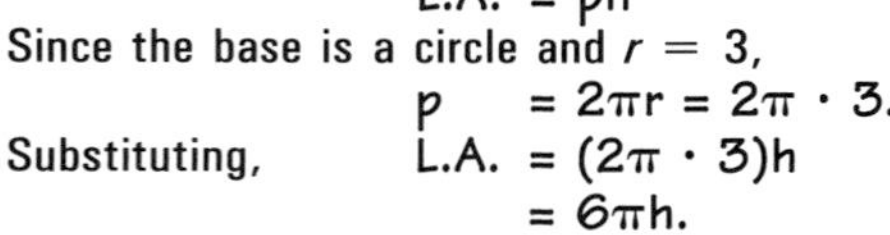

Substituting, L.A. = $(2\pi \cdot 3)h$
= $6\pi h$.
Since h = 5, L.A. = 30π square units.

b. In any cylinder, S.A. = L.A. + 2B.
Since the base is a circle, $B = \pi r^2$.
So, S.A. = L.A. + $2(\pi r^2)$
= $30\pi + 2(\pi \cdot 3^2)$ since L.A. = 30π and $r = 3$
= $30\pi + 18\pi$
= 48π square units.

Notice that, since lateral area and surface area are areas, they are measured in square units.

QUESTIONS

Covering the Reading

1. Between surface area and volume, which is a measure of the boundary of a 3-dimensional figure and which is a measure of its interior?
   Surface area measures the boundary, volume measures the interior.

Optional Activities

Activity 1 Using Physical Models
Materials: Empty boxes and food cans

As you discuss this lesson, you might provide small groups of students with models such as empty boxes and cans. Have students flatten their boxes or unroll the cans' labels in order to determine their nets. Students can then label each appropriate section, find its area, and then determine the surface area.

Activity 2
As an extension of **Question 18,** you might ask students to draw an oblique prism or oblique cylinder. Then have them explain why the formula L.A. = *ph* does not apply to the figure they have drawn. [The net for the lateral surface is not a quadrilateral.]

In 2–5, is the quantity related more to surface area or to volume?

2. how much a railroad boxcar will hold volume
3. how much metal and wood are needed to build a boxcar surface area
4. how much you weigh volume
5. how much you perspire after exercise surface area
6. A small bag has dimensions shown on the left.
   a. Draw a net for the bag. See left.
   b. What is its surface area? 1040 cm^2

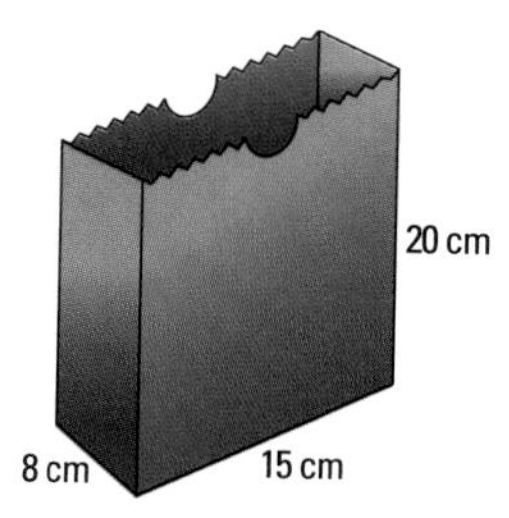

7. a. Define *lateral area.* See left.
   b. Give a formula for the lateral area of a right prism. L.A. = *ph*
8. The lateral area of a right cylinder is the product of its __?__ and the __?__ of the base. height, circumference
9. In a prism or cylinder, S.A. = __?__ + __?__. L.A., 2*B*

In 10 and 11, find the lateral area and surface area of each figure.

10.

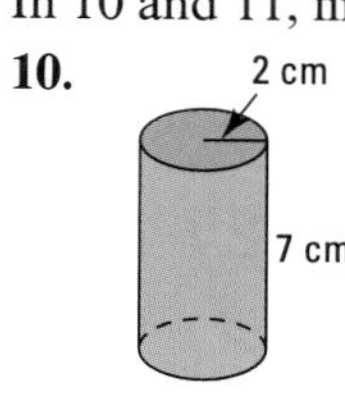

right cylinder

L.A. = $28\pi \approx 88$ cm^2
S.A. = $36\pi \approx 113$ cm^2

11.

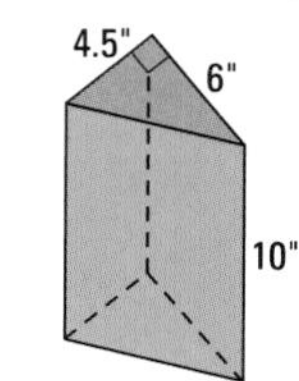

right triangular prism

L.A. = 180 in^2
S.A. = 207 in^2

Applying the Mathematics

In 12 and 13, a net for a surface is given. See left.
a. What is the surface?
b. Calculate its lateral area.
c. Calculate its surface area.

12.

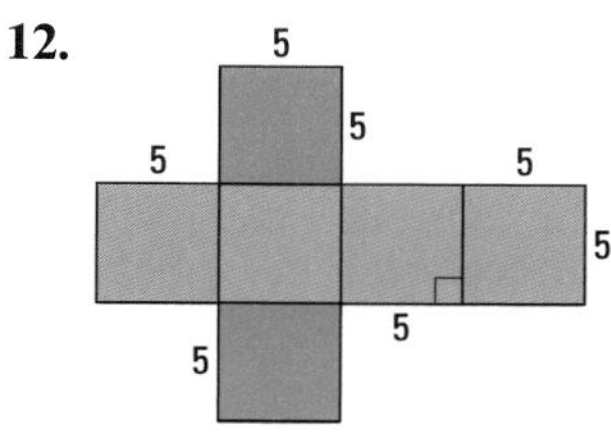

13.

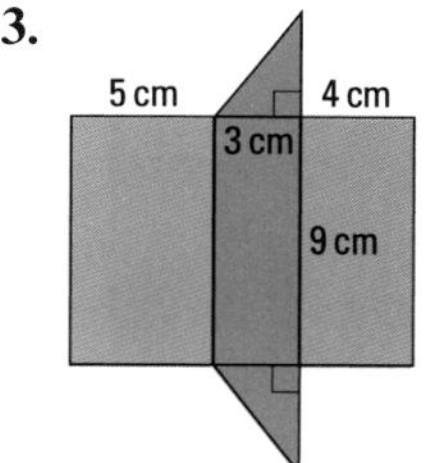

In 14–16, find the surface area of the given solid.

14. a box with dimensions 9 cm, 10 cm, and 11 cm 598 cm^2
15. a box with dimensions L, W, and H $2(LW + LH + WH)$
16. a cube with an edge of length s $6s^2$

6a) Art is shown in reduced size.

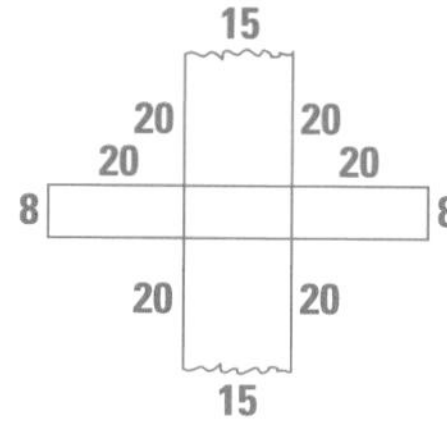

7a) the total area of the lateral surface of a solid

12a) cube
b) 100 units^2
c) 150 units^2

13a) right triangular prism
b) 108 cm^2
c) 120 cm^2

2. (cylinder: radius 7, height 15)

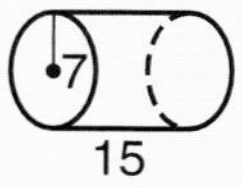

Find the lateral area and the surface area of the right cylinder above. 210π units^2; 308π units^2

Notes on Questions

Questions 2–5 It takes some students a long time to distinguish these two types of measures.

Question 12 This question is generalized in **Question 16.**

(Notes on Questions continue on page 568.)

Practice

For more questions on SPUR Objectives, use **Lesson Master 10-1A** (shown on page 565) or **Lesson Master 10-1B** (shown on pages 566–567).

Assessment

Oral/Written Communication Have students **work in pairs.** Have each student draw a box and a cylinder with the dimensions labeled. Then students should determine the surface area of their partner's figure. [Students correctly determine surface areas.]

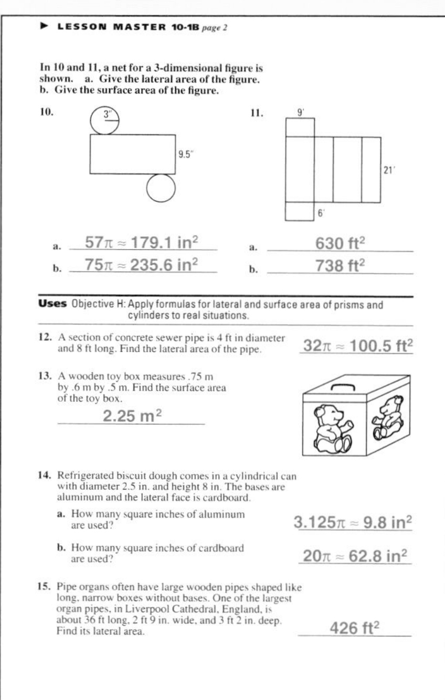

► LESSON MASTER 10-1B *page 2*

In 10 and 11, a net for a 3-dimensional figure is shown. a. Give the lateral area of the figure. b. Give the surface area of the figure.

10. (net: 3", 9.5")
a. $57\pi \approx 179.1$ in^2
b. $75\pi \approx 235.6$ in^2

11. (net: 9', 21', 6')
a. 630 ft^2
b. 738 ft^2

Uses Objective H: Apply formulas for lateral and surface area of prisms and cylinders to real situations.

12. A section of concrete sewer pipe is 4 ft in diameter and 8 ft long. Find the lateral area of the pipe. $32\pi \approx 100.5$ ft^2

13. A wooden toy box measures .75 m by .6 m by .5 m. Find the surface area of the toy box. 2.25 m^2

14. Refrigerated biscuit dough comes in a cylindrical can with diameter 2.5 in. and height 8 in. The bases are aluminum and the lateral face is cardboard.
   a. How many square inches of aluminum are used? $3.125\pi \approx 9.8$ in^2
   b. How many square inches of cardboard are used? $20\pi \approx 62.8$ in^2

15. Pipe organs often have large wooden pipes shaped like long, narrow boxes without bases. One of the largest organ pipes, in Liverpool Cathedral, England, is about 36 ft long, 2 ft 9 in. wide, and 3 ft 2 in. deep. Find its lateral area. 426 ft^2

Optional Activities

Activity 3 Technology Connection
You might consider using *Technology Sourcebook, Calculator Master 1,* with Lessons 10-1 and 10-4. In this activity, students draw a box and calculate its surface area and volume. Then students examine how changes in the dimensions of the box affect the surface area and volume.

Adapting to Individual Needs

Challenge
Have students find the surface area of each of the five platonic solids, assuming that each edge is 5 cm. [Answers are in square centimeters: tetrahedron: $25\sqrt{3}$; hexahedron: 150; octahedron: $50\sqrt{3}$; dodecahedron: $75\sqrt{25 + 10\sqrt{5}}$; icosahedron: $125\sqrt{3}$]

Extension

Have students investigate how the following changes in dimensions would affect the original surface area of the figure.

1. Doubling all dimensions of a box [Multiplies it by 4]
2. Doubling the radius and the height of a right cylinder [Multiplies it by 4]

Projects Update Project 4, *What Is Your Surface Area and Volume?* and Project 6, *Prisms and Cylinders in Packaging,* on page 614, relate to the content of this lesson.

Notes on Questions

Question 18 Activity 2 in *Optional Activities* relates to this question.

Question 19 Error Alert This type of question will be repeated many times. The initial reaction of many students for **part b** will be to say "It doubles." Show that the four copies of any side may be cut from a piece with the dimensions doubled—replacing L by $2L$, W by $2W$, and H by $2H$. The surface area is multiplied by 4 because in each term the two variables being multiplied are each multiplied by 2.

Question 20 Sometimes very accurate answers are unnecessary and may even be inappropriate.

Question 24 Be sure students can use their calculators to find the cube of a number. Some calculators have special keys for cubing numbers.

Question 26 The challenge is to use the entire 100 square inches. Since $2(LH + WH) + LW = 100$, $H = \frac{100 - LW}{2(L + W)}$. Thus, the height of the box can be determined from its length and its width.

In this Maltese version of bocce or boccie, weighted cylinders, instead of traditional spheres, are rolled with precision and accuracy.

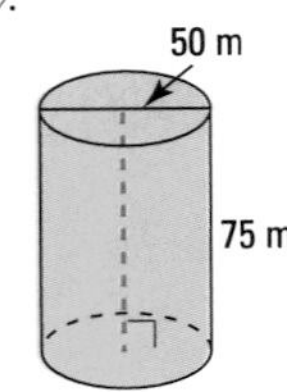

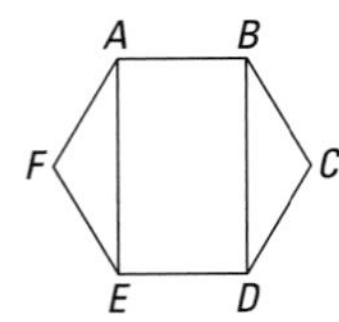

18a) Sample:

b) The formula does not hold for an oblique cylinder because the net for an oblique cylinder is not a quadrilateral and does not have constant height.

17. In one form of the game of bocce, cylindrical boules are thrown toward a cochonnet or target ball. A point is scored for each boule nearer to the cochonnet than the nearest opposing boule. How many square centimeters of metal are used to cover the lateral area of a cylindrical boule that is 10 cm high and has a base radius of 5 cm? $100\pi \approx 314.16$ cm^2
18. **a.** Draw an oblique cylinder. See left.
    b. Explain whether the Right Prism-Cylinder Lateral Area Formula holds for your cylinder in part **a.** See left.
19. Consider a box with dimensions 5, 6, and 7.
    a. Find its surface area. 214 units^2
    b. Double each dimension and find the new surface area. 856 units^2
    c. Divide your answer in **b** by the answer in **a.** 4
    d. Repeat parts **a–c** with a box of dimensions 2, 9, and 11. 278; 1112; 4
20. A fuel storage tank has diameter 50 meters and height 75 meters. If a gallon of paint can cover about 45 square meters, about how many gallons are needed for two coats of paint on the exterior sides and top of the tank? about 611 gallons

Review

21. Draw a net for a square pyramid and shade the regions that make up its lateral surface. *(Lesson 9-8)* See margin.
22. Write a proof argument.
    Given: Regular hexagon $ABCDEF$ at the left.
    To prove: $\triangle AEF \cong \triangle BDC$.
    (Lessons 6-7, 7-3) See margin.
23. Explain how to locate the center of a regular nonagon. *(Lesson 6-7)* See below.
24. What is the cube of $\frac{2}{3}$? *(Previous course)* $\frac{8}{27}$

23) Find the point of intersection of either the $\perp$ bisectors of any two sides or the bisectors of any two angles.

Exploration

25. Find a paper bag in your house. Answers will vary.
    a. What are its dimensions? Sample: 7" by $11\frac{3}{4}$" by 17"
    b. What is its surface area? Sample: 719.75 square inches
    c. To make the bag, some of the paper has to overlap for gluing. Carefully undo the seams of the bag to make it lie flat. Draw its net, including its seams. See margin.
    d. How much more paper is used to make the bag than you calculated for your answer to part **b**? Sample: ≈ 39.75 in^2
26. Suppose you have 100 square inches of cardboard, scissors, and tape, and you wish to make a box with no top. What might be its dimensions? Sample: base 5 in. by 5 in. with height 3.75 in.

Additional Answers

21. Sample:

22.

Conclusions	Justifications
1. $AF = BC$, $EF = DC$, $\angle F \cong \angle C$	def. of regular polygon
2. $\triangle AEF \cong \triangle BDC$	SAS Congruence Theorem

25c. Sample

17"
7"
$11\frac{3}{4}$"
4"
overlap area

Setting Up Lesson 10-2

Question 21 of this lesson provides an opportunity to discuss the lateral area and total surface area of pyramids. You might even want to point out that, for pyramids, S.A. = L.A. + B.

Introducing Lesson 10-2

Lateral Area of Regular Pyramids

IN-CLASS ACTIVITY

Work on this Activity with another student.

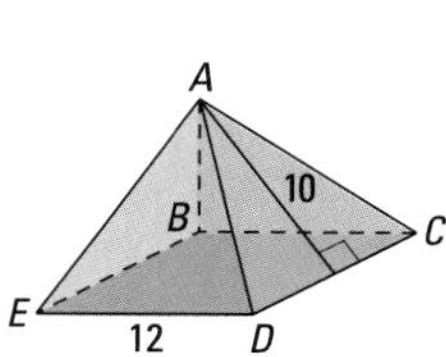

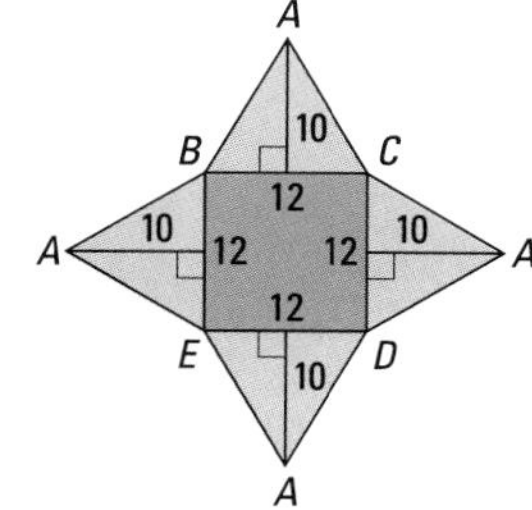

1 Shown above at the left is regular square pyramid *A-BCDE*. (Notice how the pyramid is named with the vertex, a dash, and then the name of the base.) Shown above at the right is a net for *A-BCDE*. The lateral area of *A-BCDE* is the sum of the areas of the 4 congruent triangles. Compute area($\triangle ABC$) + area($\triangle ACD$) + area($\triangle ADE$) + area($\triangle ABE$). 240 units^2

2 Shown below are regular hexagonal pyramid *K-LMNOPQ* and its net.

a. Compute the lateral area of *K-LMNOPQ*. $3s\ell$

b. Let p represent the perimeter of *LMNOPQ*. Does your answer in part **a** equal $\frac{1}{2}\ell p$? Yes

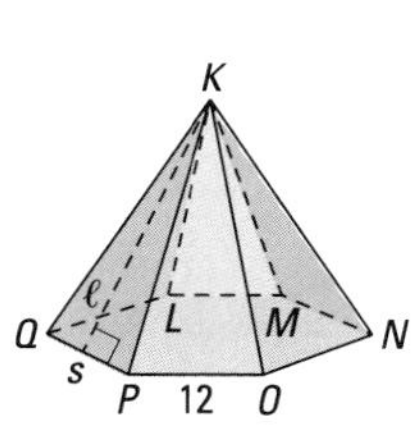

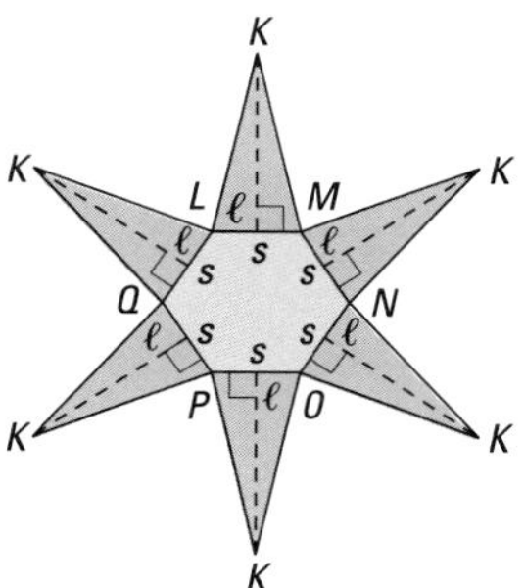

In-class Activity

Resources

From the ***Teacher's Resource File***

- Answer Master 10-2
- Teaching Aid 136: Lateral Area of Regular Pyramids

Additional Resources

- Visual for Teaching Aid 136

This In-class Activity gives students the opportunity to compute the lateral areas of two regular pyramids, in preparation for Lesson 10-2. The activity demonstrates why the slant height and the perimeter of the base are the two variables in the formula for the lateral area of a regular pyramid. Without an activity like this, students usually do not understand the role of the slant height in the formula.

Teaching Aid 136 contains the nets used to find the lateral area of the regular pyramids.

Have students record the results of the In-class Activity for use with **Questions 1 and 2** on page 573.

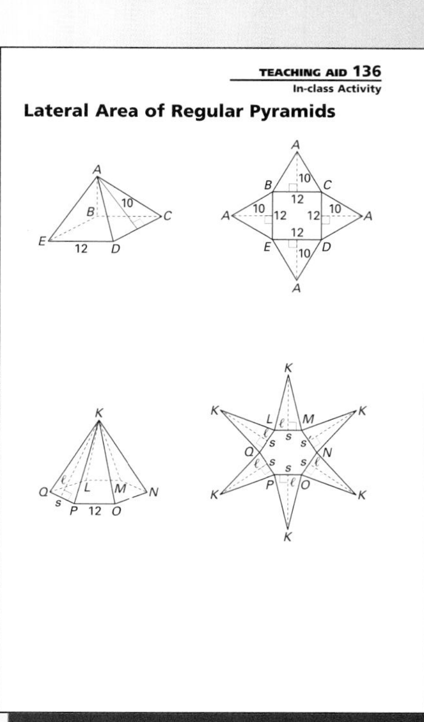
TEACHING AID 136
In-class Activity

Lateral Area of Regular Pyramids

Lesson 10-2

Objectives

B Calculate lateral areas and surface areas of pyramids and cones from appropriate lengths, and vice versa.

H Apply formulas for lateral and surface area of pyramids and cones to real situations.

Resources

From the ***Teacher's Resource File***

- Lesson Master 10-2A or 10-2B
- Answer Master 10-2
- Teaching Aids
  131 Warm-up
  137 Additional Examples

Additional Resources

- Visuals for Teaching Aids 131, 137
- Spreadsheet software

Teaching Lesson 10-2

Warm-up

Find ℓ in each figure.

1.

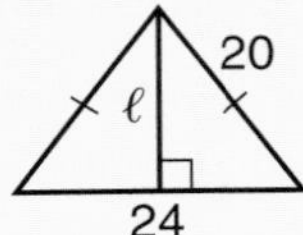

$\ell = 16$

2.

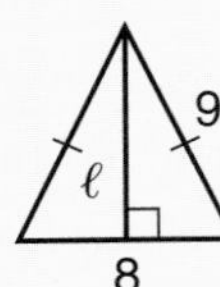

$\ell = \sqrt{65}$

LESSON

10-2 *Surface Areas of Pyramids and Cones*

Don't tread on me. *Highway cones are purposely brightly colored so drivers can see them and avoid them.*

Surface Area of Non-Regular Pyramids

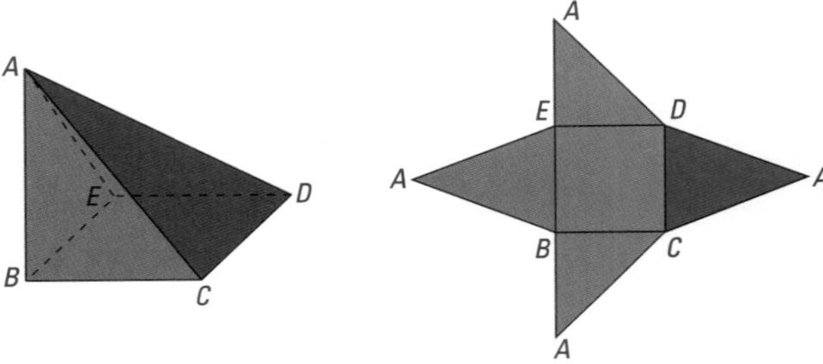

For a pyramid that is not regular, there is no simple formula for its lateral area. Above are oblique square pyramid *A-BCDE* and its net. Because its four faces are not congruent, you must calculate each of the four areas and add them.

However, all pyramids and cones have one base. So to calculate the total surface area, you can just add the area of the base to the lateral area.

> **Pyramid-Cone Surface Area Formula**
> The surface area, S.A., of any pyramid or cone is the sum of its lateral area L.A. and the area B of its base.
> $$\text{S.A.} = \text{L.A.} + B$$

Lesson 10-2 Overview

Broad Goals The goal of this lesson is to have students understand the derivation and use of the formula L.A. $= \frac{1}{2}\ell p$ for the lateral area of regular pyramids and right cones.

Perspective Generally, all formulas for pyramids and cones are more complicated than those for prisms and cylinders. Simple formulas exist for the lateral areas of right cones and regular pyramids.

There is only one basic formula in this lesson: The lateral area of a regular pyramid or right cone is $\frac{1}{2}\ell p$. Now the big questions are: Why are the variables ℓ and p involved in this formula? (The In-class Activity on page 569 is designed to answer this question.) How does one calculate ℓ, and how does one calculate p? Usually ℓ is found using the Pythagorean Theorem. For p, we need to use either ns (for a regular polygon) or $2\pi r$(for a circle). When we use $2\pi r$, we get the formula L.A. $= \pi r\ell$, for a right cone.

Lateral Areas of Regular Pyramids

There is, however, a simple formula for the lateral area of a regular pyramid.

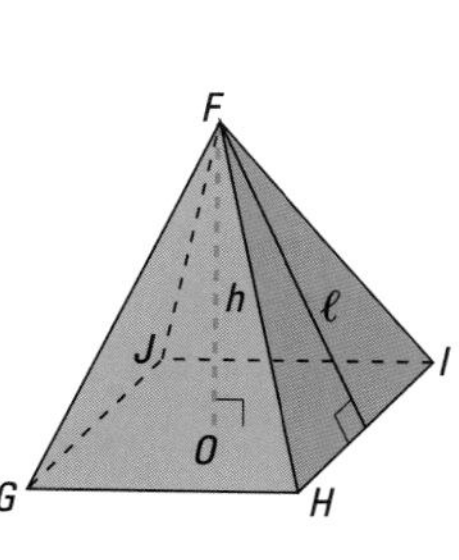

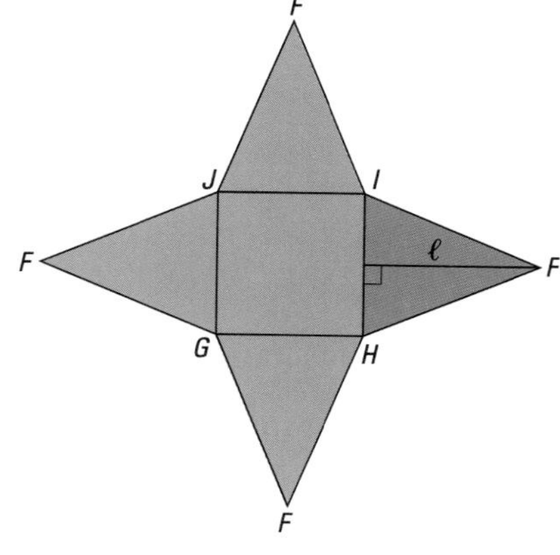

Shown above is a regular square pyramid *F-GHIJ* like the one in the In-class Activity on page 569. The lateral area of *F-GHIJ* is easy to calculate because its faces are congruent isosceles triangles. For each triangle the altitude from vertex F is the slant height ℓ of the pyramid.

❶ L.A. of *F-GHIJ* $= \text{Area}(\triangle FGH) + \text{Area}(\triangle FHI) + \text{Area}(\triangle FIJ) + \text{Area}(\triangle FJG)$

$= \frac{1}{2}\ell(GH) + \frac{1}{2}\ell(HI) + \frac{1}{2}\ell(IJ) + \frac{1}{2}\ell(GJ)$ definition of lateral area

$= \frac{1}{2}\ell(GH + HI + IJ + GJ)$ Distributive Property definition of perimeter

$= \frac{1}{2}\ell p,$

where p is the perimeter of the base.

The formula L.A. $= \frac{1}{2}\ell p$ holds for any regular pyramid. Here is a proof argument.

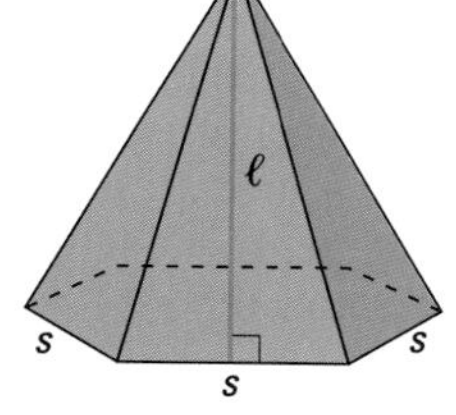

Let s be a side of the base (a regular n-gon) of a regular pyramid and ℓ be its slant height. Then the area of each lateral face is $\frac{1}{2}\ell s$. Since there are n lateral faces,

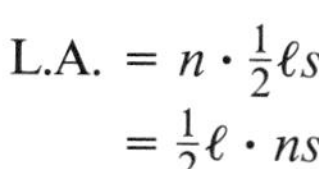

$$\text{L.A.} = n \cdot \tfrac{1}{2}\ell s$$
$$= \tfrac{1}{2}\ell \cdot ns.$$

But ns is the perimeter of the base. Substituting p for ns,

$$\text{L.A.} = \tfrac{1}{2}\ell p.$$

Sometimes, as in Example 1, you need to compute the slant height from other lengths.

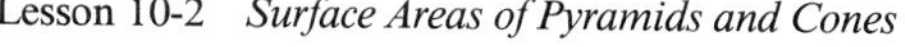

Notes on Reading

You might want to use Activity 1 in *Optional Activities* to introduce this lesson.

To find the surface area of a pyramid or cone, students should be taught to think of finding the lateral area and the area of the base separately and then adding these areas. This is true of prisms and cylinders, as well. Students should understand the Pyramid-Cone Surface Area Formula, S.A. = L.A. + *B*, as following simply from the definitions of total surface area, lateral area, and base area of a pyramid or cone. Thus formulas for lateral area are more important than formulas for surface area, because surface area can be found so easily from lateral area.

❶ In the derivation of the formula L.A. $= \frac{1}{2}\ell p$, ask students what properties allow the rewriting of $n \cdot \frac{1}{2}\ell s$ as $\frac{1}{2}\ell \cdot ns$. [Associative and Commutative Properties of Multiplication] You might also note that in a right cone, since $p = 2\pi r$ the lateral area formula becomes L.A. $= \pi r\ell$; but this formula need not be memorized.

You may need to point out and discuss the difference between the height of a pyramid or cone and its *slant height.* The slant height is the hypotenuse of the right triangle with the altitude of the pyramid or cone as a leg. (In the cone, the radius of the cone is the other leg.) Therefore, slant height is always greater than the height. The slant height of a pyramid or cone appears in surface area formulas, whereas the height of the pyramid or cone appears in their volume formulas.

Optional Activities

Activity 1 Using Physical Models
You might use this activity to introduce the lesson. Have students **work in pairs** and make paper cones and then find the lateral area of these cones. Have them try to make cones that are different sizes but which have the same lateral area.

Activity 2 You can use this activity after students have completed the lesson. Have students draw a net for a regular pyramid. Students might derive a Regular Pyramid Lateral Area Formula by thinking of the net. The area of the net shown is half the product of the height (dashed segment) of one of the triangles and the perimeter of the polygon. The height becomes the slant height of the pyramid and the perimeter of the polygon is the perimeter of the pyramid's base.

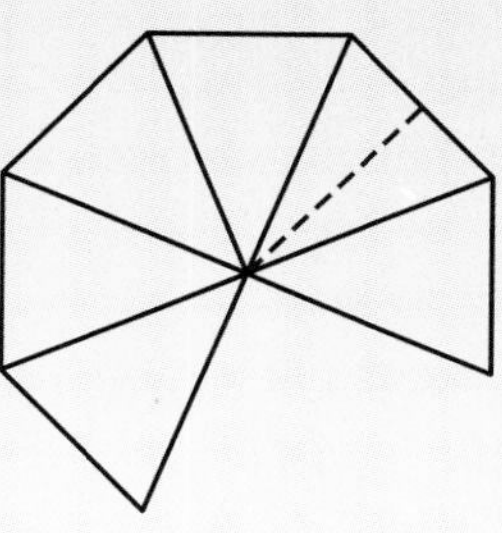

❷ **History Connection** There are three main pyramids in Giza, Egypt. The Khufu Pyramid (the largest), 481 feet tall originally, is also known as the Pyramid of Cheops, or the Great Pyramid. Khufu's son, Khafre, built a second pyramid with height just 10 feet less than that of his father's. Khafre's son Menkure had a much smaller pyramid built for himself; it stood only 218 feet tall. Nearby these three tombs stand the Great Sphinx, and several smaller pyramids and temples built for queens and other relatives. Of the so-called Seven Wonders of the Ancient World, the pyramids at Giza are the only wonder that remains.

Additional Examples

These examples are also given on **Teaching Aid 137.**

1. A small pyramid discovered recently at an Inca ceremonial site on the top of a mountain in the Andes has a square base with vertices pointed in the four directions—north, south, east, and west. The ratio of the height of the pyramid to the edges of the base are near the golden ratio—about 1.6 to 1. If the height of the pyramid is 2 meters, what are the lengths of an edge of its base, its slant height, and its lateral surface area? **Edge = 1.25 m; slant height ≈ 2.10 m; lateral area ≈ 5.24 m²**
2. A pile of sand has been stored in the shape of a cone. The yardkeeper knows that the pile is 20 feet tall and 102 feet in circumference at the base. What is the area of the conical tarpaulin needed to cover the pile? **About 1314 square feet**

❷ **Example 1**

The pyramid of Khufu, a regular square pyramid which was originally 147 m tall and 231 m on a side of a base, is the largest of the Egyptian pyramids.

a. What is the approximate slant height of this pyramid?
b. What is its lateral area?

Solution

a. Draw a picture of the pyramid. We call it *V-ABCD*. *E* is the center of its base and *F* is the midpoint of an edge.

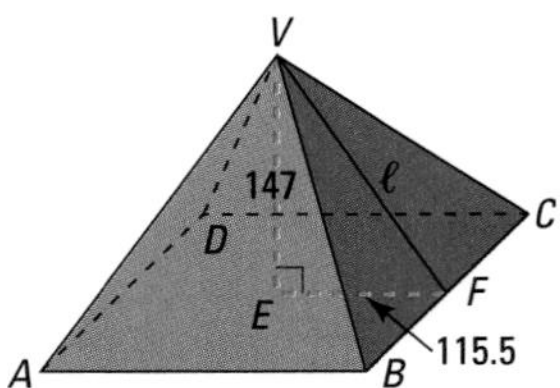

To compute the slant height ℓ, use $\triangle VEF$.
Since *V-ABCD* is a regular pyramid, $\triangle VEF$ is a right triangle.

E is the center of the square, so $EF = \frac{1}{2} \cdot 231 = 115.5$ meters.
VE is the height, 147 meters. By the Pythagorean Theorem,

$$\ell^2 = EF^2 + VE^2$$
$$= 115.5^2 + 147^2$$
$$\approx 34{,}950.$$
$$\text{So,} \quad \ell \approx 187 \text{ meters.}$$

b. To find the lateral area, use the formula L.A. $= \frac{1}{2}\ell p$. p is the perimeter of the base, so $p = 4 \cdot 231 = 924$.

$$\text{L.A.} = \frac{1}{2}\ell p$$
$$\approx \frac{1}{2} \cdot 187 \cdot 924$$
$$\approx 86{,}400 \text{ square meters}$$

Lateral Areas of Right Cones

The formula L.A. $= \frac{1}{2}\ell p$ applies also to right cones. Consider the circle containing the vertices of the base of a regular pyramid. Imagine increasing n, the number of sides of the base, keeping the altitude h constant. A cone is the limit of the regular pyramid as n increases without bound. The slant height of the pyramids becomes the length of any edge of the cone. The perimeter of the n-gon becomes the circumference of the circular base of the cone.

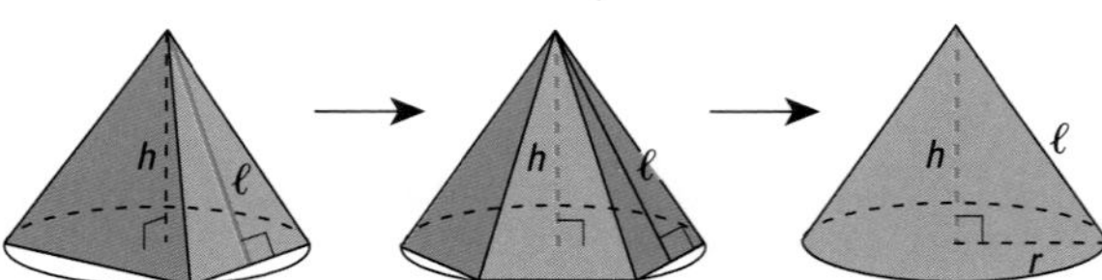

Adapting to Individual Needs

Extra Help

Some students may confuse the height of a pyramid with the slant height. Remind students that each lateral face of a pyramid is a triangle and therefore each triangular face has an altitude, even if the triangle occurs on a slant. The length of this altitude is the slant height for that face.

English Language Development

To help students learn the vocabulary associated with a formula, have them write each formula in symbols and then write the meaning of each symbol. For example, for any regular pyramid:

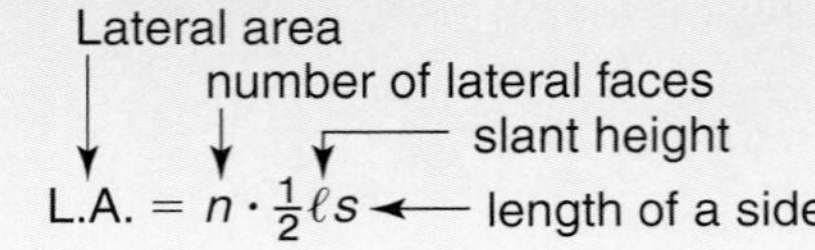

Regular Pyramid-Right Cone Lateral Area Formula
The lateral area, L.A., of a regular pyramid or right cone is half the product of its slant height ℓ and the perimeter (circumference) p of its base.

$$\text{L.A.} = \frac{1}{2}\ell p$$

Example 2

Find the surface area of a right cone with slant height 13 and base of radius 10.

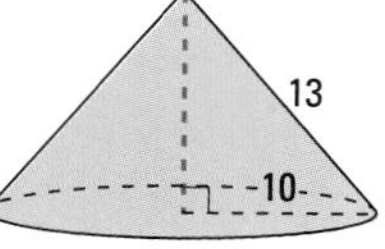

Solution

Use the formula S.A. = L.A. + B.

S.A. = L.A. + B

$= \frac{1}{2}\ell p + B$ — Since L.A. $= \frac{1}{2}\ell p$

$= \frac{1}{2}(\ell)(2\pi r) + \pi r^2$ — Since $p = 2\pi r$ and $B = \pi r^2$

$= \frac{1}{2}(13)(2 \cdot \pi \cdot 10) + \pi(10)^2$ — Substitute 13 for ℓ, and 10 for r.

$= 130\pi + 100\pi$

$= 230\pi$

Check

L.A. should be greater than B. (Do you see why?)

$130p > 100p$, a rough check.

Cheers! *Cones are an effective means of amplifying voices because they force all the sound into a small space. The megaphones' surface usually displays school names and logos.*

QUESTIONS

Covering the Reading

In 1 and 2, refer to the In-class Activity on page 569.

1. Give your answer to Part 1. 240 units^2
2. Give your answers to Part 2. a) $3s\ell$; b) yes
3. *True or false.* All the lateral faces of a regular pyramid are congruent to each other. True

In 4 and 5, consider the formula L.A. $= \frac{1}{2}\ell p$. For the figure given, what does each variable represent? Be as specific as possible.

4. regular pyramid
   L.A. = lateral area
   ℓ = slant height
   p = perimeter of base
5. right cone
   L.A. = lateral area
   ℓ = length of any edge of the cone
   p = circumference of base

3. A rubber sheet is fastened in a circular hoop 1 meter in diameter. A stick is positioned in the center and pushed up as shown, stretching the rubber sheet in the shape of a cone. How far up does the rubber sheet need to be pushed before the area of the rubber has doubled?

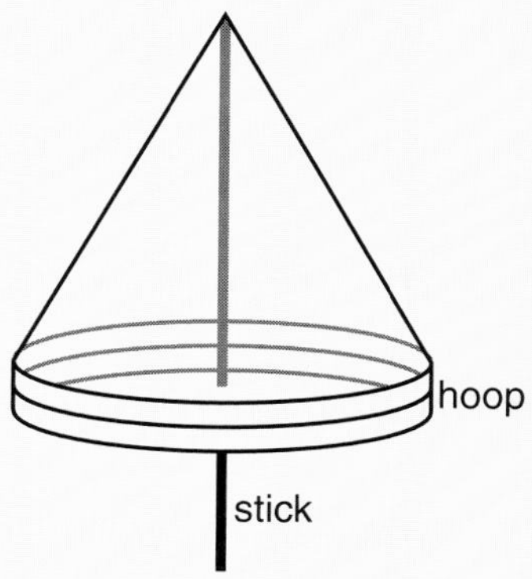

$\frac{\sqrt{3}}{2}$ or about 0.87 meter

Notes on Questions

Questions 4–5 Cooperative Learning Encourage students to make drawings of the figures, labeling the figures with the variables as appropriate.

Adapting to Individual Needs

Challenge

The formula for the surface area of a cone uses the slant height and the circumference. Suppose the radius r and the height h of a right cone are given, rather than the slant height. Find specific formulas in terms of r and h for both the lateral area and the surface area of the cone.

[L.A. $= \pi r\sqrt{h^2 + r^2}$;

S.A. $= \pi r^2 + \pi r\sqrt{h^2 + r^2}$]

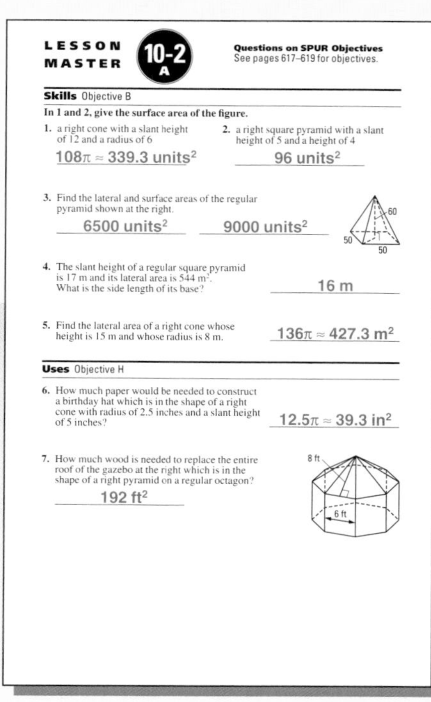

LESSON MASTER 10-2 A

Questions on SPUR Objectives
See pages 617–619 for objectives.

Skills Objective B

In 1 and 2, give the surface area of the figure.

1. a right cone with a slant height of 12 and a radius of 6 — $108\pi \approx 339.3$ units^2
2. a right square pyramid with a slant height of 5 and a height of 4 — 96 units^2
3. Find the lateral and surface areas of the regular pyramid shown at the right. — 6500 units^2 — 9000 units^2
4. The slant height of a regular square pyramid is 17 m and its lateral area is 544 m^2. What is the side length of its base? — 16 m
5. Find the lateral area of a right cone whose height is 15 m and whose radius is 8 m. — $136\pi \approx 427.3$ m^2

Uses Objective H

6. How much paper would be needed to construct a birthday hat which is in the shape of a right cone with radius of 2.5 inches and a slant height of 5 inches? — $12.5\pi \approx 39.3$ in^2
7. How much wood is needed to replace the entire roof of the gazebo at the right which is in the shape of a right pyramid on a regular octagon? — 192 ft^2

Notes on Questions

Question 11 You might point out that the area of the base of a cone is $\frac{1}{2}rp$; and the lateral area of a right cone is $\frac{1}{2}p\ell$. Thus, since $r < \ell$ the lateral area of a cone must always be greater than the area of its base. To see why this is so, suggest that students think of a rubber sheet fixed in a hoop, as pictured in Question 3 in *Additional Examples* on page 573. As the center is pushed in, the sheet must stretch, increasing the area.

Question 12 You can use the Pythagorean Theorem to prove that the slant height of a regular pyramid or cone is always greater than the height of the pyramid or cone. Since $c^2 = a^2 + b^2$ in a right triangle, then by the Equation to Inequality Property, $c^2 > a^2$. Since lengths are positive numbers, $c > a$.

Question 14 The condition "whose area is $9\sqrt{3}$" is redundant, because knowing that the length of a side of the base (an equilateral triangle) is 6 allows us to deduce that the area is $\frac{\sqrt{3}}{4} \cdot 6^2 = 9\sqrt{3}$.

Question 16 This is a hard question for most students. Some students will calculate to find the answer to **part b,** not realizing that it has to be equal to the answer to **part a. Part d** is difficult because the area of a circle is being found using the circumference of the same circle.

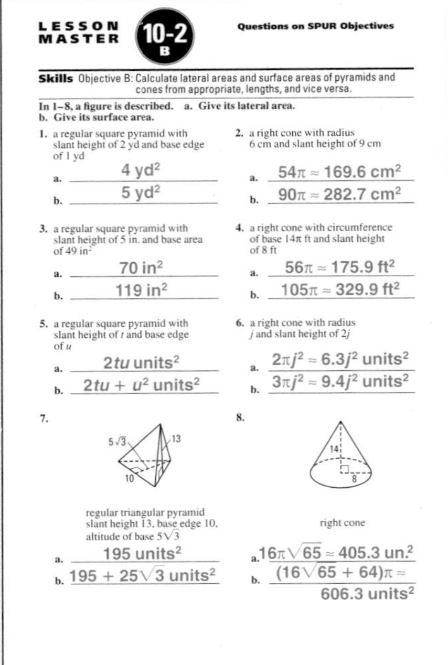

LESSON MASTER 10-2 B Questions on SPUR Objectives

Skills Objective B: Calculate lateral areas and surface areas of pyramids and cones from appropriate, lengths, and vice versa.

In 1–8, a figure is described. a. Give its lateral area. b. Give its surface area.

1. a regular square pyramid with slant height of 2 yd and base edge of 1 yd
   a. $4\ yd^2$
   b. $5\ yd^2$
2. a right cone with radius 6 cm and slant height of 9 cm
   a. $54\pi \approx 169.6\ cm^2$
   b. $90\pi \approx 282.7\ cm^2$
3. a regular square pyramid with slant height of 5 in. and base area of 49 in^2
   a. $70\ in^2$
   b. $119\ in^2$
4. a right cone with circumference of base 14π ft and slant height of 8 ft
   a. $56\pi \approx 175.9\ ft^2$
   b. $105\pi \approx 329.9\ ft^2$
5. a regular square pyramid with slant height of t and base edge of u
   a. $2tu$ units^2
   b. $2tu + u^2$ units^2
6. a right cone with radius j and slant height of $2j$
   a. $2\pi j^2 \approx 6.3j^2$ units^2
   b. $3\pi j^2 \approx 9.4j^2$ units^2
7.
   regular triangular pyramid slant height 13, base edge 10, altitude of base $5\sqrt{3}$
   a. 195 units^2
   b. $195 + 25\sqrt{3}$ units^2
8.
   right cone
   a. $16\pi\sqrt{65} \approx 405.3$ un.^{2}
   b. $(16\sqrt{65} + 64)\pi \approx 606.3$ units^2

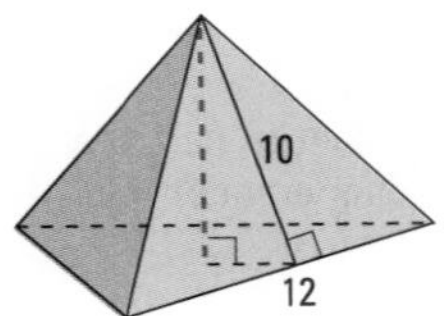

6. A regular triangular pyramid is shown at the left. Its slant height is 10 cm and a side of the base is 12 cm. Find its lateral area. $180\ cm^2$

7. Khafre, another Egyptian pyramid, is a regular square pyramid originally 143 meters tall and 216 meters on a side of the base.
   a. Draw and label a diagram. See margin.
   b. What is its approximate slant height? about 179 meters
   c. What is its approximate lateral area? about 77,300 square meters

8. A right cone is the limit of regular pyramids as the number of __?__ increases without bound. sides of its base

9. A football field measures 120 yd by $53\frac{1}{3}$ yd. About how many times as large as the area of a football field is the lateral area of the pyramid of Khufu? (1 yard = 0.9144 meters) 16

10. Use the right cone pictured at the left.
    a. Find its slant height. $\sqrt{130} \approx 11.4$ units
    b. Find its lateral area. $3\pi\sqrt{130} \approx 107.5$ units^2
    c. Find its surface area. $3\pi\sqrt{130} + 9\pi \approx 135.7$ units^2

11. *Multiple choice.* For a given cone, which is larger, its lateral area or the area of its base? a
    a. lateral area
    b. area of base
    c. neither; they are equal
    d. The answer depends on the cone.

Applying the Mathematics

12b) The slant height is the length of the hypotenuse of a right triangle, while the height is the length of a leg of the triangle.

12. a. In a regular pyramid, which is greater, its height or its slant height? slant height
    b. Explain your answer. See left.

In 13–15, a surface is described. **a.** Draw a picture. **b.** Find its lateral area. **c.** Find its surface area. a) See margin.

13. a regular square pyramid with a base side of 10 and a slant height of 50 b) 1000 units^2 c) 1100 units^2

14. a regular triangular pyramid with slant height 7 and with a base whose side is 6 and whose area is $9\sqrt{3}$
    b) 63 units^2 c) $63 + 9\sqrt{3} \approx 79$ units^2

15. a right cone with height 24 and base diameter 14
    b) $175\pi \approx 550$ units^2 c) $224\pi \approx 704$ units^2

16. A 90° sector is cut from a circle with radius 18 as shown at the left.
    a. Find the area of the shaded region. $243\pi \approx 763$ units^2
    b. If the shaded region is folded so that $\overline{AB}$ meets $\overline{CB}$, the lateral surface of a cone is formed. What is the lateral area of this cone?
    c. $\widehat{ATC}$ forms the perimeter of the base of the cone. What is the length of $\widehat{ATC}$? $27\pi \approx 85$ units
    d. Use your answer to part **c** to find the area of the base of the cone. $182.25\pi \approx 573$ units^2
    b) $243\pi \approx 763$ units^2

Additional Answers

7a.

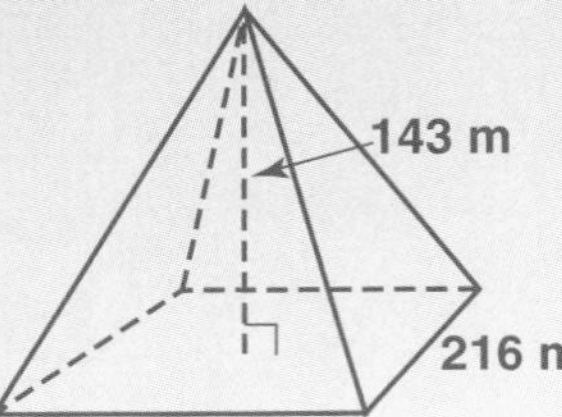

13a. Sample:

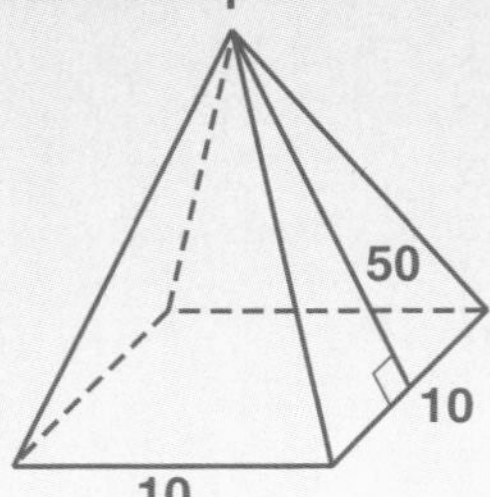

14a. Sample:

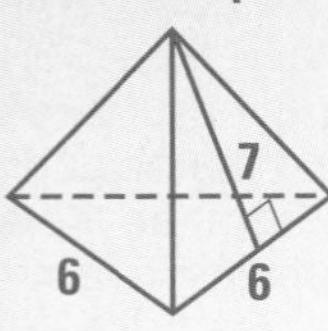

15a. Sample:

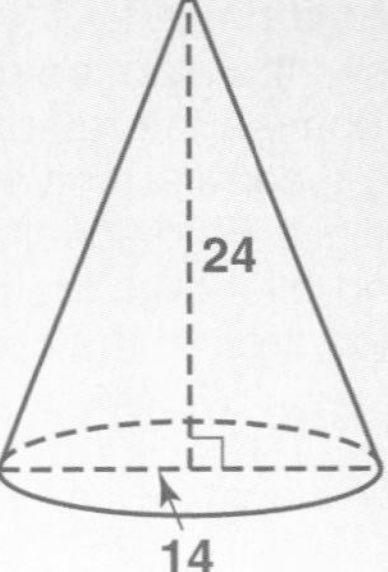

574

19) Sample:

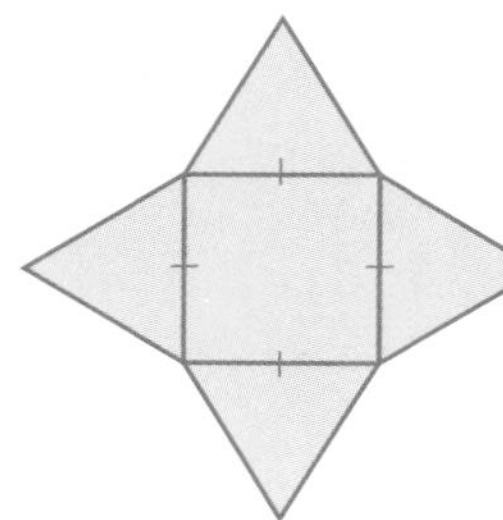

21) Uniqueness Property: Every polygonal region has a unique area. Rectangle Formula: The area of a rectangle with dimensions ℓ and w is ℓw. Congruence Property: Congruent figures have the same area. Additive Property: If A and B are nonoverlapping regions, then Area $(A \cup B)$ = Area (A) + Area (B).

Review

17. Find the surface area of a box with dimensions 1′, 15″, and 18″. *(Lesson 10-1)* 1332 sq in. = 9.25 sq ft

18. Small cans of frozen juice are about 9.5 cm tall and 5.5 cm in diameter. The tops and bottoms are metal; the rest is cardboard.
a. About how much metal is used? ≈ 47.5 cm^2
b. About how much cardboard is used? *(Lesson 10-1)* ≈ 164 cm^2

19. Draw a net for a regular square pyramid with dimensions of your choosing. *(Lesson 9-8)* See left.

20. Find the length of each lateral edge in the pyramid of Question 6. *(Lessons 8-6, 9-4)* $\sqrt{136} \approx 11.7$ cm

21. What are the four assumed properties of area? *(Lesson 8-2)* See left.

22. Line t goes through the points (6, -4) and (8, 0).
a. Graph t. See margin.
b. Find the slope of t. 2
c. Find the slope of a line perpendicular to t. *(Lessons 3-6, 3-7)* $-\frac{1}{2}$

23. Solve each equation in your head. *(Previous course)*
a. $x + 3 = 64$ $x = 61$
b. $y \cdot 3 = 64$ $y = \frac{64}{3}$
c. $z^3 = 64$ $z = 4$

Exploration

24. Draw three circles of diameter 8″. Measure central angles of 45°, 60°, and 120°, and cut out the sectors with these measures as shown in the figures below. Make a cone from each shaded portion.

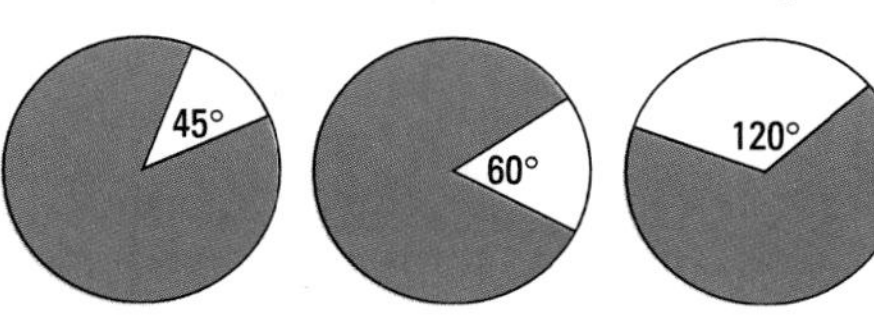

a. Which cone is the tallest? a–c) See below.
b. Which cone has the greatest lateral area?
c. Which cone's base has the greatest area?
d. Finish this sentence: As the measure of the central angle increases and a cone is formed, the height of the cone __?__, its lateral area __?__, and its base area __?__. increases, decreases, decreases

a) the cone with the 120° sector removed;
b) the cone with the 45° sector removed;
c) the cone with the 45° sector removed

These lily pads are shaped somewhat like the nets for cones found in Question 24.

Follow-up for Lesson 10-2

Practice

For more questions on SPUR Objectives, use **Lesson Master 10-2A** (shown on page 573) or **Lesson Master 10-2B** (shown on pages 574–575).

Assessment

Written Communication Have students write a paragraph comparing and contrasting the surface area formula in this lesson with the one in the preceding lesson. [Students recognize that the surface area formulas involve the same variables, but the first formula involves two bases, while the second involves one.]

Extension

Writing Ask students to explain what happens to the surface area of a cone when the radius doubles and the slant height stays the same. [The L.A. doubles and the area of the base is multiplied by 4.] Ask what happens when the slant height doubles and the radius stays the same. [The L.A. doubles and the area of the base stays the same.]

Projects Update Project 1, *Making Cones,* and Project 2, *Sizes of Pyramids of Ancient Cultures,* on page 613, relate to content of this lesson.

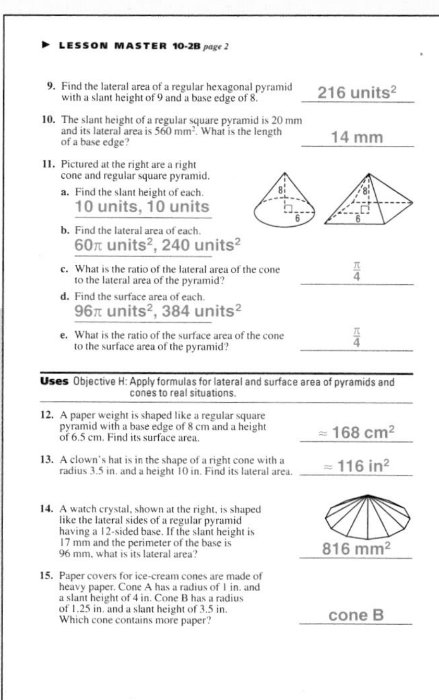

▶ LESSON MASTER 10-2B *page 2*

9. Find the lateral area of a regular hexagonal pyramid with a slant height of 9 and a base edge of 8. 216 units^2

10. The slant height of a regular square pyramid is 20 mm and its lateral area is 560 mm^2. What is the length of a base edge? 14 mm

11. Pictured at the right are a right cone and regular square pyramid.
a. Find the slant height of each. 10 units, 10 units
b. Find the lateral area of each. 60π units^2, 240 units^2
c. What is the ratio of the lateral area of the cone to the lateral area of the pyramid? $\frac{\pi}{4}$
d. Find the surface area of each. 96π units^2, 384 units^2
e. What is the ratio of the surface area of the cone to the surface area of the pyramid? $\frac{\pi}{4}$

Uses Objective H: Apply formulas for lateral and surface area of pyramids and cones to real situations.

12. A paper weight is shaped like a regular square pyramid with a base edge of 8 cm and a height of 6.5 cm. Find its surface area. ≈ 168 cm^2

13. A clown's hat is in the shape of a right cone with a radius 3.5 in. and a height 10 in. Find its lateral area. ≈ 116 in^2

14. A watch crystal, shown at the right, is shaped like the lateral sides of a regular pyramid having a 12-sided base. If the slant height is 17 mm and the perimeter of the base is 96 mm, what is its lateral area? 816 mm^2

15. Paper covers for ice-cream cones are made of heavy paper. Cone A has a radius of 1 in. and a slant height of 4 in. Cone B has a radius of 1.25 in. and a slant height of 3.5 in. Which cone contains more paper? cone B

Additional Answers

22a.

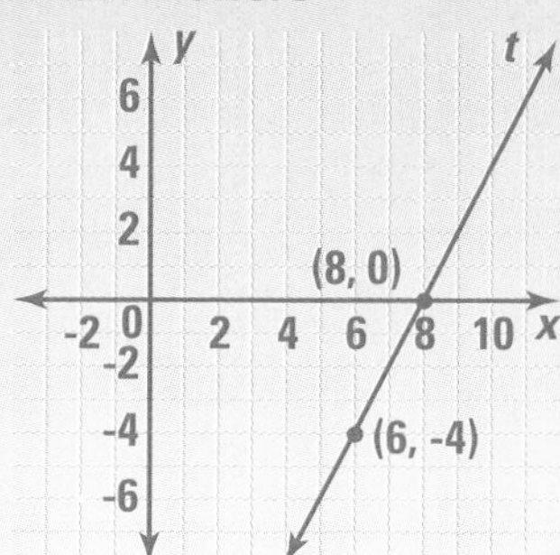

Setting Up Lesson 10-3

Discuss **Question 21** to prepare students for a discussion of the four properties of volume that are assumed in Lesson 10-3. Use **Question 23c** to review the volume of a cube.

Materials If you use *Optional Activities* on page 577, you will need containers that hold the same amount and are different shapes.

Lesson 10-3

Objectives

A Calculate volumes of rectangular prisms from appropriate lengths, and vice versa.
C Calculate cube roots.
I Apply formulas for volumes of rectangular prisms to real situations.

Resources

From the ***Teacher's Resource File***
- Lesson Master 10-3A or 10-3B
- Answer Master 10-3
- Assessment Sourcebook: Quiz for Lessons 10-1 through 10-3
- Teaching Aid 131: Warm-up

Additional Resources
- Visual for Teaching Aid 131
- Containers with different shapes that hold the same amount

Teaching Lesson 10-3

Warm-up

A child has a set of 12 alphabet blocks, all the same size. If all the blocks are arranged to form a rectangular solid, what are the possible heights for the solid?
1, 2, 3, 4, 6, or 12 blocks

Notes on Reading

Reading Mathematics Students can read this lesson independently, but be sure that they pay attention to the similarities between the Volume Postulate in this lesson and the Area Postulate in Lesson 8-2.

LESSON

10-3 *Fundamental Properties of Volume*

These stylized cubes form building blocks the computer artist Brian Yen used to fill space efficiently.

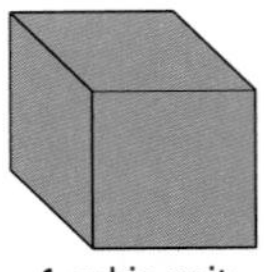

❶ The cube at the right has edges of length 1 unit, so the area of each face is 1 square unit. Since there are six faces, the surface area of this cube is 6 square units. Its *volume* is quite different from its surface area. The volume of this cube is 1 cubic unit or 1 unit^3. For this reason it is called the **unit cube.** Usually volume is measured in cubic units.

Volume is a measure of how much a figure will hold, its capacity.

Example 1

What is the volume of a paper bag with base 12″ by 7″ and height 17″?

Solution

Examine the drawing. There are 12 · 7 unit cubes in the layer along a base. There can be 17 layers. The volume is 12″ · 7″ · 17″, or 1428 cubic inches.

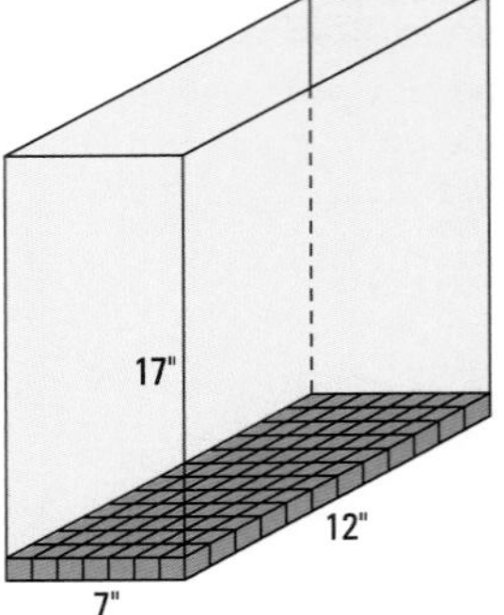

In Lesson 10-1 we found the surface area of this same bag to be 730 square inches. So volume and surface area are different quantities.

Lesson 10-3 Overview

Broad Goals This lesson introduces four basic properties of volume, reviews the volume of a cube, and discusses cube root.

Perspective The fundamental properties of volume are analogous to the fundamental properties of area. There is a uniqueness property (to ensure that there are not two different values for the volume of a figure), there is a formula for a simple figure (in area, it is a rectangle, in volume, a box), there is a congruence property (this ensures that the measure of a unit does not change as it is used again and again), and there is an additive property (this ensures that the total measure is not changed if a figure is taken apart and put together).

As with area, the volumes of some figures can be found by counting. But to find the volume of most figures, one needs to use some sort of formula or general scheme.

The capacity of solids in which cubes do not fit snugly, such as spheres, will be determined in another lesson.

Volume Postulate

Notice that the volume of the bag in Example 1 is the product of its three dimensions. This is one of the four fundamental properties of volume assumed in the Volume Postulate. Compare these assumptions with the fundamental properties of area assumed in the Area Postulate in Lesson 8-2.

Volume Postulate

a. **Uniqueness Property** Given a unit cube, every polyhedral region has a unique volume.

b. **Box Volume Formula** The volume V of a box with dimensions ℓ, w, and h is found by the formula $V = \ell wh$.

c. **Congruence Property** Congruent figures have the same volume.

d. **Additive Property** The volume of the union of two nonoverlapping solids is the sum of the volumes of the solids.

In symbols, if Volume(S) is the volume of a solid S, and A and B are nonoverlapping solids, then the Additive Property of Volume states:

$$\text{Volume}(A \cup B) = \text{Volume}(A) + \text{Volume}(B).$$

Using this property, volumes of various figures can be calculated.

Cats Cubed. *This puzzle made of eight cubes connected at the edges can be rearranged to show different views. The puzzle's volume is the sum of the volumes of the eight cubes.*

Example 2

Solids I and II are each the union of 5 unit cubes. Give the volume and surface area of each solid.

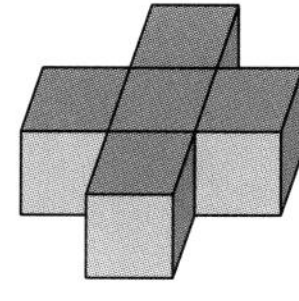

I

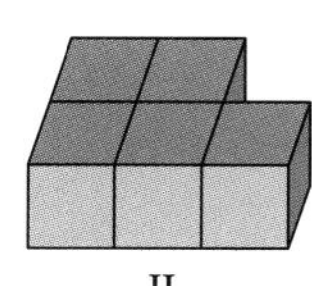

II

Solution

The volume for each solid is the same, since it is the sum of the volumes of the five cubes.

Volume(I) = Volume(II) = 5 cubic units

In solid I, there are 12 lateral faces (3 on each of the four outside cubes), each with area 1 square unit, and each base has area 5 square units.

solid I: S.A. = L.A. + 2 · B
= 12 · 1 + 2 · 5
= 22 square units.

In solid II, there are 10 lateral faces. Each base has area 5 square units.

solid II: S.A. = L.A. + 2 · B
= 10 · 1 + 2 · 5
= 20 square units.

❶ The unit cube in volume serves the same role as the unit square in area; that is, it is a convenient unit for measuring.

Emphasize that the volume of a solid can be thought of as the number of copies of a solid unit which fit inside that figure. That fundamental solid need not be a cube. The volume of a wall can be given as the number of bricks in the wall; the volume of a gasoline tank can be the number of cans of gasoline it takes to fill it, and so on.

Finding the volume of a solid as uncomplicated as those in **Example 2** still requires the use of all four properties of the Volume Postulate. First, there is the unit cube whose volume must be found (Box Volume Formula). There are five of these cubes and they all have the same volume (Congruence Property). The five volumes can be added to find the volume of the union (Additive Property). And answers found will be equal regardless of the method used (Uniqueness Property).

Uniqueness of volume is obviously a desirable attribute. Given a unit cube, the volume measure of a solid should be independent of the method of calculation. However, you might note that some boxes of food carry the caution that contents may have settled in shipping. This is to warn the consumer that the volume of the package is greater than the volume of the food inside. Also, some quantities mix so that when they are put together the volume of the result is not the sum of the two volumes. For instance, putting a teaspoon of sugar into a cup of coffee does not increase the volume by a teaspoon.

Optional Activities

Consumer Connection

Materials: Containers that hold the same amount but are different shapes

You might suggest this activity after students have completed the lesson. Have them bring items that can be purchased in a store that have the same volume but are shaped differently. For example, a box for 1 pound of margarine, a carton for 1 pound of butter, and a tub for 1 pound of margarine.

Have them find the surface area of each container. Then discuss what causes the differences in surface area and possible reasons for the different packaging.

❷ The paragraph discussing containers continues an important theme. Volume and surface area are quite different concepts, even though both measure the "size" of a figure. This is the subject of **Questions 26 and 27** in *Exploration*. Be sure to discuss these questions.

❸ **Consumer Connection** The Table of Liquid Measures contains information important for consumers. You might wish to poll your class to find out how many students knew each conversion equation before reading this lesson. Students of UCSMP *Transition Mathematics* will have seen the metric conversions before. Curiously, the conversion of a liquid gallon to cubic inches is *exact*.

Students of UCSMP *Algebra* may have a variety of ways to do **Example 3.** Here is another method.

$$8 \text{ oz} = 8 \text{ oz} \cdot \frac{1 \text{ qt}}{32 \text{ oz}} \cdot \frac{1 \text{ gal}}{4 \text{ qt}} \cdot \frac{231 \text{ in}^3}{1 \text{ gal}} =$$

$$\frac{231}{16} \text{ in}^3 = 14.4375 \text{ in}^3$$

Multicultural Connection Creamy salad dressing and yogurt, as well as cheese, whipped cream, and butter, are all dairy products, that is, products made from milk. In the U.S., most dairy goods come from cows' milk. In other countries, other animals are used. Goats' milk is popular in Europe, Latin America, Africa, and parts of Asia; camels provide milk in Central Asia and the Arabic world; reindeer provide much of the milk in Arctic regions; sheep's milk is predominant throughout the Mediterranean and Middle East; and water buffalo supply milk in Egypt, India, Pakistan, and much of Southeast Asia.

❷ Contrasting Volume and Surface Area

Example 2 illustrates that solids may have equal volumes but unequal surface areas. However, many people judge the volume of a container by its surface area. They think, "if it looks bigger, then it holds more!"

Pictured at the left are a salad dressing bottle and a yogurt container. The two containers hold the same amount; they have the same volume. The salad dressing bottle has greater surface area, which may give the false impression that it has greater volume and holds more.

Liquid Volume

In both the metric system and the U.S. customary system, special units are used to measure the volumes of liquids. The basic units are the liter and the gallon. These liquid units can be converted to cubic inches or cubic centimeters using the conversion equations in the first row of the table below. Packaged liquids you might buy in a store, such as juices and yogurt, are often measured in smaller units, such as the milliliter, quart, or pint. Some conversion facts between liquid units are in the second row of the table.

❸ **Table of Liquid Measures**

U.S. customary system	Metric system
1 liquid gallon (gal) = 231 cubic inches	1 liter (L) = 1000 cubic centimeters
1 liquid quart (qt) = $\frac{1}{4}$ liquid gallon = 32 liquid ounces (oz)	1 milliliter (mL) = $\frac{1}{1000}$ liter
1 liquid pint (pt) = 16 liquid ounces	

These units are converted to each other using methods you may have learned in previous courses.

Example 3

A small carton contains 8 oz of milk. How many cubic inches is this?

Solution

32 oz = $\frac{1}{4}$ gallon, so 128 oz = 1 gallon = 231 cubic inches.
Now form a proportion.

$$\frac{128 \text{ oz}}{231 \text{ in}^3} = \frac{8 \text{ oz}}{x \text{ in}^3}$$

Solve this proportion.

$$128x = 8 \cdot 231$$
$$x = \frac{8 \cdot 231}{128}$$
$$= 14.4375$$

8 ounces of milk occupy 14.4375 cubic inches of volume.

Adapting to Individual Needs

Extra Help

Point out to students that special units, such as gallon or liter, are commonly used to measure liquid volume. But liquid can also be measured in cubic units. For example, the capacity of a gasoline tank could be measured in cubic inches or cubic feet. Stress that the conversion equation 1 liquid gallon = 231 cubic inches can be used to convert from gallons to cubic inches if necessary.

English Language Development

Most of your students with limited English proficiency may have studied volume in their native country. Ask them to explain to you what volume means.

The Volume of a Cube

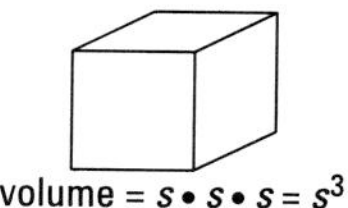

volume = $s \cdot s \cdot s = s^3$

The formula for the volume of a cube is a special case of the formula for the volume of a box, where each dimension is the same.

Cube Volume Formula
The volume V of a cube with edge s is s^3. $V = s^3$.

Because of the Cube Volume Formula, we call s^3 the "cube of s." If a cube has volume 8, its edge will satisfy $s^3 = 8$, so $s = 2$. We say that 2 is the cube root of 8, and write $2 = \sqrt[3]{8}$. In general, $\sqrt[3]{y}$ is the edge of a cube whose volume is y.

Definition
x is a **cube root of y,** written $x = \sqrt[3]{y}$, if and only if $x^3 = y$.

Calculators differ in the keys they employ to calculate a cube root. You should learn the sequence of keys you can use to find a cube root on your calculator.

Example 4

A cube has a volume of 50 cubic centimeters. What is the length of an edge, rounded to the tenths place?

Solution

Let s be the length of an edge. Since $s^3 = 50$, s is exactly $\sqrt[3]{50}$ cm. A calculator shows $\sqrt[3]{50} \approx 3.684 \ldots$.
The length of an edge is approximately 3.7 cm.

Check

Is $(3.7)^3 \approx 50$? Yes, $3.7^3 = 50.653$, which is close enough for a check.

QUESTIONS

Covering the Reading

1. What is the volume of a box with dimensions 30 cm, 70 cm, and 84 cm? $176{,}400 \text{ cm}^3$

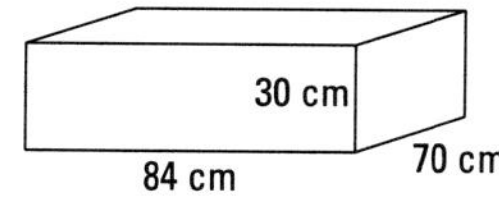

2. Two solids have the same surface area. Must they have the same volume? No

Additional Examples

1. How many sugar cubes with 1-cm edges can be packed in a box that is 12 cm wide, 5 cm long, and 20 cm tall? 1200 cubes
2. Consider a stack of h congruent cubes with edge of length s.
   a. What is the volume of the stack? hs^3
   b. Must the surface area of the stack be an even multiple of the area of one face? **Yes. The stack is a prism. Its lateral area is height × perimeter of base, which is $hs \cdot 4s = 4hs^2$; the bases have total area $2s^2$. Thus, the surface area is $(2 + 4h)s^2$, which is an even multiple of the area of a face.**
3. A 2-liter plastic liquid container has a volume of how many cubic centimeters? 2000 cm^3
4. Perry Plastic Producers advertises a plastic stacking cube for closets which "holds 2000 cubic inches of stuff." What is the length of an edge of the cube? About 12.6 inches
5. In the 1960s, an automobile manufacturer proudly announced that one of its cars had "a trunk capacity of 3000 cubic inches!" If the box-shaped trunk was 3 feet wide and 2 feet from front to back, how deep was the trunk? About 3.5 inches

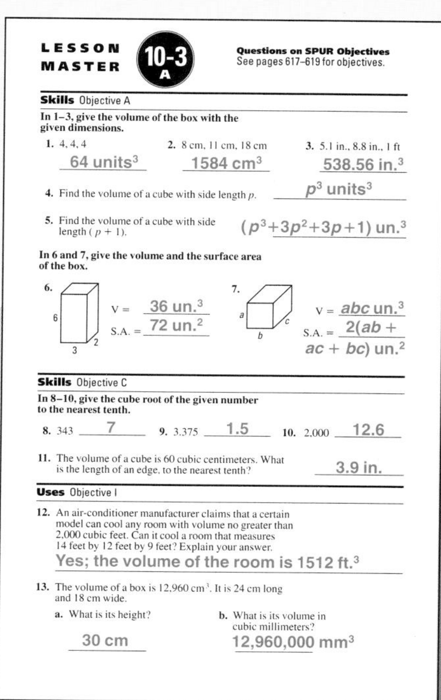

LESSON MASTER 10-3 A

Questions on SPUR Objectives
See pages 617–619 for objectives.

Skills Objective A

In 1–3, give the volume of the box with the given dimensions.

1. 4, 4, 4 64 units^3
2. 8 cm, 11 cm, 18 cm 1584 cm^3
3. 5.1 in., 8.8 in., 1 ft 538.56 in.^3
4. Find the volume of a cube with side length p. $p^3 \text{ units}^3$
5. Find the volume of a cube with side length $(p + 1)$. $(p^3+3p^2+3p+1) \text{ un.}^3$

In 6 and 7, give the volume and the surface area of the box.

6. (box 6 by 3 by 2) V = 36 un.^3 S.A. = 72 un.^2
7. (box a by b by c) V = $abc \text{ un.}^3$ S.A. = $2(ab + ac + bc) \text{ un.}^2$

Skills Objective C

In 8–10, give the cube root of the given number to the nearest tenth.

8. 343 7
9. 3.375 1.5
10. 2,000 12.6
11. The volume of a cube is 60 cubic centimeters. What is the length of an edge, to the nearest tenth? 3.9 in.

Uses Objective I

12. An air-conditioner manufacturer claims that a certain model can cool any room with volume no greater than 2,000 cubic feet. Can it cool a room that measures 14 feet by 12 feet by 9 feet? Explain your answer. Yes; the volume of the room is 1512 ft.^3
13. The volume of a box is $12{,}960 \text{ cm}^3$. It is 24 cm long and 18 cm wide.
    a. What is its height? 30 cm
    b. What is its volume in cubic millimeters? $12{,}960{,}000 \text{ mm}^3$

Adapting to Individual Needs

Challenge

An *Exploration* question in Chapter 3 mentioned the ancient problem of "duplicating the cube." Have students look in an encyclopedia or a history of mathematics to research and write a report about this problem. [The problem is to construct a cube whose volume is twice that of a given cube. The reports should give information about the various ways of solving the problem and how Euclidean tools alone (compass and straightedge) could not be used to solve the problem.]

Notes on Questions

Question 12 This question helps students distinguish between the exact answer, $\sqrt[3]{40}$, and the estimate, 3.42; the situation will determine which answer is more appropriate. The decimal for the cube root of 40 neither terminates nor repeats because the number is irrational. For a sense of the size of the cube, the estimate is useful. To express the idea that the cube holds 40 cubic units, the exact answer is more appropriate. The traditional "simplified" exact answer, $2\sqrt[3]{5}$, seems to have little utility in an age of calculators.

Question 15 Students have to determine the measure in one dimension from the measure in another dimension. An analysis of the problem should begin with asking what must be known to find the desired measure. Write down the formula; then determine how the measures needed can be found from the given data.

Question 19 In Chapter 12, the ratio of volumes as the cube of the ratio of similitude will be stressed. At this time, build the idea by having students see that four of the smaller cubes are along each edge, and that 4^2 smaller cubes are in each layer. Since there are four layers, there are 4^3 smaller cubes in the large cube.

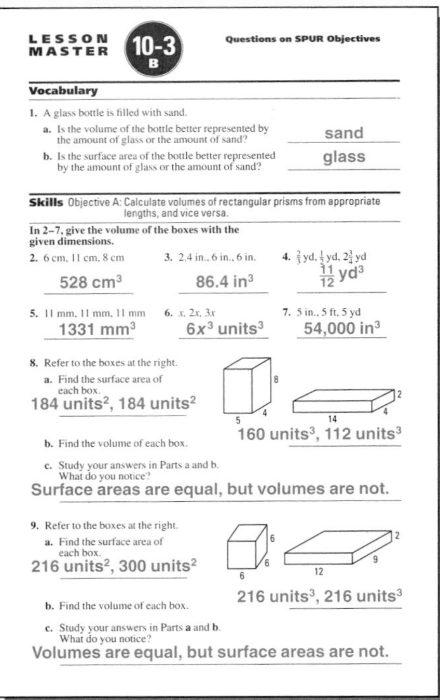

LESSON MASTER 10-3 B Questions on SPUR Objectives

Vocabulary

1. A glass bottle is filled with sand.
   a. Is the volume of the bottle better represented by the amount of glass or the amount of sand? sand
   b. Is the surface area of the bottle better represented by the amount of glass or the amount of sand? glass

Skills Objective A: Calculate volumes of rectangular prisms from appropriate lengths, and vice versa.

In 2–7, give the volume of the boxes with the given dimensions.

2. 6 cm, 11 cm, 8 cm — 528 cm^3
3. 2.4 in., 6 in., 6 in. — 86.4 in^3
4. $\frac{2}{3}$ yd, $\frac{1}{2}$ yd, $2\frac{3}{4}$ yd — $\frac{11}{12} \text{ yd}^3$
5. 11 mm, 11 mm, 11 mm — 1331 mm^3
6. x, $2x$, $3x$ — $6x^3 \text{ units}^3$
7. 5 in., 5 ft, 5 yd — $54{,}000 \text{ in}^3$

8. Refer to the boxes at the right.
   a. Find the surface area of each box. 184 units^2, 184 units^2
   b. Find the volume of each box. 160 units^3, 112 units^3
   c. Study your answers in Parts a and b. What do you notice? Surface areas are equal, but volumes are not.

9. Refer to the boxes at the right.
   a. Find the surface area of each box. 216 units^2, 300 units^2
   b. Find the volume of each box. 216 units^3, 216 units^3
   c. Study your answers in Parts **a** and **b**. What do you notice? Volumes are equal, but surface areas are not.

3. Two cubes have the same surface area. Must they have the same volume? Yes

4. Some sugar cubes have an edge length of approximately 0.6 in. What is the volume of one cube? about 0.216 in^3

5. What is the volume, in cubic inches, of a pint of milk? 28.875 in^3

6. A two-liter container contains how many milliliters? 2000

7. x is a cube root of y if and only if __?__. $x^3 = y$

In 8–11, use a calculator to find each cube root. Round to the nearest tenth if necessary.

8. 3375 15

9. 2000.376 12.6

10. 110 about 4.8

11. 6.45 about 1.9

12. A cube has volume 40 cm^3. What is the length of an edge
a. exactly? $\sqrt[3]{40}$ cm
b. to the nearest hundredth? 3.42 cm

13. How can you check to see if you have found the correct cube root of a number?
Cube your answer to see if you get the number again.

Applying the Mathematics

14. A top is put on the paper bag of Example 1.
a. By how much does the top change the bag's surface area?
b. By how much does it change the bag's volume?
a) adds 84 in^2 b) no change

15. The volume of a box is 576 in^3. If its base has area 48 in^2, what is its height? 12 inches

16. Calculate $\sqrt[3]{25} + \sqrt[3]{100}$ to the nearest hundredth. 7.57

17. Some people use the formula $V = Bh$ for the volume of a box.
a. What is B in this formula? area of a base
b. Why does this formula work? The area of the base is ℓw, so the formula $V = Bh$ is equivalent to $V = \ell wh$.

18. A cube has volume $29{,}791 \text{ cm}^3$. What is its surface area? 5766 cm^2

19. One cube has edges x centimeters long. Another cube has edges $4x$ centimeters long. Find the ratio of:
a. the total surface area of the smaller cube to that of the larger cube. a) $\frac{1}{16}$ b) $\frac{1}{64}$
b. the volume of the smaller cube to that of the larger cube.

x $4x$

20. 1 in. = 2.54 cm.
a. What is the volume, in cubic centimeters, of a cube with edge length 1 in.? about 16.39 cm^3
b. 1 cubic inch ≈ __?__ cubic centimeters 16.39

21. **a.** 1 yard = __?__ feet 3
b. 1 square yard = __?__ square feet 9
c. 1 cubic yard = __?__ cubic feet 27

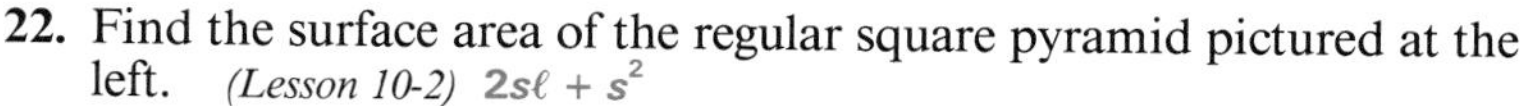

Review

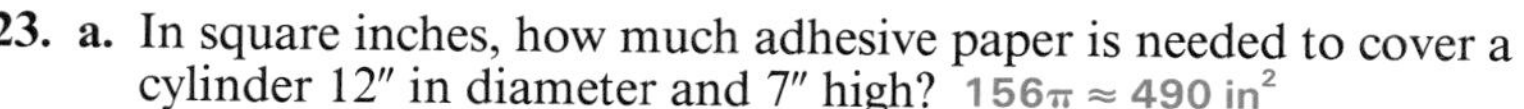

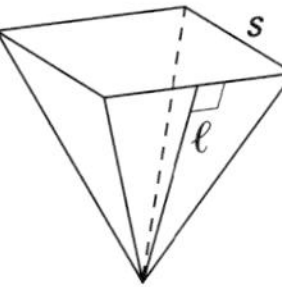

22. Find the surface area of the regular square pyramid pictured at the left. *(Lesson 10-2)* $2s\ell + s^2$

23. a. In square inches, how much adhesive paper is needed to cover a cylinder 12″ in diameter and 7″ high? $156\pi \approx 490$ in^2

b. Suppose you can buy the adhesive paper only by the square foot. How many square feet will you need to buy to cover the cylinder of part **a**? *(Lesson 10-1)* 4 square feet

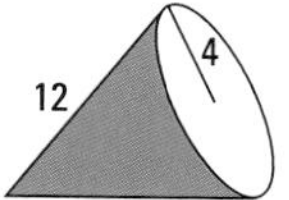

24. Determine the lateral area of the right cone at the left. *(Lesson 10-2)* $48\pi \approx 150.8$ units^2

25. The tent at the right is in the shape of a right prism with isosceles triangle *GHI* as its base.

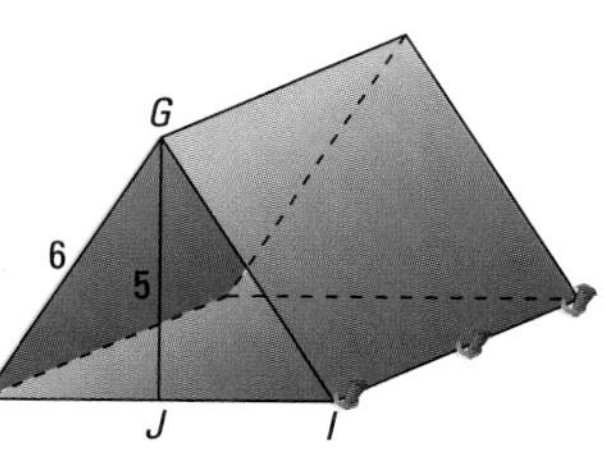

a. If the top of the tent is 5 ft above the ground, find the area of the base of this prism. $5\sqrt{11} \approx 16.6$ ft^2

b. If the length of the tent is 7 feet, find the surface area of the tent (including the floor). *(Lessons 7-7, 8-4, 9-3, 10-1)* $84 + 24\sqrt{11} \approx 163.60$ ft^2

Exploration

26. Containers holding small amounts can be made to appear to hold more than they do by making them long and thin. Give some examples of these kinds of containers. Samples: toothpaste tubes, perfume bottles

27. Two polyhedra made up of 5 unit cubes are shown in Example 2 of this lesson.

a. Draw some of the other possible polyhedra that are the union of 5 unit cubes. See margin.

b. Which has the greatest surface area? arrangements a and c

c. Which has the least surface area? arrangement b

Additional Answers
27a. Samples:

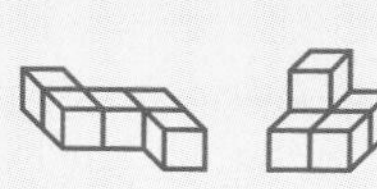
(a)

(b)

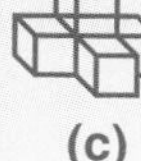
(c)

Follow-up for Lesson 10-3

Practice

For more questions on SPUR Objectives, use **Lesson Master 10-3A** (shown on page 579) or **Lesson Master 10-3B** (shown on pages 580–581).

Assessment

Quiz A quiz covering Lessons 10-1 through 10-3 is provided in the *Assessment Sourcebook.*

Oral/Written Communication Have students **work in pairs.** Have each student draw a rectangular solid with the length, width, and height labeled. Then have them exchange drawings and determine the volume and surface area for the solid. [Students correctly determine the volume and surface area for a rectangular solid.]

Extension

Writing Ask students to explain if it is possible for the number of cubic units in the volume of a cube to equal the number of square units in its surface area. [Yes. When $s = 6$, $V = 216$ units^3, S.A. $= 216$ units^2.]

Project Update Project 4, *What Is Your Surface Area and Volume?* on page 614, relates to the content of this lesson.

▶ **LESSON MASTER 10-3B** *page 2*

10. The volume of a box is 624 units^3. Two of the dimensions are 6 units and 13 units. Find the third dimension. 8 units

Skills Objective C: Calculate cube roots.

In 11–16, give the cube root of the number. Round inexact answers to the nearest tenth.

11. 512	8	12. 117.649	4.9
13. 7000	19.1	14. 0.14887	.5
15. 45	3.6	16. 100	4.6

17. Find the length of the edge of a cube whose volume is 4,096 m^3. 16 m

18. The volume of a cube is about 614 ft^3. What is the area of a face, to the nearest tenth? 72.2 ft^2

Uses Objective I: Apply formulas for volumes of rectangular prisms to real situations.

19. A carton contains 16 ounces of cream. How many cubic inches is this? ≈ 29 in^3

20. Which holds more, a metal foot locker 26 in. by 14 in. by 12 in., or a carton 22 in. by 16 in. by 13 in.? carton

21. The inside dimensions of a freezer are 32 in. by 28 in. by 60 in. Find its volume in cubic feet. ≈ 31 ft^3

22. The dimensions of each brick at the right are 2 in., 3.5 in., and 8 in.

a. Find the volume of a single brick. 56 in^3

b. Find the total volume of the 2 steps shown. 16,128 in^3

c. How many gallons of water would be displaced if the steps shown were built totally submerged into a pond? ≈ 70 gal.

Lesson 10-4

Objectives

E Determine what happens to the surface area and volume of a figure when its dimensions are multiplied by some number(s).

J Represent products of two (or three) numbers or expressions as areas of rectangles (or volumes of boxes), and vice versa.

Resources

From the ***Teacher's Resource File***

- Lesson Master 10-4A or 10-4B
- Answer Master 10-4
- Teaching Aid 132: Warm-up
- Activity Kit, Activity 22
- Technology Sourcebook, Calculator Master 1

Additional Resources

- Visual for Teaching Aid 132

Teaching Lesson 10-4

Warm-up

A gardener pointed to a rectangular flower bed and said, "If I had made that bed 2 feet wider and 3 feet longer, it would have been 64 square feet larger; but if I had made it 3 feet wider and 2 feet longer, it would then have been 68 square feet larger." Find the length and the width of the flower bed. 14 ft by 10 ft

Notes on Reading

Reading Mathematics To focus attention on how to best read the

LESSON

10-4 *Multiplication, Area, and Volume*

Packing and stacking. *A common and practical way of transporting products cross-country or worldwide is to fill large, rectangular containers which can be stacked on boats, trains, planes, or trucks.*

Picturing Multiplication with Area

To obtain the area of a rectangle, you merely have to multiply its length by its width. Any positive numbers can be the length and the width. Thus the area of a rectangle is a *model* for the multiplication of two positive numbers. This enables multiplication to be pictured. For instance, the following picture shows that $(3.5)(2.3) = (3 + 0.5)(2 + 0.3) = 3 \cdot 2 + (3)(0.3) + (0.5)(2) + (0.5)(0.3)$.

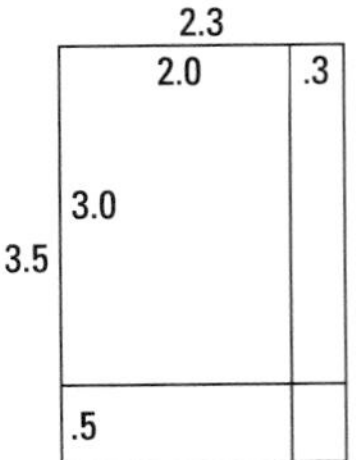

The multiplication of two polynomials can also be pictured by area. For instance, in algebra you may have seen this picture of $(a + b)(c + d)$.

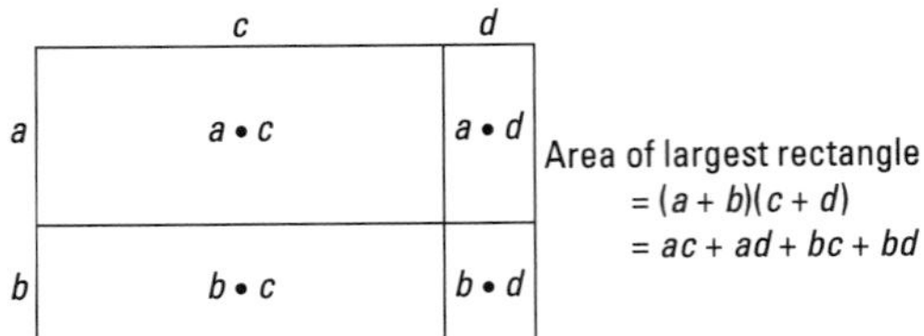

582

Lesson 10-4 Overview

Broad Goals In this lesson, the multiplication of two polynomials is reviewed and related to area. Then the multiplication of three polynomials is related to volume.

Perspective In algebra courses, students are often introduced to the Distributive Property by a diagram that uses area; it may help learning to visualize such formulas. The multiplication of three polynomials is usually not represented there because students have not yet studied volume. Here the multiplication of two and three polynomials is pictured and the skill is reviewed.

This lesson also helps set up the Fundamental Theorem of Similarity discussed in Chapter 12.

Optional Activities

Activity 1

You can use *Activity Kit, Activity 22,* as an alternate approach to **Example 3** or as a follow-up to the lesson. In this activity, students make a paper box with binomial dimensions and then relate the volume of the box to the product of three binomials.

Example 1

a. What binomial multiplication is pictured at the right?

b. Multiply the binomials.

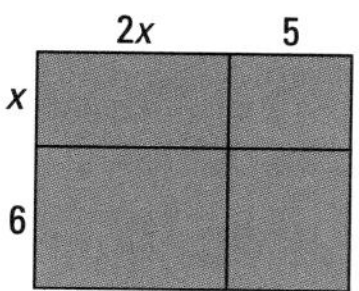

$2x^2$	$5x$
$12x$	30

Solution

a. The height is $x + 6$.
The width is $2x + 5$.
The rectangles picture $(x + 6)(2x + 5)$.

b. Add the areas of the 4 smaller rectangles.
$2x^2 + 5x + 12x + 30 = 2x^2 + 17x + 30$.
Thus $(x + 6)(2x + 5) = 2x^2 + 17x + 30$.

The multiplication of two polynomials with more terms can also be pictured with an area diagram. Here is a picture of the multiplication of two trinomials $(a + b + c)(d + e + f)$.

	d	e	f
a	$a \cdot d$	$a \cdot e$	$a \cdot f$
b	$b \cdot d$	$b \cdot e$	$b \cdot f$
c	$c \cdot d$	$c \cdot e$	$c \cdot f$

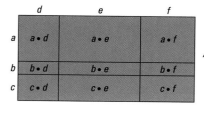

$$A = (a + b + c)(d + e + f)$$
$$= ad + ae + af + bd + be + bf + cd + ce + cf$$

Picturing Multiplication with Volume

The Box Volume Formula $V = \ell wh$ involves the multiplication of three numbers. So the volume of a box can model the multiplication of three polynomials. The biggest box below has dimensions $a + b$, $c + d$, and $e + f$. So its volume is the product of those three binomials. But its volume also is the sum of the volumes of the eight smaller boxes.

Notice that the product of the three binomials consists of all possible products in which one factor is taken from the first binomial, one from the second, and one from the third.

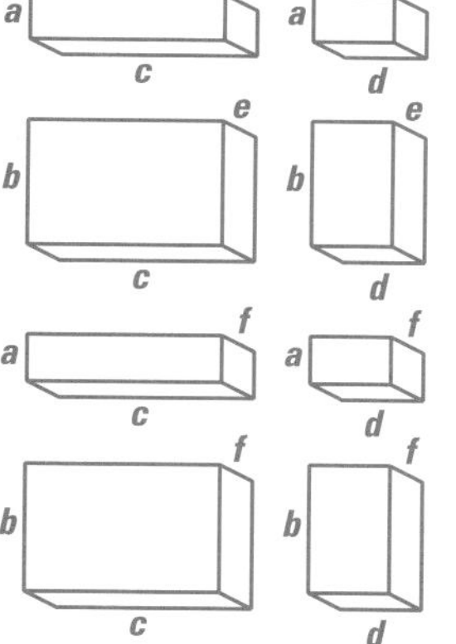

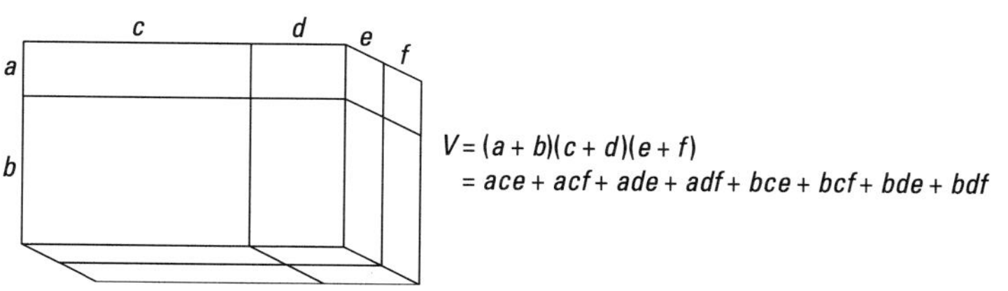

Activity

Draw each of the 8 smaller boxes that make up the above figure, and label the length, width, and height of each. See left.

equations in this lesson, you might focus on the illustrations and **Examples** as you read the lesson aloud together. Students of UCSMP *Algebra* have seen the area model for multiplication of polynomials. Still, this may be the first time that some of your students realize that they can *picture* what is going on when they multiply polynomials. Many times students have memorized the skills without any connections to properties or to potential applications.

The results of **Example 2** are very important and a surprise for many students. The question of what happens to the volume of a figure as the dimensions change can be illustrated by using open, actual models and filling them with unit cubes, sand, and so on.

Have students record the results of the **Activity** for use with **Question 6** on page 585.

Additional Examples

1. Find the product $43 \cdot 85 \cdot 61$ by expanding $(40 + 3)(80 + 5) \cdot (60 + 1)$. **Think of a box with dimensions 43, 85, and 61 cut into 8 smaller boxes; the product $= 40 \cdot 80 \cdot 60 + 40 \cdot 80 \cdot 1 + 40 \cdot 5 \cdot 60 + 40 \cdot 5 \cdot 1 + 3 \cdot 80 \cdot 60 + 3 \cdot 80 \cdot 1 + 3 \cdot 5 \cdot 60 + 3 \cdot 5 \cdot 1 = 192{,}000 + 3200 + 12{,}000 + 200 + 14{,}400 + 240 + 900 + 15 = 222{,}955$.**

(Additional Examples continue on page 584.)

Optional Activities

Activity 2 You might use this activity after discussing the **Activity** on page 583. Have students **work in pairs.** Tell one student to make up a multiplication problem such as $x(x + 3)(2x + 1)$. Tell the other student to draw the model and explain how the product of 3 numbers is similar to finding the volume of a box. Then have students switch roles. [A sample is shown at the right with width x, length $x + 3$, and height $2x + 1$. Product $= 2x^3 + 7x^2 + 3x$]

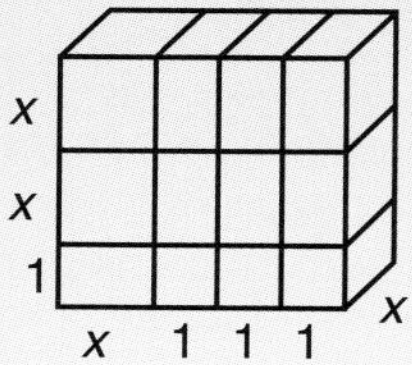

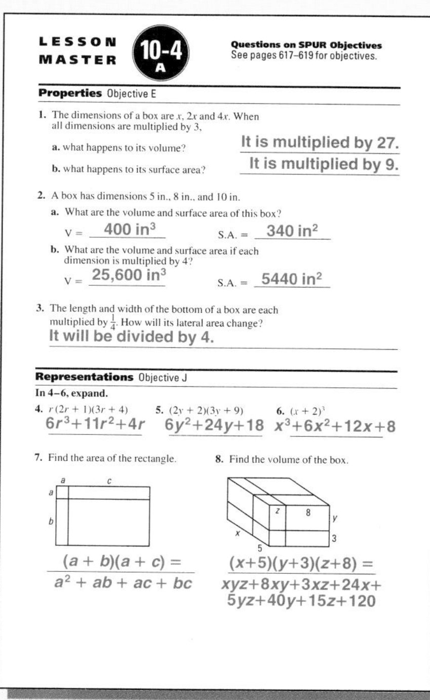

LESSON MASTER 10-4 A

Questions on SPUR Objectives
See pages 617–619 for objectives.

Properties Objective E

1. The dimensions of a box are x, $2x$ and $4x$. When all dimensions are multiplied by 3,
   a. what happens to its volume? **It is multiplied by 27.**
   b. what happens to its surface area? **It is multiplied by 9.**

2. A box has dimensions 5 in., 8 in., and 10 in.
   a. What are the volume and surface area of this box?
   V = **400 in^3** S.A. = **340 in^2**
   b. What are the volume and surface area if each dimension is multiplied by 4?
   V = **25,600 in^3** S.A. = **5440 in^2**

3. The length and width of the bottom of a box are each multiplied by $\frac{1}{4}$. How will its lateral area change?
   It will be divided by 4.

Representations Objective J

In 4–6, expand.

4. $r(2r + 1)(3r + 4)$ **$6r^3+11r^2+4r$**
5. $(2y + 2)(3y + 9)$ **$6y^2+24y+18$**
6. $(x + 2)^3$ **$x^3+6x^2+12x+8$**

7. Find the area of the rectangle.

$(a + b)(a + c) = a^2 + ab + ac + bc$

8. Find the volume of the box.

$(x+5)(y+3)(z+8) = xyz+8xy+3xz+24x+5yz+40y+15z+120$

2. A box has dimensions ℓ, w, and h. If the dimensions are reduced to $\frac{1}{2}$, $\frac{1}{3}$, and $\frac{1}{4}$ the original size, respectively, what happens to the volume? The volume of the smaller box is $\frac{1}{24}$ the volume of the original.
3. Of two bags of rice, one holds twice as much rice as the other. If corresponding dimensions of the two bags are to have the same ratio, then each dimension of the larger bag must be about how many times as large as the smaller bag? $\sqrt[3]{2} = 1.26$ times as large

Notes on Questions

Questions 7–10 You may want to have students draw rectangles or cubes as geometric interpretations for these questions.

Question 13 Error Alert Students may think that the volume is increased by 6, 36, or 216. The new volume is $(\ell + 6)wh = \ell wh + 6wh$, which indicates that it is 6wh greater than the old volume. Thus, the change in volume depends on the old width and height.

Question 14 For **part b,** assume that the size of individual grains of couscous in these bags is the same.

(Notes on Questions continue on page 586.)

LESSON MASTER 10-4 B Questions on SPUR Objectives

Properties Objective E: Determine what happens to the surface area and volume of a figure when its dimensions are multiplied by some number(s).

1. A box has a volume of 450 m³.
   a. If one dimension of the box is doubled, what is the volume of the larger box? 900 m³
   b. If two dimensions of the box are doubled, what is the volume of the larger box? 1800 m³
   c. If all three dimensions of the box are doubled, what is the volume of the larger box? 3600 m³
2. A box has a volume of 200 ft³.
   a. If one dimension of the box is multiplied by 5, what is the volume of the larger box? 1000 ft³
   b. If one dimension of the box is multiplied by 5 and another dimension is doubled, what is the volume of the larger box? 2000 ft³
   c. If one dimension of the box is multiplied by 5, another dimension is doubled, and the third dimension is tripled, what is the volume of the larger box? 6000 ft³
3. What happens to the volume of a box if all three dimensions are
   a. tripled? It is multiplied by 27.
   b. multiplied by 5? It is multiplied by 125.
   c. multiplied by $\frac{1}{2}$? It is multiplied by $\frac{1}{8}$.
   d. multiplied by k? It is multiplied by k^3.
4. A box has dimensions ℓ, w, and h. If the dimensions are changed as indicated, give the volume of the new box.
   a. Just the length is multiplied by 4. $4\ell wh$
   b. Its length is multiplied by 3, its width by 6, and its height by 10. $180\ell wh$
   c. Five is added to each dimension. $(\ell + 5)(w + 5)(h + 5)$ or $\ell wh + 5wh + 5\ell h + 5\ell w + 25h + 25w + 25\ell + 125$

Changing Dimensions of a Box

If you *multiply* each side of a box by a number, the change in volume is easy to find.

Example 2

A box has dimensions ℓ, w, and h. If the dimensions are multiplied by 2, 3, and 4, respectively, how is the volume of the box changed?

Solution

Draw a picture of the situation. The new volume is $(2\ell)(3w)(4h)$, which is $24\ell wh$, or 24 times the original volume.

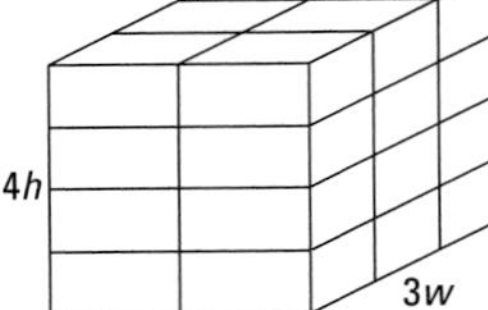

In general, multiplying any one dimension of a box by a particular number (and leaving the others constant) multiplies the volume of the box by that number. For example, if the length of a box is doubled but nothing is done to the other dimensions, the volume is doubled. Adding to a dimension of a box does not affect the volume in such a simple way.

Example 3

The dimensions of a box are increased by 2, 3, and 4. What happens to the volume of the box?

Solution

Let the original dimensions of the box be x, y, and z. So the original volume is xyz. Let the new dimensions be ℓ, w, and h, where $\ell = z + 4$, $w = y + 3$, and $h = x + 2$.

$V = \ell wh = (z + 4)(y + 3)(x + 2)$

First, multiply two of the binomials.

$(z + 4)(y + 3) = yz + 3z + 4y + 12$

Then multiply $x + 2$ by your result.

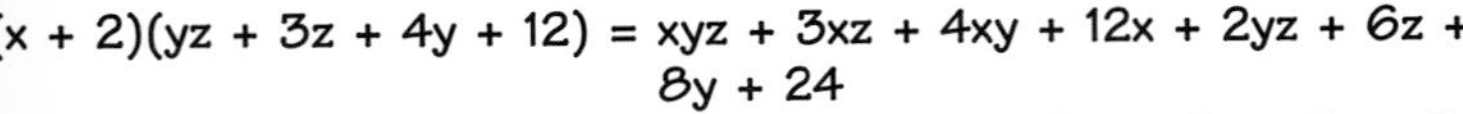

$(x + 2)(yz + 3z + 4y + 12) = xyz + 3xz + 4xy + 12x + 2yz + 6z + 8y + 24$

The volume is increased by $3xz + 4xy + 12x + 2yz + 6z + 8y + 24$.

Another shape. Same volume. *This is another configuration of the puzzle shown on page 577.*

Check

Let $x = 6$, $y = 8$, $z = 10$. The volume of the original box was 480. The volume of the new box is $(6 + 2)(8 + 3)(10 + 4) = 8 \cdot 11 \cdot 14 = 1232$. Now substitute into the answer.

$3 \cdot 6 \cdot 10 + 4 \cdot 6 \cdot 8 + 12 \cdot 6 + 2 \cdot 8 \cdot 10 + 6 \cdot 10 + 8 \cdot 8 + 24$
$= 180 + 192 + 72 + 160 + 60 + 64 + 24$
$= 752$, which is $1232 - 480$. It checks.

Example 3 points out how complicated the change in volume is if you *add* to the dimensions of a figure.

Adapting to Individual Needs

Extra Help

For the drawing of the box on page 584, remind students that not all sides are shown because a box represents a 3-dimensional figure. For some students it might be helpful to draw in the dashed lines to show the missing sides.

Challenge

Show students the figure at the far right. Explain that squares of equal size are cut from each corner of the rectangle. Tell them to imagine the edges are folded along the dashed lines to form a box without a top. Then have students do the following:

1. Describe the volume of the box with a third-degree polynomial in x. $[V = x(12 - 2x)(14 - 2x) = 168x - 52x^2 + 4x^3]$

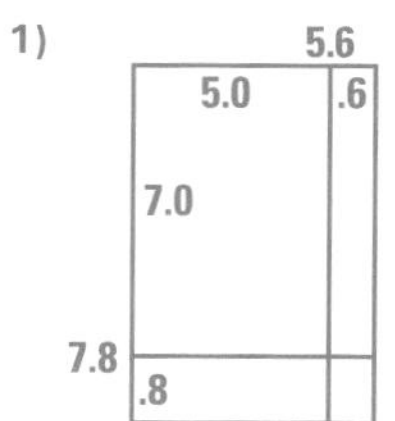

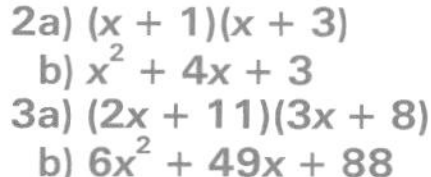
2a) $(x + 1)(x + 3)$
b) $x^2 + 4x + 3$
3a) $(2x + 11)(3x + 8)$
b) $6x^2 + 49x + 88$

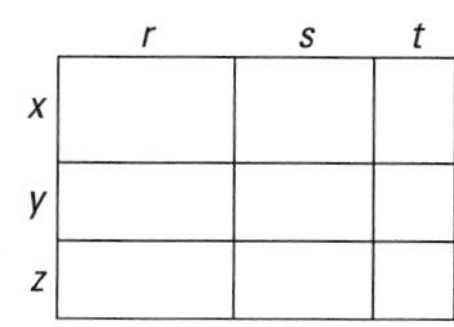

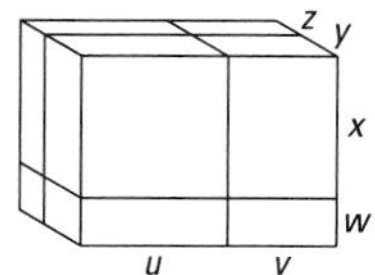

5a) $(u + v)(w + x)(y + z)$
b) $uwy + uwz + uxy + uxz + vwy + vwz + vxy + vxz$
c) $uwy + uwz + uxy + uxz + vwy + vwz + vxy + vxz$; yes

7) $2x^2 + 21x + 27$

8) $21a^2 + 53a + 30$

9) $a^3 + 6a^2 + 11a + 6$

10) $3a^2 + 6a + 11ab + 16b + 8b^2$

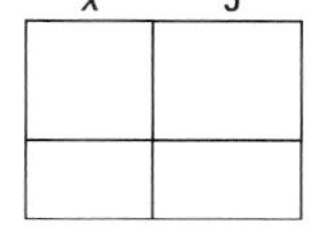

QUESTIONS

Covering the Reading

1. Use the area model for multiplication to write $5.6 \cdot 7.8$ as the sum of four products. $5 \cdot 7 + (5)(.8) + (.6)(7) + (.6)(.8)$; See left.

In 2 and 3, a binomial multiplication is pictured. **a.** What multiplication is pictured? **b.** Multiply the binomials. See left.

2.

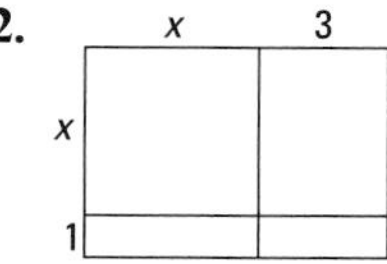

3.

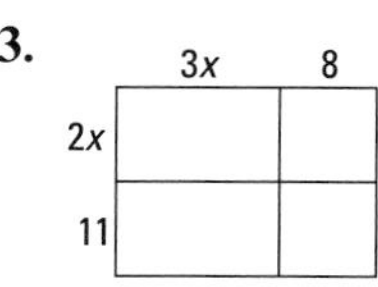

4. a. What trinomial multiplication is pictured at the left?
b. Multiply the trinomials. a) $(r + s + t)(x + y + z)$ $rx + ry + rz + sx + sy + sz + tx + ty + tz$

5. a. What multiplication of three binomials is pictured at the left?
b. What is the sum of the volumes of the eight boxes at the left?
c. Multiply the three binomials of part **a.** Does your product check with your answer to part **b**? a–c) See left.

6. What is your answer to the Activity in this lesson? See page 583.

In 7–10, perform the multiplication. See left.

7. $(x + 9)(2x + 3)$ **8.** $(3a + 5)(7a + 6)$

9. $(a + 1)(a + 2)(a + 3)$ **10.** $(a + b + 2)(3a + 8b)$

In 11–13, a box has dimensions ℓ, w, and h. Describe how the volume is changed if the box's dimensions are changed in the indicated way.

11. Its length is multiplied by 5, and all other dimensions stay the same. multiplied by 5

12. Its length, width, and height are all multiplied by 4. multiplied by 64

13. Six is added to the length, and all other dimensions are kept the same. increased by six times the product of height and width

Applying the Mathematics

14. In a store you see two bags X and Y of couscous ("koos′-koos"), coarse grains of wheat that are prepared by steaming. (Couscous is a common dish in North Africa.) Bag X is 1.4 times as high, 1.2 times as wide, and 1.2 times as deep as bag Y.
a. How do the capacities of these bags compare? Bag X holds about twice as much as bag Y.
b. How should their prices compare? Bag X should cost about twice as much as bag Y.

15. The sum of the areas of the small rectangles at the left is $x^2 + 8x + 15$. If the length of the large rectangle is $x + 5$, what is its width? $x + 3$

16. Expand $(a + b)^3$ See margin.
a. by finding the volume of an appropriate cube and by finding the volume of the eight boxes that make up the cube.
b. by multiplying $(a + b)(a + b)(a + b)$.

2. Give the range of values for x. $[0 < x < 6]$

3. Experiment with different values of x. What value of x do you think produces a box with the greatest volume? What is that volume? [Answers may vary. Through maximization techniques of calculus, the best value of x is about 2.15 units, with maximum volume about 160.58 cubic units.]

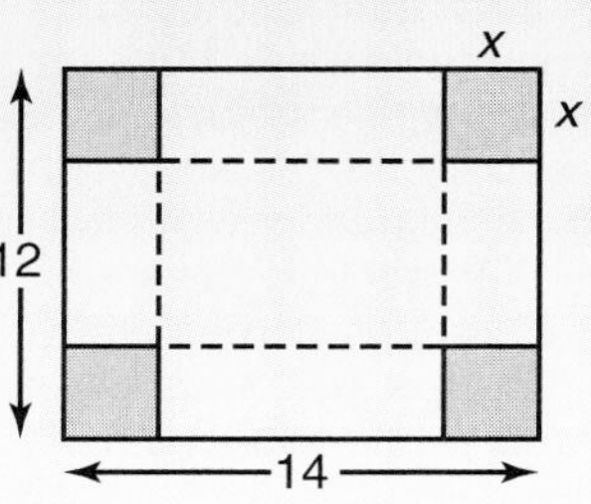

Follow-up for Lesson 10-4

Practice

For more questions on SPUR Objectives, use **Lesson Master 10-4A** (shown on page 583) or **Lesson Master 10-4B** (shown on pages 584–585).

Assessment

Oral/Written Communication Have students **work in pairs.** Have each student draw a diagram similar to one of those in **Questions 2–4.** Have them exchange papers and write the multiplication problem that is illustrated by the diagram. [Students provide meaningful diagrams of the required type and correctly identify the multiplication associated with the diagrams.]

(Follow-up continues on page 586.)

Additional Answers

16a. The volume is $(a + b)^3$ and also $a^3 + 3a^2b + 3ab^2 + b^3$. So $(a + b)^3 = a^3 + 3a^2b + 3ab^2 + b^3$

Sample:

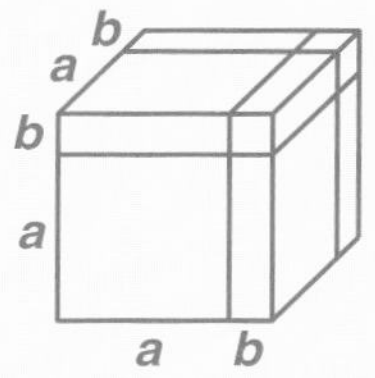

b. $(a^2 + 2ab + b^2)(a + b) = a^3 + 3a^2b + 3ab^2 + b^3$

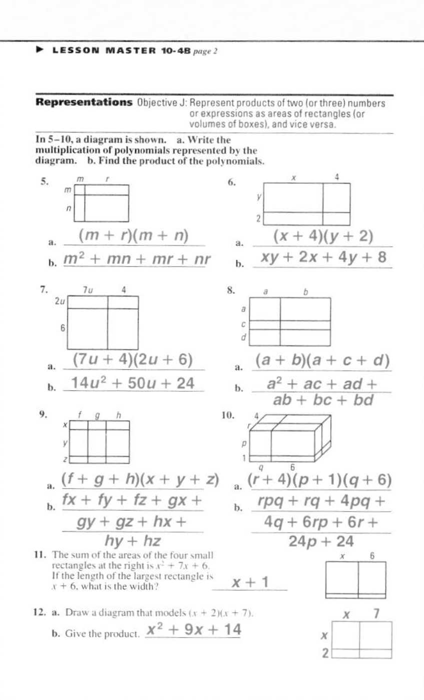
LESSON MASTER 10-4B *page 2*

Representations Objective J: Represent products of two (or three) numbers or expressions as areas of rectangles (or volumes of boxes), and vice versa.

In 5–10, a diagram is shown. a. Write the multiplication of polynomials represented by the diagram. b. Find the product of the polynomials.

5. a. $(m + r)(m + n)$ b. $m^2 + mn + mr + nr$

6. a. $(x + 4)(y + 2)$ b. $xy + 2x + 4y + 8$

7. a. $(7u + 4)(2u + 6)$ b. $14u^2 + 50u + 24$

8. a. $(a + b)(a + c + d)$ b. $a^2 + ac + ad + ab + bc + bd$

9. a. $(f + g + h)(x + y + z)$ b. $fx + fy + fz + gx + gy + gz + hx + hy + hz$

10. a. $(r + 4)(p + 1)(q + 6)$ b. $rpq + rq + 4pq + 4q + 6rp + 6r + 24p + 24$

11. The sum of the areas of the four small rectangles at the right is $x^2 + 7x + 6$. If the length of the largest rectangle is $x + 6$, what is the width? $x + 1$

12. a. Draw a diagram that models $(x + 2)(x + 7)$.
b. Give the product. $x^2 + 9x + 14$

Extension

Extend **Questions 7–10** by having students draw an area model for $(a + b)^2$, $(a + b)(a - b)$, and $(a - b)^2$, where $a > b$. Some students might also be able to draw volume models for $(a + b)^3$ and $(a - b)^3$. [Check students' drawings.]

Projects Update Project 4, *What Is Your Surface Area and Volume?* and Project 6, *Prisms and Cylinders in Packaging,* on page 614, relate to the content of this lesson.

Notes on Questions

Question 18 Health Connection Popcorn, although considered a junk food by many, is actually quite healthy. When not heavily salted or saturated with butter or cheese, popcorn is a good source of dietary fiber and is very low in calories.

Question 18b You might wish to ask how the volume is affected when this is done. [The new volume is (1.25)(.75) times the old, so it is .9375 times the old volume.]

Question 23 It is not uncommon to measure a great number n of congruent items and then divide by n in order to find the measure of one of them. Cards and paper, often thought of as models of rectangles, can also be thought of as boxes with a very small height. In this situation, a typical school ruler would not be adequate to measure the thickness of a single card. For instance, the thickness of a sheet of notebook paper is about $\frac{1}{500}$ the thickness of a ream; its volume is about $\frac{1}{500}$ the volume of a ream. The idea of a solid as a stack of very thin solids is an idea with an important application in Lesson 10-5, and is the foundation for finding volumes in calculus.

17) $33\frac{1}{3}$ cm

17. The makers of Bubblesuds laundry detergent increased the height of the container by 4 cm, keeping other dimensions the same. If this change increased the volume by 12%, what was the original height? See left.

18. *Multiple choice.* A popcorn distributor wants to change the shape of popcorn boxes. The box is 6″ wide, 9″ high, and 2″ thick. Which change will keep the volume constant? c
(a) Add 1″ to the width, subtract 1″ from the height.
(b) Increase the thickness by 25%, decrease the width by 25%.
(c) Double the thickness, halve the height.

19. One dimension of a cube is increased by 5 units. Another dimension is decreased by 4 units. The third dimension is kept the same. Is it possible for the resulting prism to have the same volume as the original cube? Why or why not? Yes; if s is the side length of the cube and if $s = 20$, then $s \cdot (s + 5) \cdot (s - 4) = s^3$.

Review

20. Follow these steps to determine the number of gallons of liquid in a cubic foot. *(Lesson 10-3)*
a. Finish the conversion equation: 1 gallon = ___ cubic inches. 231
b. 1 foot = ___ inches, so 1 cubic foot = ___ cubic inches. 12; 1728
c. Use the answers to parts **a** and **b** to complete the equation 1 cubic foot = ___ gallons. about 7.48

21. Find the cube root of π to the nearest hundredth. *(Lesson 10-3)* 1.46

22. A cube has volume 27 in^3. What is its surface area? *(Lessons 10-1, 10-3)* 54 in^2

23. A playing card is about 5.6 cm by 8.7 cm. If a stack of 72 cards is about 2.7 cm high, what is the volume of a single card? *(Lesson 10-3)* about 1.8 cm^3

24. Find the surface area of the right cone at the left. *(Lesson 10-2)* $200\pi \approx 628$ units^2

25. Find the lateral area of the right triangular prism at the right. *(Lesson 10-1)* 2.88 units^2

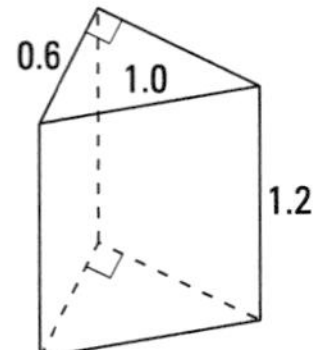

26. Solve $\pi r^2 = 10$ for r. *(Previous course)* $\pm\sqrt{\frac{10}{\pi}} \approx \pm 1.8$

Exploration

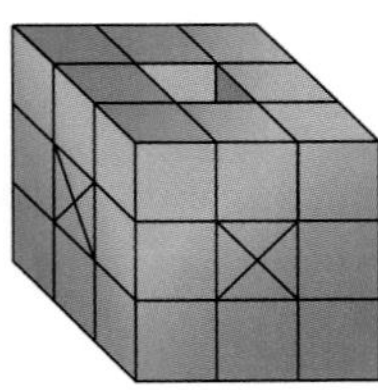

27. A hole is cut through the 3 × 3 × 3 cube at the left, from top to bottom, as indicated. This leaves 24 cubes. Then the large cube with the hole is dipped in green paint.
a. What is the surface area of the large cube with the hole? (Think of all faces with green paint.) 64 square units
How many of the smaller cubes that are left are green on
b. 3 faces? 16 **c.** 2 faces? 8 **d.** 1 face? 0 **e.** no faces? 0

28. Repeat Question 27 if two more holes are cut through the cube, one at each place marked with an X.
a) 72 square units b) 8 c) 0 d) 0 e) 0

Setting Up Lesson 10-5

Materials During their study of surface area and volume, students should use the formulas with actual physical objects. Some teachers set up several stations around the room. Students go from station to station in pairs, taking the measures they think are necessary to find the surface areas and volumes of prisms, cylinders, pyramids, cones, spheres, and irregular shapes such as soma-cube puzzle pieces. Such an activity is suggested in *Optional Activities* on page 589. At that time, finding volume is limited to prisms and cylinders. This activity is extended to include cones and pyramids in Lesson 10-7 and to include spheres in Lessons 10-8 and 10-9.

You will need a large rectangular box that holds water, such as a plastic storage box or food container, a gallon jug, and water for *Warm-up* in Lesson 10-5. You will need to give students the dimensions of the box.

LESSON

10-5

Volumes of Prisms and Cylinders

Tanks a lot. *After oil is pumped from the ground, it is stored in tank farms like the one shown here. On the average, a tank farm can hold the total of one week of production from the wells in its cylindrical tanks.*

Oil, water, and other products are often stored in huge cylindrical tanks like those pictured above. It is natural to wonder how much water or oil is stored in each tank. The amount can be calculated if you know the dimensions of the tank and a formula for the volume of a cylinder. This formula, and other formulas for the volumes of other common 3-dimensional figures, can be derived from the Area and Volume Postulates you already have studied, using one other postulate given in this lesson.

Volumes of Right Prisms and Cylinders

Consider a prism or cylinder with a base of area B. Think of B unit squares covering the region. We think of this even if B is not an integer.

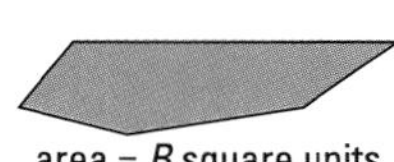
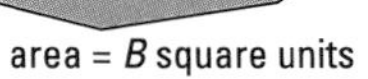

area = B square units

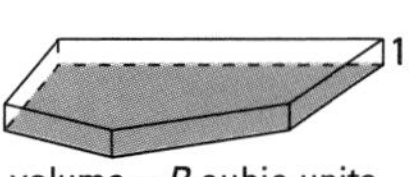

volume = B cubic units

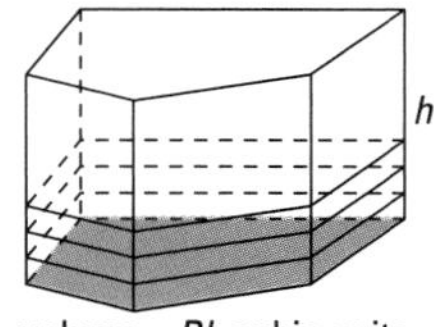

volume = Bh cubic units

If a prism with this base has height 1 unit, the prism contains B unit cubes, and so the volume of the 1-unit-high prism is B cubic units. This is pictured in the middle figure above. If you can stack h of these prisms, as in the figure above at the right, you form a prism with base B and height h. That prism has h times the volume of the middle prism, and so its volume is Bh. This argument shows that if a right prism or cylinder has a base with area B and height h, then a formula for its volume V is $V = Bh$.

Lesson 10-5

Objectives

A Calculate volumes of cylinders and prisms from appropriate lengths, and vice versa.

G Know the conditions under which Cavalieri's Principle can be applied.

I Apply formulas for volumes of prisms and cylinders to real situations.

Resources

From the ***Teacher's Resource File***

- Lesson Master 10-5A or 10-5B
- Answer Master 10-5
- Teaching Aids
  132 Warm-up
  138 Cavalieri's Principle

Additional Resources

- Visuals for Teaching Aids 132, 138
- Gallon jug, large rectangular box that will hold water, and water
- Objects shaped like prisms and cylinders; rulers and tape measures

Teaching Lesson 10-5

Warm-up

Your teacher will show you a large rectangular box and will give you the dimensions of the box.

1. Estimate how many gallons of water the box will hold.

(Warm-up continues on page 588.)

Lesson 10-5 Overview

Broad Goals This lesson discusses only one formula, $V = Bh$. Its importance is due to the fact that it applies to *all* prisms and cylinders. The postulate known as Cavalieri's Principle is required for its proof.

Perspective Cavalieri's Principle was first realized and used (to calculate the volume of a sphere) by two Chinese mathematicians, Zu Chongzhi (429-500 A.D.) and his son Zu Geng in the 5th century. In China, it is called Zu Geng's Principle. In this book, we still use the name of "Cavalieri's Principle," but you might point out this history, and remind students that the Pythagorean Theorem also has different names in different countries. This illustrates the universality of mathematics.

Cavalieri, one of the great mathematicians of the early 17th century, was a student of Galileo. The principle he asserted was one of the ideas that led to the development of calculus later in the century. In using Cavalieri's principle, one sums an infinite number of areas of infinitely small thickness to find volume. In calculus, one takes the limit of the sums of many thin volumes to find the total volume. Each section in Cavalieri's principle is called a *lamina,* the source of the word "laminate." (A credit card

(Overview continues on page 588.)

2. Determine the volume of the box in gallons. Use the fact that a cubic foot of liquid contains about 7.48 gallons to find how much water the box will hold.
3. As a class, check your estimates using water and a gallon jug. All answers will depend on the dimensions of the box.

Notes on Reading

Pacing It might take longer than a single period to discuss the questions in this lesson, so you may wish to spend two days here, with the first day having a quiz on Lessons 10-1 through 10-3.

Cooperative Learning There is a substantial amount of mathematics for students to understand in this lesson, so it may be an appropriate lesson for a cooperative effort. **Examples 1–2** can be read aloud and explained thoroughly as can the key ideas behind Cavalieri's Principle. Students should discuss the derivations of the formulas and how they are applied to find the volume of a solid.

Remind students that a cube and a box are prisms, so they have already calculated the volumes of some prisms. Specifically, the formula $V = \ell wh$ for the volume of a box can be interpreted as $V = Bh$, where the dimensions of the base are ℓ and w and $B = \ell w$.

The use of physical models in this lesson will greatly enhance students' understanding. A stack of congruent sheets of paper or a deck of playing cards are appropriate to illustrate Cavalieri's Principle. Note that the act of transforming the stack of paper (a transformation called "shearing") is not the same as "bending" an oblique wire prism. In shearing, the height of the stack of paper remains constant and the slant edge becomes longer. If the

A cubic foot of liquid contains about 7.48 gallons. (This is the correct answer for Question 20c of Lesson 10-4.) This information, combined with the volume formula derived on page 587, enables you to find the capacity (in gallons) of an oil storage tank.

Example 1

If a cylindrical oil tank has a diameter of 100 feet and is 70 feet high, how many gallons of oil can it hold? Make a guess before you go on.

Solution

It helps to draw a picture like the one at the right. We use the formula $V = Bh$. The radius of the base is 50′, so $B = \pi(50)^2 = 2500\pi \approx 7854$ sq ft.

Thus,
$$\begin{aligned} V &= Bh \\ &\approx 7854 \cdot 70 \\ &= 549{,}780 \text{ cubic feet} \\ &\approx 550{,}000 \text{ cubic feet.} \end{aligned}$$

We round because our calculations cannot be more accurate than the given data. Now we use the fact that each cubic foot contains about 7.48 gallons of fuel. So the capacity of the tank is

$$550{,}000 \text{ ft}^3 \cdot 7.48 \frac{\text{gal}}{\text{ft}^3} \approx 4{,}110{,}000 \text{ gallons.}$$

This is more than many people would estimate.

Volumes of Oblique Prisms and Cylinders

Now suppose you have an *oblique* prism or cylinder. Recall that in these figures, the lateral edges are not perpendicular to the planes of the bases. Pictured here are a right prism and an oblique prism with congruent bases and equal heights.

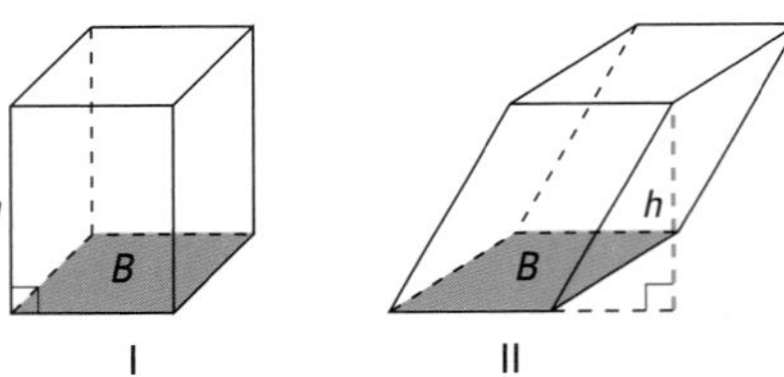

Imagine Prism I to be made up of a stack of thin slices like congruent sheets of paper. You can shift the slices until it takes the form of Prism II.

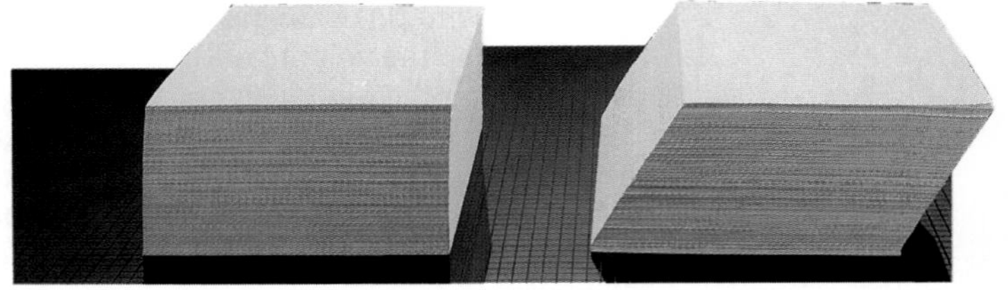

Lesson 10-5 Overview, continued

is covered or *laminated* with a very thin layer of plastic.)

Cavalieri's Principle is difficult to state and drawings for it are not easy, so teachers sometimes slight this idea. But it gives intuitive meanings to the concept of volume, it is essential for the derivation of the formulas for the volumes of pyramids, cones, cylinders, and spheres, and it exemplifies an idea that will later be used in calculus. In this lesson, the figures look very much the same; in later lessons Cavalieri's Principle is applied to figures that look quite different (but have the same cross-sectional areas).

Note that the height, area of the base, and number of slices are the same in Prism I and Prism II. Consequently,

$$\text{Volume(Prism II)} = \text{Volume(Prism I)}.$$

Or, since the two prisms have equal heights and congruent bases,

$$\text{Volume(Prism II)} = Bh.$$

Cavalieri's Principle

The key ideas of this argument are: (1) the prisms have their bases in the same planes; (2) each slice is parallel to the bases; and (3) the slices in each prism have the same area. The conclusion is that these solids have the same volume. The first individuals to use these ideas to obtain volumes seem to have been the Chinese mathematician Zu Chongzhi (429–500) and his son Zu Geng. However, in the West, Francesco Bonaventura Cavalieri (1598–1647), an Italian mathematician, first realized the importance of this principle. So, in the West, the principle is named after him.

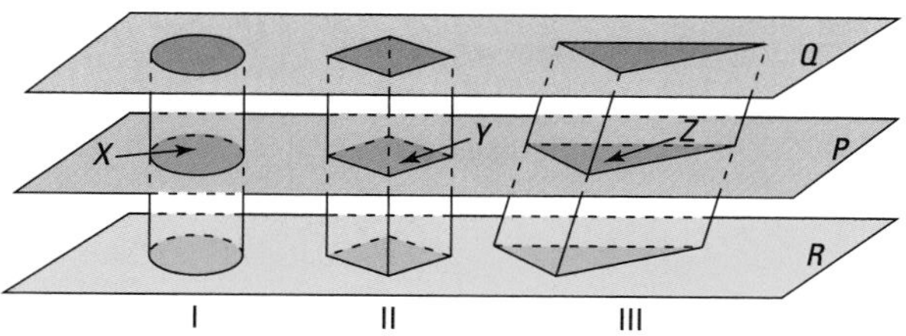

> **Volume Postulate**
>
> e. **Cavalieri's Principle** Let I and II be two solids included between parallel planes. If every plane P parallel to the given planes intersects I and II in sections with the same area, then Volume(I) = Volume(II).

Above, plane P is parallel to planes Q and R containing the bases, and all three solids have bases with area B. Since plane sections X, Y, and Z are translation images of the bases (this is how prisms and cylinders are defined), each also has area B. Thus the conditions for Cavalieri's Principle are satisfied. These solids have the same volume. But we know the volume of the box:

$$\begin{aligned}\text{Volume(II)} &= \ell \cdot w \cdot h \\ &= B \cdot h\end{aligned}$$

Thus, using Cavalieri's Principle,

$$\begin{aligned}\text{Volume(I)} &= B \cdot h \text{ and} \\ \text{Volume(III)} &= B \cdot h.\end{aligned}$$

This proves the following theorem for all cylinders and prisms.

wire prism is bent, the height is shortened and thus volume is reduced. **Teaching Aid 138** can help illustrate this idea.

Oblique prisms and cylinders are to right prisms and cylinders as parallelograms are to rectangles. The space inside does not change, although the boundaries (perimeters or surface areas) do. The key things to measure are the height and the base. Thus, just as parallelograms and rectangles both have the area formula $A = hb$, so prisms and right prisms both have the volume formula $V = Bh$.

Additional Examples

1. A silo is a tall cylindrically-shaped container and holds chopped grain for cattle feed. Which holds more, a silo 50 feet tall with a diameter of 10 feet, or one 35 feet tall with a diameter of 12 feet? **The latter holds more, but they are very close in volume.**
2. Some computer paper is $8\frac{1}{2}" \times 11"$ inches. Suppose a stack of it has a volume of 748 cubic inches. If the stack is sheared into an oblique parallelepiped with the same height as the original stack, what will be the volume of the new stack? **748 cubic inches**

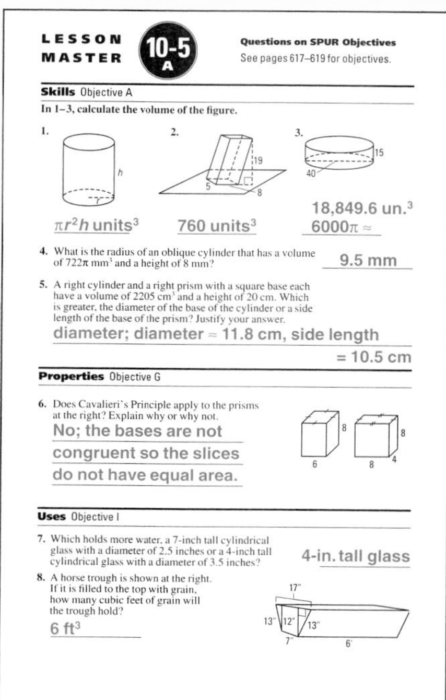

LESSON MASTER 10-5 A

Questions on SPUR Objectives
See pages 617–619 for objectives.

Skills Objective A

In 1–3, calculate the volume of the figure.

1. $\pi r^2 h$ units³
2. 760 units³
3. $6000\pi \approx$ 18,849.6 un.³

4. What is the radius of an oblique cylinder that has a volume of 722π mm³ and a height of 8 mm? 9.5 mm

5. A right cylinder and a right prism with a square base each have a volume of 2205 cm³ and a height of 20 cm. Which is greater, the diameter of the base of the cylinder or a side length of the base of the prism? Justify your answer. diameter; diameter ≈ 11.8 cm, side length = 10.5 cm

Properties Objective G

6. Does Cavalieri's Principle apply to the prisms at the right? Explain why or why not. No; the bases are not congruent so the slices do not have equal area.

Uses Objective I

7. Which holds more water, a 7-inch tall cylindrical glass with a diameter of 2.5 inches or a 4-inch tall cylindrical glass with a diameter of 3.5 inches? 4-in. tall glass

8. A horse trough is shown at the right. If it is filled to the top with grain, how many cubic feet of grain will the trough hold? 6 ft³

Optional Activities

Using Physical Models

Materials: Objects shaped like prisms and cylinders; rulers and tape measures

You might set up stations with objects students can measure and calculate the surface area and volume. (At this time, limit finding volume to prisms and cylinders.) After discussing this lesson, have students **work in pairs** and go from station to station taking the measures they think are necessary to find the surface areas and volumes of the objects. Surface areas can be verified by covering the objects with paper; volumes can be verified by immersing them in water.

Notes on Questions

Question 5 You might compare the volume of the sewer to the amount of rain water which may fall on a given region in a period of time. For example, a parking lot might be 200' by 150'. If one inch of rain falls in an hour, would the sewer pipe hold all the drainage from the lot? [The volume of water over the lot is $200 \cdot 150 \cdot \frac{1}{12}$ cubic feet, or 2500 cubic feet. This sewer pipe would hold just that amount.]

Question 15 Point out that neither the shape of the base nor the angle of slant of the prism is needed.

(Notes on Questions continue on page 592.)

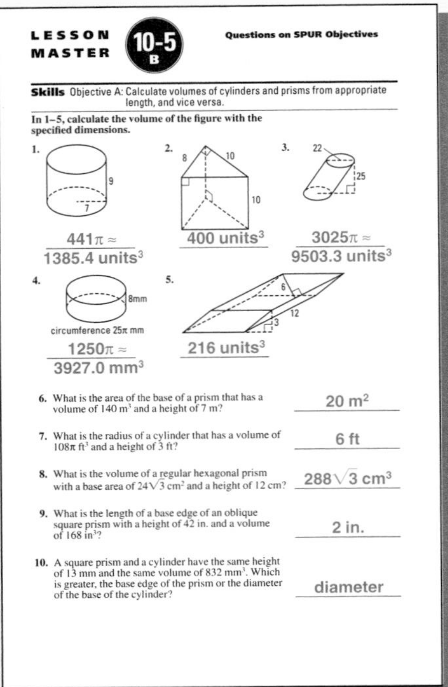

LESSON MASTER 10-5 B Questions on SPUR Objectives

Skills Objective A: Calculate volumes of cylinders and prisms from appropriate length, and vice versa.

In 1–5, calculate the volume of the figure with the specified dimensions.

1. $441\pi \approx 1385.4$ units^3
2. 400 units^3
3. $3025\pi \approx 9503.3$ units^3
4. circumference 25π mm — $1250\pi \approx 3927.0$ mm^3
5. 216 units^3

6. What is the area of the base of a prism that has a volume of 140 m^3 and a height of 7 m? 20 m^2
7. What is the radius of a cylinder that has a volume of 108π ft^3 and a height of 3 ft? 6 ft
8. What is the volume of a regular hexagonal prism with a base area of $24\sqrt{3}$ cm^2 and a height of 12 cm? $288\sqrt{3}$ cm^3
9. What is the length of a base edge of an oblique square prism with a height of 42 in. and a volume of 168 in^3? 2 in.
10. A square prism and a cylinder have the same height of 13 mm and the same volume of 832 mm^3. Which is greater, the base edge of the prism or the diameter of the base of the cylinder? diameter

Prism-Cylinder Volume Formula
The volume V of any prism or cylinder is the product of its height h and the area B of its base. $V = Bh$

In an oblique prism or cylinder, the height sometimes can be determined using the Pythagorean Theorem.

Example 2

Find the volume of the oblique prism with parallelogram base pictured below.

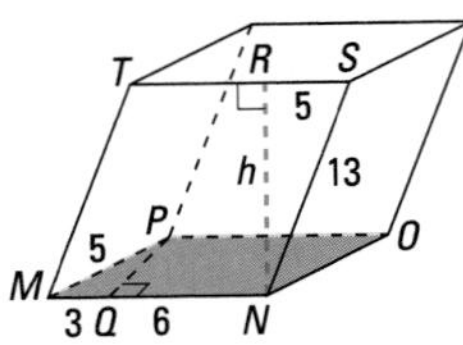

Solution

$V = Bh$. To find B, first look at the base parallelogram $MNOP$. Use the Pythagorean Theorem to find its height PQ.

$$MQ^2 + PQ^2 = MP^2$$
$$3^2 + PQ^2 = 5^2$$

So, $PQ = 4$

Thus, $B = MN \cdot PQ = 9 \cdot 4 = 36$ square units.

The height h of the prism also can be found by applying the Pythagorean Theorem.

$$RN^2 + RS^2 = NS^2$$
$$h^2 + 5^2 = 13^2$$

So, $h = 12$

Thus $V = Bh = 36 \cdot 12 = 432$ cubic units.

Questions

Covering the Reading

1. A cubic foot of liquid is how many gallons? about 7.48
2. How many gallons of oil can a cylindrical tank with diameter 120 feet and height 60 feet hold? $\approx$ 5,076,000
3. *Multiple choice.* In this lesson, a stack of paper is used to illustrate all but which one of the following? d
   (a) Cavalieri's Principle
   (b) An oblique prism and a right prism can have the same volume.
   (c) The volume of an oblique prism is *Bh.*
   (d) A cylinder and a prism have the same volume formula.

Adapting to Individual Needs

Extra Help
Have students use a large stack of typing paper (or other congruent sheets) to illustrate Cavalieri's Principle. Have them split the stack into two equal amounts. Then point out that both stacks would have the same volume since each is made from the same number of sheets. Have them shear one of the stacks. Point out that the height and volume of the sheared stack stays the same as the height and volume of the other stack.

English Language Development
It is suggested in the *Notes on Reading* that students work together through the reading and the examples. Be sure that you pair students with limited English proficiency with English-speaking students who are good readers.

In 4–9, find the volume of each figure.

4. a square prism whose base has edge 5 meters, and whose height is 20 meters 500 m^3

5. a sewer pipe 200′ long with a radius of 2′ $800\pi \approx 2513$ ft^3

6. the oblique prism with parallelogram base drawn at the right $\approx$ 4796 $units^3$

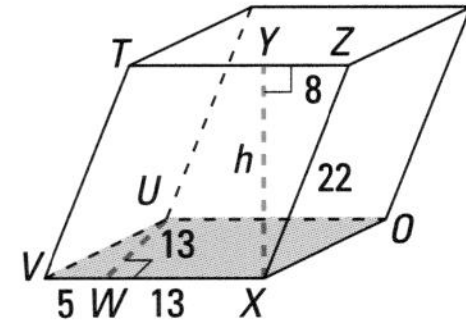

7.

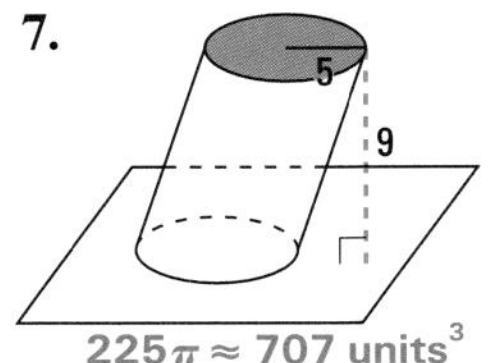

$225\pi \approx 707$ $units^3$

8.

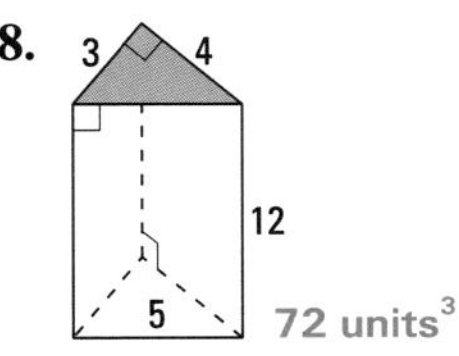

72 $units^3$

9. a right rectangular prism whose base is 3 feet by 7 feet and whose height is 10 feet 210 ft^3

10. Cavalieri's Principle was discovered by mathematicians of what two nationalities? Italian and Chinese

11. State Cavalieri's Principle. See left.

11) Let I and II be two solids included between parallel planes. If every plane *P* parallel to the given planes intersects I and II in sections with the same area, then Volume(I) = Volume(II).

Applying the Mathematics

12. The cylindrical storage tank in Example 1 has a diameter of about 30 meters and a height of about 21 meters. About how many liters of oil does it hold? $\approx 1.5 \times 10^7$

13. If a cylinder has a height *h* and base with radius *r*, find a formula for its volume in terms of *h* and *r*. $V = \pi r^2 h$

14. Suppose eight pennies are stacked vertically as below at the left. Then they are moved to lean, as below at the right.

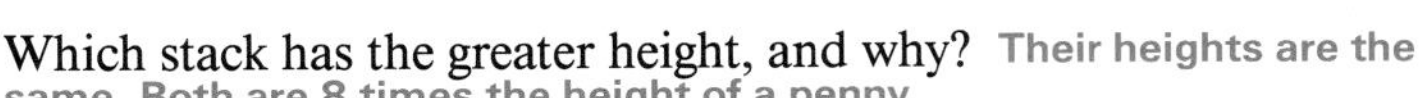

Which stack has the greater height, and why? Their heights are the same. Both are 8 times the height of a penny.

15. The volume of an oblique prism is 38 cubic meters. Its height is 4 meters. Find the area of each base. 9.5 m^2

16. An artist constructed a large cylindric solid as shown in the sketch at the left. What is its volume? 189 m^3

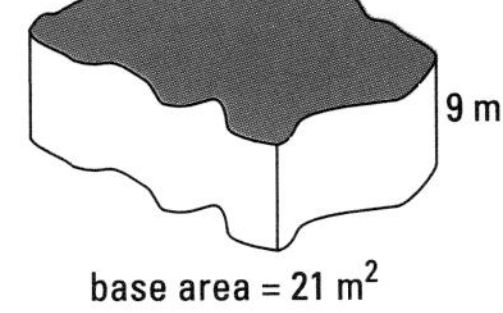

base area = 21 m^2

Practice

For more questions on SPUR Objectives, use **Lesson Master 10-5A** (shown on page 589) or **Lesson Master 10-5B** (shown on pages 590–591).

Assessment

Oral / Written Communication
Write questions similar to **Questions 4–9** on the chalkboard. Choose students to draw and label an appropriate diagram, and then find the volume of the figure. Have each student explain his or her work to the class. Repeat this process until all students have had an opportunity to respond to a question. [Students correctly draw and label the diagrams and use the appropriate volume formulas.]

(Follow-up continues on page 592.)

Adapting to Individual Needs

Challenge
Have students use the table of liquid measures in Lesson 10-3 and find the dimensions of a can that holds 64 liquid ounces. (Have them give at least two different answers, rounded to the nearest tenth of an inch.) Have students experiment to determine which dimensions produce containers that are reasonable. [Sample answers: $r = 2"$, $h \approx 9.2"$; $r = 3"$, $h \approx 4.1"$]

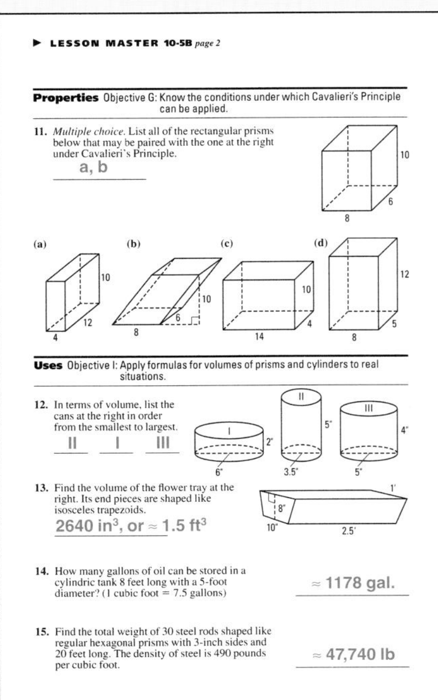

▶ **LESSON MASTER 10-5B** *page 2*

Properties Objective G: Know the conditions under which Cavalieri's Principle can be applied.

11. *Multiple choice.* List all of the rectangular prisms below that may be paired with the one at the right under Cavalieri's Principle. a, b

(a) (b) (c) (d)

Uses Objective I: Apply formulas for volumes of prisms and cylinders to real situations.

12. In terms of volume, list the cans at the right in order from the smallest to largest. II I III

13. Find the volume of the flower tray at the right. Its end pieces are shaped like isosceles trapezoids. 2640 in^3, or $\approx$ 1.5 ft^3

14. How many gallons of oil can be stored in a cylindric tank 8 feet long with a 5-foot diameter? (1 cubic foot = 7.5 gallons) $\approx$ 1178 gal.

15. Find the total weight of 30 steel rods shaped like regular hexagonal prisms with 3-inch sides and 20 feet long. The density of steel is 490 pounds per cubic foot. $\approx$ 47,740 lb

Extension

Question 19 can be extended by asking students to compare the volume of a cylinder with the same height h as the one in the problem, but a radius four times as long. [The volume is 16 times greater than the original.] Also, students may investigate in general how a change in the radius of a cylinder affects its volume. [If the radius is multiplied by x, then the volume is multiplied by x^2.]

Project Update Project 3, *Prismoids,* Project 4, *What Is Your Surface Area and Volume?* and Project 6, *Prisms and Cylinders in Packaging,* on pages 613–614, relate to the content of this lesson.

Notes on Questions

Question 17 In general, if the height of a cylinder is kept the same, the diameter needs to be multiplied by $\sqrt{2}$ in order to double the volume.

Questions 19 and 22 Students should try to verify these relationships by writing the volume formulas and substituting into them. For instance, for **Question 19,** the larger cylinder has volume $V_1 = \pi r^2 h$, and the smaller cylinder has volume $V_2 = \pi(0.5r)^2 h = 0.25\pi r^2 h$, so $V_1 = 4V_2$.

Question 23 Science Connection Plutonium is silvery in appearance, and gives off a natural warmth thanks to energy being released from its rapid decay. Besides being used for nuclear weapons, various isotopes of plutonium are used in power plants, medical research, and long-life batteries, such as those installed in pacemakers. Lead is used to make containers holding plutonium and other radioactive metals because it has the highest density of all common metals, thus making it an effective shield against radiation release. Plutonium is one of the most highly toxic substances known.

18) The plane sections parallel to the base do not have the same area.

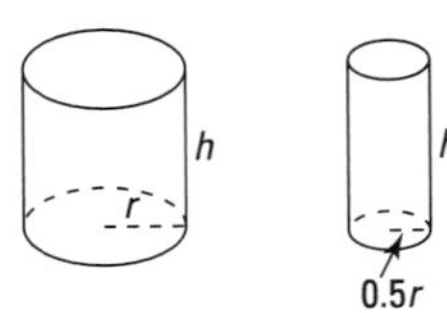

17. Two cylindrical glasses have the same height, but the diameters of the glasses are 2.3″ and 3.3″.
 a. Can the second glass hold twice as much as the first? Yes
 b. Why or why not? For the second glass, $V \approx 2.7\pi h$. For the first glass, $V \approx 1.3\pi h$.
18. A cylinder and cone have equal heights and bases of the same area. Why can't Cavalieri's Principle be applied in this situation? See left.
19. Compare the volumes of two cylinders with the same height, but the radius of the second cylinder is half that of the first. The first cylinder has four times the volume of the second cylinder.
20. A milliliter of water has a mass of 1 gram and occupies 1 cm^3 of space. If a cylindrical can is 15 cm high, has radius 3 cm, and is filled with water, what is the mass of the water (to the nearest gram)? 424 grams

Review

21. Perform the multiplication $(4x - 5y)(x + 2y + 7)$. *(Lesson 10-4)* $4x^2 + 3xy + 28x - 10y^2 - 35y$
22. The height of a box is multiplied by 4 and the length and width are each multiplied by 5. By how much is the volume of the box multiplied? *(Lesson 10-4)* by 100
23. A lead box for vials of plutonium measures 4 cm by 3.5 cm by 2.5 cm on the outside. The inside dimensions are 3 cm by 2.5 cm by 2 cm. How much lead was used to make the box? *(Lesson 10-1)* 20 cm^3

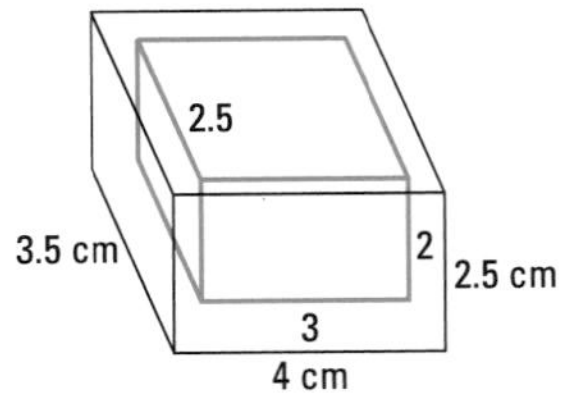

24. Find the surface area of the prism in Question 8. *(Lesson 10-1)* 156 square units
25. Arrange these quadrilateral area formulas from most general to most specific: $A = s^2$, $A = \frac{1}{2}h(b_1 + b_2)$, $A = \ell w$, $A = hb$. *(Lesson 8-5)* $A = \frac{1}{2}h(b_1 + b_2)$; $A = bh$; $A = \ell w$; $A = s^2$

Exploration

26. Stack pennies obliquely as in Question 14. Try to get the top penny as far to the right as possible, as in the picture at the right. How long can you make the distance LR? Answers may vary. In theory, LR can be made as long as one wishes, though in practice it is difficult to make LR much longer than the width of two pennies.

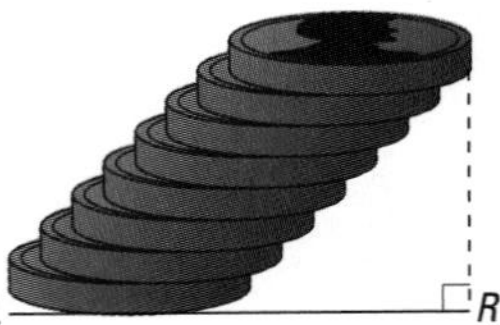

Setting Up Lesson 10-6

Materials Students using *Challenge* on page 596, will need a paper cup that is truncated (has a circular base that is smaller than the rim), a tape measure, and a ruler. They will also need to know the capacity of the cup.

LESSON

10-6

Organizing Formulas

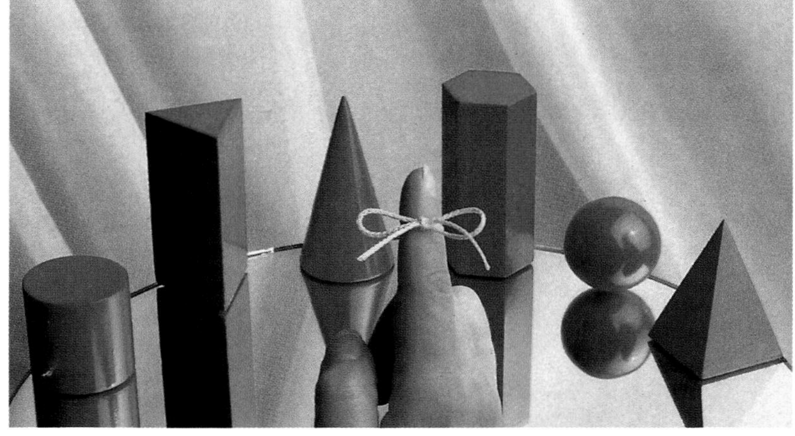

Now, why did I tie that string around my finger? *Many people have gimmicks for trying to remember names, birthdates, or other bits of information. The formulas for area and volume of various shapes are related. Use your hierarchy to make these connections, so you do not have to rely upon strict memorization.*

At this point, you have encountered formulas for perimeters and areas of many 2-dimensional regions and for lateral areas, surface areas, and volumes of some 3-dimensional figures. You will see more formulas later in this chapter. At this point, you may wonder which formulas to remember. The answer is simple: *Remember the formulas which apply to the most figures.*

Summarizing Surface Area and Volume Formulas

In this chapter there are eight—only eight—basic formulas. So far you have seen five of the eight. The chart below also includes the three other surface area and volume formulas you will see in the next three lessons. The chart is organized into columns based on the number of bases a figure has. Prisms and cylinders have two parallel bases. Cones and pyramids have one base. Spheres have no bases.

Surface Area and Volume Formulas of 3-Dimensional Figures

	Prisms/Cylinders (two parallel bases)	Pyramids/Cones (one base)	Sphere (no bases)
Lateral Area	L.A. $= ph$	L.A. $= \frac{1}{2}\ell p$	
Surface Area	S.A. = L.A. + $2B$	S.A. = L.A. + B	S.A. $= 4\pi r^2$
Volume	$V = Bh$	$V = \frac{1}{3}Bh$	$V = \frac{4}{3}\pi r^3$

Lesson 10-6

Objectives

F Develop formulas for specific figures from more general formulas.

Resources

From the ***Teacher's Resource File***
- Lesson Master 10-6A or 10-6B
- Assessment Sourcebook: Quiz for Lessons 10-4 through 10-6
- Answer Master 10-6
- Teaching Aids
  132 Warm-up
  139 Surface Area and Volume Formulas

Additional Resources
- Visuals for Teaching Aids 132, 139
- Truncated paper cup, tape measure, ruler

Teaching Lesson 10-6

Warm-up

1. How is a cone like a pyramid? **Sample: Both have a single base and one vertex that is not on the base.**
2. How is a prism like a cylinder? **Sample: Both have two congruent, parallel bases.**
3. What is the formula for the surface area of a prism or cylinder? **S.A. = L.A. + 2*B***
4. What is the formula for the surface area of a cone or pyramid? **S.A. = L.A. + *B***

Lesson 10-6 Overview

Broad Goals This lesson serves two purposes, one of which is to provide an extra day to work on surface area and volume. The other, more important purpose, is to serve as an organizer for the formulas in the chapter and thus help students to learn them.

Perspective This is an easier lesson than the two lessons preceding it and should help students master the ideas of those lessons. Here we repeat what you may have discussed in Lesson 10-1 regarding the way formulas are organized in this book. We do not give formulas for all figures. Rather, we give formulas that will apply to the most figures and expect students to substitute to get more specific formulas.

There is an analogy with learning the multiplication tables. There are 81 facts to be remembered, from 1×1 to 9×9. But, by using commutativity of multiplication, you can reduce the number of facts greatly. If you know 7×9, you employ commutativity to get 9×7. In this chapter, we employ the circle formulas $C = 2\pi r$ and $A = \pi r^2$ in much the same way.

The five key points of the lesson are in italics on pages 593–594: (1) Remember

(Overview continues on page 594.)

Notes on Reading

As they read this lesson, students should pay close attention to the advice given in the five sentences in italics in the lesson. After they complete the reading, you might ask students to close their books, and see how many of these points they remember.

It will be very helpful to students if they take notes as they read this lesson, particularly on the pointers listed in italics. Call attention to the structure of the chart on page 593. Ask students to share ways to learn the chart with other members of the class. As you discuss this information, you may want to use **Teaching Aid 139** which contains the chart.

Because students will need to calculate areas and volumes of figures throughout the remainder of this course and in subsequent courses, encourage students to memorize the formulas rather than look them up or derive them.

Additional Examples

1. Find a formula for the volume of material needed to make a cylindric pipe of length h if the inner radius is r and the outer radius is R. **The pipe is the material between two cylinders. A cylinder has volume Bh, where B is the area of the base. Since the base is a circle, its area is πr^2. So the volume of the cylinder is $\pi r^2 h$. Letting R be the outer radius of the pipe and r be its inner radius, the amount of material in the pipe is $\pi R^2 h - \pi r^2 h = \pi h(R^2 - r^2)$.**
2. Name some objects other than pipes to which the formula of Additional Example 1 applies. **Samples: straws, CDs with holes in the middle, some lampshades**

If you organize the formulas in this way, you will find them easier to remember because the links between them are clearer. Of course, one thing is true for every formula: *To use a formula, you must know what each variable in the formula represents.*

Secret formula. *Formulas in mathematics are usually not secret, but chemical formulas are often protected for safety. In the MGM film,* Dr. Jekyll and Mr. Hyde, *Spencer Tracy portrays the scientist who creates a potion that transforms his appearance and personality in a sinister way.*

Deriving Formulas

You may have seen some formulas that are not in the chart. For instance, the formula L.A. = $2\pi rh$ gives the lateral area of a right cylinder. This is not listed because a few general ideas help reduce the load of formulas to remember. *For special formulas for prisms and pyramids, substitute the formulas for the particular base area or perimeter. For special formulas for cones and cylinders, substitute the circle formulas πr^2 for B or $2\pi r$ for p.* The idea is simple: cones and cylinders are like pyramids and prisms, but with circular bases instead of polygonal bases.

For example, to obtain a specific formula for the lateral area of a right cylinder, use the formula L.A. = ph from the chart. Substitute $2\pi r$ for p to get L.A. = $(2\pi r)h = 2\pi rh$. You do not need to memorize a special formula for the lateral area of a right cylinder or a right cone.

In Lesson 10-3, you saw a formula for the volume of a box: $V = \ell wh$. You probably had seen this formula before. From this formula, all the other volume formulas can be deduced. The process we used—the process of proof—is the most powerful idea of all for remembering formulas. *If you cannot remember a formula, try to derive it from some simpler formulas you know to be true.* That is the way mathematicians recall many of the formulas they have to use. The difficulty with this advice is that finding a proof may take some time. Often there is not the time. So, if you do not want to spend your time proving formulas, you must either learn some of them by heart or have access to a list of the formulas.

Using General Formulas

Another way to avoid learning lots of formulas needlessly is to *use general formulas to obtain formulas for special types of figures.* These ideas are applied in the Example.

Example

Find a formula for the surface area of a box in terms of its height h, length ℓ, and width w.

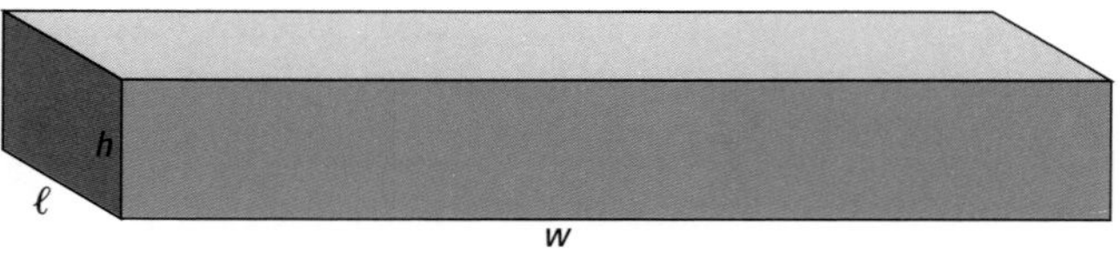

▶

Lesson 10-6 Overview, continued

formulas which apply to the most figures. (2) To use a formula, you must know what each variable in the formula represents. (3) For special formulas for cones and cylinders, substitute the circle formulas $B = \pi r^2$ and $p = 2\pi r$ in the corresponding formulas for pyramids and prisms. (4) If you cannot remember a formula, try to derive it from some simpler formulas you know to be true. (5) Use general formulas to get formulas for special types of figures. All but the third of these hints apply to all mathematics.

Throughout the remainder of this course and even in subsequent courses, students will need to calculate areas and volumes of figures. While in theory it is always possible to look up the formulas necessary or to derive them, having formulas committed to memory will facilitate student work.

Optional Activities

Cooperative Learning Have each student make a list of all of the formulas for area, surface area, and volume that he or she knows. Then have students **work in groups** and compare lists. Have each group share its method for remembering the formulas or for making them easier to learn.

Solution

A box is a prism. Begin with the formula for the lateral area of a prism.

$$\text{L.A.} = ph$$

Since h is given, it need not be touched. But p is the perimeter of the base. Since the base is a rectangle with length ℓ and width w, its perimeter is $2\ell + 2w$. Substituting,

$$\text{L.A.} = (2\ell + 2w)h.$$

For the surface area, the areas of the two bases must be added to the lateral area.

$$\text{S.A.} = \text{L.A.} + 2B$$

Each base has area $B = \ell w$. Thus a formula is

$$\text{S.A.} = (2\ell + 2w)h + 2\ell w.$$

Using the Distributive Property, the formula can be rewritten as

$$\text{S.A.} = 2\ell h + 2wh + 2\ell w$$
$$= 2(\ell h + wh + \ell w).$$

That is to say, the surface area of the box pictured on page 594 is the sum of the areas of the faces visible in the drawing, times two.

QUESTIONS

Covering the Reading

1. What are the best formulas to remember? formulas that apply to the most figures

In 2 and 3, choose from the following: boxes, cones, cylinders, prisms, pyramids, spheres.

2. In which figures does S.A. = L.A. + $2B$? boxes, cylinders, prisms
3. In which figures does S.A. = L.A. + B? cones, pyramids
4. a. List the five formulas in the chart which are in earlier lessons.
   b. List the three formulas in the chart that are in later lessons in this chapter. S.A. = $4\pi r^2$, $V = \frac{1}{3}Bh$, $V = \frac{4}{3}\pi r^3$

   a) See left.
5. In the formula L.A. = ph, what does each variable represent? See left.
6. Describe the process for obtaining special formulas for cones and cylinders. Substitute the circle formulas $B = \pi r^2$ and $p = 2\pi r$ in the corresponding formulas for pyramids and prisms.
7. How do many mathematicians recall formulas? They try to prove them from simpler formulas known to be true.

In 8 and 9, consider a right cylinder with height h and base with radius r. From the general formulas,

8. deduce a specific formula for its lateral surface area. L.A. = $2\pi rh$
9. deduce a specific formula for its volume. $V = \pi r^2 h$

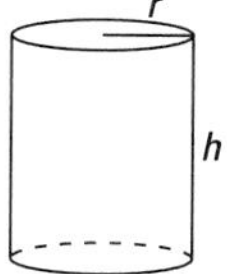

4a) L.A. = ph; L.A. = $\frac{1}{2}\ell p$, S.A. = L.A. + $2B$, S.A. = L.A. + B, $V = Bh$

5) L.A. = lateral area of prism or cylinder, p = perimeter of its base, h = its height

Notes on Questions

Questions 2–3, and 6 Cooperative Learning These questions are good for discussion. In order to answer them, students have to review the classification shown on page 593 and discuss how to do substitutions to obtain the special formulas from the general ones.

Questions 8–9 These exercises have students do mathematics, not just memorize math facts. The tacit assumption here is that the formulas should be in terms of h and r. Students should start with the formulas L.A. = ph and $V = Bh$.

Adapting to Individual Needs

Extra Help

Some students will try to memorize formulas without having any understanding of how the formulas are derived. Point out that they are much more likely to remember the formulas at a later date if they use the five points listed in italics. It might be helpful for students to copy these five points into their notes.

English Language Development

If you use *Optional Activities* on page 594, be sure to pair students with limited English proficiency with English-speaking students for the first part of the activity.

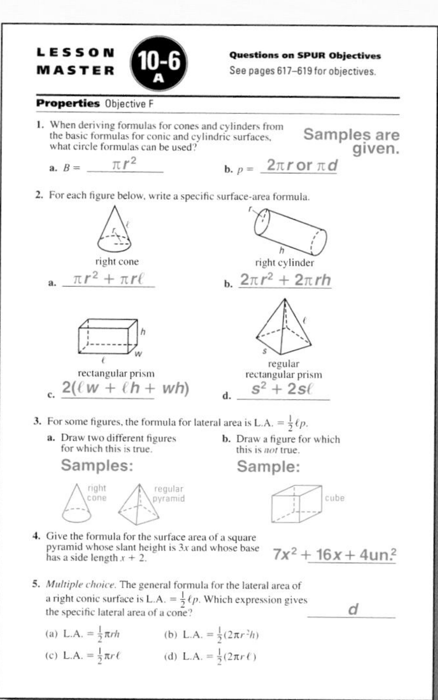

LESSON MASTER 10-6 A

Questions on SPUR Objectives
See pages 617–619 for objectives.

Properties Objective F

1. When deriving formulas for cones and cylinders from the basic formulas for conic and cylindric surfaces, what circle formulas can be used? Samples are given.
   a. $B = \pi r^2$
   b. $p = 2\pi r$ or πd
2. For each figure below, write a specific surface-area formula.
   a. right cone: $\pi r^2 + \pi r\ell$
   b. right cylinder: $2\pi r^2 + 2\pi rh$
   c. rectangular prism: $2(\ell w + \ell h + wh)$
   d. regular rectangular prism: $s^2 + 2s\ell$
3. For some figures, the formula for lateral area is L.A. = $\frac{1}{2}\ell p$.
   a. Draw two different figures for which this is true. Samples: right cone, regular pyramid
   b. Draw a figure for which this is *not* true. Sample: cube
4. Give the formula for the surface area of a square pyramid whose slant height is $3x$ and whose base has a side length $x + 2$. $7x^2 + 16x + 4$ un.^{2}
5. *Multiple choice.* The general formula for the lateral area of a right conic surface is L.A. = $\frac{1}{2}\ell p$. Which expression gives the specific lateral area of a cone? d
   (a) L.A. = $\frac{1}{2}\pi rh$
   (b) L.A. = $\frac{1}{2}(2\pi r^2 h)$
   (c) L.A. = $\frac{1}{2}\pi r\ell$
   (d) L.A. = $\frac{1}{2}(2\pi r\ell)$

Notes on Questions

Question 20 History Connection The city of Teotihuacán, where the Pyramid of the Sun is located, is only a short distance from Mexico City, the country's modern-day capital. Before the Spanish conquest, Teotihuacán was the premier city in the Americas and one of the largest cities in the world. Built 2300 meters above sea level, it covered 150 square kilometers. At its height it contained a quarter of a million people. It is the site of several of Mexico's most famous temples and monuments. The Aztecs referred to it as "The Place Where Men Become Gods."

Question 25 This question provides a very good opportunity for students to learn how to use their knowledge of algebra in a geometric situation. Note that from the answer to **Question 10,** we have S.A. = $2\pi rh + 2\pi r^2$. From $2\pi rh + 2\pi r^2 = 200\pi$ ($r > 0$, $h > 0$) we can get the equation, $r^2 + rh - 100 = 0$, then $h = \frac{100 - r^2}{r}$. There are infinitely many solutions (r, h) to this equation, such as (5, 15), (8, 4.5), and so on.

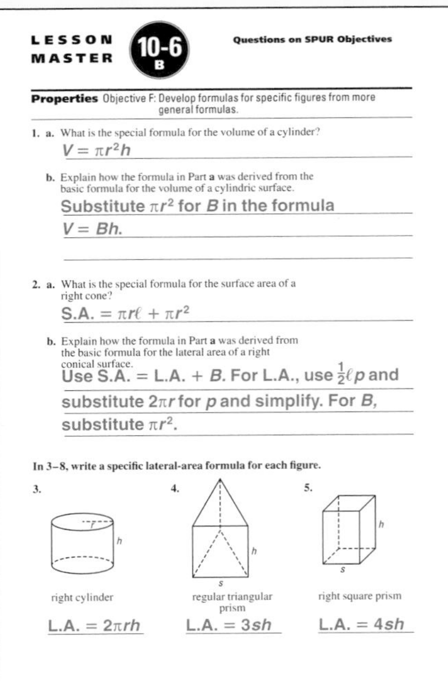
LESSON MASTER 10-6 B

Questions on SPUR Objectives

Properties Objective F: Develop formulas for specific figures from more general formulas.

1. a. What is the special formula for the volume of a cylinder? $V = \pi r^2 h$

   b. Explain how the formula in Part a was derived from the basic formula for the volume of a cylindric surface. Substitute πr^2 for B in the formula $V = Bh$.

2. a. What is the special formula for the surface area of a right cone? S.A. = $\pi r\ell + \pi r^2$

   b. Explain how the formula in Part a was derived from the basic formula for the lateral area of a right conical surface. Use S.A. = L.A. + B. For L.A., use $\frac{1}{2}\ell p$ and substitute $2\pi r$ for p and simplify. For B, substitute πr^2.

In 3–8, write a specific lateral-area formula for each figure.

3. right cylinder — L.A. = $2\pi rh$
4. regular triangular prism — L.A. = $3sh$
5. right square prism — L.A. = $4sh$

11a) L.A. = $\frac{1}{2}\ell(2\pi r) = \pi r\ell$
b) S.A. = $\pi r\ell + \pi r^2 = \pi r(\ell + r)$

13a) $192 + 192x$ units^2
b) S.A. = L.A. + 2B

14a) $7qy\pi$ units^2
b) L.A. = $\frac{1}{2}\ell p$ or L.A. = $\pi r\ell$

15a) $144wz$ units^3
b) $V = Bh$

The Pyramids Office Building in Indianapolis, Indiana

Applying the Mathematics

10. Find a formula for the surface area of the right cylinder of Questions 8 and 9 in terms of its height h and the radius r of its base. S.A. = $2\pi rh + 2\pi r^2$

11. A right cone has slant height ℓ and its base has radius r.
a. Find a formula for its L.A. in terms of ℓ and r. See left.
b. Find a formula for its S.A. in terms of ℓ and r. See left.

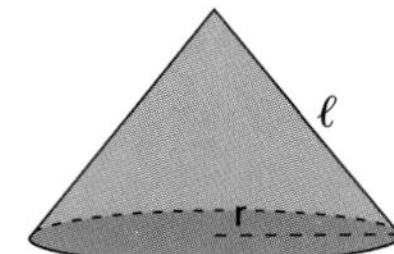

12. A cube has edges of length $2t$.
a. What is its surface area? $24t^2$ units^2
b. What is its volume? $8t^3$ units^3

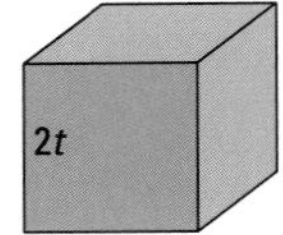

In 13–15, a figure is shown. **a.** Determine the desired measure. **b.** Tell which formula(s) you used. See left.

13. surface area of the right triangular prism

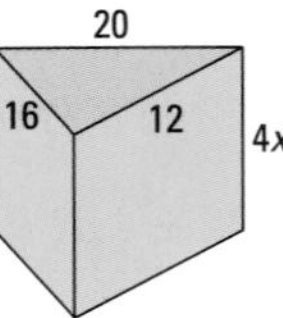

14. lateral area of the right cone

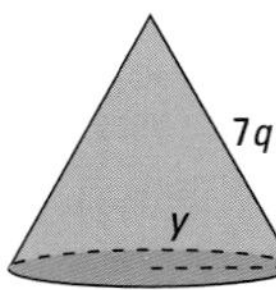

15. volume of oblique rectangular prism

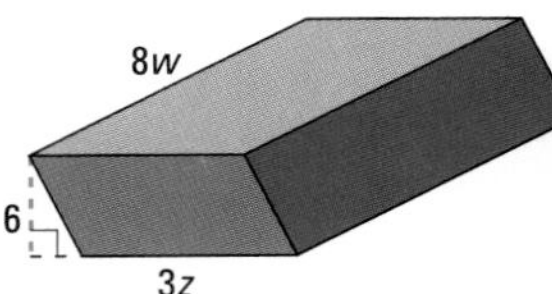

Review

16. Suppose each base of a right prism is an isosceles trapezoid with dimensions as shown below. *(Lessons 10-1, 10-5)*
a. Find the volume of the prism. 480 units^3
b. Find its lateral area. 420 units^2
c. Find its surface area. 516 units^2

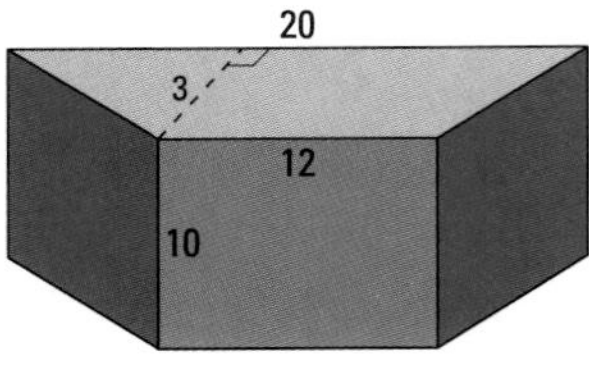

17. Suppose the volume of a cylinder is $39{,}366\pi$ cm^3. If the radius of the base is 27 cm, what is the cylinder's height? *(Lesson 10-5)* 54 cm

Adapting to Individual Needs

Challenge

Materials: Truncated paper cup, tape measure, ruler

Most paper or plastic cups are not cylinders, but truncated cones. Have students look up a formula for finding the volume of a truncated cone or frustum. Then give students a cup that contains a known number of liquid ounces and have them make the appropriate measurements and calculate the cup's volume. Have them convert their calculations into liquid ounces and compare their answer with the volume stated in the packaging of the product. [$V = \frac{\pi(r^2 + rR + R^2)h}{3}$, where r and R are the radii of the top and base, respectively.]

19)

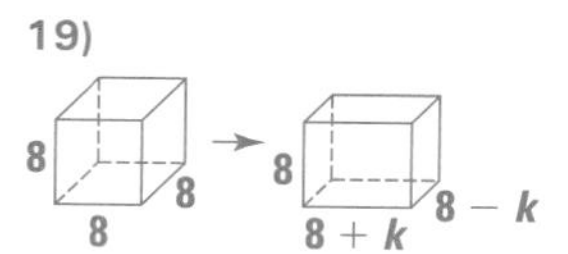

20b) The Mexico pyramid has lateral area about $\frac{5}{8}$ that of Khufu pyramid.

18. Expand $(x + y)^2$. *(Lesson 10-4)* $x^2 + 2xy + y^2$

19. By how much is the volume of a cube of side 8 changed if k is added to the length, k is subtracted from the width, and the height remains 8? Draw a picture of the original cube and the resulting box. *(Lesson 10-4)* Volume is decreased by $8k^2$. See left.

20. Pyramids were built throughout the ancient world. Northeast of Mexico City is Teotihuacán's Pyramid of the Sun. This pyramid is presently 66 m high and has a rectangular base measuring 232 m by 200 m. *(Lesson 10-2)*

a. What is its lateral area? (Note: There are faces of two different sizes.)

b. How does its lateral area compare with that of the pyramid of Khufu?

a) ≈ 54,500 m^2 b) See left.

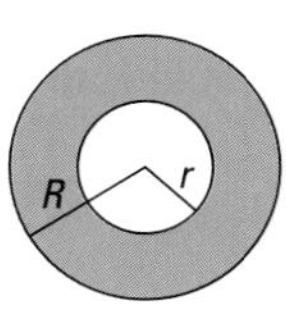

21. A ring between two concentric circles is shaded as shown at the left. If the radius of the small circle is r and the radius of the large circle is R, what is the area of the ring? *(Lesson 8-8)* $\pi(R^2 - r^2)$

22. In right triangle ABC at the right, find

a. $m\angle C$. 45 **b.** BC. 7 **c.** AC. $7\sqrt{2} \approx 9.9$

(Lessons 6-2, 8-6)

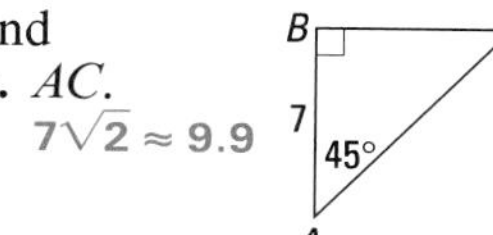

23. Find the slope of line ℓ below. *(Lesson 3-6)* $-\frac{b}{a}$

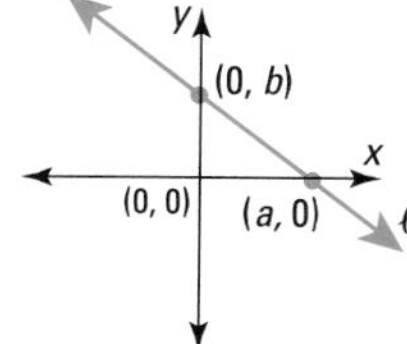

24)

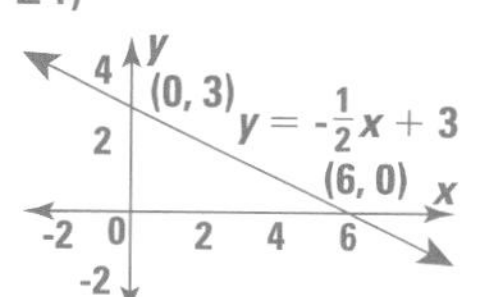

24. Graph $y = -\frac{1}{2}x + 3$. *(Lesson 1-3)* See left.

Exploration

25. a. Give a possible set of dimensions for a cylinder whose surface area is 200π units^2.

b. Give dimensions for a second cylinder, not congruent to the first, whose surface area is 200π units^2.

a, b) Samples:

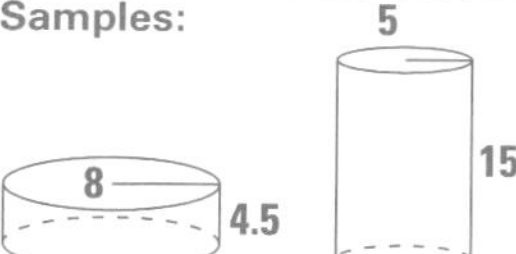

Follow-up for Lesson 10-6

Practice

For more questions on SPUR Objectives, use **Lesson Master 10-6A** (shown on page 595) or **Lesson Master 10-6B** (shown on pages 596–597).

Assessment

Quiz A quiz covering Lessons 10-4 through 10-6 is provided in the *Assessment Sourcebook.*

Oral Communication Have students **work in groups** to make a complete list of all the formulas presented in this chapter and identify what each variable represents. Suggest that students include diagrams. [Students demonstrate an understanding of the various formulas.]

Extension

You might give students this problem from *The Mathematics Teacher,* (Volume 81, Number 1, January, 1988). A stone is thrown into a cylindrical water tank 2 feet in diameter, causing the water to rise 1.5 inches. What is the stone's volume? [$\frac{\pi}{8}$ ft³]

Project Update Project 1, *Making Cones,* on page 613, relates to the content of this lesson.

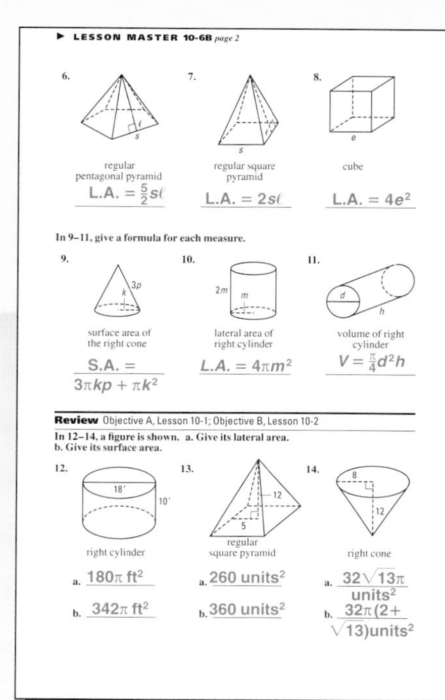

▸ LESSON MASTER 10-6B *page 2*

6. regular pentagonal pyramid — L.A. = $\frac{5}{2}s\ell$

7. regular square pyramid — L.A. = $2s\ell$

8. cube — L.A. = $4e^2$

In 9–11, give a formula for each measure.

9. surface area of the right cone — S.A. = $3\pi kp + \pi k^2$

10. lateral area of right cylinder — L.A. = $4\pi m^2$

11. volume of right cylinder — $V = \frac{\pi}{4}d^2h$

Review Objective A, Lesson 10-1; Objective B, Lesson 10-2

In 12–14, a figure is shown. a. Give its lateral area. b. Give its surface area.

12. right cylinder — a. 180π ft² b. 342π ft²

13. regular square pyramid — a. 260 units² b. 360 units²

14. right cone — a. $32\sqrt{13}\pi$ units² b. $32\pi(2+\sqrt{13})$units²

Setting Up Lesson 10-7

Be sure students do the In-Class Activity on page 598 before reading Lesson 10-7.

Materials For Activity 1 in *Optional Activities* on page 600, students will need objects shaped like prisms, cones, cylinders, and pyramids; rulers, and tape measures. For Activity 2, they will need a pyramid and a prism (or a cone and a cylinder) with the same height and identical bases that can be filled with sand or water, along with sand or water to fill them.

In-class Activity

Resources

From the ***Teacher's Resource File***
- Answer Master 10-7
- Teaching Aid 140: Building a Prism from Pyramids

Additional Resources
- Visual for Teaching Aid 140

This In-class Activity is designed to prepare students for Lesson 10-7. It has students create a prism from three pyramids, paralleling the discussion that begins Lesson 10-7.

This activity is not easy for students, with the main difficulties occurring in Steps 3 and 4, so it may be advantageous to have them **work in groups. Teaching Aid 140** contains the nets needed for the activity.

The labels are important and need to be done accurately.

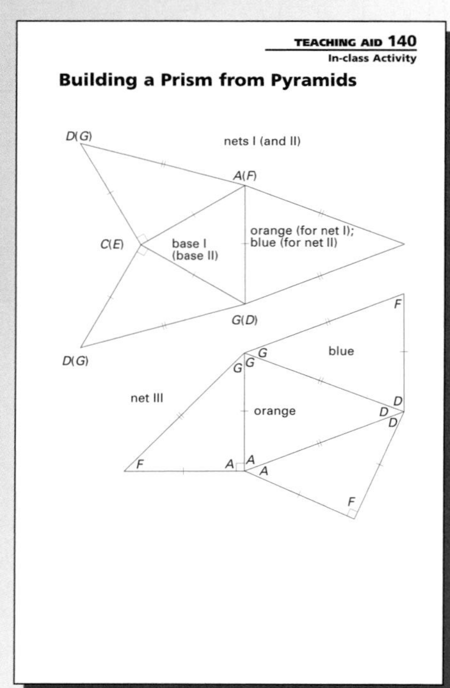
TEACHING AID 140
In-class Activity
Building a Prism from Pyramids

Introducing Lesson 10-7

Building a Prism from Pyramids

IN-CLASS ACTIVITY

Work in small groups. You will need orange and blue pencils, scissors, and tape.

1 Trace two copies of the first net shown below. Label the first tracing "net I," and copy the first of each pair of vertex names onto net I. Label the second tracing "net II," and copy the second of each pair of vertex names onto your tracing. Copy the word *base* on the equilateral face of both nets. On net I color $\triangle ADG$ orange, and on net II color $\triangle FGD$ blue.

2 Trace one copy of net III and copy the vertex names onto it. Color $\triangle ADG$ orange and $\triangle FGD$ blue.

3 Make a pyramid from each net, keeping the tracing marks and the labels on the exterior of the pyramids. See margin.

4 By placing one base on top and one on bottom, and by matching the blue and orange triangles, form a regular triangular prism from the three pyramids. See margin.

5 Use these models as you read Lesson 10-7.

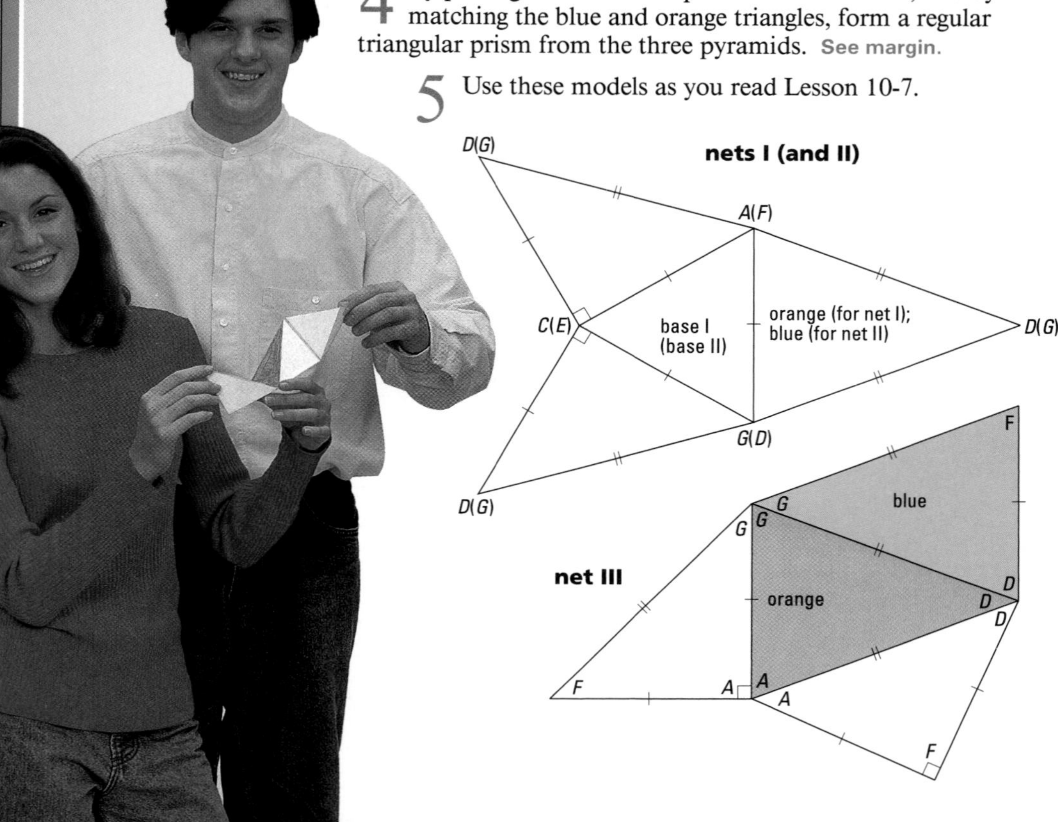

Additional Answers
Step 3.

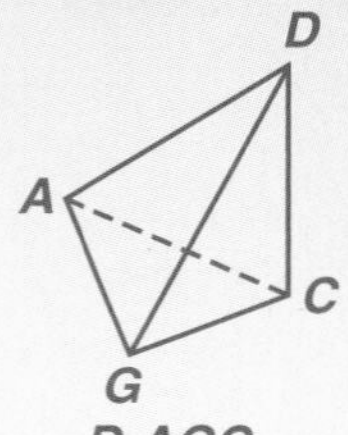

D-AGC from net I

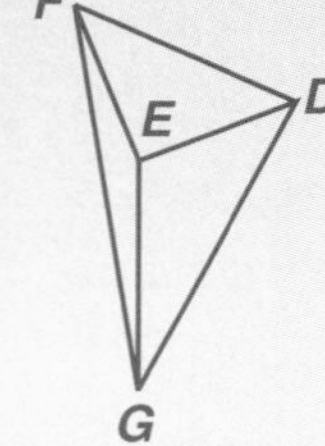

G-DEF or *D-GEF* from net II

F, D, A, G

D-AGF from net III

Step 4. Sample:

F, E, D, A, C, G

LESSON

10-7

Volumes of Pyramids and Cones

This computer-generated art shows two cones with the same volume.

In this lesson you will learn a simple formula for the volume of any pyramid or cone. The proof of that formula, however, is not so simple. Use the pyramids you constructed in the In-class Activity and examine the figures drawn as you read.

Creating a Prism from Pyramids

Consider the triangular pyramid *D-AGC* below at the left in which $\overline{DC}$ is perpendicular to the plane of the base $\triangle AGC$. (This is the pyramid from net I of the In-class Activity.) Let B = Area($\triangle AGC$) and $h = DC$. We want to compute the volume of *D-AGC*.

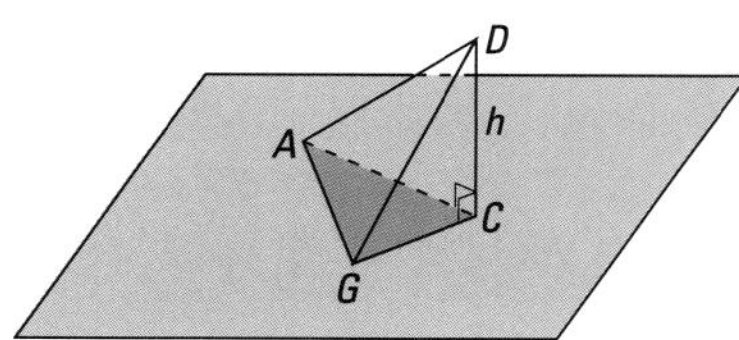

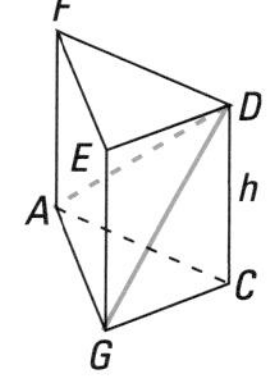

In the In-class Activity, you saw that three pyramids could be put together to form a triangular *prism* with congruent bases *AGC* and *FED* and height *DC*. This prism is pictured above at the right and has volume *Bh*.

Lesson 10-7

Objectives

B Calculate volumes of pyramids and cones from appropriate lengths, and vice versa.

I Apply formulas for volumes of pyramids and cones to real situations.

Resources

From the ***Teacher's Resource File***

- Lesson Master 10-7A or 10-7B
- Answer Master 10-7
- Teaching Aids
  133 Warm-up
  141 Three Pyramids Forming a Prism
- Technology Sourcebook, Calculator Master 2

Additional Resources

- Visuals for Teaching Aids 133, 141
- Geometric solids; rulers
- Pyramid and prism (or cone and cylinder) with the same height and congruent bases
- Sand

Teaching Lesson 10-7

Warm-up

1. A triangle has the same area as a circle with a radius of 6 inches. If the base of the triangle is 3 inches, what is its height? **24π inches**
2. Another circle has the same area as a triangle whose base is 12 cm and whose height is 10 cm. What is the radius of the circle? **$\approx$ 4.4 cm**

Lesson 10-7 Overview

Broad Goals This lesson derives and applies the volume formula for pyramids and cones. The derivation uses the idea of the In-class Activity and Cavalieri's Principle.

Perspective Why are the derivations of the volume formulas so difficult? The reason is that we are starting from only a formula for the volume of a box. The power of deduction is that so much can be deduced from so little. The arguments may be difficult to follow, but each line can be justified, and the results are true if the postulates are true.

The derivation given for the formula $V = \frac{1}{3}Bh$ for any pyramid and cone is standard: dissect a prism into three equal-volume pyramids to get the volume of each pyramid; then use Cavalieri's principle to note that the volume of a cone has the same formula.

Not all things in two dimensions generalize so easily to three dimensions. In two dimensions, any two polygons with the same area can be dissected and rearranged into congruent pieces. Max Dehn proved in 1902 that in three dimensions, there can exist two triangular pyramids with equal altitudes and with bases of equal area that cannot be dissected and rearranged into congruent solids. This was the first of David Hilbert's famous 23 problems to be solved.

Notes on Reading

Pacing The questions in this lesson and the next may take more than a day each to cover. You may wish to save some of the discussion for the days of review.

Reading Mathematics This is a difficult lesson to read. That is the reason that an In-class Activity is included to precede it. While reading, students should pay particular attention to the notation for pyramids. The vertex is given first, a hyphen follows, and then the vertices of the base of the pyramid are given. This notation should help students classify the pyramids (how many vertices are in the base?) and also see the corresponding prism with bases congruent to the named base in the prism. **Teaching Aid 141** contains the diagrams of the three pyramids that form a prism and can be used to help students.

For many students, proofs are not as convincing as demonstrations. You might want to use Activity 2 in *Optional Activities* below to show the correspondence between the volumes of pyramids and prisms and of cones and cylinders.

The following mnemonic device may also help students: The area of a triangle is $\frac{1}{2}$ the area of a rectangle, and area is 2-dimensional. The volume of a pyramid is $\frac{1}{3}$ the volume of a prism, and volume is 3-dimensional.

The power of Cavalieri's Principle is that the range of shapes that cones and pyramids may take is infinite, but there is a single formula which applies to all of them.

When you discuss the volume of the pyramid of Khufu in **Example 1**, you may want to ask students what the volume of a single stone in the

We can show that the prism on page 599 has 3 times the volume of the pyramid *D-AGC*. First, split the prism into the three pyramids of the In-class Activity.

the three pyramids forming the prism

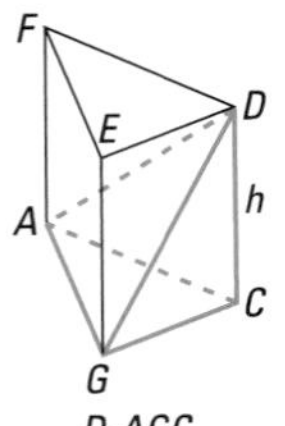

D-AGC
formed by net I

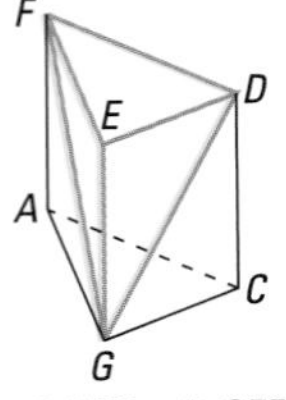

G-DEF or *D-GEF*
formed by net II

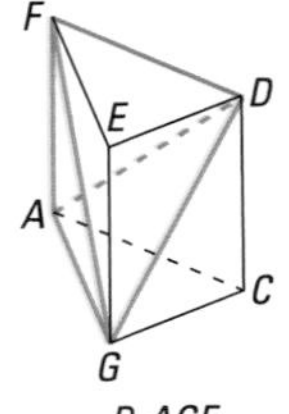

D-AGF
formed by net III

The pyramids formed by nets I and II, *D-AGC* and *G-DEF*, have the same volume since they are formed by the same net. Now we show that the pyramid formed by net III also has the same volume. Look at face *AGEF* of the prism. It is a rectangle with diagonal $\overline{FG}$, so $\triangle AFG \cong \triangle EGF$.

Now the pyramids *D-AGF* and *D-GEF* have the same volume since the height of each is from *D* to the plane of parallelogram *AGEF*, and the bases are congruent. But *D-GEF* and *G-DEF* are the same pyramid. So, by the Transitive Property of Equality, the three pyramids have the same volume. So each pyramid has a volume that is one third the volume of the prism.

Consequently, the volume of pyramid *D-AGC* is $\frac{1}{3}Bh$.

Volumes of Any Pyramids

By Cavalieri's Principle, the volume of any pyramid or cone is equal to the volume of a particular pyramid of the same height with a triangular base of equal area. For instance, if a cone has base area 6π units^2 and height h, a triangular pyramid with the same volume can be constructed if its base has area 6π units^2 and its height is h. Furthermore, these need not be regular pyramids or right cones.

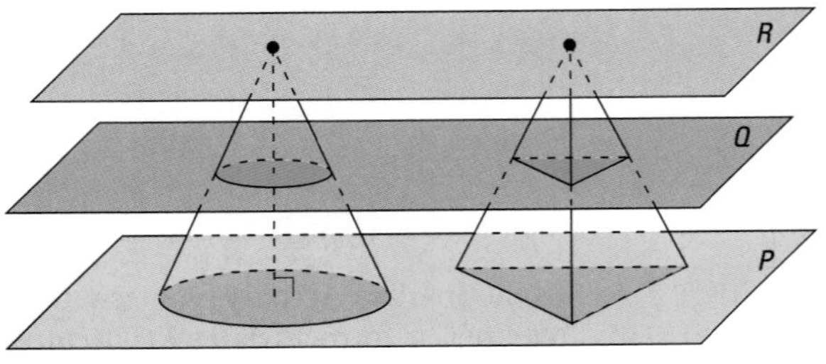

This argument proves the following theorem.

Optional Activities

Activity 1 Using Physical Models
Materials: Objects shaped like prisms, cones, cylinders, and pyramids; rulers and tape measures

After discussing finding the volumes of pyramids and cones, you might continue having students find the volumes and surface areas of actual objects, as suggested in the Activity in *Optional Activities* on page 589.

Activity 2 Using Physical Models
Materials: Pyramid and prism (or cone and cylinder) with the same height and identical bases that can be filled with sand or water

You can use this activity to demonstrate that the volume of a pyramid is $\frac{1}{3}$ the volume of a prism with the same height and base. Or, you can do a similar demonstration with a cone and cylinder. Fill the pyramid with sand or water and empty it into the prism. Show that this can be done three times. It surprises students because of the coefficient $\frac{1}{2}$ found in many area formulas; many students think that the volume should be twice as much, not three times as much.

Pyramid-Cone Volume Formula
The volume V of any pyramid or cone equals $\frac{1}{3}$ the product of its height h and its base area B.

$$V = \frac{1}{3}Bh$$

Thus, a pyramid or a cone which has the same base area and same height as a prism or cylinder has $\frac{1}{3}$ the volume of the prism or cylinder. Often the volume of a pyramid is easier to calculate than its surface area.

Example 1

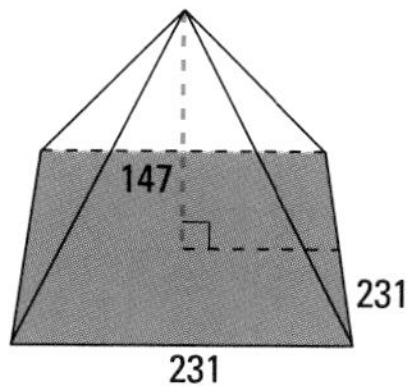

Find the volume of the pyramid of Khufu. (Recall that this pyramid is a regular square pyramid 147 m high, and each side of its base is 231 m.)

Solution

Use the Pyramid-Cone Volume Formula

$$V = \frac{1}{3}Bh.$$

The base is a square, so $B = (231)^2 = 53{,}361$ square meters. From the given, $h = 147$ meters.

Thus,

$$V = \frac{1}{3} \cdot 53{,}361 \cdot 147$$
$$\approx 2{,}610{,}000 \text{ cubic meters.}$$

The volume is about 2,610,000 m^3. This is over 5000 times the capacity of a middle-size house or large apartment.

If you know all but one quantity in a formula, you can solve an equation to determine the unknown.

Example 2

If a cone has a height of 6 in. and a volume of 40 in^3, what is the radius of its base?

Solution

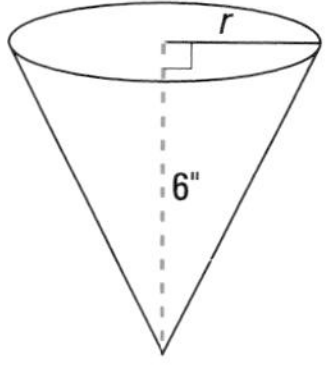

The relevant formula is $V = \frac{1}{3}Bh$.

Here $h = 6$ and $V = 40$.

Substituting, $40 = \frac{1}{3}B \cdot 6.$

$40 = 2B$

So, $B = 20.$

But $B = \pi r^2$. So, $\pi r^2 = 20.$

$r^2 = \frac{20}{\pi}$

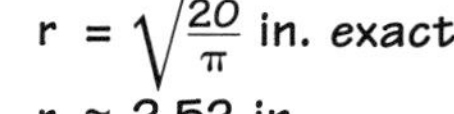

So, $r = \sqrt{\frac{20}{\pi}}$ in. exactly,

or $r \approx 2.52$ in.

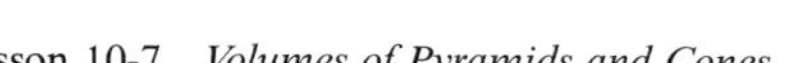

pyramid might be. Even a stone with volume 1 cubic meter is extremely heavy. This pyramid would contain over 2,500,000 such stones. Suppose 1,000 people worked on building the pyramid and a team of five of them could put 10 one-cubic-meter stones in place each day. How long would it take them to build the pyramid? [It would take about 1250 days or 3.5 years. This is probably a fast pace and there may have been more than 1000 people who worked on the pyramid.]

Using the volume formula for pyramids and cones should be straightforward for students, but caution them to find the *height* of the pyramid or cone, not the *slant height,* before substituting into the formula.

Additional Examples

1. A bin at a granary is in the shape of a cube with a pyramid underneath. If the cube is 5 feet tall and the entire bin is 9 feet tall, how many cubic feet of grain will it hold? **$\frac{475}{3} \approx 158$ cubic feet**
2. An ice cream cone holds $\frac{1}{8}$ pint of ice cream. (The rest of the ice cream will be above the cone.) If the cone has a diameter of 2 inches, how high does it need to be? **From Lesson 10-3, $\frac{1}{8}$ pint ≈ 3.6 cubic inches. $\frac{\pi}{3}h \approx 3.6$, so $h \approx 3.4$ inches.**

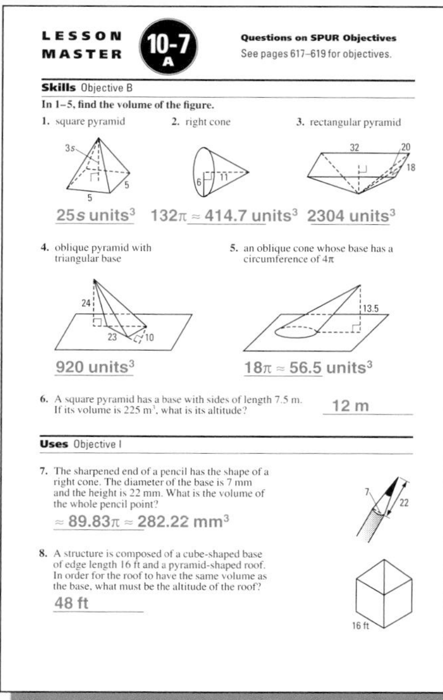

LESSON MASTER 10-7 A

Questions on SPUR Objectives
See pages 617–619 for objectives.

Skills Objective B

In 1–5, find the volume of the figure.

1. square pyramid

$25s$ units^3

2. right cone

$132\pi \approx 414.7$ units^3

3. rectangular pyramid

2304 units^3

4. oblique pyramid with triangular base

920 units^3

5. an oblique cone whose base has a circumference of 4π

$18\pi \approx 56.5$ units^3

6. A square pyramid has a base with sides of length 7.5 m. If its volume is 225 m^3, what is its altitude? 12 m

Uses Objective I

7. The sharpened end of a pencil has the shape of a right cone. The diameter of the base is 7 mm and the height is 22 mm. What is the volume of the whole pencil point?

$\approx 89.83\pi \approx 282.22$ mm^3

8. A structure is composed of a cube-shaped base of edge length 16 ft and a pyramid-shaped roof. In order for the roof to have the same volume as the base, what must be the altitude of the roof?

48 ft

Optional Activities

Activity 3 Technology Connection To make **Question 9** more dynamic, students can use a spreadsheet. Rather than ask what the radius is if the height is 5 cm, make two columns listing corresponding heights and radii of cones that have a volume of 40 cm^3. Have the radius column range from .5 to 15 in increments of .5. The height-column values h will depend on the corresponding radius values, with $h = \frac{120}{\pi r^2}$.

Activity 4 Consumer Connection
Question 13 is an excellent question to lead into a discussion about finding the best value when buying soft drinks at a fast-food restaurant. Have students investigate the cost of various sizes of drinks at fast-food chains. Have them determine the best value in purchasing a soft drink, that is, what is the best size soft drink to purchase for a given unit of money. Usually (but not always) the largest size is the best value.

Notes on Questions

Question 4 There are infinitely many pyramids *A-BCDE* with fixed base *BCDE* and vertex *A*, some point on the top of the box. They all have the same volume but not necessarily the same surface area.

Question 9 Activity 3 in *Optional Activities* on page 601 relates to this question.

Question 13 Activity 4 in *Optional Activities* on page 601 relates to this question.

Questions 15–16 These questions can be used to review algebra. Since $(kx)^2 = k^2x^2$, if x is multiplied by k, then its square is multiplied by k^2. Thus, if dimensions of a square are multiplied by k, the area is multiplied by k^2. Similarly, since $(kx)^3 = k^3x^3$, if dimensions of a cube are multiplied by k, the volume is multiplied by k^3.

Question 22 Students should know the answer to **part c** before beginning, so the task here is to verify that the formulas really work.

QUESTIONS

Covering the Reading

In 1–3, refer to the splitting of a prism into pyramids in this lesson.

1. Why do pyramids *D-AGC* and *G-DEF* have the same volume?
   Sample: They are formed from the same net.
2. Why do pyramids *G-DEF* and *D-GEF* have the same volume?
   They are the same pyramid.
3. Why do pyramids *D-GEF* and *D-AGF* have the same volume?
   They have congruent bases and heights.
4. At the left, how does the volume of *A-BCDE* compare with the volume of the box?
   The volume of the pyramid is $\frac{1}{3}$ the volume of the box.
5. Find the volume of a cone with height 8′ and base of radius 2′.
   $\frac{32\pi}{3} \approx 33.5 \text{ ft}^3$

In 6–8, find the volume of the solid.

6. pyramid with right triangular base PCD and height AP
7. trapezoidal pyramid with height 12
8. right cone with height 27 and diameter 18

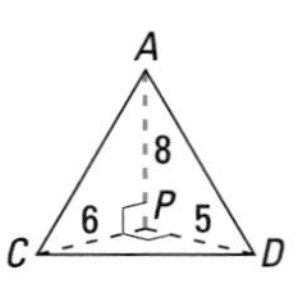

40 units^3

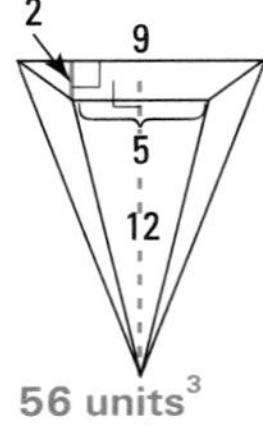

56 units^3

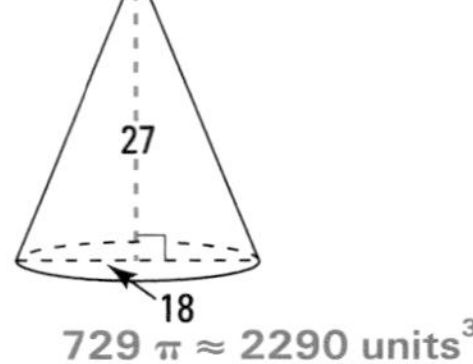

$729\pi \approx 2290$ units^3

9. A cone has a volume of 40 cm^3. Its height is 5 cm. What is the radius of the base? $\sqrt{\frac{24}{\pi}} \approx 2.8$ cm
10. A cone and a cylinder have identical bases and equal heights. If the volume of the cylinder is V, then the volume of the cone is __?__. $\frac{1}{3}V$

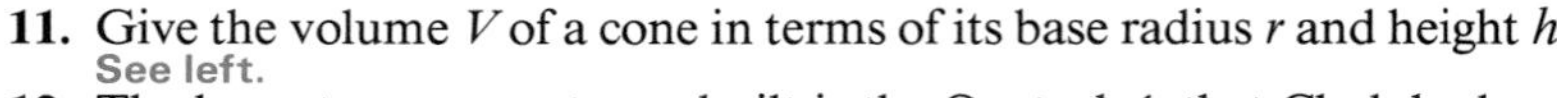

Applying the Mathematics

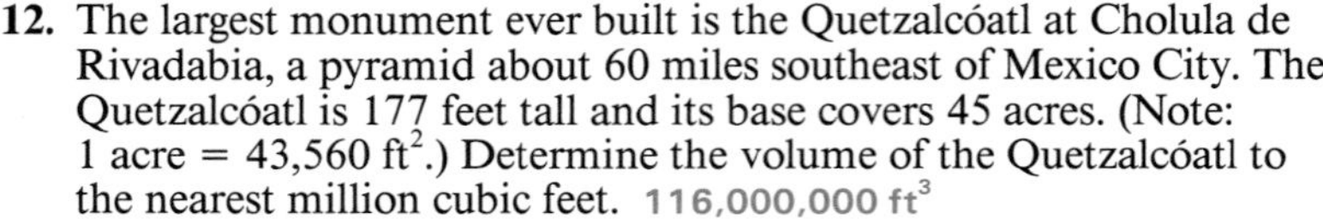

11. Give the volume V of a cone in terms of its base radius r and height h.
    See left.
12. The largest monument ever built is the Quetzalcóatl at Cholula de Rivadabia, a pyramid about 60 miles southeast of Mexico City. The Quetzalcóatl is 177 feet tall and its base covers 45 acres. (Note: 1 acre = 43,560 ft^2.) Determine the volume of the Quetzalcóatl to the nearest million cubic feet. 116,000,000 ft^3
13. What happens to the volume of a pyramid if its base is kept the same but its height is multiplied by 31.8? The volume is multiplied by 31.8.
14. What happens to the volume of a cone if the height is kept the same but the radius of the base is multiplied by 7?
    The volume is multiplied by 49.

Largest monument. *The Quetzalcóatl pyramid is named for the Aztec god, Quetzalcóatl.*

11) $V = \frac{\pi r^2 h}{3}$

Optional Activities

Activity 5 Technology Connection

You may want to consider using *Technology Sourcebook, Calculator Master 2,* with Lessons 10-7 and 10-8. In this activity, students calculate the volumes of cones and spheres and then explore how the volume of a figure is affected by changes in dimensions.

Adapting to Individual Needs

Challenge

Have students solve this problem: Sand is falling off a conveyer belt onto a conical pile. The diameter of the base is always about 3 times the height of the cone. The belt dumps about 100 cubic feet of sand per minute. When the pile is 10 feet high, the conveyor stops and moves to form another pile. How long does it take for a pile of the required height to be formed? [About 23.6 minutes]

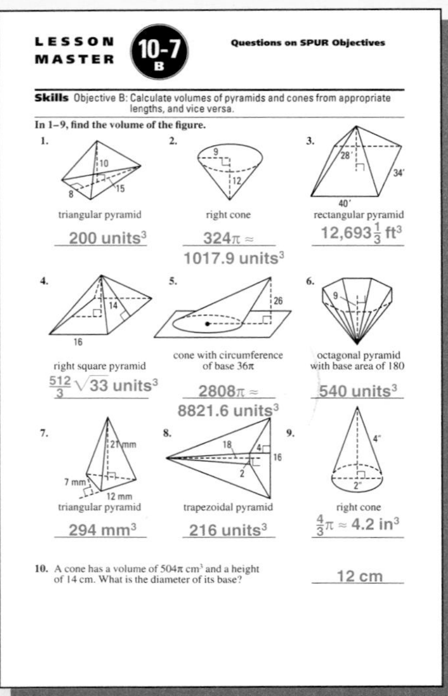

LESSON MASTER 10-7 B — Questions on SPUR Objectives

Skills Objective B: Calculate volumes of pyramids and cones from appropriate lengths, and vice versa.

In 1–9, find the volume of the figure.

1. triangular pyramid — 200 units^3
2. right cone — $324\pi \approx$ 1017.9 units^3
3. rectangular pyramid — $12{,}693\frac{1}{3}$ ft^3
4. right square pyramid — $\frac{512}{3}\sqrt{33}$ units^3
5. cone with circumference of base 36π — $2808\pi \approx$ 8821.6 units^3
6. octagonal pyramid with base area of 180 — 540 units^3
7. triangular pyramid — 294 mm^3
8. trapezoidal pyramid — 216 units^3
9. right cone — $\frac{4}{3}\pi \approx 4.2$ in^3

10. A cone has a volume of 504π cm^3 and a height of 14 cm. What is the diameter of its base? 12 cm

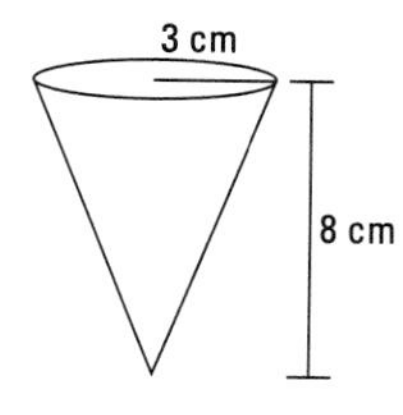

15. Consider the water cooler cup pictured at the left. See left.
    a. How many cubic centimeters of liquid will it hold?
    b. How many times will it need to be used in order to fill a liter jug?
    c. How much paper is needed to make the cup?

15a) $\frac{72}{3}\pi \approx 75$ cm^3
b) 14
c) $3\pi\sqrt{73} \approx 81$ cm^2

16. A pyramid has a volume of 250 cubic centimeters. Its base is a square and its height is 7.5 centimeters. Find the length of a base edge. 10 cm

Review

17. How much paper is needed to wrap a box that is 20 inches long, 13 inches wide, and 4.5 inches high? *(Lesson 10-6)*
    at least 817 square inches

18. Give the lateral area of the regular square pyramid pictured at the left. *(Lesson 10-6)* $6\ell s$

19. Find the volume and surface area of the right triangular prism pictured at the right. *(Lessons 10-1, 10-5)*
    volume = 216 units^3; S.A. = $174 + 8\sqrt{117} \approx$ 261 units^2

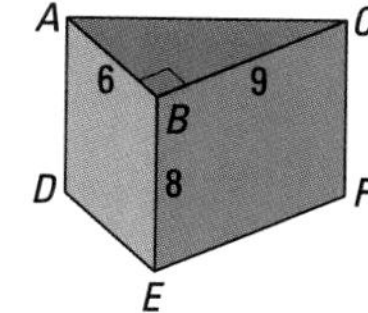

20. In parts **a** and **b,** express the volume of the largest rectangular prism pictured below.
    a. as a product of binomials $(x + 3)(y + 8)(z + 5)$
    b. as the sum of the volumes of eight smaller rectangular prisms *(Lesson 10-4)*
    $8zx + 24z + xyz + 3yz + 40x + 5xy + 15y + 120$

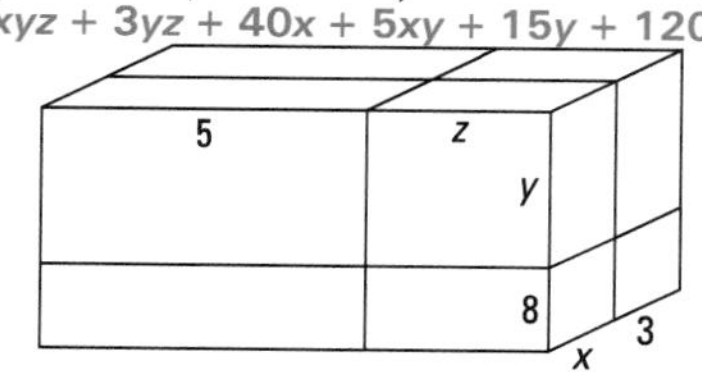

21. A two-by-four is a piece of wood that starts out measuring 2″ by 4″ by k' (it can have any length) but is planed to $1\frac{5}{8}$″ by $3\frac{5}{8}$″ by k'. What percent of the wood is lost in the planing? *(Lesson 10-3)*
    ≈ 26%

Exploration

22. a. Make a cone using a net like that at the right, with $\ell \geq 3$ in. Answers may vary.
    b. After the cone is made, make an open-top cylinder with the same height and base with the same radius as the cone. Answers may vary.
    c. Fill the cone with dirt or sand. How many times must you empty the cone into the cylinder in order to fill up the cylinder? three

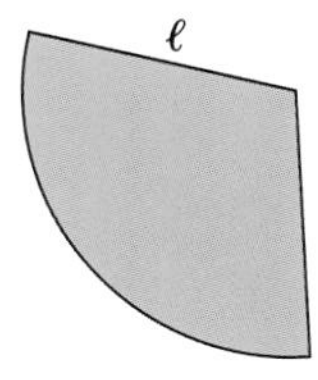

Follow-up for Lesson 10-7

Practice

For more questions on SPUR Objectives, use **Lesson Master 10-7A** (shown on page 601) or **Lesson Master 10-7B** (shown on pages 602–603).

Assessment

Oral/Written Communication
Have students **work in groups** to make up two problems similar to **Examples 1–2.** Then have them work together to write an explanation of how each problem could be solved. [Students provide meaningful problems and provide a correct explanation of how to solve each problem.]

Extension

Have students draw a cube and choose a vertex. Then have the students connect the vertex to all vertices on the opposite face. Ask students what figure is formed. [A square pyramid] Suppose that the edge of the cube is 2 inches, ask the students to find the volume of the pyramid. [$\frac{8}{3}$ in^3]

Projects Update Project 1, *Making Cones,* Project 2, *Sizes of Pyramids of Ancient Cultures,* and Project 3, *Prismoids,* on page 613, relate to the content of this lesson.

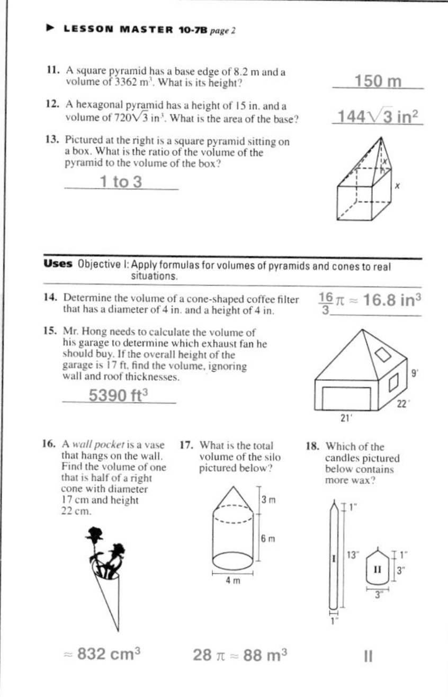
► **LESSON MASTER 10-7B** *page 2*

11. A square pyramid has a base edge of 8.2 m and a volume of 3362 m^3. What is its height? 150 m
12. A hexagonal pyramid has a height of 15 in. and a volume of $720\sqrt{3}$ in^3. What is the area of the base? $144\sqrt{3}$ in^2
13. Pictured at the right is a square pyramid sitting on a box. What is the ratio of the volume of the pyramid to the volume of the box? 1 to 3

Uses Objective I: Apply formulas for volumes of pyramids and cones to real situations.

14. Determine the volume of a cone-shaped coffee filter that has a diameter of 4 in. and a height of 4 in. $\frac{16}{3}\pi \approx 16.8$ in^3
15. Mr. Hong needs to calculate the volume of his garage to determine which exhaust fan he should buy. If the overall height of the garage is 17 ft, find the volume, ignoring wall and roof thicknesses. 5390 ft^3
16. A *wall pocket* is a vase that hangs on the wall. Find the volume of one that is half of a right cone with diameter 17 cm and height 22 cm. ≈ 832 cm^3
17. What is the total volume of the silo pictured below? $28\pi \approx 88$ m^3
18. Which of the candles pictured below contains more wax? II

Setting Up Lesson 10-8

Materials Students will need a variety of balls, such as baseballs, basketballs, tennis balls, golf balls, and tape measures for Activity 2 in *Optional Activities* on page 606. You may want a globe for the suggestions given in *English Language Development.*

Lesson 10-8

Objectives

D Calculate the volume of a sphere from appropriate lengths, and vice versa.

E Determine what happens to the volume of a sphere when its dimensions are multiplied by some number(s).

I Apply the formula for volume of a sphere to real situations.

Resources

From the ***Teacher's Resource File***

- Lesson Master 10-8A or 10-8B
- Answer Master 10-8
- Teaching Aids
  133 Warm-up
  142 Sphere and Cylinder
- Technology Sourcebook, Calculator Master 2

Additional Resources

- Visuals for Teaching Aids 133, 142
- A variety of balls, such as baseballs, basketballs, tennis balls, and golf balls; tape measure
- Globe

Teaching Lesson 10-8

Warm-up

Find the area of the shaded region between the circles.

64π square units

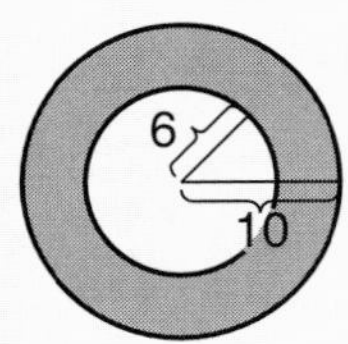

LESSON

10-8 The Volume of a Sphere

Here is how the volume formulas of this chapter have been developed. We began with this postulate in Lesson 10-3.

$V = \ell wh$ volume of a box

Cavalieri's Principle was presented in Lesson 10-5, and the following formula was deduced.

$V = Bh$ volume of a prism or cylinder

In Lesson 10-7 we saw that a prism can be split into three pyramids with the same height and base. Using Cavalieri's Principle again, this led to another formula.

$V = \frac{1}{3}Bh$ volume of a pyramid or cone

In this lesson, still another application of Cavalieri's Principle results in a formula for the volume of a sphere. In this application, figures that look quite different will be shown to have the same volume.

Comparing a Sphere with Another Surface

Both the sphere and cylinder below have a height of $2r$. Each cone inside the cylinder has height r. An amazing result is that the volume of the sphere equals the volume between the cylinder and the two cones. The argument that follows uses plane sections and Cavalieri's Principle to prove this result.

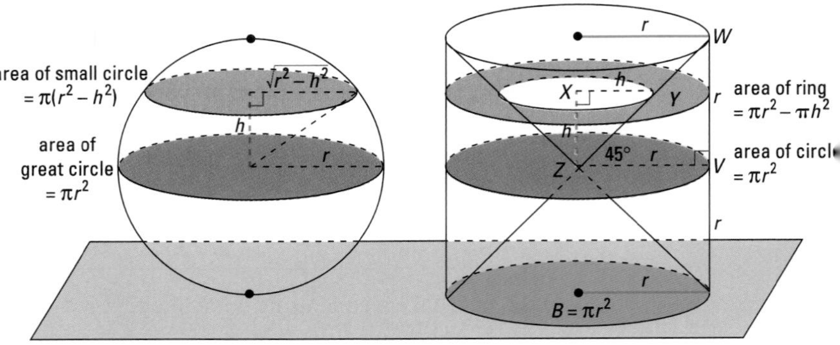

Lesson 10-8 Overview

Broad Goals In this lesson, the volume of a sphere is shown (using Cavalieri's principle once again) to be equal to the volume lying between a cylinder and two cones. The volume is thus found by subtraction.

Perspective The derivations in this lesson and the next are ingenious. Ingenuity is required because no part of the surface of a sphere contains a planar region; and as discussed in Lesson 9-9, there is no plane net for any part of a sphere.

In the Japanese texts translated by UCSMP, the formulas of this and the next lesson appear in grade 7 and are derived as follows. It is known that the volume of a sphere is $\frac{2}{3}$ the volume of a cylinder into which the sphere is enclosed. Thus, since the volume of that cylinder would be $V = hB = 2r(\pi r^2)$, the volume of the sphere is $\frac{4}{3}\pi r^3$. It is also known that the surface area of that sphere equals the lateral area of the cylinder. (See **Question 12** of Lesson 10-9.) The lateral area of the cylinder is $2\pi rh$; but in this case $h = 2r$, so we get $4\pi r^2$ for the lateral area of the sphere. These are pretty derivations, but they assume some statements that themselves are very difficult to prove from scratch.

The purple sections in the figures on page 604 are the sections formed when a plane slices these figures in their middles. These sections are congruent circular regions with area πr^2. At h units above each horizontal section are two red sections. We now show that the areas of the red circle and the red ring are equal.

In the sphere, the red section is a small circle. By the Pythagorean Theorem, its radius is $\sqrt{r^2 - h^2}$. The area of the small circle is found using the familiar formula for the area of a circle.

$$\text{Area(small circle)} = \pi\left(\sqrt{r^2 - h^2}\right)^2 = \pi(r^2 - h^2)$$

For the region between the cylinder and the cones, the section is the red ring. The outside circle of the ring has radius r. The inside circle of the ring has radius XY. To find XY, examine $\triangle WVZ$. Since $VZ = WV = r$, $\triangle WVZ$ is an isosceles right triangle. Thus $m\angle VZW = 45$. This makes $m\angle XZY = 45$, so $\triangle XYZ$ must also be an isosceles right triangle. Thus $XY = XZ = h$.

The area of the ring now can be computed.

$$\text{Area(ring)} = \pi r^2 - \pi h^2 = \pi(r^2 - h^2)$$

Thus the red sections have equal area. Since the area of the small red circle equals the area of the ring no matter what height h is chosen, Cavalieri's Principle can be applied.

Finding the Formula

The volume of a sphere is thus the difference in the volume of the cylinder ($B \cdot 2r$) and the volume of the two cones (each with volume $\frac{1}{3}B \cdot r$).

$$\begin{aligned}\text{Volume of sphere} &= (B \cdot 2r) - 2 \cdot \left(\tfrac{1}{3}B \cdot r\right)\\ &= 2Br - \tfrac{2}{3}Br\\ &= \tfrac{4}{3}Br\end{aligned}$$

But here the base of the cone and cylinder is a circle with radius r. So $B = \pi r^2$. Substituting,

$$\begin{aligned}\text{Volume of sphere} &= \tfrac{4}{3} \cdot \pi r^2 \cdot r\\ &= \tfrac{4}{3}\pi r^3.\end{aligned}$$

Sphere Volume Formula

The volume V of any sphere is $\frac{4}{3}\pi$ times the cube of its radius r.

$$V = \tfrac{4}{3}\pi r^3$$

Notes on Reading

Reading Mathematics You may wish to read this lesson aloud with as much use of visual aids as possible. Even if students do not understand the derivation, they should be able to appreciate the interrelationship of the cylinder, cone, and sphere.

For all other figures, we derived the surface-area formulas first, then the volume formulas. Students may wonder why the order is reversed here. The order could have been reversed before; no surface area formula was used in deriving volume. However, in Lesson 10-9 the formula for the surface area of a sphere will be found with the aid of the formula for the volume.

The diagram used in the derivation of the Sphere Volume Formula is very complicated. This diagram is shown on **Teaching Aid 142,** which we suggest you use for the discussion. A couple of images may help students visualize this drawing. Have them imagine a solid cylinder of wood from which two cones are carved out at either end. The remaining wood has the same volume as a sphere of the same radius as the cylinder. Then have them imagine a beaker filled with water and a cone pushed in from each end, displacing the water. The water that remains would fill the sphere.

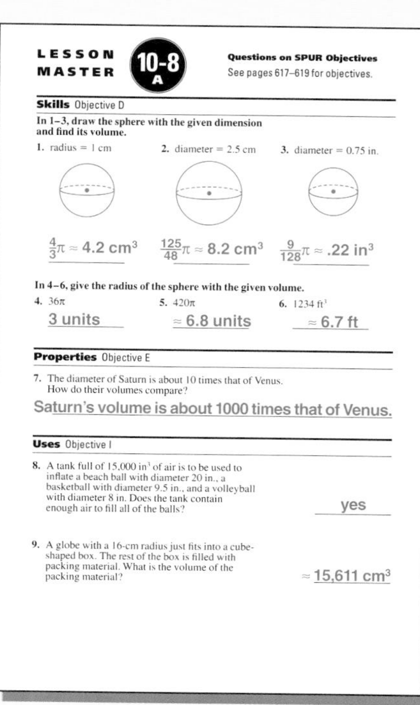
LESSON MASTER 10-8 A

Questions on SPUR Objectives
See pages 617–619 for objectives.

Skills Objective D

In 1–3, draw the sphere with the given dimension and find its volume.

1. radius = 1 cm — $\frac{4}{3}\pi \approx 4.2$ cm^3
2. diameter = 2.5 cm — $\frac{125}{48}\pi \approx 8.2$ cm^3
3. diameter = 0.75 in. — $\frac{9}{128}\pi \approx .22$ in^3

In 4–6, give the radius of the sphere with the given volume.

4. 36π — 3 units
5. 420π — $\approx$ 6.8 units
6. 1234 ft^3 — $\approx$ 6.7 ft

Properties Objective E

7. The diameter of Saturn is about 10 times that of Venus. How do their volumes compare? Saturn's volume is about 1000 times that of Venus.

Uses Objective I

8. A tank full of 15,000 in^3 of air is to be used to inflate a beach ball with diameter 20 in., a basketball with diameter 9.5 in., and a volleyball with diameter 8 in. Does the tank contain enough air to fill all of the balls? yes

9. A globe with a 16-cm radius just fits into a cube-shaped box. The rest of the box is filled with packing material. What is the volume of the packing material? $\approx$ 15,611 cm^3

Optional Activities

Activity 1 Technology Connection This activity relates to **Question 10.** Students may not realize that the situation described would constitute an emergency situation, because to have so little water in storage would be unhealthy. They also may not realize that water in storage tanks ultimately has to come from rainfall or snowfall. You might use a spreadsheet in which one column lists the different amounts of water removed per day. A second column could list how many days the water will last if x amount of water is replaced each day, where x is the value stored in a cell (hence students can see the effect as x changes).

Some students may still think of π as a variable. Point out that variables in volume and surface area formulas are often those that determine the figure. For instance, a right cylinder is determined by its height h and the radius r of its base, so the surface area and volume formulas involve h and r. Thus, since a sphere is determined by its radius (all spheres with the same radius are congruent), a volume formula can involve only the radius. And the radius is cubed because volume implies three dimensions. Thus, a formula for the volume of the sphere has the form $V = kr^3$. The value of k, which is $\frac{4}{3}\pi$, is determined in the proof.

Additional Examples

1. Racquetballs come two to a can. The can is a cylinder and the balls are spheres. If the diameter of the can is d, what is the volume of a racquetball? $\frac{1}{6}\pi d^3$
2. Jacques made a spherical cheese ball for a party. He formed it from a block of cheese 8 cm by 8 cm by 20 cm. What is the diameter of the cheese ball? $\frac{4}{3}\pi r^3 = 1280$, so $r \approx 6.74$ cm, and $d \approx 13.5$ cm.

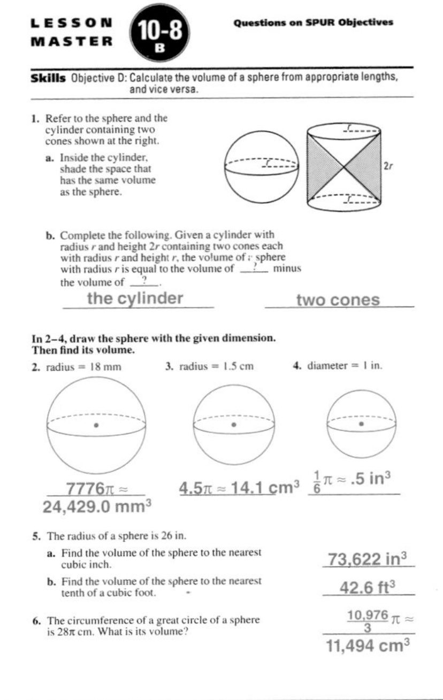

LESSON MASTER 10-8 B Questions on SPUR Objectives

Skills Objective D: Calculate the volume of a sphere from appropriate lengths, and vice versa.

1. Refer to the sphere and the cylinder containing two cones shown at the right.
   a. Inside the cylinder, shade the space that has the same volume as the sphere.
   b. Complete the following. Given a cylinder with radius r and height $2r$ containing two cones each with radius r and height r, the volume of a sphere with radius r is equal to the volume of __?__ minus the volume of __?__.
   the cylinder; two cones

In 2–4, draw the sphere with the given dimension. Then find its volume.

2. radius = 18 mm — $7776\pi \approx 24{,}429.0 \text{ mm}^3$
3. radius = 1.5 cm — $4.5\pi \approx 14.1 \text{ cm}^3$
4. diameter = 1 in. — $\frac{1}{6}\pi \approx .5 \text{ in}^3$

5. The radius of a sphere is 26 in.
   a. Find the volume of the sphere to the nearest cubic inch. $73{,}622 \text{ in}^3$
   b. Find the volume of the sphere to the nearest tenth of a cubic foot. 42.6 ft^3
6. The circumference of a great circle of a sphere is 28π cm. What is its volume? $\frac{10{,}976}{3}\pi \approx 11{,}494 \text{ cm}^3$

The Sphere Volume Formula seems first to have been discovered by Archimedes (287–212 B.C.). Today, we apply his old formula using modern calculators.

Example 1

Find the volume of a sphere with radius 12.

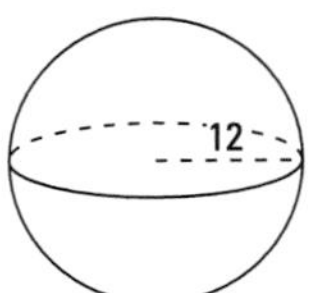

Solution

Substitute into the volume formula.

$$V = \frac{4}{3}\pi r^3$$
$$= \frac{4}{3}\pi(12)^3$$
$$= 2304\pi \approx 7238 \text{ units}^3$$

Example 2

A standard bowling ball cannot be more than 27 inches in circumference. What is the maximum volume of such a ball (to the nearest cubic inch) before the holes are drilled?

Solution

First find the radius of the ball.
Use the circumference formula.

$$C = 2\pi r$$
$$27 = 2\pi r$$

So, $$r = \frac{27}{2\pi} \approx 4.3''.$$

Now substitute into the volume formula $V = \frac{4}{3}\pi r^3$.

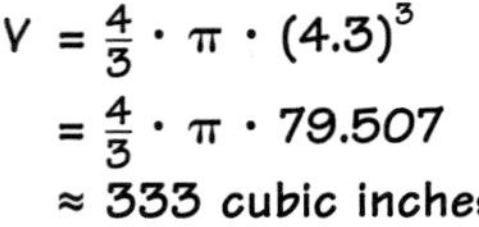

$$V = \frac{4}{3} \cdot \pi \cdot (4.3)^3$$
$$= \frac{4}{3} \cdot \pi \cdot 79.507$$
$$\approx 333 \text{ cubic inches}$$

Even after drilling the holes, there are more than 300 cubic inches of material in a standard bowling ball.

QUESTIONS

Covering the Reading

1. Cavalieri's Principle is used to derive three formulas in this chapter. Name them. Prism-Cylinder Volume Formula; Pyramid-Cone Volume Formula; Sphere Volume Formula.
2. Who discovered the Sphere Volume Formula? Archimedes

Optional Activities

Activity 2 Using Physical Objects

Materials: A variety of balls—baseballs, basketballs, golf balls, tennis balls, and so on; tape measures

After completing the lesson, have students **work in pairs** to find the volumes of various kinds of balls. Do not tell them how to find the radius of the ball—let them discover a method on their own. After completing the activity, have students compare results.

In 3 and 4, use the drawings below of a sphere and a cylinder with two cones inside it.

3. a. Give the area of the shaded cross section of the sphere. 20π units^2
b. Give the area of the shaded ring between the cylinder and the cone. 20π units^2

4. Give the volume of
a. the cylinder. $432\pi \approx 1357.2$ units^3
b. the two cones. $144\pi \approx 452.4$ units^3
c. the solid region between the cylinder and the two cones. $288\pi \approx 904.8$ units^3
d. the sphere. $288\pi \approx 904.8$ units^3

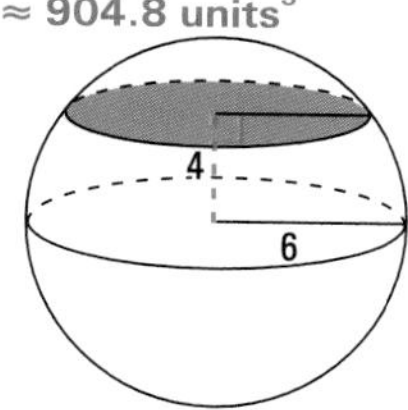

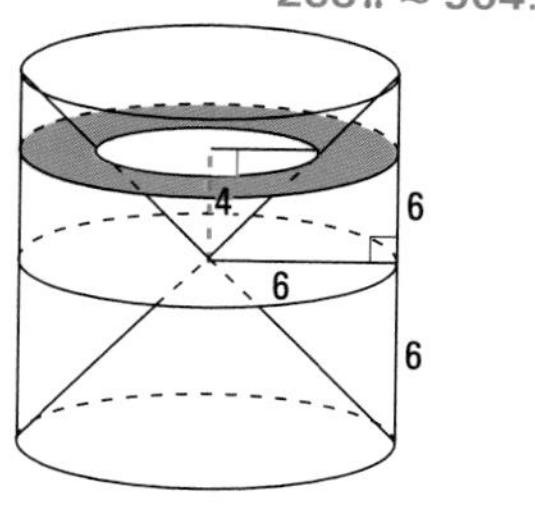

5a) Art is shown in reduced size.

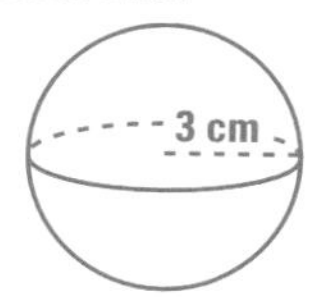

5. a. Draw a sphere with radius 3 cm. See left.
b. Find its volume. $36\pi \approx 113$ cm^3

6. *Multiple choice.* How much material is needed to make a standard bowling ball before the holes are drilled? d
(a) less than 100 cubic inches
(b) between 100 and 200 cubic inches
(c) between 200 and 300 cubic inches
(d) between 300 and 400 cubic inches

Applying the Mathematics

7. The volume of a sphere is 268 cubic meters. Find its radius, to the nearest meter. 4 m

8. An inflated basketball has a diameter of about 9.4 inches. If it is shipped in a cube-shaped box with edge 9.4 inches, what percent of the box is filled by the basketball? $\approx 52\%$

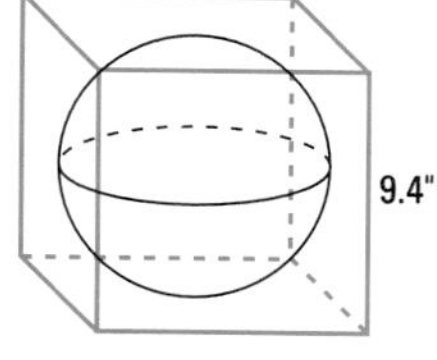

9. A filled ice cream cone has the shape of a **hemisphere** (half a sphere) atop a cone.
a. If the cone has height 10 cm, and the radius of the hemisphere is 3 cm, how much ice cream is there? $48\pi \approx 151$ cm^3
b. What percent of the ice cream have you eaten when only the ice cream in the cone is left? 37.5%

Notes on Questions

Question 3 This question leads students to review the arguments used in the lesson and should be discussed.

Question 8 The answer will surprise many students. Almost half of the cube is outside the basketball. Point out that it is easier to do this problem with diameter *d* than diameter 9.4". Often algebra is easier than arithmetic. Students might check out a sporting-goods store. Do basketballs come in cube-shaped boxes? [In our experience, some do and some don't.]

(Notes on Questions continue on page 608.)

Follow-up for Lesson 10-8

Practice

For more questions on SPUR Objectives, use **Lesson Master 10-8A** (shown on page 605) or **Lesson Master 10-8B** (shown on pages 606–607).

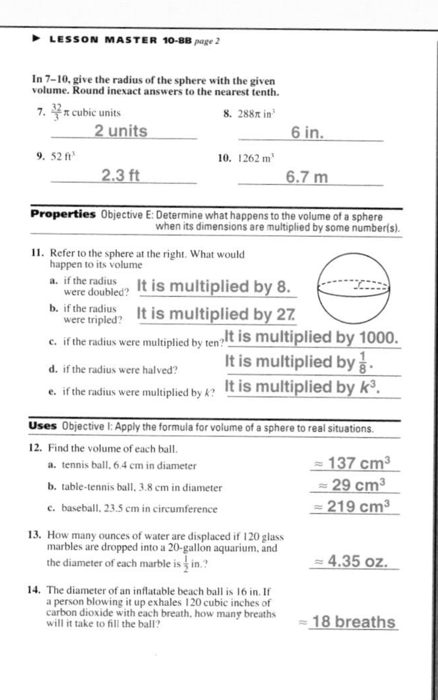

LESSON MASTER 10-8B *page 2*

In 7–10, give the radius of the sphere with the given volume. Round inexact answers to the nearest tenth.

7. $\frac{32}{3}\pi$ cubic units 2 units
8. 288π in^3 6 in.
9. 52 ft^3 2.3 ft
10. 1262 m^3 6.7 m

Properties Objective E: Determine what happens to the volume of a sphere when its dimensions are multiplied by some number(s).

11. Refer to the sphere at the right. What would happen to its volume
a. if the radius were doubled? It is multiplied by 8.
b. if the radius were tripled? It is multiplied by 27.
c. if the radius were multiplied by ten? It is multiplied by 1000.
d. if the radius were halved? It is multiplied by $\frac{1}{8}$.
e. if the radius were multiplied by k? It is multiplied by k^3.

Uses Objective I: Apply the formula for volume of a sphere to real situations.

12. Find the volume of each ball.
a. tennis ball, 6.4 cm in diameter ≈ 137 cm^3
b. table-tennis ball, 3.8 cm in diameter ≈ 29 cm^3
c. baseball, 23.5 cm in circumference ≈ 219 cm^3

13. How many ounces of water are displaced if 120 glass marbles are dropped into a 20-gallon aquarium, and the diameter of each marble is $\frac{1}{2}$ in.? ≈ 4.35 oz.

14. The diameter of an inflatable beach ball is 16 in. If a person blowing it up exhales 120 cubic inches of carbon dioxide with each breath, how many breaths will it take to fill the ball? ≈ 18 breaths

Adapting to Individual Needs

English Language Development
Materials: Globe

To help students with limited English proficiency understand the word *hemisphere* in **Question 9,** identify the northern and southern hemispheres on a globe. Explain that each hemisphere is half of the globe. Ask students if any of them have lived in the southern hemisphere.

Assessment

Written Communication Have students consider at least one spherical object with which they are familiar, for example, a basketball. Then have them do necessary research to determine the radius of the object and then determine the volume. [Students provide one example of a spherical object and then correctly determine the volume.]

Extension

Give students the picture below. Have them find the volume of the "rocket." [$V \approx 2225.29$ m^3]

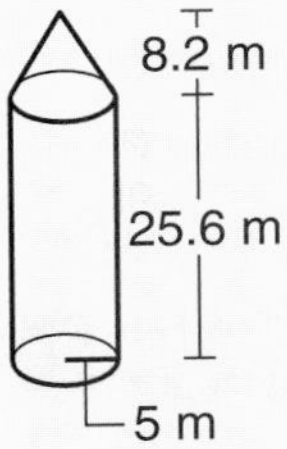

Projects Update Project 3, *Prismoids,* and Project 5, *Domes,* on pages 613–614, relate to the content of this lesson.

Notes on Questions

Question 10 Activity 1 in *Optional Activities* on page 605 relates to this question.

Question 11 The simplicity of the answer suggests that a formula for the volume would be easier to remember in terms of the diameter than in terms of the radius. But it is tradition to learn the formula with radius.

Question 19 Error Alert The answer 4.3 probably indicates that students simplified $\sqrt[3]{85} - \sqrt[3]{5}$ incorrectly to $\sqrt[3]{80}$.

Questions 22–23 These questions involve two multiplications which are found in Lesson 10-9. They should be discussed as a lead-in to the discussion of that lesson.

Question 24 History Connection We encourage you to ask students to learn about Archimedes, a legend in his own day, considered by some historians of mathematics to have been the greatest mathematician of ancient times.

10. A spherical water tank with diameter 16 meters supplies water to a small town. The town uses about 500 cubic meters of water per day. How long would a full tank last if
- **a.** 300 cubic meters were replaced each day? 10.7, or about 11 days
- **b.** due to drought conditions no water were replaced? 4.3, or about 4 days

11. Derive a formula for the volume of a sphere with diameter d. $V = \frac{\pi}{6}d^3$ units^3

Review

In 12 and 13, find the volume of the solid. *(Lessons 10-3, 10-7)*

12.

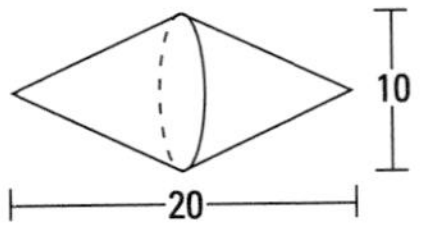

union of two right cones with same base

$\frac{500}{3}\pi \approx 524$ units^3

13.

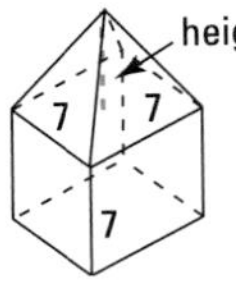

height = 6.5 regular pyramid atop cube

≈ 449 units^3

In 14 and 15, choose from the following: boxes, cones, cylinders, prisms, pyramids, spheres. *(Lesson 10-6)*

14. In which figure does $V = Bh$? boxes, cylinders, prisms

15. In which figures does L.A. $= \frac{1}{2}\ell p$? cones, pyramids

16. *True or false.* If two prisms have congruent bases and equal heights, and one of the solids is oblique and one is right, then
- **a.** the solids have the same volume. True
- **b.** the solids have the same surface area. *(Lesson 10-5)* False

17. Perform the multiplication: $(x + 3)(2y)(z + 4)$. *(Lesson 10-4)* $2xyz + 8xy + 6yz + 24y$

18. All the dimensions of a box are tripled.
- **a.** What happens to its surface area? It is multiplied by 9.
- **b.** What happens to its volume? *(Lesson 10-4)* It is multiplied by 27.

19. Calculate $\sqrt[3]{85} - \sqrt[3]{5}$ to the nearest tenth. *(Lesson 10-3)* 2.7

20. What is the volume of a 14-oz glass of water, to the nearest cubic inch? *(Lesson 10-3)* 25 cubic inches

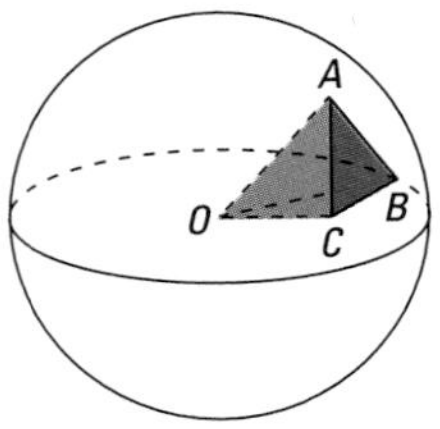

21. On the sphere shown at the left, points A, B, and C have been chosen so that $\triangle ABC$ is equilateral. Prove that m$\angle OAB$ = m$\angle OCB$. *(Lessons 6-2, 7-3, 9-4, 9-5)* See margin.

In 22 and 23, multiply. *(Previous course)*

22. $\frac{3}{r} \cdot \frac{1}{3} \cdot r \cdot x$ x

23. $\frac{3}{r} \cdot \frac{4}{3}\pi r^3$ $4\pi r^2$

Exploration

24. Archimedes was an extraordinary scientist as well as a mathematician. Look in an encyclopedia or other reference and identify two scientific discoveries made by Archimedes. See left.

24) Sample: Archimedes invented a screw (now called the Archimedean screw) for irrigating fields. He found formulas for the area of a segment of a parabola, and for the volumes of segments of paraboloids, hyperboloids, and spheroids.

Additional Answers

21.

Conclusions	Justifications
1. $AB = CB$	def. of equilateral △
2. $OB = OB$	Reflexive Prop. of Equality
3. $OA = OC$	def. of sphere
4. $\triangle OBC \cong \triangle OBA$	SSS Congruence Theorem
5. m$\angle OCB$ = m$\angle OAB$	CPCF Theorem

Setting Up Lesson 10-9

Discuss **Questions 22–23** in this lesson. These simplifications are used in Lesson 10-9.

Materials You will want to have objects that can be measured including spheres, cones, cylinders, pyramids, and rectangular prisms; rulers and tape measures for Activity 2 in *Optional Activities.* You will need a beach ball for Activity 3 in *Optional Activities.*

LESSON

10-9

The Surface Area of a Sphere

A sphere of action. *A geodesic dome is a spherical shape supported by a lightweight frame of triangles. Shown here is B.C. Stadium in Vancouver.*

Shown below are a sphere and its net made out of gores. The surface area of the sphere is equal to the area of its net. But there is no easy way to compute the area of this net. Another strategy is needed.

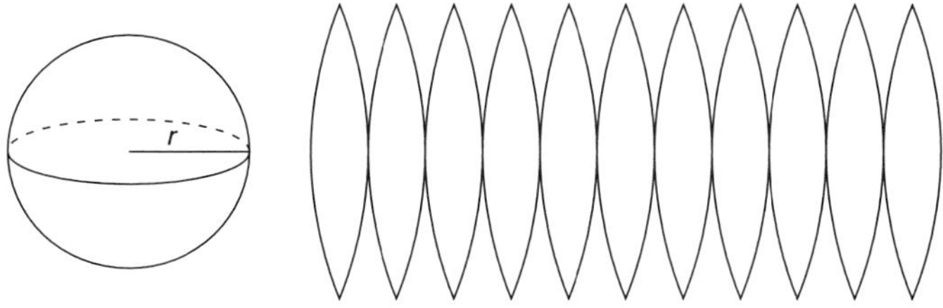

Breaking a Sphere into Pyramids

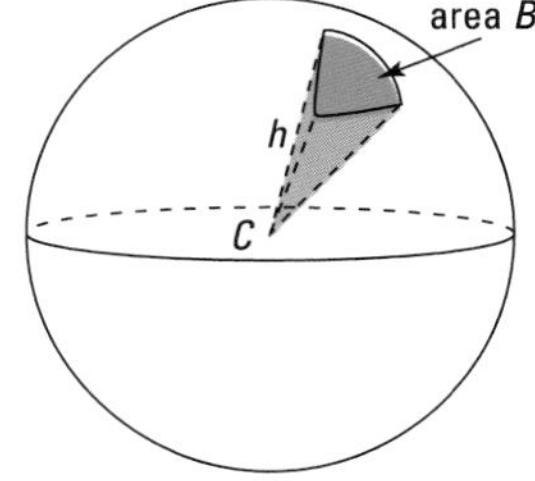

Surprisingly, we derive the surface area formula from the volume formula. The idea is to consider a solid sphere as being made up of "almost pyramids" with vertices at the center of the sphere. One such "pyramid," with height h and base area B, is drawn in the sphere at the right. The solid is not exactly a pyramid because its base is not exactly a polygon. Even so, when the "almost pyramid" is small, its volume is close to that of a pyramid, namely $\frac{1}{3}Bh$. Since h equals r, the radius of the sphere, each "almost pyramid" has volume $\frac{1}{3}Br$.

Lesson 10-9

Objectives

D Calculate the surface area of a sphere from appropriate lengths, and vice versa.

E Determine what happens to the surface area of a sphere when its dimensions are multiplied by some number(s).

H Apply the formula for the surface area of a sphere to real situations.

Resources

From the ***Teacher's Resource File***

- Lesson Master 10-9A or 10-9B
- Answer Master 10-9
- Teaching Aids 133: Warm-up

Additional Resources

- Visual for Teaching Aid 133
- Spheres, cones, cylinders, pyramids, and rectangular prisms; rulers, tape measures
- Beach ball

Teaching Lesson 10-9

Warm-up

Explain why it is difficult to wrap a basketball with paper. **Sample: the surface is not flat.**

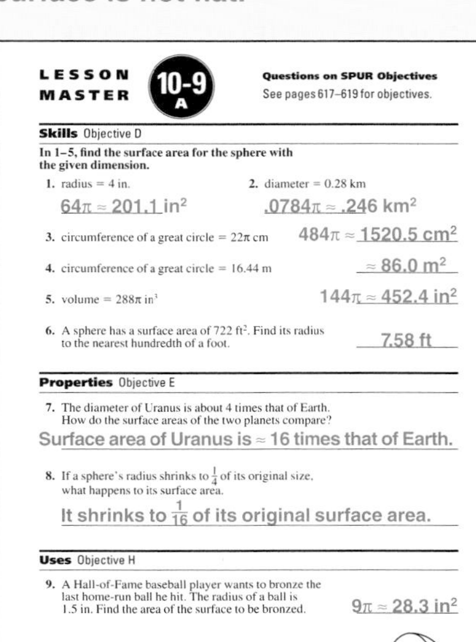

LESSON MASTER 10-9 A — **Questions on SPUR Objectives** See pages 617–619 for objectives.

Skills Objective D

In 1–5, find the surface area for the sphere with the given dimension.

1. radius = 4 in. — $64\pi \approx 201.1$ in^2
2. diameter = 0.28 km — $.0784\pi \approx .246$ km^2
3. circumference of a great circle = 22π cm — $484\pi \approx 1520.5$ cm^2
4. circumference of a great circle = 16.44 m — ≈ 86.0 m^2
5. volume = 288π in^3 — $144\pi \approx 452.4$ in^2
6. A sphere has a surface area of 722 ft^2. Find its radius to the nearest hundredth of a foot. — 7.58 ft

Properties Objective E

7. The diameter of Uranus is about 4 times that of Earth. How do the surface areas of the two planets compare?
   Surface area of Uranus is $\approx$ 16 times that of Earth.
8. If a sphere's radius shrinks to $\frac{1}{4}$ of its original size, what happens to its surface area.
   It shrinks to $\frac{1}{16}$ of its original surface area.

Uses Objective H

9. A Hall-of-Fame baseball player wants to bronze the last home-run ball he hit. The radius of a ball is 1.5 in. Find the area of the surface to be bronzed. — $9\pi \approx 28.3$ in^2
10. A concert shell, in the shape of a quarter of a sphere with a radius of 80 feet, is to be painted. If one gallon of paint covers 400 square feet, how much paint is needed to cover the outside of the shell? — $16\pi \approx 51$ gal.
11. The planet Mercury has a radius of about 2400 km. If a surveying satellite can take a picture which covers an area of 30,000 km^2, what is the least number of pictures that will need to be taken to completely survey the surface? — 2413 pictures

Lesson 10-9 Overview

Broad Goals This brief lesson contains the derivation of a formula for the surface area of a sphere from the formula for the volume.

Perspective To find the area of a circle, we split it into sectors ("almost triangles") and added their areas (Lesson 8-8). Analogously, to derive a formula for the volume of a sphere, we begin by splitting it into "almost pyramids" and add their volumes. This gives a formula for the volume in terms of the sum of the bases of these "almost pyramids." Since the sum of the bases of the "almost pyramids" is the surface area of the sphere, the surface area of the sphere can now be found.

Some students may think there is a base "at the bottom" of the sphere. Point out that the entire surface of a sphere can be thought of as its lateral area, so the total surface area and lateral area are the same.

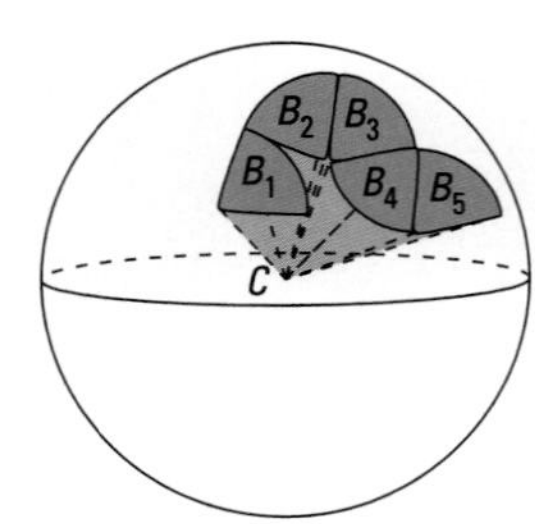

Now break up the entire sphere into "almost pyramids" with bases of areas B_1, B_2, B_3, and so on. The sum of all the B's is the surface area of the sphere.

The volume V of the sphere is the sum of the volumes of all the "almost pyramids" with base area B_1, B_2, B_3, . . .

$$\begin{aligned} V &= \tfrac{1}{3}B_1 r + \tfrac{1}{3}B_2 r + \tfrac{1}{3}B_3 r + \tfrac{1}{3}B_4 r + \ldots \\ &= \tfrac{1}{3}r(B_1 + B_2 + B_3 + B_4 + \ldots) \\ &= \tfrac{1}{3} \cdot r \cdot \text{S.A.} \end{aligned}$$

Finding the Formula

Now substitute $\frac{4}{3}\pi r^3$ for the volume V.

$$\tfrac{4}{3}\pi r^3 = \tfrac{1}{3} r \cdot \text{S.A.}$$

To solve for the surface area, multiply both sides by 3, then divide by r.

$$4\pi r^3 = r \cdot \text{S.A.}$$

Thus, $$4\pi r^2 = \text{S.A.}$$

Sphere Surface Area Formula
The total surface area S.A. of a sphere with radius r is $4\pi r^2$.

$$\text{S.A.} = 4\pi r^2$$

This formula indicates that the surface area of a sphere is equal to 4 times the area of a great circle of the sphere.

Example

Find the surface area of a beach ball with radius 20 cm.

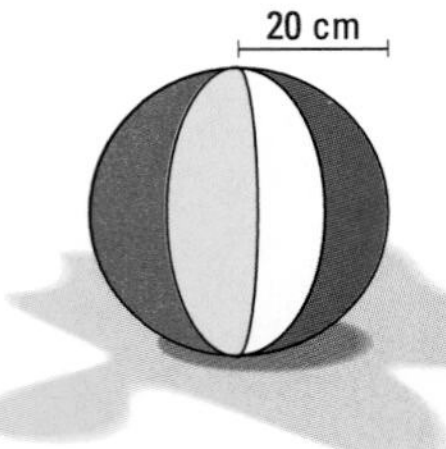

Solution

S.A. = $4\pi r^2 = 4 \cdot \pi \cdot 20^2 = 1600\pi$ exactly, or approximately 5027 square centimeters.

In the Example, the surface area measures how much plastic is needed to make the beach ball. To determine how much air is inside the inflated beach ball, volume is needed. The volume of the beach ball above is $\frac{4}{3}\pi r^3 = \frac{4}{3}\pi(20^3) \approx 33{,}500 \text{ cm}^3$.

Notes on Reading

The proof in this lesson is easier than those of the previous two lessons, but it still may be difficult for students to follow. Point out that there is no 2-dimensional surface for a sphere, which is one reason why its surface area formula is derived from its volume formula.

The derivation of the formula for the surface area of a sphere seems to come from nowhere, but its general features can be explained. Since at this point we do not know much about the sphere except the volume, we use that. It is natural to split up the sphere into other figures we have discussed, and pyramids are more appropriate than prisms.

You might want to use Activity 3 in *Optional Activities* on page 611, when discussing the **Example.**

In developing the formula for the surface area of a sphere, we use the concept of a limit implicitly. Students need to imagine the number of pyramids as getting very great, while the sphere itself does not change. Thus, each pyramid gets smaller. As each pyramid gets smaller, its base becomes flatter and its volume is better approximated by the formula for the volume of a pyramid.

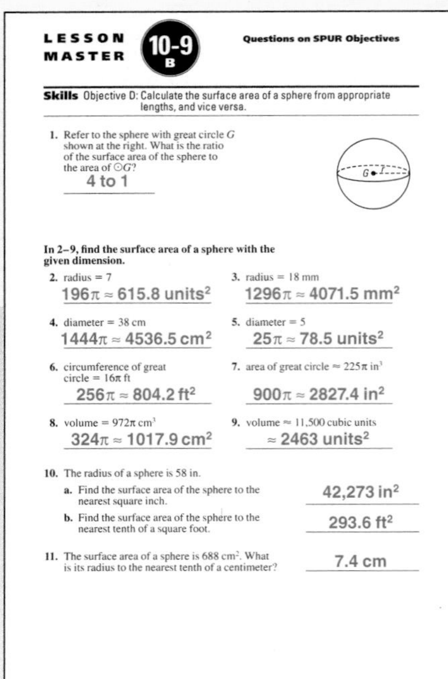
LESSON MASTER 10-9 B Questions on SPUR Objectives

Skills Objective D: Calculate the surface area of a sphere from appropriate lengths, and vice versa.

1. Refer to the sphere with great circle G shown at the right. What is the ratio of the surface area of the sphere to the area of $\odot G$? 4 to 1

In 2–9, find the surface area of a sphere with the given dimension.

2. radius = 7 — $196\pi \approx 615.8$ units²
3. radius = 18 mm — $1296\pi \approx 4071.5$ mm²
4. diameter = 38 cm — $1444\pi \approx 4536.5$ cm²
5. diameter = 5 — $25\pi \approx 78.5$ units²
6. circumference of great circle = 16π ft — $256\pi \approx 804.2$ ft²
7. area of great circle ≈ 225π in³ — $900\pi \approx 2827.4$ in²
8. volume = 972π cm³ — $324\pi \approx 1017.9$ cm²
9. volume ≈ 11,500 cubic units — ≈ 2463 units²
10. The radius of a sphere is 58 in.
    a. Find the surface area of the sphere to the nearest square inch. 42,273 in²
    b. Find the surface area of the sphere to the nearest tenth of a square foot. 293.6 ft²
11. The surface area of a sphere is 688 cm². What is its radius to the nearest tenth of a centimeter? 7.4 cm

Optional Activities

Activity 1
Have students draw the net for a sphere on another sheet of paper (either by tracing or drawing it on an overhead and enlarging it). Then have them put their nets together to convince themselves that they actually get a sphere. The spheres could then be decorated and hung in the room.

Activity 2 Using Physical Models
Materials: Objects that can be measured, including spheres, cones, cylinders, pyramids, and rectangular prisms; rulers, tape measures

After completing this lesson, you might continue the measuring activities suggested in previous lessons, but now you can include spheres.

QUESTIONS

Covering the Reading

1) There is no easy way to compute the area of its net, which is not 2-dimensional.

1. Why is it hard to calculate the surface area of a sphere from its net? See left.

2. A sphere can be imagined as the union of __?__, whose base areas add to the __?__ of the sphere. "almost pyramids," surface area

3. State the Sphere Surface Area Formula. The surface area S.A. of a sphere with radius r is $4\pi r^2$.

4. The surface area of a sphere is __?__ times the area of one of its great circles. 4

In 5 and 6, a sphere is described. **a.** Find its exact surface area. **b.** Approximate its surface area to the nearest integer.

5. a sphere with radius 6
a) 144π units^2 b) 452 units^2

6. a sphere with diameter 100″
a) $10{,}000\pi$ in^2 b) 31,416 in^2

Applying the Mathematics

7. The area of the United States is about 3,600,000 square miles. What percent is this of the area of Earth, which is approximately a sphere with radius 3960 miles? ≈ 1.83%

8. Derive a formula for the surface area of a sphere with diameter d.
S.A. $= d^2\pi$

9. B.C. Stadium in Vancouver, which was built as a pavilion at the 1986 Expo, has a geodesic dome with a diameter of about 215 meters. The geodesic dome can be approximated by a sphere. Estimate the cost of covering the dome if the gold foil that covered it cost \$3.20 per square meter.
≈ \$464,704

10a) The moon has about $\frac{1}{16}$ the surface area of Earth.
b) The moon has about $\frac{1}{64}$ the volume of Earth.
c) $\frac{1}{16} = \left(\frac{1}{4}\right)^2$, $\frac{1}{64} = \left(\frac{1}{4}\right)^3$

10. The moon has a diameter about $\frac{1}{4}$ that of Earth. See left.
a. How do their total surface areas compare?
b. How do their volumes compare?
c. How do your answers for parts **a** and **b** relate to the number $\frac{1}{4}$?

11. A sphere has volume 36π cubic meters. What is its surface area?
$36\pi \approx 113$ m^2

12. A sphere of radius r fits exactly into a cylinder, touching the cylinder at the top, bottom, and sides. How does the total surface area of the sphere compare to the lateral surface area of the cylinder?
They are the same; both are $4\pi r^2$.

13. Two figure-8 pieces of cowhide are used to cover a baseball. The diameter of the baseball is about 2.9 inches.

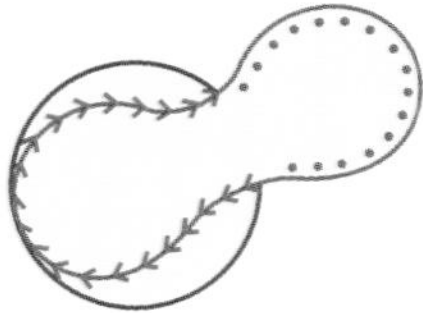

a. Find its surface area, to the nearest square inch.
b. What must be the area of one cover?
a) 26 square inches b) ≈ 13 square inches

Additional Examples

Round beads 1 cm in diameter are to be gilded with a thin layer of gold. If one container of gold will cover 100 square cm of surface with the desired thickness, how many beads can be covered with one container of gold? About 32 beads

Notes on Questions

Question 7 Geography Connection Some students may be surprised at how little of the earth is covered by the United States. Since the earth is about $\frac{2}{3}$ water, you could ask how much of the land area is covered by the United States. **Questions 23–24** are related to this question.

Question 8 Formulas for the sphere are stated more simply in terms of the diameter, but it is traditional to use the radius. The justification for using the radius is that formulas for the circle use the radius and thereby avoid fractions. However, in real-world applications, spheres, such as ball bearings, are often described by their diameters.

Question 12 Extend this question to compare a cylinder, cone, and sphere all with the same height and base thinking of a great-circle cross section as the "base" of the sphere. If the height is 2r, the volume of the cylinder is $2\pi r^2$, the volume of the cone is $\frac{2}{3}\pi r^3$, and the volume of the sphere is $\frac{4}{3}\pi r^3$.

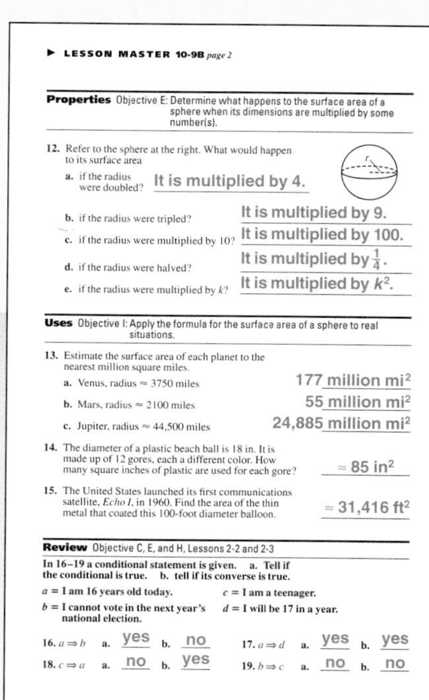

▸ **LESSON MASTER 10-9B** *page 2*

Properties Objective E: Determine what happens to the surface area of a sphere when its dimensions are multiplied by some number(s).

12. Refer to the sphere at the right. What would happen to its surface area
a. if the radius were doubled? It is multiplied by 4.
b. if the radius were tripled? It is multiplied by 9.
c. if the radius were multiplied by 10? It is multiplied by 100.
d. if the radius were halved? It is multiplied by $\frac{1}{4}$.
e. if the radius were multiplied by k? It is multiplied by k^2.

Uses Objective I: Apply the formula for the surface area of a sphere to real situations.

13. Estimate the surface area of each planet to the nearest million square miles.
a. Venus, radius ≈ 3750 miles 177 million mi^2
b. Mars, radius ≈ 2100 miles 55 million mi^2
c. Jupiter, radius ≈ 44,500 miles 24,885 million mi^2

14. The diameter of a plastic beach ball is 18 in. It is made up of 12 gores, each a different color. How many square inches of plastic are used for each gore? ≈ 85 in^2

15. The United States launched its first communications satellite, *Echo I*, in 1960. Find the area of the thin metal that coated this 100-foot diameter balloon. ≈ 31,416 ft^2

Review Objective C, E, and H, Lessons 2-2 and 2-3

In 16–19 a conditional statement is given. a. Tell if the conditional is true. b. tell if its converse is true.

a = **I am 16 years old today.** c = **I am a teenager.**
b = **I cannot vote in the next year's national election.** d = **I will be 17 in a year.**

16. $a \Rightarrow b$ a. yes b. no
17. $a \Rightarrow d$ a. yes b. yes
18. $c \Rightarrow a$ a. no b. yes
19. $b \Rightarrow c$ a. no b. no

Optional Activities

Activity 3 Using Physical Objects
Materials: Beach ball

The beach ball in the **Example** can make a good physical aid to demonstrate the formula for the surface area of a sphere. Deflate a beach ball as much as possible until it is apparently two discs (stuck together). If the ball is cut apart and laid out flat onto a disc of the same diameter as the original sphere, the pieces should fit into the circle four times. This method can show only an approximation, but it is easy to believe that the sphere has a surface area which is equal to four times the area of a great circle of the sphere. An alternate method is cut out four discs with the same diameter as the beach ball, cut them apart, cover the beach ball with the pieces (like a puzzle), and show that it takes four discs to cover the sphere.

Notes on Questions

Question 17 Even if for no other reason than its applicability, this question should be discussed.

Question 21 Consumer Connection Immigrants from Switzerland started making cheese in the U.S. in the 1850s. Today, swiss cheese is second only to cheddar in American cheese consumption.

Questions 23–24 Students' percentages in these two questions may be slightly different if they used different resources as references.

Follow-up for Lesson 10-9

Practice

For more questions on SPUR Objectives, use **Lesson Master 10-9A** (shown on page 609) or **Lesson Master 10-9B** (shown on pages 610–611).

Assessment

Written Communication Have students write a paragraph discussing how they can remember which formulas to use for volume and surface area of a sphere. Have them refer to memory devices that might help them. [Answers will vary. Students should recognize that the surface area formula involves an exponent of 2, and area is expressed in square units. Analogously, the volume formula involves an exponent of 3, and volume is expressed in cubic units.]

Extension

Give students this problem: A cone with a height of 5.7 meters and a diameter of 2.1 meters is inscribed in a square prism with a base 2.1 meters on each side and a height of 5.7 meters. What percent of the prism's volume is the cone's volume? [≈ 26 %]

Project Update Project 5, *Domes*, on page 614, relates to the content of this lesson.

16) no base: sphere; one base: pyramid, cone, regular pyramid, right cone; two bases: prism, cylinder, right prism, box

Review

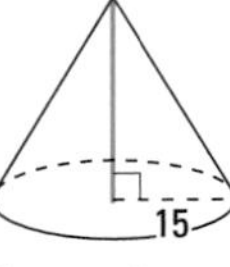

14. Refer to Question 7. Give the volume of Earth, to the nearest million cubic miles. *(Lesson 10-8)* $2.6 \cdot 10^{11}$ miles³

15. A right cone has a base radius of 15 and a volume of 1800π. Find its height. *(Lesson 10-7)* 24 units

16. Name the no-base, one-base, and two-base figures in the chart of 3-dimensional figures you have studied in this chapter. *(Lesson 10-6)* See left.

17. Consider two cylindrical jars of jam. One jar of jam is twice as tall as the other, but only half as wide. Which jar holds more jam? *(Lessons 10-4, 10-5)* The shorter jar holds twice as much jam.

18. You can make the lateral surface of two different cylinders by rolling an 8.5″ by 11″ piece of notebook paper along one or the other of its sides.
  a. What is the lateral area of each cylinder? 93.5 square inches
  b. Which has more volume? *(Lessons 10-1, 10-5)* the one with height of 8.5″

19. One cube has edges of length 13. A second cube has 125 times the volume of the first cube. To the nearest tenth, what is the length of an edge of the second cube? *(Lesson 10-4)* 65.0 units

A, B, z, a, a, D, x, a, C, y

20. Use the box at the left.
  a. Write an expression for Area($ABCD$). $(x + a)(z + a)$
  b. Write an expression for the volume of the box. $(x + a)(y + a)(z + a)$
  c. Expand the expression in part **b.** *(Lessons 8-5, 10-4)* $xyz + axy + axz + ayz + a^2x + a^2y + a^2z + a^3$

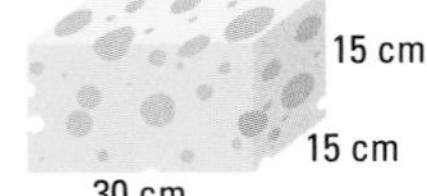

21. Cheese is aged in large blocks. The block at the right is to be removed from the aging cellar, wrapped in foil, and shipped. *(Lesson 10-1)*
  a. At a minimum, with no overlap, how many square centimeters of foil are needed? 2250 cm²
  b. A distributor cuts the block up into 15 cm × 7.5 cm × 3 cm slabs to sell to grocery stores. At a minimum, how much foil is needed to wrap all the slabs from the block? 7200 cm²

22. Write the statement *A trapezoid is a quadrilateral that has at least two parallel sides* as a conditional. *(Lesson 2-2)* If a quadrilateral is a trapezoid, then it has at least two parallel sides.

Exploration

In 23 and 24, use an almanac, atlas, dictionary, or other reference book.

23. What three countries each cover more of the surface of Earth than the United States covers? What percent (to the nearest tenth) of the surface does each cover? Canada (≈ 2.0%), China (≈ 1.9%), Russia (≈ 3.4%)

24. What percent (to the nearest tenth) of the surface of Earth is covered by **a.** the Pacific Ocean? **b.** the Atlantic Ocean? **c.** all the oceans together? a) 32.7% b) 17.0% c) 66.8%

612

Adapting to Individual Needs

Challenge

Suppose that a sphere is circumscribed by a cylinder. Ask students to prove the following results, which are ascribed to Archimedes.

1. The volume of the sphere is $\frac{2}{3}$ that of the circumscribed cylinder.
2. The surface area of the sphere is $\frac{2}{3}$ that of the total area of the circumscribed cylinder.

[Let r be the radius of the sphere, which is also the radius of the base of the cylinder. The height of the cylinder is $2r$.

1. $V(\text{cylinder}) = \pi r^2h = \pi r^2(2r) = 2\pi r^3$
   $V(\text{sphere}) = \frac{4}{3}\pi r^3 = \frac{2}{3}V(\text{cylinder})$
2. $\text{S.A. (cylinder)} = 2\pi r^2 + 2\pi rh = 2\pi r^2 + 2\pi r(2r) = 2\pi r^2 + 4\pi r^2 = 6\pi r^2$
   $\text{S.A. (sphere)} = 4\pi r^2 = \frac{2}{3}\text{S.A. (cylinder)}$

Notice that the lateral area of the cylinder equals the surface area of the sphere.]

A project presents an opportunity for you to extend your knowledge of a topic related to the material of this chapter. You should allow more time for a project than you do for typical homework questions.

PROJECTS 10 CHAPTER TEN

1 Making Cones

In Question 24 of Lesson 10-2 you were asked to construct cones from sectors of circular disks of the same radius. Do this again and attempt to answer the question: Which central angle yields the cone with the most volume?

2 Sizes of Pyramids of Ancient Cultures

Choose one of the following:

a. the pyramids at Giza, Egypt
b. the pyramids near Mexico City
c. the step pyramids of ancient Babylon.

Look in an encyclopedia or other book for the dimensions of at least two pyramids from the location you have chosen. Draw an accurate picture of them. Calculate the lateral surface area and the volumes of these pyramids.

3 Prismoids

A prismoid (or prismatoid) is a polyhedron that has two parallel bases (that need not be congruent) and whose lateral faces are either quadrilaterals or triangles. The volume of a prismoid is given by the formula $V = \frac{1}{6}h(B_1 + 4B_m + B_2)$, where h is the height, B_1 and B_2 are the areas of the bases, and B_m is the area of a plane section midway between and parallel to the bases. Show that this formula works

a. for any prism or cylinder.
b. for any pyramid or cone (think of one base as being a point and use the fact that sides of the plane section are half the length of sides of the bases.).
c. for any sphere (think of both bases as being points).

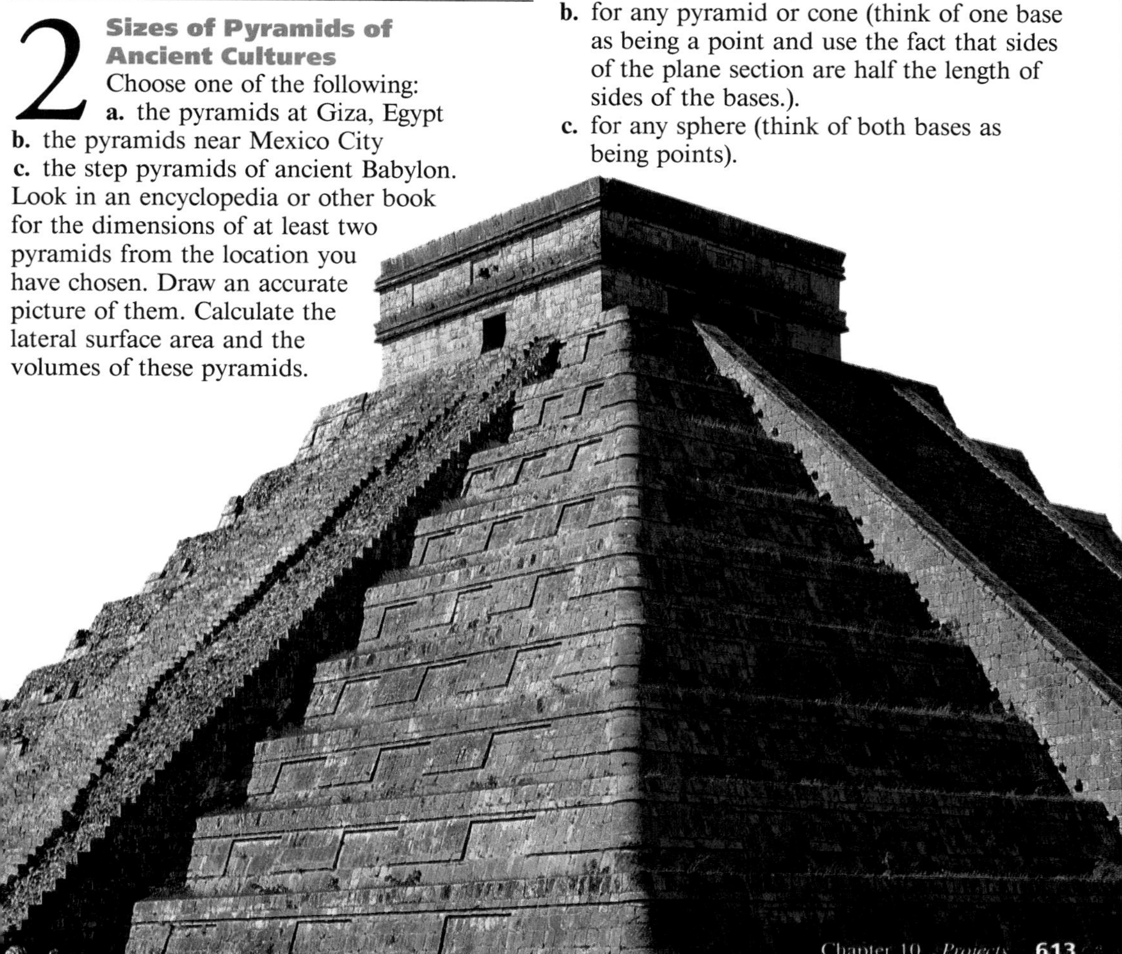

Chapter 10 Projects

The projects relate chiefly to the content of the lessons of this chapter as follows:

Project	Lesson(s)
1	10-2, 10-6, 10-7
2	10-2, 10-7
3	10-5, 10-7, 10-8
4	10-1, 10-3, 10-4, 10-5
5	10-8, 10-9
6	10-1, 10-4, 10-5

1 Making Cones Some students will calculate the volume for the three cones in **Question 24** on page 575 and conclude that the cone with the greatest volume occurs when the angle removed measures 60 degrees. Other students may carry the project further and determine the volume is maximum at about 66 degrees.

2 Sizes of Pyramids of Ancient Cultures The calculations in the *Possible Responses* assume smooth faces for the pyramids.

3 Prismoids This is a straightforward project. It will help students appreciate the convenience of using a general result rather than a host of individual formulas. Student responses should include appropriate diagrams.

Possible responses

1. Some students will use a spreadsheet like the one shown below. The largest volume occurs when the central angle removed is 60°.

central angle	circumference of base	radius of base	area of base	height of cone	volume of cone
45	21.9911	3.5000	38.4845	1.9365	24.8416
60	20.9333	3.3333	34.8889	2.2111	25.7141
120	16.7552	2.6667	22.3402	2.9814	22.2019

Some students may carry the project further and determine which central angle maximizes the volume. The spreadsheet shows calculations for angles from 57° to 69°. The maximum volume is 25.7832 cubic units which occurs when the central angle removed is about 66°.

(Responses continue on page 614.)

4 What Is Your Surface Area and Volume? For **part a,** students can use tape to mark the original and final water levels, then use standard containers to see how many quarts of water must be added to raise the water from the original to the final level. Paper towels (slightly moistened) might be a good idea for **part b.** Since the areas are nearly equal for all the sheets, the total area should be relatively easy to estimate.

5 Domes Textbook and reference works on architecture are good sources for this project.

6 Prisms and Cylinders in Packaging Students are apt to think of the convenience aspect of container design only from the point of view of the end user. Remind them that manufacturing, shipping, and unloading at the point of sale are also important considerations.

(continued)

5 Domes

Temples and other buildings are sometimes topped off with domes. Write an essay about at least two famous domes, including at least the following information:

a. their names and locations,
b. their shapes, dimensions, surface areas, and volumes, and
c. how and why they were built.

4 What Is Your Surface Area and Volume?

Do these three activities to estimate your surface area and volume.

a. Partially fill a bathtub with water. Then estimate your volume as accurately as you can by immersing yourself in the bathwater, determining the new level of the bathwater, and estimating how much volume of the bathtub you have occupied.
b. Estimate your surface area by covering all parts of your body with rectangular pieces of paper or cloth and adding up the areas.
c. Compare the two estimates in parts **a** and **b** with the surface area and volume of a cylinder that is your height and whose circumference is equal to the circumference of your waist. Do the surface area and volume of this cylinder provide a good approximation to your surface area and volume? Why or why not?

6 Prisms and Cylinders in Packaging

Imagine that you are asked to design containers for a new line of juices. You are to create a Family Size to hold 1200 mL in the shape of a cylinder and a Solo Size to hold 270 mL in the shape of a box. Design and construct two models for each of these sizes. Each model should have the required volume but different dimensions. Finally, write about the pros and cons of each model if used as a juice container.

Additional responses, page 613

central angle	lateral of area	circumference of base	radius of base	area of base	height of cone	volume of cone
56	42.4249	21.2124	3.3778	35.8255	2.1426	25.5862
57	42.2853	21.1427	3.3667	35.5902	2.1600	25.6248
58	42.1458	21.0729	3.3556	35.3556	2.1772	25.6589
59	42.0062	21.0031	3.3444	35.1219	2.1942	25.6886
60	41.8667	20.9333	3.3333	34.8889	2.2111	25.7141
61	41.7271	20.8636	3.3222	34.6557	2.2277	25.7354
62	41.5876	20.7938	3.3111	34.4253	2.2442	25.7527

SUMMARY

The lateral and total surface areas of a 3-dimensional figure are measures of its boundary, which is 2-dimensional. So these areas are given in square units. Volume is a measure of the space enclosed by a 3-dimensional figure, and is given in cubic units. Areas of rectangles can picture the product of two polynomials. Volumes of boxes can picture the product of three polynomials.

From the formula $V = \ell wh$ for the volume of a box, formulas for the volumes of other figures are developed. Pyramids and cones have $\frac{1}{3}$ the volume of the prism or cylinder with congruent bases and the same height. The volume of a sphere has the same volume as a cylinder of the same height and radius, minus two cones.

Eight key formulas to remember are given in the table below. In all cases r represents radius, h represents height, ℓ represents slant height, p represents perimeter, and B represents area of a base. From these eight formulas you can derive other formulas. If you multiply any one dimension of a 3-dimensional figure by a particular number, the volume of the figure is multiplied by that number.

Surface Areas and Volumes of Common 3-Dimensional Figures

	Prisms/Cylinders (two parallel bases)	Pyramids/Cones (one base)	Sphere (no bases)
Lateral Area	L.A. $= ph$	L.A. $= \frac{1}{2}\ell p$	
Surface Area	S.A. $=$ L.A. $+ 2B$	S.A. $=$ L.A. $+ B$	S.A. $= 4\pi r^2$
Volume	$V = Bh$	$V = \frac{1}{3}Bh$	$V = \frac{4}{3}\pi r^3$

VOCABULARY

Below are the most important terms and phrases for this chapter. For the starred (*) terms you should be able to give a definition of the term. For the other terms you should be able to give a general description and specific example of each.

Lesson 10-1
surface area, S.A.
lateral area, L.A.
*Right Prism-Cylinder Lateral Area Formula
*Prism-Cylinder Surface Area Formula

Lesson 10-2
*Pyramid-Cone Surface Area Formula
*Regular Pyramid-Right Cone Lateral Area Formula

Lesson 10-3
unit cube
volume, capacity
Volume Postulate:
*Uniqueness Property
*Box Volume Formula
*Congruence Property
*Additive Property
Cube Volume Formula
*cube root

Lesson 10-5
Volume Postulate:
*Cavalieri's Principle
*Prism-Cylinder Volume Formula

Lesson 10-7
*Pyramid-Cone Volume Formula

Lesson 10-8
*Sphere Volume Formula
hemisphere

Lesson 10-9
*Sphere Surface Area Formula

Additional responses, page 613

central angle	lateral of area	circumference of base	radius of base	area of base	height of cone	volume of cone
63	41.4480	20.7240	3.3000	34.1946	2.2605	25.7660
64	41.3084	20.6542	3.2889	33.9647	2.2767	25.7754
65	41.1689	20.5844	3.2778	33.7356	2.2926	25.7811
66	41.0293	20.5147	3.2667	33.5073	2.3084	25.7832
67	40.8898	20.4449	3.2556	33.2797	2.3241	25.7816
68	40.7502	20.3751	3.2444	33.0530	2.3396	25.7766
69	40.6107	20.3053	3.2333	32.8270	2.3549	25.7681

Summary

The Summary gives an overview of the entire chapter and provides an opportunity for students to consider the material as a whole. Thus, the Summary can be used to help students relate and unify the concepts presented in the chapter.

Vocabulary

Terms, symbols, and properties are listed by lesson to provide a checklist of concepts a student must know. Emphasize to students that they should read the vocabulary list carefully before starting the Progress Self-Test. If students do not understand the meaning of a term, they should refer to the indicated lesson.

2a. Samples: In Giza Egypt: Cheops (or Khufu, or Great Pyramid)—original square base 230 m on each side and 147 m high; $V \approx 2{,}595{,}000$ m^3; L.A. $\approx 86{,}000$ m^2
Khafre, or Chephren—originally about 216 m on each side and 144 m high; $V \approx 2{,}227{,}000$ m^3; L.A. $\approx 77{,}500$ m^2
Mankaure, or Mycerinus—originally about 109 m on each side and 66.4 m high; $V \approx 261{,}500$m^3; L.A. $\approx 18{,}700$ m^2

b. Near Mexico City: Quetzalcóatl at Cholula de Rivadabia—247 m on each side and about 54 m high; $V \approx 1{,}098{,}900$ m^3; L.A. $\approx 66{,}700$ m^2
Teotihuacán—square base 442 m on each side and 66 m high; $V \approx 4{,}298{,}000$ m^3; L.A. $\approx 204{,}000$ m^2

c. Babylon (now Iraq) did not have pyramids, but *ziggurats,* which are like pyramids with slightly curved walls: Etemenanki Ziggurat commonly known as the Tower of Babel—91 m tall and square base 91 m on each side; $V \approx 251{,}000$ m^3; L.A. $\approx 18{,}500$ m^2
Nanna Ziggurat—12 m tall with base 64 m by 46 m; $V \approx 11{,}800$ m^3; L.A. ≈ 3250 m^2

(Responses continue on page 616.)

Progress Self-Test

For the development of mathematical competence, students need feedback and correction, along with the opportunity to practice. The Progress Self-Test provides the opportunity for feedback and correction; the Chapter Review provides additional opportunities and practice. We cannot overemphasize the importance of these end-of-chapter materials. It is at this point that the material "gels" for many students, allowing them to solidify skills and understanding. In general, student performance should be markedly improved after these pages.

Assign the Progress Self-Test as a one-night assignment. Answers to all questions are in the Selected Answers section of the student book. Encourage students to take the Progress Self-Test honestly, grade themselves, and then be prepared to discuss the test in class.

Advise students to pay special attention to those Chapter Review questions (pages 617–619) which correspond to questions missed on the Progress Self-Test.

Additional Answers

7. S.A. ≈ 4536 units^2
$V \approx$ 28731 units^3

12. The volume of the larger box is 343 times that of the smaller one.

13. Jupiter's area is 121 times that of Earth.

14a. Yes

b. They have congruent bases and heights, and both volumes are $64\pi h$ units^3.

15. The volume of the pyramid is one-third the volume of the prism.

18. $V \approx$ 59,734,000 miles^3

PROGRESS SELF-TEST

Directions: Take this test as you would take a test in class. You will need a calculator. Then check your work with the solutions in the Selected Answers section in the back of the book. 7, 12–15, 18) See margin.

1. In the right prism at the right, the bases are right triangles.
   a. Find its lateral area. 1440 units^2
   b. Find its volume. 2880 units^3
2. Find the height of a right cylinder whose base has radius 7″ and whose lateral area is 84π square inches. 6 inches
3. A box has a volume of 400 cm^3, a height of 10 cm, and a width of 5 cm. What is its length? 8 cm 4a) 1040 units^2
4. Refer to the regular square pyramid at the right that has base edges of length 20 and slant height of length 26.

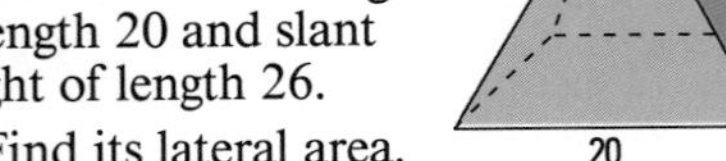

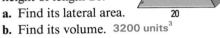

   a. Find its lateral area.
   b. Find its volume. 3200 units^3
5. Find the volume of a right cone with height 15 and base radius 8. $320\pi \approx$ 1005.3 units^3
6. If a pyramid has volume 96 cm^3 and height 18 cm, what is the area of its base? 16 cm^2
7. Give the surface area and volume of a sphere with radius 19 inches.
8. A sphere has a surface area of 100π units^2. What is its exact radius? 5 units
9. Give the cube root of 400 to the nearest whole number. 7
10. A right cone has slant height ℓ and base radius r. Find a formula for its lateral area in terms of ℓ and r. L.A. = $\pi r\ell$
11. A cube has edges of length $9t$.
    a. Find its surface area. $486t^2$ units^2
    b. Find its volume. $729t^3$ units^3
12. Suppose each edge of one box is 7 times the length of the corresponding edge of another box. How do their volumes compare?
13. Jupiter has a diameter about 11 times that of Earth. How do their total surface areas compare?
14. The two figures below have bases in parallel planes and the same height.
    a. Do they have the same volume?
    b. Why or why not?

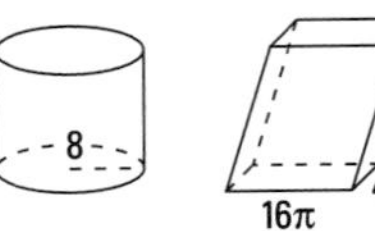

15. If a prism and a pyramid have congruent bases and their heights are equal, how do their volumes compare?
16. How many square meters of fabric do you need to cover a suitcase with dimensions 0.9 m by 0.7 m by 0.2 m? 1.9 m^2
17. How much paper covers the outside of a cone-shaped megaphone whose large end has radius 4″ and whose slant height is 18″? (Ignore the small open end.) $72\pi \approx$ 226 in^2
18. The largest asteroid, Ceres, has a diameter of about 485 miles. If Ceres were spherical in shape, what would be its volume?
19. Find the volume inside of a pipe 20 cm long with an inside radius of 3 cm, as drawn below.

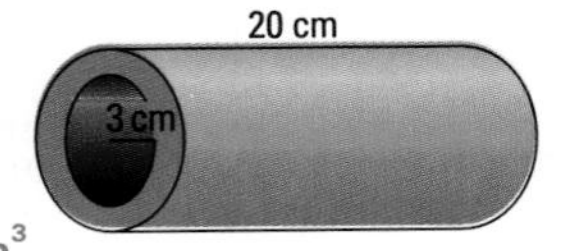

≈ 565 cm^3

20. Multiply $(3x + 1)(2x + 8)$. $6x^2 + 26x + 8$
21. Give two expressions for the volume of the box pictured below. $(y + 2)(x + 1)(z + 6)$; $xyz + yz + 2xz + 2z + 6xy + 6y + 12x + 12$

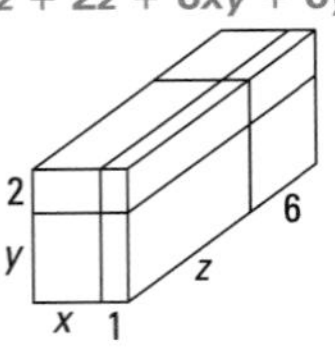

Additional responses, page 613

3a. The volume for a prism or cylinder is $V = Bh$, where B represents the area of the base. In a cylinder, the base is a circle, so $B = \pi r^2$, where r represents the radius of the circle. In a prism or cylinder, the bases must be congruent, so $B_1 = B_2$. From Lesson 9-5, we know that the plane section will be equal to the area of the base ofa prism or cylinder, so $B_m = B_2$. So $B_1 = B_2 = B_m$. Let B = area of B_1. $V = \frac{1}{6}h(B_1 + B_2 + 4B_m) = \frac{1}{6}h(B + B + 4B) = \frac{1}{6}h(6B) = Bh$. So the volume of a prism or cylinder can be found using this formula.

b. The volume of a pyramid or cone is $V = \frac{1}{3}Bh$, where B represents the area of the bottom base. Using this formula, the top base is a point, and has area of zero. Consider the pyramid and the cone at the right. For the pyramid, ℓ_m is parallel to and $\frac{1}{2}$ the length of ℓ_2. The area of the bottom base B_2 is four times the area of middle base B_m, so $.25B_2 = B_m$. Let $B = B_2$.
$V = \frac{1}{6}h(B_1 + B_2 + 4B_m) = \frac{1}{6}h(0 + B + 4(.25B)) = \frac{1}{6}(2B) = \frac{1}{3}Bh$.

CHAPTER REVIEW

Questions on SPUR Objectives

SPUR stands for **S**kills, **P**roperties, **U**ses, and **R**epresentations. The Chapter Review questions are grouped according to the SPUR Objectives for this chapter.

SKILLS DEAL WITH THE PROCEDURES USED TO GET ANSWERS.

Objective A: *Calculate lateral areas, surface areas, and volumes of cylinders and prisms from appropriate lengths, and vice versa.*
(Lessons 10-1, 10-3, 10-5) 1a) $72\pi \approx 226$ units^2

1. Refer to the right cylinder at the right. Find its
   a. lateral area.
   b. surface area. $104\pi \approx 327$ units^2
   c. volume. $144\pi \approx 452$ units^3

2. Refer to the right square prism at the right. Find its
   a. volume. 90 units^3
   b. surface area. 138 units^2

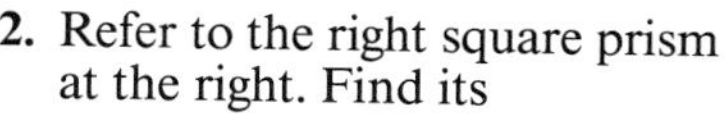

3. The base of the prism at the right is a right triangle with legs of lengths 5 and 12. The distance between the bases of the prism is 24. Find the volume of the prism. 720 units^3

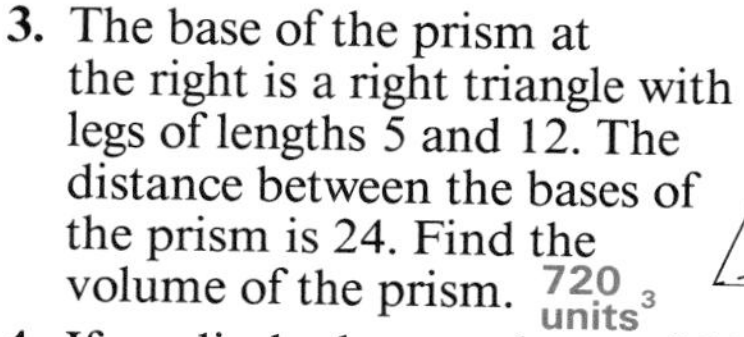

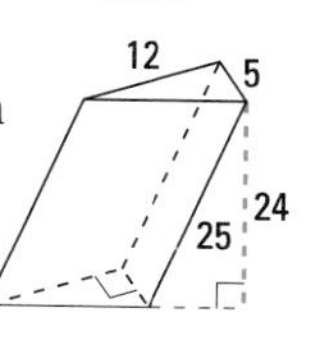

4. If a cylinder has a volume of 30π cubic units and a base with radius 3, what must its height be? ≈ 3.33 units
5. Find the surface area of a cube whose volume is 125 cubic units. 150 units^2
6. Find the volume of a right cylinder whose lateral area is 60π square centimeters and whose base has diameter 12 centimeters.
7. A cube has surface area $54e^2$. Find: **a.** the length of an edge. **b.** its volume.
8. Find the volume of a cylinder with diameter $8p$ and height equal to the radius of its base. $64p^3\pi$ units^3

6) $180\pi \approx 565.5$ cm^3
7a) $3e$ units
b) $27e^3$ units^3
9) S.A. ≈ 155 units^2; $V \approx 128.3$ units^3

Objective B: *Calculate lateral areas, surface areas, and volumes of pyramids and cones from appropriate lengths, and vice versa.*
(Lessons 10-2, 10-7)

9. Find the surface area and volume of the right cone at the right. See below.

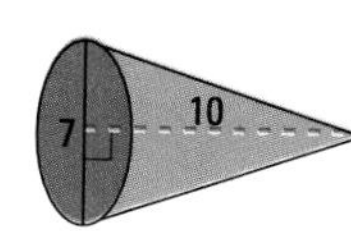

In 10 and 11, refer to the regular square pyramid at the right.

10. Find its volume.
11. Find its 10) 64,000 units^3
    a. slant height. 50 units
    b. lateral area. 8000 units^2
    c. surface area. 14,400 units^2
12. Find the volume of the cone at the right. $18\pi \approx 56.5$ units^3

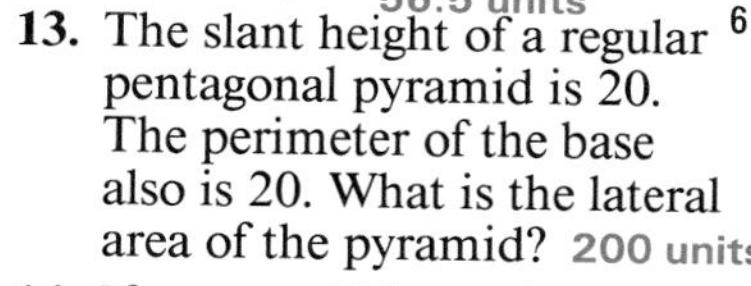

13. The slant height of a regular pentagonal pyramid is 20. The perimeter of the base also is 20. What is the lateral area of the pyramid? 200 units^2

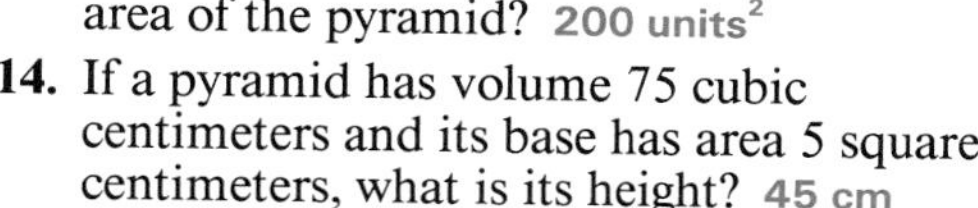

14. If a pyramid has volume 75 cubic centimeters and its base has area 5 square centimeters, what is its height? 45 cm
15. A cone has volume 900 ft^3. Its height is 20 ft. Find the radius of the base. ≈ 6.6 ft
16. Find the volume of pyramid X-$ABCD$ below whose base is a rectangle with one side 11 and diagonal 61 and whose altitude is 20. 4400 units^3

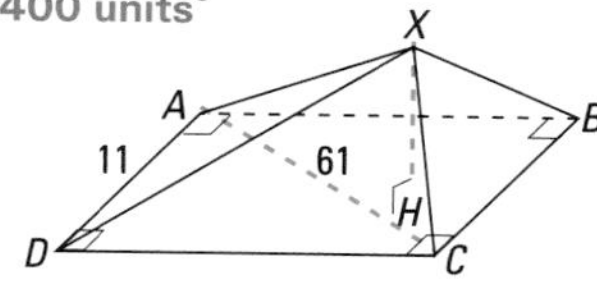

Chapter 10 Review

Resources

From the ***Teacher's Resource File***
- Answer Master for Chapter 10 Review
- Assessment Sourcebook: Chapter 10 Test, Forms A–D Chapter 10 Test, Cumulative Form

Additional Resources
- Quiz and Test Writer

The main objectives for the chapter are organized in the Chapter Review under the four types of understanding this book promotes—Skills, Properties, Uses, and Representations.

Whereas end-of-chapter material may be considered optional in some texts, in UCSMP *Geometry* we have selected these objectives and questions with the expectation that they will be covered. Students should be able to answer these questions with about 85% accuracy after studying the chapter.

You may assign these questions over a single night to help students prepare for a test the next day, or you may assign the questions over a two-day period. If you work the questions over two days, then we recommend assigning the evens for homework the first night so that students get feedback in class the next day, then assigning the odds the night before the test, because answers are provided to the odd-numbered questions.

It is effective to ask students which questions they still do not understand and to use the day or days for a general class discussion of the material which the class finds most difficult.

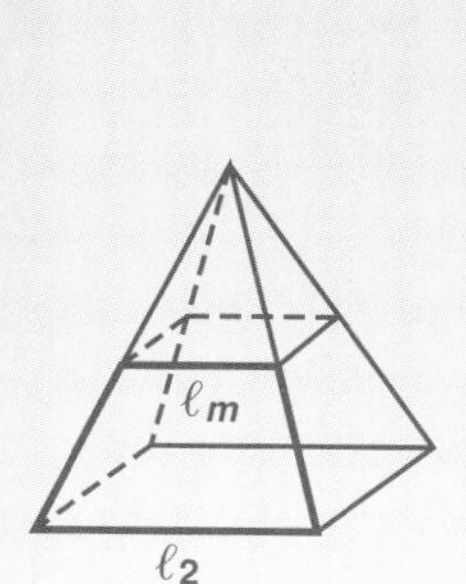

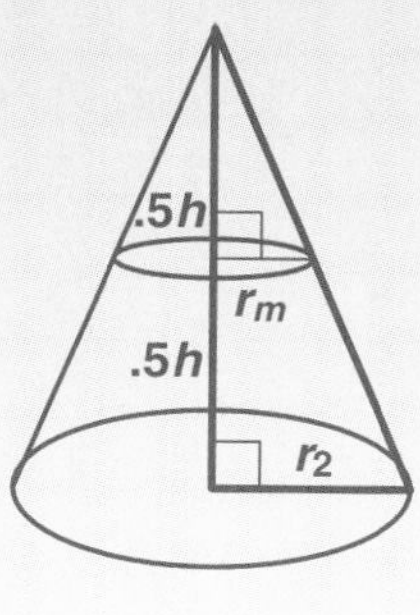

For the cone, r_m is parallel to r_2 and one-half of r_2; the area of the bottom base B_2 is four times the area of the middle base B_m, so $.25B_2 = B_m$. Let $B = B_2$. $V = \frac{1}{6}h(B_1 + B_2 + 4B_m) = \frac{1}{6}h(0 + B + 4(.25B) = \frac{1}{6}(2B) = \frac{1}{3}Bh$. So the volume of a pyramid or cone can be found using this formula.

3c. The volume of a sphere is $\frac{4}{3}\pi r^3$. In a sphere, both the top and bottom bases are points, and have area of zero. The middle base is the area of the great circle, with radius r; that is, πr^2. The height of the sphere is the diameter $2r$.

(Responses continue on page 618.)

Assessment

Evaluation The *Assessment Sourcebook* provides five forms of the Chapter 10 Test. Forms A and B present parallel versions in a short-answer format. Forms C and D offer performance assessment. The fifth test is Chapter 10 Test, Cumulative Form. About 50% of this test covers Chapter 10; 25% of it covers Chapter 9, and 25% covers earlier chapters.

For information on grading, see *General Teaching Suggestions; Grading* in the *Professional Sourcebook,* which begins on page T00 in this Teacher's Edition.

Additional responses, pages 613–614

3c. $V = \frac{1}{6}h(B_1 + B_2 + 4B_m) = \frac{1}{6}2r(0 + 0 + 4(\pi r^2)) = \frac{1}{6}2r(4\pi r^2) = \frac{4}{3}\pi r^3$. So the volume of a sphere can be found using this formula.

4. Responses will vary.

5. Sample Responses:
(1) Dome of the Rock, also called Qubbat As-Sakhrah and Mosque of Omar, is the oldest Islamic monument. It was built in Jerusalem between 685 and 691 A.D. by the caliph 'Abd al-Malik ibn Marwan as a shrine for pilgrims. A wooden dome approximately 18 meters in diameter is mounted on an elevated drum which sits atop a basically octagonal arcade. The dome and the exterior walls contain many windows. The surface area of this dome is approximately 525 m^2 and the volume is approximately 4800 m^3.
(2) The U.S. Capitol, located in Washington D.C., was designed originally by William Thornton. The purpose of the Capitol is to house the U.S. Congress. The dome was not built before the original building was burnt by the British, but was added on when the Capitol was rebuilt. The first dome was built in 1827 and was later upgraded in 1857. The diameter of this dome is 287 ft; S.A. ≈ 124,400 ft^2 and $V \approx$ 6,189,000 ft^3

Objective C: *Calculate cube roots.* *(Lesson 10-3)*

17. Give the cube root of 27,000. 30
18. Approximate the cube root of 40 to the nearest tenth. 3.4
19. A cube has volume of 150. To the nearest hundredth, what is the length of an edge of the cube? 5.31
20. Calculate $\sqrt[3]{15} + \sqrt[3]{21}$ to the nearest hundredth. 5.23

25a) It is multiplied by 9. b) It is multiplied by 27.
26) It is multiplied by 729.
27) The new volume is 4 times as large.

Objective D: *Calculate the surface area and volume of a sphere from appropriate lengths, and vice versa.* *(Lessons 10-8, 10-9)*

21. Give the surface area and volume of a sphere with radius 72. See margin.
22. Give the surface area and volume of a sphere with diameter 3 mm. See margin.
23. A sphere has volume 288π. What is its radius? 6 units
24. A sphere has volume 40π cubic units. What is its surface area? ≈ 121.3 units^2

PROPERTIES DEAL WITH THE PRINCIPLES BEHIND THE MATHEMATICS.

Objective E: *Determine what happens to the surface area and volume of a figure when its dimensions are multiplied by some number(s).* *(Lessons 10-4, 10-8, 10-9)* See above.

25. All of the dimensions of a box are tripled.
    a. What happens to the surface area?
    b. What happens to the volume?
26. The edges of a cube are multiplied by 9. What happens to its volume?
27. The diameter of a pizza is doubled. If its thickness remains the same, how do the volumes of the two pizzas compare?
28. The diameter of the Sun is about 109 times the diameter of Earth. How do their volumes compare? See margin.

Objective F: *Develop formulas for specific figures from more general formulas.* *(Lesson 10-6)*

29. At the right, the regular square pyramid has slant height ℓ and a base with side length s.

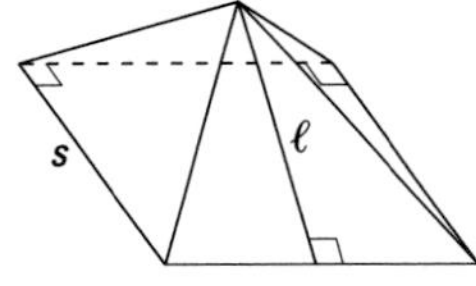

    a. Find a formula for the lateral area. $2s\ell$
    b. Find a formula for the surface area. $s^2 + 2s\ell$
30. A right cylinder has base radius r and height h.
    a. Find a formula for its lateral area. $2\pi rh$
    b. Find a formula for its volume. $\pi r^2 h$

31. A right cone has slant height ℓ and its base has radius r.
    a. Give a formula for its surface area. $\pi r^2 + \pi r\ell$
    b. Give a formula for its volume. $\frac{1}{3}\pi r^2\sqrt{\ell^2 - r^2}$
32. A cube has edges of $2x$. Find
    a. its surface area. $24x^2$ units^2
    b. its volume. $8x^3$ units^3

Objective G: *Know the conditions under which Cavalieri's Principle can be applied.* *(Lesson 10-5)*

33. A prism and pyramid have bases of the same area and equal heights. Can Cavalieri's Principle be applied in this situation? Why or why not? See margin.
34. Two cylindric solids have congruent bases and equal heights. One of the solids is oblique and one is right. *True or false.*
    a. The solids have the same volume. True
    b. The solids have the same surface area. False

In 35 and 36, the two figures have the same height. **a.** Do they have the same volume? **b.** Why or why not? See margin.

35.

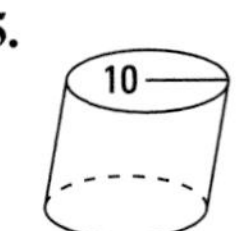

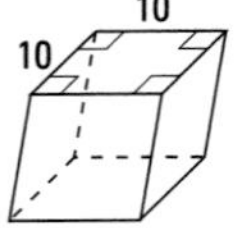

36.

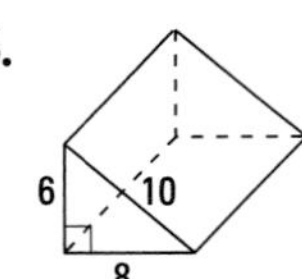

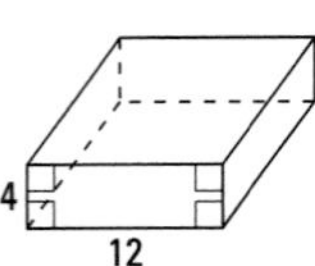

6. Sample information students might find: For the cylinder, the dimensions r and h must be such that $\pi r^2h = 1200$. To the nearest hundredth, the dimensions shown in the chart at the right yield a cylinder which has volume 1200 cm^3, or 1200 mL.

r (cm)	h (cm)
1	381.97
2	95.49
3	42.44
4	23.87

r (cm)	h (cm)
5	15.28
6	10.61
7	7.80
8	5.97

For the box, or rectangular prism, the dimensions must be ℓ, w, and h such that $\ell wh = 270$ cm^3. One possibility is to hold the length constant at a single value.

CHAPTER TEN

USES DEAL WITH APPLICATIONS OF MATHEMATICS IN REAL SITUATIONS.

Objective H: *Apply formulas for lateral and surface area to real situations.* *(Lessons 10-1, 10-2, 10-9)*

37. A jewelry box measures 12″ by 7″ by 4″. Find, to the nearest square inch, the amount of wrapping paper needed to exactly cover it. 320 square inches

38. How much paper is needed to make a cylindrical paper cup with a base diameter of 10 cm and a height of 12 cm? $\approx 455.5 \text{ cm}^2$

39. The sides of the base of an ancient square pyramid are 100 cubits (an ancient unit). The pyramid is 50 cubits high. Find its lateral area. $\approx 14{,}142 \text{ cubits}^2$

40. A paper holder for an ice cream cone is in the shape of a right cone. If its slant height is 6 cm and its radius is 2 cm, what is its lateral area? $\approx 37.7 \text{ cm}^2$

41. Venus is almost spherical with a radius of about 3000 km. To survey Venus completely, about how many square kilometers must be covered? $\approx 1.13 \cdot 10^8 \text{ km}^2$

42. To the nearest square foot, how much leather is needed to make a basketball that is 9.4″ in diameter? 2 ft^2

44) No; the suitcase has volume $10{,}368 \text{ in}^3$, but the bills have volume $62{,}769 \text{ in}^3$.

Objective I: *Apply formulas for volume to real situations.* *(Lessons 10-3, 10-5, 10-7, 10-8)*

43. How much wood is in a solid cube 2.5″ on a side? 15.625 in^3

44. Can a suitcase 3′ long, 1′ wide, and 2′ high hold one million one-dollar bills if a dollar bill is 6.125″ long, 2.562″ wide, and 0.004″ thick? See below.

45. A silo is a cylinder whose base is a circle. One silo has base diameter 6 m and height 10 m. What is the volume of this silo? $\approx 282.7 \text{ m}^3$

46. How much can the paper cup of Question 38 hold? $\approx 942.5 \text{ cm}^3$

47. Find the volume of the pyramid in Question 39. $\approx 167{,}000 \text{ cubits}^3$

48. An ice cream cone has diameter 2″ and a slant height of 3″. Find its volume to the nearest tenth of a cubic inch. ≈ 3.0 cubic inches

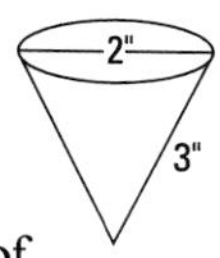

49. A chocolate golf ball has a radius of 2.6 cm. Ignoring the "dimples" on the ball, find its volume. $\approx 73.6 \text{ cm}^3$

50. The Hagia Sophia in Istanbul was built in 532 A.D. Its great dome is a hemisphere with diameter 107′. Find the volume of the dome to the nearest thousand cubic feet. 321,000 cubic feet

REPRESENTATIONS DEAL WITH PICTURES, GRAPHS, OR OBJECTS THAT ILLUSTRATE CONCEPTS.

Objective J: *Represent products of two (or three) numbers or expressions as areas of rectangles (or volumes of boxes), and vice versa.* *(Lesson 10-4)*

In 51 and 52, perform the multiplication.

51. $(5x + 2)(4y + 3)$ $20xy + 15x + 8y + 6$

52. $(a + 6)(2a + 1)(a + 8)$ $2a^3 + 29a^2 + 110a + 48$

In 53 and 54, give two expressions for the area of the rectangle.

53.

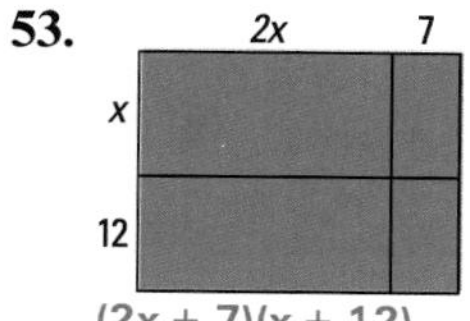

$(2x + 7)(x + 12)$
$2x^2 + 31x + 84$

54.

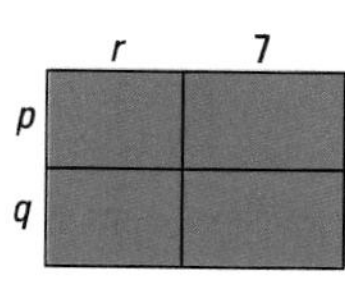

$(r + 7)(p + q)$
$rp + 7p + rq + 7q$

In 55 and 56, give two expressions for the volume of the box. See margin.

55.

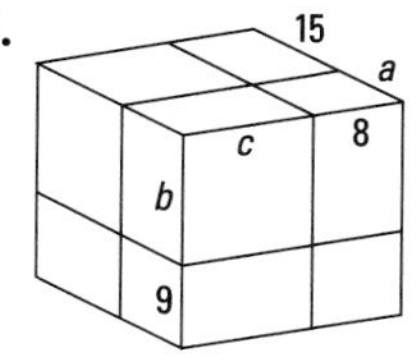

56.

10 z y 5 x w

Feedback After students have taken the test for Chapter 10 and you have scored the results, return the tests to students for discussion. Class discussion of the questions that caused trouble for the most students can be very effective in identifying and clarifying misunderstandings. You might want to have them write down the items they missed and work, either in groups or at home, to correct them. It is important for students to receive feedback on every chapter test, and we recommend that students see and correct their mistakes before proceeding too far into the next chapter.

Additional Answers

21. S.A. $= 20{,}736\pi \approx 65{,}144$ units^2; $V = 497{,}664\pi \approx 1{,}563{,}458$ units^3
22. S.A. $= 9\pi \approx 28$ mm^2; $V = 4.5\pi \approx 14$ mm^3
28. The volume of the sun is approximately 1,300,000 times the volume of the earth.
33. Plane sections at any level other than the base do not have the same area.

35a. No
b. Plane sections at any level do not have the same area.

36a. No
b. Plane sections at any level do not have the same area.

55. $(a + 15)(b + 9)(c + 8)$; $abc + 8ab + 9ac + 72a + 15bc + 120b + 135c + 1080$
56. $(x + w)(y + 5)(z + 10)$; $xyz + wyz + 5xz + 5wz + 10xy + 10wy + 50x + 50w$

In this case, let $\ell = 10$ cm. All measurements in the table are in centimeters.

ℓ	10	10	10	10	10
w	9	3	4	5	8
h	3	9	6.75	5.4	3.375

Each of the models above allows no space for air. Typically, containers of liquid allow for a small space for air at the top.

Containers with a height greater than 30 cm may not fit well in standard refrigerators. Boxes with thin widths are sometimes easier to hold; however, taken to an extreme, this is not true. The containers with the dimensions closer to that of a cube will require the least amount of space for storage, but containers with non-standard shapes sometimes are more eye-catching and better for advertising. People tend to associate container shapes with the products—such as Coca-Cola™ bottles.

Chapter 11 Planner

Adapting to Individual Needs

The student text is written for the vast majority of students. The chart at the right suggests two pacing plans to accommodate the needs of your students. Students in the Full Course should complete the entire text by the end of the year. Students in the Minimal Course will spend more time when there are quizzes and more time on the Chapter Review. Therefore, these students may not complete all of the chapters in the text.

Options are also presented to meet the needs of a variety of teaching and learning styles. For each lesson, the Teacher's Edition provides a section entitled *Adapting to Individual Needs.* This section regularly includes **Optional Activities, Challenge** problems, **English Language Development** suggestions, and suggestions for providing **Extra Help.** The Teacher's Edition also frequently includes an **Error Alert,** an **Extension,** and an **Assessment** alternative. The options available in Chapter 11 are summarized in the chart below.

Chapter 11 Pacing Chart

Day	Full Course	Minimal Course
1	11-1	11-1
2	11-2	11-2
3	11-3	11-3
4	11-4	11-4
5	Quiz*; 11-5	Quiz*; begin 11-5.
6	11-6	Finish 11-5.
7	11-7	11-6
8	Quiz*; 11-8	11-7
9	11-9	Quiz*; begin 11-8.
10	Self-Test	Finish 11-8.
11	Review	11-9
12	Test*	Self-Test
13		Review
14		Review
15		Test*

*in the Teacher's Resource File

In the Teacher's Edition...

Lesson	Optional Activities	Extra Help	Challenge	English Language Development	Error Alert	Extension	Cooperative Learning	Ongoing Assessment
11-1	●	●	●	●	●	●	●	Written
11-2	●	●	●		●	●	●	Written
11-3	●	●	●	●		●	●	Oral/Written
11-4	●		●	●		●	●	Oral/Written
11-5	●	●	●		●	●		Written
11-6	●		●			●	●	Oral/Written
11-7	●		●			●	●	Oral/Written
11-8	●		●	●		●		Written
11-9	●	●	●	●		●		Oral/Written

Chapter 11 Block Schedule

Day	Recommended Pacing
1	Lessons 11-1, 11-2
2	Lesson 11-3
3	Lessons 11-4, 11-5
4	Lessons 11-6, 11-7
5	Lesson 11-8
6	Lesson 11-9, Self-Test, Chapter Review
7	Chapter Review, Chapter Test

In the Additional Resources...

	In the Teacher's Resource File								
Lesson	Lesson Masters, A and B	Teaching Aids*	Activity Kit*	Answer Masters	Technology Sourcebook	Assessment Sourcebook	Visual Aids**	Technology	Video Segments
11-1	11-1	143, 146		11-1			143, 146, AM		
11-2	11-2	143, 147		11-2			143, 147, AM		
11-3	11-3	104, 143, 148, 149		11-3			104, 143, 148, 149, AM		
11-4	11-4	144, 150, 151		11-4	22	Quiz	144, 150, 151, AM	GeoExplorer	
11-5	11-5	4, 105, 144, 152		11-5			4, 105, 144, 152, AM		
11-6	11-6	4, 144		11-6			4, 144, AM		11-6
11-7	11-7	4, 145, 153		11-7		Quiz	4, 145, 153, AM		
In-class Activity				11-8					
11-7	11-8	145, 154	23	11-8	23		145, 154 AM	GeoExplorer	
11-8	11-9	145, 155, 156	24	11-9			145, 155, 156, AM		
End of Chapter				Review		Tests			

*Teaching Aids are pictured on pages 620C and 620D. The activities in the Activity Kit are pictured on page 620C.

**Visual Aids provide transparencies for all Teaching Aids and all Answer Masters.

Also available is the Study Skills Handbook which includes study-skill tips related to reading, note-taking, and comprehension.

Integrating Strands and Applications

	11-1	11-2	11-3	11-4	11-5	11-6	11-7	11-8	11-9
Mathematical Connections									
Number Sense		●		●	●	●	●	●	●
Algebra	●		●	●	●	●	●	●	●
Geometry	●	●	●	●	●	●	●	●	●
Measurement		●				●	●	●	●
Logic and Reasoning	●	●	●	●	●	●	●	●	●
Statistics/Data Analysis			●					●	
Patterns and Functions					●	●	●	●	
Discrete Mathematics		●							
Interdisciplinary and Other Connections									
Music			●						
Literature	●								
Science			●		●			●	
Social Studies		●				●		●	●
Multicultural				●				●	
Technology				●		●		●	
Career			●	●					
Sports	●	●		●		●	●		●

Teaching and Assessing the Chapter Objectives

				In the Teacher's Resource File		
Chapter 11 Objectives (Organized into the SPUR categories—Skills, Properties, Uses, and Representations)	**Lessons**	**Progress Self-Test Questions**	**Chapter Review Questions**	**Chapter Test, Forms A and B**	**Chapter Test, Forms C**	**D**
Skills						
A: Determine the length and the coordinates of the midpoint of a segment in the coordinate plane.	11-6, 11-8	1, 2, 3	1–8	1, 2	3	
B: Apply the Midpoint Connector Theorem.	11-8	12, 13	9–12	18, 19	1	
C: Plot points, find distances between them, and find coordinates of midpoints in 3-dimensional space.	11-9	4	13–16	13, 14	3	
Properties						
D: Follow the basic laws of reasoning to make conclusions.	11-1, 11-2, 11-3, 11-4	5, 6	17–22	3, 4	4	
E: Write the converse, inverse, or contrapositive of a conditional.	11-2	7	23–26	11, 12		
F: Write indirect proofs.	11-4, 11-5, 11-6	8, 9	27–32	10, 21	5	✓
G: Use coordinate geometry to deduce properties of figures and prove theorems.	11-5, 11-6, 11-8	10, 11	33–38	5	5	✓
Uses						
H: Apply laws of reasoning in real situations.	11-1, 11-2, 11-3, 11-4	14, 15	39–44	20	4	
I: Apply the Distance and Box Diagonal Formulas in real situations.	11-6, 11-9	16, 17	45–48	8, 17		
Representations						
J: Graph and write an equation for a circle or a sphere given its center and radius, and vice versa.	11-7, 11-9	18, 19	49–54	6, 7, 15, 16	2	
K: Give convenient locations for triangles and quadrilaterals in the coordinate plane.	11-5	20	55–58	9		

Assessment Sourcebook
Quiz for Lessons 11-1 through 11-4
Quiz for Lessons 11-5 through 11-7
Chapter 11 Test, Forms A–D
Chapter 11 Test, Cumulative Form

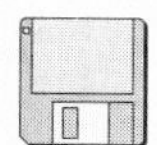
Quiz and Test Writer

Activity Kit

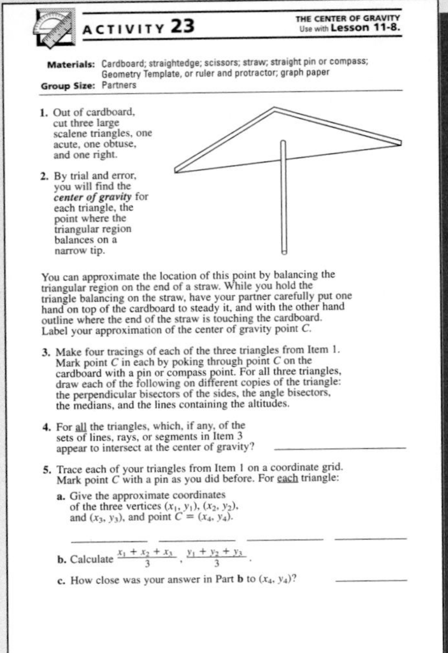

ACTIVITY 23 THE CENTER OF GRAVITY Use with **Lesson 11-8.**

Materials: Cardboard; straightedge; scissors; straw; straight pin or compass; Geometry Template, or ruler and protractor; graph paper
Group Size: Partners

1. Out of cardboard, cut three large scalene triangles, one acute, one obtuse, and one right.
2. By trial and error, you will find the ***center of gravity*** for each triangle, the point where the triangular region balances on a narrow tip.

You can approximate the location of this point by balancing the triangular region on the end of a straw. While you hold the triangle balancing on the straw, have your partner carefully put one hand on top of the cardboard to steady it, and with the other hand outline where the end of the straw is touching the cardboard. Label your approximation of the center of gravity point *C*.

3. Make four tracings of each of the three triangles from Item 1. Mark point *C* in each by poking through point *C* on the cardboard with a pin or compass point. For all three triangles, draw each of the following on different copies of the triangle: the perpendicular bisectors of the sides, the angle bisectors, the medians, and the lines containing the altitudes.
4. For all the triangles, which, if any, of the sets of lines, rays, or segments in Item 3 appear to intersect at the center of gravity? ______
5. Trace each of your triangles from Item 1 on a coordinate grid. Mark point *C* with a pin as you did before. For each triangle:
   a. Give the approximate coordinates of the three vertices (x_1, y_1), (x_2, y_2), and (x_3, y_3), and point $C = (x_4, y_4)$.
   ______ ______ ______ ______
   b. Calculate $\frac{x_1 + x_2 + x_3}{3}, \frac{y_1 + y_2 + y_3}{3}$.
   c. How close was your answer in Part **b** to (x_4, y_4)? ______

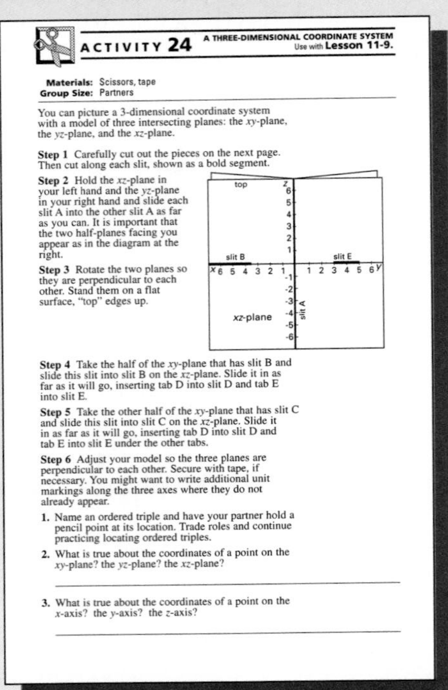

ACTIVITY 24 A THREE-DIMENSIONAL COORDINATE SYSTEM Use with **Lesson 11-9.**

Materials: Scissors, tape
Group Size: Partners

You can picture a 3-dimensional coordinate system with a model of three intersecting planes: the *xy*-plane, the *yz*-plane, and the *xz*-plane.

Step 1 Carefully cut out the pieces on the next page. Then cut along each slit, shown as a bold segment.

Step 2 Hold the *xz*-plane in your left hand and the *yz*-plane in your right hand and slide each slit A into the other slit A as far as you can. It is important that the two half-planes facing you appear as in the diagram at the right.

Step 3 Rotate the two planes so they are perpendicular to each other. Stand them on a flat surface, "top" edges up.

Step 4 Take the half of the *xy*-plane that has slit B and slide this slit into slit B on the *xz*-plane. Slide it in as far as it will go, inserting tab D into slit D and tab E into slit E.

Step 5 Take the other half of the *xy*-plane that has slit C and slide this slit into slit C on the *xz*-plane. Slide it in as far as it will go, inserting tab D into slit D and tab E into slit E under the other tabs.

Step 6 Adjust your model so the three planes are perpendicular to each other. Secure with tape, if necessary. You might want to write additional unit markings along the three axes where they do not already appear.

1. Name an ordered triple and have your partner hold a pencil point at its location. Trade roles and continue practicing locating ordered triples.
2. What is true about the coordinates of a point on the *xy*-plane? the *yz*-plane? the *xz*-plane?
3. What is true about the coordinates of a point on the *x*-axis? the *y*-axis? the *z*-axis?

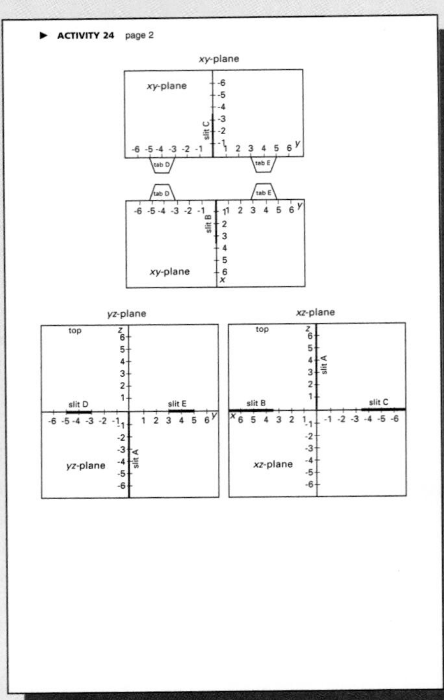

► ACTIVITY 24 page 2

Teaching Aids

Teaching Aid 4, Coordinate Plane (shown on page 4D), can be used with **Lessons 11-5** through **11-7.**
Teaching Aid 104, Map of the United States (shown on page 434C), can be used with **Lesson 11-3.**
Teaching Aid 105, Graph Paper (shown on page 434C), can be used with **Lesson 11-5.**

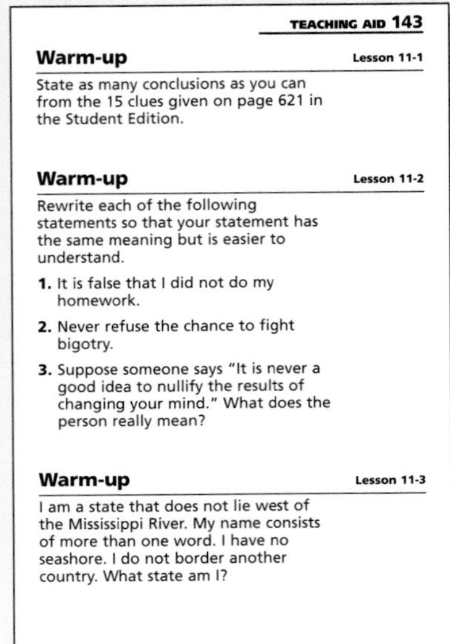

TEACHING AID 143

Warm-up Lesson 11-1

State as many conclusions as you can from the 15 clues given on page 621 in the Student Edition.

Warm-up Lesson 11-2

Rewrite each of the following statements so that your statement has the same meaning but is easier to understand.

1. It is false that I did not do my homework.
2. Never refuse the chance to fight bigotry.
3. Suppose someone says "It is never a good idea to nullify the results of changing your mind." What does the person really mean?

Warm-up Lesson 11-3

I am a state that does not lie west of the Mississippi River. My name consists of more than one word. I have no seashore. I do not border another country. What state am I?

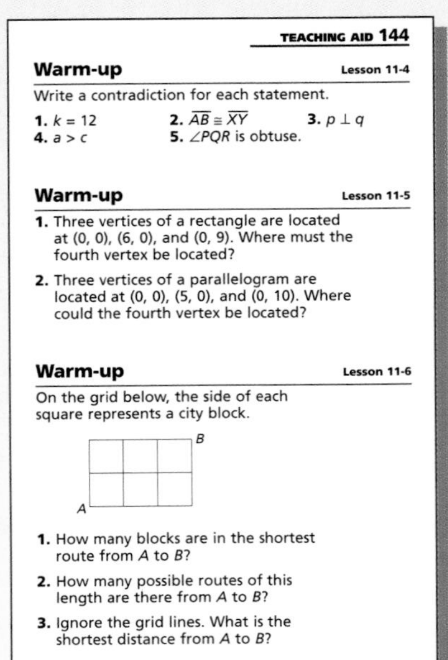

TEACHING AID 144

Warm-up Lesson 11-4

Write a contradiction for each statement.

1. $k = 12$ 2. $\overline{AB} \cong \overline{XY}$ 3. $p \perp q$
4. $a > c$ 5. $\angle PQR$ is obtuse.

Warm-up Lesson 11-5

1. Three vertices of a rectangle are located at (0, 0), (6, 0), and (0, 9). Where must the fourth vertex be located?
2. Three vertices of a parallelogram are located at (0, 0), (5, 0), and (0, 10). Where could the fourth vertex be located?

Warm-up Lesson 11-6

On the grid below, the side of each square represents a city block.

1. How many blocks are in the shortest route from *A* to *B*?
2. How many possible routes of this length are there from *A* to *B*?
3. Ignore the grid lines. What is the shortest distance from *A* to *B*?

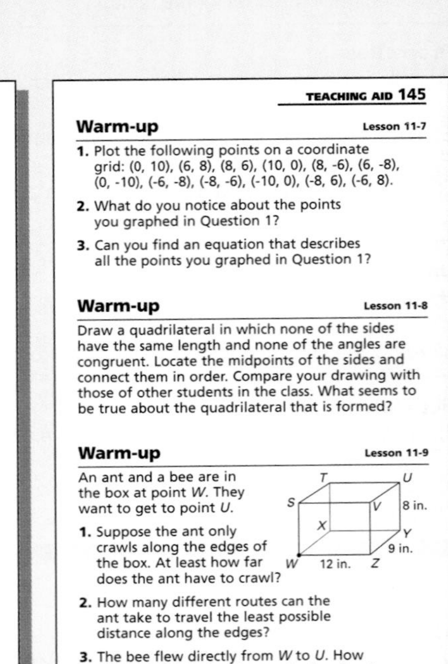

TEACHING AID 145

Warm-up Lesson 11-7

1. Plot the following points on a coordinate grid: (0, 10), (6, 8), (8, 6), (10, 0), (8, -6), (6, -8), (0, -10), (-6, -8), (-8, -6), (-10, 0), (-8, 6), (-6, 8).
2. What do you notice about the points you graphed in Question 1?
3. Can you find an equation that describes all the points you graphed in Question 1?

Warm-up Lesson 11-8

Draw a quadrilateral in which none of the sides have the same length and none of the angles are congruent. Locate the midpoints of the sides and connect them in order. Compare your drawing with those of other students in the class. What seems to be true about the quadrilateral that is formed?

Warm-up Lesson 11-9

An ant and a bee are in the box at point *W*. They want to get to point *U*.

1. Suppose the ant only crawls along the edges of the box. At least how far does the ant have to crawl?
2. How many different routes can the ant take to travel the least possible distance along the edges?
3. The bee flew directly from *W* to *U*. How might you find the distance the bee flew?

TEACHING AID 146
Lesson 11-1

Additional Examples

1. Maria's father said, "If you go to computer camp, we will buy you a computer." Her mother said, "If you make an A in geometry, you can go to computer camp." What conclusion can Maria make?
2. What conclusion can be made using all of these statements?
   (1) Every rectangle is an isosceles trapezoid.
   (2) *ABCD* is a rectangle.
   (3) The perpendicular bisector of the bases of an isosceles trapezoid is a symmetry line for the isosceles trapezoid.
3. Here is another Lewis Carroll puzzle. What can you conclude?
   (1) All puddings are nice.
   (2) This dish is a pudding.
   (3) No nice things are wholesome.
4. A contest states "The deadline is May 1." Jack entered on April 29.
   a. How are these two facts related to the given of the Law of Detachment?
   b. What conclusion is desired?
5. What can you conclude from these statements of famous writers?
   (1) "A little knowledge is a dangerous thing." Alexander Pope
   (2) "If a little knowledge is dangerous, then no one is out of danger." Thomas Huxley
6. Consider these steps in solving an equation. Give justifications for: $p \Rightarrow q$, $q \Rightarrow r$, and $p \Rightarrow r$.
   p: $5t - 11 = 24$ *q*: $5t = 35$ *r*: $t = 7$

TEACHING AID 147
Lesson 11-2

Additional Examples

1. Write the converse, inverse, and contrapositive of the following statement: If you live in an air-conditioned place, then you have the opportunity to be cool in the summer.
2. Make a conclusion from these two statements.
   (1) Bill cannot become an eagle scout.
   (2) If a person is a boy scout, he can become an eagle scout.
3. Make a conclusion using all three statements.
   (1) If we hang an Escher print on this wall, people will smile as they enter the room.
   (2) If we do not put up an Escher print on this wall, I will be bothered.
   (3) I will not be bothered if we remove these paintings from this wall.

TEACHING AID 148
Lesson 11-3

Example

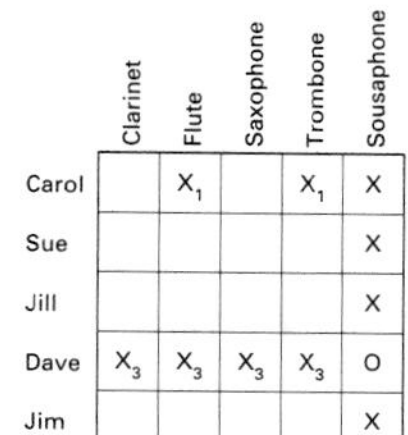

	Clarinet	Flute	Saxophone	Trombone	Sousaphone
Carol		X_1		X_1	X
Sue					X
Jill					X
Dave	X_3	X_3	X_3	X_3	O
Jim					X

Activity Grids

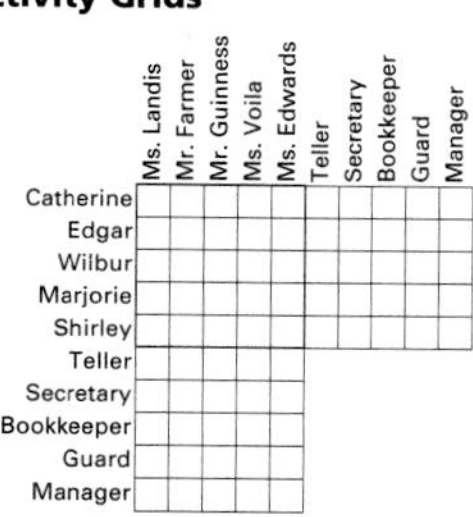

TEACHING AID 149
Lesson 11-3

Additional Examples

1. Presidents Buchanan, Grant, Johnson, and Lincoln were four consecutive presidents of the United States. From the clues below, determine the order in which they served.
   (1) Buchanan served before Johnson, who became president when the president before him was assassinated.
   (2) Grant won the election because of his popularity during the Civil War.
   (3) Lincoln served during almost the entire Civil War and was the only one of these presidents to die in office.
2. I am thinking of a one-digit number from 0 through 9. From the clues, determined my number.
   (1) It is not prime.
   (2) It cannot be the last digit of the square of an integer.

TEACHING AID 150
Lesson 11-4

Laws of Reasoning

Law of Detachment
From a true conditional $p \Rightarrow q$ and a statement or given information *p*, you may conclude *q*.

Law of Transitivity
If $p \Rightarrow q$ and $q \Rightarrow r$ are true, then $p \Rightarrow r$ is true.

Law of Contrapositive
A conditional ($p \Rightarrow q$) and its contrapositive (not-$q \Rightarrow$ not-p) are either both true or both false.

Law of Ruling Out Possibilities
When statement *p* or statement *q* is true, and *q* is not true, then *p* is true.

Law of Indirect Reasoning
If valid reasoning from a statement *p* leads to a false conclusion, then *p* is false.

TEACHING AID 151
Lesson 11-4

Additional Examples

1. Are the statements contradictory?
   a. *ABCD* is a square. *ABCD* is a trapezoid.
   b. Billy is 15. Billy has an airplane pilot's license.
   c. $|x| = -4$. $|x| = 4$.
   d. $|33| = y$. $|-33| = y$.
   e. $m = 5$. $m \leq 5$.
2. What statement is contradicted by each statement below?
   a. $m\angle ABC + m\angle BCA + m\angle CAB = 360$.
   b. *M* is the midpoint of $\overline{AB}$, $AM = 50$, and $MB = 40$.
3. Show that $5(2x + 3) = 10(x + 1)$ is never true.
4. Prove that $\sqrt[3]{9} \neq 2$.
5. Prove that a convex pentagon cannot have four acute angles.

TEACHING AID 152
Lesson 11-5

Convenient Locations

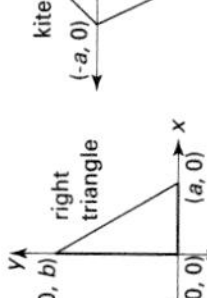

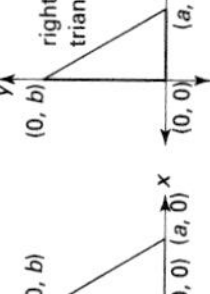

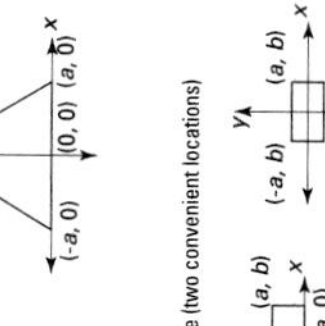

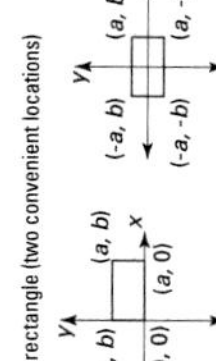

parallelogram (two convenient locations)
(-c, b) (a, b) (-a, -b) (c, -b)
(b, c) (a + b, c) (0, 0) (a, 0)

TEACHING AID 153
Lesson 11-7

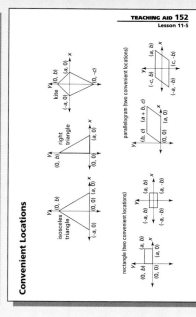

Graph of a Circle

Equation for a Circle:
The circle with center (*h*, *k*) and radius *r* is the set of points (*x*, *y*) satisfying $(x - h)^2 + (y - k)^2 = r^2$.

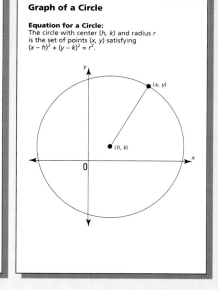

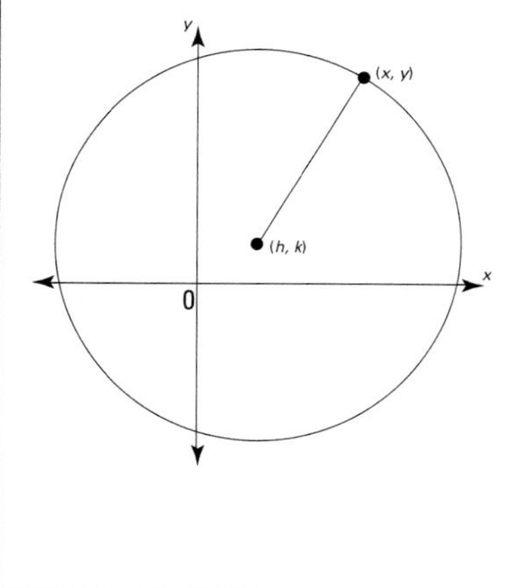

TEACHING AID 154
Lesson 11-8

Additional Examples

1. What is the midpoint of the segment connecting (5, -7) and (2, 9)?
2. In $\triangle DEF$, sides $\overline{DE}$, $\overline{EF}$, and $\overline{FD}$ have lengths of 28, 44, and 35, respectively. $\triangle GHI$ is formed by connecting the midpoints of $\triangle DEF$. What are the lengths of the sides of $\triangle GHI$?

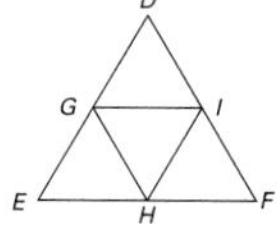

3. If $P = (-10, 6)$ and the midpoint of $\overline{PQ}$ is (-5, 9), what are the coordinates of *Q*?
4. Use a coordinate proof to show that the diagonals of a parallelogram bisect each other.

TEACHING AID 155
Lesson 11-9

Additional Examples

1. Give the coordinates of the vertices of the box shown below.

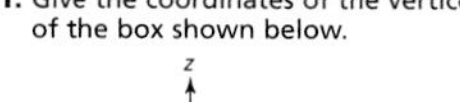
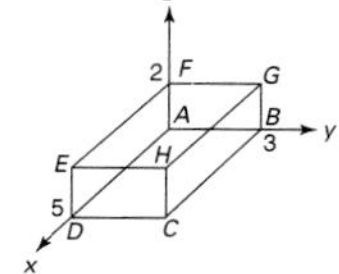

2. Find the distance between (4, -1, 8) and (10, 20, 5).
3. Find an equation for the sphere with center (-4, 5, 0) and which intersects the origin.
4. What is the midpoint of the segment joining (1, 2, 3) and (11, 0, -9)?

TEACHING AID 156
Lesson 11-9

3-Dimensional Coordinate System

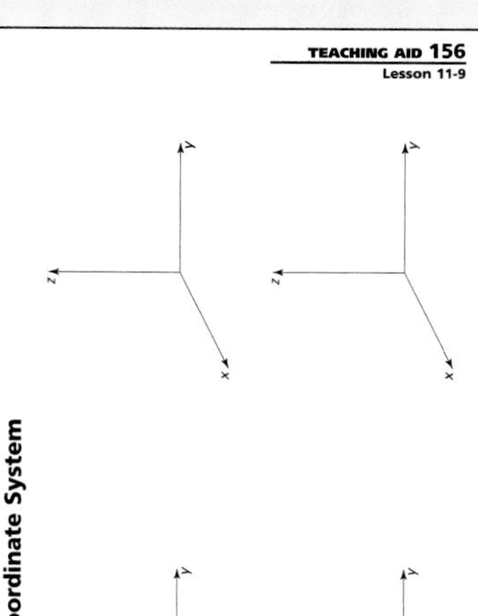

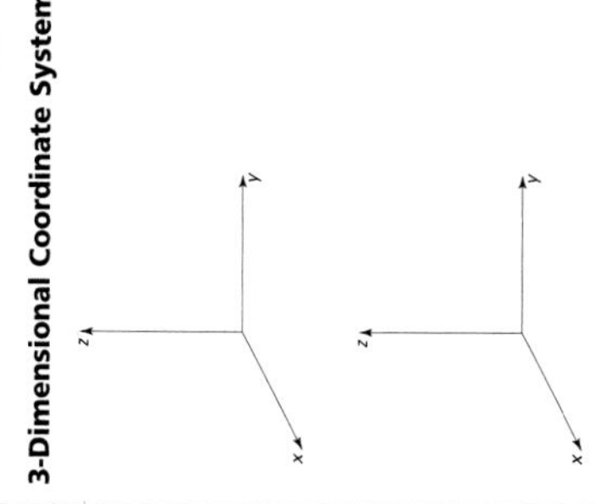

Chapter Opener 11

Pacing

All lessons in this chapter are designed to be covered in one day. Be careful not to spend too much time on the logic puzzles introduced in Lesson 11-3. They are captivating for many students and teachers, but are best treated as a recreational application. At the end of the chapter, you should plan to spend 1 day to review the Progress Self-Test, 1–2 days for the Chapter Review, and 1 day for a test. You may wish to spend a day on projects, and possibly a day is needed for quizzes. Therefore, this chapter should take 12–15 days. We recommend that you not spend more than 16 days on this chapter.

Using Pages 620–621

The origin of "Who Owns the Zebra?" is unknown to the authors. It is quite difficult to solve even if you have experience with these kinds of logic puzzles. The solver must go through the clues again and again, each time checking for a little bit of information. Do not make solving this puzzle a requirement; it should be pure fun and/or extra credit.

Those familiar with older versions of this puzzle will note that we have replaced the context of smoking with that of gardening, and the brands of cigarettes with names of flowers.

Literature Connection Descartes' dream is the idea behind the book *Descartes' Dream: The World According to Mathematics,* by Philip J. Davis and Rueben Hersh (San Diego: Harcourt, Brace, Jovanovich, 1986).

CHAPTER

11

620

Chapter 11 Overview

What makes mathematics interesting to many professional mathematicians is the variety of proofs that exist. The number of different types of proofs seems infinite. It is a challenge and a pleasure to discover or rediscover them.

However, this same quality that is so enticing to mathematicians can be extremely frustrating to students. It can be depressing to learn that a subject is, for all practical purposes, infinite. It's much nicer to think that you've learned all of the ways to do proofs.

Still, there is a bit of consolation. All of the proofs mathematicians do are based on a small number of laws of logic. Although for students, proofs can be difficult, this chapter's work with logic along with indirect and coordinate proofs has been very popular. Students see it as worthwhile and applicable.

Two laws of logic, Detachment and Transitivity, are discussed in Lesson 11-1. The other laws, Contrapositive, Ruling Out Possibilities, and Indirect Reasoning, are introduced in Lessons 11-2 through 11-4. A student who masters the content of Lessons 11-1 through 11-4 has enough knowledge to follow the logic in most mathematical proofs.

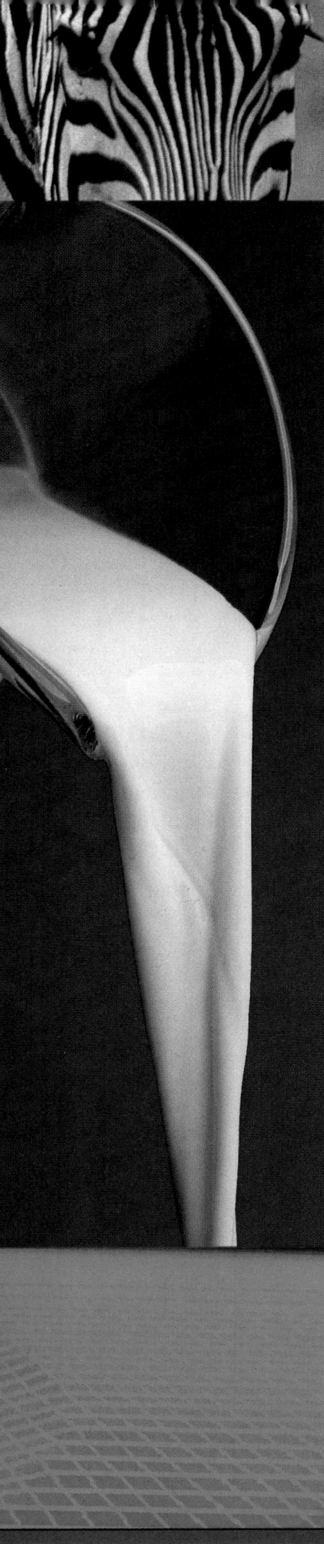

INDIRECT AND COORDINATE PROOFS

The 15 clues below are adapted from a famous puzzle called "Who Owns The Zebra?"

1. There are five houses in a row, each of a different color and inhabited by people of different nationalities, with different pets, drinks, and flowers.
2. The English person lives in the red house.
3. The Spaniard owns the dog.
4. Coffee is drunk in the green house.
5. The Ukrainian drinks tea.
6. The green house is immediately to the right (*your* right) of the ivory house.
7. The geranium grower owns snails.
8. Roses are in front of the yellow house.
9. Milk is drunk in the middle house.
10. The Norwegian lives in the first house on the left.
11. The person who grows marigolds lives in the house next to the person with the fox.
12. Roses are grown at the house next to the house where the horse is kept.
13. The person who grows lilies drinks orange juice.
14. The Japanese person grows gardenias.
15. The Norwegian lives next to the blue house.

Now, who drinks water? And who owns the zebra?

In this chapter, you will learn about the logic of indirect reasoning, and see and write some indirect proofs. Indirect reasoning is used to solve logic puzzles like "Who Owns the Zebra?" and also to prove many theorems. You may find that some indirect proofs are easier to write than direct proofs.

Recall that René Descartes, along with Pierre Fermat, invented the idea of coordinate graphs. Descartes was thrilled with his invention, which he called a *method*, for it used algebra to combine arithmetic and geometry, and so unified all the mathematics known up to that time. He used his method, which is now called **coordinate geometry** or **analytic geometry,** to solve many problems which were then considered to be very difficult or unsolvable. Descartes thought that mathematics and logic could provide the means to solve any problem in any field of endeavor. In this chapter, you will use coordinates the way Descartes used them, to *deduce* properties of figures.

You might want to make a distinction between *analytic geometry* and *coordinate geometry.* Analytic geometry refers to the study of graphs, including geometric curves and surfaces. Coordinate geometry refers to the use of the coordinate plane to study geometric figures. That is, in coordinate geometry the figure comes first and it is placed on a coordinate plane for study. In analytic geometry, an equation often comes first, and geometry is used to study the equation.

Photo Connection

The photo collage makes real-world connections to the content of the chapter: indirect and coordinate proofs.

Zebras: Much like the fact that no two human beings have the same fingerprint, no two zebras have identical stripe patterns.

Dogs: The beagle is a friendly dog with a strong sense of smell. It originated in ancient Rome, and developed in its present form in England in the 1600s.

Roses: The rose family is the largest family of flowering plants with 3,400 species of trees, shrubs, and herbs.

Milk: Milk is a favorite drink of people all over the world, and is also a nourishing food.

3-D Graphic: Just as 2-dimensional coordinate grids can be used to locate points in a plane, it is possible to locate points in space by using a 3-dimensional coordinate system.

Chapter 11 Projects

At this time you might want to have students look over the projects on pages 675–676.

Lesson 11-5 reviews slope and introduces the idea of coordinate proof. The Distance Formula is derived in Lesson 11-6 and used in Lesson 11-7 to find the equation for a circle. In Lesson 11-8, the Midpoint Formula is proved and then used to prove the Midpoint Connector Theorem. Lesson 11-9 introduces the 3-dimensional analogues to the 2-dimensional ideas presented earlier.

This work extends much of the earlier work in the course. Students first studied logic with if-then statements in Lesson 2-2. The connection with proof was made in Lesson 3-5, and since that time students have seen and have been writing *direct* proofs. They were introduced to the descriptive aspect of coordinate geometry in Lesson 1-3, in which points and lines were graphed. The coordinate descriptions of parallel and perpendicular lines were presented in Chapter 3 and of reflections and other transformations in Chapter 4. The use of coordinates to deduce information about figures was first presented in Chapter 3, where lines were concluded to be parallel or perpendicular based on their slopes. In Chapter 8, coordinate descriptions of polygons were used to calculate the areas of polygons.

Lesson 11-1

Objectives

D Follow the Law of Detachment and the Law of Transitivity to make conclusions.
H Apply the Law of Detachment and the Law of Transitivity in real situations.

Resources

From the ***Teacher's Resource File***
- Lesson Master 11-1A or 11-1B
- Answer Master 11-1
- Teaching Aids
  143 Warm-up
  146 Additional Examples

Additional Resources
- Visuals for Teaching Aids 143, 146

Teaching Lesson 11-1

Warm-up

State as many conclusions as you can from the 15 clues given on page 621. **Answers will vary.**

Notes on Reading

Warm-up gives students some time in class to make conclusions from the 15 clues given in *Chapter Opener.* Do not publicly announce more than a couple of conclusions. If you do so, you will take the fun out of students' finding conclusions on their own.

Consider these statements: "If a person is over 17, that person can vote. A person is 20." What can be concluded? [The person can vote.]

LESSON

11-1 *The Logic of Making Conclusions*

The "Who Owns the Zebra?" puzzle on page 621 is famous partially because nothing in the clues seems to have anything to do with water or zebras. Consequently, it doesn't seem as if there is enough information to figure out the answer to the question. However, by carefully using logic and ruling out possibilities, the owner of the zebra can be determined.

The logic used to solve this kind of puzzle is the same logic that is used in mathematics. Instead of reasoning from clues, mathematicians reason from postulates, definitions, and previously proved theorems. Instead of finding out who owns the zebra or who drinks water, mathematicians try to find out what is true about figures or numbers or other mathematical ideas.

Logic in Proofs

To begin the study of logic, look at the proof below. We have identified each statement with a letter so that the logic becomes clearer.

Given: $ABCD$ is a parallelogram. (p)
To prove: $m\angle 1 = m\angle 2$. (r)

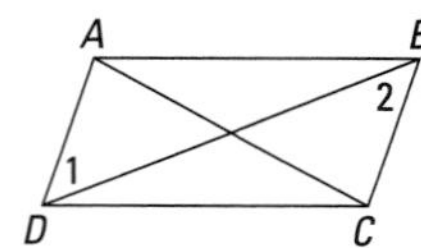

Argument:

Conclusions	Justifications
0. $ABCD$ is a parallelogram. (p)	Given
1. $\overline{AD} \parallel \overline{BC}$ (q)	definition of parallelogram ($p \Rightarrow q$)
2. $m\angle 1 = m\angle 2$ (r)	// Lines $\Rightarrow$ AIA $\cong$ Theorem ($q \Rightarrow r$)

622

Lesson 11-1 Overview

Broad Goals Two laws of logic are discussed in this lesson, namely, the Law of Detachment (If p and ($p \Rightarrow q$), then q) and the Law of Transitivity (If $p \Rightarrow q$ and $q \Rightarrow r$, then $p \Rightarrow r$). The goal of the lesson is for students to see how these laws are applied in a variety of situations.

Perspective There are three major reasons for stating laws such as the Law of Detachment and the Law of Transitivity. The first is to catalog the ways in which conclusions are made. The Law of Detachment is the simplest. Second, these laws characterize the reasoning used in mathematical proofs. And third, some laws of reasoning to be encountered in later lessons, such as the Law of Indirect Reasoning, are not so obvious.

In typical two-column proofs, the Law of Detachment is found in almost every line. In them, q is the "conclusion," while $p \Rightarrow q$ is the "justification" for q. It is p, the given, that is sometimes lost when thinking about each line. Another name for the Law of Detachment is *modus ponens.*

Without the Law of Transitivity, it would not be possible to use conclusions to make other conclusions or to be able to say that the last statement deduced follows from the original given. The important point is that a

The Law of Detachment

Recall that in a proof argument each justification for a conclusion is a true conditional, with the conclusion as the consequent. This idea is used in step 1 of the argument on page 622. The conditional $p \Rightarrow q$ is the justification for concluding q from the given. The general logical principle is called the *Law of Detachment* because q is "detached" from $p \Rightarrow q$. It is a generalization of the common sense idea that when $p \Rightarrow q$ is a true conditional and p is true, then q also must be true.

> **Law of Detachment**
> From a true conditional $p \Rightarrow q$ and a statement or given information p, you may conclude q.

The Law of Transitivity

Conclusions can be antecedents for making other conclusions. In step 2 of the proof argument on page 622, we use the conclusion q and a theorem $q \Rightarrow r$, to conclude r, giving the theorem as the justification. From steps 1 and 2, we can conclude $p \Rightarrow r$. This logic can be diagrammed as follows:

If $p \Rightarrow q$
and $q \Rightarrow r$,
then $p \Rightarrow r$.

This logical principle is called the *Law of Transitivity*. (It is sometimes called the *Transitive Property of Implication*.)

> **Law of Transitivity**
> If $p \Rightarrow q$ and $q \Rightarrow r$ are true, then $p \Rightarrow r$ is true.

Using Laws of Logic in Everyday Situations

Logical principles can be applied in everyday thinking.

Example 1

A commercial states:

If you want to be popular, you must dress well.
If you dress well, you must wear Brand X jeans.

What conclusion does the commercial want you to make?

Solution

Assign variables to the statements.

p: You want to be popular.
d: You dress well.
x: You must wear Brand X jeans.

The commercial states: If p, then d. If d, then x.
Using the symbol $\Rightarrow$, you can write: $p \Rightarrow d$ and $d \Rightarrow x$. ▶

The answer is obvious. Every student in your classes could reach this conclusion. Humans have a natural logic. The task in mathematics is to harness this ability. The danger is that by formalizing the process you may encourage students to think there is more to reasoning in mathematics than there really is, and to think that mathematics makes the easy things hard. In this chapter we try to use these (simple) principles to arrive at nonobvious conclusions.

There are three types of examples given in the lesson. **Example 1** involves a real-life situation, **Example 2** is a geometric example, and **Example 3** is a puzzle.

You may also wish to include an example from algebra:

p	$3n + 18 > 16$	Given
$\Rightarrow q$	$3n > -2$	Addition Property of Inequality $[p \Rightarrow q]$
$\Rightarrow r$	$n > -\frac{2}{3}$	Multiplication Property of Inequality $[q \Rightarrow r]$

Write the steps and the justifications, but not the logic. Ask students to identify p, q, and r. What can be concluded using the Law of Transitivity? $[p \Rightarrow r]$ Fill in the logic as students give you the answers.

Literature Connection *Alice's Adventures in Wonderland* (1865) was originally written and illustrated for Alice Liddell, the daughter of the dean of Christ Church College, Oxford. Later, the story was professionally illustrated and published. It has become one of the most famous children's books of all time.

conclusion made from a conclusion is just as valid as the first conclusion. This runs counter to the intuition of many people, who believe that long chains of if-then statements are not as trustworthy as short chains. This comes from the fact that long chains of work are more likely to harbor errors. However, if each step is correct, the end result is just as valid.

IF. . .THEN statements in computer programs ignore false antecedents. If-then statements in formal logic are considered true if the antecedent is false. For instance, a statement such as "If 3 = 4, then triangles have six sides" is true, because the antecedent 3 = 4 is false. The rationale for this is that if a false antecedent is chosen, then with valid logic, both true and false conclusions follow. Since the logic is valid, the if-then statement is considered true.

Additional Examples

These examples are also given on **Teaching Aid 146.**

1. Maria's father said, "If you go to computer camp, we will buy you a computer." Her mother said, "If you make an A in geometry, you can go to computer camp." What conclusion can Maria make? **If she makes an A in geometry, her parents will buy her a computer.**
2. What conclusion can be made using all of these statements?
   (1) Every rectangle is an isosceles trapezoid.
   (2) *ABCD* is a rectangle.
   (3) The perpendicular bisector of the bases of an isosceles trapezoid is a symmetry line for the isosceles trapezoid.
   From (1) and (3) by the Law of Transitivity, (4) the perpendicular bisector of the bases of every rectangle is a symmetry line for the rectangle; from (2) and (4) by the Law of Detachment, the perpendicular bisector of the bases of *ABCD* is a symmetry line for *ABCD*.
3. Here is another Lewis Carroll puzzle. What can you conclude?
   (1) All puddings are nice.
   (2) This dish is a pudding.
   (3) No nice things are wholesome. **This dish is not wholesome.**
4. A contest states: "The deadline is May 1." Jack entered on April 29.
   a. How are these two facts related to the given of the Law of Detachment? **The first statement is: If a person enters by May 1, then he or she meets the deadline. The second statement is: Jack entered by May 1.**
   b. What conclusion is desired? **Jack met the deadline.**

By the Law of Transitivity, you can conclude $p \Rightarrow x$. In words:
If you want to be popular, you must wear Brand X jeans.

Of course, the commercial wants you to believe that $p \Rightarrow d$ and $d \Rightarrow x$ are true conditionals. Then you would have to accept $p \Rightarrow x$. But many people would *not* accept $p \Rightarrow d$ and $d \Rightarrow x$. If either $p \Rightarrow d$ or $d \Rightarrow x$ is false, you have no reason to conclude $p \Rightarrow x$.

Using Laws of Logic in Geometry

In Example 2, the Law of Detachment and the Law of Transitivity are combined to make a conclusion about a geometric figure.

Example 2

What conclusion about *MBUS* can be made using all three statements below?
(1) Every rhombus is a kite.
(2) The diagonals of a kite are perpendicular.
(3) *MBUS* is a rhombus.

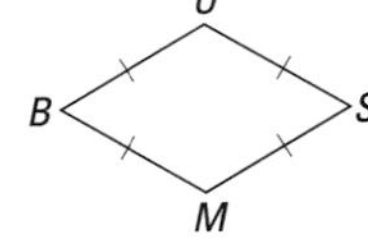

Solution

First, rewrite the first two statements as conditionals.
(1) If a figure is a rhombus, then it is a kite.
(2) If a figure is a kite, then its diagonals are perpendicular.
Next, represent each statement by means of appropriate letters.
(1) $r \Rightarrow k$
(2) $k \Rightarrow p$
(3) MBUS is an instance of r.

From (1) and (2), using the Law of Transitivity, you can conclude $r \Rightarrow p$:
If a figure is a rhombus, then its diagonals are perpendicular.
From r and $r \Rightarrow p$, using the Law of Detachment, you can conclude p:
The diagonals of MBUS are perpendicular.
Since the given statements (1)–(3) are true, the conclusion is also true.

Using Laws of Logic to Solve Puzzles

Lewis Carroll [1832–1898], the Englishman best known for writing *Alice's Adventures in Wonderland* and *Through the Looking Glass*, was a logician. That is, he studied the process of reasoning. Under his given name, Charles L. Dodgson, he was a professor at Oxford University and wrote books on logic. Here is a puzzle from one of his books.

Example 3

What can you conclude using all three statements?
(1) My gardener is well worth listening to on military subjects.
(2) No one can remember the battle of Waterloo, unless he is very old.
(3) Nobody is really worth listening to on military subjects, unless he can remember the battle of Waterloo.

Optional Activities

You might use this activity after students complete the lesson. Have students **work in small groups.** One student makes up a true conditional statement of the form $p \Rightarrow q$. Then a second student should use the consequent q to write another true conditional $q \Rightarrow r$. Finally a third student should use the Law of Transitivity to form a third conditional $p \Rightarrow r$. Refer students to **Example 1** if they need ideas.

The battle of Waterloo is one of the subjects in logic puzzles by Charles Dodgson. See Example 3 on page 624.

Solution

Assign a letter to each statement or clause in the given statements.

Let m: A person is worth listening to on military subjects.
w: A person can remember the battle of Waterloo.
o: A person is very old.

Now analyze the three numbered statements.

(1) is an instance of m (the gardener).
(2) is $w \Rightarrow o$.
(3) is $m \Rightarrow w$.

From (1) and (3), using the Law of Detachment, you can conclude *w*, for the gardener. Together with (2), using the Law of Detachment, you get an instance of *o*, again for the gardener. Lewis Carroll's desired conclusion is: My gardener is very old.

Conditionals with False Antecedents

Consider this statement:

If the moon is made of green cheese, then the sun is made of salsa.

The antecedent is "the moon is made of green cheese," a false statement. Is it possible to show an instance of the conditional? No, since an instance requires that the antecedent be true. Is it possible to state a counterexample? No, a counterexample also requires that the antecedent be true. Thus, if an antecedent is not true, you cannot trust any conclusions made from it. They could be true. They could be false.

QUESTIONS

Covering the Reading

1. What did Descartes think mathematics and logic could provide? the means to solve any problem in any field of endeavor
2. Which two logical principles are used in the proof on page 622? Law of Detachment, Law of Transitivity
3. If p is given and $p \Rightarrow q$ is true, then _?_ can be concluded. q

In 4–6, what can be concluded from the pair of given statements?

4. (1) Every square is a rectangle.
(2) Every rectangle is a parallelogram.
Every square is a parallelogram.
5. (1) You will look better if you wear designer clothes.
(2) The better you look, the more popular you will be.
If you wear designer clothes, you will be more popular.
6. (1) If a figure is a prism, then the figure is a polyhedron.
(2) A figure is a polyhedron if it is a pyramid.
No conclusion can be made.
7. Name the law of logic used.
All cats like fish.
Garfield is a cat.
So Garfield likes fish. Law of Detachment

5. What can you conclude from these statements of famous writers?
(1) "A little learning is a dangerous thing." Alexander Pope
(2) "If a little knowledge is dangerous, then no one is out of danger." Thomas Huxley
No one is out of danger.
6. Consider these steps in solving an equation. Give justifications for: $p \Rightarrow q$, $q \Rightarrow r$, and $p \Rightarrow r$.
p: $5t - 11 = 24$
q: $5t = 35$
r: $t = 7$
Addition Property of Equality; Multiplication Property of Equality; Law of Transitivity

Notes on Questions

Question 4 This transitivity can be shown on the quadrilateral hierarchy.

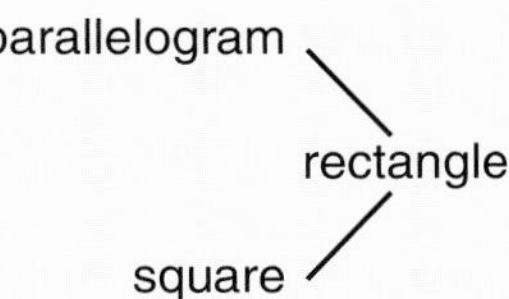

The transitivity means: if *a* is below and attached to *b* on the hierarchy and *b* is below and attached to *c*, then *a* is below and attached to *c*.

Adapting to Individual Needs

Extra Help

In **Example 3,** some students may not recognize that statement (2) can be restated as "If a person can remember the battle of Waterloo, then he is very old." Also, statement (3) can be restated as "If a person is worth listening to on military subjects, then he can remember the battle of Waterloo." Remind students that many statements are not necessarily written in "if -then" form, but they can be restated that way. However, students must be careful that their rewording does indeed mean the same thing as the original statement.

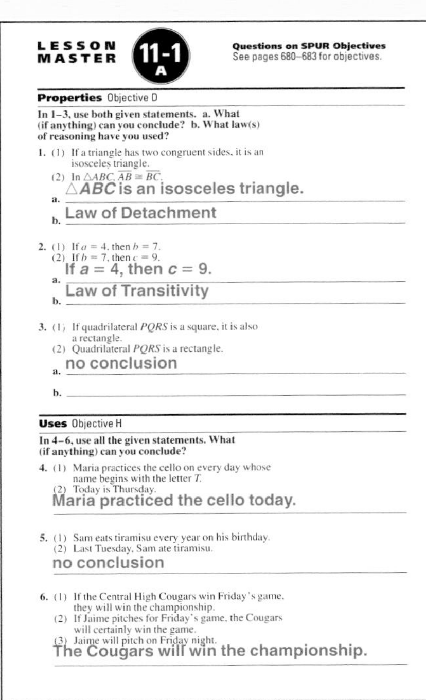

LESSON MASTER 11-1 A

Questions on SPUR Objectives
See pages 680–683 for objectives.

Properties Objective D

In 1–3, use both given statements. a. What (if anything) can you conclude? b. What law(s) of reasoning have you used?

1. (1) If a triangle has two congruent sides, it is an isosceles triangle.
(2) In $\triangle ABC$, $\overline{AB} \cong \overline{BC}$.
a. $\triangle ABC$ is an isosceles triangle.
b. Law of Detachment

2. (1) If $a = 4$, then $b = 7$.
(2) If $b = 7$, then $c = 9$.
a. If $a = 4$, then $c = 9$.
b. Law of Transitivity

3. (1) If quadrilateral *PQRS* is a square, it is also a rectangle.
(2) Quadrilateral *PQRS* is a rectangle.
a. no conclusion
b. ___

Uses Objective H

In 4–6, use all the given statements. What (if anything) can you conclude?

4. (1) Maria practices the cello on every day whose name begins with the letter *T*.
(2) Today is Thursday.
Maria practiced the cello today.

5. (1) Sam eats tiramisu every year on his birthday.
(2) Last Tuesday, Sam ate tiramisu.
no conclusion

6. (1) If the Central High Cougars win Friday's game, they will win the championship.
(2) If Jaime pitches for Friday's game, the Cougars will certainly win the game.
(3) Jaime will pitch on Friday night.
The Cougars will win the championship.

Notes on Questions

Questions 12–14, 17, 18 The Law of Detachment states if $p \Rightarrow q$ is true and p' is or satisfies p, then $p' \Rightarrow q$. In each of these questions, p' does not satisfy p, so the Law of Detachment cannot apply to deducing $p' \Rightarrow q$.

Question 13 Sports Connection Arthur Ashe did win Wimbledon in 1975. You may want to explain that *Wimbledon,* a tennis tournament held every summer in Wimbledon, England, is the most highly regarded of the world's major championships for men and women.

Question 14 Error Alert Remind students to notice that in the first statement, the antecedent p is that a triangle is equilateral. Some students may conclude that $\triangle ABC$ is an equilateral triangle. You can draw an isosceles $\triangle ABC$ that is not equilateral to show that the conclusion is wrong. This could also be related to the converse of a conditional, which will be reviewed in Lesson 11-2.

Questions 24–25 These questions review coordinate geometry in anticipation of Lesson 11-5.

Question 27 Discuss this question, listing the valid conclusions offered by your students. Here is a conclusion, rather easily proved via coordinates, which they may not have seen: If $ABCD$ is a rectangle and P is any point in the plane, then $PA^2 + PC^2 = PB^2 + PD^2$.

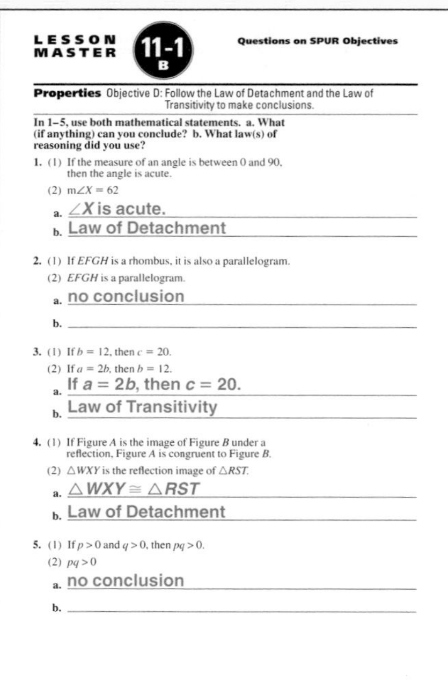

LESSON MASTER 11-1 B Questions on SPUR Objectives

Properties Objective D: Follow the Law of Detachment and the Law of Transitivity to make conclusions.

In 1–5, use both mathematical statements. a. What (if anything) can you conclude? b. What law(s) of reasoning did you use?

1. (1) If the measure of an angle is between 0 and 90, then the angle is acute.
   (2) $m\angle X = 62$
   a. $\angle X$ is acute.
   b. Law of Detachment

2. (1) If $EFGH$ is a rhombus, it is also a parallelogram.
   (2) $EFGH$ is a parallelogram.
   a. no conclusion
   b. _____

3. (1) If $b = 12$, then $c = 20$.
   (2) If $a = 2b$, then $b = 12$.
   a. If $a = 2b$, then $c = 20$.
   b. Law of Transitivity

4. (1) If Figure A is the image of Figure B under a reflection, Figure A is congruent to Figure B.
   (2) $\triangle WXY$ is the reflection image of $\triangle RST$.
   a. $\triangle WXY \cong \triangle RST$
   b. Law of Detachment

5. (1) If $p > 0$ and $q > 0$, then $pq > 0$.
   (2) $pq > 0$
   a. no conclusion
   b. _____

8. Name the law of logic used in the proof argument below.
$s \Rightarrow t$ and $r \Rightarrow s$ are true.
So $r \Rightarrow t$ is true.
Law of Transitivity

9. Explain why you cannot give an instance of the statement *If 2 = 3, then 100 = 200.* An instance requires that the antecedent be true, but 2 = 3 is not true.

Arthur Ashe (1943–1993)

Applying the Mathematics

In 10–13, assume this statement is true: *If a tennis player has won Wimbledon, then the player is world-class.* Using the Law of Detachment only, what (if anything) can you conclude if you also know the given statement is true?

10. Steffi Graf has won Wimbledon.
Steffi Graf is world-class.

11. Pete Sampras has won Wimbledon.
Pete Sampras is world-class.

12. Gabriela Sabatini has not won Wimbledon (as of 1995).
No conclusion can be made.

13. Arthur Ashe has won the U.S. Open Tennis Tournament.
No conclusion can be made.

14. What can you conclude from these two statements? Explain your answer in words.
(1) A triangle has two congruent angles if it is equilateral.
(2) $\triangle ABC$ has two congruent angles.
Nothing can be concluded. There is no instance of the antecedent.

In 15–18, use this information: In some states if a person has a driver's license, then the person's age is greater than or equal to 16. Tell what you can conclude in those states if you also know the following:

15. Thayer has a driver's license.
Thayer is 16 or older.

16. Neesham drives a car legally.
Neesham is 16 or older.

17. Florence is 18 years old.
Nothing can be concluded.

18. Isabel does not drive a car.
Nothing can be concluded.

19. Lewis Carroll asked if this reasoning is correct. Is it?
(1) Dictionaries are useful.
(2) Useful books are valuable.
Conclusion: Dictionaries are valuable.
Yes

In 20 and 21, use the drawing at the right.

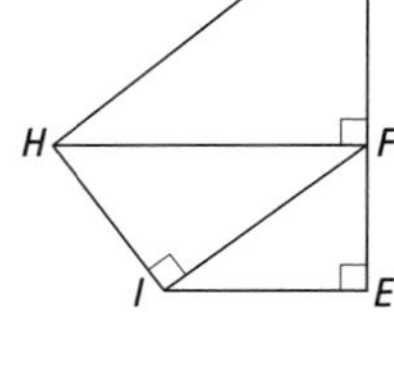

20. Let $HI = 15$, $EF = 12$, $EI = 16$, and $FG = 20$.
   a. Find FI. 20
   b. Find FH. 25
   c. Find GH. ≈ 32
   d. *Multiple choice.* Which, if any, of the following has not been used in finding GH?
      (i) Law of Detachment
      (ii) Law of Transitivity
      (iii) Pythagorean Theorem
      (iv) All of these are used. iv

21. Explain why $GH^2 = FG^2 + HI^2 + IE^2 + EF^2$.
$GH^2 = FG^2 + FH^2$, but $FH^2 = HI^2 + FI^2$, so by substituting, $GH^2 = FG^2 + HI^2 + FI^2$. But $FI^2 = IE^2 + EF^2$, so by substituting, $GH^2 = FG^2 + HI^2 + IE^2 + EF^2$.

Adapting to Individual Needs

English Language Development
You might have students with limited English proficiency begin by making up conditionals using numerical examples from mathematics. Then pair the students with English-speaking students and have them try giving statements using words.

626

22) Yes; $11x + 18 + 15x + 6 + 16x + 8x + 36 = 360$, so $x = 6$. Therefore, $m\angle N = 84 = m\angle T$, and $m\angle G = 96 = m\angle A$. By the Sufficient Conditions for a Parallelogram, *TANG* is a parallelogram.

23) Sample:

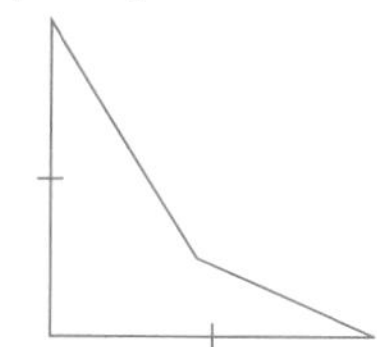

Review

22. In quadrilateral *TANG*, angles have measures as marked. Is *TANG* a parallelogram? How do you know? *(Lesson 7-8)* See left.

N, A, G, T; $(11x + 18)°$, $(16x)°$, $(15x + 6)°$, $(8x + 36)°$

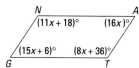

23. Draw a counterexample to this statement: *If a quadrilateral has two consecutive sides congruent, then it is a kite.* *(Lesson 6-4)* See left.

24. **a.** Graph the lines with equations $y = 2x + 1$ and $y = 2x + 2$.
b. Are these lines parallel, intersecting, or coincident?
c. Are these lines horizontal, vertical, or oblique? *(Lessons 1-3, 3-6)*
a) See below. b) parallel c) oblique

25. Find the slope of the line through each pair of points. *(Lesson 3-6)*
a. (7, 5) and (-3, 1) $\frac{2}{5}$
b. (a, b) and $(2a, 2b)$ (Assume $a \neq 0$.) $\frac{b}{a}$
c. (a, b) and (b, a) (Assume $a \neq b$.) -1

26. Fill in the blanks. $\sqrt{200} = \sqrt{\underline{\ ?\ }} \cdot \sqrt{2} = \underline{\ ?\ } \cdot \sqrt{2}$ *(Previous course)*
100, 10

Exploration

27. Let p be the statement *a figure is a rectangle.* State as many theorems as you can of the form $p \Rightarrow q$. For each theorem, tell what q means for rectangle *ABCD*. Sample: If a figure is a rectangle, then its diagonals are congruent. q: $\overline{AC} \cong \overline{BD}$.

28. Examine the clues in "Who Owns the Zebra?" Make a conclusion that is not given in the clues.
Samples: The second house from the left is the blue house.
The first house is the yellow house.
The horse is kept at the blue house.

24a)

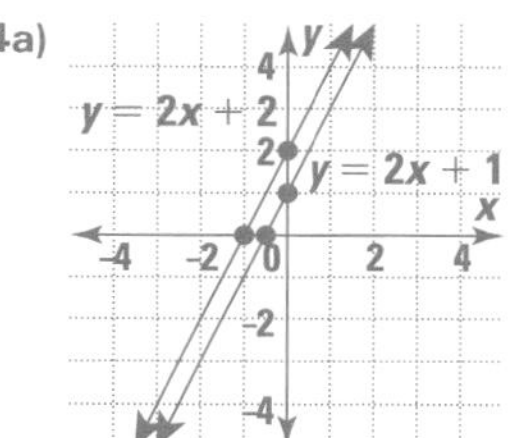

Who owns the snail?

Follow-up for Lesson 11-1

Practice

For more questions on SPUR Objectives, use **Lesson Master 11-1A** (shown on page 625) or **Lesson Master 11-1B** (shown on pages 626–627).

Assessment

Written Communication Have each student write a paragraph to explain and give an example of each of the logical principles discussed in this lesson. [Students provide a clear explanation, including an example, of the Law of Detachment and the Law of Transitivity.]

Extension

Have students look for examples of advertisements in which it would be useful to have a knowledge of the Laws of Logic discussed in this lesson. Suggest that they try to find advertisements in which the advertiser uses false conditionals or hopes a person will assume a false conditional. [Answers will vary.]

Project Update Project 1, *Logic Puzzle,* Project 2, *Lewis Carroll,* and Project 6, *Truth Tables,* on pages 675–676, relate to the content of this lesson.

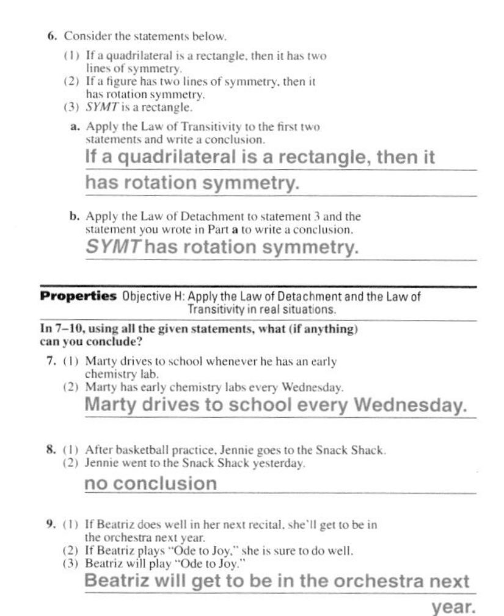

▶ LESSON MASTER 11-1B *page 2*

6. Consider the statements below.
(1) If a quadrilateral is a rectangle, then it has two lines of symmetry.
(2) If a figure has two lines of symmetry, then it has rotation symmetry.
(3) *SYMT* is a rectangle.
a. Apply the Law of Transitivity to the first two statements and write a conclusion.
If a quadrilateral is a rectangle, then it has rotation symmetry.
b. Apply the Law of Detachment to statement 3 and the statement you wrote in Part **a** to write a conclusion.
SYMT has rotation symmetry.

Properties Objective H: Apply the Law of Detachment and the Law of Transitivity in real situations.

In 7–10, using all the given statements, what (if anything) can you conclude?

7. (1) Marty drives to school whenever he has an early chemistry lab.
(2) Marty has early chemistry labs every Wednesday.
Marty drives to school every Wednesday.

8. (1) After basketball practice, Jennie goes to the Snack Shack.
(2) Jennie went to the Snack Shack yesterday.
no conclusion

9. (1) If Beatriz does well in her next recital, she'll get to be in the orchestra next year.
(2) If Beatriz plays "Ode to Joy," she is sure to do well.
(3) Beatriz will play "Ode to Joy."
Beatriz will get to be in the orchestra next year.

10. (1) City Hall is closed on national holidays.
(2) Building permits are issued only at City Hall.
(3) Today is July 4.
Building permits are not issued today.

Adapting to Individual Needs

Challenge Writing

Logicians have noted paradoxes that come from certain statements that involve self-reference. Have students write a paragraph about the paradox that comes from this statement: "This sentence is false." [If the sentence is true, then it is false. If it is false, then it is true.] Another example is: A barber shaves exactly those people in town who do not shave themselves. Who shaves the barber? [If the barber does not shave himself, then he does shave himself, and conversely. This kind of contradiction can be avoided by restricting the use of self-referencing sentences in logic.]

Lesson 11-2

Objectives

D Follow the Law of the Contrapositive to make conclusions.
E Write the converse, inverse, or contrapositive of a conditional.
H Apply the Law of the Contrapositive in real situations.

Resources

From the ***Teacher's Resource File***
- Lesson Master 11-2A or 11-2B
- Answer Master 11-2
- Teaching Aid
  143 Warm-up
  147 Additional Examples

Additional Resource
- Visuals for Teaching Aids 143, 147

Teaching Lesson 11-2

Warm-up

Writing Rewrite each of the following statements so that your statement has the same meaning but is easier to understand. **Sample responses are given.**

1. It is false that I did not do my homework. **It is true that I did my homework.**
2. Never refuse the chance to fight bigotry. **Accept every chance to fight bigotry.**
3. Suppose someone says, "It is never a good idea to nullify the results of changing your mind." What does the person really mean? **Once you change your mind, stick to your decision.**

LESSON

11-2 *Negations*

Logicians . . . NOT! *Wayne and Garth are two gnarly negators who comically demonstrate how just to say "NOT!"*

In the movie *Wayne's World*, Wayne's friend Garth is unexpectedly left to host the Wayne's World television show alone. He says: "I'm having a good time. NOT!"

Writing Negations

The quote above and all indirect reasoning uses the idea of *negation*. The **negation** of a statement *p*, called **not-*p*,** is a statement that is true whenever statement *p* is false, and is false whenever statement *p* is true. We say the truth or falseness of a statement is its **truth value.** A statement and its negation always have opposite truth values.

Statement: You study for the next test.

Negation: You do not study for the next test.

Often you can write a negation by just inserting the word *not* in the statement. If the sentence already is negative, then the negation takes out the "not."

p: The quadrilateral *ABCD* is not a parallelogram.

not-p: The quadrilateral *ABCD* is a parallelogram.

Sometimes the word *not* can be avoided by considering all the alternatives.

p: $\triangle ABC$ is isosceles.

not-p: $\triangle ABC$ is scalene.

Lesson 11-2 Overview

Broad Goals This lesson discusses negations, inverses, and contrapositives, culminating in the Law of the Contrapositive.

Perspective Given that $p \Rightarrow q$ is the original statement, negating and/or switching both *p* and *q* results in one of the following three statements:

$q \Rightarrow p$:	converse
not-$p \Rightarrow$ not-q:	inverse
not-$q \Rightarrow$ not-p:	contrapositive

The Law of the Contrapositive states that when $p \Rightarrow q$ is true, then its contrapositive is true. If the converse $q \Rightarrow p$ is also true, then the biconditional $p \Leftrightarrow q$ is true, and all four of the above statements are true. Thus there can never be an odd number of true statements within this group of four.

The Law of the Contrapositive is discussed in most geometry books, although it is not always named. In this lesson, the law is applied to logic puzzles. Surprisingly, this law is not used often in proofs even though many theorems that are proved with an indirect proof can be proved quite easily if the law is used. For instance, consider the theorem that $\sqrt{2}$ is irrational. That theorem can be stated as a conditional as follows: If $\frac{a}{b}$ is in lowest terms and *a* and *b* are positive integers, then $\sqrt{2} \neq \frac{a}{b}$. The usual indirect proof really proves the contrapositive

p:	Coplanar lines ℓ and m intersect at exactly one point.
correct *not-p*:	Coplanar lines ℓ and m are parallel.
incorrect *not-p*:	Coplanar lines ℓ and m have no points in common. This statement is not the negation of p because it does not include all alternatives to p (the lines may be identical).

The negation of a negation is the original statement. The statements p and *not*-(*not-p*) have the same truth value.

Inverses and Contrapositives of Conditionals

Recall that from any conditional $p \Rightarrow q$, you can form its converse $q \Rightarrow p$. Let p = a triangle is equilateral, and q = a triangle has three acute angles.

Original $p \Rightarrow q$: If a triangle is equilateral, then it has three acute angles.

Converse $q \Rightarrow p$: If a triangle has three acute angles, then it is equilateral.

Here the original conditional is true, and its converse is false.

Negating *both* the antecedent and the consequent of the original conditional gives a new conditional of the form **not-*p* ⇒ not-*q*,** called the **inverse** of the original.

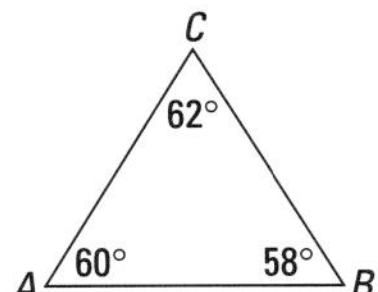

Inverse *not-p* ⇒ *not-q*: If a triangle is not equilateral, then it does not have three acute angles.

This inverse is false. The triangle at the left is not equilateral, yet it has three acute angles.

If both parts of the original are negated and the antecedent and consequent are switched, the result is a statement of the form **not-*q* ⇒ not-*p*.** This statement is called the **contrapositive** of the original.

Contrapositive *not-q* ⇒ *not-p*: If a triangle does not have three acute angles, then it is not equilateral.

Notice that this statement is true, just as $p \Rightarrow q$ was true.

Example 1

Given the conditional *If you live in California, then you need a mountain bike,* write its converse, inverse, and contrapositive.

Solution

Converse ($q \Rightarrow p$): If you need a mountain bike, then you live in California.

Inverse (not-p ⇒ not-q): If you do not live in California, then you do not need a mountain bike.

▶

Notes on Reading

You might wish to point out to students that the inverse and the converse of a statement are either both true or both false. This is because the inverse is the contrapositive of the converse.

Reading Mathematics As students read the lesson, ask them to use proper grammar and English when writing the negation, converse, inverse, or contrapositive of a statement. That is, what they write should not be an awkward statement. Ask them to reread their statements very carefully.

directly; that is, if $\sqrt{2} = \frac{a}{b}$ and a and b are positive integers, then $\frac{a}{b}$ cannot be in lowest terms. Thus, one could prove the contrapositive and then apply the Law of the Contrapositive to conclude that $\sqrt{2}$ is irrational. This would not be considered a direct proof because the Law of the Contrapositive is considered to introduce "indirection" to the argument.

Logicians often use the symbol ~*p* where we use *not-p*. We avoid ~*p* because the tilde ~ might be confused with the symbol ~ for similarity, and because *not-p* more easily conveys the idea of negation. But you may wish to use ~*p*.

Your school library may have one or more of the puzzle books of Lewis Carroll. We warn you that he was, by current standards, a very bigoted man, a characteristic reflected in many of his puzzles. Therefore, we do not suggest doing too much with the books themselves.

Additional Examples

These examples are also given on **Teaching Aid 147.**

1. Write the converse, inverse, and contrapositive of the following statement: If you live in an air-conditioned place, then you have the opportunity to be cool in the summer. **Converse: If you have the opportunity to be cool in the summer, then you live in an air-conditioned place. Inverse: If you do not live in an air-conditioned place, then you do not have the opportunity to be cool in the summer. Contrapositive: If you do not have the opportunity to be cool in the summer, then you do not live in an air-conditioned place.**
2. Make a conclusion from these two statements.
   (1) Bill cannot become an eagle scout.
   (2) If a person is a boy scout, he can become an eagle scout.
   Bill is not a boy scout.
3. Make a conclusion using all three statements.
   (1) If we hang an Escher print on this wall, people will smile as they enter the room.
   (2) If we do not put up an Escher print on this wall, I will be bothered.
   (3) I will not be bothered if we remove these paintings from this wall.
   If we remove these paintings from this wall, then people will smile as they enter the room.

(Notes on Questions begin on page 632.)

Contrapositive (not-$q \Rightarrow$ not-p): **If you do not need a mountain bike, then you do not live in California.**

The given and all three statements in the solution of Example 1 are false. Both Example 1 and the equilateral triangle example preceding it are instances of the following law of logic.

Law of the Contrapositive
A conditional ($p \Rightarrow q$) and its contrapositive (not-$q \Rightarrow$ not-p) are either both true or both false.

That is, a statement and its contrapositive have the same truth value. To summarize: If a given conditional is true, you may conclude that its contrapositive is true, but its converse and inverse may be either true or false.

Making Conclusions Using the Law of the Contrapositive

The Law of the Contrapositive used along with the Law of Detachment and the Law of Transitivity allows you to make many more conclusions.

Example 2

Given are two statements.
(1) Every square is a kite.
(2) Quadrilateral *POTS* is not a kite.
What conclusion can be made using both statements?

Solution

First change statement (1) into a conditional: **(1) If a figure is a square, then it is a kite. This is a true conditional. Thus, its contrapositive is also true: If a figure is not a kite, then it is not a square.** Now, since **(2) POTS is not a kite,** you can use the Law of Detachment to conclude that **POTS is not a square.**

You now have studied enough laws of logic to figure out many logic puzzles. Here is a version of another one of Lewis Carroll's puzzles. Notice how the Law of the Contrapositive and the Law of Transitivity are both used.

Example 3

Given these statements, what can you conclude?
(1) Babies are illogical.
(2) Any person who can manage an alligator is not despised.
(3) Illogical persons are despised.

Optional Activities

You can use this activity after students have completed the lesson. Have students **work in groups.** Tell them to try to find examples of conditional statements in songs and literature. (For example, an old song is titled, "If I Knew You Were Coming, I'd Have Baked a Cake.") For each example they find, have them write the converse, the inverse, and the contrapositive.

Adapting to Individual Needs

Extra Help

In the student text, we give the following definitions for the inverse and the contrapositive of a conditional statement $p \Rightarrow q$.

not-p $\Rightarrow$ *not-q*: inverse
not-q $\Rightarrow$ *not-p*: contrapositive

Although "*not-p*" stands for the negation of statement p, the word "not" may or may not appear in the actual statement of the inverse or contrapositive, depending on the wordings for p and q.

Why did the alligator cross the road? *Police officers in North Carolina protected this 12-foot long alligator for an hour while it soaked up the warmth of the asphalt in the early morning.*

Solution

To avoid lots of writing, use variables to name the parts of the statements.

Let
B = A person is a baby.
D = A person is despised.
M = A person can manage an alligator.
I = A person is illogical.

Now (1) becomes $B \Rightarrow I$.
(2) becomes $M \Rightarrow$ not-D.
(3) becomes $I \Rightarrow D$.

From (1) and (3) you can conclude (using transitivity) $B \Rightarrow D$.

The contrapositive of (2) is $D \Rightarrow$ not-M. Using transitivity again, $B \Rightarrow$ not-M: A baby cannot manage an alligator.

QUESTIONS

Covering the Reading

In 1–4, write the negation of the statement.

1. $\angle A$ is acute.
   $\angle A$ is not acute, or $\angle A$ is either zero, straight, right, or obtuse.
2. The perimeter of an n-gon with side s is ns.
   The perimeter of an n-gon with side s is not ns.
3. You were not late for school today.
   You were late for school today.
4. $\triangle GHI$ is scalene.
   $\triangle GHI$ is not scalene, or $\triangle GHI$ is isosceles.
5. The negation of a statement p is written _?_.
   not-p

In 6–8, a statement is given.
a. Write its converse.
b. Write its contrapositive.
c. Write its inverse.
d. Tell which (if any) of these are true.

6. If m$\angle T$ = 45, then $\angle T$ is acute. See left.
7. $p \Rightarrow q$ (Assume $p \Rightarrow q$ is true.) a) $q \Rightarrow p$ b) not-$q \Rightarrow$ not-p c) not-$p \Rightarrow$ not-q d) b, the contrapositive
8. If an equation of a line is $y = k$, then the line is horizontal. See left.

6a) If $\angle T$ is acute, then m$\angle T$ = 45.
b) If $\angle T$ is not acute, then m$\angle T \neq 45$.
c) If m$\angle T \neq 45$, then $\angle T$ is not acute.
d) b, the contrapositive

8a) If a line is horizontal, then an equation of the line is $y = k$.
b) If a line is not horizontal, then an equation of the line is not $y = k$.
c) If the equation of a line is not $y = k$, then the line is not horizontal.
d) All three are true.

In 9–11, *multiple choice.* The four choices are
(a) negation
(b) converse
(c) inverse
(d) contrapositive.

9. If a statement is true, its _?_ must be true. d
10. If a statement is true, its _?_ must be false. a
11. If a statement is false, its _?_ must be false. d

Follow-up for Lesson 11-2

Practice

For more questions on SPUR Objectives, use **Lesson Master 11-2A** (shown on page 631) or **Lesson Master 11-2B** (shown on pages 632–633).

Assessment

Written Communication Have students **work in pairs.** Each student should write a conditional statement. Then students should exchange papers and write the converse, the inverse, and the contrapositive of the given statement. [Students correctly write the converse, the inverse, and the contrapositive of a given conditional statement.]

(Follow-up continues on page 632.)

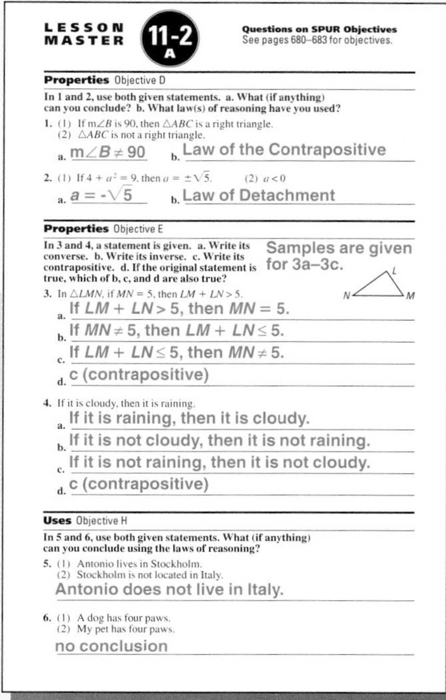

LESSON MASTER 11-2 A

Questions on SPUR Objectives
See pages 680–683 for objectives.

Properties Objective D

In 1 and 2, use both given statements. a. What (if anything) can you conclude? b. What law(s) of reasoning have you used?

1. (1) If m$\angle B$ is 90, then $\triangle ABC$ is a right triangle.
   (2) $\triangle ABC$ is not a right triangle.
   a. m$\angle B \neq 90$ b. Law of the Contrapositive
2. (1) If $4 + a^2 = 9$, then $a = \pm\sqrt{5}$. (2) $a < 0$
   a. $a = -\sqrt{5}$ b. Law of Detachment

Properties Objective E

In 3 and 4, a statement is given. a. Write its converse. b. Write its inverse. c. Write its contrapositive. d. If the original statement is true, which of b, c, and d are also true? Samples are given for 3a–3c.

3. In $\triangle LMN$, if $MN = 5$, then $LM + LN > 5$.
   a. If $LM + LN > 5$, then $MN = 5$.
   b. If $MN \neq 5$, then $LM + LN \leq 5$.
   c. If $LM + LN \leq 5$, then $MN \neq 5$.
   d. c (contrapositive)
4. If it is cloudy, then it is raining.
   a. If it is raining, then it is cloudy.
   b. If it is not cloudy, then it is not raining.
   c. If it is not raining, then it is not cloudy.
   d. c (contrapositive)

Uses Objective H

In 5 and 6, use both given statements. What (if anything) can you conclude using the laws of reasoning?

5. (1) Antonio lives in Stockholm.
   (2) Stockholm is not located in Italy.
   Antonio does not live in Italy.
6. (1) A dog has four paws.
   (2) My pet has four paws.
   no conclusion

Adapting to Individual Needs

Challenge

In each of the situations at the right, a statement p and a statement q are given. Have students explain why q is not a negation of p, and then have them give the proper negation. [In each case, p and q do not have the opposite truth values. For instance, in the first example, both p and q could be false. Correct negations can sometimes be worded in different ways. A sample is given for each instance.]

1. p: All students passed the last test.
   q: All students failed the last test.
   [not p: There is at least one student that failed the test.]
2. p: Some math teachers are hard.
   q: Some math teachers are easy.
   [not p: All math teachers are easy.]
3. p: Today is Friday, and it is hot.
   q: Today is not Friday, and it is not hot.
   [not p: Today is not Friday, or it is not hot.]

Extension

Writing Have students **work in groups** to write instances of each of the following types of conditionals. [Answers will vary.]

1. Both the conditional and its converse are true.
2. The conditional is true, but the converse is false.
3. The conditional is false, but the converse is true.
4. Both the conditional and the converse are false.

Project Update Project 1, *Logic Puzzle,* Project 2, *Lewis Carroll,* and Project 6, *Truth Tables,* on pages 675–676, relate to the content of this lesson.

Notes on Questions

Question 13 Error Alert In this question and elsewhere, when statements are numbered, students should try to use *all* the statements in making their conclusions. One could conclude—from (1) by using the Law of the Contrapositive—that if a network is not traversable, then it does not have only even vertices. That is not the best response, however, because it does not use (2).

Question 15 You might want students to give other examples from other areas of mathematics.

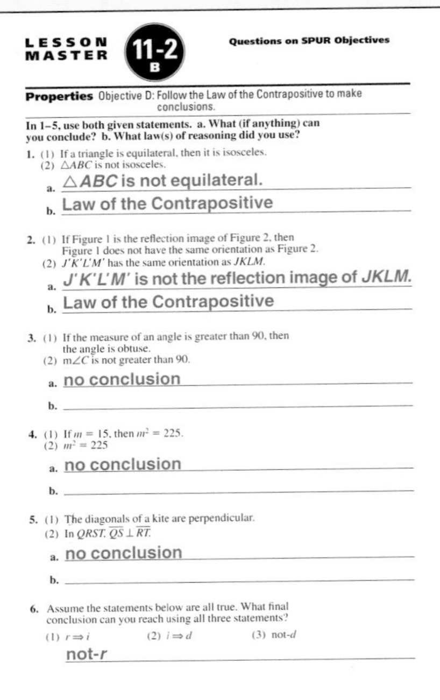

LESSON MASTER 11-2 B — Questions on SPUR Objectives

Properties Objective D: Follow the Law of the Contrapositive to make conclusions.

In 1–5, use both given statements. a. What (if anything) can you conclude? b. What law(s) of reasoning did you use?

1. (1) If a triangle is equilateral, then it is isosceles.
   (2) $\triangle ABC$ is not isosceles.
   a. $\triangle ABC$ is not equilateral.
   b. Law of the Contrapositive

2. (1) If Figure 1 is the reflection image of Figure 2, then Figure 1 does not have the same orientation as Figure 2.
   (2) $J'K'L'M'$ has the same orientation as $JKLM$.
   a. $J'K'L'M'$ is not the reflection image of $JKLM$.
   b. Law of the Contrapositive

3. (1) If the measure of an angle is greater than 90, then the angle is obtuse.
   (2) $m\angle C$ is not greater than 90.
   a. no conclusion
   b.

4. (1) If $m = 15$, then $m^2 = 225$.
   (2) $m^2 = 225$
   a. no conclusion
   b.

5. (1) The diagonals of a kite are perpendicular.
   (2) In $QRST$, $\overline{QS} \perp \overline{RT}$.
   a. no conclusion
   b.

6. Assume the statements below are all true. What final conclusion can you reach using all three statements?
   (1) $r \Rightarrow i$ (2) $i \Rightarrow d$ (3) not-d
   not-r

12a) If the Pythagorean Theorem holds for $\triangle ABC$, then $\triangle ABC$ is a right triangle.

13) The network does not have only even vertices.

17) Yes; let a = Joanne apologized and d = Joanne went on her date. Her mother said not-$a \Rightarrow$ not-d. It is true, so $d \Rightarrow a$ is also true. Since d is true, you can conclude a: Joanne apologized.

12. a. Give the contrapositive of this statement: *If $\triangle ABC$ is not a right triangle, then the Pythagorean Theorem does not hold for $\triangle ABC$.* a) See left.
b. Is the contrapositive true? Yes
c. Is the original statement true? Yes

In 13 and 14, make a conclusion using both of the statements.

13. (1) If a network has only even vertices, it is traversable.
(2) The network below is not traversable. See left.

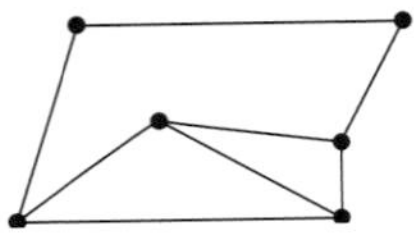

14. (1) If a line rises to the right, it has a positive slope.
(2) The line $2x + 3y = 5$ has a slope of $-\frac{2}{3}$.
The line $2x + 3y = 5$ does not rise to the right.

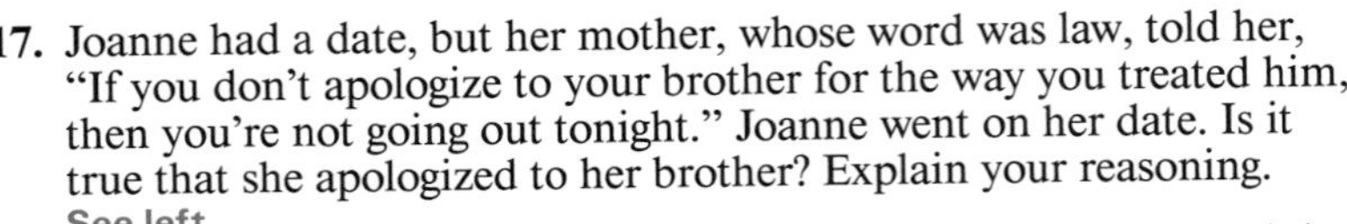

Applying the Mathematics

15. a. Make a conclusion using both these statements.
(1) If $x = 3$, then $y = 4$.
(2) $y = 5$ $x \neq 3$
b. Which two of the three laws—Detachment, Transitivity, and Contrapositive—are needed to make your conclusion?
Detachment and Contrapositive

16. Assuming these three statements are true, what final conclusion can you draw based on all three statements?
(1) $p \Rightarrow q$
(2) $q \Rightarrow r$
(3) not-r not-p

17. Joanne had a date, but her mother, whose word was law, told her, "If you don't apologize to your brother for the way you treated him, then you're not going out tonight." Joanne went on her date. Is it true that she apologized to her brother? Explain your reasoning.
See left.

18. José heard an ad that claimed "If you try our product, you won't be sorry." Later on, José was not sorry. Does that mean he tried the product?
No

In 19 and 20, make a final conclusion based on all the given statements.

19. (1) All equilateral triangles have three 60° angles.
(2) $m\angle ABC = 59$
$\triangle ABC$ is not equilateral.

20. (1) All unripe fruit is unwholesome.
(2) All these apples are wholesome.
(3) No fruit grown in the shade is ripe.
(This question is adapted from a Lewis Carroll puzzle.)
None of these apples was grown in the shade.

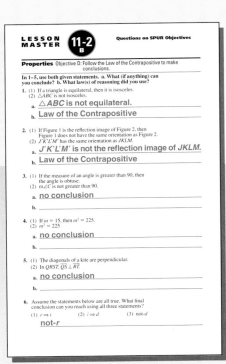

21) From a true conditional $p \Rightarrow q$ and a statement or given information p, you may conclude q.

Review

21. Write the Law of Detachment. *(Lesson 11-1)* See left.

22. Make a conclusion about $ABCD$ from all three statements. *(Lesson 11-1)*
(1) $ABCD$ is a rhombus.
(2) If a figure is a rhombus, then it is a parallelogram.
(3) Opposite sides of a parallelogram are parallel.
The opposite sides of $ABCD$ are parallel.

23. Find PQ. *(Lesson 8-6)* $\sqrt{130}$

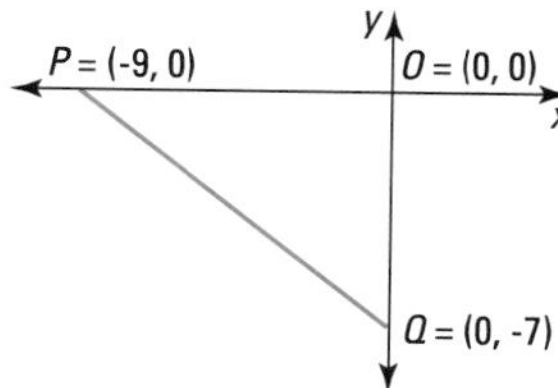

24. Write a proof argument using at least one triangle congruence theorem.
Given: $\overline{AD} \parallel \overline{BC}$, $\overline{AB} \parallel \overline{CD}$.
To prove: $\overline{AB} \cong \overline{CD}$. *(Lessons 7-2, 7-7)*
See margin.

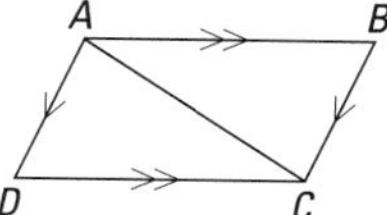

25. *Multiple choice.* In Question 24, what have you proved? b
(a) In a parallelogram, opposite sides are parallel.
(b) In a parallelogram, opposite sides are congruent.
(c) If opposite sides of a quadrilateral are congruent, the quadrilateral is a parallelogram.
(d) If opposite sides of a quadrilateral are parallel, the quadrilateral is a parallelogram. *(Lessons 7-7, 7-8)*

In 26 and 27, solve. *(Previous course)*

26. $6z^2 = 150$ 5, -5

27. $(w + 5)^2 = 289$ 12, -22

28. Give a counterexample to prove that $\sqrt{x^2 + y^2}$ is not always equal to $x + y$. *(Previous course)* Sample: $x = 1$, $y = 2$. $\sqrt{x^2 + y^2} = \sqrt{5}$, $x + y = 3$

29. Fill in the blanks. *(Previous course)*
$\sqrt{4a^2 + 4b^2} = \sqrt{4(\underline{\ ?\ })} = \sqrt{4}\sqrt{\underline{\ ?\ }} = \underline{\ ?\ }\sqrt{\underline{\ ?\ }}$
$a^2 + b^2$; $a^2 + b^2$; 2; $a^2 + b^2$

Exploration

30. Make up your own logic puzzle like the one in Example 3.
Sample: Given these four statements, what can you conclude? (1) Anything that squips isn't a wozzle. (2) Only wozzles tibble. (3) Everything is red unless it tibbles. (4) Ip is green. Conclusion: Ip doesn't squip.

Question 18 In this situation, the advertisers want the listener to think the inverse: "If I do not try the product, I will be sorry." Even if the original ad is true, the inverse does not have to be true. Advertisements usually are technically true, but they often want the listener or reader to reason that the converse or inverse is true.

Questions 28–29 Be sure to review these questions; they are preparation for later work in the chapter in connection with coordinate geometry.

Question 30 You might wish to give students a few days to do this question, or give a prize for the best or most interesting puzzle. One possible criterion for *best* is that the given statements are sayings that people usually take as true while the conclusion is surprising.

Additional Answers

24. Sample:

Conclusions	Justifications
0. $\overline{AD} \parallel \overline{BC}$, $\overline{AB} \parallel \overline{CD}$	Given
1. $\angle DAC \cong \angle BCA$, $\angle DCA \cong \angle BAC$	// Lines ⇒ AIA ≅ Theorem
2. $\overline{AC} \cong \overline{CA}$	Reflexive Prop. of Congruence
3. $\triangle ADC \cong \triangle CBA$	ASA Congruence Theorem
4. $\overline{AB} \cong \overline{CD}$	CPCF Theorem

▸ **LESSON MASTER 11-2B** *page 2*

7. What final conclusion can you reach using all three statements?
(1) A reflection or composite of reflections is an isometry.
(2) If a transformation is an isometry, then distance is preserved.
(3) W is a transformation that does not preserve distance.
W is not a reflection nor a composite of reflections.

Properties Objective E: Write the converse, inverse, or contrapositive of a conditional.

In 8 and 9, a statement is given. a. Write its converse. b. Write its inverse. c. Write its contrapositive. d. Assuming the original statement is true, which of a, b, and c are also true? Samples are given for 8a–8c and 9a–9c.

8. If $\angle X$ and $\angle Y$ are vertical angles, then $m\angle X = m\angle Y$.
a. If $m\angle X = m\angle Y$, $\angle X$ and $\angle Y$ vertical $\angle$s.
b. If $\angle X$ and $\angle Y$ not vertical $\angle$s, $m\angle X \neq m\angle Y$.
c. If $m\angle X \neq m\angle Y$, $\angle X$ and $\angle Y$ not vertical $\angle$s.
d. c (contrapositive)

9. If you are a teen, you were born after 1975.
a. If you were born after '75, you are a teen.
b. If not a teen, you were not born after '75.
c. If not born after '75, you are not a teen.
d. c (contrapositive)

Properties Objective H: Apply the Law of the Contrapositive in real situations.

In 10 and 11, using both given statements, what (if anything) can you conclude using the laws of logic?

10. (1) If Joe does not get a scholarship, he will not attend Yale.
(2) Joe will attend Yale.
Joe will get a scholarship.

11. (1) Today I bought a leather purse.
(2) If I don't get a raise, I won't buy a leather purse.
I got a raise.

Setting Up Lesson 11-3

Materials Students will need a map of the United States or **Teaching Aid 104** for *Warm-up* in Lesson 11-3.

Lesson 11-3

Objectives

D Follow the Law of Ruling Out Possibilities to make conclusions.
H Apply the Law of Ruling Out Possibilities in real situations.

Resources

From the ***Teacher's Resource File***
- Lesson Master 11-3A or 11-3B
- Answer Master 11-3
- Teaching Aids
  - 104 Map of the United States
  - 143 Warm-up
  - 148 Example and Activity Grids
  - 149 Additional Examples

Additional Resources
- Visuals for Teaching Aids 104, 143, 148–149

Teaching Lesson 11-3

Warm-up

Have students refer to a map of the United States or **Teaching Aid 104** to solve the following puzzle.

I am a state that does not lie west of the Mississippi River. My name consists of more than one word. I have no seashore. I do not border another country. What state am I?
West Virginia

LESSON

11-3 *Ruling Out Possibilities*

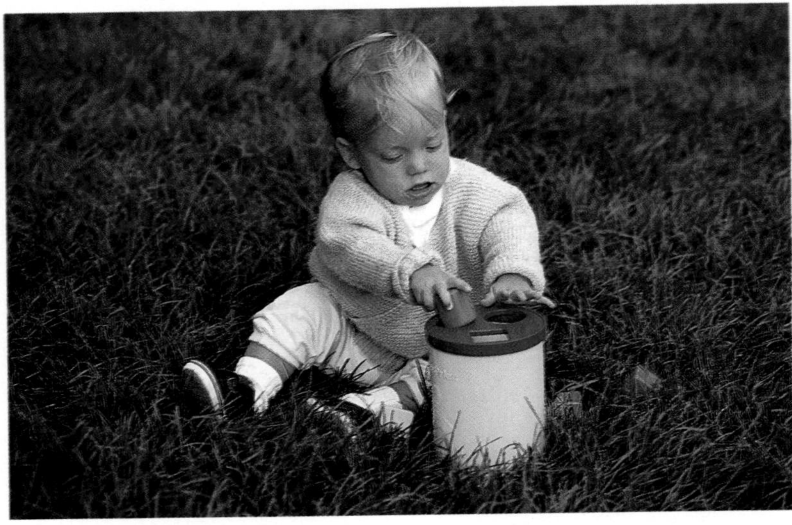

Process of elimination. *Toddlers' toys can help develop the ability to reason.*

The Law of Ruling Out Possibilities

Indirect reasoning is based on the idea of ruling out possibilities. The idea is simple, and is used even by animals and babies. If a child knows that a toy is either in a parent's right hand or in the parent's left hand, and the right hand is opened and found empty, the child will know to look in the left hand for the toy. This innate principle of reasoning is called the *Law of Ruling Out Possibilities.*

> **Law of Ruling Out Possibilities**
> When statement p or statement q is true, and q is not true, then p is true.

In mathematics, ruling out possibilities is often easy. For example, you know every angle in a triangle is either acute, right, or obtuse. If $\angle A$ in $\triangle ABC$ is not acute or right, then using the Law of Ruling Out Possibilities, you can conclude that $\angle A$ is obtuse. There is no other possibility.

In real life, if words are not carefully defined, you may not be able to rule out possibilities so easily. For example, if a person is not young, that does not necessarily mean the person is old.

Solving Logic Puzzles

In the questions for this lesson, you are asked to solve some logic puzzles. These puzzles use the idea of ruling out possibilities again and again. Notice how little information is given and how much you can deduce. The same thing happens in geometry.

Lesson 11-3 Overview

Broad Goals There are two reasons for this challenging lesson. The mathematical reason is that the idea of ruling out possibilities forms the basis for indirect reasoning, the focus of Lesson 11-4. The pedagogical reason is that logic puzzles of the type given in the lesson are very motivating for students.

Perspective An important aspect of the Law of Ruling Out Possibilities is that there must be a finite number of possibilities, and you must be able to rule out every possibility but one in order to arrive at a definitive answer.

Two logic puzzles by Wayne Williams were selected for this lesson. Other logic puzzles written by him are in the books *Quizzles* and *More Quizzles,* which are distributed by Dale Seymour Publications of Palo Alto, California. They are in a blackline master form for duplicating. Each puzzle is on a separate page and the grid is drawn. Some students will become very interested in these puzzles, and all students will remember that they did some in their geometry class. Small groups are appropriate for solving the more complicated puzzles.

Here are some hints for doing these puzzles: (1) Logic puzzles take a lot of time and analysis, so do not hurry. (2) Construct a grid and place an X in the square whenever something *cannot* occur. Place an O in the square when the situation *must* occur.

The famous composer and band conductor, John Philip Sousa (1854-1932) designed the sousaphone.

Example

Carol, Sue, Jill, Dave, and Jim each play a different instrument in the school band. The instruments they play are: clarinet, flute, saxophone, trombone, and sousaphone. From the clues below, determine which instrument each student plays.

(1) Carol plays either the clarinet, saxophone, or sousaphone.
(2) Sue does not play the flute.
(3) Dave does not play the trombone, saxophone, flute, or clarinet.
(4) Jim plays either the sousaphone or the saxophone.

Solution

The grid below can be used to solve this puzzle.

The first clue tells you that Carol does not play the flute and that Carol does not play the trombone. Two X_1s in the first row of the grid show this. (We call it X_1 so you can tell it comes directly from clue (1).)

The third clue tells you the four instruments Dave does not play. The four X_3s in the fourth row show this. Of course, this means that Dave must play the sousaphone. We show this with an O. Now we know that no one else plays the sousaphone, so we place four Xs in the column labeled "sousaphone."

	Clarinet	Flute	Saxophone	Trombone	Sousaphone
Carol		X_1		X_1	X
Sue					X
Jill					X
Dave	X_3	X_3	X_3	X_3	O
Jim					X

You are asked to complete this puzzle in Question 4.

Sometimes a single piece of given information may yield many conclusions, as in the following Activity.

Notes on Reading

Reading Mathematics You might need to read this lesson aloud with students. Discuss in detail how the grid is constructed in the **Example** and how the Xs and Os are determined. Encourage students to give some of their own valid conclusions from the statements in the **Example** and in the **Activity** on page 636. Ask them how their conclusions relate to the grids that have been set up. **Teaching Aid 148** can be used for this discussion.

Reiterate one quality of mathematics: From a few statements, you may be able to deduce a great deal. Indeed, a major attraction of logic puzzles is that it doesn't seem as if you could deduce everything asked for from such few statements, but you can. However, also remind students that sometimes you may not see how to solve a problem at first glance. By reading over the clues and looking at your grid, you may find something you missed. Thus, this lesson deals with some important problem-solving strategies: reading carefully, making a diagram, and having patience and persistence.

These puzzles are not easy to invent. You may wish to collect the puzzles that are found by students as a result of *Exploration* (**Question 22** on page 638). You may also wish to go to your favorite store that sells magazines and pick up one of the many puzzle books that contain these kinds of puzzles.

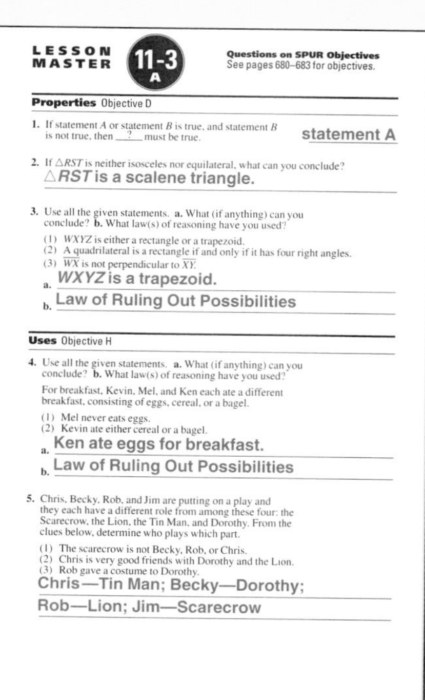

LESSON MASTER 11-3 A — **Questions on SPUR Objectives** See pages 680–683 for objectives.

Properties Objective D

1. If statement *A* or statement *B* is true, and statement *B* is not true, then __?__ must be true. statement A

2. If $\triangle RST$ is neither isosceles nor equilateral, what can you conclude? $\triangle RST$ is a scalene triangle.

3. Use all the given statements. **a.** What (if anything) can you conclude? **b.** What law(s) of reasoning have you used?
   (1) *WXYZ* is either a rectangle or a trapezoid.
   (2) A quadrilateral is a rectangle if and only if it has four right angles.
   (3) $\overline{WX}$ is not perpendicular to $\overline{XY}$.
   a. *WXYZ* is a trapezoid.
   b. Law of Ruling Out Possibilities

Uses Objective H

4. Use all the given statements. **a.** What (if anything) can you conclude? **b.** What law(s) of reasoning have you used?
   For breakfast, Kevin, Mel, and Ken each ate a different breakfast, consisting of eggs, cereal, or a bagel.
   (1) Mel never eats eggs.
   (2) Kevin ate either cereal or a bagel.
   a. Ken ate eggs for breakfast.
   b. Law of Ruling Out Possibilities

5. Chris, Becky, Rob, and Jim are putting on a play and they each have a different role from among these four: the Scarecrow, the Lion, the Tin Man, and Dorothy. From the clues below, determine who plays which part.
   (1) The scarecrow is not Becky, Rob, or Chris.
   (2) Chris is very good friends with Dorothy and the Lion.
   (3) Rob gave a costume to Dorothy.
   Chris—Tin Man; Becky—Dorothy; Rob—Lion; Jim—Scarecrow

Optional Activities

You might give students this problem after they complete the lesson. Once they have solved the problem, suggest that they select a different topic and rewrite this problem.

Mr. Potato, Ms. Carrot, Mrs. Squash, and Mr. Spinach are eating potatoes, carrots, squash, and spinach. None of them is eating the same thing as their last name. Mr. Potato is not eating spinach. Mrs. Squash is not eating carrots. Neither Ms. Carrot nor Mrs. Squash is eating potatoes. Who is eating what? [Mr. Potato–carrot, Ms. Carrot–squash, Mrs. Squash–spinach, Mr. Spinach–potatoes]

Have students record the results of the **Activity** for use with **Questions 5–7** on page 637.

Additional Examples

These examples are also given on **Teaching Aid 149.**

1. Presidents Buchanan, Grant, Johnson, and Lincoln were four consecutive presidents of the United States. From the clues below, determine the order in which they served.
   (1) Buchanan served before Johnson, who became president when the president before him was assassinated.
   (2) Grant won the election because of his popularity during the Civil War.
   (3) Lincoln served during almost the entire Civil War and was the only one of these presidents to die in office. **Buchanan, Lincoln, Johnson, Grant**
2. I am thinking of a one-digit number from 0 through 9. From the clues, determine my number.
   (1) It is not prime.
   (2) It cannot be the last digit of the square of an integer.
   The number is 8.

Activity
a) Sample:
1. Edgar and Ms. Voila are not the same person.
2. Edgar is not the teller.
3. Ms. Voila is not the teller.
4. Edgar is not the guard.
5. Ms. Voila is not the guard.

Activity

a. In Question 11, clue (4) is "Neither Edgar nor Ms. Voila is the guard or the teller." Write five conclusions from this clue. See left.

b. A grid is often very helpful for solving a logic problem like this one. The grid should have a space for each *last name-first name* pair, and also for each *first name-bank job* pair, and also each *bank job-last name* pair. Copy and mark the grid below with X_4s for the conclusions made in part **a.** Save your grid for Questions 5, 6, 7, and 11. The grid shows the X_4s and the solution to Question 11.

	Ms. Landis	Mr. Farmer	Mr. Guinness	Ms. Voila	Ms. Edwards	Teller	Secretary	Bookkeeper	Guard	Manager
Catherine	X_3	X	X	O	X_1	X_1	O	X	X	X
Edgar	X	X_5	O	X_4	X	X_4	X_3	X_5	X_4	O
Wilbur	X	O	X	X	X	O	X_3	X	X	X
Marjorie	O	X	X	X	X_1	X_1	X	X	O	X
Shirley	X	X	X	X	O	X_1	X	O	X_2	X
Teller	X	O	X	X_4	X_1					
Secretary	X	X_3	X_3	O	X					
Bookkeeper	X	X_5	X	X	O					
Guard	O	X	X	X_4	X					
Manager	X	X	O	X	X					

QUESTIONS

Covering the Reading

1. Marilyn tossed a coin. The face that showed was not "heads." You conclude that the face that showed was "tails." What principle of reasoning have you used? Law of Ruling Out Possibilities
2. If statement m or statement n is true, and m is not true, then __?__ must be true. n
3. **a.** What are the two possibilities for the intersection of two lines in a plane? no points or exactly one point
   b. If you know that two coplanar lines s and t are not parallel, what can you conclude? s and t have exactly one point in common.
4. Finish the Example of this lesson. Carol plays the clarinet. The other pairings are Sue: trombone, Jill: flute, Dave: sousaphone, Jim: saxophone.

636

LESSON MASTER 11-3 B Questions on SPUR Objectives

Properties Objective D: Follow the Law of Ruling Out Possibilities to make conclusions.

1. Explain the *Law of Ruling Out Possibilities.*
   When one or the other of two statements is true, if one is not true the other is true.

In 2 and 3, what can you conclude from the given statements?

2. (1) $x > 19$ or $x \leq 19$.
   (2) x is not greater than 19.
   $x \leq 19$
3. (1) $\angle U$ is either right or obtuse.
   (2) $m\angle U \neq 90$
   $\angle U$ is obtuse.

In 4–6 use all the given statements. a. What (if anything) can you conclude? b. What law(s) of reasoning did you use?

4. (1) F is either a circle or a sphere.
   (2) A sphere is a 3-dimensional figure.
   (3) F is not a 3-dimensional figure
   a. F is a circle.
   b. Laws of Contrap. and Ruling Out Poss.
5. (1) b is either even or odd.
   (2) An odd number has an odd square.
   (3) b^2 is not odd.
   a. b is even.
   b. Laws of Contrap. and Ruling Out Poss.
6. (1) N is either a rotation or a translation.
   (2) A rotation is the composite of two reflections over two intersecting lines.
   (3) The two lines of reflection defining transformation N do not intersect.
   a. N is a translation.
   b. Laws of Contrap. and Ruling Out Poss.

Adapting to Individual Needs

Extra Help

Some students may have already solved logic puzzles and have not been asked to include the subscripts to keep track of the clues that are being used. Point out that the subscripts are not mandatory, but they certainly are helpful. Stress that a subscript appears with X only when a clue is applied directly. When no subscript appears, this means that two or more clues were applied.

Challenge

1. Have students research DeMorgan's Laws for Logic and translate them into words:
   a. $\sim(p \vee q) \equiv \sim p \wedge \sim q$ [The negation of (p or q) has the same truth value as (not p and not q).]
   b. $\sim(p \wedge q) \equiv \sim p \vee \sim q$ [The negation of (p and q) has the same truth value as (not p or not q).]

In 5–7, refer to Question 11 below. Record your responses in the grid you made for the Activity in this lesson. For grid, see page 636.

5. From clue (3) alone, who cannot be the secretary? Edgar, Wilbur, Mr. Farmer, and Mr. Guinness
6. Write at least two conclusions that follow from clue (1). Sample: The teller is male. Catherine and Marjorie are not Ms. Edwards.
7. Write at least two conclusions that follow from clue (5). Sample: Edgar is not the bookkeeper. Edgar is not Mr. Farmer.

Applying the Mathematics

In 8 and 9, make a conclusion from the given information.

8. Line m is not parallel to plane X and m is not in plane X. m intersects plane X in exactly one point.
9. $ABCD$ is a trapezoid with $\overline{AB} \parallel \overline{CD}$, but $ABCD$ is not a parallelogram. $\overline{BC}$ and $\overline{AD}$ are not parallel.
10. The **Trichotomy Law** for real numbers is: Of two real numbers a and b, either $a < b$, $a = b$, or $a > b$, and no two of these can be true at the same time. Suppose you know that $\sqrt{2} \neq \frac{41}{29}$. What can you conclude by using the Trichotomy Law? Either $\sqrt{2} < \frac{41}{29}$ or $\sqrt{2} > \frac{41}{29}$.

11) Catherine Voila: secretary, Edgar Guinness: manager, Wilbur Farmer: teller, Marjorie Landis: guard, Shirley Edwards: bookkeeper

11. The Smalltown Bank has a teller, secretary, bookkeeper, guard, and manager named Mr. Farmer, Mr. Guinness, Ms. Landis, Ms. Voila, and Ms. Edwards, though not necessarily in that order. The two men are Edgar and Wilbur, while the three women are Catherine, Marjorie, and Shirley. From the clues below, determine the first and last names of each person and his or her position at the bank. (Use the grid you copied for the Activity in the lesson.)
    (1) Neither Catherine nor Marjorie is the teller, and neither is Ms. Edwards.
    (2) Shirley is not the guard.
    (3) The secretary is either Catherine or Ms. Landis.
    (4) Neither Edgar nor Ms. Voila is the guard or the teller.
    (5) Mr. Farmer, Edgar, and the bookkeeper have worked at the bank for more than five years. See left. For grid, see page 636.
12. Seven seniors, Joyce, Mike, Darlene, Gary, Wanda, Ken, and Brad, were asked about their career plans. These occupations were mentioned: lawyer, farmer, teacher, doctor, dentist, car dealer, and chemist. No occupation was selected by more than one student. Using the following clues, find out who mentioned which occupation.
    (1) Joyce doesn't want to be a doctor, car dealer, or chemist.
    (2) Mike doesn't want to be a doctor or car dealer either.
    (3) Gary wants to be either a teacher, dentist, or farmer.
    (4) Ken wants to be either a dentist or farmer.
    (5) Brad doesn't want to be a car dealer.
    (6) Darlene wants to be a dentist.
    Joyce: lawyer, Mike: chemist, Darlene: dentist, Gary: teacher, Wanda: car dealer, Ken: farmer, Brad: doctor

Notes on Questions

Question 4 This question should be discussed in detail. There will be students who do not know where to begin, even with the information that is given.

Question 10 The Trichotomy Law is sometimes used as the justification for the statement that either $a = b$ or $a \neq b$. If you wish to use this justification, be certain to review this question in class. The Trichotomy Law is used in some of the indirect proofs in the next lesson.

Questions 11–12 It will take some time to review these questions. The grid on **Teaching Aid 148** can be used with **Question 11.**

Career Connection The seniors making career plans in **Question 12** might have considered these facts: in 1993, according to the Bureau of the Census, there were 4,397,000 teachers, 1,170,000 farm operators, 777,000 lawyers, 605,000 doctors, 152,000 dentists, and 133,000 chemists employed in the United States. The Bureau had no figures on car dealers, but over 14 million people were employed in sales occupations in 1993.

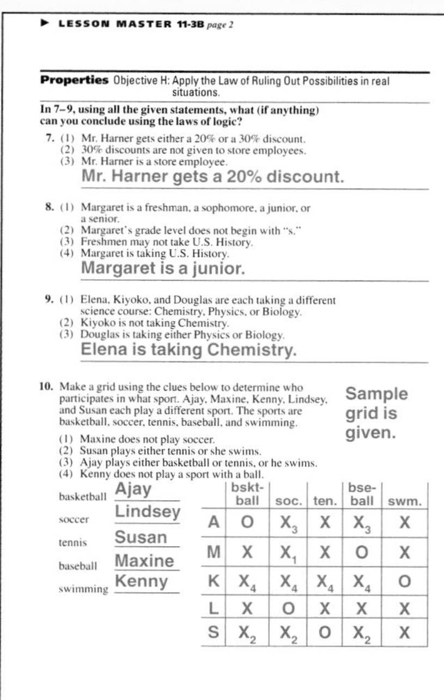

▸ **LESSON MASTER 11-3B** *page 2*

Properties Objective H: Apply the Law of Ruling Out Possibilities in real situations.

In 7–9, using all the given statements, what (if anything) can you conclude using the laws of logic?

7. (1) Mr. Harner gets either a 20% or a 30% discount.
   (2) 30% discounts are not given to store employees.
   (3) Mr. Harner is a store employee.
   Mr. Harner gets a 20% discount.
8. (1) Margaret is a freshman, a sophomore, a junior, or a senior.
   (2) Margaret's grade level does not begin with "s."
   (3) Freshmen may not take U.S. History.
   (4) Margaret is taking U.S. History.
   Margaret is a junior.
9. (1) Elena, Kiyoko, and Douglas are each taking a different science course: Chemistry, Physics, or Biology.
   (2) Kiyoko is not taking Chemistry.
   (3) Douglas is taking either Physics or Biology.
   Elena is taking Chemistry.
10. Make a grid using the clues below to determine who participates in what sport. Ajay, Maxine, Kenny, Lindsey, and Susan each play a different sport. The sports are basketball, soccer, tennis, baseball, and swimming. Sample grid is given.
    (1) Maxine does not play soccer.
    (2) Susan plays either tennis or she swims.
    (3) Ajay plays either basketball or tennis, or he swims.
    (4) Kenny does not play a sport with a ball.

basketball Ajay
soccer Lindsey
tennis Susan
baseball Maxine
swimming Kenny

	bskt-ball	soc.	ten.	bse-ball	swm.
A	O	X_3	X	X_3	X
M	X	X_1	X	O	X
K	X_4	X_4	X_4	X_4	O
L	X	O	X	X	X
S	X_2	X_2	O	X_2	X

2. Now have students use a truth table to prove one of DeMorgan's Laws. This is the proof of law **a**.

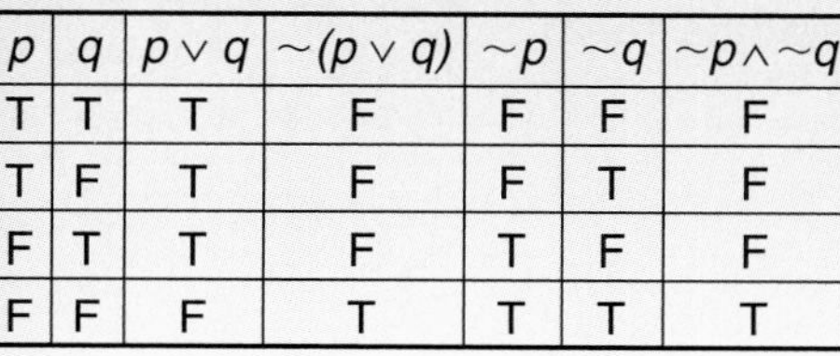

p	q	$p \vee q$	$\sim(p \vee q)$	$\sim p$	$\sim q$	$\sim p \wedge \sim q$
T	T	T	F	F	F	F
T	F	T	F	F	T	F
F	T	T	F	T	F	F
F	F	F	T	T	T	T

[The left side has the same truth value as the right side for all possible truth values of p and q. Therefore, $\sim(p \vee q) \equiv \sim p \wedge \sim q$.]

Notes on Questions

Questions 13–16 Cooperative Learning You might ask students to **work in groups** and go over these questions. Ask each group to list all correct answers for each question.

Follow-up for Lesson 11-3

Practice

For more questions on SPUR Objectives, use **Lesson Master 11-3A** (shown on page 635) or **Lesson Master 11-3B** (shown on pages 636–637).

Assessment

Oral/Written Communication Have students **work in groups** to make a list of hints that would be useful in solving logic puzzles. [Possible answers include: make a grid and place an X in the square whenever something cannot occur. Place an O in the square when the situation must occur. Allow any hints that students feel are useful.]

Extension

You might want to extend **Question 22** by asking students to give some suggestions on how to write a logic puzzle. [These might include statements like the following: Pick an interesting topic and construct a grid for related items. Put Os in the grid and start making up sentences to go along with what "aren't Os" and so on.]

Project Update Project 1, *Logic Puzzle,* and Project 6, *Truth Tables,* on pages 675–676, relate to the content of this lesson.

13) Converse: If I eat my hat, my cousin is a good cook.
Inverse: If my cousin is not a good cook, then I will not eat my hat.
Contrapositive: If I don't eat my hat, then my cousin is not a good cook.

Review

13. Consider this statement: *If my cousin is a good cook, I'll eat my hat!* Write its converse, inverse, and contrapositive. *(Lesson 11-2)*
See left.

In 14 and 15, make a conclusion using all three of these true statements. *(Lessons 11-1, 11-2)*

14. (1) Every integer is a real number.
(2) Every natural number is an integer.
(3) The complex number i is not a real number.
The complex number *i* is not a natural number.

15. (1) Every square is a rhombus.
(2) Diagonals in a kite are perpendicular.
(3) A figure is a kite if it is a rhombus.
Diagonals in a square are perpendicular.

16. Write the negation of this statement in two different ways: $\triangle ABC$ *is isosceles.* *(Lesson 11-2)* $\triangle ABC$ is not isosceles, or $\triangle ABC$ is scalene.

17. Write a proof argument.
Given: Diagonals of quadrilateral *ABED* intersect at *C*. $\triangle ABC$ and $\triangle DCE$ are isosceles, both with vertex angle *C*.
To prove: $\triangle ACD \cong \triangle BCE$.
(Lesson 7-3)

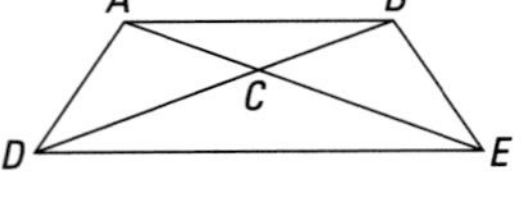

See margin.

18. *Multiple choice.* In which geometry is there exactly one single line through two points? *(Lessons 1-1, 1-2, 1-4)* c
(a) discrete geometry
(b) graph theory
(c) synthetic geometry

19. a. Write an equation for the horizontal line through the point (2, 11).
b. Write an equation for the vertical line through the point (*h*, *k*).
c. What is the intersection of the lines in parts **a** and **b**? *(Lesson 1-3)*
a) $y = 11$ b) $x = h$ c) $(h, 11)$

20. Rewrite without the radical sign $\sqrt{\ }$ or with a smaller number under the radical sign. *(Previous course)* Samples are given.
a. $\sqrt{50}$ $5\sqrt{2}$ **b.** $\sqrt{108}$ $6\sqrt{3}$ **c.** $\sqrt{\frac{1}{4}}$ $\frac{1}{2}$

21. If *z* is positive, then $\sqrt{16z^2}$ can be simplified to __?__. *(Previous course)*
$4z$

Exploration

22. Question 11 and the Example in the lesson are adapted from puzzles found in *Pencil Puzzle Treasury*, by Wayne Williams, Grosset and Dunlap, publishers, New York, 1978. Logic puzzles of this type can be found in *Games Magazine*, magazines by Dell Publishing Co., and other places. Find an example of a logic puzzle different from the ones given in this lesson, and solve it. Answers will vary.

Adapting to Individual Needs

English Language Development
Logic puzzles sometimes involve subtleties of the language, so this lesson may be difficult for students with limited English proficiency. It would be ideal if you could give these students puzzles written in their native language. If this is not possible, let students with limited English proficiency work through the puzzles with English-speaking students.

Additional Answers

17.

Conclusions	Justifications
1. $AC = BC$, $DC = EC$	def. of isosceles △
2. $\angle ACD \cong \angle BCE$	Vertical Angles Theorem
3. $\triangle ACD \cong \triangle BCE$	SAS Congruence Theorem (steps 1 and 2)

Setting Up Lesson 11-4

Discuss **Question 10** in preparation for Lesson 11-4. Also, to help set up later lessons in the chapter, discuss **Questions 18–21.**

LESSON

11-4

Indirect Proof

Reasoning it out. *In some trials, it is the lawyer's job to convince the jury by stating facts, showing contradictions, and building a sound argument.*

A lawyer, summing up a case for a jury, says, "The defendant, my client, is either guilty or not guilty. The prosecutors assume that my client committed the crime. In that case, my client must have been at the scene of the crime. But, as you remember, we brought in witnesses and telephone records that demonstrate my client was on a farm 15 miles away at the time the crime was committed. A person can't be in two places at one time! My client could not have been both on the farm and at the scene of the crime at the same time. So the prosecution's assumption that my client committed the crime cannot be true. Therefore it must be false. Ladies and gentlemen of the jury, the defendant is not guilty."

In this summing up, the lawyer has used *indirect reasoning.*

In **direct reasoning,** a person begins with given information known to be true. The Laws of Detachment and Transitivity are used to reason from that information to a conclusion. The proofs you have written so far in this book have been **direct proofs.**

In **indirect reasoning,** a person examines, and tries to rule out, all the possibilities other than the one thought to be true. This is exactly what you did in solving the logic puzzles of the previous lesson. You marked Xs in boxes to show which possibilities could not be true. When you had enough Xs, you knew that the only possibility left must be correct.

Lesson 11-4

Objectives

D Follow the Law of Indirect Reasoning to make conclusions.
F Write indirect proofs.
H Apply the Law of Indirect Reasoning in real situations.

Resources

From the ***Teacher's Resource File***

- Lesson Master 11-4A or 11-4B
- Answer Master 11-4
- Assessment Sourcebook: Quiz for Lessons 11-1 through 11-4
- Teaching Aids
  144 Warm-up
  150 Laws of Reasoning
  151 Additional Examples
- Technology Sourcebook, Calculator Master 3

Additional Resources

- Visuals for Teaching Aids 144, 150–151

Teaching Lesson 11-4

Warm-up

Write a contradiction for each statement.

1. $k = 12$ — **$k \neq 12$**
2. $\overline{AB} \cong \overline{XY}$ — **$\overline{AB} \ncong \overline{XY}$**
3. $p \perp q$ — **$p \not\perp q$**
4. $a > c$ — **$a \ngtr c$ ($a < c$ or $a = c$)**
5. $\angle PQR$ is obtuse. — **$\angle PQR$ is not obtuse. ($\angle PQR$ is an acute angle or a right angle.)**

Lesson 11-4 Overview

Broad Goals An indirect proof is a proof that uses indirect reasoning. This lesson discusses indirect reasoning in a variety of contexts: geometry, law, and arithmetic.

Perspective Many teachers believe indirect proof is more difficult than direct proof. We disagree, believing that in some cases indirect proof is easier and more natural. However, there are two things which may create difficulty. One is requiring that an indirect proof be placed in two-column format. That format doesn't work well because some of the justifications in an indirect proof are logical laws.

The second is confusing students by saying that an indirect proof begins by reasoning from a false statement. That is not what happens. If you were reasoning from a false statement, the conclusions could be either true or false. In indirect reasoning, we reason from a statement *whose truth value we do not know.* We use only valid reasoning and known justifications. When we find out that we get a false conclusion, then we know we must have started from a false statement. If we use valid reasoning from a true statement, only true statements can arise. Thus the falseness of the statement is not known until after the proof. This is akin to direct proof, where the truth of a

(Overview continues on page 640.)

Notes on Reading

You might begin the lesson by asking students how they know a statement is false. Point out that one indication that a statement is false is that it contradicts another statement known or assumed to be true. At the beginning of the lesson, the lawyer points out that a person being in one place contradicts the fact that a person was in another place. In **Example 3,** the true statement $12 \neq 6$ is contradicted. In **Example 4,** the statements $149^2 = 22{,}200$ and $149^2 = 22{,}201$ contradict each other. In **Example 5,** the reasoning leads to a statement contradicting the Triangle-Sum Theorem. Generally, it is easier to understand an indirect proof if a well-known statement is contradicted.

Stress that indirect reasoning is just as valid as direct reasoning, and point out that indirect reasoning was used earlier in the course. One of the first indirect arguments was in Lesson 1-7. It was explained in that lesson that two lines could not intersect in two different points *A* and *B*. If that were the case, then there would be two lines through *A* and *B*, which would contradict a postulate.

Review **Examples 4 and 5** carefully, as they show students what can be written in order to have a valid indirect proof. The task here is as much a writing task as a mathematical task. The three steps are given simply to organize the task and should not be considered as the only way to write the proof.

Contradictory Statements

You can rule out a possibility if you know it is false. But how can you tell if a statement is false? One way to tell that a statement is false is if you know its negation is true. For instance, suppose you know that $y = 5$ is true. Then $y \neq 5$ must be false. As another example, suppose you know $\triangle ABC$ is isosceles. Then the statement *$\triangle ABC$ is scalene* must be false.

You also know a statement is false if it contradicts another statement known to be true. For instance, if your friend Lillian is a senior, then she cannot be a junior. If you know 8 is a solution to an equation, and there is only one solution to that equation, then 3 cannot be a solution.

Definition
Two statements *p* and *q* are **contradictory** if and only if they cannot both be true at the same time.

Example 1

Let *p* be the statement *$\angle V$ is acute*. Let *q* be the statement *$\angle V$ is right*. Are *p* and *q* contradictory? Explain your answer.

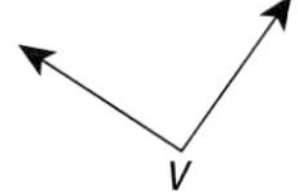

Solution

Yes. An acute angle has a measure of less than 90. A right angle has measure 90. From the Angle Measure Postulate, an angle has only one measure, so it cannot be both acute and right at the same time.

Example 2

Let *p* = *ABCD is a rhombus*. Let *q* = *ABCD is a rectangle*. Are *p* and *q* contradictory? Explain your answer.

Solution

No. p and q can be true at the same time. For instance, square ABCD at the right is both a rhombus and a rectangle.

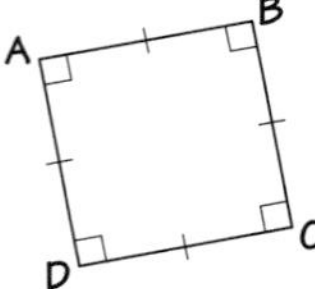

A **contradiction** is a situation in which two contradictory statements *p* and *q* are both asserted as true. Contradictions are false statements. In Example 1, the statement *p and q* ($\angle V$ is acute *and* $\angle V$ is right) is false, because *p* and *q* are contradictory. However, in Example 2, the statement *p and q* (*ABCD* is a rhombus *and ABCD* is a rectangle) is not a contradiction, because both *p* and *q* can be true at the same time.

Lesson 11-4 Overview, continued

conclusion is not known until after the proof. Until then, the truth of conclusion is basically undecided.

We often use the word "suppose," rather than "assume," in our indirect proofs when we start the reasoning from the statement we want to prove false. Then we say later that the supposition is false, and avoid having to explain why an assumption (which could be confused with a postulate) might be false.

Optional Activities

Technology Connection
In *Technology Sourcebook, Calculator Master 3,* students use a calculator to do complicated calculations needed in the arguments of indirect proofs.

Adapting to Individual Needs

English Language Development
You might have students with limited English proficiency discuss an indirect proof with an English-speaking student. Then the two students can work together to write the proof.

Indirect Reasoning

Sometimes it is not easy to tell whether a statement is true or false. However, you may be able to employ the logic used by the lawyer in the situation described at the beginning of this lesson. This is an **indirect argument.**

Step 1: If you want to prove a statement to be false, start by reasoning from it. (The prosecutors thought the defendant was guilty. The lawyer reasoned from this.)

Step 2: Using valid logic, try to make the reasoning lead to a contradiction or other false statement. (The lawyer argued that the defendant would then have been in two places at the same time.)

Step 3: If the reasoning leads to a contradiction or other false statement, the assumed statement must be false. (The lawyer concluded that the defendant was not guilty.)

This logic exemplifies the *Law of Indirect Reasoning.* It is the fifth and last law of logic discussed in this book.

> **Law of Indirect Reasoning**
> If valid reasoning from a statement p leads to a false conclusion, then p is false.

Example 3

Show that the statement $3(4 + 2x) = 6(x + 1)$ is never true.

Solution

Step 1: Begin with the equation and reason from it as you would any normal equation to see what happens. Suppose there is a value of x with $3(4 + 2x) = 6(x + 1)$. Then, using the Distributive Property,

$$12 + 6x = 6x + 6.$$

Step 2: Adding $-6x$ to each side leads to the conclusion

$$12 = 6.$$

Step 3: $12 = 6$ is a false conclusion. So, by the Law of Indirect Reasoning, the original statement $3(4 + 2x) = 6(x + 1)$ is false for all values of x. So $3(4 + 2x) = 6(x + 1)$ is never true.

Indirect Proof

A proof whose argument uses the Law of the Contrapositive, the Law of Ruling Out Possibilities, or the Law of Indirect Reasoning is called an **indirect proof.** To write an argument for an indirect proof, you *suppose* that a statement is true, then reason from that statement, or *supposition.* Following are two examples of indirect proof.

All the laws of reasoning that are needed in this course have now been discussed. They are summarized on **Teaching Aid 150.**

Multicultural Connection As noted in the first paragraph of the lesson, lawyers sometimes use indirect reasoning. However, lawyers work in different ways throughout the world. In this country, attorneys tend to specialize in one area, such as criminal, divorce, corporate, probate, or personal injury law; but they perform all duties for their clients in that area. In France and England, various attorneys do office and paper work, while a barrister (*avocat* in France) does nothing but plead cases in court. German attorneys also do courtroom presentations, but are often restricted to practicing only in certain districts or courts; notaries take on all other legal work. In countries that were formerly Communist, lawyers serve mostly as advisors to government bureaus, and rarely represent individuals.

Adapting to Individual Needs

Challenge

Have students solve this problem. One of four persons drank the last cup of coffee. When asked about drinking the last cup, they responded in the following ways.

Lou: Elena drank it.
Katrina: I didn't drink it.
Elena: Lou is lying.
Antonio: Lou drank it.

If only one of the four persons lied, who drank the last cup of coffee? [Lou]

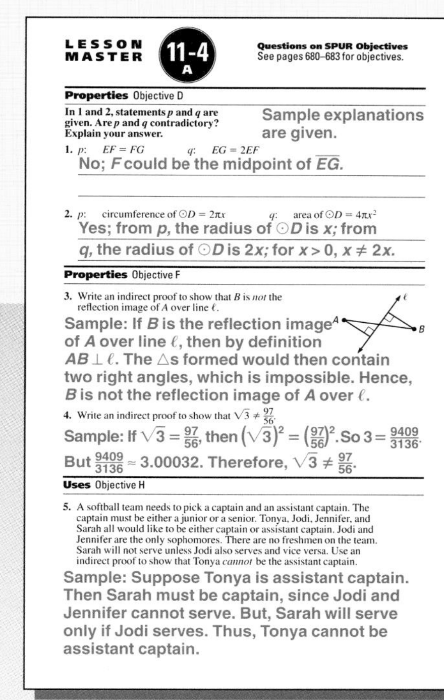

LESSON MASTER 11-4 A

Questions on SPUR Objectives
See pages 680–683 for objectives.

Properties Objective D

In 1 and 2, statements p and q are given. Are p and q contradictory? Explain your answer.

Sample explanations are given.

1. p: $EF = FG$ q: $EG = 2EF$
No; F could be the midpoint of $\overline{EG}$.

2. p: circumference of $\odot D = 2\pi x$ q: area of $\odot D = 4\pi x^2$
Yes; from p, the radius of $\odot D$ is x; from q, the radius of $\odot D$ is $2x$; for $x > 0$, $x \neq 2x$.

Properties Objective F

3. Write an indirect proof to show that B is *not* the reflection image of A over line ℓ.
Sample: If B is the reflection image of A over line ℓ, then by definition $AB \perp \ell$. The $\triangle$s formed would then contain two right angles, which is impossible. Hence, B is not the reflection image of A over ℓ.

4. Write an indirect proof to show that $\sqrt{3} \neq \frac{97}{56}$.
Sample: If $\sqrt{3} = \frac{97}{56}$, then $(\sqrt{3})^2 = (\frac{97}{56})^2$. So $3 = \frac{9409}{3136}$. But $\frac{9409}{3136} \approx 3.00032$. Therefore, $\sqrt{3} \neq \frac{97}{56}$.

Uses Objective H

5. A softball team needs to pick a captain and an assistant captain. The captain must be either a junior or a senior. Tonya, Jodi, Jennifer, and Sarah all would like to be either captain or assistant captain. Jodi and Jennifer are the only sophomores. There are no freshmen on the team. Sarah will not serve unless Jodi also serves and vice versa. Use an indirect proof to show that Tonya *cannot* be the assistant captain.
Sample: Suppose Tonya is assistant captain. Then Sarah must be captain, since Jodi and Jennifer cannot serve. But, Sarah will serve only if Jodi serves. Thus, Tonya cannot be assistant captain.

Additional Examples

These examples are also given on **Teaching Aid 151.**

1. Are the statements contradictory?
   a. *ABCD* is a square. *ABCD* is a trapezoid. No
   b. Billy is 15. Billy has an airplane pilot's license. No
   c. $|x| = -4$. $|x| = 4$. Yes
   d. $|33| = y$. $|-33| = y$. No
   e. $m = 5$. $m \le 5$. No
2. What statement is contradicted by each statement below?
   a. $m\angle ABC + m\angle BCA + m\angle CAB = 360$. Triangle-Sum Theorem
   b. *M* is the midpoint of $\overline{AB}$, $AM = 50$, and $MB = 40$. Definition of midpoint
3. Show that $5(2x + 3) = 10(x + 1)$ is never true. **Suppose $5(2x + 3) = 10(x + 1)$. Using the Distributive Property, $10x + 15 = 10x + 10$. Add $-10x$ to each side. Then $15 = 10$. Since $15 = 10$ is a false conclusion, by the Law of Indirect Reasoning, the original statement is false for all values of x.**
4. Prove that $\sqrt[3]{9} \ne 2$. **Either $\sqrt[3]{9} \ne 2$ or $\sqrt[3]{9} = 2$. Suppose $\sqrt[3]{9} = 2$. By substitution, $(\sqrt[3]{9})^3 = 2^3$, from which $9 = 8$. This contradicts the fact that $9 \ne 8$. By the Law of Indirect Reasoning, the supposition is false, and thus $\sqrt[3]{9} \ne 2$.**

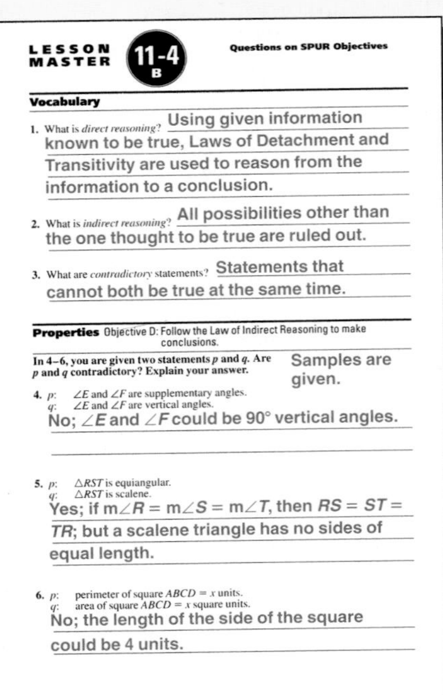
LESSON MASTER 11-4 B Questions on SPUR Objectives

Vocabulary

1. What is *direct reasoning*? Using given information known to be true, Laws of Detachment and Transitivity are used to reason from the information to a conclusion.
2. What is *indirect reasoning*? All possibilities other than the one thought to be true are ruled out.
3. What are *contradictory* statements? Statements that cannot both be true at the same time.

Properties Objective D: Follow the Law of Indirect Reasoning to make conclusions.

In 4–6, you are given two statements *p* and *q*. Are *p* and *q* contradictory? Explain your answer. Samples are given.

4. *p*: $\angle E$ and $\angle F$ are supplementary angles.
   q: $\angle E$ and $\angle F$ are vertical angles.
   No; $\angle E$ and $\angle F$ could be 90° vertical angles.
5. *p*: $\triangle RST$ is equiangular.
   q: $\triangle RST$ is scalene.
   Yes; if $m\angle R = m\angle S = m\angle T$, then $RS = ST = TR$; but a scalene triangle has no sides of equal length.
6. *p*: perimeter of square $ABCD = x$ units.
   q: area of square $ABCD = x$ square units.
   No; the length of the side of the square could be 4 units.

Example 4

Write an indirect proof argument to show that $\sqrt{22{,}200} \ne 149$.

Given: The real numbers $\sqrt{22{,}200}$ and 149.

To prove: $\sqrt{22{,}200} \ne 149$.

Solution

No drawing is needed. We begin by analyzing the problem. There are only two possibilities here. To show that the first possibility is false, reason from it to produce a contradiction.

Argument:
1. Either $\sqrt{22{,}200} = 149$ or $\sqrt{22{,}200} \ne 149$. Suppose $\sqrt{22{,}200} = 149$.
2. Then, squaring both sides, $22{,}200 = 149^2$. However, by the meaning of power, $149^2 = 149 \cdot 149 = 22{,}201$.
3. The two statements in step 2 are contradictory. The supposition of step 1, $\sqrt{22{,}200} = 149$, has led to a false conclusion. By the Law of Indirect Reasoning, $\sqrt{22{,}200} = 149$ is false. Thus $\sqrt{22{,}200} \ne 149$.

Notice the steps in the argument. Start by stating all possibilities. Then pick one of the possibilities you think is *not* true (step 1 above) and make conclusions from it (step 2 above). Reason until you get a contradiction or a false statement. Then apply the Law of Indirect Reasoning to rule out the possibility. Rule out all other possibilities in the same way until the statement you wish to prove is the only one left (step 3 above).

Example 5

Write an indirect proof argument to show that no triangle has two obtuse angles.

Given: $\triangle ABC$

To prove: No two angles of $\triangle ABC$ are obtuse.

Solution

Argument:
1. It helps to draw a triangle $\triangle ABC$. First, list the possibilities. Either $\triangle ABC$ has two obtuse angles (say $\angle A$ and $\angle B$) or it does not. Suppose both $\angle A$ and $\angle B$ are obtuse.
2. Then, by the definition of obtuse, $m\angle A > 90$ and $m\angle B > 90$. By the Addition Property of Inequality, $m\angle A + m\angle B > 180$. Then, because $m\angle C > 0$ for any angle in a triangle, by the Angle Measure Postulate, $m\angle A + m\angle B + m\angle C > 180$. But the Triangle-Sum Theorem says that $m\angle A + m\angle B + m\angle C = 180$.
3. The last two statements in step 2 are contradictory. A false conclusion has been reached. By the Law of Indirect Reasoning, the supposition of step 1 is false. $\angle A$ and $\angle B$ cannot both be obtuse. Thus, no triangle has two obtuse angles.

Additional Answers

3b. A triangle can be both isosceles and equilateral, so *p* and *q* can both be true at the same time.

4b. An obtuse angle has measure greater than 90, and a right angle has measure exactly 90, so *p* and *q* cannot both be true at the same time.

9. Suppose that a triangle has two right angles. Then the sum of the interior angles is greater than 180, which contradicts the Triangle-Sum Theorem. So the supposition is false. Therefore, a triangle cannot have two right angles.

10. Either $\triangle GHI$ is scalene or $\triangle GHI$ is isosceles. Suppose $\triangle GHI$ is isosceles. Then by the definition of isosceles triangle, two of its sides will be

In Example 5, the following statement was proved: (1) *If a figure is a triangle, then it does not have two obtuse angles.* Its contrapositive is (2) *If a figure has two obtuse angles, then it is not a triangle.* By the Law of the Contrapositive, statement (2) is also true.

QUESTIONS

Covering the Reading

1. What is *indirect reasoning*? See left.

2. When are two statements contradictory? when they cannot both be true at the same time

In 3 and 4, you are given statements p and q.
a. Are p and q contradictory? **b.** Explain your answer. See margin.

3. p: $\triangle ABC$ is isosceles. a) No
   q: $\triangle ABC$ is equilateral.

4. p: $\angle U$ is obtuse. a) Yes
   q: $\angle U$ is right.

5. State the Law of Indirect Reasoning. If valid reasoning from a statement p leads to a false conclusion, then p is false.

6. Show that the statement $2 + 5x = 5x - 8$ is never true. Adding $-5x$ to both sides yields $2 = -8$, which is false.

7. Write an indirect proof to show that $\sqrt{9800} \neq 99$. See left.

8. Write an indirect proof to show that a quadrilateral cannot have four obtuse angles. See left.

1) the way of proof which examines and tries to rule out all the possibilities other than the one thought to be true

7) Suppose $\sqrt{9800} = 99$. Then $9800 = 99^2 = 9801$, which is false. Therefore, $\sqrt{9800} \neq 99$.

8) Suppose a quadrilateral has four obtuse angles. Then the sum of the interior angle measures is greater than 360, which contradicts the Quadrilateral-Sum Theorem. Then the supposition is false, and a quadrilateral cannot have four obtuse angles.

Applying the Mathematics

9. Write an indirect proof to prove that a triangle cannot have two right angles. See margin.

In 10 and 11, write an indirect proof argument.

10. Refer to $\triangle GHI$ at the right.
    Given: $m\angle G > m\angle H > m\angle I$.
    To prove: $\triangle GHI$ is scalene.

G H I

11. Given: In the figure at the right, $PX > QX$.
    To prove: X is not on the $\perp$ bisector of $\overline{PQ}$.

X

10, 11) See margin.

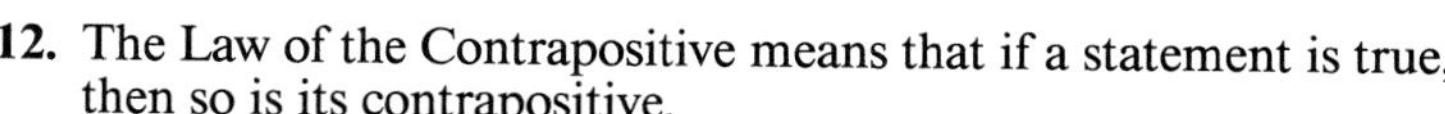

•Q

P•

12. The Law of the Contrapositive means that if a statement is true, then so is its contrapositive.
    a. State the contrapositive of the Pythagorean Theorem. See left.
    b. If in $\triangle ABC$ at the left, $\overline{AC}$ is the longest side and $AB^2 + BC^2 \neq AC^2$, what can be concluded? See left.

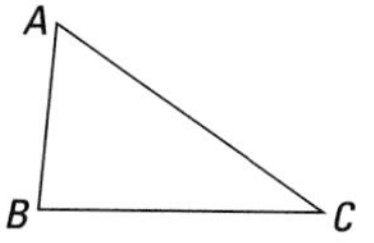

12a) If in a triangle with sides of lengths a, b, and c (and c is the greatest), $a^2 + b^2 \neq c^2$, then the triangle is not a right triangle.
b) $\triangle ABC$ is not a right triangle.

5. Prove that a convex pentagon cannot have four acute angles. The pentagon either has or does not have four acute angles. Suppose that it does and that the angles are A, B, C, and D. Then the sum of their measures is less than 360. But the sum of the measures of all five angles of a convex pentagon is 540. This means that $\angle E$ has a measure greater than 180, which contradicts the Angle Measure Postulate. Thus, by the Law of Indirect Reasoning, the supposition is false and the pentagon does not have four acute angles.

Notes on Questions

Question 10 Cooperative Learning You might ask several students to put their proofs on the chalkboard so that the steps can be compared and discussed.

11. Suppose that X is on the $\perp$ bisector of $\overline{PQ}$. By the Perpendicular Bisector Theorem, $PX = QX$, which contradicts the given information. So the supposition is false. Thus, X is not on the $\perp$ bisector of $\overline{PQ}$.

congruent. The angles opposite those sides will then be congruent by the Isosceles Triangle Base Angles Theorem. This contradicts the given. So, by the Law of Indirect Reasoning, the supposition that $\triangle GHI$ is isosceles is false. Thus, $\triangle GHI$ is scalene.

Setting Up Lesson 11-5

To help prepare students for Lesson 11-5, give them a point on the coordinate plane, say (3, 9). Ask for the image of this point under each of the following transformations:

reflection over the x-axis: [-3, 9]
reflection over the y-axis: [3, -9]
rotation of 180° about the origin: [-3, -9]

Then have them generalize these findings to the preimage (a, b).

▶ **LESSON MASTER 11-4B** *page 2*

Properties Objective F: Write indirect proofs.

7. Use an indirect argument to prove that a right triangle *cannot* have an obtuse angle.
   Sample: Suppose in $\triangle ABC$, $m\angle A = 90$ and $m\angle B > 90$. Then $m\angle A + m\angle B + m\angle C > 180$, which contradicts the Triangle-Sum Theorem. Therefore, a right triangle cannot have an obtuse angle.

8. Use an indirect argument to prove that $\sqrt{7} \neq \frac{111}{42}$.
   Sample: Suppose $\sqrt{7} = \frac{111}{42}$. Then $7 = \left(\frac{111}{42}\right)^2$. But $=\left(\frac{111}{42}\right)^2 \approx 6.98$. Since $7 \neq 6.98$, $\sqrt{7} \neq \frac{111}{42}$.

9. Finish the proof with an indirect argument.
   Given: In acute triangle UOE, $\overleftrightarrow{DN}$ is the perpendicular bisector of $\overline{EO}$.
   To prove: $\overleftrightarrow{DN}$ is *not* parallel to $\overline{UO}$. Sample:
   If $\overleftrightarrow{DN} \parallel \overline{UO}$, $m\angle DNE = m\angle UOE$ because // lines ⇒ corr. ∠s ≅. But $m\angle DNE = 90$, while $m\angle UOE < 90$ by definition. Thus, $\overleftrightarrow{DN}$ is not parallel to $\overline{UO}$.

U D E N O

Properties Objective H: Apply the Law of Indirect Reasoning in real situations.

10. Pam has three coins. They are either all the same, or all different. They may be pennies, nickels, dimes, and quarters. The sum of their values is an odd number. Use an indirect proof to show that Pam has *no* dimes.
    Sample: Suppose Pam has at least one dime. Then if all alike, the possible coins are 3 dimes whose value is even (30¢). If all different, the possible coins are: penny, nickel, dime—even (16¢); penny, dime, quarter—even (36¢); nickel, dime, quarter—even (40¢). Thus, Pam has no dimes.

Notes on Questions

Question 15 Use an expanded grid like the one used in **Question 11** of Lesson 11-3. Have students discuss how they got the answer.

Question 21 This equality will come in handy when discussing the Distance Formula in Lesson 11-6.

Question 22 Have students discuss their examples.

Follow-up for Lesson 11-4

Practice

For more questions on SPUR Objectives, use **Lesson Master 11-4A** (shown on page 641) or **Lesson Master 11-4B** (shown on pages 642–643).

Assessment

Quiz A quiz covering Lessons 11-1 through 11-4 is provided in the *Assessment Sourcebook.*

Oral/Written Communication Have students **work in groups** and write a problem that can be solved by using an indirect proof. Then have them write the proof. [Students provide a meaningful problem that can be solved by using an indirect proof and then provide a valid indirect proof.]

Extension

When asked the ages of his children, a math teacher said. "If you multiply the ages of all my children, the result is 60. Dividing 60 by the age of the eldest gives you the sum of the ages of all three." What are the ages of the children? [3, 4, and 5 years.]

13. Refer to page 43 in Lesson 1-7. Write out the argument for the Line Intersection Theorem as an indirect proof. See margin.

14. Write an indirect argument to prove that there is no integer which is greater than all other integers. See margin.

Review

15. (This puzzle is taken from *Quizzles*, by Wayne Williams.) Mary, Isobel, Marcia, Grace, and Ruth are on the Grand Avenue School basketball team. Each girl has a different hair color. The hair colors are blond, red, auburn, black, and brunette. As it happens, no two girls on the team are the same height; they are 5′11″, 5′10″, 5′8″, 5′7″, and 5′6″. From the clues given, try to determine the hair color and height of each girl on the team. (Hint: Use a grid like the ones shown in Lesson 11-3.)

(1) Mary is taller than Ruth, who is two inches taller than the redhead.
(2) The brunette is not 5′8″ tall.
(3) Marcia and Mary are neither the tallest nor the shortest.
(4) The girl with black hair is two inches taller than Ruth.
(5) Isobel is taller than the blond, who is one inch taller than Grace.
(Lesson 11-3) See left.

16. Can you draw a logical conclusion that combines the following statements? Explain your reasoning. *(Lesson 11-3)*
(1) Lines ℓ and m have no points in common.
(2) Lines ℓ and m are not parallel.
See left.

17. Give the negation of this statement: $\triangle ABC \cong \triangle DEF$. *(Lesson 11-2)*
$\triangle ABC$ is not congruent to $\triangle DEF$.

In 18 and 19, a statement is given. **a.** Write its contrapositive. **b.** Write its converse. **c.** Write its inverse. **d.** Indicate the true statement(s). *(Lesson 11-2)*

18. If $\triangle ABC \cong \triangle DEF$, then $\angle A \cong \angle D$. See margin.

19. Every prism is a box. See margin.

20. Can you draw a logical conclusion that combines the following statements? Explain your reasoning. *(Lesson 11-1)*
(1) Every square is a parallelogram.
(2) All rectangles are parallelograms.
See left.

21. *True or false.* If y_1 and y_2 are real numbers, then $(y_1 - y_2)^2 = (y_2 - y_1)^2$. *(Previous course)* True

Exploration

22. In everyday life, indirect reasoning is often used as follows. If you do *A*, then *B* will happen. But *B* is horrible (or dangerous or some other bad thing). Therefore, you should not do *A*. Give two examples of possible *A*s and *B*s. Samples: *A*: drive too fast, *B*: have an accident; *A*: run without stretching first, *B*: pull a muscle

15) Isobel: 5′11″ and brunette, Mary: 5′10″ and black, Ruth: 5′8″ and auburn, Marcia: 5′7″ and blond, Grace: 5′6″ and red

16) Yes, lines ℓ and m are not coplanar. If we suppose that these two distinct lines are coplanar, then either they intersect or they are parallel. But since they do not intersect and are not parallel, ℓ and m are not coplanar.

20) No further conclusion can be drawn. The statements are of the form $s \Rightarrow p$ and $r \Rightarrow p$, so the Law of Transitivity cannot be applied.

Additional Answers

13. Suppose that two different lines intersect in more than one point, for instance, two points *P* and *Q*. This contradicts the Unique Line Assumption of the Point-Line-Plane Postulate. So the assumption is false. Therefore, two different lines intersect in at most one point.
14. Suppose that integer *a* is greater than all other integers. However, $a + 1 > a$, and $a + 1$ is an integer. So the supposition is false. Therefore, there is no integer which is greater than all other integers.

18a. If $\angle A \not\cong \angle D$, then $\triangle ABC \not\cong \triangle DEF$.
b. If $\angle A \cong \angle D$, then $\triangle ABC \cong \triangle DEF$.
c. If $\triangle ABC \not\cong \triangle DEF$, then $\angle A \not\cong \angle D$.
d. its contrapositive

19a. If a surface is not a box, then it is not a prism.
b. If a surface is a box, then it is a prism.
c. If a surface is not a prism, then it is not a box.
d. its converse and inverse (The original statement is not true.)

LESSON

11-5

Proofs with Coordinates

So far, the proofs that you have seen have been in synthetic geometry, where points are locations. But figures in coordinate geometry have the same properties as those in synthetic geometry. So it is not surprising that there are proofs in coordinate geometry.

Proofs in coordinate geometry have two main differences from proofs in synthetic geometry. First, they involve ideas from algebra. Second, coordinate proofs are often nearly automatic, involving little more than a few calculations.

Recall that the slope m determined by two points (x_1, y_1) and (x_2, y_2) is defined as $m = \frac{y_2 - y_1}{x_2 - x_1}$. Recall also that two lines are parallel if and only if they have the same slope. These ideas are utilized in Example 1.

Example 1

Consider quadrilateral *ABCD* with vertices $A = (0, 0)$, $B = (8, 0)$, $C = (11, 12)$, and $D = (3, 12)$ as shown at the right. Prove or disprove that *ABCD* is a parallelogram.

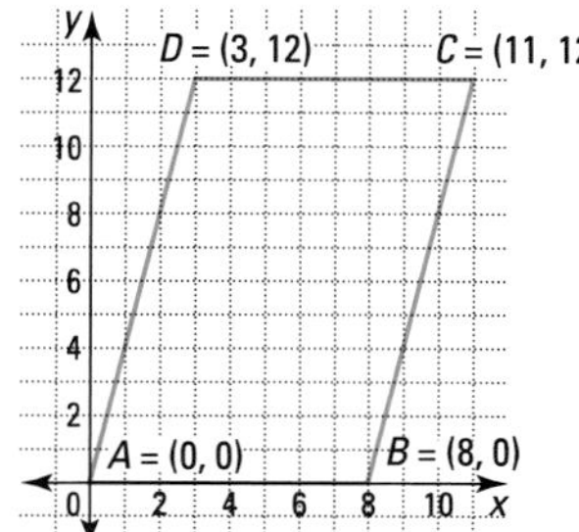

Solution

In the drawing, it appears that *ABCD* is a parallelogram. *ABCD* is a parallelogram if both pairs of opposite sides are parallel. So calculate the slopes of the sides of *ABCD*.

We write this argument in two-column form.

Conclusions	Justifications
1. slope of $\overline{AD} = \frac{12 - 0}{3 - 0} = 4$	definition of slope
slope of $\overline{BC} = \frac{12 - 0}{11 - 8} = 4$	
slope of $\overline{DC} = \frac{12 - 12}{11 - 3} = \frac{0}{8} = 0$	
slope of $\overline{AB} = \frac{0 - 0}{8 - 0} = \frac{0}{8} = 0$	
2. $\overline{AD} // \overline{BC}$, $\overline{DC} // \overline{AB}$	Parallel Lines and Slopes Theorem
3. ABCD is a parallelogram.	definition of parallelogram

Lesson 11-5

Objectives

F Write indirect proofs involving coordinates.
G Use coordinate geometry to deduce properties of figures and prove theorems.
K Give convenient locations for triangles and quadrilaterals in the coordinate plane.

Resources

From the ***Teacher's Resource File***
- Lesson Master 11-5A or 11-5B
- Answer Master 11-5
- Teaching Aids
  - 4 Coordinate Plane
  - 105 Graph paper
  - 144 Warm-up
  - 152 Convenient Locations

Additional Resource
- Visuals for Teaching Aids 4, 105, 144, 152

Teaching Lesson 11-5

Warm-up

1. Three vertices of a rectangle are located at (0, 0), (6, 0), and (0, 9). Where must the fourth vertex be located? (6, 9)
2. Three vertices of a parallelogram are located at (0, 0), (5, 0), and (0, 10). Where could the fourth vertex be located? **There are three possible answers: (5, 10), (5, –10), or (–5, 10)**

Lesson 11-5 Overview

Broad Goals This lesson discusses three types of coordinate proofs: (1) proofs that lines are parallel; (2) proofs that lines are perpendicular; and (3) proofs that a polygon is a special type of polygon using parallelism and perpendicularity. Convenient locations for many of the special types of polygons are identified.

Perspective In this lesson, students are asked to think about or prove statements that were presented in previous lessons. Figures in this lesson, however, are described with coordinates. Therefore, the emphasis is on finding algebraic ways to justify statements and interpret theorems and definitions.

We place the material on coordinate geometry here for several reasons. First, we use coordinates (in particular, the Distance Formula) for the study of similarity. Second, the proofs serve as a nice counterpart to the synthetic proofs students have been writing. Third, coordinate proofs help the understanding of all types of proof. Fourth, coordinate arguments will be encountered by these students throughout the courses in mathematics they will take.

Coordinate proofs are easier for some students than are synthetic proofs

(Overview continues on page 646.)

Notes on Reading

You might begin by going over **Example 1** carefully with the class, emphasizing what needs to be written. You may wish to state a preference for either the paragraph or two-column format.

After plotting the coordinates of the figures in **Examples 1–3,** it may occur to some students that there is much more that could be proved about those figures. It might be appropriate at this time to encourage a discussion of which properties could be applied to determine more about the figure.

Some students may still confuse "a line has *no* slope" with "a line has slope of *zero*." A visual example is to consider how rapidly one ascends or descends a line moving from left to right. Since one cannot move from left to right on a vertical line, there is no slope on a vertical line.

Students may find coordinate proofs quite difficult if the algebra gets too complicated. The easiest proof is usually done with the least number of variables for vertices, and that is often accomplished by using the *x*- and *y*-axis as lines containing the sides of the figure.

You can use **Teaching Aid 152** as you discuss convenient locations of figures.

Students will need graph paper or **Teaching Aid 4 or Teaching Aid 105** for *Additional Examples* and **Questions.**

Additional Examples

1. If a quadrilateral has vertices $A = (13, 9)$, $B = (8, 11)$, $C = (5, -11)$, and $D = (2, -4)$, prove that the quadrilateral is a trapezoid with a right angle. **First draw a picture to determine the**

The proof in Example 1 is about a single parallelogram. To prove a theorem that applies to many parallelograms, the coordinates of the vertices must be variables.

Example 2

Write a proof argument.

Given: Quadrilateral *PQRS* with $P = (a, b)$, $Q = (c, b)$, $R = (-a, -b)$, $S = (-c, -b)$, such that $a \neq c$ and $-a \neq c$.

To prove: *PQRS* is a parallelogram.

Solution

As in Example 1, calculate slopes.

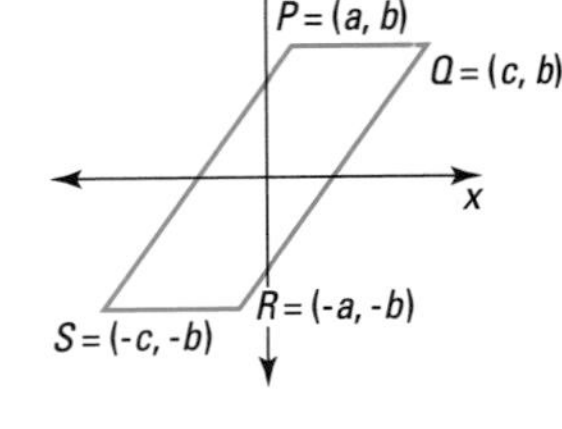

Argument:

Slope of $\overline{PQ} = \frac{b - b}{c - a} = \frac{0}{c - a} = 0$

Slope of $\overline{RS} = \frac{-b - (-b)}{-a - (-c)} = \frac{0}{-a + c} = 0$

Slope of $\overline{PS} = \frac{b - (-b)}{a - (-c)} = \frac{2b}{c + a}$

Slope of $\overline{QR} = \frac{b - (-b)}{c - (-a)} = \frac{2b}{c + a}$

By the Parallel Lines and Slopes Theorem, $\overline{PQ} \parallel \overline{RS}$ and $\overline{PS} \parallel \overline{QR}$. So, by the definition of parallelogram, PQRS is a parallelogram.

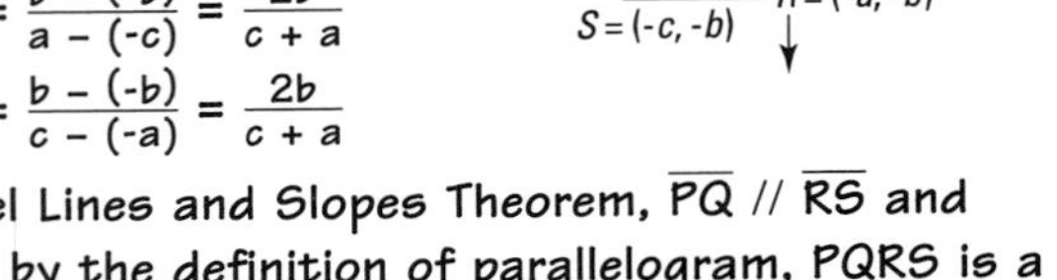

Convenient Locations

The coordinates of the vertices in Example 2 were carefully chosen. Coordinate axes can always be positioned so that the vertices of a parallelogram have the locations of *P*, *Q*, *R*, and *S* above. Just put the origin at the intersection of its diagonals and make the x-axis parallel to one side. This is called a *convenient location* for the parallelogram. A **convenient location** for a figure is one in which its key points are described with the fewest possible number of variables. In Example 2, the vertices of the parallelogram are described with only the three variables *a*, *b*, and *c*.

The location in Example 2 turns out to be convenient because the parallelogram is rotation-symmetric with center of rotation (0, 0). When a polygon is reflection-symmetric, a convenient location can usually be found by locating the polygon so that it is symmetric to the *x*-axis or the *y*-axis. Otherwise, a convenient location can be found by placing the polygon with one vertex at (0, 0) and another vertex on one of the axes.

To remember convenient locations, recall how to find certain reflection and rotation images on a coordinate plane.

The reflection image of (a, b) over the *x*-axis is $(a, -b)$.
The reflection image of (a, b) over the *y*-axis is $(-a, b)$.
The image of (a, b) under a rotation of 180° about the origin is $(-a, -b)$.

Lesson 11-5 Overview, continued

because what is given and what is to be proved is clear, and because the proof arguments are automatic, usually involving only computation and algebraic manipulation.

Except for the parallelogram, the convenient coordinates for the various special triangles and quadrilaterals shown on page 647 all result either from the definition of the figure or from its symmetry. For the parallelogram, the only nonobvious vertex is $(a + b, c)$.

The second coordinate is *c* because one side is parallel to the *x*-axis. Let the first coordinate be *x*. Now the oblique sides must be parallel, and since the slope of the left side is $\frac{c}{b}$, the slope of the right side must be $\frac{c}{b}$. From the slope formula $\frac{c - 0}{x - a} = \frac{c}{b}$, from which $x - a = b$, and therefore $x = a + b$.

Optional Activities

Materials: Graph paper or **Teaching Aid 4**

After students complete the lesson have them use a "convenient location" on a coordinate system and graph (a) a trapezoid, (b) a quadrilateral for which opposite sides are neither parallel nor congruent, and (c) an isosceles right triangle. [Graphs will vary. It is convenient to have at least one side on the *x*- or *y*-axis with a vertex at (0, 0).]

The point (a, b) and the images $(a, \text{-}b)$, $(\text{-}a, b)$, and $(\text{-}a, \text{-}b)$ are the vertices of a rectangle. This is one of the convenient locations for a rectangle. Here are convenient locations for some of the figures you have studied.

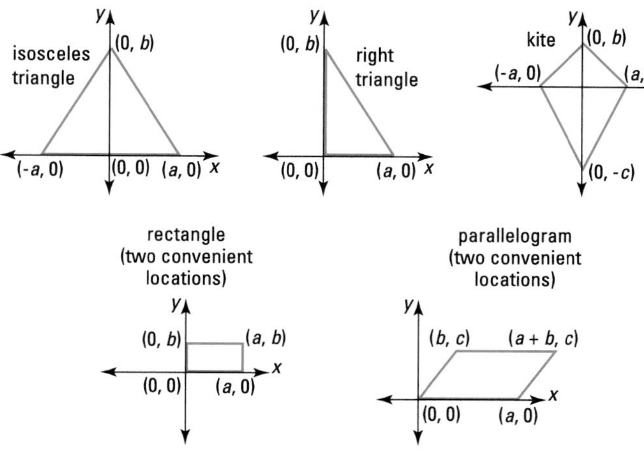

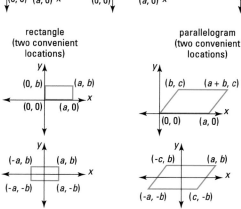

Indirect Coordinate Proofs

Coordinate proofs may be direct or indirect. Example 3 uses indirect reasoning to show that two lines are not perpendicular.

Example 3

If $T = (3, 6)$, $O = (-1, -2)$, and $W = (-3, 1)$, use an indirect argument to show that $\overleftrightarrow{WO}$ is *not* perpendicular to $\overleftrightarrow{WT}$.

Solution

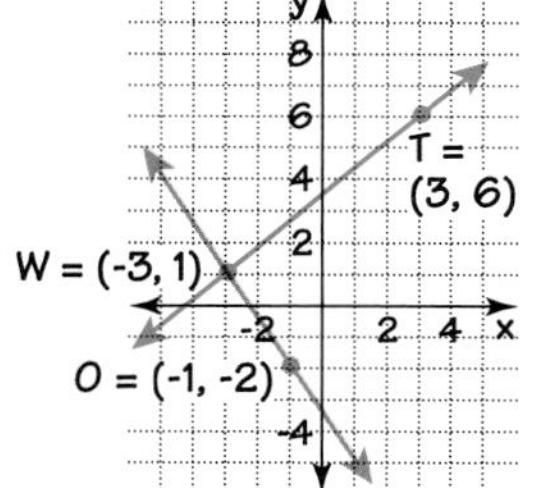

A drawing shows that the lines look nearly perpendicular.

1. Either $\overleftrightarrow{WO} \perp \overleftrightarrow{WT}$ or they are not perpendicular. Suppose $\overleftrightarrow{WO} \perp \overleftrightarrow{WT}$. Then, by the Perpendicular Lines and Slopes Theorem, the product of their slopes is -1.
2. But by the definition of slope, Slope of $\overleftrightarrow{WT} = \frac{6 - 1}{3 - (-3)} = \frac{5}{6}$ and slope of $\overleftrightarrow{WO} = \frac{-2 - 1}{-1 - (-3)} = \frac{-3}{2}$.
   The product of the slopes is $\left(\frac{5}{6}\right)\left(\frac{-3}{2}\right) = \frac{-15}{12}$.
3. The statements in steps 1 and 2 are contradictory. By the Law of Indirect Reasoning, the supposition of step 1 is false. $\overleftrightarrow{WO}$ is not perpendicular to $\overleftrightarrow{WT}$.

order of vertices in the quadrilateral. The quadrilateral is $ABDC$. The slopes of $\overline{BD}$ and $\overline{AC}$ are each $\frac{5}{2}$, so they are parallel. The slope of $\overline{AB}$ is $-\frac{2}{5}$ so the product of slopes is -1 and thus $\overline{AB}$ is perpendicular to each of the parallel sides.

2. Consider quadrilateral $JKLM$ with vertices $J = (a, 0)$, $K = (0, b)$, $L = (-a, b + c)$, and $M = (0, c)$. Prove that $JKLM$ is a parallelogram. $\overline{JK}$ and $\overline{LM}$ have slope $-\frac{b}{a}$, so they are parallel; $\overline{JM}$ and $\overline{KL}$ have slope $-\frac{c}{a}$, so they are parallel. $JKLM$ is a parallelogram by the definition of parallelogram.
3. If $A = (1, 5)$, $B = (2, 10)$, and $C = (10, 3)$, use an indirect argument to show that $\overline{AB}$ is not perpendicular to $\overline{AC}$. Suppose $\overline{AB} \perp \overline{AC}$. Then the product of their slopes should be -1. But the slope of $\overline{AB}$ is 5 and the slope of $\overline{AC}$ is $-\frac{2}{9}$. So the product of their slopes is $-\frac{10}{9}$. By the Law of Indirect reasoning, the original supposition is false, and $\overline{AB}$ is not perpendicular to $\overline{AC}$.

Adapting to Individual Needs

Extra Help

Students may have difficulty working with variable coordinates. You may want to spend some time discussing the variable coordinates used in the convenient locations of the figures on page 647.

Challenge

Materials: Graph paper or **Teaching Aid 4**

As a generalization of **Question 14,** ask the students to answer the following. Graph all possible ordered pairs (x, y) such that $a \le x \le b$ and $c \le y \le d$. Describe the graph. [A rectangular region with vertices (a, c), (b, c), (b, d), and (a, d).]

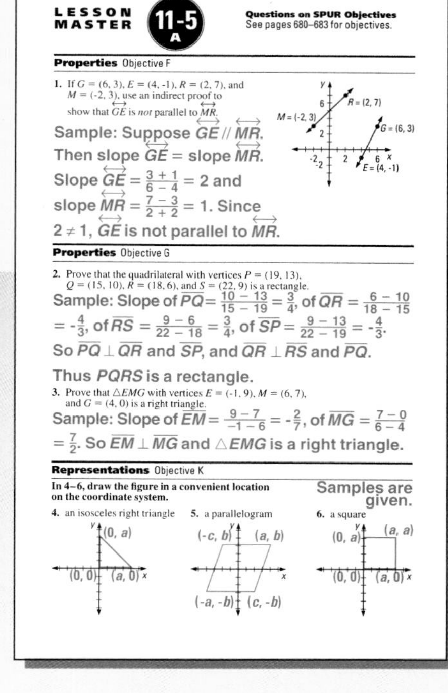

LESSON MASTER 11-5 A Questions on SPUR Objectives See pages 680–683 for objectives.

Properties Objective F

1. If $G = (6, 3)$, $E = (4, -1)$, $R = (2, 7)$, and $M = (-2, 3)$, use an indirect proof to show that $\overleftrightarrow{GE}$ is *not* parallel to $\overleftrightarrow{MR}$.
Sample: Suppose $\overleftrightarrow{GE} \parallel \overleftrightarrow{MR}$. Then slope $\overleftrightarrow{GE}$ = slope $\overleftrightarrow{MR}$. Slope $\overleftrightarrow{GE} = \frac{3+1}{6-4} = 2$ and slope $\overleftrightarrow{MR} = \frac{7-3}{2+2} = 1$. Since $2 \ne 1$, $\overleftrightarrow{GE}$ is not parallel to $\overleftrightarrow{MR}$.

Properties Objective G

2. Prove that the quadrilateral with vertices $P = (19, 13)$, $Q = (15, 10)$, $R = (18, 6)$, and $S = (22, 9)$ is a rectangle.
Sample: Slope of $\overline{PQ} = \frac{10-13}{15-19} = \frac{3}{4}$, of $\overline{QR} = \frac{6-10}{18-15} = -\frac{4}{3}$, of $\overline{RS} = \frac{9-6}{22-18} = \frac{3}{4}$, of $\overline{SP} = \frac{9-13}{22-19} = -\frac{4}{3}$. So $\overline{PQ} \perp \overline{QR}$ and $\overline{SP}$, and $\overline{QR} \perp \overline{RS}$ and $\overline{PQ}$. Thus $PQRS$ is a rectangle.
3. Prove that $\triangle EMG$ with vertices $E = (-1, 9)$, $M = (6, 7)$, and $G = (4, 0)$ is a right triangle.
Sample: Slope of $\overline{EM} = \frac{9-7}{-1-6} = -\frac{2}{7}$, of $\overline{MG} = \frac{7-0}{6-4} = \frac{7}{2}$. So $\overline{EM} \perp \overline{MG}$ and $\triangle EMG$ is a right triangle.

Representations Objective K

In 4–6, draw the figure in a convenient location on the coordinate system. Samples are given.

4. an isosceles right triangle (0, a) (0, 0) (a, 0)
5. a parallelogram (-c, b) (a, b) (-a, -b) (c, -b)
6. a square (0, a) (a, a) (0, 0) (a, 0)

Notes on Questions

Questions 2–3, and 9–12 Each of these proofs should be discussed.

Question 3 This is the only question in which the coordinates are variables. Ask students to draw a picture with convenient locations. Although it is common to think of *a*, *b*, and *c* as being positive, if the proof works, it should work for all real values of *a*, *b*, and *c*.

Question 8 Coordinates make it possible to prove that something is not so. In this case it is easy to show that the segments are not perpendicular.

Question 10 It is not necessary to first prove *EFGH* is a parallelogram.

Additional Answers

3.

Conclusions	Justifications
1. The slope of $\overline{WX}$ is $\frac{0-0}{0-a} = \frac{0}{-a} = 0$; $\overline{ZY}$ is $\frac{c-c}{a+b-b} = \frac{0}{a} = 0$; $\overline{WZ}$ is $\frac{c-0}{b-0} = \frac{c}{b}$; $\overline{XY}$ is $\frac{c-0}{a+b-a} = \frac{c}{b}$.	def. of slope
2. $\overline{WX} // \overline{ZY}$, $\overline{WZ} // \overline{XY}$	// Lines and Slopes Thm.
3. *WXYZ* is a parallelogram.	def. of parallelogram

LESSON MASTER 11-5 B Questions on SPUR Objectives

Properties Objective F: Write indirect proofs involving coordinates.

1. If $V = (-3, 0)$, $M = (0, -4)$, $T = (0, 3)$, and $J = (4, 0)$, use an indirect proof to show that $\overleftrightarrow{VM}$ is *not* parallel to $\overleftrightarrow{TJ}$. Sample:
If $\overleftrightarrow{VM} // \overleftrightarrow{TJ}$, then slope of $\overleftrightarrow{VM}$ = slope of $\overleftrightarrow{TJ}$. Slope of $\overleftrightarrow{VM} = \frac{0+4}{-3-0} = -\frac{4}{3}$ and of $\overleftrightarrow{TJ} = \frac{3-0}{0-4} = -\frac{3}{4}$.
Since $-\frac{4}{3} \neq -\frac{3}{4}$, $\overleftrightarrow{VM}$ is not parallel to $\overleftrightarrow{TJ}$.

2. Let $A = (0, 4)$, $B = (6, 0)$, $C = (0, -4)$, and $D = (-6, 0)$. Use an indirect proof to show that *ABCD* is *not* a square. Sample:
If *ABCD* is a square, $\overline{AB} \perp \overline{BC}$ and slope of $\overline{AB}$ times slope of $\overline{BC} = -1$. Slope of $\overline{AB} = \frac{4-0}{0-6} = -\frac{2}{3}$ and of $\overline{BC} = \frac{0+4}{6-0} = \frac{2}{3}$.
Since $-\frac{2}{3} \cdot \frac{2}{3} \neq -1$, *ABCD* is not a square.

Properties Objective G: Use coordinate geometry to deduce properties of figures and prove theorems.

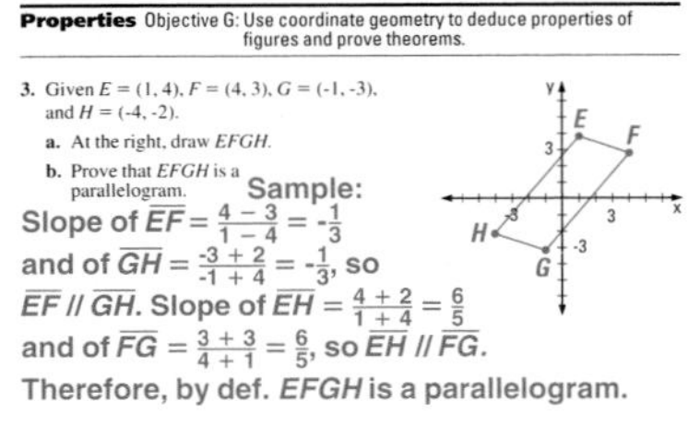

3. Given $E = (1, 4)$, $F = (4, 3)$, $G = (-1, -3)$, and $H = (-4, -2)$.
a. At the right, draw *EFGH*.
b. Prove that *EFGH* is a parallelogram. Sample:
Slope of $\overline{EF} = \frac{4-3}{1-4} = -\frac{1}{3}$ and of $\overline{GH} = \frac{-3+2}{-1+4} = -\frac{1}{3}$, so $\overline{EF} // \overline{GH}$. Slope of $\overline{EH} = \frac{4+2}{1+4} = \frac{6}{5}$ and of $\overline{FG} = \frac{3+3}{4+1} = \frac{6}{5}$, so $\overline{EH} // \overline{FG}$.
Therefore, by def. *EFGH* is a parallelogram.

Notice how automatic coordinate proofs of parallelism and perpendicularity can be. Just calculate and compare slopes! This helps explain why Descartes was so optimistic about his method.

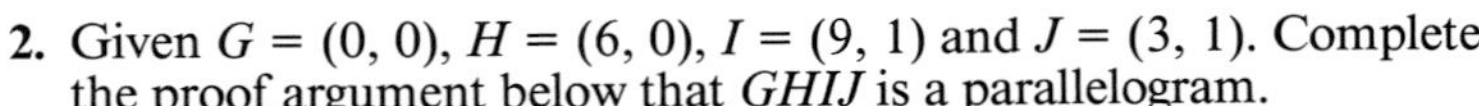

QUESTIONS

Covering the Reading

1. *True or false.* Most of the proofs in this text have been in synthetic geometry. True

2. Given $G = (0, 0)$, $H = (6, 0)$, $I = (9, 1)$ and $J = (3, 1)$. Complete the proof argument below that *GHIJ* is a parallelogram.

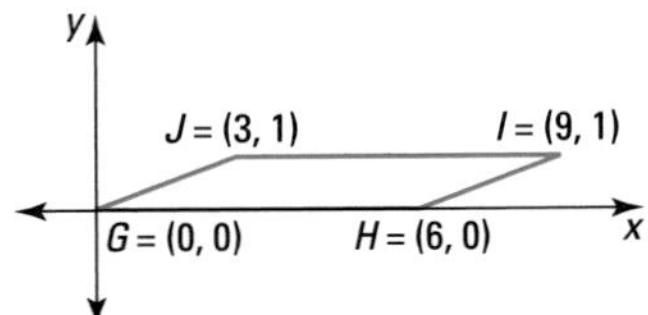

Argument:

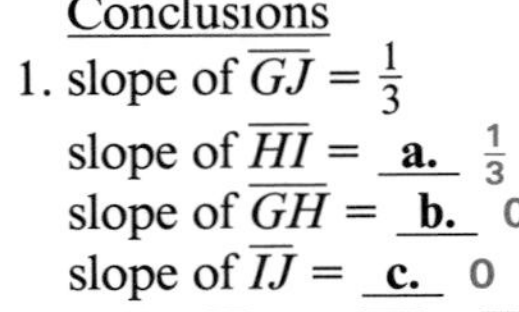

Conclusions	Justifications
1. slope of $\overline{GJ} = \frac{1}{3}$	**d.** definition of slope
slope of $\overline{HI}$ = **a.** $\frac{1}{3}$	
slope of $\overline{GH}$ = **b.** 0	
slope of $\overline{IJ}$ = **c.** 0	
2. $\overline{GH} // \overline{IJ}$ and $\overline{HI} // \overline{GJ}$	**e.** Parallel Lines and Slopes Theorem
3. **f.** *GHIJ* is a parallelogram.	definition of parallelogram

3. In quadrilateral *WXYZ*, $W = (0, 0)$, $X = (a, 0)$, $Y = (a + b, c)$, and $Z = (b, c)$. If $a \neq 0$ and $b \neq 0$, prove that *WXYZ* is a parallelogram. See margin.

In 4–7, draw a figure of the indicated type in a convenient location on a coordinate system. See left.

4. right triangle

5. rectangle

6. isosceles triangle

7. kite

8. If $X = (3, 7)$, $Y = (11, 3)$, and $Z = (4, 10)$, use an indirect proof to show that $\overleftrightarrow{XZ}$ is not perpendicular to $\overleftrightarrow{XY}$. See margin.

4) Sample:

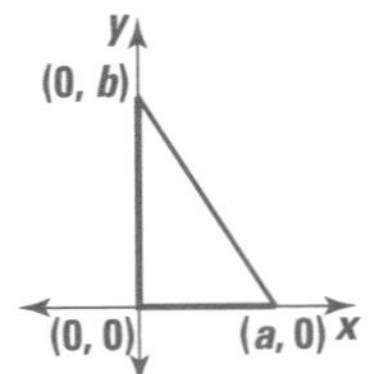

5) Sample:

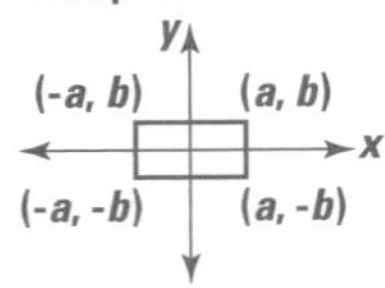

6) Sample:

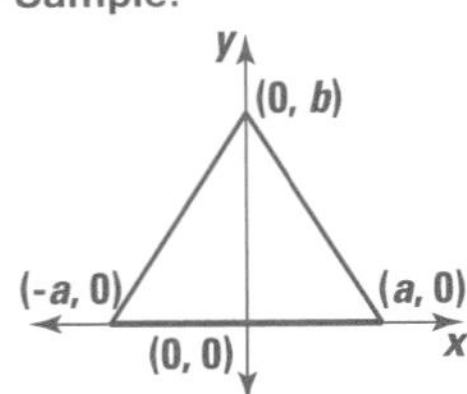

7) Sample:

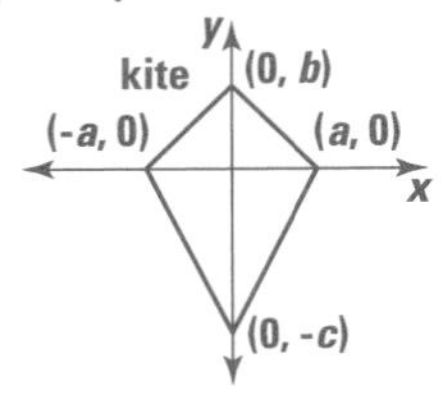

Additional Answers, continued

8. Either $\overleftrightarrow{XY} \perp \overleftrightarrow{XZ}$ or $\overleftrightarrow{XY}$ is not $\perp \overleftrightarrow{XZ}$. Suppose $\overleftrightarrow{XY} \perp \overleftrightarrow{XZ}$. The product of their slopes is -1. The slope of $\overleftrightarrow{XY}$ is $-\frac{1}{2}$ and the slope of $\overleftrightarrow{XZ}$ is 3. $-\frac{1}{2} \cdot 3 = -\frac{3}{2} \neq -1$, so our supposition has led to a false conclusion. By the Law of Indirect Reasoning, the supposition is false. Thus, $\overleftrightarrow{XY}$ is not $\perp \overleftrightarrow{XZ}$.

9.

Conclusions	Justifications
1. The slopes of $\overline{EF} = \overline{GH} = 1$; $\overline{EH} = \overline{FG} = -1$.	def. of slope
2. $\overline{EF} // \overline{GH}$, $\overline{EH} // \overline{FG}$	// Lines and Slopes Thm.
3. *EFGH* is a parallelogram.	def. of parallelogram

Applying the Mathematics

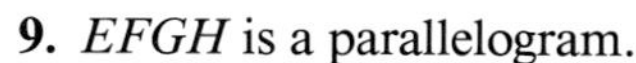

In 9–11, use quadrilateral $EFGH$ shown at the right. Write an argument to prove each statement. See margin.

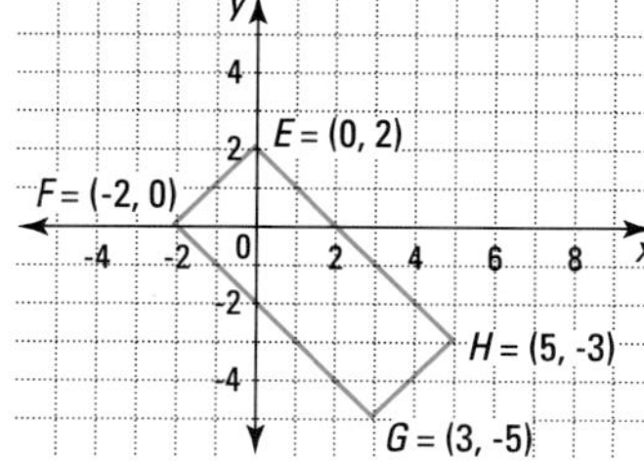

9. $EFGH$ is a parallelogram.

10. $EFGH$ is a rectangle.

11. $\overline{EG}$ and $\overline{FH}$ (not drawn) are not perpendicular.

12. Given $S = (1, 3)$, $P = (4, 4)$, $A = (3, 1)$, and $T = (0, 0)$.
  a. Draw $SPAT$. **b.** Prove that $\overline{SA} \perp \overline{PT}$.
  See left.

13. a. Draw a square in a convenient location on a coordinate system. (Hint: only one variable is needed.)
  b. Using this location, prove that its diagonals are perpendicular.
  See left.

14. Full-grown zebras can range from 46 to 55 inches high at the shoulder and their weights can range from 550 to 650 pounds. Let h be these possible heights and w be these possible weights. See left.
  a. Graph all possible ordered pairs (h, w).
  b. Describe the graph.

Review

15. Give an indirect proof to show that $\sqrt{39{,}600} \neq 199$. *(Lesson 11-4)*
See margin.

16. a. Draw a quadrilateral with exactly
  (i) no right angles
  (ii) one right angle
  (iii) two right angles
  (iv) four right angles
  b. Use an indirect proof to show that no quadrilateral has exactly three right angles. *(Lesson 11-4)*
  a, b) See margin.

In 17 and 18, what (if anything) can you conclude using all of the statements?

17. (1) Either Julie walks to school or she rides her bicycle to school.
(2) Julie's bicycle is being repaired. *(Lesson 11-3)*
Julie walks to school.

18. (1) All people who grew up in Mississippi have a southern accent.
(2) If you did not grow up in Mississippi, then you do not know the Ole Miss fight song.
(3) Murray does not have a southern accent. *(Lessons 11-1, 11-2)*
Murray does not know the Ole Miss fight song.

12a)

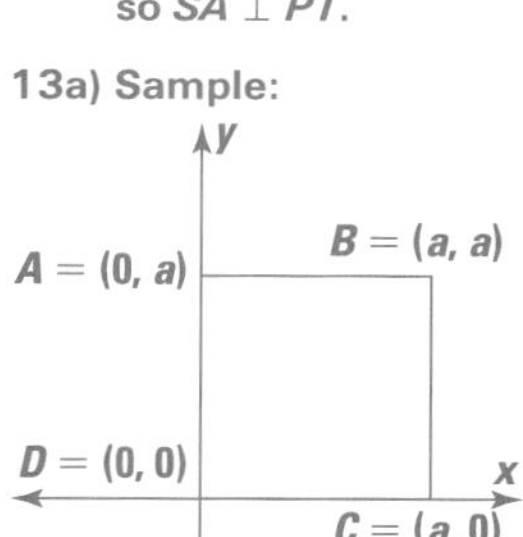

b) The slope of $\overline{SA}$ is -1, and the slope of $\overline{PT}$ is 1. $-1 \cdot 1 = -1$, so $\overline{SA} \perp \overline{PT}$.

13a) Sample:

$A = (0, a)$, $B = (a, a)$, $D = (0, 0)$, $C = (a, 0)$

b) The slope of $\overline{BD}$ is 1, and the slope of $\overline{AC}$ is -1. Therefore, the product of the slopes is -1. By the Perpendicular Lines and Slopes Theorem, $\overline{AC} \perp \overline{BD}$.

14a)

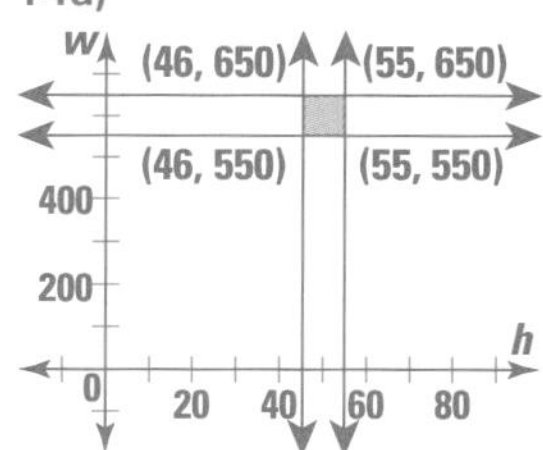

b) The graph is the rectangular region with vertices (46, 550), (55, 550), (55, 650), and (46, 650).

10. The products of the slopes of adjacent sides are -1, so $\overline{EF} \perp \overline{FG}$, $\overline{FG} \perp \overline{GH}$, $\overline{GH} \perp \overline{EH}$, and $\overline{EH} \perp \overline{EF}$ by the Perpendicular Lines and Slopes Theorem. Thus, $EFGH$ is a rectangle by the definition of rectangle.

11. The slope of $\overline{EG} = -\frac{7}{3}$, and the slope of $\overline{FH} = -\frac{3}{7}$. $-\frac{7}{3} \cdot -\frac{3}{7} = 1 \neq -1$, so $\overline{EG}$ is not perpendicular to $\overline{FH}$.

15. Either $\sqrt{39{,}600} = 199$ or $\sqrt{39{,}600} \neq 199$. Suppose $\sqrt{39{,}600} = 199$. Then, squaring both sides: $39{,}600 = 199^2$. However, by the definition of square, $199^2 = 199 \cdot 199 = 39{,}601$. This contradicts $39{,}600 = 199^2$. By the Law of Indirect Reasoning, the supposition is false. Thus $\sqrt{39{,}600} \neq 199$.

16a. Samples:

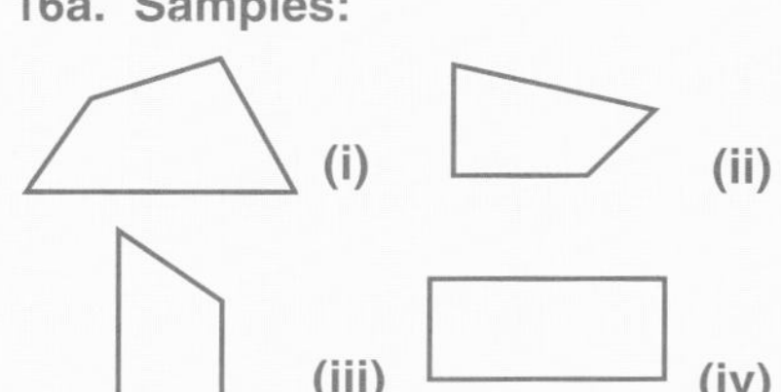

16b. Suppose that a quadrilateral has exactly three right angles. Then, according to the Quadrilateral-Sum Theorem, the sum of four interior angles is 360°, so the fourth angle is also a right angle, which contradicts the given information. By the Law of Indirect Reasoning, the supposition is false. Thus, no quadrilateral has exactly three right angles.

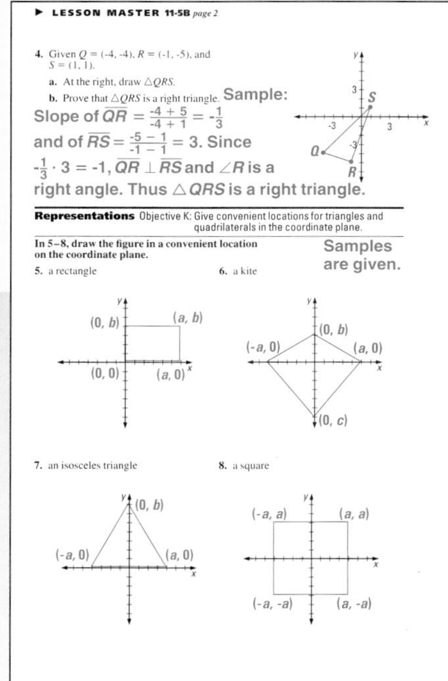

▶ LESSON MASTER 11-5B *page 2*

4. Given $Q = (-4, -4)$, $R = (-1, -5)$, and $S = (1, 1)$.
a. At the right, draw $\triangle QRS$.
b. Prove that $\triangle QRS$ is a right triangle. Sample:
Slope of $\overline{QR} = \frac{-4+5}{-4+1} = -\frac{1}{3}$
and of $\overline{RS} = \frac{-5-1}{-1-1} = 3$. Since $-\frac{1}{3} \cdot 3 = -1$, $\overline{QR} \perp \overline{RS}$ and $\angle R$ is a right angle. Thus $\triangle QRS$ is a right triangle.

Representations Objective K: Give convenient locations for triangles and quadrilaterals in the coordinate plane.

In 5–8, draw the figure in a convenient location on the coordinate plane. Samples are given.

5. a rectangle — (0, b), (a, b), (0, 0), (a, 0)

6. a kite — (0, b), (-a, 0), (a, 0), (0, c)

7. an isosceles triangle — (0, b), (-a, 0), (a, 0)

8. a square — (-a, a), (a, a), (-a, -a), (a, -a)

Notes on Questions

Question 21 This question deals with the distance between two points on a horizontal line in a coordinate plane.

Questions 22–23 Error Alert You may need to remind students when square roots of squares can be simplified.

Question 24 Graphing is necessary to understand this question. The three given vertices are taken in a different order for each possible fourth vertex. The *Warm-up* on page 645 is similar to this question.

Practice

For more questions on SPUR Objectives, use **Lesson Master 11-5A** (shown on page 647) or **Lesson Master 11-5B** (shown on pages 648–649).

Assessment

Written Communication Have students write a paragraph explaining how they could use coordinate geometry to show whether two lines in the coordinate plane are perpendicular. [Students recognize that they can use the coordinates of any two points on a line to determine the slope. Once they know the slope of both lines, they can multiply to see if the product is -1. Or, if one slope is zero and the other is undefined, the lines are also perpendicular.]

Extension

Give students this problem from *The Mathematics Teacher,* Volume 80, Number 7, October, 1987. Draw the figure that comes next.

   [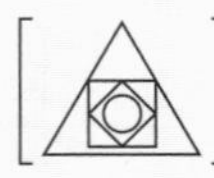]

Project Update Project 4, *Varignon's Theorem,* on page 676, relates to the content of this lesson.

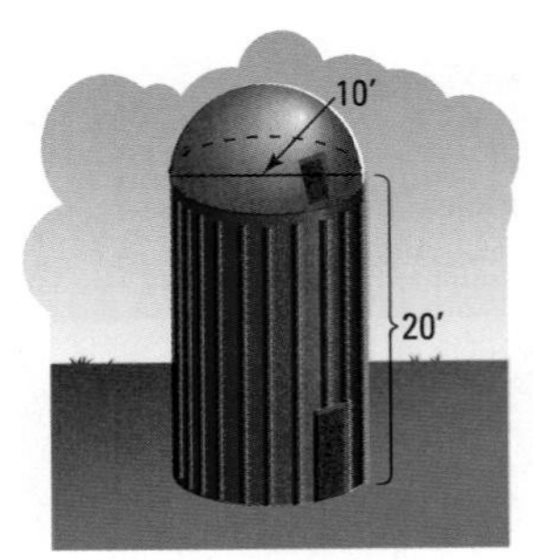

19. a. A silo is shaped with a hemisphere atop a cylinder. The cylinder is 10′ in diameter and 20′ high. If the outside is to be painted, what is the measure of the area to be painted? ≈ 785 sq ft

b. If the volume of a bushel of corn is about $\frac{1}{14}$ cubic feet, about how many bushels of corn could be stored in this silo? *(Lessons 10-1, 10-5, 10-8, 10-9)* ≈ 25,656 bushels

20. The orange scheelite crystal below is in the shape of a regular octahedron. Give the number of vertices, faces, and edges of this crystal. *(Lesson 10-7)* six vertices, eight faces, twelve edges

21. a. What is the distance between two points on a number line with coordinates 50 and 500? 450 units

b. What is the distance between (50, 100) and (500, 100)? *(Lesson 1-2)* 450 units

In 22 and 23, simplify if $a \geq 0$ and $b \geq 0$. *(Previous course)*

22. $\sqrt{a^2b^2}$ *ab*

23. $\sqrt{a^2 + b^2}$ cannot be simplified

Exploration

24. Three vertices of a parallelogram are (2, 6), (-1, 5), and (0, -4).

a. Find at least two possible locations of the fourth vertex.

b. Are there other possible locations for the fourth vertex?

a) Samples: (3, -3), (1, 15); b) Yes. In this case, (-3, -5)

650

LESSON

11-6 *The Distance Formula*

Going the distance. *Running distances has been an event in the Special Olympics since they began in 1968.*

Distances on the Coordinate Plane

In the Example below, we find the distance between two points. The method is to draw a right triangle whose hypotenuse represents the distance, and then to apply the Pythagorean Theorem.

Example 1

Find the distance d between (-8, 50) and (30, -11).

Solution

Draw a rough graph. Then identify the coordinates of the third vertex of a right triangle, as shown here. The lengths of the legs are 30 − (-8), or 38, and 50 − (-11), or 61. Now use the Pythagorean Theorem.

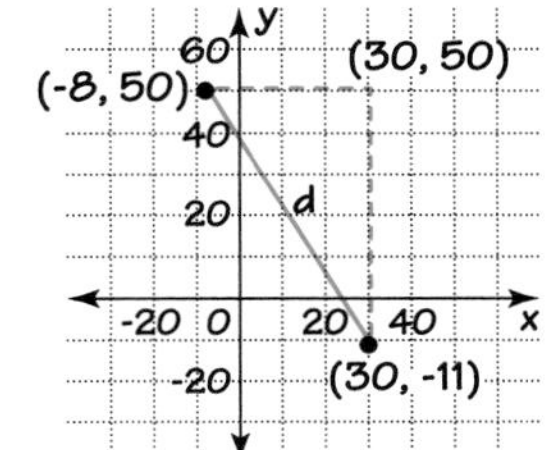

$d^2 = 38^2 + 61^2 = 5165$. So
$d = \sqrt{5165} \approx 71.87$.

Activity

1. On a sheet of graph paper plot points $A = (3, 6)$ and $B = (-4, -2)$.
2. Draw a vertical line through A and a horizontal line through B. Let these lines intersect at C. 1,2)See Question 4 on page 654.
3. $\triangle ABC$ is a right triangle. Give the coordinates of C. (3, -2)
4. Find AC and BC. $AC = 8$, $BC = 7$
5. Use the Pythagorean Theorem to find AB.
   $AB = \sqrt{8^2 + 7^2} = \sqrt{113} \approx 10.6$

Lesson 11-6

Objectives

A Determine the length of a segment in the coordinate plane.
F Write indirect proofs involving the use of the Distance Formula.
G Use coordinate geometry to deduce properties of figures and prove theorems.
I Apply the Distance Formula in real situations.

Resources

From the ***Teacher's Resource File***
- Lesson Master 11-6A or 11-6B
- Answer Master 11-6
- Teaching Aids
  4 Coordinate Plane
  144 Warm-up

Additional Resources
- Visuals for Teaching Aids 4, 144
- Videodisc

Teaching Lesson 11-6

Warm-up

On the grid below, the side of each square represents a city block.

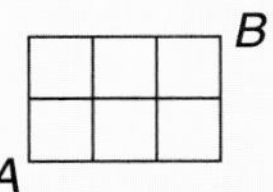

1. How many blocks are in the shortest route from A to B? 5 blocks
2. How many possible routes of this length are there from A to B? 10 routes
3. Ignore the grid lines. What is the shortest distance from A to B? $\sqrt{13} \approx 3.6$ blocks

Lesson 11-6 Overview

Broad Goals This lesson covers the derivation and use of the formula for the distance between two points (x_1, y_1) and (x_2, y_2).

Perspective The application of the Pythagorean Theorem to prove the Distance Formula is simple and powerful. Students should be expected not only to know the formula but also to know the idea (not necessarily the details) behind its derivation. Students who have studied UCSMP *Algebra* should have seen this formula before.

The Distance Formula enables us to prove segments congruent. Therefore, by using the Distance Formula, we can prove triangles equilateral or isosceles, quadrilaterals to be kites, and so on.

The formula of this lesson is the Distance Formula for *Euclidean* geometry. In *taxicab* geometry, where distances can be measured along only horizontal or vertical lines, there is a different formula for the distance between (x_1, y_1) and (x_2, y_2), namely $d = |x_1 - x_2| + |y_1 - y_2|$.

Notes on Reading

Every line in the coordinate plane is a number line, but only horizontal and vertical lines have points whose coordinates allow us to find distances using subtraction. To find the distance between two points with coordinates a and b along these lines, we can use the familiar distance formula $|a - b|$; all one does is ignore the coordinates that are alike. However, along an oblique line segment, the coordinates are not obvious (and, in fact, they are seldom indicated), and the Pythagorean Theorem is needed.

It is important to go through the proof of the Distance Formula in detail. Students need to understand that one reason for a proof is to save work. Once the Distance Formula is proved, it can be used to find distances because it always works. Thus, it is not necessary to draw a right triangle every time a distance must be found.

A possible confusing step in the derivation of the Distance Formula is the move from absolute value to parentheses. The logic is as follows: Either $|a| = a$ or $|a| = -a$, and since $a^2 = (-a)^2$, the number a and its absolute value (either a or $-a$, depending on whether a is positive or negative) have the same square.

Example 1 is straightforward. **Example 2** points out the usefulness of the Distance Formula. It is more difficult to answer this type of question without using coordinates. **Example 3** shows the applicability of the formula in proofs.

Have students record the results of the **Activity** for use with **Question 4** on page 654.

You could draw a right triangle every time you need to calculate distances on an oblique line, but it is easier to have a general formula. The process is the same as in Example 1 and the Activity.

Let $P = (x_1, y_1)$ be the first point and $R = (x_2, y_2)$ be the second point.

Find a third point Q so that $\overline{PR}$ is the hypotenuse of a right triangle $\triangle PQR$. Such a point is $Q = (x_2, y_1)$.

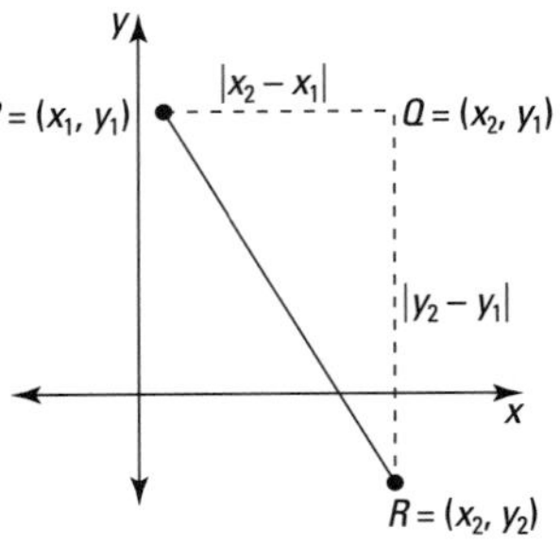

Using the Pythagorean Theorem,

$$PR^2 = PQ^2 + QR^2.$$
$$= (x_2 - x_1)^2 + (y_2 - y_1)^2$$

Taking the square roots of both sides,

$$PR = \sqrt{(x_2 - x_1)^2 + (y_2 - y_1)^2}.$$

This is a formula you should memorize.

Distance Formula on the Coordinate Plane
The distance d between two points (x_1, y_1) and (x_2, y_2) in the coordinate plane is given by the formula

$$d = \sqrt{(x_2 - x_1)^2 + (y_2 - y_1)^2}.$$

With the Distance Formula, Example 1 can be solved without drawing a figure.

Let $(x_1, y_1) = (-8, 50)$ and let $(x_2, y_2) = (30, -11)$. If d is the distance between these points,

$$\begin{aligned} d &= \sqrt{(x_2 - x_1)^2 + (y_2 - y_1)^2}. \\ &= \sqrt{(30 - -8)^2 + (-11 - 50)^2} \\ &= \sqrt{(38)^2 + (-61)^2} \\ &= \sqrt{1444 + 3721} \\ &= \sqrt{5165} \\ &\approx 71.87 \end{aligned}$$

A grid can be put behind any drawing (blueprint, map, picture, and so on) to assign coordinates to points. With the Distance Formula, you can calculate distances between any two points on the drawing without having to measure.

Video

Wide World of Mathematics The segment, *Sailing the Seas,* features a woman attempting to sail around the world; she runs into storms but survives. The segment may be used to extend this lesson on the Distance Formula by having students compute distances between the boat's various locations. Related questions and an investigation are provided in videodisc stills and in the Video Guide. A related CD-ROM activity is also available.

Videodisc Bar Codes

Search Chapter 54

Play

Optional Activities

Technology Connection You can use this activity after discussing the lesson. Students who can program a calculator or computer may be interested in writing a short program to find the distance between two points which have been input. The program also can be extended to print out whether the segment is horizontal, vertical, or oblique.

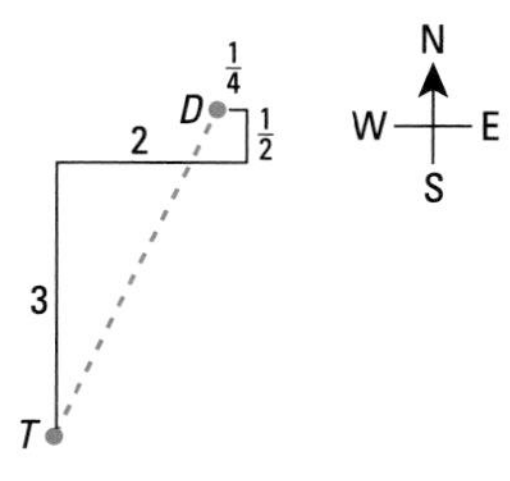

Example 2

Tom likes to bike from his apartment to Doris's house following the path shown at the left: 3 miles north, then 2 miles east, then $\frac{1}{2}$ mile north, then $\frac{1}{4}$ mile west. How far apart do they live?

Solution

Think of the path as being on a coordinate grid with Tom's apartment T at (0, 0). Doris's house D is at the point (1.75, 3.5). The distance between them is the length of $\overline{TD}$. Using the distance formula,

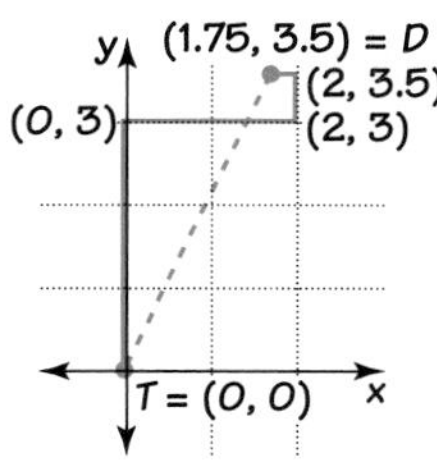

$$TD = \sqrt{(1.75 - 0)^2 + (3.5 - 0)^2}$$
$$= \sqrt{15.3125}$$
$$\approx 3.9.$$

They live about 3.9 miles apart.

Using the Distance Formula in Proofs

You can use the Distance Formula to prove that segments on the coordinate plane are congruent. Example 3 presents a coordinate proof of a theorem you have known for some time.

Example 3

Use coordinates to prove that the diagonals of a rectangle are congruent.

Solution

First, write the given and to prove in terms of a representative figure.
Given: RSTU is a rectangle.
To prove: RT = US.

Drawing:
One of the convenient locations for any rectangle RSTU is with R = (0, 0), S = (a, 0), T = (a, b), and U = (0, b).

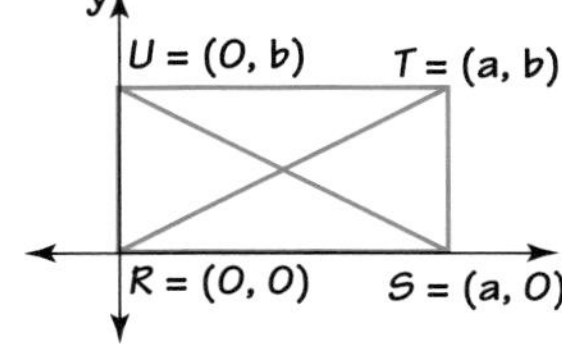

Argument:
Using the Distance Formula,

$$RT = \sqrt{(0 - a)^2 + (0 - b)^2} = \sqrt{a^2 + b^2}$$
$$\text{and } US = \sqrt{(a - 0)^2 + (0 - b)^2} = \sqrt{a^2 + b^2}.$$

By substitution, RT = US.

Again notice that the coordinate proof is simple and straightforward. However, it does require a knowledge of algebra and how to find square roots.

Additional Examples

1. Find the distance between (3, 7) and (7, 3). $\sqrt{32} \approx 5.66$
2. On a coordinate grid, Karim's home is 2800 north and 1200 west of the (0, 0) point. His friend Sanjay lives 3500 south and 400 east. If each 100 in an address equals $\frac{1}{8}$ mile, how far apart are their homes? $8\frac{1}{8}$ miles
3. Use coordinates to prove that the diagonals of a square are congruent. Sample: Put the square in a convenient location, say (0, 0), (a, 0), (a, a), and (0, a). The distance between (0, 0) and (a, a) is $\sqrt{(a - 0)^2 + (a - 0)^2}$. The distance between ($a$, 0) and (0, a) is $\sqrt{(0 - a)^2 + (a - 0)^2}$. Each distance is $\sqrt{2a^2}$.

LESSON MASTER 11-6 A

Questions on SPUR Objectives
See pages 680–683 for objectives.

Skills Objective A

In 1 and 2, find the distance between the given points.

1. (4, -3) and (-2, 6) $\sqrt{117} \approx 10.8$
2. (1.5, 3.9) and (-0.4, -9.2) $\sqrt{175.22} \approx 13.2$
3. What is the radius of the circle at the right with center D? $\sqrt{41} \approx 6.4$

Properties Objective F

4. Use the figure at the right. Write an indirect proof to show that $ABCD$ is *not* a kite.
Sample: If $ABCD$ is a kite, then $AD = CD$ or AB. But $AD = \sqrt{1^2 + 4^2} = \sqrt{17}$, $CD = \sqrt{3^2 + 2^2} = \sqrt{13}$, and $AB = \sqrt{8^2 + 6^2} = \sqrt{100}$. Therefore, $ABCD$ is not a kite.

Properties Objective G

5. $\triangle XYZ$ has vertices $X = (85, 150)$, $Y = (115, 110)$, and $Z = (125, 180)$. Prove that $\triangle XYZ$ is isosceles.
Sample: $XY = \sqrt{30^2 + 40^2} = \sqrt{2500}$; $YZ = \sqrt{10^2 + 70^2} = \sqrt{5000}$; $ZX = \sqrt{30^2 + 40^2} = \sqrt{2500}$. So $XY = ZX$, and $\triangle XYZ$ is isosceles.

Uses Objective I

6. Gary Ozawa gave you the following directions to get from school to his home: Go six blocks east, then 15 blocks north, then 4 more blocks east, then 1 block south, and finally 1 block west. By air to his home, about how many kilometers is it, if 5 blocks is about 1 kilometer? ≈ 3.3 km

Adapting to Individual Needs

Challenge

Materials: Graph paper or **Teaching Aid 4**

Have students graph the parabola $y = \frac{1}{4}x^2$, the point (0, 1) and the line $y = -1$. Have them complete the chart at the right for several points on the parabola and make a conjecture based on the results. Suggest that they look up the definition of parabola and relate their results to this definition.

Point on the parabola	Distance from (0, 1)	Distance from $y = -1$
(0, 0)	[1]	[1]
(2, 1)	[2]	[2]
(-2, 1)	[2]	[2]
(3, 2.25)	[3.25]	[3.25]

[A parabola is the set of all points equidistant from a fixed point (the focus), and a fixed line (the directrix). For this parabola, the focus is (0, 1) and the directrix is the line $y = -1$.]

Notes on Questions

Question 10 Drawing a picture can shorten work by indicating which sides are probably the same length.

Question 11 Without coordinates, this would be a more difficult question, but it could be done using the Pythagorean Theorem.

Question 15 Cooperative Learning Have groups of students graph the triangle, assigning each group a different value for z. Discuss that the triangles are the same shape but different sizes.

Question 21 The algebraic manipulation here is similar to algebraic manipulation used in Lesson 11-8 in the proof of the midpoint formula.

Question 22 Discuss this question in preparation for Lesson 11-8.

Additional Answers

9. Given: Isosceles trapezoid $PQRS$ with $P = (a, 0)$, $Q = (b, c)$, $R = (-b, c)$, and $S = (-a, 0)$.
To prove: $SQ = PR$.
From the Distance Formula, $SQ = \sqrt{(c-0)^2 + (b+a)^2} = \sqrt{c^2 + (b+a)^2}$ and $PR = \sqrt{(c-0)^2 + (-b-a)^2} = \sqrt{c^2 + ((-1)(b+a))^2} = \sqrt{c^2 + ((-1)^2(b+a)^2)} = \sqrt{c^2 + (b+a)^2}$.
Thus, by the Transitive Property of Equality, $SQ = PR$.

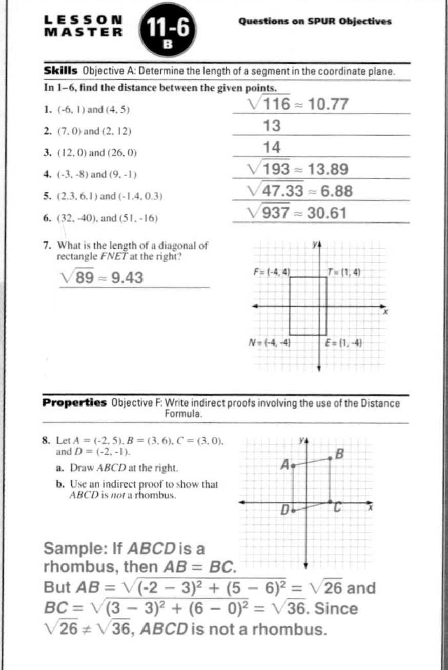

LESSON MASTER 11-6 B — Questions on SPUR Objectives

Skills Objective A: Determine the length of a segment in the coordinate plane.

In 1–6, find the distance between the given points.

1. (-6, 1) and (4, 5) — $\sqrt{116} \approx 10.77$
2. (7, 0) and (2, 12) — 13
3. (12, 0) and (26, 0) — 14
4. (-3, -8) and (9, -1) — $\sqrt{193} \approx 13.89$
5. (2.3, 6.1) and (-1.4, 0.3) — $\sqrt{47.33} \approx 6.88$
6. (32, -40), and (51, -16) — $\sqrt{937} \approx 30.61$
7. What is the length of a diagonal of rectangle $FNET$ at the right? $\sqrt{89} \approx 9.43$

Properties Objective F: Write indirect proofs involving the use of the Distance Formula.

8. Let $A = (-2, 5)$, $B = (3, 6)$, $C = (3, 0)$, and $D = (-2, -1)$.
   a. Draw $ABCD$ at the right.
   b. Use an indirect proof to show that $ABCD$ is *not* a rhombus.

Sample: If $ABCD$ is a rhombus, then $AB = BC$. But $AB = \sqrt{(-2-3)^2 + (5-6)^2} = \sqrt{26}$ and $BC = \sqrt{(3-3)^2 + (6-0)^2} = \sqrt{36}$. Since $\sqrt{26} \neq \sqrt{36}$, $ABCD$ is not a rhombus.

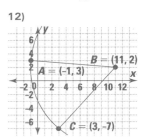

4) $A = (3, 6)$, $B = (-4, -2)$, $C = (3, -2)$

10a) $KL = \sqrt{82}$ and $LJ = \sqrt{82}$ by the Distance Formula. $KL = LJ$ by the Transitive Property of Equality. Thus $\triangle JKL$ is isosceles, by the definition of isosceles triangle.

11a) School (0, 0); Cynthia (-2, -0.8); Charles (1, -1.5)

12) $A = (-1, 3)$, $B = (11, 2)$, $C = (3, -7)$

$BC = \sqrt{145}$ and $BA = \sqrt{145}$. Thus, by the definition of circle, C and A are on the same circle with center B.

QUESTIONS

Covering the Reading

In 1–3, use the figure at the right to find the distance.

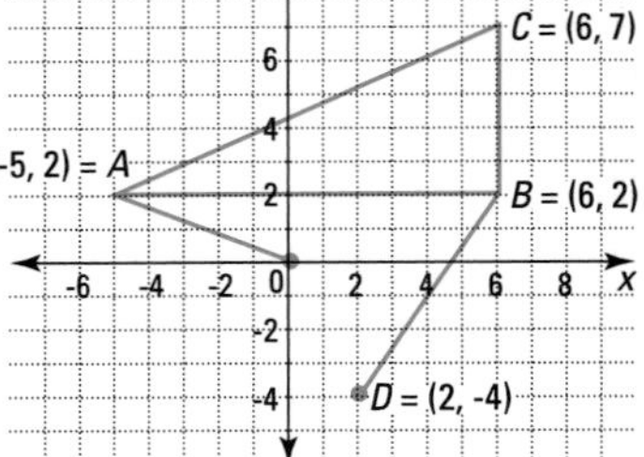

1. AB 11
2. BC 5
3. AC ≈ 12.08
4. Give your answers to the Activity on page 651.
See left. $C = (3, -2)$, $AC = 8$, $BC = 7$, $AB \approx 10.6$
5. Give the distance between (x_1, y_1) and (x_2, y_2). $\sqrt{(x_2 - x_1)^2 + (y_2 - y_1)^2}$

In 6 and 7, find the distance between the points.

6. (14, -7), (28, 90) ≈ 98.0
7. (-10, 11), (-31, -25) ≈ 41.7
8. To get to a hospital from the middle of a nearby town, you can drive 8 miles east, turn right and go 4 miles south, and then turn right again and go 1 mile west. By helicopter, how far is it from the middle of the town to the hospital? (Ignore the altitude of the helicopter.)
$\sqrt{65} \approx 8.06$ miles
9. A convenient location for an isosceles trapezoid is pictured at the right. Use this location to prove that the diagonals of an isosceles trapezoid are congruent.
See margin.

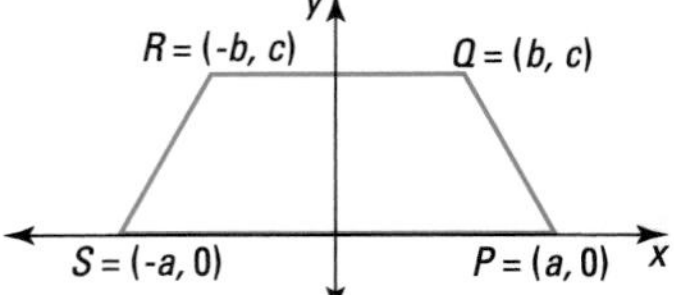

Applying the Mathematics

10. Let $J = (-5, 0)$, $K = (5, 8)$, and $L = (4, -1)$.
   a. Prove that $\triangle JKL$ is isosceles by using the Distance Formula.
   b. Is $\triangle JKL$ equilateral? Explain why or why not.
   a) See left. b) No, because $JK = \sqrt{164} \neq \sqrt{82}$.
11. On a map, it can be seen that Charles lives one mile east and 1.5 miles south of school, while Cynthia lives 2 miles west and 0.8 mile south of the same school.
   a. Draw a graph with appropriate coordinates for the school, Charles's residence, and Cynthia's residence. See left.
   b. How far do Charles and Cynthia live from each other?
   $\sqrt{9.49} \approx 3.08$ miles
12. Let $A = (-1, 3)$ and $B = (11, 2)$. Prove that the point $C = (3, -7)$ is on the circle with center B and radius BA. Include a picture.
See left.
13. Using coordinates, prove that each pair of opposite sides of a parallelogram are congruent. See margin.

Additional Answers, continued

13. Given: Parallelogram $WXYZ$ in the convenient position as shown below, with $a > 0$.
To prove: $WX = YZ$ and $WZ = YX$.

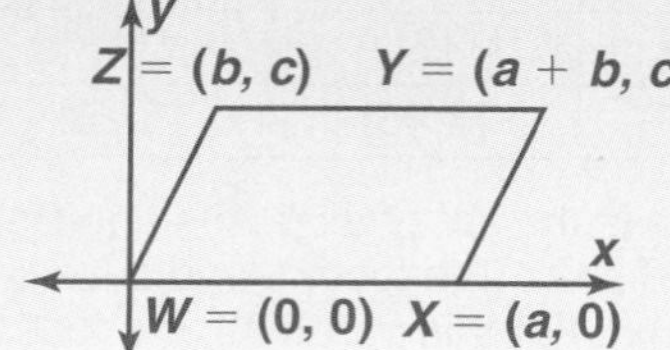

According to the Distance Formula, $WX = |a|$, $YZ = \sqrt{(a+b-b)^2 + (c-c)^2} = \sqrt{a^2} = |a|$; $WZ = \sqrt{(0-b)^2 + (0-c)^2} = \sqrt{b^2 + c^2}$; $XY = \sqrt{(a+b-a)^2 + (c-0)^2} = \sqrt{b^2 + c^2}$. By the Transitive Property of Equality, $WX = YZ$ and $WZ = YX$. Therefore, both pairs of opposite sides are congruent.

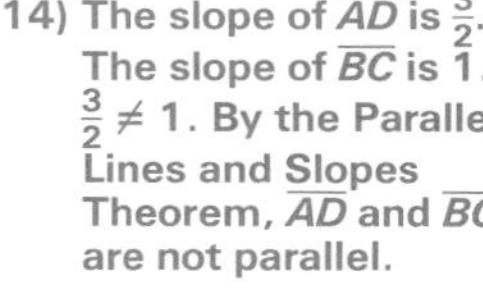

14) The slope of $\overline{AD}$ is $\frac{3}{2}$. The slope of $\overline{BC}$ is 1. $\frac{3}{2} \neq 1$. By the Parallel Lines and Slopes Theorem, $\overline{AD}$ and $\overline{BC}$ are not parallel.

Review

14. Given: $A = (1, 0)$, $B = (4, 0)$, $C = (5, 1)$, and $D = (3, 3)$. Prove that $\overline{BC}$ is not parallel to $\overline{AD}$. *(Lesson 11-5)* See left.

15. Prove that, when $z \neq 0$, the triangle with vertices $P = (3z, 4z)$, $Q = (7z, 2z)$, and $R = (2z, -8z)$ is a right triangle. *(Lesson 11-5)* See left.

16. Show by indirect reasoning that a quadrilateral cannot have four acute angles. *(Lesson 11-4)* See margin.

In 17 and 18, what (if anything) can you conclude from the given statements, using the rules of logic? *(Lessons 11-1, 11-2, 11-3)*

17. (1) You are elected President of the U.S. if you win the majority of electoral votes.
(2) In 1960, Richard Nixon was not elected President. In 1960 Richard Nixon did not receive the majority of electoral votes.

18. (1) Last Saturday Notre Dame won the football game 6–3.
(2) You can score six points in football with three safeties, two field goals, or one touchdown.
(3) Notre Dame did not have any safeties or touchdowns. Notre Dame had two field goals.

19. A parallelogram and a triangle have the same base and same altitude. How are their areas related? *(Lessons 8-5, 8-6)* Area of the triangle is one-half the area of the parallelogram.

20. The measure of one acute angle of a right triangle is 45 more than the measure of the other.
a. Is this possible? Yes
b. If so, find the measures. If not, tell why not. *(Lesson 3-3)* 22.5 and 67.5

21. Write $a - \frac{a+b}{2}$ as a single fraction. *(Previous course)* $\frac{a-b}{2}$

22. Lynne has scored 92, 83, and 95 on her three tests so far this grading period. What is her average (or mean) score so far? *(Previous course)* 90

Notre Dame vs. University of Michigan

15) The slope of $\overline{PQ} = \frac{2z - 4z}{7z - 3z} = -\frac{1}{2}$ and the slope of $\overline{QR} = \frac{-8z - 2z}{2z - 7z} = 2$ by the definition of slope. $-\frac{1}{2} \cdot 2 = -1$. So $\overline{PQ} \perp \overline{QR}$ by the Perpendicular Lines and Slopes Theorem. Thus, $\triangle PQR$ is a right triangle by the definition of right triangle.

Exploration

23. The distance from point X to (2, 8) is 17.
a. Show that X could be (10, 23).
b. Name five other possible locations for point X. (Hint: Draw a picture.)

a) $\sqrt{(10-2)^2 + (23-8)^2} = \sqrt{64 + 225} = \sqrt{289} = 17$
b) Samples: (2, 25), (2, -9), (19, 8), (-15, 8), (10, -7)
All points X will be on a circle with radius 17 and center (2, 8).

16. Either $ABCD$ has four acute angles or it does not. Suppose $ABCD$ has four acute angles. Then, by the definition of acute, $m\angle A < 90$, $m\angle B < 90$, $m\angle C < 90$, and $m\angle D < 90$. Then $m\angle A + m\angle B + m\angle C + m\angle D < 360$, which contradicts the Quadrilateral-Sum Theorem. So the supposition is false. Therefore, a quadrilateral cannot have four acute angles.

Follow-up for Lesson 11-6

Practice

For more questions on SPUR Objectives, use **Lesson Master 11-6A** (shown on page 653) or **Lesson Master 11-6B** (shown on pages 654–655).

Assessment

Oral/Written Communication
Have students **work in pairs.** Each student should name two points in the coordinate plane. Then partners should exchange papers and find the distance between the points. [Students correctly find the distance between two points by applying the Distance Formula.]

Extension

Extend *Additional Example 1* by asking students to generalize and give the distance between (a, b) and (b, a). [$|a - b|\sqrt{2}$]

Project Update Project 4, *Varignon's Theorem,* on page 676, relates to the content of this lesson.

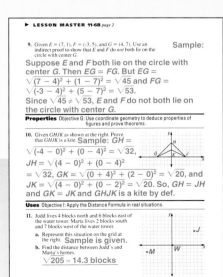

▶ **LESSON MASTER 11-6B** *page 2*

9. Given $E = (7, 1)$, $F = (-3, 5)$, and $G = (4, 7)$. Use an indirect proof to show that E and F do *not* both lie on the circle with center G. Sample:
Suppose E and F both lie on the circle with center G. Then $EG = FG$. But $EG = \sqrt{(7-4)^2 + (1-7)^2} = \sqrt{45}$ and $FG = \sqrt{(-3-4)^2 + (5-7)^2} = \sqrt{53}$.
Since $\sqrt{45} \neq \sqrt{53}$, E and F do not both lie on the circle with center G.

Properties Objective G: Use coordinate geometry to deduce properties of figures and prove theorems.

10. Given $GHJK$ as shown at the right. Prove that $GHJK$ is a kite. Sample: $GH = \sqrt{(-4-0)^2 + (0-4)^2} = \sqrt{32}$, $JH = \sqrt{(4-0)^2 + (0-4)^2} = \sqrt{32}$, $GK = \sqrt{(0+4)^2 + (2-0)^2} = \sqrt{20}$, and $JK = \sqrt{(4-0)^2 + (0-2)^2} = \sqrt{20}$. So, $GH = JH$ and $GK = JK$ and $GHJK$ is a kite by def.

Uses Objective I: Apply the Distance Formula in real situations.

11. Judd lives 4 blocks north and 6 blocks east of the water tower. Marta lives 2 blocks south and 7 blocks west of the water tower.
a. Represent this situation on the grid at the right. Sample is given.
b. Find the distance between Judd's and Marta's homes.
$\sqrt{205} \approx 14.3$ blocks

12. Mrs. Kurinsky's car phone works within a 75-mile radius of her office. She made a sales call 26 miles east and 58 miles south of her office. From there, she made a second call by driving 8 miles north and 17 miles west. Then she drove 14 miles west and 3 miles south for lunch at a restaurant. Could Mrs. Kurinsky use her car phone from the parking lot of the restaurant? Explain your answer.
Yes; she is about 53 miles from her office.

Lesson 11-7

Objectives

J Graph and write an equation for a circle given its center and radius, and vice versa.

Resources

From the ***Teacher's Resource File***

- Lesson Master 11-7A or 11-7B
- Answer Master 11-7
- Assessment Sourcebook: Quiz for Lessons 11-5 through 11-7
- Teaching Aids
  4 Coordinate Plane
  145 Warm-up
  153 Graph of a Circle

Additional Resources

- Visuals for Teaching Aids 4, 145, 153

Teaching Lesson 11-7

Warm-up

1. Plot the following points on a coordinate grid: (0, 10), (6, 8), (8, 6), (10, 0), (8, -6), (6, -8), (0, -10), (-6, -8), (-8, -6), (-10, 0), (-8, 6), (-6, 8). **Check students' graphs. The points should all lie on a circle with center (0, 0) and radius 10.**
2. What do you notice about the points you graphed in Question 1? **They lie on a circle.**
3. Can you find an equation that describes all the points you graphed in Question 1? $x^2 + y^2 = 100$

LESSON

11-7 *Equations for Circles*

Round and round they go. *As a carousel turns, the path a carved animal follows is a circle. The equation of each circle is determined by the distance each animal is from the center.*

Distance and Circles

A wonderful application of the Distance Formula is in finding an equation for a circle. At the right, a circle is drawn with center (3, 2) and radius 10. By adding or subtracting 10 from either coordinate of (3, 2), four points on the circle can be found. They are (13, 2), (3, 12), (-7, 2), and (3, -8). We seek an equation satisfied by the coordinates of these four points and all other points on the circle, and by no other points.

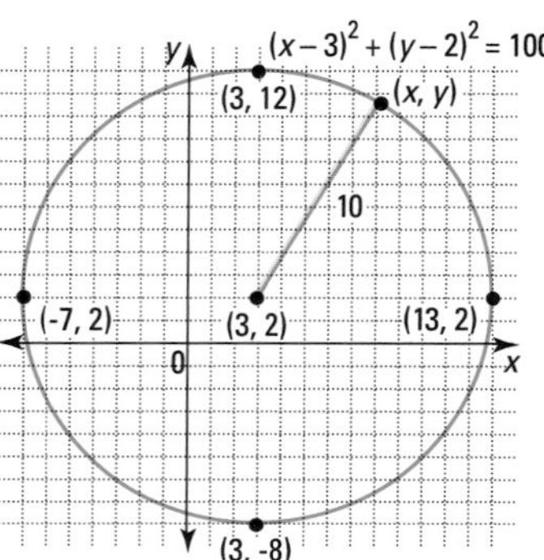

If a point (x, y) is on this circle, then it is 10 units away from the center. So, by the Distance Formula:

$$\sqrt{(x - 3)^2 + (y - 2)^2} = 10.$$

This is an equation for the circle.

However, most people prefer equations without square roots. Squaring both sides gives an equivalent equation.

$$(x - 3)^2 + (y - 2)^2 = 100$$

To check if this equation is correct, try the point (-7, 2), which is known to be on the circle. It should satisfy the equation. Substitute -7 for x and 2 for y.

Lesson 11-7 Overview

Broad Goals The goal of this lesson is to apply the Distance Formula to obtain the formula for an equation of a circle.

Perspective This lesson is a nice application of the Pythagorean Theorem to circles. The content is important and will be seen again in later courses. Why do we do this in geometry when students will see it again in *UCSMP Advanced Algebra?* Because it is important content and the first "locus" definition to yield an equation for a curve. When students see such equations in their next course, they should have had something like it before. Also, it is important that students realize that there can be equations for curves. If they do not take more mathematics, and leave having never seen equations for curves, they cannot hope to comprehend the idea behind equations for functions or non-linear descriptions of data.

Optional Activities

Activity 1 You can use this activity after students complete the lesson. Consider the circle with radius 15 and center (5, -7). Have students use what they know about the equation of a circle to describe the coordinates (x, y) of all of the points in the interior of the circle, and to describe the coordinates (x, y) of all of the points in the exterior of the circle.
[Interior of circle: $(x - 5)^2 + (y + 7)^2 < 225$
Exterior of circle: $(x - 5)^2 + (y + 7)^2 > 225$]

Does $(-7 - 3)^2 + (2 - 2)^2 = 100$?
Does $(-10)^2 + 0^2 = 100$? Yes.

It is easy to generalize this example.

❶ **Equation for a Circle**
The circle with center (h, k) and radius r is the set of points (x, y) satisfying

$$(x - h)^2 + (y - k)^2 = r^2.$$

Drawing

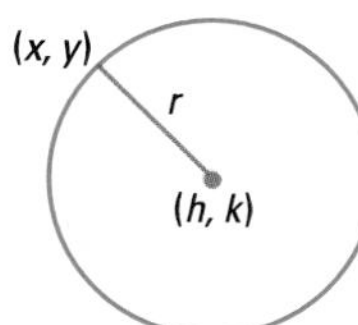

Proof

Given: The circle with center (h, k) and radius r, and a point (x, y) on the circle.

To prove: $(x - h)^2 + (y - k)^2 = r^2$.

Argument:
It is given that r is the radius. By the definition of circle, the distance from (h, k) to (x, y) is r. Express the distance from (h, k) to (x, y) using the Distance Formula.

$$\sqrt{(x - h)^2 + (y - k)^2} = r$$

Squaring both sides: $(x - h)^2 + (y - k)^2 = r^2$.

Example 1

Write an equation for the circle with center (0, -4) and radius 7.

Solution

Here $r = 7$ and $(h, k) = (0, -4)$. So $h = 0$ and $k = -4$. Write the general equation for a circle, and substitute the values of h, k, and r into it.

$$(x - h)^2 + (y - k)^2 = r^2$$
$$(x - 0)^2 + (y - -4)^2 = 7^2$$

After simplifying, $x^2 + (y + 4)^2 = 49$ is the desired equation.

Check

Draw a picture and find the coordinates of a point on the circle. One point on the circle is (7, -4). Does (7, -4) satisfy the equation? Substitute 7 for x and -4 for y.

Does $7^2 + (-4 + 4)^2 = 49$?
Does $7^2 + 0^2 = 49$? Yes.

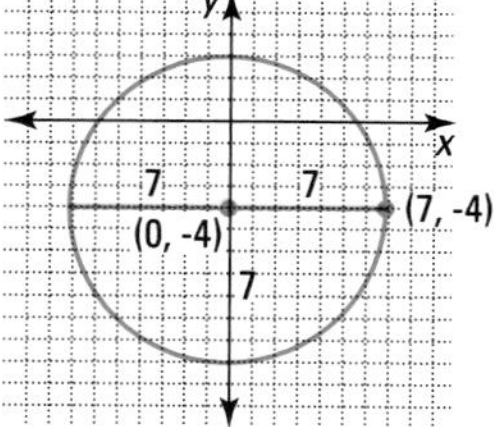

Other easily found points to check are (0, 3), (-7, -4), or (0, -11). Remember that the center is not on the circle, so its coordinates will not satisfy the equation.

If you are given an equation for a circle, you can determine its center and radius.

Notes on Reading

❶ A major difficulty some students have in understanding the equation for a circle is that the use of the variables x and y in the formula is different from the uses of the variables h, k, and r. The variables x and y may stand for any point on the circle, but h, k, and r are constants. You might point out that the expression $\sqrt{(x-3)^2 + (y-2)^2}$ gives the distance from *any* point (x, y) to (3, 2). By setting the expression equal to 10, only those points 10 units away from (3, 2) will satisfy the equation. The constants are 3, 2, and 10. **Teaching Aid 153** contains a graph of a circle.

Using the standard form of the equation of a circle can be difficult for some students because of the subtraction, which represents a difference in coordinates. Caution students to read the equation in **Example 2** as a circle with center (-1, -3), not (1, 3).

At this time you might wish to discuss **Question 14.** Then consider the equation $(x - 4)^2 + (y - 11)^2 = 25$. This equation has many lattice-point solutions, among them the obvious four points (9, 11), (-1, 11), (4, 16), and (4, 6). But there are also the solutions from the relationship $3^2 + 4^2 = 25$. Some of the other points are (7, 15), (1, 15), (8, 14), (8, 8), (0, 14), (0, 8), (7, 7), (1, 7). Have students graph these points to show that they all lie on a circle. The equation $(x - 4)^2 + (y - 11)^2 = 25$ is

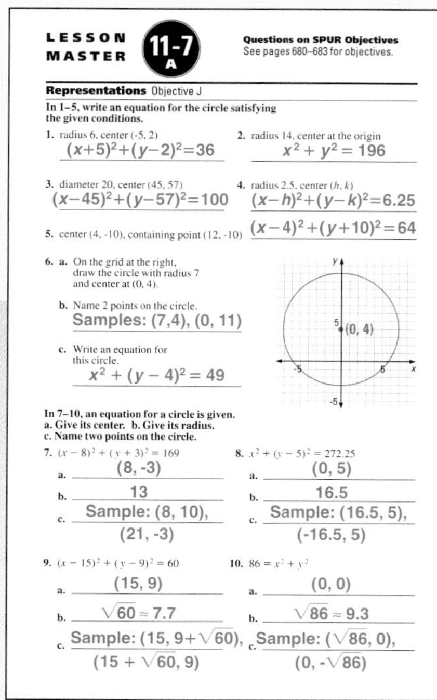

LESSON MASTER 11-7 A

Questions on SPUR Objectives
See pages 680–683 for objectives.

Representations Objective J

In 1–5, write an equation for the circle satisfying the given conditions.

1. radius 6, center (-5, 2) $(x+5)^2+(y-2)^2=36$
2. radius 14, center at the origin $x^2 + y^2 = 196$
3. diameter 20, center (45, 57) $(x-45)^2+(y-57)^2=100$
4. radius 2.5, center (h, k) $(x-h)^2+(y-k)^2=6.25$
5. center (4, -10), containing point (12, -10) $(x-4)^2+(y+10)^2=64$
6. a. On the grid at the right, draw the circle with radius 7 and center at (0, 4).
   b. Name 2 points on the circle. Samples: (7,4), (0, 11)
   c. Write an equation for this circle. $x^2 + (y - 4)^2 = 49$

In 7–10, an equation for a circle is given. a. Give its center. b. Give its radius. c. Name two points on the circle.

7. $(x - 8)^2 + (y + 3)^2 = 169$
   a. (8, -3)
   b. 13
   c. Sample: (8, 10), (21, -3)
8. $x^2 + (y - 5)^2 = 272.25$
   a. (0, 5)
   b. 16.5
   c. Sample: (16.5, 5), (-16.5, 5)
9. $(x - 15)^2 + (y - 9)^2 = 60$
   a. (15, 9)
   b. $\sqrt{60} \approx 7.7$
   c. Sample: $(15, 9+\sqrt{60})$, $(15 + \sqrt{60}, 9)$
10. $86 = x^2 + y^2$
   a. (0, 0)
   b. $\sqrt{86} \approx 9.3$
   c. Sample: $(\sqrt{86}, 0)$, $(0, -\sqrt{86})$

Optional Activities

Activity 2
Materials: Graph paper or **Teaching Aid 4**

You can use these questions after students complete the lesson. Have them superimpose a circle on a coordinate plane and tell what changes will occur in the equation of the circle $(x - h)^2 + (y - k)^2 = r^2$, when a circle is

1. translated horizontally. [The value of h will vary, but k and r will remain constant.]
2. translated vertically. [The value of k will vary, but the values of h and r will remain constant.]
3. translated along an oblique line. [Both h and k will vary, but r will remain constant.]
4. expanded or contracted with center (0, 0) and magnitude m. [The equation becomes $(x - mh)^2 + (y - mk)^2 = (mr)^2$.]

an equation for this circle. Though there are many equations equivalent to this one, this equation is *the* equation written in standard form.

Some students might think that the coordinates of points on a circle must be integers. To help students see that this is not true, pick one of the circles in the lesson and have each student find the coordinates of a point that is not a lattice point. The process is found in the last paragraph of the lesson.

Some students may also think that the coefficients in an equation for a circle must be integers. Point out that they can be any real numbers. Students have to consider noninteger coefficients in order to answer **Question 24.**

❷ Point out the simplicity of the equation for a circle whose center is at the origin. Tell students that there are reasonably simple equations for certain placements of conic sections. They may have seen equations for some parabolas ($y = ax^2 + bx + c$) and some hyperbolas ($xy = k$) in their previous study of algebra. If students did not find the equation for the circle in the *Warm-up,* you might have them do so after this discussion.

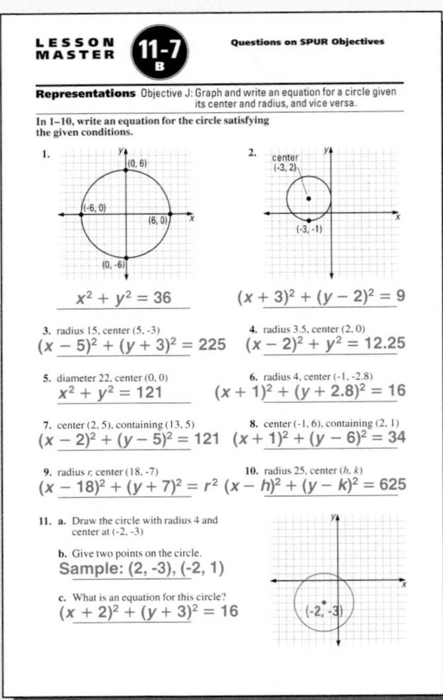

LESSON MASTER 11-7 B — Questions on SPUR Objectives

Representations Objective J: Graph and write an equation for a circle given its center and radius, and vice versa.

In 1–10, write an equation for the circle satisfying the given conditions.

1. $x^2 + y^2 = 36$

2. $(x + 3)^2 + (y - 2)^2 = 9$

3. radius 15, center (5, -3) $(x - 5)^2 + (y + 3)^2 = 225$

4. radius 3.5, center (2, 0) $(x - 2)^2 + y^2 = 12.25$

5. diameter 22, center (0, 0) $x^2 + y^2 = 121$

6. radius 4, center (-1, -2.8) $(x + 1)^2 + (y + 2.8)^2 = 16$

7. center (2, 5), containing (13, 5) $(x - 2)^2 + (y - 5)^2 = 121$

8. center (-1, 6), containing (2, 1) $(x + 1)^2 + (y - 6)^2 = 34$

9. radius r, center (18, -7) $(x - 18)^2 + (y + 7)^2 = r^2$

10. radius 25, center (h, k) $(x - h)^2 + (y - k)^2 = 625$

11. a. Draw the circle with radius 4 and center at (-2, -3).

b. Give two points on the circle. Sample: (2, -3), (-2, 1)

c. What is an equation for this circle? $(x + 2)^2 + (y + 3)^2 = 16$

Example 2

Find the center and radius of the circle with equation $(x + 1)^2 + (y + 3)^2 = 25$.

Solution

Compare the general equation to the given equation.

$$(x - h)^2 + (y - k)^2 = r^2$$
$$(x + 1)^2 + (y + 3)^2 = 25$$

h must be -1 to get $(x + 1)$. k must be -3 to get $(y + 3)$. The center is (-1, -3). We know $r^2 = 25$, so $r = 5$ or $r = -5$. Since r is a length, r cannot be negative. The radius is 5.

Check

Draw a circle with center (-1, -3) and radius 5. One point on the circle is (-1, 2). Does it satisfy the equation?

Does $(-1 + 1)^2 + (2 + 3)^2 = 25$?
$0^2 + 5^2 = 25$? Yes.

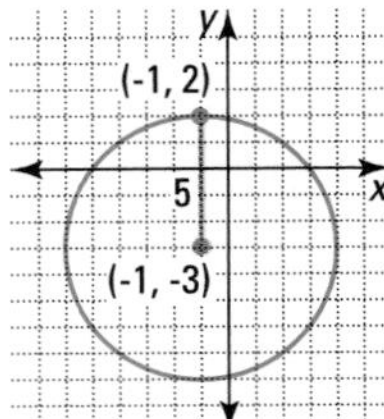

Circles Centered at the Origin

❷ The circles with the simplest equations are those with center (0, 0), the origin. Then $h = 0$ and $k = 0$. So an equation is

$$(x - 0)^2 + (y - 0)^2 = r^2,$$

or just

$$x^2 + y^2 = r^2.$$

Pictured below is the circle with center (0, 0) and radius 9. Its equation is $x^2 + y^2 = 81$.

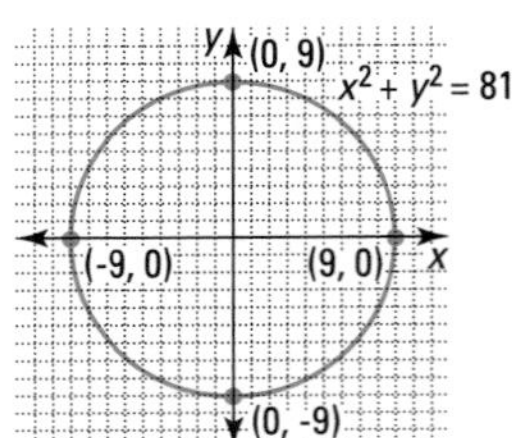

Four points on the circle are shown above. Others can be found by substituting values for x or y. For instance, consider the points of intersection of the circle with the line $x = 5$, as shown at the right. To find the coordinates of these points, substitute 5 for x in the equation. Then $5^2 + y^2 = 81$, making $y^2 = 56$, and so $y = \pm\sqrt{56}$. So the points $(5, \sqrt{56})$ and $(5, -\sqrt{56})$ are on this circle.

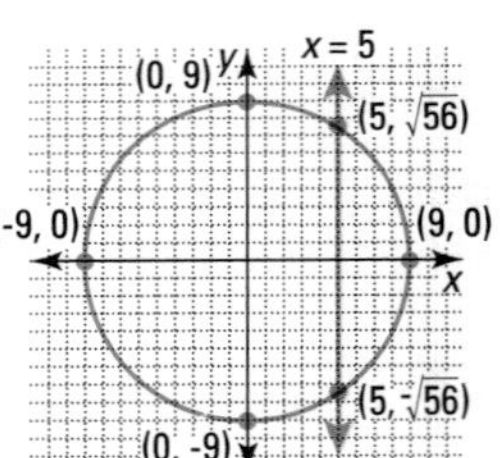

658

Adapting to Individual Needs

Challenge

Materials: Graph paper or **Teaching Aid 4**

Have students graph the circle $x^2 + y^2 = 9$, draw a circumscribed square around the circle crossing the axes at the same place the circle does, and draw a circumscribed circle around that square. Then have them give the equation of the outer circle. Ask which has greater area, the smaller circle or the ring between the circles. [The equation of the outer circle is $x^2 + y^2 = 18$. The areas of both the inner circle and the ring are 9π.]

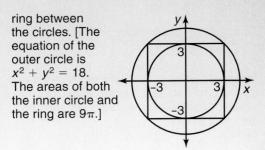

QUESTIONS

Covering the Reading

1. Is the point on the circle with center (3, 2) and radius 10?
   a. (13, 2) Yes b. (3, -8) Yes
   c. (8, 7) No d. (9, -6) Yes
2. Write the general form of the Equation for a Circle. Explain what each letter represents. See left.
3. The equation for a circle is derived from what formula? Distance Formula
4. a. Write an equation for the circle with center (-3, 5) and radius 1.
   b. Give the coordinates of four points on this circle. See left.
5. a. What is the distance between (x, y) and (7, 1)? $\sqrt{(x-7)^2 + (y-1)^2}$
   b. Give an equation for the circle with center (7, 1) and radius 5.
   c. Graph this circle. See left. b) $(x - 7)^2 + (y - 1)^2 = 25$
   d. Give the coordinates of four points on this circle. Sample: (7, 6), (7, -4), (12, 1), (2, 1)
6. The circle at the left has center at the origin and contains (3, 0). What is an equation for this circle? $x^2 + y^2 = 9$
7. Consider the circle $x^2 + y^2 = 81$ graphed on page 658. Where does this circle intersect the line $x = 4$? $(4, \sqrt{65})$, $(4, -\sqrt{65})$

Applying the Mathematics

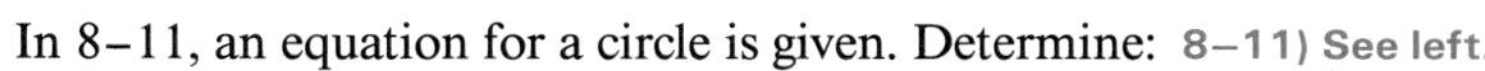

In 8–11, an equation for a circle is given. Determine: 8–11) See left.
a. its center. b. its radius. c. one point on the circle.

8. $(x - 5)^2 + (y - 11)^2 = 81$
9. $(x + 1)^2 + y^2 = 2$
10. $x^2 + y^2 = \frac{4}{25}$
11. $(x + 6)^2 + (y + 2)^2 = 1$

In 12 and 13, consider the circle $x^2 + y^2 = 121$.

12. Identify the coordinates of 10 points on this circle. See margin.
13. Find the circumference of this circle. 22π units
14. Give the coordinates of the 12 lattice points on the circle $x^2 + y^2 = 25$. (Recall that a lattice point is a point with integer coordinates.) Graph the points and the circle that contains them. See margin.
15. A circle is called **tangent** to a line if the circle and line have exactly one point in common. That point is called the **point of tangency.** A circle with center (2, -1) is tangent to the x-axis.
    a. Draw a picture. See margin.
    b. What are the coordinates of the point of tangency? (2, 0)
    c. Find an equation for the circle. $(x - 2)^2 + (y + 1)^2 = 1$
    d. Find the area of this circle. π square units

2) $(x - h)^2 + (y - k)^2 = r^2$. (h, k) are the coordinates of the center of the circle; r is the radius.

4a) $(x + 3)^2 + (y - 5)^2 = 1$
b) Samples: (-3, 4), (-3, 6), (-2, 5), (-4, 5)

(3, 0)

5c) $(x - 7)^2 + (y - 1)^2 = 25$

8a) (5, 11)
b) 9
c) Sample: (5, 20)

9a) (-1, 0)
b) $\sqrt{2}$
c) Sample: (0, 1)

10a) (0, 0)
b) $\frac{2}{5}$
c) Sample: $(0, -\frac{2}{5})$

11a) (-6, -2)
b) 1
c) Sample: (-6, -3)

Additional Examples

1. Write an equation for the circle with center at (2, 3) which contains the point (5, 6). $(x - 2)^2 + (y - 3)^2 = 18$
2. Find the center and radius of the circle with equation $(x + 11)^2 + (y + 7)^2 = 2$. Center (-11, -7), radius $\sqrt{2}$

Notes on Questions

Question 14 Any Pythagorean triple will yield a circle with at least 12 lattice points. For example, $x^2 + y^2 = 289$ employs the triple (8, 15, 17). A cutout of a triangle placed over a circle transparency may help students visualize the 8 points not on the axes.

Question 15 You might ask: What is an equation of a circle which is tangent to both axes and contains the point (0, 4)? [There is not a unique answer.]

Additional Answers

12. Sample: (0, 11), (0, -11), (11, 0), (-11, 0), $(6, \sqrt{85})$, $(6, -\sqrt{85})$, $(-6, \sqrt{85})$, $(-6, -\sqrt{85})$, $(\sqrt{85}, 6)$, $(\sqrt{85}, -6)$

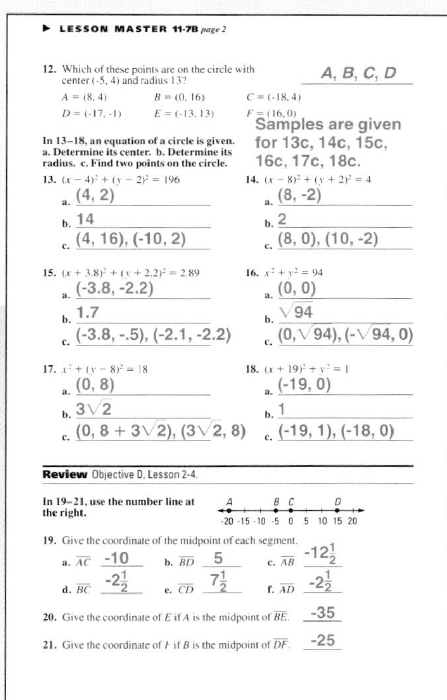

▶ LESSON MASTER 11-7B *page 2*

12. Which of these points are on the circle with center (-5, 4) and radius 13? A, B, C, D
    $A = (8, 4)$ $B = (0, 16)$ $C = (-18, 4)$
    $D = (-17, -1)$ $E = (-13, 13)$ $F = (16, 0)$

In 13–18, an equation of a circle is given. a. Determine its center. b. Determine its radius. c. Find two points on the circle. Samples are given for 13c, 14c, 15c, 16c, 17c, 18c.

13. $(x - 4)^2 + (y - 2)^2 = 196$
    a. (4, 2)
    b. 14
    c. (4, 16), (-10, 2)
14. $(x - 8)^2 + (y + 2)^2 = 4$
    a. (8, -2)
    b. 2
    c. (8, 0), (10, -2)
15. $(x + 3.8)^2 + (y + 2.2)^2 = 2.89$
    a. (-3.8, -2.2)
    b. 1.7
    c. (-3.8, -.5), (-2.1, -2.2)
16. $x^2 + y^2 = 94$
    a. (0, 0)
    b. $\sqrt{94}$
    c. $(0, \sqrt{94})$, $(-\sqrt{94}, 0)$
17. $x^2 + (y - 8)^2 = 18$
    a. (0, 8)
    b. $3\sqrt{2}$
    c. $(0, 8 + 3\sqrt{2})$, $(3\sqrt{2}, 8)$
18. $(x + 19)^2 + y^2 = 1$
    a. (-19, 0)
    b. 1
    c. (-19, 1), (-18, 0)

Review Objective D, Lesson 2-4.

In 19–21, use the number line at the right.

A B C D
-20 -15 -10 -5 0 5 10 15 20

19. Give the coordinate of the midpoint of each segment.
    a. $\overline{AC}$ -10 b. $\overline{BD}$ 5 c. $\overline{AB}$ $-12\frac{1}{2}$
    d. $\overline{BC}$ $-2\frac{1}{2}$ e. $\overline{CD}$ $7\frac{1}{2}$ f. $\overline{AD}$ $-2\frac{1}{2}$
20. Give the coordinate of E if A is the midpoint of $\overline{BE}$. -35
21. Give the coordinate of F if B is the midpoint of $\overline{DF}$. -25

Additional Answers, continued

14.

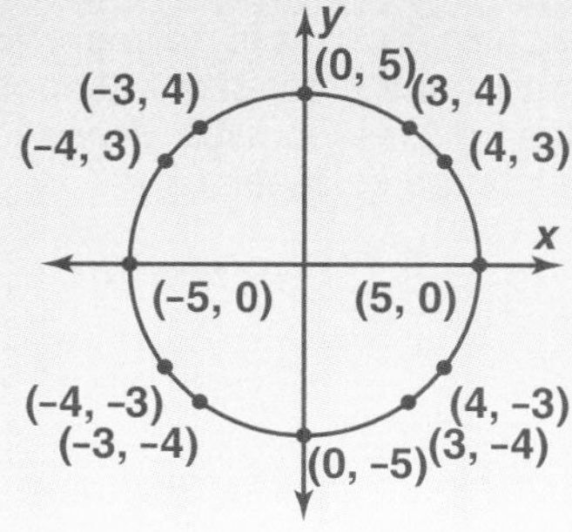

15a.

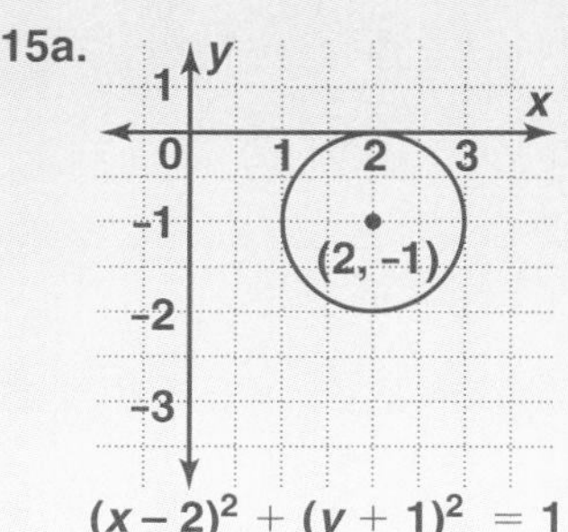

Follow-up for Lesson 11-7

Practice

For more questions on SPUR Objectives, use **Lesson Master 11-7A** (shown on page 657) or **Lesson Master 11-7B** (shown on pages 658–659).

Assessment

Quiz A quiz covering Lessons 11-5 through 11-7 is provided in the *Assessment Sourcebook.*

Oral/Written Communication Have students **work in pairs.** Each student should write the equation of a circle with a center that is not at the origin. Then students should exchange papers, find the center and the radius of their partner's circle, and graph the circle. [Students correctly identify the center and radius of a circle when given the equation. They also correctly graph the circle.]

Extension

Writing You might ask students to explain how they would find the area of a circle inscribed in a square whose coordinates are (2, 3), (6, 0), (3, -4), and (-1, -1). [Use the Distance Formula to find the length of a side of the square; 5; this is the diameter of the circle. Half the diameter is the radius. Then use the Circle Area Formula $A = \pi r^2$.]

21) By the definition of isosceles triangle, $YX = ZX$. V is the midpoint of $\overline{XY}$, W is the midpoint of $\overline{XZ}$. Therefore, $XV = VY = \frac{1}{2}XY$ and $XW = WZ = \frac{1}{2}XZ$. Therefore, by the Transitive Property of Equality, $XV = XW$. By the definition of isosceles triangle, $\triangle XVW$ is isosceles.

Review

In 16 and 17, calculate the distance between the points. Assume $x > 0$. *(Lesson 11-6)*

16. (4, -7) and (-1, 5) 13

17. $(9x, -40x)$ and the origin $41x$

18. Nancy lives 6 blocks west and 3 blocks north of the train station. Domaso lives 5 blocks south of the station. How many blocks is it from where Nancy lives to where Domaso lives? *(Lesson 11-6)*
10 blocks

19. Prove that the quadrilateral $QRST$ with vertices $Q = (9a, 4b)$, $R = (6a, 2b)$, $S = (a, -7b)$, and $T = (-a, -14b)$ is a trapezoid. *(Lesson 11-5)*
See margin.

20. In the box at the right, $CG = 8$, $HG = 12$ and $EH = 16$.

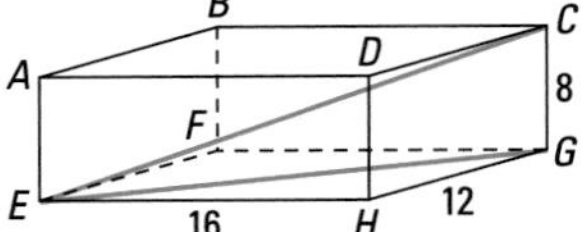

a. Find EG. 20 units

b. Find CE. *(Lessons 8-6, 9-2)*
$\sqrt{464} \approx 21.5$ units

21. Write a proof argument using the given figure.
Given: $\triangle XYZ$ at the right is isosceles with vertex angle X. V is the midpoint of $\overline{XY}$, and W is the midpoint of $\overline{XZ}$.
To prove: $\triangle XVW$ is isosceles. *(Lesson 6-2)*
See left.

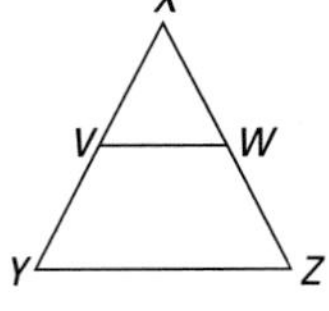

22. Where can you aim to putt a golf ball G into the hole at H in one shot? *(Lesson 4-3)*

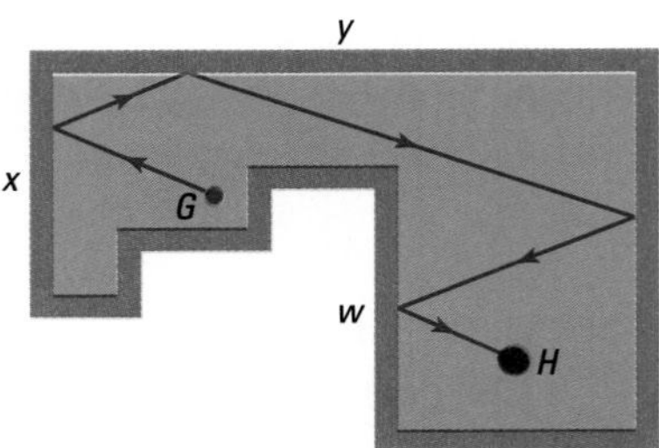

23. Suppose $\overleftrightarrow{AB}$ and $\overleftrightarrow{BC}$ have the same slope. What can you conclude about points A, B, and C? *(Lessons 1-7, 3-6)* They are collinear.

Exploration

24. Give an equation for a circle on which there are no lattice points and whose interior contains no lattice points. (See Question 14 if you have forgotten the meaning of *lattice point*.)
Sample: $(x - \frac{1}{2})^2 + (y - \frac{1}{2})^2 = \frac{1}{4}$

Additional Answers

19. Given: $Q = (9a, 4b)$; $R = (6a, 2b)$, $S = (a, -7b)$, and $T = (-a, -14b)$.
To prove: $QRST$ is a trapezoid.

Conclusions	Justifications
1. slope of $\overline{TQ} = \frac{-14b - 4b}{-a - 9a} = \frac{-18b}{-10a} = \frac{9b}{5a}$	def. of slope
2. slope of $\overline{SR} = \frac{-7b - 2b}{a - 6a} = \frac{-9b}{-5a} = \frac{9b}{5a}$	def. of slope
3. $\overline{TQ} \parallel \overline{SR}$	// Lines and Slopes Thm.
4. $QRST$ is a trapezoid.	def. of trapezoid

Setting Up Lesson 11-8

Discuss **Question 23.** This is an important question because the proof of the Midpoint Formula in the next lesson uses slopes to show that points are collinear.

Introducing Lesson 11-8

Connecting Midpoints in a Triangle

IN-CLASS ACTIVITY

Work with a partner. You will need an automatic drawer for this activity.

1 Place a $\triangle ABC$ on the screen. Let D be the midpoint of $\overline{AB}$ and E be the midpoint of $\overline{AC}$. Draw $\overline{DE}$. See figure below.

2 Place the following measurements on the screen: DE, BC, slope of $\overline{BC}$, slope of $\overline{DE}$, $\frac{BC}{DE}$. (Sample measurements are shown below.)

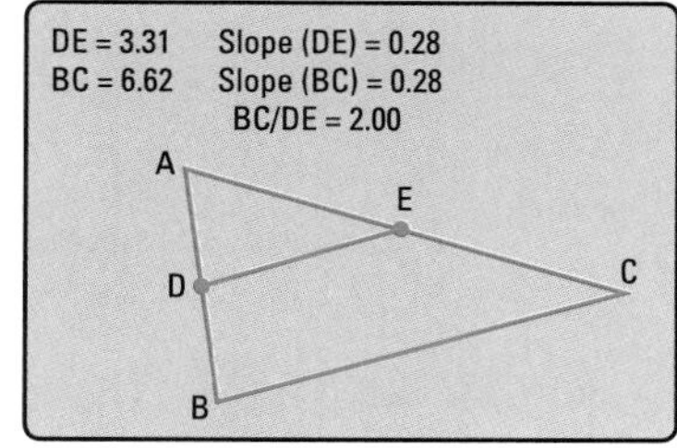

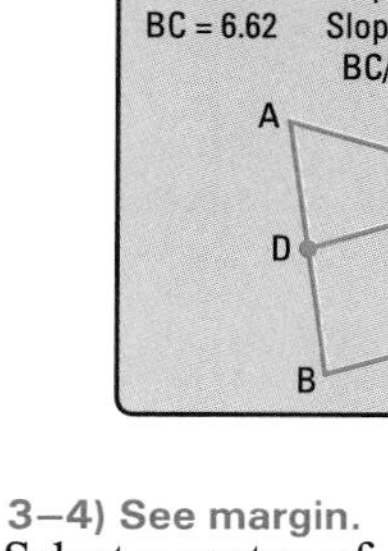

3–4) See margin.

3 Select a vertex of $\triangle ABC$, and distort the figure by moving that vertex. Record the screen for at least two other positions of $\triangle ABC$.

4 Repeat Step 3, but move a different vertex.

5 What conjecture can you make about the slopes of $\overline{DE}$ and $\overline{BC}$? They are equal.

6 What conjecture can you make about the lengths of $\overline{DE}$ and $\overline{BC}$? $DE = \frac{1}{2}BC$

In-class Activity

Resources

From the ***Teacher's Resource File***

- Answer Master 11-8

This In-class Activity is designed to give students some idea of the Midpoint Connector Theorem, which will be introduced in the next lesson. It is expected that after students do this In-class Activity, most of them will conjecture the theorem. If an automatic drawer is not available, then you might wish to have students draw a large triangle on a sheet of paper and do all but Step 4 for that triangle.

Additional Answers

3.

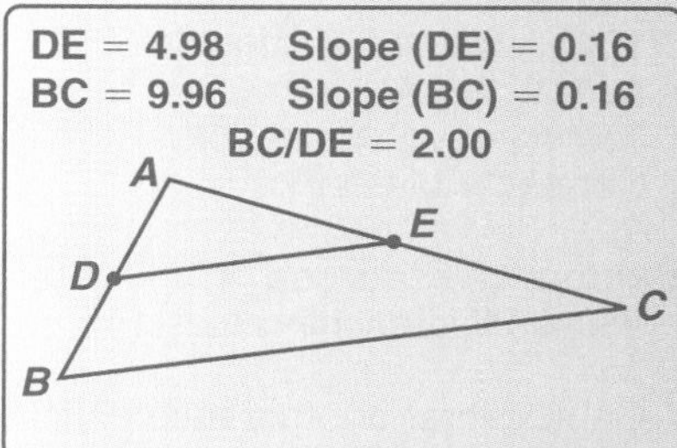

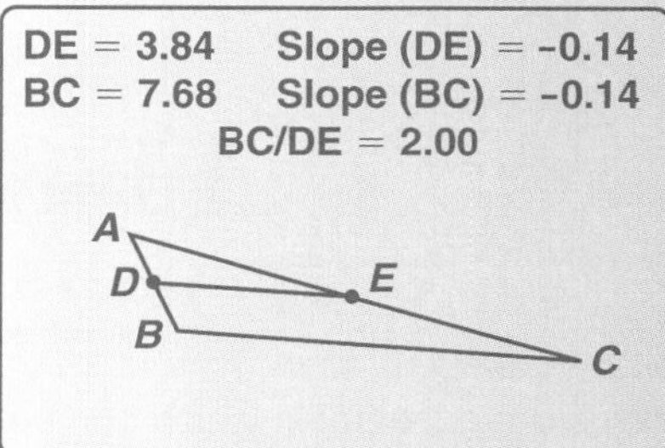

4.

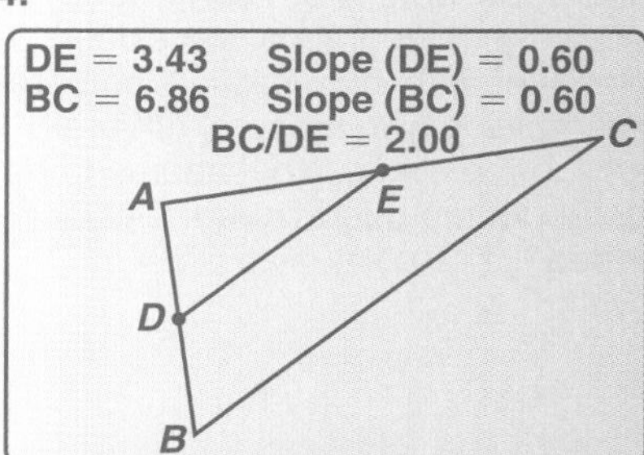

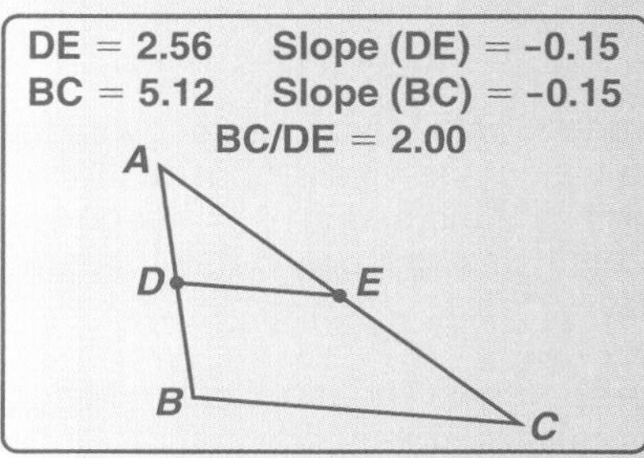

Lesson 11-8

Objectives

A Determine the coordinates of the midpoint of a segment in the coordinate plane.
B Apply the Midpoint Connector Theorem.
G Use coordinate geometry to deduce properties of figures and prove theorems.

Resources

From the ***Teacher's Resource File***
- Lesson Master 11-8A or 11-8B
- Answer Master 11-8
- Teaching Aids
  145 Warm-up
  154 Additional Examples
- Activity Kit, Activity 23
- Technology Sourcebook, Computer Master 20

Additional Resources
- Visuals for Teaching Aids 145, 154
- GeoExplorer or other automatic drawers

Teaching Lesson 11-8

Warm-up

Draw a quadrilateral in which none of the sides have the same length and none of the angles are congruent. Locate the midpoints of the sides and connect them in order. Compare your drawing with those of other students in the class. What seems to be true about the quadrilateral that is formed? **The quadrilateral is a parallelogram.**

LESSON

11-8 *Means and Midpoints*

A Geometric Interpretation of the Mean of Two Numbers

Suppose you score 90 and 83 on two tests. Your average or **mean** score is the sum of these numbers divided by 2. It is

$$\frac{90 + 83}{2} = 86.5.$$

❶ The mean has a physical interpretation. Think of a ruler with hooks for attaching weights (assume the ruler itself is weightless). If equal weights are hung from 90 and 83, the ruler will be horizontal if it is hung from a string at 86.5, or if it is placed to balance on a sharp object at 86.5.

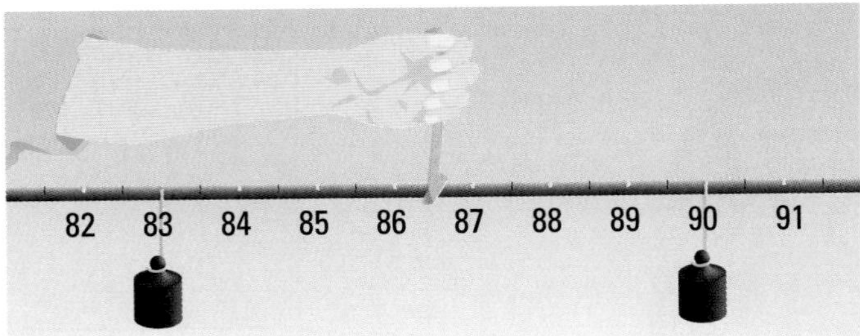

Notice that 86.5 is the *midpoint* of the segment connecting 90 and 83. It is 3.5 units away from both 90 and 83. With some algebra, the relationship between a mean and a midpoint can be proven for any segment on a number line.

Number Line Midpoint Formula
On a number line, the coordinate of the midpoint of the segment with endpoints a and b is $\frac{a+b}{2}$.

Proof:
Given: $\overline{PQ}$ with endpoint coordinates a and b.
To prove: The midpoint of $\overline{PQ}$ has coordinate $\frac{a+b}{2}$.
First, draw a picture. Let M be the point with coordinate $\frac{a+b}{2}$.

Argument: $MP = \left|\frac{a+b}{2} - a\right| = \left|\frac{a+b-2a}{2}\right| = \left|\frac{b-a}{2}\right|$

$QM = \left|b - \frac{a+b}{2}\right| = \left|\frac{2b-(a+b)}{2}\right| = \left|\frac{b-a}{2}\right|$

So $MP = QM$, and so M is the midpoint of $\overline{PQ}$.

Lesson 11-8 Overview

Broad Goals This lesson covers the derivation and applications of the formula for finding the midpoint of a segment, including its application to the center of gravity.

Perspective The proof of the Midpoint Formula is tedious; the authors debated whether to include it. It is not the kind of proof students at this level should be expected to reproduce. We include it for completeness, to show that the formula can be proved, and to illustrate the occasional need for rather complicated algebra. In contrast, the proof of the Midpoint Connector Theorem is one that students should be expected to follow, and better students should be able to reproduce.

Historically, the Midpoint Connector Theorem was proved without coordinates and was a mathematical link from congruence to similarity. The Greeks were troubled by the fact that ratios of sides in similar figures could be irrational. The ratio of the sides of the squares formed by connecting the midpoints of a square, as shown at the right, is $\sqrt{2}$. The Greeks called these ratios *incommensurable,* which means unmeasurable. They did not want an additional postulate to deal with similarity.

A Formula for the Midpoint in Two Dimensions

In two dimensions, the same idea holds. The coordinates of the midpoint of a segment are the averages of the coordinates of the endpoints. Notice that we state the theorem using the points (x_1, y_1) and (x_2, y_2) as endpoints. This makes the pattern easy to see. But in the proof we replace (x_1, y_1) by (a, b) and (x_2, y_2) by (c, d). This makes the algebra easier to follow.

> **Coordinate Plane Midpoint Formula**
> In the coordinate plane, the midpoint of the segment with endpoints (x_1, y_1) and (x_2, y_2) is $\left(\frac{x_1 + x_2}{2}, \frac{y_1 + y_2}{2}\right)$.

Drawing:

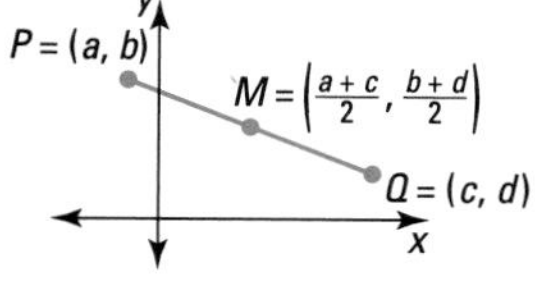

❷ **Proof**

Given: $\overline{PQ}$ with $P = (a, b)$, $Q = (c, d)$, and $M = \left(\frac{a+c}{2}, \frac{b+d}{2}\right)$.

To prove: M is the midpoint of $\overline{PQ}$.

Argument:
Recall the definition of midpoint. To show that M is the midpoint of $\overline{PQ}$, we need to show that $PM = MQ$ and M is on $\overleftrightarrow{PQ}$.

The algebra that follows is cumbersome but straightforward. To show that $PM = MQ$, we calculate distances using the Distance Formula.

$$PM = \sqrt{\left(\frac{a+c}{2} - a\right)^2 + \left(\frac{b+d}{2} - b\right)^2}$$
$$= \sqrt{\left(\frac{a+c-2a}{2}\right)^2 + \left(\frac{b+d-2b}{2}\right)^2}$$
$$= \sqrt{\left(\frac{c-a}{2}\right)^2 + \left(\frac{d-b}{2}\right)^2}$$
$$MQ = \sqrt{\left(c - \frac{a+c}{2}\right)^2 + \left(d - \frac{b+d}{2}\right)^2}$$
$$= \sqrt{\left(\frac{2c-(a+c)}{2}\right)^2 + \left(\frac{2d-(b+d)}{2}\right)^2}$$
$$= \sqrt{\left(\frac{c-a}{2}\right)^2 + \left(\frac{d-b}{2}\right)^2}$$

Thus $PM = MQ$. To show that M is on $\overleftrightarrow{PQ}$, we calculate the slopes of $\overleftrightarrow{PM}$ and $\overleftrightarrow{MQ}$.

$$\text{slope of } \overleftrightarrow{PM} = \frac{\frac{b+d}{2} - b}{\frac{a+c}{2} - a} = \frac{b+d-2b}{a+c-2a} = \frac{d-b}{c-a}$$

$$\text{slope of } \overleftrightarrow{MQ} = \frac{d - \frac{b+d}{2}}{c - \frac{a+c}{2}} = \frac{2d-(b+d)}{2c-(a+c)} = \frac{d-b}{c-a}$$

The slopes are equal so $\overleftrightarrow{PM} \parallel \overleftrightarrow{MQ}$. Both lines contain point M, so $\overleftrightarrow{PM} = \overleftrightarrow{MQ}$ and M is on $\overleftrightarrow{PQ}$. So M is the midpoint of $\overline{PQ}$.

Fortunately, applying the Midpoint Formula is easier than proving it.

Notes on Reading

❶ Students have probably seen means only in connection with calculating averages; they may be quite surprised with seeing means used in a geometric context. Remind them that they also might have been surprised to see quadratics with the equations of circles, and square roots in connection with lengths in right triangles. The applicability of such a variety of arithmetic and algebraic concepts in studying geometry exemplifies the structural unity of mathematics.

❷ We use (a, b) and (c, d) in the proof of the Midpoint Formula on the plane, because to have the subscripts in a formula that involves fractions would make the proof look even more forbidding than it already does. The number 2 would appear in the proof in four different ways: as the denominator of a fraction, as a coefficient, as a subscript, and as an exponent. Nevertheless, we state the Midpoint Formula for points (x_1, y_1) and (x_2, y_2) as mathematics books usually do. We suggest you relate it to the notation used for the Distance Formula and emphasize that the answer is a *point,* not a distance.

The use of convenient coordinates, such as $2a$, when a midpoint is to be obtained, is a difficult idea for some students. Point out that mathematicians try to do things easily, and one way to simplify computations is to avoid fractions.

The Midpoint Connector Theorem implies that a triangle whose sides are half the length of those of a second triangle has congruent angles and so is similar to the larger triangle. They then used the idea with points one third of the way along the sides of a triangle, then two thirds, then one fourth of the way, and so on. See the triangle at the right. This enabled them to ultimately prove that if $\frac{AD}{DB}$ is rational and equals $\frac{AE}{EC}$, then $DE \parallel BC$. So the triangles have the same angle measures, and thus are similar.

Today's conception of real numbers covers both rationals and irrationals, and the use of coordinates enables us to prove the general theorem (the Side-Splitting Converse Theorem) without an additional postulate. This will be done in Lesson 13-3.

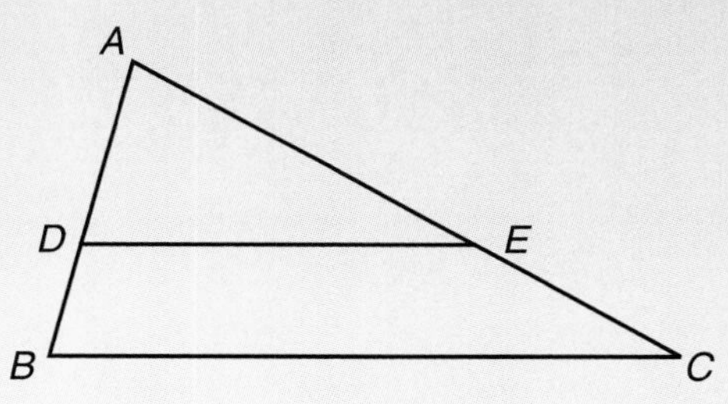

Additional Examples

These examples are also given on **Teaching Aid 154.**

1. What is the midpoint of the segment connecting (5, -7) and (2, 9)? (3.5, 1)
2. In $\triangle DEF$, sides DE, EF, and FD have lengths of 28, 44, and 35, respectively. $\triangle GHI$ is formed by connecting the midpoints of $\triangle DEF$. What are the lengths of the sides of $\triangle GHI$?

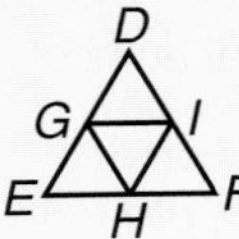

$GH = 17.5$, $HI = 14$, $IG = 22$

3. If $P = (-10, 6)$ and the midpoint of $\overline{PQ}$ is (-5, 9), what are the coordinates of Q? (0, 12)
4. Use a coordinate proof to show that the diagonals of a parallelogram bisect each other. Let the vertices be (a, b), (c, d), $(-a, -b)$, and $(-c, -d)$. Then each diagonal has midpoint (0, 0), and so they bisect each other.

Notes on Questions

Questions 1–3 Science Connection In the U. S., the highest temperature ever recorded was 134°F at Greenland Ranch, Death Valley, California, on July 10, 1913. The lowest was -79.8°F in Prospect Creek, Alaska, on January 23, 1971.

(Notes on Questions continue on page 666.)

Follow-up for Lesson 11-8

Practice

For more questions on SPUR Objectives, use **Lesson Master 11-8A** (shown on page 665) or **Lesson Master 11-8B** (shown on pages 666–667).

Example 1

If $P = (-10, 6)$ and $Q = (1, 8)$, find the midpoint of $\overline{PQ}$.

Solution

Call the midpoint M. Use the Midpoint Formula.

$$M = \left(\frac{-10+1}{2}, \frac{6+8}{2}\right) = \left(\frac{-9}{2}, \frac{14}{2}\right) = (-4.5, 7)$$

Check

Sketch a coordinate plane. (-4.5, 7) looks halfway between (-10, 6) and (1, 8). This gives a rough check. You can calculate the slopes and lengths of $\overline{PM}$ and $\overline{MQ}$ for an exact check.

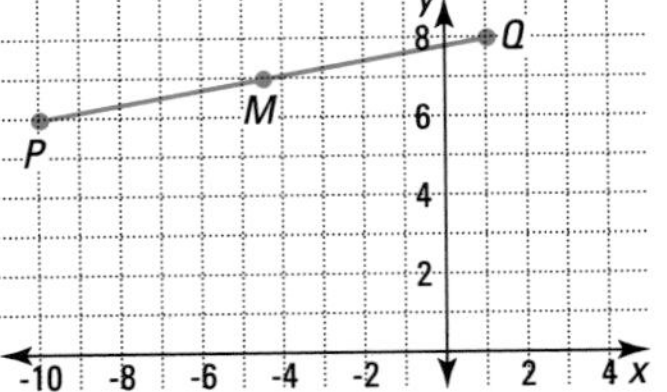

The Midpoint Connector Theorem

In the In-class Activity on page 661, you connected the midpoints of two sides of a triangle. You may have made a conjecture similar to the following theorem.

Midpoint Connector Theorem
The segment connecting the midpoints of two sides of a triangle is parallel to and half the length of the third side.

In this proof, we use $2a$, $2b$, and $2c$ as coordinates of vertices in the convenient location for the triangle. This avoids fractions when coordinates of midpoints are calculated.

Proof:

Given: $\triangle PQR$ with $Q = (0, 0)$, $R = (2a, 0)$, $P = (2b, 2c)$, M the midpoint of $\overline{PQ}$, and N the midpoint of $\overline{PR}$.

To prove: (1) $\overline{MN} \parallel \overline{QR}$.
(2) $MN = \frac{1}{2}QR$.

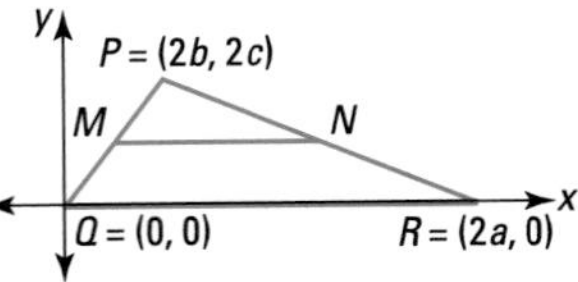

Argument:
First use the Coordinate Plane Midpoint Formula to find the coordinates of M and N.

$$M = \left(\frac{2b+0}{2}, \frac{2c+0}{2}\right) = (b, c)$$

$$N = \left(\frac{2b+2a}{2}, \frac{2c+0}{2}\right) = \left(\frac{2(a+b)}{2}, \frac{2c}{2}\right) = (a+b, c)$$

(1) Slopes help prove $\overline{MN} \parallel \overline{QR}$.

slope of $\overline{MN} = \frac{c-c}{(a+b)-b} = \frac{0}{a} = 0$

slope of $\overline{QR} = \frac{0-0}{2a-0} = \frac{0}{2a} = 0$

Since the slope of $\overline{MN}$ equals the slope of $\overline{QR}$, $\overline{MN} \parallel \overline{QR}$. ▸

Optional Activities

Activity 1

You may use *Activity Kit, Activity 23,* as a follow-up to the lesson. This activity is an introduction to the concept of *center of gravity.* In this activity, students work together to approximate the center of gravity by balancing cardboard triangular regions on the end of a straw.

Activity 2 Technology Connection

In *Technology Sourcebook, Computer Master 20,* students draw segments connecting the midpoints of the sides of various polygons. Then students develop conjectures about the perimeter, area, and other properties of the new figure.

(2) The Distance Formula is used to prove $MN = \frac{1}{2} QR$.

$$MN = \sqrt{((b + a) - b)^2 + (c - c)^2} = \sqrt{a^2 + 0} = |a|$$
$$QR = \sqrt{(2a - 0)^2 + (0 - 0)^2} = \sqrt{4a^2} = 2|a|$$

Thus $QR = 2MN$.

So $MN = \frac{1}{2}QR$.

Example 2

$\triangle ABC$ has sides of lengths 15, 27, and 38. $\triangle LMN$ is formed by connecting the midpoints of $\triangle ABC$. What are the lengths of the sides of $\triangle LMN$?

Solution

Use the Midpoint Connector Theorem.

$LM = \frac{1}{2} AB = \frac{1}{2} \cdot 15 = 7.5$

$MN = \frac{1}{2} BC = \frac{1}{2} \cdot 38 = 19$

$LN = \frac{1}{2} AC = \frac{1}{2} \cdot 27 = 13.5$

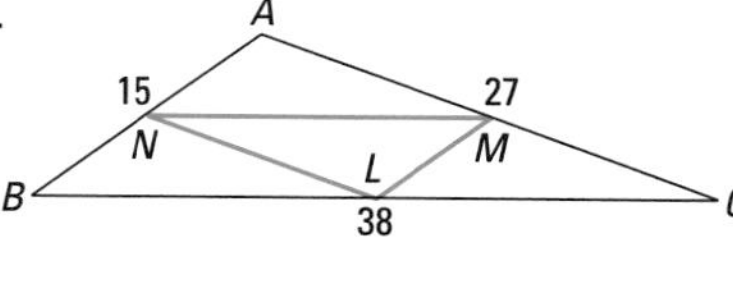

5) L M H on a number line from -6 to 6, temperature

6) On a number line, the midpoint of the segment with endpoints a and b has coordinate $\frac{a+b}{2}$.

Notice in Example 2 that the sides of $\triangle LMN$ are parallel to the sides of $\triangle ABC$. $\triangle LMN$ is called the *medial triangle* of $\triangle ABC$. You are asked to explore other properties of this medial triangle in the Questions.

QUESTIONS

Covering the Reading

In 1–3, use this information: The U.S. Weather Bureau calculates the mean temperature for a particular place on a particular day by averaging the high and low temperatures. Find the mean temperature if

1. the high is 20°C and the low is 12°C. 16°C
2. the high is 6°C and the low is -7°C. -0.5°C
3. the high is -1°C and the low is -9°C. -5°C
4. Suppose you score 95 and 87 on two tests. What is your mean score? 91
5. Give a number-line interpretation of the mean in Question 2. See left.
6. What is the Number Line Midpoint Formula? See left.
7. Give the coordinates of the midpoint of the segment connecting (x_1, y_1) to (x_2, y_2). $\left(\frac{x_1 + x_2}{2}, \frac{y_1 + y_2}{2}\right)$
8. Find the midpoint of the segment with endpoints (-5, 11) and (13, 1). (4, 6)

Whether or not we have weather. *This temperature sign is on a building near the Shibuya Railway Station in Tokyo, Japan.*

Assessment

Written Communication Have students write two examples similar to **Examples 1 and 2.** Their examples should also include the solutions. [Students provide examples and solutions to illustrate the Midpoint Theorem and the Midpoint Connector Theorem.]

Extension

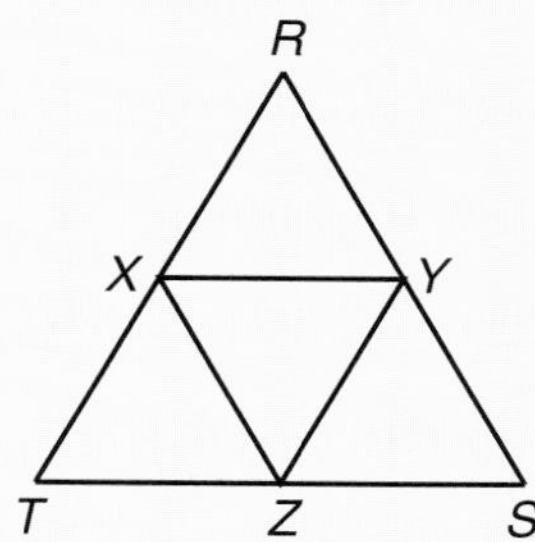

Use the figure to answer the following questions.

1. If $RS = 2x + 4$ and $XZ = 3x - 6$, find the length of $\overline{XZ}$. [$x = 4$, $XZ = 6$]
2. If $RT = 3x - 4$ and $YZ = 2x - 6$, find the length of $\overline{YZ}$. [$x = 8$, $YZ = 10$]
3. If $TS = 8x - 4$ and $XY = 6x - 8$, find the length of $\overline{XY}$. [$x = 3$, $XY = 10$]
4. Find the perimeter of $\triangle RST$ and $\triangle XYZ$. [52, 26]

Project Update Project 4, *Varignon's Theorem,* on page 676, relates to the content of this lesson.

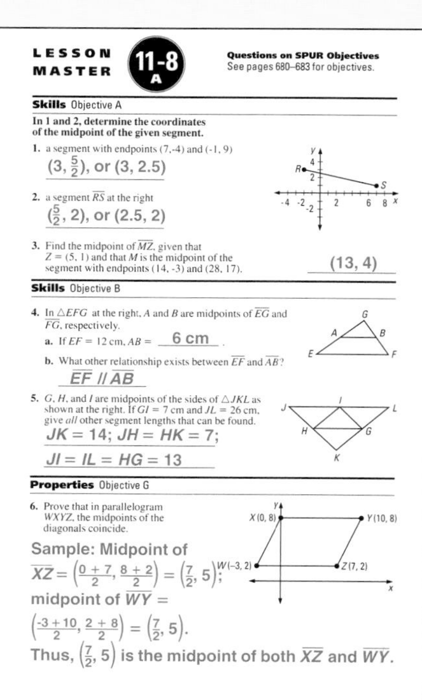

LESSON MASTER 11-8 A

Questions on SPUR Objectives
See pages 680–683 for objectives.

Skills Objective A

In 1 and 2, determine the coordinates of the midpoint of the given segment.

1. a segment with endpoints (7, -4) and (-1, 9) $(3, \frac{5}{2})$, or (3, 2.5)
2. a segment $\overline{RS}$ at the right $(\frac{5}{2}, 2)$, or (2.5, 2)
3. Find the midpoint of $\overline{MZ}$, given that $Z = (5, 1)$ and that M is the midpoint of the segment with endpoints (14, -3) and (28, 17). (13, 4)

Skills Objective B

4. In $\triangle EFG$ at the right, A and B are midpoints of $\overline{EG}$ and $\overline{FG}$, respectively.
   a. If $EF = 12$ cm, $AB =$ 6 cm
   b. What other relationship exists between $\overline{EF}$ and $\overline{AB}$? $\overline{EF} \parallel \overline{AB}$
5. G, H, and I are midpoints of the sides of $\triangle JKL$ as shown at the right. If $GI = 7$ cm and $JL = 26$ cm, give *all* other segment lengths that can be found. $JK = 14$; $JH = HK = 7$; $JI = IL = HG = 13$

Properties Objective G

6. Prove that in parallelogram $WXYZ$, the midpoints of the diagonals coincide.

Sample: Midpoint of $\overline{XZ} = \left(\frac{0 + 7}{2}, \frac{8 + 2}{2}\right) = \left(\frac{7}{2}, 5\right)$; midpoint of $\overline{WY} = \left(\frac{-3 + 10}{2}, \frac{2 + 8}{2}\right) = \left(\frac{7}{2}, 5\right)$. Thus, $\left(\frac{7}{2}, 5\right)$ is the midpoint of both $\overline{XZ}$ and $\overline{WY}$.

Adapting to Individual Needs

English Language Development

Point out to students with limited English proficiency that the word *medial* means "in the middle." The medial triangle is formed by connecting the midpoints of the sides of a triangle. Thus, the medial triangle is in the middle of another triangle.

Challenge

Have students solve the following problem: The mean of three test grades is 74. What must the fourth test grade be to increase the mean to 78? [90]

Notes on Questions

Question 12 Note that the sides of the medial triangle form four congruent triangles. In the next chapter, students will learn that these four triangles are all similar to the original. Students can verify this by folding a paper triangle.

Question 17 Social Studies Connection You might want to introduce the word *interpolation* for making estimates between two values, as is done here. Ask students if it is reasonable to assume that the population of nonwhite families in 1983 could be found from the midpoint of the segment. Note that if the population were more than the midpoint predicts, then the rate of growth has decreased. The corresponding word *extrapolation* is also common in the real world; often one wishes to extrapolate from current data to estimate what will happen in the future or what happened in the past.

Question 20 This question reveals another type of application of the Midpoint Formula. Students should be aware of that application and know when and how to use it.

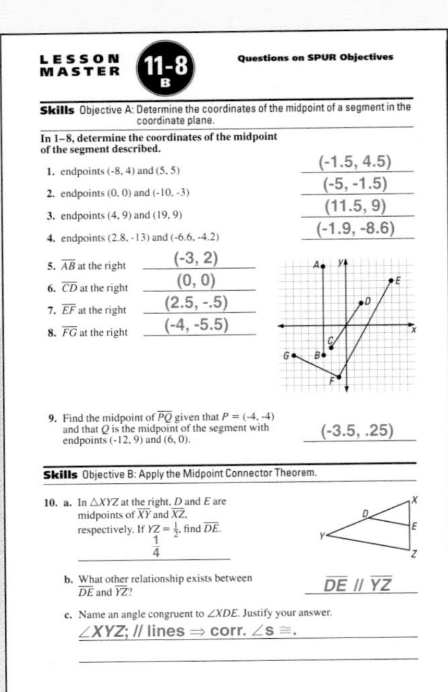
LESSON MASTER 11-8 B — Questions on SPUR Objectives

Skills Objective A: Determine the coordinates of the midpoint of a segment in the coordinate plane.

In 1–8, determine the coordinates of the midpoint of the segment described.

1. endpoints (-8, 4) and (5, 5) — (-1.5, 4.5)
2. endpoints (0, 0) and (-10, -3) — (-5, -1.5)
3. endpoints (4, 9) and (19, 9) — (11.5, 9)
4. endpoints (2.8, -13) and (-6.6, -4.2) — (-1.9, -8.6)
5. $\overline{AB}$ at the right — (-3, 2)
6. $\overline{CD}$ at the right — (0, 0)
7. $\overline{EF}$ at the right — (2.5, -.5)
8. $\overline{FG}$ at the right — (-4, -5.5)

9. Find the midpoint of $\overline{PQ}$ given that P = (-4, -4) and that Q is the midpoint of the segment with endpoints (-12, 9) and (6, 0). — (-3.5, .25)

Skills Objective B: Apply the Midpoint Connector Theorem.

10. a. In △XYZ at the right, D and E are midpoints of $\overline{XY}$ and $\overline{XZ}$, respectively. If $YZ = \frac{1}{2}$, find DE. — $\frac{1}{4}$

b. What other relationship exists between $\overline{DE}$ and $\overline{YZ}$? — $\overline{DE} \parallel \overline{YZ}$

c. Name an angle congruent to ∠XDE. Justify your answer. — ∠XYZ; // lines ⇒ corr. ∠s ≅.

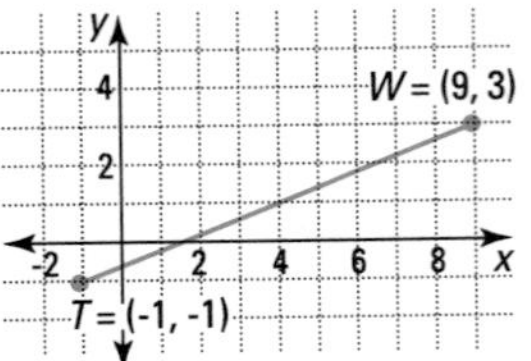

9. Give the coordinates of the midpoint of $\overline{TW}$ at the left. (4, 1)

10. Give the coordinates of the midpoint of the segment with endpoints (a, b) and the origin. $\left(\frac{a}{2}, \frac{b}{2}\right)$

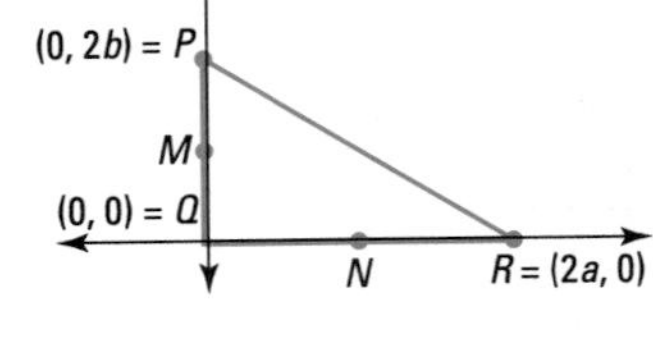

11. At the right is a conveniently located right △PQR. Let M be the midpoint of $\overline{PQ}$ and N the midpoint of $\overline{QR}$.
   a. Give the coordinates of M and N.
   b. Without using the Midpoint Connector Theorem, write a proof argument to show that $\overline{MN} \parallel \overline{PR}$ and $MN = \frac{1}{2}PR$.
   a) M = (0, b), N = (a, 0) b) See margin.

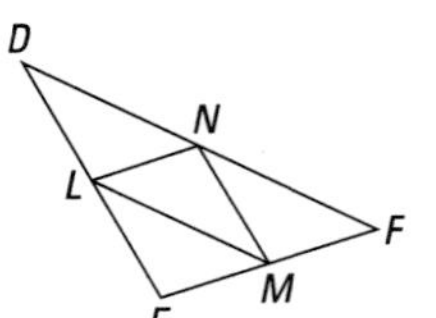

12. △LMN is the medial triangle of △DEF at the left. If DE = 20, EF = 16, and DF = 24, what are the lengths of the sides of △LMN? LN = 8, MN = 10, LM = 12

Applying the Mathematics

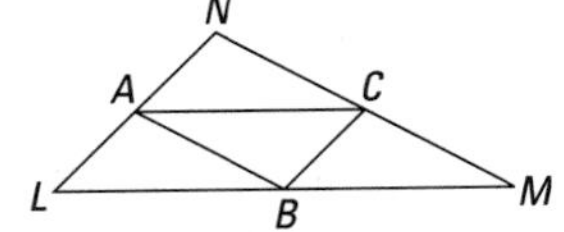

In 13–16, △ABC is the medial triangle of △LMN at the right.

13. If LN = 12, what other length(s) can be found? BC = 6

14. If AB = 5.2, what other length(s) can be found? MN = 10.4

15. Explain why ANCB is a parallelogram. $\overline{AB} \parallel \overline{NC}$ and $\overline{AN} \parallel \overline{BC}$ by the Midpoint Connector Theorem. Therefore, ANCB is a parallelogram.

16. Write a proof argument to show that △ANC ≅ △BCM. See margin.

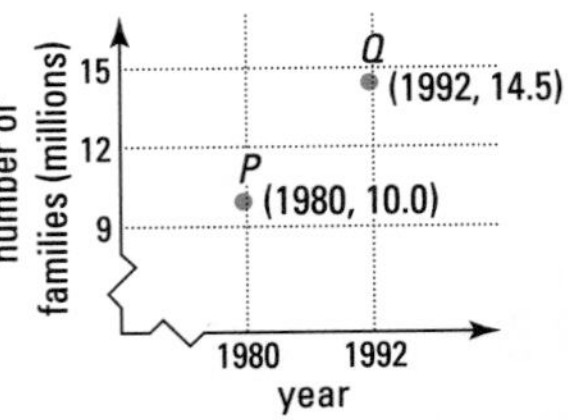

17. At the right is a graph of the total number of African-American, Hispanic, and Asian families in the United States for 1980 and 1992.
   a. Find the midpoint of $\overline{PQ}$.
   b. What does the midpoint represent?
   a) (1986, 12.25); b) See left.

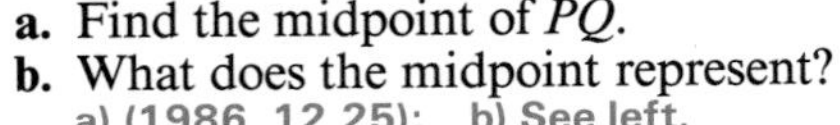

17b) In 1986 one might estimate that there were 12.25 million African-American, Hispanic, and Asian families in the United States.

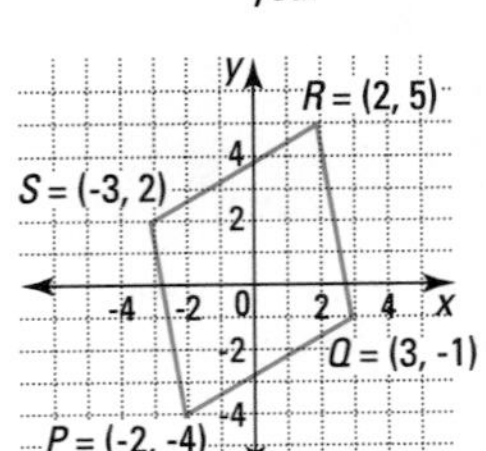

18. Use quadrilateral PQRS at the right.
   a. Show that the diagonals of PQRS bisect each other. See left.
   b. What type of quadrilateral is PQRS? parallelogram

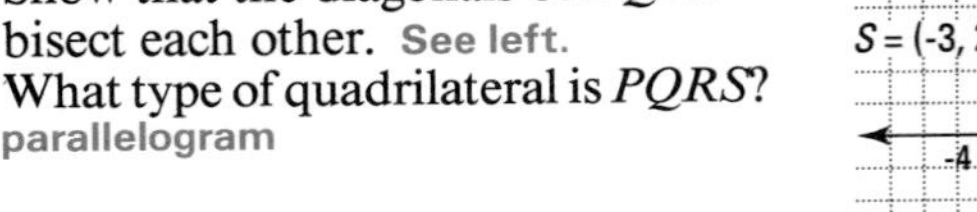

18a) The midpoint of $\overline{PR}$ is (0, 0.5). The midpoint of $\overline{QS}$ is (0, 0.5). Thus, the diagonals bisect each other.

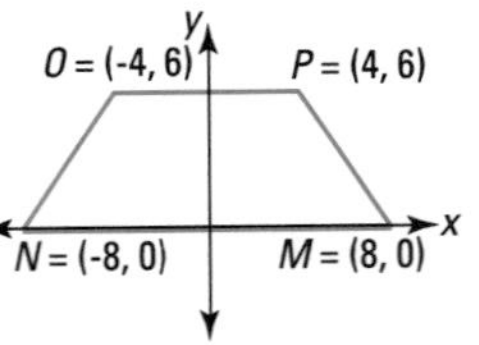

19. Use quadrilateral MNOP at the right. Use indirect reasoning to show that the diagonals of MNOP do *not* bisect each other. See margin.

Additional Answers

11b. By the definition of slope, the slope of $\overline{PR} = \frac{0-2b}{2a-0} = \frac{-b}{a}$, and the slope of $\overline{MN} = \frac{0-b}{a-0} = \frac{-b}{a}$. Thus, $\overline{MN} \parallel \overline{PR}$ by the Parallel Lines and Slopes Theorem. By the Distance Formula on the Coordinate Plane, $PR = \sqrt{(2a-0)^2 + (0-2b)^2} = \sqrt{4a^2 + 4b^2} = 2\sqrt{a^2 + b^2}$ and $MN = \sqrt{(a-0)^2 + (0-b)^2} = \sqrt{a^2 + b^2}$. Thus, $MN = \frac{1}{2}PR$.

16. In Question 15 it is shown that ANCB is a parallelogram. Thus $\overline{AN} \cong \overline{BC}$, because opposite sides of a parallelogram are congruent. For the same reasons, ACMB is a parallelogram, and so $\overline{AC} \cong \overline{BM}$. By the definition of midpoint, $\overline{NC} \cong \overline{MC}$. So △ANC ≅ △BCM, by the SSS Congruence Theorem.

20. $\overline{UV}$ has midpoint M. The coordinates of U are (9, 11) and the coordinates of M are (-1, 7). Find the coordinates of V. (-11, 3)

21. The endpoints of a diameter of a circle are (-3, 5) and (5, -10). Find
  a. The center of the circle. (1, -2.5)
  b. the radius of the circle. 8.5 units
  c. an equation for the circle. $(x - 1)^2 + (y + 2.5)^2 = 72.25$

Review

22. Consider the circle with equation $x^2 + y^2 = 75$.
  a. Find its center. (0, 0)
  b. Find its radius. $\sqrt{75} \approx 8.66$ units
  c. Graph it. See left.
  d. Find its area. *(Lesson 11-7)* $75\pi \approx 235.6$ units^2

(-7, 0) -6 -4 -2 0 2 (3, 0) 6 4 2 -2 -4 -6 y x

23. The circle at the left has center (-2, 0). What is an equation for it? *(Lesson 11-7)* $(x + 2)^2 + y^2 = 25$

24. Write an indirect proof to show that $ABCD$ at the right is *not* a rhombus. *(Lessons 11-4, 11-6)* See margin.

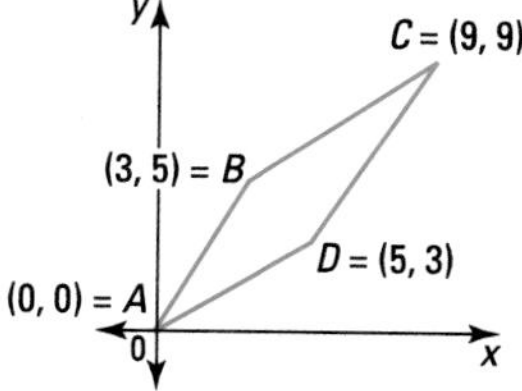

22c)

y 8 4 x -8 -4 0 4 8 -4 -8

$x^2 + y^2 = 75$

25. What can you conclude from all four statements (adapted from Lewis Carroll) using the laws of logic? *(Lessons 11-1, 11-2, 11-3)*
  (1) The only kinds of foods that my doctor allows me are kinds that are not very rich.
  (2) Nothing that agrees with me is unsuitable for dinner.
  (3) Birthday cake is always very rich.
  (4) My doctor allows me all kinds of food that are suitable for dinner.
  Birthday cake does not agree with me.

26. The right square pyramid at the right has a height of 30 cm. The perimeter of the base is 64 cm. See left.
  a. Find the volume of the pyramid.
  b. Find its surface area. *(Lessons 10-2, 10-7)*

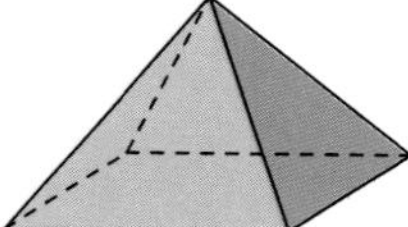

26a) 2560 cm^3
b) $\approx$ 1249.5 cm^2

27. Draw a map with 6 regions that can be colored with 3 colors. *(Lesson 9-9)* See left.

27) Sample:

Exploration

28. The Midpoint Connector Theorem tells how the sides of a medial triangle and its original triangle are related. See left.
  a. How are the angles related?
  b. How are the areas related?
  c. How are the perimeters related?

28) Let $\triangle LMN$ be the medial triangle of $\triangle ABC$.
  a) Sample: $\angle MNL \cong \angle C$, $\angle NLM \cong \angle A$, $\angle LMN \cong \angle B$
  b) Area of $\triangle ABC$ is four times the area of $\triangle MNL$.
  c) The perimeter of $\triangle ABC$ is twice the perimeter of $\triangle MNL$.

Question 26 Have students conjecture about the result of joining the midpoints of the lateral edges of the pyramid. How would the lateral area of the "top" pyramid compare with that of the original? [It is one fourth that of the original.] How would its volume compare? [It is one eighth.] How do we know? (We need to use the Fundamental Theorem of Similarity in Chapter 12.)

Question 28 An automatic drawer can be helpful for students who have difficulty finding the answers based on reading this lesson.

Additional Answers

19. Either the diagonals of $MNOP$ bisect each other or they do not. Suppose they do. Thus, $\overline{MO}$ and $\overline{NP}$ have the same midpoint. The midpoint of $\overline{MO} = \left(\frac{8 + -4}{2}, \frac{0 + 6}{2}\right) = \left(\frac{4}{2}, \frac{6}{2}\right) =$ (2, 3). The midpoint of $\overline{NP} = \left(\frac{-8 + 4}{2}, \frac{0 + 6}{2}\right) = \left(\frac{-4}{2}, \frac{6}{2}\right) =$ (-2,3). These midpoints are not the same. Thus, the supposition has led to a false conclusion. Consequently, by the Law of Indirect Reasoning, the diagonals of $MNOP$ do not bisect each other.

24. Suppose that $ABCD$ is a rhombus. Then $AB = CD$. However, $AB = \sqrt{34}$, and $CD = \sqrt{16 + 36} = \sqrt{52} \neq AB$. This is a contradiction. So, the supposition is false. Therefore, $ABCD$ is not a rhombus.

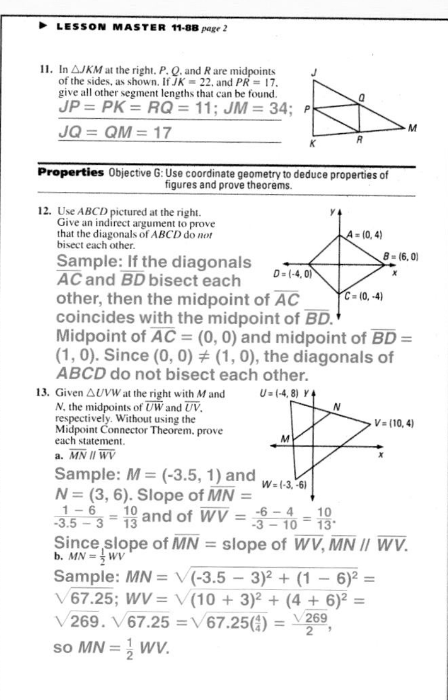

LESSON MASTER 11-8B *page 2*

11. In $\triangle JKM$ at the right, P, Q, and R are midpoints of the sides, as shown. If $JK = 22$, and $PR = 17$, give all other segment lengths that can be found.
$JP = PK = RQ = 11$; $JM = 34$; $JQ = QM = 17$

Properties Objective G: Use coordinate geometry to deduce properties of figures and prove theorems.

12. Use $ABCD$ pictured at the right. Give an indirect argument to prove that the diagonals of $ABCD$ do *not* bisect each other.
Sample: If the diagonals $\overline{AC}$ and $\overline{BD}$ bisect each other, then the midpoint of $\overline{AC}$ coincides with the midpoint of $\overline{BD}$. Midpoint of $\overline{AC} = (0, 0)$ and midpoint of $\overline{BD} = (1, 0)$. Since $(0, 0) \neq (1, 0)$, the diagonals of $ABCD$ do not bisect each other.

13. Given $\triangle UVW$ at the right with M and N, the midpoints of $\overline{UW}$ and $\overline{UV}$, respectively. Without using the Midpoint Connector Theorem, prove each statement.
  a. $\overline{MN} \parallel \overline{WV}$
  Sample: $M = (-3.5, 1)$ and $N = (3, 6)$. Slope of $\overline{MN} = \frac{1 - 6}{-3.5 - 3} = \frac{10}{13}$ and of $\overline{WV} = \frac{-6 - 4}{-3 - 10} = \frac{10}{13}$. Since slope of $\overline{MN}$ = slope of $\overline{WV}$, $\overline{MN} \parallel \overline{WV}$.
  b. $MN = \frac{1}{2} WV$
  Sample: $MN = \sqrt{(-3.5 - 3)^2 + (1 - 6)^2} = \sqrt{67.25}$; $WV = \sqrt{(10 + 3)^2 + (4 + 6)^2} = \sqrt{269}$. $\sqrt{67.25} = \sqrt{67.25(\frac{4}{4})} = \frac{\sqrt{269}}{2}$, so $MN = \frac{1}{2} WV$.

Setting Up Lesson 11-9

Materials If you ask students to do *Challenge* on page 672, they will make a model of a 3-dimensional coordinate system. They may use cardboard or plastic as the planes. They will also need markers, glue, tape, and wire to locate a point in the system.

Lesson 11-9

Objectives

C Plot points, find distances between them, and find coordinates of midpoints in 3-dimensional space.

I Apply the Box Diagonal Formula in real situations.

J Graph and write an equation for a sphere given its center and radius, and vice versa.

Resources

From the ***Teacher's Resource File***
- Lesson Master 11-9A or 11-9B
- Answer Master 11-9
- Teaching Aids
  145 Warm-up
  155 Additional Examples
  156 3-Dimensional Coordinate System
- Activity Kit, Activity 24

Additional Resources
- Visuals for Teaching Aids 145, 155–156

Teaching Lesson 11-9

Warm-up

An ant and a bee are in the box at point W. They want to get to point U.

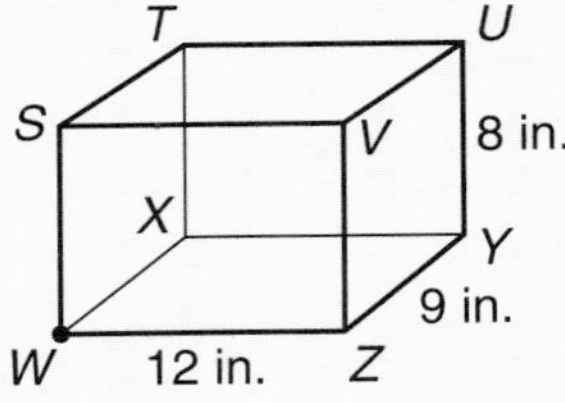

LESSON

11-9 *Three-Dimensional Coordinates*

Off the wall. *Racquetball players bounce balls off planes which are perpendicular or parallel. Notice the three mutually perpendicular planes meeting at the corner.*

Coordinatizing Space

Points in space can be located using a **three-dimensional coordinate system.** For instance, you can locate points in a room by letting the origin be at a corner of the room where two walls and the floor intersect. Then with two coordinates, x and y, you can describe the location of any point on the floor. To describe an object in the room which is not on the floor (such as the bottom of a light hanging from the ceiling), you can use a third number to indicate the height from the floor. This is the ***z*-coordinate.** Thus, if the bottom of the light is 4 ft from the origin in the x-direction, 7 ft in the y-direction, and 8 ft in the z-direction (up), you could uniquely specify the position of the light by the **ordered triple** (4, 7, 8). The x-coordinate is 4, the y-coordinate is 7, and the z-coordinate is 8. The three lines where the walls and floor meet are the **axes** of this 3-dimensional coordinate system.

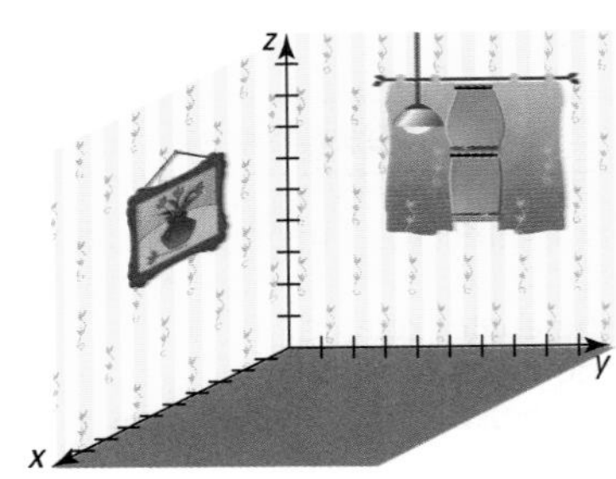

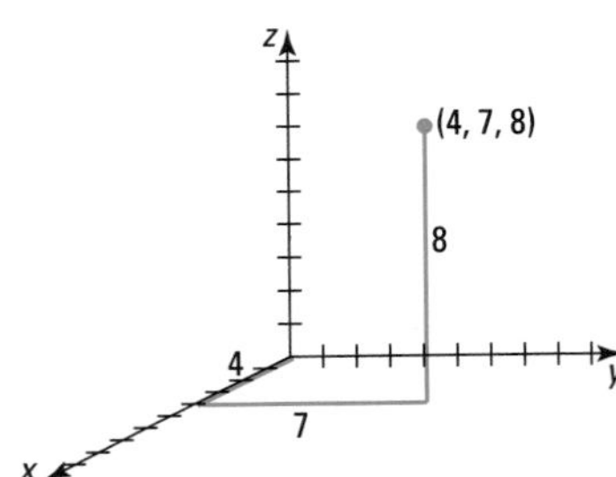

Lesson 11-9 Overview

Broad Goals The Distance and Midpoint Formulas and the equation of a circle are extended in this lesson to three dimensions.

Perspective Now that students are familiar with coordinates, it is natural and appropriate to expose them to 3-dimensional coordinates. This continues a consistent theme throughout the book: extend 2-dimensional ideas to higher dimensions.

The formulas presented earlier in the chapter on distance, circles, and midpoints all find their 3-dimensional counterpart included in this lesson. Thus, this lesson can serve as a review of the chapter. The Diagonal of a Box Formula is also included since it is an immediate application of the Distance Formula in Three Dimensions.

Now imagine extending each axis in its negative direction, as shown in the figure at the right. The three axes are called the **x-axis,** the **y-axis,** and the **z-axis.** The ordered triple (x, y, z) represents a point in *3-space*. The position of a point is given by its three distances from the origin (0, 0, 0). The following example shows how to plot a point in three dimensions.

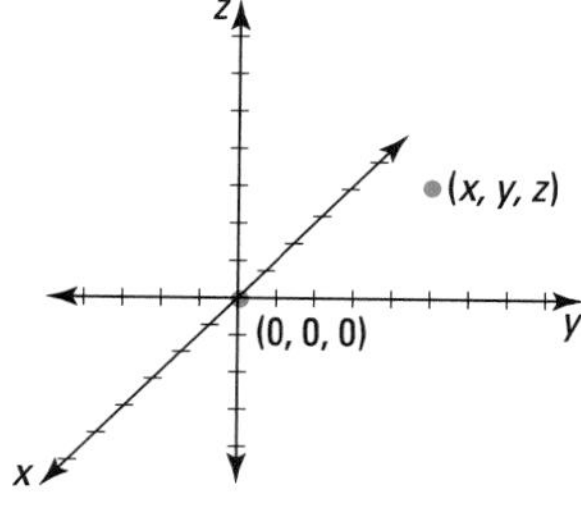

Example 1

Plot the point $R = (-7, 4, 3)$ on a 3-dimensional coordinate system.

Solution

Step 1: Draw or copy the axes from above.

Step 2: Move 7 units backward (in a negative direction) on the x-axis.

Step 3: From there move 4 units to the right, parallel to the y-axis.

Step 4: From there move 3 units up parallel to the z-axis.

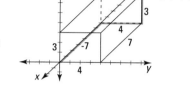

It helps to think of the point as the back upper right vertex of a box with base dimensions 7 and 4 and height 3.

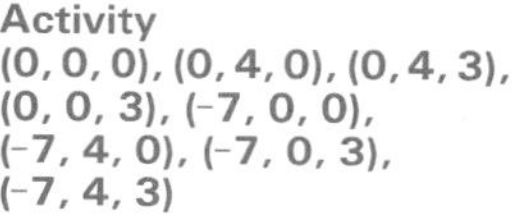
Activity
(0, 0, 0), (0, 4, 0), (0, 4, 3), (0, 0, 3), (-7, 0, 0), (-7, 4, 0), (-7, 0, 3), (-7, 4, 3)

Activity

List the x, y, z coordinates of each of the eight vertices of the box in Example 1. (Hint: Each vertex other than (-7, 4, 3) has at least one coordinate that is 0.)
See left.

The Distance Formula in Space

Many of the formulas for 2-dimensional coordinates have counterparts in three dimensions. For instance, the Coordinate Plane Distance Formula states that the distance between (x_1, y_1) and (x_2, y_2) is $\sqrt{(x_2 - x_1)^2 + (y_2 - y_1)^2}$. Its counterpart is the 3-dimensional Distance Formula below.

Three-Dimension Distance Formula
The distance d between two points (x_1, y_1, z_1) and (x_2, y_2, z_2) is given by the formula

$$d = \sqrt{(x_2 - x_1)^2 + (y_2 - y_1)^2 + (z_2 - z_1)^2}.$$

The proof of this formula, which is given on the following page, is based on two successive applications of the Pythagorean Theorem.

1. Suppose the ant only crawls along the edges of the box. At least how far does the ant have to crawl? 29 in.
2. How many different routes can the ant take to travel the least possible distance along the edges? 6
3. The bee flew directly from W to U. How might you find the distance the bee flew? **Sample: Use the Pythagorean Theorem with sides $\overline{WZ}$ and $\overline{ZY}$ to find the length WY. Then use the Pythagorean Theorem with $\overline{WY}$ and $\overline{YU}$ to find the length of WU.**

Notes on Reading

This lesson can be read independently, even though many students have never worked with 3-dimensional graphing before. Point out that all of the theorems in this lesson are analogous to theorems in two dimensions. Encourage students to summarize the theorems and their analogues in two dimensions and to make sure they can justify the calculations given in the **Examples.**

Plotting points in three dimensions with paper and pencil is not easy. **Teaching Aid 156** can be used to help students graph in three dimensions. A grid is needed, as the picture on the bottom of page 668 indicates. In that picture, (x, y, z) could be in the xy-plane and behind the y-axis, or directly below the x-axis, or near the viewer and quite high above the xy-plane. The lines, as shown for the point (4, 7, 8), or a box, as shown for (-7, 4, 3) in the **Activity,** are needed. Do not expect your students to become expert graphers, but do expect them to know how to graph a point.

Optional Activities

You may use *Activity Kit, Activity 24,* as a follow-up to the lesson. In this activity, students make a model of a 3-dimensional coordinate system.

Some automatic graphers enable the user to plot points in three dimensions. You may wish to have students explore these graphs.

Students may wonder why x is not the horizontal axis in 3-dimensional graphing. Point out that in the normal way that points are plotted in three dimensions, the xy-plane is viewed as the horizontal *plane,* and the x-axis and y-axis are in their usual positions.

An everyday example of the use of three coordinates is in identifying the position of an airplane relative to an airport. This position may be given as the airplane's distance east and south of the airport and its altitude above sea level or above ground level.

Have students record the results of the **Activity** for use with **Question 4** on page 672.

Proof:

Given: $P = (x_1, y_1, z_1)$ and $Q = (x_2, y_2, z_2)$.

To prove: $PQ = \sqrt{(x_2 - x_1)^2 + (y_2 - y_1)^2 + (z_2 - z_1)^2}$.

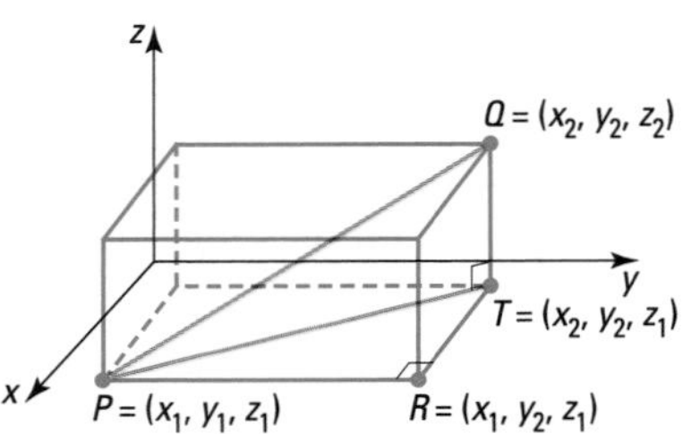

Argument:

In right $\triangle PRT$, $PT^2 = RT^2 + PR^2$.

In right $\triangle PTQ$, $PQ^2 = PT^2 + QT^2$

Substituting $RT^2 + PR^2$ for PT^2 gives

$$PQ^2 = RT^2 + PR^2 + QT^2.$$

So $$PQ^2 = (x_2 - x_1)^2 + (y_2 - y_1)^2 + (z_2 - z_1)^2.$$

Example 2

Find the distance between points P and Q, where: $P = (-5, 2, 1)$ and $Q = (4, 0, -3)$.

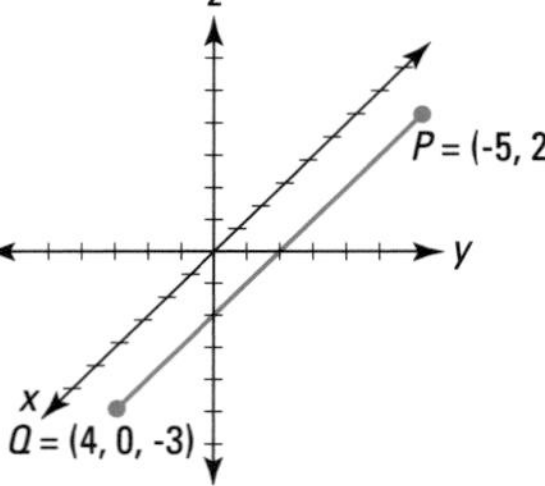

Solution

Let $P = (-5, 2, 1) = (x_1, y_1, z_1)$ and $Q = (4, 0, -3) = (x_2, y_2, z_2)$. Then

$$\begin{aligned} PQ &= \sqrt{(x_2 - x_1)^2 + (y_2 - y_1)^2 + (z_2 - z_1)^2} \\ &= \sqrt{(4 - -5)^2 + (0 - 2)^2 + (-3 - 1)^2} \\ &= \sqrt{(81 + 4 + 16)} \\ &= \sqrt{(101)} \\ &\approx 10.05 \text{ units.} \end{aligned}$$

The Three-Dimension Distance Formula helps answer this question: What is the length of the diagonal of a box? A box with dimensions ℓ, w, and h is conveniently located below with one endpoint of the diagonal at the origin and the other at (ℓ, w, h).

The diagonal has length PQ.

$$\begin{aligned} PQ &= \sqrt{(\ell - 0)^2 + (w - 0)^2 + (h - 0)^2} \\ &= \sqrt{\ell^2 + w^2 + h^2} \end{aligned}$$

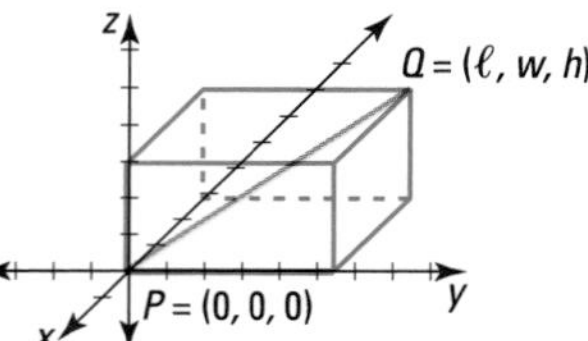

This argument proves the following formula.

Adapting to Individual Needs

Extra Help

Some students will be confused by the fact that in 3-dimensional graphing the xy-plane is horizontal. It might be helpful for them to draw a coordinate plane on a sheet of grid paper and label it in the usual way to show positive and negative numbers. Then have them lay the grid on a desk top and orient it so that the positive x-axis extends toward them. Have them hold a pencil in the vertical position at the origin. The pencil will represent the z-axis with positive coordinates above the plane of the desk.

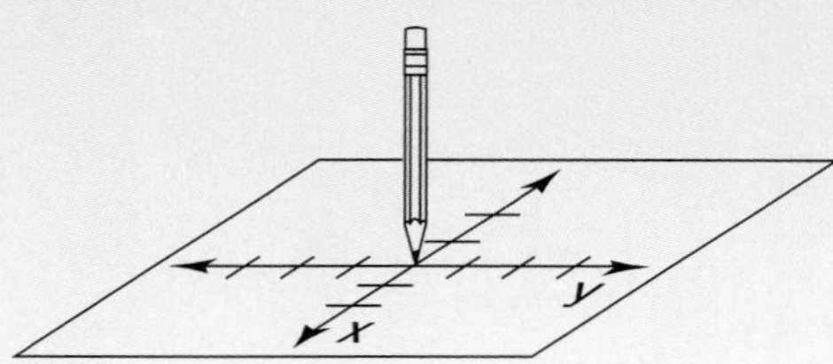

Box Diagonal Formula
In a box with dimensions ℓ, w, and h, the length d of the diagonal is given by the formula

$$d = \sqrt{\ell^2 + w^2 + h^2}.$$

Spheres

In Lesson 11-7, an equation for the circle with center (h, k) and radius r was shown to be $(x - h)^2 + (y - k)^2 = r^2$. The 3-dimensional counterpart to the circle is the sphere. An equation for the sphere is analogous to the equation for a circle. Its proof uses the Three-Dimension Distance Formula.

Equation for a Sphere
The sphere with center (h, k, j) and radius r is the set of points (x, y, z) satisfying

$$(x - h)^2 + (y - k)^2 + (z - j)^2 = r^2.$$

Proof

Given: The sphere with center (h, j, k) and radius r.

To prove: The sphere is the set of points (x, y, z) that satisfy $(x - h)^2 + (y - k)^2 + (z - j)^2 = r^2$.

Drawing:

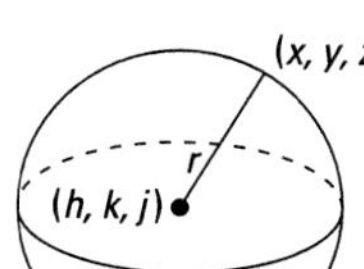

Argument:
Since r is the radius, by the definition of sphere, the distance from (h, k, j) to (x, y, z) is r. That distance is given by the Three-Dimension Distance Formula:

$$\sqrt{(x - h)^2 + (y - k)^2 + (z - j)^2} = r.$$

Squaring both sides results in the theorem.

$$(x - h)^2 + (y - k)^2 + (z - j)^2 = r^2$$

Example 3

Find an equation for the sphere with center (3, 0, -1) and radius 8.

Solution

Here $(h, k, j) = (3, 0, -1)$. So $h = 3$, $k = 0$, and $j = -1$. Also, $r = 8$. Substitute these values into the equation for a sphere.

$$(x - 3)^2 + (y - 0)^2 + (z - -1)^2 = 8^2$$

Simplify. $(x - 3)^2 + y^2 + (z + 1)^2 = 64$ is the desired equation.

Additional Examples

These examples are also given on **Teaching Aid 155.**

1. Give the coordinates of the vertices of the box shown below.

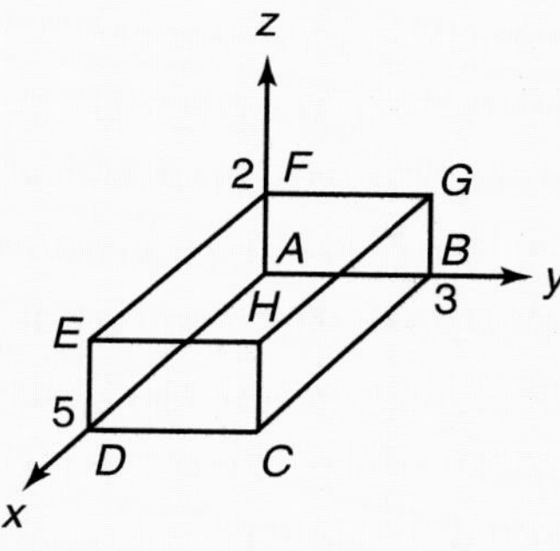

$A = (0, 0, 0)$, $B = (0, 3, 0)$, $C = (5, 3, 0)$, $D = (5, 0, 0)$, $E = (5, 0, 2)$, $F = (0, 0, 2)$, $G = (0, 3, 2)$, $H = (5, 3, 2)$

2. Find the distance between (4, -1, 8) and (10, 20, 5). $\sqrt{486}$

3. Find an equation for the sphere with center (-4, 5, 0) and which intersects the origin. The radius is $\sqrt{41}$, so an equation is $(x + 4)^2 + (y - 5)^2 + z^2 = 41$.

4. What is the midpoint of the segment joining (1, 2, 3) and (11, 0, -9)? (6, 1, -3)

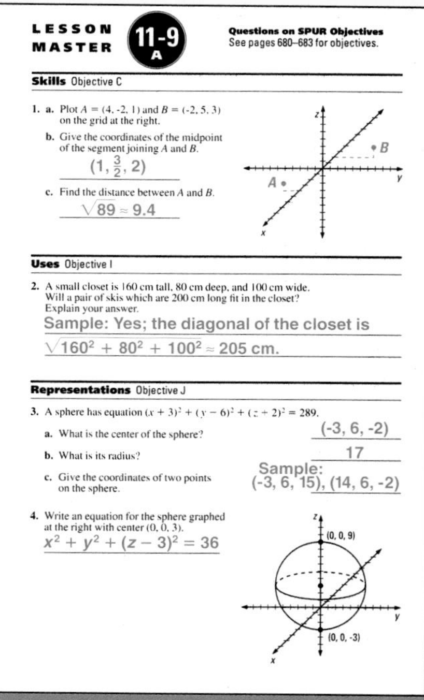

LESSON MASTER 11-9 A

Questions on SPUR Objectives
See pages 680–683 for objectives.

Skills Objective C

1. a. Plot $A = (4, -2, 1)$ and $B = (-2, 5, 3)$ on the grid at the right.
   b. Give the coordinates of the midpoint of the segment joining A and B. $(1, \frac{3}{2}, 2)$
   c. Find the distance between A and B. $\sqrt{89} \approx 9.4$

Uses Objective I

2. A small closet is 160 cm tall, 80 cm deep, and 100 cm wide. Will a pair of skis which are 200 cm long fit in the closet? Explain your answer.
   Sample: Yes; the diagonal of the closet is $\sqrt{160^2 + 80^2 + 100^2} \approx 205$ cm.

Representations Objective J

3. A sphere has equation $(x + 3)^2 + (y - 6)^2 + (z + 2)^2 = 289$.
   a. What is the center of the sphere? (-3, 6, -2)
   b. What is its radius? 17
   c. Give the coordinates of two points on the sphere. Sample: (-3, 6, 15), (14, 6, -2)

4. Write an equation for the sphere graphed at the right with center (0, 0, 3).
   $x^2 + y^2 + (z - 3)^2 = 36$

Notes on Questions

Question 6 You might want students to find the lengths of other diagonals of this box. Ask which diagonals are equal. [All of them are equal.]

Question 11c Remind students that figures graphed in three dimensions have all the same properties as if they were not graphed.

Question 14 If the tube were thick, it could not be considered a line segment; the thickness would have to be considered when fitting it into the case. Of course, it makes a difference if the case is flexible or not, but even most flexible cases cannot be extended at their seams.

Question 15 Ask students to find lattice points on this sphere other than the three given. [There are many: the other points of intersection with the axes, (-5, 0, 0), (0, -5, 0), and (0, 0, -5), and also many points like (3, 4, 0) and (0, -3, 4).]

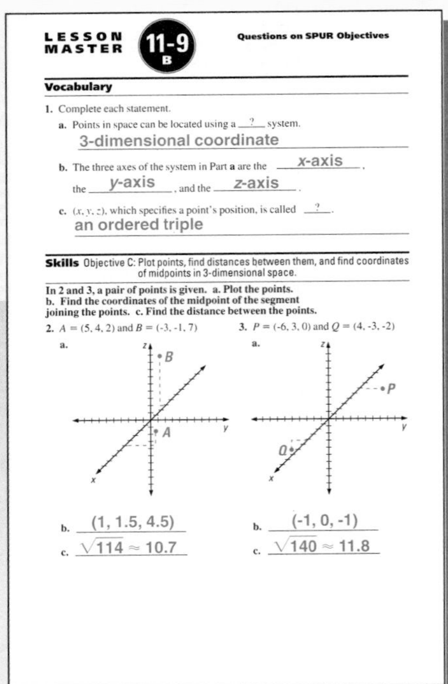

LESSON MASTER 11-9 B Questions on SPUR Objectives

Vocabulary

1. Complete each statement.
   a. Points in space can be located using a ___?___ system. 3-dimensional coordinate
   b. The three axes of the system in Part **a** are the x-axis, the y-axis, and the z-axis.
   c. (x, y, z), which specifies a point's position, is called ___?___. an ordered triple

Skills Objective C: Plot points, find distances between them, and find coordinates of midpoints in 3-dimensional space.

In 2 and 3, a pair of points is given. a. Plot the points. b. Find the coordinates of the midpoint of the segment joining the points. c. Find the distance between the points.

2. A = (5, 4, 2) and B = (-3, -1, 7)
   b. (1, 1.5, 4.5)
   c. $\sqrt{114} \approx 10.7$

3. P = (-6, 3, 0) and Q = (4, -3, -2)
   b. (-1, 0, -1)
   c. $\sqrt{140} \approx 11.8$

3)

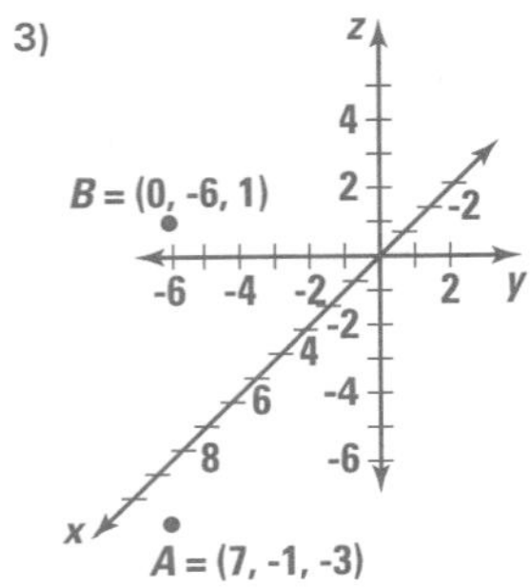

4) (0, 0, 0), (0, 4, 0), (0, 4, 3), (0, 0, 3), (-7, 0, 0), (-7, 4, 0), (-7, 0, 3), (-7, 4, 3)

The Midpoint Formula in Space

The Midpoint Formula from Lesson 11-8 also extends easily to three dimensions.

> **Three-Dimension Midpoint Formula**
> In space, the midpoint of the segment with endpoints (x_1, y_1, z_1) and (x_2, y_2, z_2) is
> $$\left(\frac{x_1 + x_2}{2}, \frac{y_1 + y_2}{2}, \frac{z_1 + z_2}{2}\right).$$

You can verify the Three-Dimension Midpoint Formula by calculating the distances between the endpoints and the midpoint, just as in two dimensions.

QUESTIONS

Covering the Reading

1. Any point in three dimensions can be located with an ordered ___?___. triple
2. *True or false.* The intersection of two walls and the floor of a room can represent the origin of a coordinate system in three dimensions. True
3. Draw a coordinate system and plot the points $A = (7, -1, -3)$ and $B = (0, -6, 1)$. See left.
4. Give the list you wrote for the Activity in this lesson. See left.
5. Find PQ when $P = (3, 7, -2)$ and $Q = (5, -11, 0)$. $\sqrt{332} \approx 18.22$ units
6. In the box pictured below, calculate CF. $\sqrt{227} \approx 15.07$ units

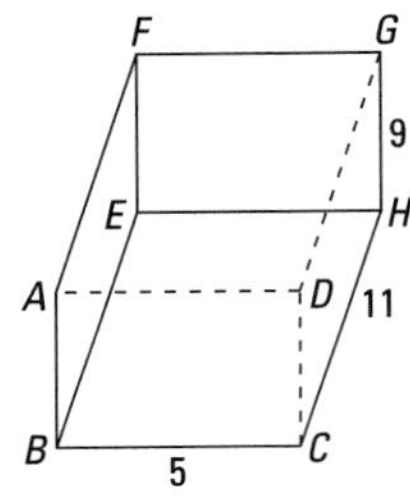

7. Find an equation for the sphere with center (-5, 3, -10) and radius 13. $(x + 5)^2 + (y - 3)^2 + (z + 10)^2 = 169$
8. Refer to Question 5. Find the midpoint of $\overline{PQ}$. (4, -2, -1)
9. Here is an equation for a sphere: $(x - 18)^2 + (y - 5)^2 + (z + 11)^2 = 36$.
   a. What point is the center of the sphere? (18, 5, -11)
   b. What is the radius of the sphere? 6
   c. Give the coordinates of two points on the sphere. Samples: (12, 5, -11) and (18, 11, -11)

Adapting to Individual Needs

Challenge

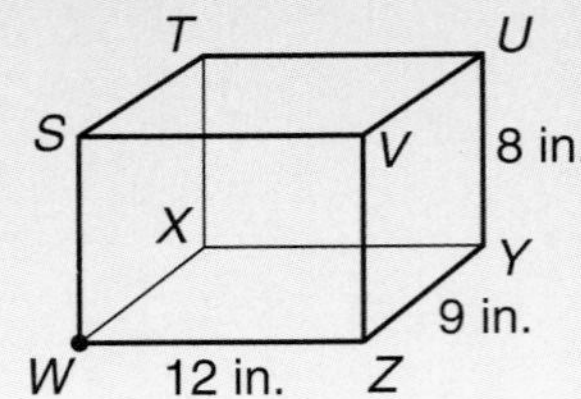

You might give students this additional problem related to *Warm-up* on pages 668–669. Have students assume that the ant can crawl on the sides of the box as well as along the edges. Then have them find the shortest distance from W to U. [All six possible paths will traverse two faces. The net at the right shows that the paths which intersect $\overline{SV}$ and $\overline{XY}$ are the shortest with length $\sqrt{433} = \sqrt{12^2 + 17^2}$.]

Applying the Mathematics

10. A box has the following vertices: the origin, (0, 1, 0), (3, 0, 0), (3, 1, 0), (3, 1, 9), (3, 0, 9), (0, 0, 9), and (0, 1, 9). a) See left.

a. Draw the box on a 3-dimensional coordinate system.

b. Determine its volume. 27 units^3

11. In the rectangular box at the left, $D = (10, 1, 6)$ and F is the origin.

a. Find the coordinates of the points A, B, C, E, G, and H. See left.

b. Determine the volume of the box. 60 units^3

c. Determine its surface area. 152 units^2

In 12 and 13, triangle ABC has vertices $A = (2, -1, 7)$, $B = (4, 0, -5)$, and $C = (-11, 8, 2)$.

12. Find the perimeter of $\triangle ABC$. $\sqrt{149} + \sqrt{338} + \sqrt{275} \approx 47.17$ units

13. Find the midpoints of the three sides of $\triangle ABC$. $\overline{AB}$: (3, -.5, 1); $\overline{BC}$: (-3.5, 4, -1.5); $\overline{AC}$: (-4.5, 3.5, 4.5)

14. What is the length of the longest thin cylindrical tube that can be carried in a 16″ × 18″ × 5″ carrying case? ≈ 24.59 inches

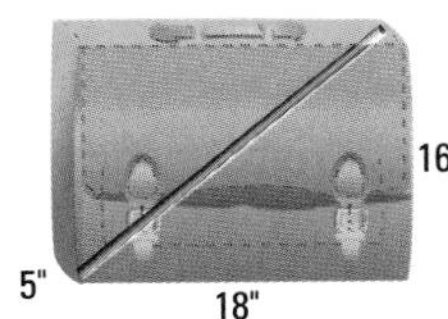

15. Find an equation for the sphere below with center (0, 0, 0). $x^2 + y^2 + z^2 = 25$

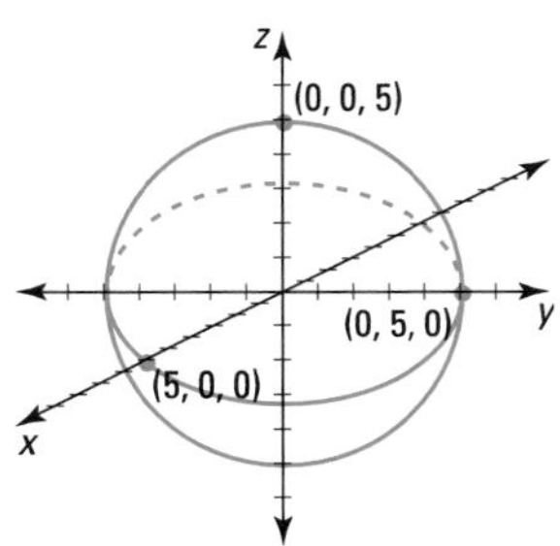

10a)

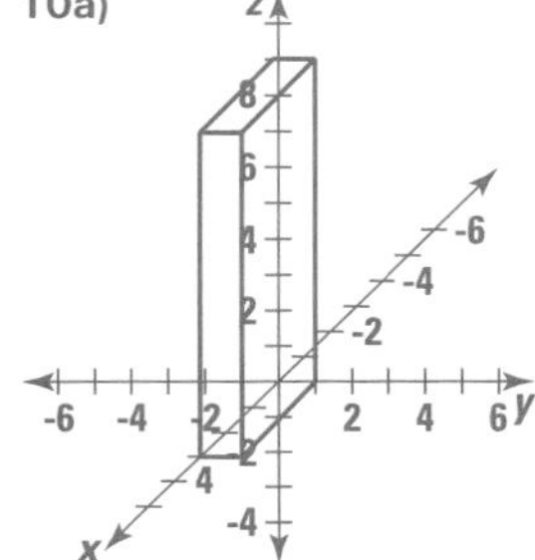

11a) $A = (10, 0, 6)$, $B = (0, 0, 6)$, $C = (0, 1, 6)$, $E = (10, 0, 0)$, $G = (0, 1, 0)$, $H = (10, 1, 0)$

16b) By the Midpoint Formula, the midpoints are located at (b, c) and $(a + d, c)$. The slope of the segment joining the midpoint is 0, and the slope of the bases is 0. Thus the segment joining the midpoints is parallel to the bases, by the Parallel Lines and Slopes Theorem.

Review

16. a. The figure below is a(n) __?__. trapezoid

b. Use this figure to complete the sentence. Then prove it. The segment joining the midpoints of the non-base sides of a(n) __?__ is parallel to the bases. *(Lessons 6-5, 11-8)* trapezoid; for proof see left.

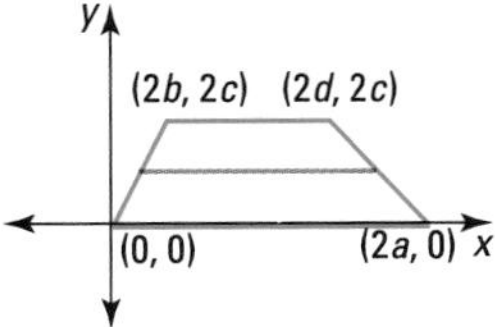

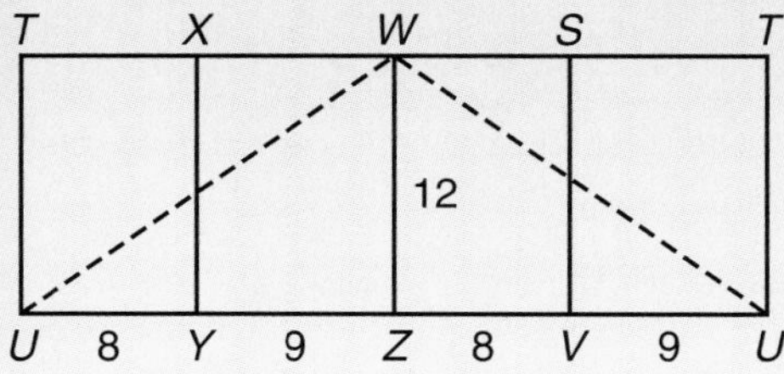

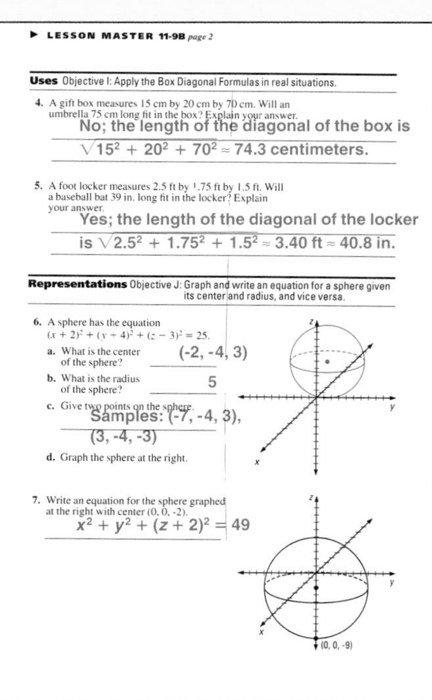

▶ **LESSON MASTER 11-9B** *page 2*

Uses Objective I: Apply the Box Diagonal Formulas in real situations.

4. A gift box measures 15 cm by 20 cm by 70 cm. Will an umbrella 75 cm long fit in the box? Explain your answer.
No; the length of the diagonal of the box is $\sqrt{15^2 + 20^2 + 70^2} \approx 74.3$ centimeters.

5. A foot locker measures 2.5 ft by 1.75 ft by 1.5 ft. Will a baseball bat 39 in. long fit in the locker? Explain your answer.
Yes; the length of the diagonal of the locker is $\sqrt{2.5^2 + 1.75^2 + 1.5^2} \approx 3.40$ ft ≈ 40.8 in.

Representations Objective J: Graph and write an equation for a sphere given its center and radius, and vice versa.

6. A sphere has the equation $(x + 2)^2 + (y + 4)^2 + (z - 3)^2 = 25$.

a. What is the center of the sphere? (-2, -4, 3)

b. What is the radius of the sphere? 5

c. Give two points on the sphere. Samples: (-7, -4, 3), (3, -4, -3)

d. Graph the sphere at the right.

7. Write an equation for the sphere graphed at the right with center (0, 0, -2).
$x^2 + y^2 + (z + 2)^2 = 49$

Notes on Questions

Question 23 This question should be discussed, because students are expected to be able to solve proportions as they study similarity in the next chapter.

Practice

For more questions on SPUR Objectives, use **Lesson Master 11-9A** (shown on page 671) or **Lesson Master 11-9B** (shown on pages 672–673).

Assessment

Oral/Written Communication
For each of the three formulas in the lesson, have each student make up an example to illustrate how the formula is used. Then have students present their examples to the rest of the class. [Students correctly apply the formulas of the lesson.]

Extension

Refer students to **Question 9.** Have them find the coordinates of several other points on the sphere. Then have them make up a similar problem with a sphere that has a different radius and center. [Answers will vary. Sample: (21, 10, -11)]

Project Update Project 3, *3-Dimensional Locations,* Project 4, *Varignon's Theorem,* and Project 5, *Equations for Planes,* on pages 675–676, relate to the content of this lesson.

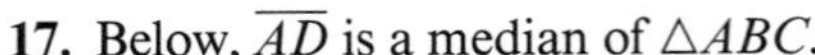

17. Below, $\overline{AD}$ is a median of $\triangle ABC$.
a. Find the coordinates of D. (14, 5)
b. Calculate the length of AD. *(Lesson 11-8)* $\sqrt{109} \approx 10.44$ units

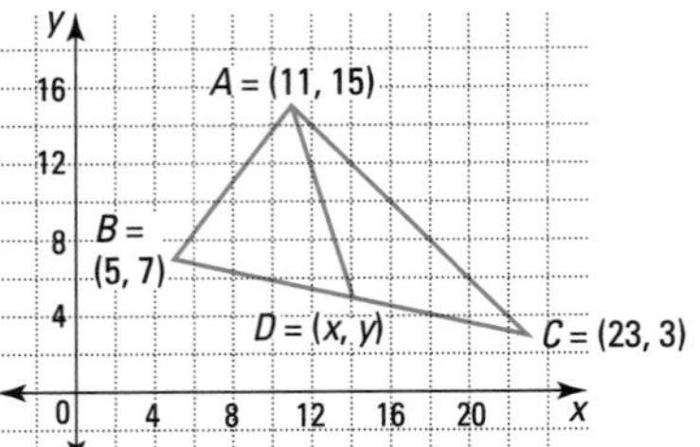

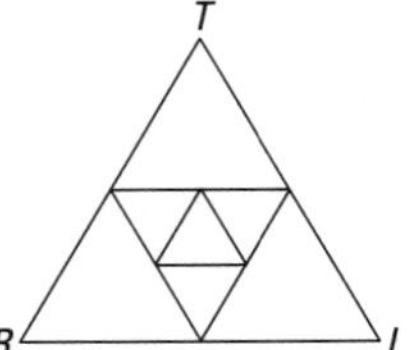

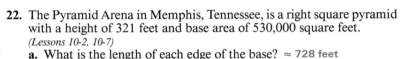

18. $\triangle TRI$ at the left is equilateral with each side having length $2a$. The smaller triangles are formed by joining the midpoints of the sides of the larger triangles. Find the perimeter of the smallest triangle shown. *(Lesson 11-8)* 1.5*a*

19. A circle has center (3, -2) and passes through $P = (4, 1)$.
a. What is its radius? $\sqrt{10}$
b. Write an equation for it. *(Lessons 11-6, 11-7)* $(x - 3)^2 + (y + 2)^2 = 10$

20. A right triangle has sides of lengths 12, 16, and 20. To study this triangle on a coordinate plane, what would be convenient coordinates for its vertices? *(Lesson 11-5)* Sample: with the vertex of the right angle at (0, 0) and the other vertices at (0, 12) and (16, 0)

21. Given: not-$m \Rightarrow n$,
$m \Rightarrow p$,
not-n.
Draw a conclusion. *(Lesson 11-1)* *p*

Pyramid Arena, Memphis, Tennessee

22. The Pyramid Arena in Memphis, Tennessee, is a right square pyramid with a height of 321 feet and base area of 530,000 square feet. *(Lessons 10-2, 10-7)*
a. What is the length of each edge of the base? ≈ 728 feet
b. What is the volume of this pyramid? 56,710,000 cubic feet
c. A newspaper reported that this pyramid is two-thirds the size of the pyramid of Khufu. Refer back to page 572. Is the newspaper correct? In terms of volume, the ratio is about .61, so the newspaper is roughly correct.

23. Solve each equation. *(Previous course)*
a. $\frac{x}{5} = \frac{11}{2}$ $x = \frac{55}{2} = 27.5$
b. $\frac{2}{y} = \frac{4}{2.3}$ $y = 1.15$
c. $\frac{3}{5} = \frac{2z}{13}$ $z = 3.9$

Exploration

24. Measure the three dimensions of a rectangular bedroom or classroom. Set up a coordinate system for the room and determine the coordinates of the lights and windows. Include a drawing. Answers will vary.

25. What is a *hypersphere*? What is a *hypercube*? A hypersphere is all points that are a given distance from a given point in four dimensions. A hypercube is a four-dimensional cube.

A project presents an opportunity for you to extend your knowledge of a topic related to the material of this chapter. You should allow more time for a project than you do for typical homework questions.

PROJECTS 11 CHAPTER ELEVEN

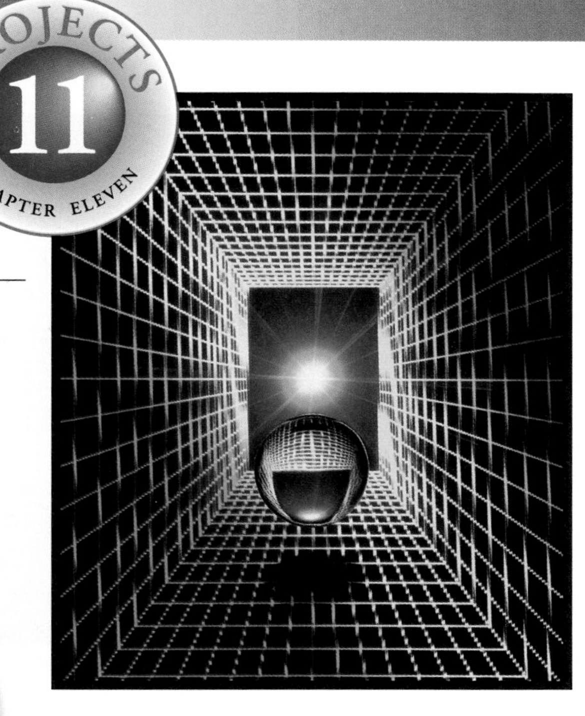

1 Logic Puzzle

Make up your own logic puzzle that has at least 3 categories and at least 8 necessary clues that would require a grid to solve. Make the grid and solve the puzzle.

2 Lewis Carroll

Write a report on the life of Lewis Carroll (Charles Dodgson), including his mathematical and non-mathematical writings.

3 3-Dimensional Locations

Pick a corner of your classroom or a room in your house and locate several objects using 3-dimensional coordinates. Make a poster showing the axes and the locations of the objects. Use the Distance Formula to calculate distances between the objects.

Chapter 11 Projects

The projects relate chiefly to the content of the lessons of this chapter as follows:

Project	Lesson(s)
1	11-1, 11-2, 11-3
2	11-1, 11-2
3	11-9
4	11-5, 11-6, 11-8 11-9
5	11-9
6	11-1, 11-2, 11-3

1 Logic Puzzle It may be easier to make up the grid first, and then write the clues accordingly.

2 Lewis Carroll General information about Lewis Carroll is available in most encyclopedias. For more information about his mathematical writings, students may need to refer to books of recreational mathematics or mathematics history.

3 3-Dimensional Locations The coordinates for objects will depend upon the corner students choose as the origin.

Possible responses

1. Answers will vary.
2. Sample information students might include: Dodgson was born January 27, 1832, in Daresbury, Cheshire, England. He graduated from Christ Church College, Oxford with a degree in mathematics. He then became a lecturer in mathematics and a deacon in the Church of England. He wrote several books on mathematics including *Euclid and His Modern Rivals, Symbolic Logic, The Game of Logic, Pillow Problems,* and *A Tangled Tale.* Of his other books, *Alice in Wonderland* and *Through the Looking-Glass* and *What Alice Found There,* are among the most famous children's books in the world. His pseudonym, Lewis Carroll, which he used for nonacademic work, came from translating his first and middle name into Latin, switching the order, and then translating them back into English. Dodgson died on January 14, 1898.
3. Answers will vary. A suggestion is to let one corner of the room be the origin.

4a. Drawings will vary. At least one of the quadrilaterals should be nonconvex.

b. Sample outlines for both proofs are provided below.
Given: Quad. *ABCD* with midpoints of consecutive sides *E, F, G, H.*
To prove: Quad. *EFGH* is a parallelogram.

Using coordinate geometry:
Graph Quad. *ABCD* with $A = (0, 0)$, $B = (2b, 2c)$, $C = (2d, 2e)$, and $D = (2a, 0)$. By the Midpoint Formula, $E = (b, c)$, $F = (d + b, e + c)$, $G = (d + a, e)$, and $H = (a, 0)$. To show that Quad. *EFGH* is a parallelogram, it is sufficient to show that $EF = GH$ and $FG = EH$ because a quadrilateral

(Responses continue on page 676.)

4 Varignon's Theorem This theorem is quite interesting to see when illustrated using an automatic drawer. It allows all types of quadrilaterals to be shown with the resulting parallelogram.

5 Equations for Planes Remind students that any equation in slope-intercept form can be rewritten in $ax + by = c$ form.

6 Truth Tables A chapter on logic is included in UCSMP *Precalculus and Discrete Mathematics.*

Additional responses, page 676

4b. with both pairs of opposite sides congruent is a parallelogram. By the Distance Formula, $EF = GH = \sqrt{d^2 + e^2}$; $FG = EH = \sqrt{(b-a)^2 + c^2}$. So $EFGH$ is a parallelogram. Using synthetic geometry: In Quad. $ABCD$, draw $\overline{BD}$ to form $\triangle ABD$ and $\triangle CBD$. Then draw $\overline{EH}$ and $\overline{FG}$. By the Midpoint Connector Theorem, $\overline{EH} \parallel \overline{BD}$ and $\overline{FG} \parallel \overline{BD}$. So by the Transitivity of Parallelism, $\overline{EH} \parallel \overline{FG}$. Similarly, draw $\overline{AC}$, and get $\overline{EF} \parallel \overline{HG}$. Hence, Quad. $EFGH$ is a parallelogram, by definition.

c. Varignon's Theorem does hold for space quadrilaterals. Consider the quadrilateral with vertices at $A = (0, 0, 0)$, $B = (0, 2b, 2c)$, $C = (2d, 2e, 2f)$, and $D = (2a, 0, 0)$. By the Midpoint Formula
E = Midpoint of $\overline{AB} = (0, b, c)$
F = Midpoint of $\overline{BC} = (d, e + b, c + f)$
G = Midpoint of $\overline{CD} = (a + d, e, f)$
H = Midpoint of $\overline{DA} = (a, 0, 0)$.
To show that Quad. $EFGH$ is a parallelogram, it is sufficient to show that $EF = GH$ and $FG = EH$ because a quadrilateral with opposite sides congruent is a parallelogram. It can be shown that: $EF = GH = \sqrt{d^2 + e^2 + f^2}$; $FG = EH = \sqrt{a^2 + b^2 + c^2}$. Hence, Quadrilateral $EFGH$ is a parallelogram.

(continued)

4 Varignon's Theorem

An amazing property of all quadrilaterals was discovered and proved by Pierre Varignon, a French mathematician (1654–1722): If the midpoints of consecutive sides of any quadrilateral are connected, then the quadrilateral so formed is a parallelogram.

a. Draw instances of Varignon's Theorem using quadrilaterals with different shapes, with at least one of them nonconvex.

b. Prove Varignon's Theorem for the plane using coordinate geometry or using synthetic geometry. (Hint: If you use coordinate geometry, begin with vertices (0, 0), $(2a, 0)$, $(2b, 2c)$, and $(2d, 2e)$ to simplify the algebra. If you use synthetic geometry, use diagonals of the original quadrilateral as auxiliary lines.)

c. Consider a *space quadrilateral* as one that is formed by connecting four points in space that are not necessarily in the same plane. Does Varignon's Theorem hold for space quadrilaterals? Give evidence to support your answer.

5 Equations for Planes

A line in a 2-dimensional rectangular coordinate system is the set of points (x, y) that satisfy an equation of the form $ax + by = c$. Similarly, in a 3-dimensional rectangular coordinate system like the one in Lesson 11-9, a plane is the set of points (x, y, z) that satisfy an equation of the form $ax + by + cz = d$. Find an automatic drawer that graphs planes. Use it to graph planes that intersect all three axes, exactly two axes, and exactly one axis. Show these graphs.

6 Truth Tables

Examine a book on symbolic logic to find out what is meant by a *truth table*. Then show how each of the five logical principles in this chapter can be analyzed using truth tables.

5. Graphs will vary. Given the equation of a plane $ax + by + cz = d$, where a, b, c, and d are all real numbers the following happens:

When	The plane intersects
$d = 0$	the axis at the origin.
$a, b, c \neq 0$	all three axes.

SUMMARY

Every mathematical argument follows rules of logic. In this chapter, five rules are stated.

Law of Detachment: From a statement or given information p and a conditional $p \Rightarrow q$, you may conclude q.

Law of Transitivity: If $p \Rightarrow q$ and $q \Rightarrow r$, then $p \Rightarrow r$.

Law of the Contrapositive: A conditional ($p \Rightarrow q$) and its contrapositive (not-$q \Rightarrow$ not-p) are either both true or both false.

Law of Ruling Out Possibilities: When p or q is true and q is not true, then p is true.

Law of Indirect Reasoning: If reasoning from a statement p leads to a false conclusion, then p is false.

The last three of these laws comprise the basic logic used in indirect proofs. If you can prove that the contrapositive of a statement is true, then the statement is true. If you can rule out all possibilities but one, then the possibility left is true. If you reason from the negation of what you want to prove and arrive at a contradiction, then the negation is false, so what you want to prove must be true.

In coordinate geometry, figures are described by equations or by giving coordinates of key points. To deduce a general property of a polygon using coordinates, it is efficient to place the polygon in a convenient location on the coordinate plane. Either the figure is placed with one vertex at the origin and one or more sides on the axes, or the figure is placed so that it is symmetric to the x-axis or y-axis or origin.

Three formulas are involved in the coordinate proofs of this chapter. Let (x_1, y_1) and (x_2, y_2) be two points. The distance between them is $\sqrt{(x_2 - x_1)^2 + (y_2 - y_1)^2}$. This gives a way to tell whether segments are congruent. The midpoint of the segment joining the points is $\left(\frac{x_1 + x_2}{2}, \frac{y_1 + y_2}{2}\right)$. Many theorems which involve midpoints can be proved using the Midpoint Formula.

Just as there are equations for lines, there are equations for circles. An equation for the circle with center (h, k) and radius r is $(x - h)^2 + (y - k)^2 = r^2$.

A coordinate geometry of three dimensions can be built by extending the 2-dimensional coordinate system. An ordered pair becomes an ordered triple. The equation for a circle has an analogous equation for a sphere. The Distance Formula and the Midpoint Formula have their 3-dimensional counterparts. Many properties of 3-dimensional figures can be deduced using 3-dimensional coordinates. One example given in this chapter was the formula for the length of a diagonal of a box.

When	The plane is // to the
$a = 0$	x-axis. (If $d = 0$ it contains the x-axis.)
$b = 0$	y-axis. (If $d = 0$ it contains the y-axis.)
$c = 0$	z-axis. (If $d = 0$ it contains the z-axis.)
$a = b = 0$	x- and y-axes (called xy-plane).
$a = c = 0$	x- and z-axes (called xz-plane).
$b = c = 0$	y- and z-axes (called yz-plane).

Summary

The Summary gives an overview of the entire chapter and provides an opportunity for students to consider the material as a whole.

Teaching Aid 151 contains a summary of the Laws of Reasoning discussed in this chapter.

Additional responses, page 676

6. A truth table summarizes all of the possible combinations of true and false statements and shows the truth or falsity of compound statements. Here are the basic principles.

p	q	~ p	p and q	$p \Rightarrow q$	p or q	$p \Leftrightarrow q$
T	T	F	T	T	T	T
T	F	F	F	F	T	F
F	T	T	F	T	T	F
F	F	T	F	T	F	T

The Law of Detachment is that the truth value of [p and ($p \Rightarrow q$)] $\Rightarrow q$ is always T. This can be shown by building up the truth value of the statement for the four possible combinations of truth values of p and q.

p	q	$p \Rightarrow q$	p and $p \Rightarrow q$	(p and $p \Rightarrow q$) $\Rightarrow q$
T	T	T	T	T
T	F	F	F	T
F	T	T	F	T
F	F	T	F	T

Similar analyses can be done for the Law of Transitivity and the Law of the Contrapositive. Law of Transitivity: The truth value of [($p \Rightarrow q$) and ($q \Rightarrow r$)] $\Rightarrow$ ($p \Rightarrow r$) is always T. Law of the Contrapositive: The statement ($p \Rightarrow q$) and the statement (~$q \Rightarrow$ ~p) always have the same truth value. Law of Ruling Out Possibilities: When the truth value of (p or q) is T and that of q is F, then the truth value of p is T. This can be seen by examining the first table. Only the second row satisfies the given conditions, and in that row the truth value of p is T. Law of Indirect Reasoning: If the truth value of ($p \Rightarrow q$) is T and the truth value of q is F, then the truth value of p is F.

Vocabulary

Terms, symbols, and properties are listed by lesson to provide a checklist of concepts a student must know. Emphasize to students that they should read the vocabulary list carefully before starting the Progress Self-Test. If students do not understand the meaning of a term, they should refer back to the indicated lesson.

Additional Answers

4a.

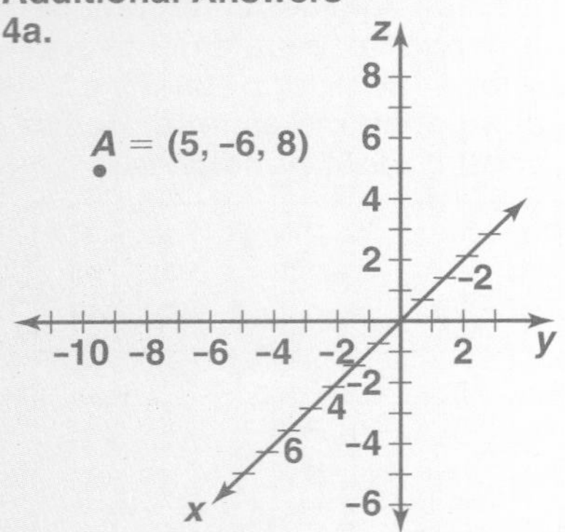

b. ≈ 11.18 units

c. (2.5, -3, 4)

5a. △*ABC* is a right triangle.

b. Law of Ruling Out Possibilities and Law of Detachment

6a. The volume of figure Q is the area of its base times its height.

b. Law of Detachment

7a. If a figure is a polygon, then it is a hexagon. False

b. If a figure is not a hexagon, then it is not a polygon. False

c. If a figure is not a polygon, then it is not a hexagon. True

8. Either △*ABC* has all angles with measure less than 60 or it does not. Suppose that there exists a △*ABC* in which $m\angle A < 60$, $m\angle B < 60$, and $m\angle C < 60$. By the Addition Property of Inequality, $m\angle A + m\angle B + m\angle C < 180$. But this contradicts the Triangle-Sum Theorem. So by the Law of Indirect Reasoning, there is no triangle with three angles all with measure less than 60.

9. Either $\sqrt{80} = 40$ or $\sqrt{80} \neq 40$. Suppose $\sqrt{80} = 40$. Then squaring both sides, $80 = 1600$. This is a false statement. By the Law of Indirect Reasoning, the supposition $\sqrt{80} = 40$ is false. So $\sqrt{80} \neq 40$.

VOCABULARY

Below are the most important terms and phrases for the chapter. For the starred (*) terms you should be able to give a definition of the term. For the other terms you should be able to give a general description and a specific example of each.

Introduction
coordinate geometry
analytic geometry

Lesson 11-1
*Law of Detachment
*Law of Transitivity

Lesson 11-2
negation, not-*p*
truth value
not-*p* ⇒ not-*q*, inverse
not-*q* ⇒ not-*p*, contrapositive
*Law of the Contrapositive

Lesson 11-3
*Law of Ruling Out Possibilities
Trichotomy Law

Lesson 11-4
direct reasoning
direct proofs
indirect reasoning
*contradictory
*contradiction
indirect argument
*Law of Indirect Reasoning
*indirect proof

Lesson 11-5
convenient location for a figure

Lesson 11-6
*Distance Formula on the Coordinate Plane

Lesson 11-7
*Equation for a Circle

Lesson 11-8
mean
*Number Line Midpoint Formula
*Coordinate Plane Midpoint Formula
*Midpoint Connector Theorem
medial triangle

Lesson 11-9
three-dimensional coordinate system
z-coordinate
ordered triple
x-axis, *y*-axis, *z*-axis
*Three-Dimension Distance Formula
*Box Diagonal Formula
Equation for a Sphere
Three-Dimension Midpoint Formula

Additional Answers, continued

10. $HM = \sqrt{6^2 + 8^2} = 10$,
$RB = \sqrt{(16-10)^2 + (8-0)^2} = 10$,
$HR = \sqrt{(16-6)^2 + (8-8)^2} = 10$,
$MB = \sqrt{10^2 + 0^2} = 10$.
So, $HM = RB = HR = MB$.
Therefore, *RHMB* is a rhombus.

11. By the Midpoint Formula, the midpoint of $\overline{XZ}$ is $\left(\frac{2a+2b}{2}, \frac{0+2c}{2}\right) = (a+b, c)$, and the midpoint of $\overline{YW}$ is $\left(\frac{2a+2b+0}{2}, \frac{2c+0}{2}\right) = (a+b, c)$. So the two midpoints are identical.

12. $\overline{DF} \parallel \overline{BE}$ and $\overline{EF} \parallel \overline{BD}$ by the Midpoint Connector Theorem. By the definition of a parallelogram, *BDFE* is a parallelogram.

PROGRESS SELF-TEST

Directions: Take this test as you would take a test in class. Then check your work with the solutions in the Selected Answers section in the back of the book.

4–11) See margin.

In 1 and 2, use points $P = (7, 15)$ and $Q = (30, -7)$.

1. Find PQ. ≈ 31.8 units
2. If M is the midpoint of $\overline{PQ}$, give the coordinates of M. (18.5, 4)
3. Let $R = (3, 4)$, $S = (8, 4)$, and $T = (11, 8)$. Find the perimeter of $\triangle RST$. ≈ 18.94 units
4. a. Draw a three-dimensional coordinate system and plot $A = (5, -6, 8)$.
   b. Find AO, where O is the origin.
   c. What are the coordinates of the midpoint of $\overline{AO}$?

In 5 and 6, consider the two statements (i) and (ii). **a.** What can you conclude using both statements? **b.** What law(s) of logic have you used to arrive at your answer to part **a**?

5. (i) $\angle A$ is an angle of $\triangle ABC$.
   (ii) $\angle A$ is neither acute nor obtuse.
6. (i) If a figure is a right cylinder, then its volume is the area of the base times its height.
   (ii) Figure Q is a right cylinder.
7. Consider this statement: *If a figure is a hexagon, then it is a polygon.* Write its
   a. converse.
   b. inverse.
   c. contrapositive.
   d. Tell which (if any) of these are true.
8. Write an argument to show why no triangle can have three angles all with measures less than 60.
9. Write an indirect proof to show that $\sqrt{80} \neq 40$.
10. $RHMB$ is located on the coordinate plane with coordinates $R = (16, 8)$, $B = (10, 0)$, $M = (0, 0)$, and $H = (6, 8)$. Write a proof argument to show $RHMB$ is a rhombus.

20) Sample: $(-a, 0)$, $(a, 0)$, (b, c), $(-b, c)$

11. Write a proof argument to show that the diagonals of the quadrilateral at the right have the same midpoint.

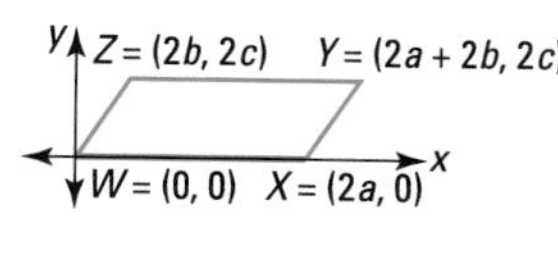

12–13) See margin.

In 12 and 13, D, E, and F are midpoints of the sides of $\triangle ABC$, as shown below.

12. Explain why $BDFE$ is a parallelogram.
13. If $AB = 11$ and $BC = 22.3$, find as many other lengths as you can.
14. What (if anything) can you conclude using all the following statements?
    (1) All babies are happy.
    (2) If someone is teething, then that person is a baby.
    (3) Nate is sad. Nate is not teething.
15. Four cards—the Jack, Queen, King, and Ace—are from the seventeenth, eighteenth, nineteenth, and twentieth centuries, but not necessarily in that order. From the clues below, match each card to its century. (Note: the seventeenth century covers the years 1601–1700; the eighteenth: 1701–1800; and so on.) See margin.
    (1) The Queen is older than the King.
    (2) The Jack is exactly 100 years older than the Queen.
    (3) The Ace is older than the Jack.
16. Goodland, Kansas, is about 60 miles north and 12 miles west of Selkirk. Garden City is about 36 miles south and 34 miles east of Selkirk. What is the flying distance from Goodland to Garden City? ≈ 106.5 miles
17. A grocery bag measures 7″ by 12″ by 17″. What is the length of the longest straw that will fit in the bag without sticking out of it? $\approx 21.95''$
18. Graph the circle with the equation $(x + 1)^2 + (y - 9)^2 = 25$. See margin.
19. What is an equation for a sphere with center (0, -19, 4) and radius 6? See margin.
20. Give convenient coordinates for the vertices of an isosceles trapezoid. See left.

Progress Self-Test

For the development of mathematical competence, feedback and correction, along with the opportunity to practice, are necessary. The Progress Self-Test provides the opportunity for feedback and correction; the Chapter Review provides additional opportunities and practice. We cannot overemphasize the importance of these end-of-chapter materials. It is at this point that the material "gels" for many students, allowing them to solidify skills and understanding. In general, student performance should be markedly improved after these pages.

Assign the Progress Self-Test as a one-night assignment. Answers to all questions are in the Selected Answers section of the student book. Encourage students to take the Progress Self-Test honestly, grade themselves, and then be prepared to discuss the test in class.

Advise students to pay special attention to those Chapter Review questions (pages 680–683) which correspond to questions missed on the Progress Self-Test.

13. $AE = EB = DF = \frac{1}{2}AB = 5.5$;
$EF = BD = DC = \frac{1}{2}BC = 11.15$

15. The Ace is from the 17th century, the Jack is from the 18th century, the Queen is from the 19th century, and the King is from the 20th century.

18. $(x + 1)^2 + (y - 9)^2 = 25$

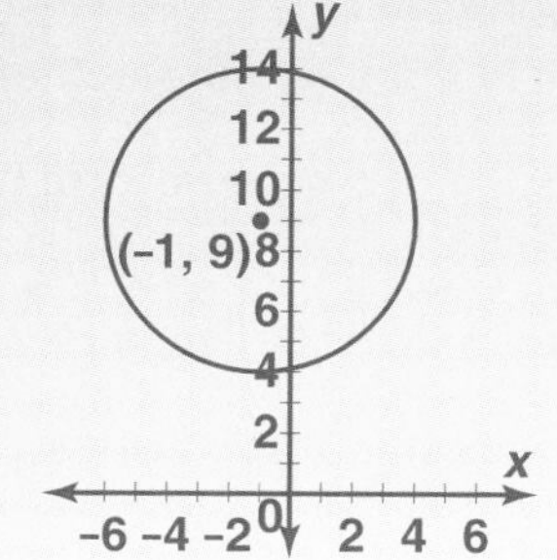

19. $x^2 + (y + 19)^2 + (z - 4)^2 = 36$

Chapter 11 Review

Resources

From the ***Teacher's Resource File***

- Answer Master for Chapter 11 Review
- Assessment Sourcebook: Chapter 11 Test, Forms A–D Chapter 11 Test, Cumulative Form

Additional Resources

- Quiz and Test Writer

The main objectives for the chapter are organized in the Chapter Review under the four types of understanding this book promotes—Skills, Properties, Uses, and Representations.

Additional Answers

10. From the Midpoint Connector Theorem, $\overline{WY} \parallel \overline{VZ}$. Thus, m∠*XWY* = m∠*XVZ* by // lines ⇒ corresponding ∠s ≅.
11. Applying the Midpoint Connector Theorem to △*BCD*, $\overline{EF} \parallel \overline{DB}$. Thus, *BDEF* is a trapezoid by the definition of trapezoid.

13–14.

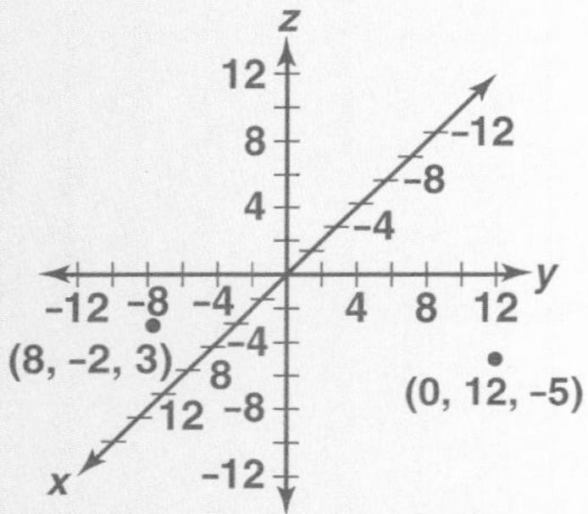

17a. *LOVE* is a trapezoid.
b. Law of Detachment
18a. If alternate interior angles formed by a transversal are congruent, then two lines are parallel.
b. Law of Transitivity
19a. $x = 11$
b. Law of Ruling Out Possibilities
20a. ℓ is not perpendicular to *m*.
b. Law of the Contrapositive and Law of Detachment
23a. If $x^2 = 9$, then $x = 3$.
b. If $x \neq 3$, then $x^2 \neq 9$.
c. If $x^2 \neq 9$, then $x \neq 3$.
d. original, contrapositive.

CHAPTER REVIEW

Questions on SPUR Objectives

SPUR stands for **S**kills, **P**roperties, **U**ses, and **R**epresentations. The Chapter Review questions are grouped according to the SPUR Objectives for this chapter.

SKILLS DEAL WITH THE PROCEDURES USED TO GET ANSWERS.

Objective A: *Determine the length and the coordinates of the midpoint of a segment in the coordinate plane.* (*Lessons 11-6, 11-8*)

In 1 and 2, find the distance between the given points.

1. (3, 5) and (-7, -1) $\sqrt{136} \approx 11.66$ units
2. (55, 90) and (64, 50) $\sqrt{1681} = 41$ units

In 3 and 4, give the coordinates of the midpoint of the segment with the given endpoints.

3. (3, -1) and (-7, -11) (-2, -6)
4. (3, 2) and (6, -2) (4.5, 0)

In 5 and 6, a triangle has vertices (3, 2), (3, 7), and (6, 11).

5. What is its perimeter? 19.49 units
6. What are the coordinates of the midpoints of the sides? (3, 4.5), (4.5, 6.5), (4.5, 9)

In 7 and 8, refer to segment $\overline{AO}$ at the right.

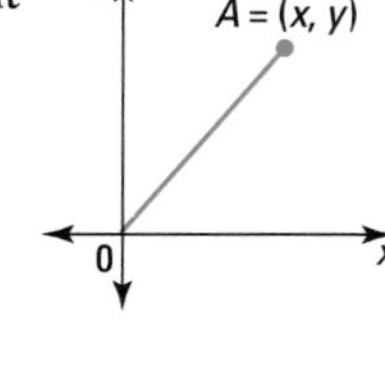

7. Find *AO*. $\sqrt{x^2 + y^2}$
8. If *M* is the midpoint of $\overline{AO}$, give the coordinates of *M*. $\left(\frac{x}{2}, \frac{y}{2}\right)$

Objective B: *Apply the Midpoint Connector Theorem.* (*Lesson 11-8*)

In 9 and 10, *W* and *Y* are the midpoints of $\overline{XV}$ and $\overline{XZ}$ in the figure at the right.

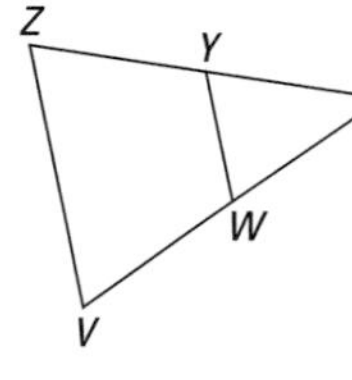

9. If *YW* = 40, and *WV* = 41, determine all the other lengths that you can. *WX* = 41, *VX* = 82, *VZ* = 80
10. Write a proof argument to show that m∠*XWY* = m∠*XVZ*. See margin.

In 11 and 12, △*EFG* is the medial triangle of △*BCD*, as shown below.

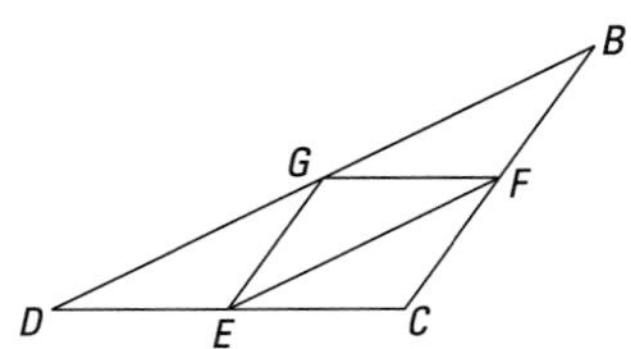

11. Explain why *BDEF* is a trapezoid. See margin.
12. If *BD* = 10, *DC* = 7, and *BC* = 6, find the lengths of as many other segments as possible. *DE* = *EC* = *GF* = 3.5; *CF* = *BF* = *EG* = 3; *EF* = *DG* = *BG* = 5

Objective C: *Plot points, find distances between them, and find coordinates of midpoints in 3-dimensional space.* (*Lesson 11-9*)

In 13 and 14, draw a coordinate system and plot the points. 13, 14) See margin.

13. (8, -2, 3)
14. (0, 12, -5)

In 15 and 16, two points are given. **a.** Find the coordinates of the midpoint of the segment joining them. **b.** Find the distance between them.

15. *P* = (-2, 3, 6) and *Q* = (0, -5, 1).
16. *R* = (13, -5, 8) and *S* = (0, 16, -3).

15a) (-1, -1, 3.5); b) ≈ 9.64 units
16a) (6.5, 5.5, 2.5); b) ≈ 27.04 units

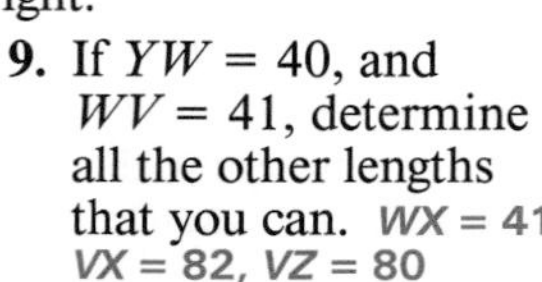

Additional Answers, continued

24a. If a figure is a square, then it is a rectangle.
b. If a figure is not a rectangle, then it is not a square.
c. If a figure is not a square, then it is not a rectangle.
d. converse, inverse
25a. All people in the U.S. live in New York.
b. If a person is not a New Yorker, then that person does not live in the U.S.
c. If a person does not live in the U.S., then that person is not a New Yorker.
d. original, contrapositive
26a. If m∠*DBC* = 140, then m∠*ABC* = 40.
b. If m∠*ABC* ≠ 40, then m∠*DBC* ≠ 140.
c. If m∠*DBC* ≠ 140, then m∠*ABC* ≠ 40.
d. All are true.

PROPERTIES DEAL WITH THE PRINCIPLES BEHIND THE MATHEMATICS.

17–20) See margin.

Objective D: *Follow the basic laws of reasoning to make conclusions.* *(Lessons 11-1, 11-2, 11-3, 11-4)*

In 17–20, use all the statements. **a.** What (if anything) can you conclude? **b.** What laws of reasoning have you used?

17. (1) If a figure is a rectangle, then it is a trapezoid.
(2) *LOVE* is a rectangle.

18. (1) If corresponding angles formed by a transversal are congruent, then two lines are parallel.
(2) If alternate interior angles formed by a transversal are congruent, then so are corresponding angles.

19. (1) $x = 11$ or $y = 10$.
(2) $y = 7$

20. (1) If $\ell \perp m$, then $m\angle A = 90$.
(2) $m\angle A = 75$

21. *Multiple choice.*

a. If the conditional $p \Rightarrow q$ is true, which of the following must also be true? d
(a) $p \Rightarrow$ not-q (b) $q \Rightarrow p$
(c) not-$p \Rightarrow$ not-q (d) not-$q \Rightarrow$ not-p

b. How is the correct answer to part **a** related to the given conditional? b
(a) inverse (b) contrapositive
(c) converse (d) negation

22. Solving $(2x - 5)(3x + 4) = (x - 1)(6x - 1)$, Nella came up with the equation $-20 = 1$.

a. What should Nella conclude?

b. What law of logic is being used to make this conclusion? Law of Indirect Reasoning
a) The original equation has no solution.

Objective E: *Write the converse, inverse, or contrapositive of a conditional.* *(Lesson 11-2)*

In 23–26, write **a.** the converse, **b.** the inverse, and **c.** the contrapositive of the statement. **d.** Tell which (if any) of these are true. See margin.

23. If $x = 3$, then $x^2 = 9$.

24. If a figure is a rectangle, then it is a square.

25. All New Yorkers live in the U.S.

26. Use the figure at the right. If $m\angle ABC = 40$, then $m\angle DBC = 140$.

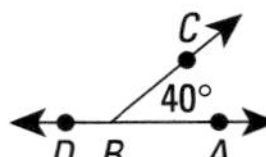

Objective F: *Write indirect proofs.* *(Lessons 11-4, 11-5, 11-6)* See margin.

27. Explain why a quadrilateral cannot have four acute angles.

28. Give an indirect proof to show that $\sqrt{2400} \neq 49$.

29. Give an indirect proof to show that $\sqrt{2} \neq \frac{239}{169}$.

30. Use the figure below. Write an indirect proof to show that $\triangle ABC$ is not isosceles.

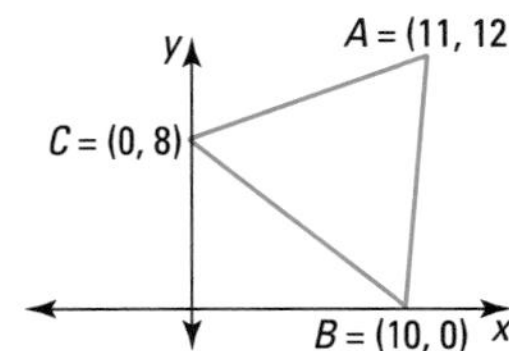

31. Write an indirect proof to show that *ABCD* below is not a trapezoid.

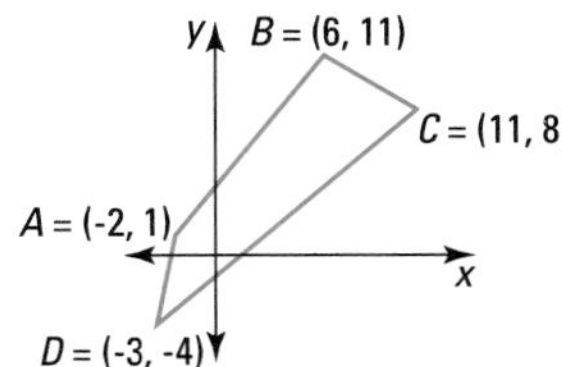

32. What is the difference between a direct proof and an indirect proof?

Objective G: *Use coordinate geometry to deduce properties of figures and prove theorems.* *(Lessons 11-5, 11-6, 11-8)* 33–34) See margin.

33. Prove that the triangle with vertices $A = (11, 2)$, $B = (23, 1)$, and $C = (2, 10)$ is isosceles.

34. Prove that the triangle with vertices $X = (q, 0)$, $Y = (0, q)$, and $Z = (2q, 3q)$ is a right triangle.

Additional Answers, continued

27. Either quadrilateral $ABCD$ has four acute angles or it does not. Suppose that in quadrilateral $ABCD$, $\angle A$, $\angle B$, $\angle C$, and $\angle D$ are acute. Thus, $m\angle A < 90$, $m\angle B < 90$, $m\angle C < 90$, and $m\angle D < 90$. So $m\angle A + m\angle B + m\angle C + m\angle D < 360$, which contra-dicts the Quadrilateral-Sum Theorem. So by the Law of Indirect Reasoning, the supposition is false. Thus, a quadrilateral cannot have four acute angles.

28. Either $\sqrt{2400} = 49$ or $\sqrt{2400} \neq 49$. Suppose $\sqrt{2400} = 49$. Then, squaring both sides, $2400 = 2401$. This is a false conclusion; so by the Law of Indirect Reasoning, the supposition is false. So $\sqrt{2400} \neq 49$.

29. Either $\sqrt{2} = \frac{239}{169}$ or $\sqrt{2} \neq \frac{239}{169}$. Suppose $\sqrt{2} = \frac{239}{169}$. Then $2 = (\frac{239}{169})^2 = \frac{57{,}121}{28{,}561}$. Then $2 \cdot 28{,}561 = 57{,}121$; so $57{,}122 = 57{,}121$. This is a false conclusion; so by the Law of Indirect Reasoning, the supposition is false. So $\sqrt{2} \neq \frac{239}{169}$.

30. Either $\triangle ABC$ is isosceles or it is not. Suppose that $\triangle ABC$ is isosceles. Then $AB = BC$, $AB = AC$, or $BC = AC$. Suppose $AB = BC$, then $AB = \sqrt{1^2 + 12^2} = \sqrt{145}$. $BC = \sqrt{10^2 + 8^2} = \sqrt{164} \neq AB$. This is a contradiction. So $AB \neq BC$. Similarly, since $AC = \sqrt{11^2 + 4^2} = \sqrt{137}$, $AB \neq AC$, and $BC \neq AC$. So, by the Law of Indirect Reasoning, the supposition is false. So $\triangle ABC$ is not isosceles.

31. Either $ABCD$ is a trapezoid or it is not. Suppose $ABCD$ is a trapezoid. Then by the definition of trapezoid, either $\overline{AB} \parallel \overline{CD}$ or $\overline{AD} \parallel \overline{BC}$. Slope of $\overline{AB} = \frac{10}{8} = \frac{5}{4}$; slope of $\overline{CD} = \frac{12}{14} = \frac{6}{7}$. So, by the Parallel Lines and Slopes Theorem, $\overline{AB}$ is not parallel to $\overline{CD}$. Then by the Law of Ruling Out Possibilities $\overline{AD} \parallel \overline{BC}$ is the other possibility. Slope of $\overline{AD} = \frac{-5}{-1} = 5$; slope of $\overline{BC} = \frac{3}{-5} = \frac{-3}{5}$. So by the Parallel Lines and Slopes Theorem, $\overline{AD}$ is not parallel to $\overline{BC}$. Therefore, the supposition is false and by the Law of Indirect Reasoning, $ABCD$ is not a trapezoid.

32. A direct proof begins with information known to be true. An indirect proof supposes a statement thought to be false and tries to derive a contradiction. A direct proof uses the Laws of Detachment and Transitivity to reach a conclusion. An indirect proof uses the Law of the Contrapositive, the Law of Indirect Reasoning, and/or the Law of Ruling Out Possibilities.

33. $AB = \sqrt{145}$; $AC = \sqrt{145}$. Since $AB = AC$, $\triangle ABC$ is isosceles by definition of isosceles triangle.

(Additional Answers continue on page 682.)

Assessment

Evaluation The *Assessment Sourcebook* provides five forms of the Chapter 11 Test. Forms A and B present parallel versions in a short-answer format. Forms C and D offer performance assessment. The fifth test is Chapter 11 Test, Cumulative Form. About 50% of this test covers Chapter 11; 25% of it covers Chapter 10, and 25% covers earlier chapters.

For information on grading, see *General Teaching Suggestions; Grading* in the *Professional Sourcebook,* which begins on page T20 in this Teacher's Edition.

Additional Answers

34. Slope of $\overline{XY} = \frac{q-0}{0-q} = \frac{q}{-q} = -1$; slope of $\overline{YZ} = \frac{3q-q}{2q-0} = \frac{2q}{2q} = 1$. Since $1 \cdot -1 = -1$, $\overline{XY} \perp \overline{YZ}$ by the $\perp$ Lines and Slopes Theorem. So $\triangle XYZ$ is a right triangle by the definition of right triangle.

35. Slopes of: $\overline{XY} = \frac{-2}{7}$; $\overline{YZ} = \frac{10}{3}$; $\overline{ZW} = \frac{-2}{7}$; $\overline{WX} = \frac{10}{3}$. By the Parallel Lines and Slopes Theorem, $\overline{XY} \parallel \overline{ZW}$ and $\overline{YZ} \parallel \overline{WX}$. Thus, $XYZW$ is a parallelogram by the definition of a parallelogram.

36. Midpoint of $\overline{AB} = E = (6, -1.5)$; midpoint of $\overline{BC} = F = (4, 5)$; midpoint of $\overline{CD} = G = (-4.5, 3.5)$; midpoint of $\overline{AD} = H = (-2.5, -3)$. Slope of $\overline{EF} = \frac{6.5}{-2}$ = slope of $\overline{GH}$. Slope of $\overline{FG} = \frac{1.5}{8.5}$ = slope of $\overline{EH}$. So $\overline{EF} \parallel \overline{GH}$ and $\overline{FG} \parallel \overline{EH}$. $EFGH$ is a parallelogram by the definition of parallelogram.

37. Slope of $\overline{WY} = \frac{s-0}{s-0} = \frac{s}{s} = 1$; slope of $\overline{XZ} = \frac{s-0}{0-s} = \frac{s}{-s} = -1$. Since $1 \cdot -1 = -1$, by the Perpendicular Lines and Slopes Theorem, $\overline{WY} \perp \overline{XZ}$.

35. Prove that $X = (-1, 10)$, $Y = (6, 8)$, $Z = (3, -2)$, and $W = (-4, 0)$ are vertices of a parallelogram. See margin.

36. Show that the quadrilateral formed by joining midpoints of $ABCD$ shown below is a parallelogram. See margin.

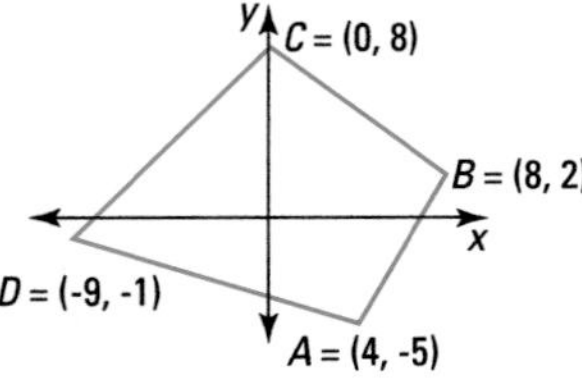

In 37 and 38, use the square below. See margin.

37. Prove that its diagonals are perpendicular to each other.

38. Prove that its diagonals have the same length.

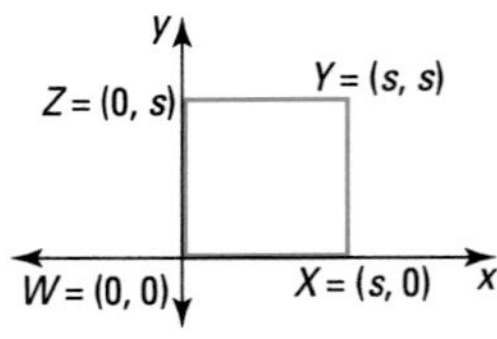

USES DEAL WITH APPLICATIONS OF MATHEMATICS IN REAL SITUATIONS.

39–44) See margin.

Objective H: *Apply laws of reasoning in real situations.* *(Lessons 11-1, 11-2, 11-3, 11-4)*

In 39–41, given the statements, what (if anything) can you conclude using the rules of logic?

39. (1) I am allowed to watch TV at 8 P.M. if I have finished my homework.
(2) I am not allowed to watch TV at 8 P.M.

40. (1) Either Mary is too old for camp or she can go to camp.
(2) Mary cannot go to camp.

41. (1) All bats are mammals.
(2) No mammal can live without air.
(3) Air is not found on the moon.

42. Ted is looking for his lost homework paper. It isn't in his notebook. It isn't in his school locker. So he concludes that it is at home.
  a. What reasoning law has he used?
  b. What, if anything, is wrong with his reasoning?

In 43 and 44, the puzzles are from Lewis Carroll. What can you conclude?

43. (1) No name in this list is unsuitable for the hero of a romance.
(2) Names beginning with a vowel are always melodious.
(3) No name is suitable for the hero of a romance, if it begins with a consonant.

44. (1) Nobody who really appreciates Beethoven fails to keep silent while the Moonlight Sonata is being played.
(2) Guinea pigs are hopelessly ignorant of music.
(3) No one who is hopelessly ignorant of music ever keeps silent while the Moonlight Sonata is being played.

Ludwig van Beethoven (1770-1827)

Objective I: *Apply the Distance and Box Diagonal formulas in real situations.* *(Lessons 11-6, 11-9)*

45. A car drives 5 miles north, 2 miles east, then another 6 miles north, and another 3 miles east. By plane, how far is the car from its starting point? $\sqrt{146} \approx 12.1$ miles

46. A ship is located 2.3 km south and 1.4 km west of a lighthouse. Another ship is 1.6 km south and 0.8 km east of the lighthouse.
  a. Draw a picture of this situation.
  b. Calculate the distance between the ships.

b) $\sqrt{5.33} \approx 2.3$ km a) See page 683.

Additional Answers, continued

38. $ZX = \sqrt{(s-0)^2 + (0-s)^2} = \sqrt{2s^2}$; $WY = \sqrt{(0-s)^2 + (s-0)^2} = \sqrt{2s^2} = ZX$

39. I have not finished my homework.

40. Mary is too old for camp.

41. No bat can live on the moon.

42a. Law of Ruling Out Possibilities
b. He may not have included all the possibilities.

43. All the names on this list are melodious.

44. Guinea pigs do not really appreciate Beethoven.

CHAPTER ELEVEN

47. A storage box is 8 inches by 12 inches by 24 inches. What is the longest dowel rod that can fit in it? 28 inches

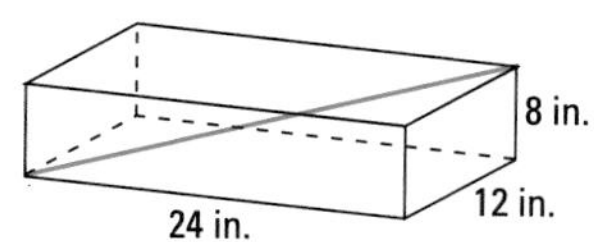

48. A wooden crate is 45 mm by 30 mm by 80 mm. What is the length of the longest straw that will fit in it?
$\sqrt{9325} \approx 96.6$ mm

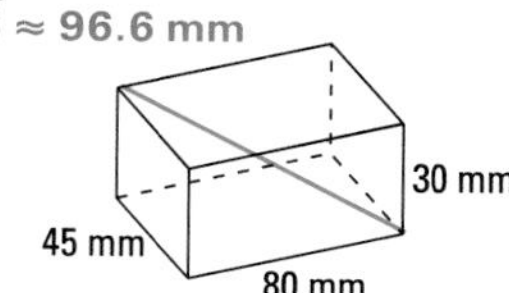

REPRESENTATIONS DEAL WITH PICTURES, GRAPHS, OR OBJECTS THAT ILLUSTRATE CONCEPTS.

Objective J: *Graph and write an equation for a circle or a sphere given its center and radius, and vice versa.* *(Lessons 11-7, 11-9)*

49. What is an equation for the circle with center (8, -1) and radius 15? $(x - 8)^2 + (y + 1)^2 = 225$

50. Write an equation for the circle below.
$(x - 4)^2 + (y - 5)^2 = 36$

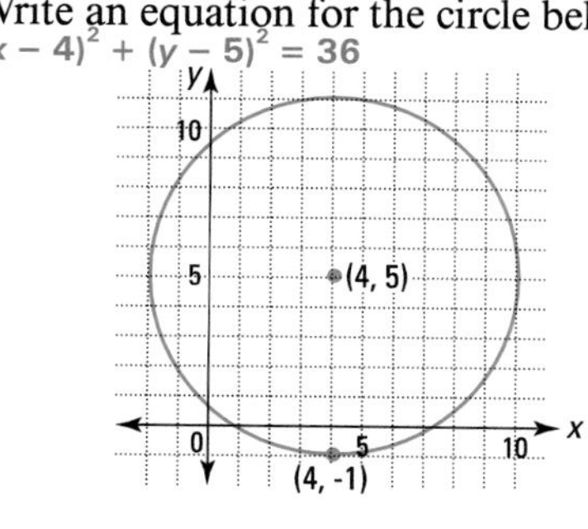

In 51 and 52, graph the given equation. See below.

51. $(x + 1)^2 + (y - 4)^2 = 9$

52. $x^2 + y^2 = 36$

53. Find an equation for the sphere with center (4, -3, 0) and radius 10. See below.

54. Find the center and the radius of the sphere $(x - 1)^2 + (y + 2)^2 + (z - 5)^2 = 4$.
(1, -2, 5); 2

Objective K: *Give convenient locations for triangles and quadrilaterals in the coordinate plane.* *(Lesson 11-5)*

In 55–58, give convenient locations for the figure. 55. Sample: $(-a, 0)$, $(a, 0)$, $(0, b)$

55. an isosceles triangle

56) See below.

56. a rectangle is symmetric to the x- and y-axes

57. a kite Sample: $(-a, 0)$, $(a, 0)$, $(0, b)$, $(0, -c)$

58. a square $(0, 0)$, $(a, 0)$, (a, a), $(0, a)$

53) $(x - 4)^2 + (y + 3)^2 + z^2 = 100$

56) (a, b), $(a, -b)$, $(-a, -b)$, $(-a, b)$

46a)

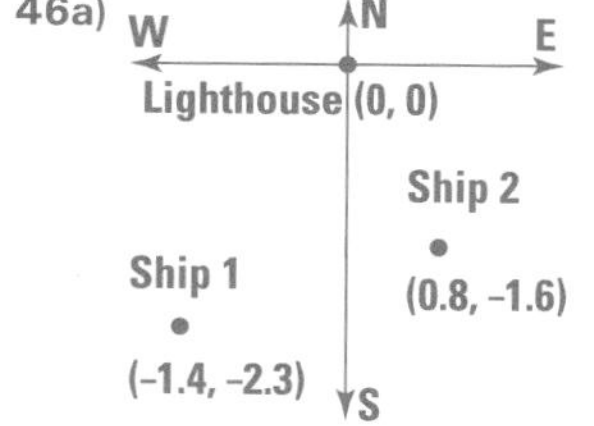

51)

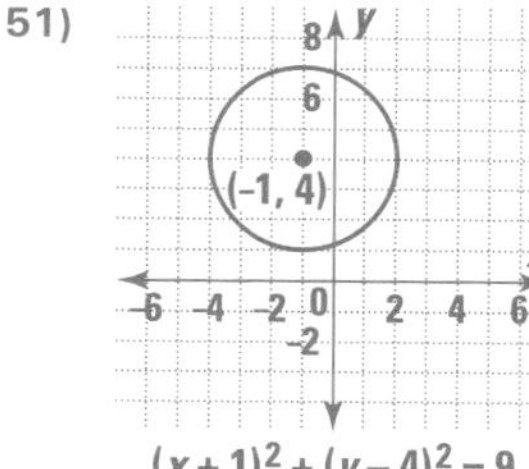

$(x+1)^2+(y-4)^2=9$

52)

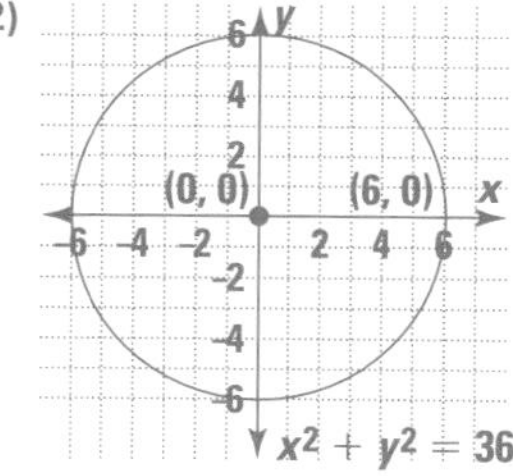

$x^2 + y^2 = 36$

Feedback After students have taken the test for Chapter 11 and you have scored the results, return the tests to students for discussion. Class discussion of the questions that caused trouble for the most students can be very effective in identifying and clarifying misunderstandings. You might want to have them write down the items they missed and work, either in groups or at home, to correct them. It is important for students to receive feedback on every chapter test, and we recommend that students see and correct their mistakes before proceeding too far into the next chapter.

Chapter 12 Planner

Adapting to Individual Needs

The student text is written for the vast majority of students. The chart at the right suggests two pacing plans to accommodate the needs of your students. Students in the Full Course should complete the entire text by the end of the year. Students in the Minimal Course will spend more time when there are quizzes and more time on the Chapter Review. Therefore, these students may not complete all of the chapters in the text.

Options are also presented to meet the needs of a variety of teaching and learning styles. For each lesson, the Teacher's Edition provides a section entitled *Adapting to Individual Needs.* This section regularly includes **Optional Activities, Challenge** problems, **English Language Development** suggestions, and suggestions for providing **Extra Help.** The Teacher's Edition also frequently includes an **Error Alert,** an **Extension,** and an **Assessment** alternative. The options available in Chapter 12 are summarized in the chart below.

Chapter 12 Pacing Chart

Day	Full Course	Minimal Course
1	12-1	12-1
2	12-2	12-2
3	12-3	12-3
4	12-4	12-4
5	Quiz*; 12-5	Quiz*; begin 12-5.
6	12-6	Finish 12-5.
7	12-7	12-6
8	Self-Test	12-7
9	Review	Self-Test
10	Test*	Review
11		Review
12		Test*

*in the Teacher's Resource File

Chapter 12 Block Schedule

Day	Recommended Pacing
1	Lessons 12-1, 12-2
2	Lessons 12-3, 12-4
3	Lesson 12-5
4	Lesson 12-6
5	Lesson 12-7, Self-Test, Chapter Review
6	Chapter Review, Chapter Test

In the Teacher's Edition...

Lesson	Optional Activities	Extra Help	Challenge	English Language Development	Error Alert	Extension	Cooperative Learning	Ongoing Assessment
12-1	●		●					Written
12-2	●	●	●	●	●	●		Written
12-3	●	●	●			●	●	Oral/Written
12-4	●	●	●	●	●	●	●	Group
12-5	●	●	●	●	●	●		Written
12-6	●	●		●		●	●	Group
12-7	●		●			●	●	Written

In the Additional Resources...

	In the Teacher's Resource File								
Lesson	Lesson Masters, A and B	Teaching Aids*	Activity Kit*	Answer Masters	Technology Sourcebook	Assessment Sourcebook	Visual Aids**	Technology	Video Segments
12-1	12-1	105, 157, 160		12-1			157, 160, AM		
In-class Activity		161		12-2			161, AM		
12-2	12-2	157, 162–164		12-2	24		157, 162–164, AM	GeoExplorer	
12-3	12-3	105, 157, 165–167		12-3	24		105, 157, 165–167, AM	GeoExplorer	
12-4	12-4	158, 168		12-4		Quiz	158, 168, AM		
12-5	12-5	158, 169	25	12-5			158, 169, AM		
12-6	12-6	105, 159, 170		12-6			105, 159, 170, AM		12-6
12-7	12-7	159		12-7			159, AM		
End of Chapter				Review		Tests			

*Teaching Aids are pictured on pages 684C and 684D. The activities in the Activity Kit are pictured on page 684C. Teaching Aid 161 which accompanies the In-class Activity preceding Lesson 12-2 is pictured with the lesson notes on page 691.

**Visual Aids provide transparencies for all Teaching Aids and all Answer Masters.

Also available is the Study Skills Handbook which includes study-skill tips related to reading, note-taking, and comprehension.

Integrating Strands and Applications

	12-1	12-2	12-3	12-4	12-5	12-6	12-7
Mathematical Connections							
Number Sense	●			●	●	●	●
Algebra	●	●	●	●	●		●
Geometry	●	●	●	●	●	●	●
Measurement	●	●	●	●	●	●	●
Logic and Reasoning	●	●	●	●	●	●	
Patterns and Functions	●	●	●	●	●	●	
Discrete Mathematics		●	●				
Interdisciplinary and Other Connections							
Art	●	●					
Music	●						
Literature							●
Science			●				●
Social Studies					●	●	●
Multicultural		●	●	●		●	●
Technology		●	●			●	
Career					●	●	●
Consumer				●			●
Sports							●

Teaching and Assessing the Chapter Objectives

Chapter 12 Objectives (Organized into the SPUR categories—Skills, Properties, Uses, and Representations)	**Lessons**	**Progress Self-Test Questions**	**Chapter Review Questions**	**In the Teacher's Resource File: Chapter Test, Forms A and B**	**Chapter Test, Forms C**	**Chapter Test, Forms D**
Skills						
A: Draw size transformation images of figures.	12-2, 12-3	1, 2, 3	1–6	1, 2	1	
B: Use proportions to find missing parts in similar figures.	12-4, 12-5	5, 6, 9, 12	7–12	4, 6	4	
Properties						
C: Recognize and apply properties of size transformations.	12-2, 12-3	4, 7, 8	13–18	3, 5, 7, 16	1	
D: Use the Fundamental Theorem of Similarity to find lengths, perimeters, areas, and volumes in similar figures.	12-6	10, 11	19–22	8, 9		✓
Uses						
E: Identify and determine proportional lengths and distances in real situations.	12-4, 12-5	13, 14, 16	23–28	11, 12	3	
F: Apply the Fundamental Theorem of Similarity in real situations.	12-6, 12-7	15, 17	29–34	10, 13	5	✓
Representations						
G: Perform and analyze size transformations on figures in the coordinate plane.	12-1	18, 19, 20	35–40	14–17	2	✓

Assessment Sourcebook
Quiz for Lessons 12-1 through 12-4
Chapter 12 Test, Forms A–D
Chapter 12 Test, Cumulative Form

Quiz and Test Writer

Activity Kit

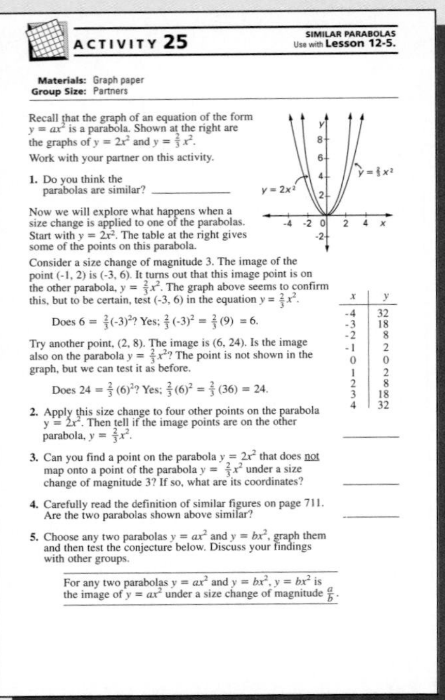

ACTIVITY 25 — SIMILAR PARABOLAS
Use with **Lesson 12-5.**

Materials: Graph paper
Group Size: Partners

Recall that the graph of an equation of the form $y = ax^2$ is a parabola. Shown at the right are the graphs of $y = 2x^2$ and $y = \frac{2}{3}x^2$.

Work with your partner on this activity.

1. Do you think the parabolas are similar? ________

Now we will explore what happens when a size change is applied to one of the parabolas. Start with $y = 2x^2$. The table at the right gives some of the points on this parabola.

Consider a size change of magnitude 3. The image of the point (-1, 2) is (-3, 6). It turns out that this image point is on the other parabola, $y = \frac{2}{3}x^2$. The graph above seems to confirm this, but to be certain, test (-3, 6) in the equation $y = \frac{2}{3}x^2$.

Does $6 = \frac{2}{3}(-3)^2$? Yes; $\frac{2}{3}(-3)^2 = \frac{2}{3}(9) = 6$.

Try another point, (2, 8). The image is (6, 24). Is the image also on the parabola $y = \frac{2}{3}x^2$? The point is not shown in the graph, but we can test it as before.

Does $24 = \frac{2}{3}(6)^2$? Yes; $\frac{2}{3}(6)^2 = \frac{2}{3}(36) = 24$.

x	y
-4	32
-3	18
-2	8
-1	2
0	0
1	2
2	8
3	18
4	32

2. Apply this size change to four other points on the parabola $y = 2x^2$. Then tell if the image points are on the other parabola, $y = \frac{2}{3}x^2$. ________

3. Can you find a point on the parabola $y = 2x^2$ that does not map onto a point of the parabola $y = \frac{2}{3}x^2$ under a size change of magnitude 3? If so, what are its coordinates? ________

4. Carefully read the definition of similar figures on page 711. Are the two parabolas shown above similar? ________

5. Choose any two parabolas $y = ax^2$ and $y = bx^2$, graph them and then test the conjecture below. Discuss your findings with other groups.

For any two parabolas $y = ax^2$ and $y = bx^2$, $y = bx^2$ is the image of $y = ax^2$ under a size change of magnitude $\frac{a}{b}$.

Teaching Aids

Teaching Aid 105, Graph Paper (shown on page 434C), can be used with **Lessons 12-1, 12-3, and 12-6.**

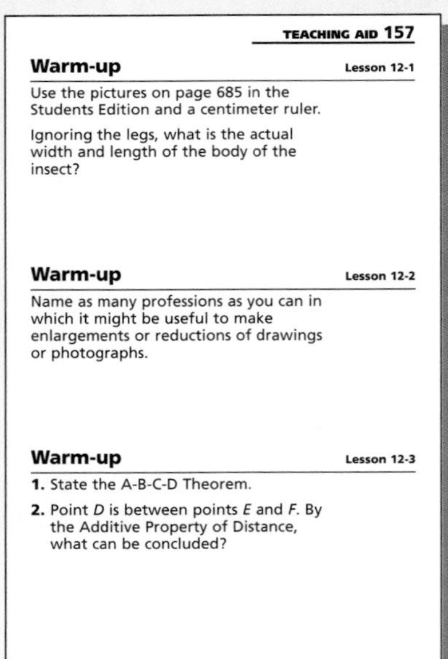

TEACHING AID 157

Warm-up — Lesson 12-1

Use the pictures on page 685 in the Students Edition and a centimeter ruler.

Ignoring the legs, what is the actual width and length of the body of the insect?

Warm-up — Lesson 12-2

Name as many professions as you can in which it might be useful to make enlargements or reductions of drawings or photographs.

Warm-up — Lesson 12-3

1. State the A-B-C-D Theorem.

2. Point D is between points E and F. By the Additive Property of Distance, what can be concluded?

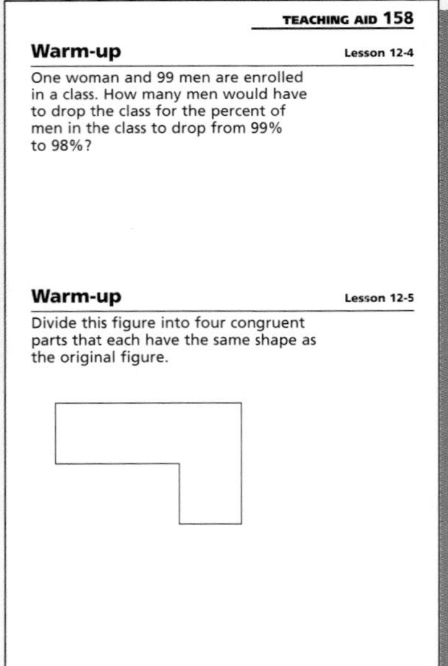

TEACHING AID 158

Warm-up — Lesson 12-4

One woman and 99 men are enrolled in a class. How many men would have to drop the class for the percent of men in the class to drop from 99% to 98%?

Warm-up — Lesson 12-5

Divide this figure into four congruent parts that each have the same shape as the original figure.

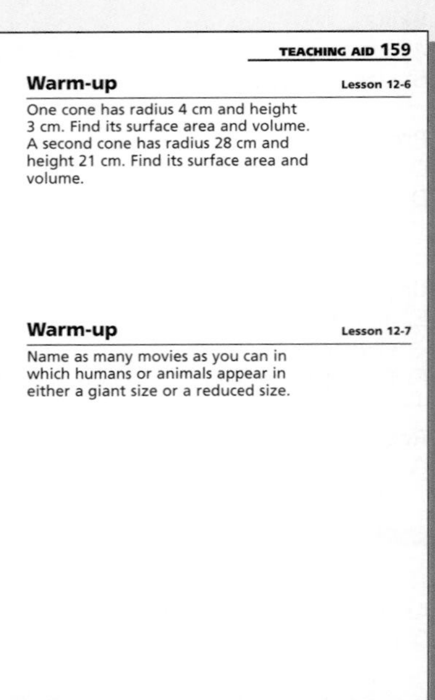

TEACHING AID 159

Warm-up — Lesson 12-6

One cone has radius 4 cm and height 3 cm. Find its surface area and volume. A second cone has radius 28 cm and height 21 cm. Find its surface area and volume.

Warm-up — Lesson 12-7

Name as many movies as you can in which humans or animals appear in either a giant size or a reduced size.

TEACHING AID 160
Lesson 12-1

Question 11

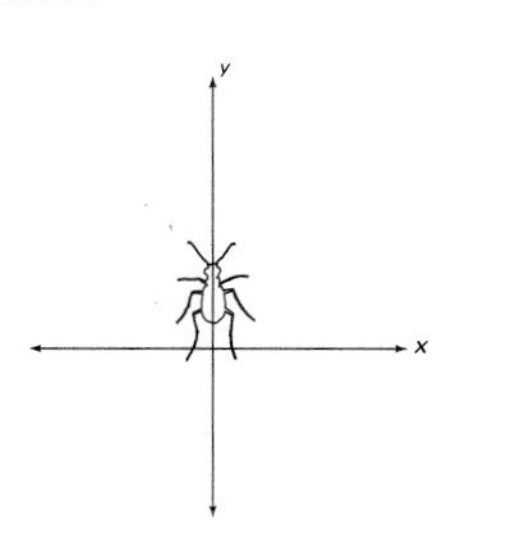

TEACHING AID 162
Lesson 12-2

Additional Examples

1. *KITE* is the image of *PLAY* under a size change. Find the center and magnitude of the size change.

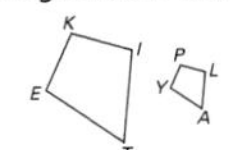

2. Trace the flag of Questions 4-5 on page 695 of the Student Edition. Find its image under the size change with center *D* and magnitude 1.5.

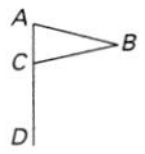

TEACHING AID 163
Lesson 12-2

Questions

4.-5.

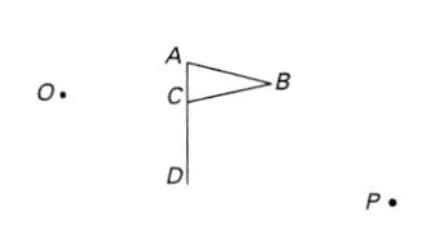

10.

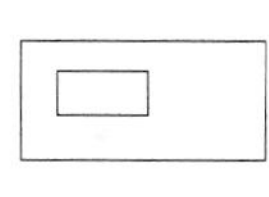

TEACHING AID 164
Lesson 12-2

Questions

11.

12.

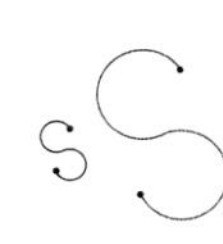

19.

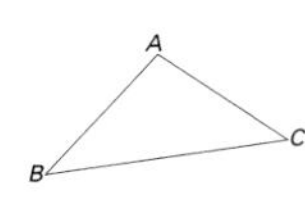

TEACHING AID 165
Lesson 12-3

Additional Examples

1. Let S be a size transformation with magnitude 1.75 and center *O*. Draw *S(HAT)*.

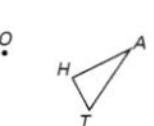

2. Every size change maps any line onto a line that is parallel to it. Which, if any, isometries have this same property?

3. Circle *P* has radius 5. Circle *Q* has radius 22. Is there a size change that maps circle *P* onto circle *Q*? If so, what is its magnitude? If not, why not?

TEACHING AID 166
Lesson 12-3

Example

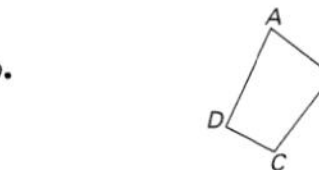

Question 1

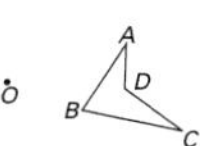

TEACHING AID 167
Lesson 12-3

Questions

14.

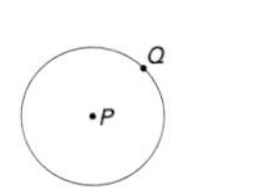

15.

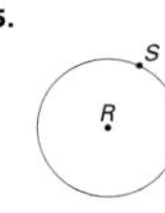

16.

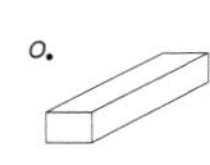

TEACHING AID 168
Lesson 12-4

Additional Examples

1. $\triangle DEF$ is the image of $\triangle ABC$ under a size change with center *O*. If $AB = 20$, $DE = 12$, and $DF = 16.5$, find AC.

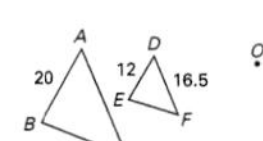

2. A toy train is $\frac{1}{48}$ actual size. If the locomotive of the train is $10\frac{7}{8}''$ long and $2\frac{1}{4}''$ high, how long and how high is the actual locomotive?

3. A Boeing 747 is about 70.5 meters long and has a wingspan of about 59.6 meters. The wingspan on a model of this plane is 40 centimeters. What will be the length of the model?

TEACHING AID 169
Lesson 12-5

Additional Examples

1. In the figure, $S_{1.25} \circ r_m(\triangle RST) = \triangle JLK$, and the center of $S_{1.25}$ is point *O*.
   a. If $m\angle K = 67$, what angle in $\triangle RST$ has measure 67?
   b. If $JK = 11$, what length in $\triangle RST$ can be determined, and what is this length?

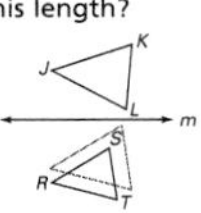

2. $\triangle NUT \sim \triangle SQR$, with angle measures and lengths as indicated. Find as many angle measures and lengths in $\triangle NUT$ as possible using the Similar Figures Theorem.

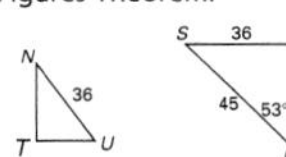

3. Suppose $\triangle ABC \sim \triangle XYZ$, with a ratio of similitude of 3.5. If $BC = 2$ and $m\angle Y = 15$, what other angle measures and lengths can be determined using the Similar Figures Theorem?

TEACHING AID 170
Lesson 12-6

Additional Examples 1-3

1. $RSTU \sim WXYZ$. Give the ratios of the perimeters and the areas of these rectangles.

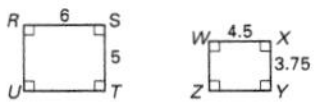

2. Hexagons *ABCDEF* and *UVWXYZ* are similar with ratio of similitude $\frac{4}{5}$. If *ABCDEF* has area 56 square units, what is the area of *UVWXYZ*?

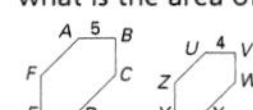

3. Two toy trucks are shown. Each is similar to the same type of truck, so they are similar to each other. The larger toy is 18 cm long, and the smaller is 6 cm long.

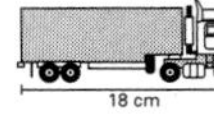

   a. How do the heights of the toy trucks compare?
   b. How do the areas of the floors of the holds (where the cargo is stored) compare?
   c. How do the volumes of the holds compare?

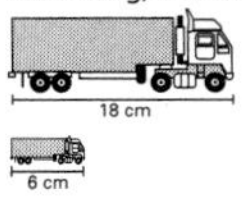

Chapter Opener 12

Pacing

All lessons in this chapter are designed to be covered in one day. At the end of the chapter, you should plan to spend 1 day to review the Progress Self-Test, 1 day for the Chapter Review, and 1 day for a test. You may wish to spend a day on projects, and you may need another day for activities and quizzes. Therefore, this chapter should take 10–12 days. We strongly advise that you not spend more than 13 days on this chapter; the ideas are reviewed in the next chapter.

Using Pages 684–685

A number of vocations and hobbies are mentioned in the reading. These can provide the focus for a discussion of similarity. You might begin with hobbies and ask if any students have ever collected dolls or figurines. How big were these dolls or figurines? How did their sizes compare to the actual sizes of the people they represented? Then ask if any students have built model planes, cars, trains, or ships. Again ask how big these models were. Do the students know how the size of each model related to the actual size of the object it represented? If students still have the original packaging for their models at home, they may be able to find a quite precise answer to this question on the box or in the instructions. Ask if any students have a pair of binoculars. If so, ask, "What is its power?" The point of the discussion should be that similarity is a very important concept and that similar figures can be found everywhere.

At this time, you also should ask if students have studied size changes before and, if so, elicit what they

684

Chapter 12 Overview

This is the first of two chapters that deal with similar figures. This chapter addresses the general concepts of similarity that apply to all figures. Chapter 13 details the concepts that apply specifically to triangles, together with their applications to trigonometry.

If several students were asked to draw a rectangle with length 6 and width 3, their rectangles would not necessarily be congruent, because they could use any unit of measure. However, their rectangles all would be similar. All the formulas and relationships students have learned about figures—area formulas, theorems about midpoints, the Pythagorean Theorem, and so on—will apply in these figures. In this sense, Euclidean geometry can be thought of as the study of similar figures.

When geometry is developed with transformations, similarity becomes analogous to congruence. While the reflection is the transformation from which the properties of all congruence transformations are derived, the *size change* or *size transformation* is basic to the study of similarity transformations. Lesson 12-1 introduces this transformation on the coordinate plane, naming it S_k, and deduces two of its properties. Lesson 12-2 and the In-class Activity preceding it show students how to do size changes without coordinates.

SIMILARITY

Figures with different sizes but the same shape are found both in fun and serious pursuits. Models of planes, cars, trains, and ships, and dolls and dollhouses are scale models of real figures. Clothes designers, inventors, architects, and city planners use scale models to see how an object will look before the full-size version is made. Scientists magnify small things like insects or the atom, or make models of large objects, like Earth or our solar system, in order to study them.

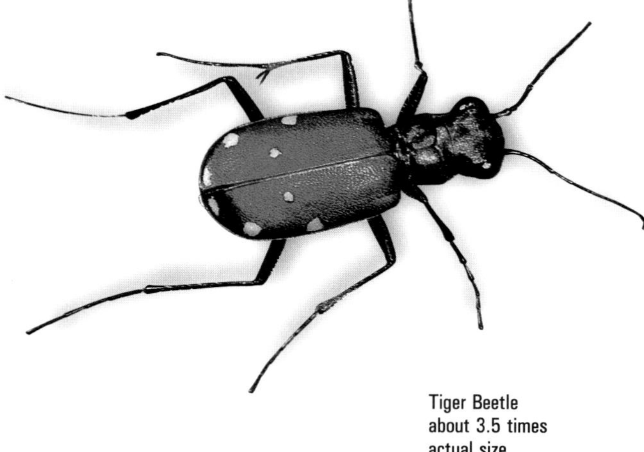

Tiger Beetle
about 3.5 times
actual size

Figures with the same shape (but not necessarily the same size) are *similar figures*. The concept of *similarity* is as important in analyzing figures as the concept of congruence. In this chapter, you will learn how to draw similar figures. Then you will study their basic properties and the transformations relating them, and see a few of their many applications.

remember about these changes. They may remember that a size change of magnitude k and center (0, 0) can be performed on the coordinate plane by multiplying the coordinates of each point by k. This discussion leads naturally into Lesson 12-1.

Photo Connections

These pictures show ways in which we use similarity—we enlarge small objects and we reduce large objects. The study of similar figures is the study of the relationships between figures and their *expansion* and *contraction* images.

The photo collage makes real-world connections to the content of the chapter: similarity.

Ship Model: In the past, scale models were made to aid in the building of ships. Today, ship designers make and test models to see how a ship will react in various conditions.

Microscope: In an optical microscope, light rays that shine through an object are refracted by lenses to enlarge the appearance of the object.

Vitamin C: Most of us know what vitamin C is and how to get it in our daily diet. But do we know what it looks like? A microscope shows vitamin C as a vivid array of color.

Telescope: Stars might be many times the size of the earth, but without telescopes we would know very little about them.

Common Fungus: Like vitamin C, common fungus looks very different when seen under a microscope.

Chapter 12 Projects

At this time, you might want to have students look over the projects on pages 729–730.

The properties of these transformations are summarized in Lesson 12-3. The preservation properties of size changes are like those of reflections, except that distances are multiplied by a constant. As a result, the ratios of lengths of images and their preimages are equal, forming proportions. Solving proportions is reviewed in Lesson 12-4. At this point, students have studied similar figures for almost a week without formalization. They are ready for a formal definition, which is given in Lesson 12-5. As with the definition of congruence, the definition of similarity allows for similar figures of any shape. Lesson 12-6 covers the Fundamental Theorem of Similarity, which may be the most important theorem in geometry. It gives the relations among length, perimeter, area, and volume in similar figures.

Lesson 12-7 presents a very nice application of this theorem—why there cannot be humans twice the height of normal humans. Many students do not understand Lesson 12-6 until they see this concrete application.

Students who have studied UCSMP *Transition Mathematics* or UCSMP *Algebra* will have studied size changes on the coordinate plane and will have solved proportions using corresponding sides in similar figures.

Lesson 12-1

Objectives

G Perform and analyze size transformations on figures in the coordinate plane.

Resources

From the ***Teacher's Resource File***

- Lesson Master 12-1A or 12-1B
- Answer Master 12-1
- Teaching Aids
  105 Graph paper
  157 Warm-up
  160 Question 11

Additional Resources

- Visuals for Teaching Aids 105, 157, 160

Teaching Lesson 12-1

Warm-up

Use the picture on page 685 and a centimeter ruler. **Figure appears smaller in Teacher's Edition than in Pupil's Edition. Measurements given correspond to figures given in Pupil's Edition.**

Ignoring the legs, what is the actual width and length of the body of the insect? **Width ≈ .5 cm; length: ≈ 1.3 cm**

Notes on Reading

Before beginning the lesson, you may want to review the definition of *transformation* and the notation used for transformations, the preservation properties of reflections, and the procedure for reflecting complicated figures.

LESSON

12-1 *The Transformation S_k*

Relative size. *Many individual portraits are sized for the wallets, desktops, and photo albums of relatives and friends.*

A Specific Example

The transformations in this lesson are easy to do on a coordinate plane. You need only multiply the coordinates of points on the figure by a fixed number.

Example

In pentagon *ABCDE*, *A* = (-9, 15), *B* = (-15, -6), *C* = (0, 3), *D* = (12, 0), and *E* = (3, 12). Describe the result when all the coordinates of the points of this figure are multiplied by $\frac{2}{3}$.

Solution

First draw *ABCDE*. Then multiply the coordinates of the vertices of *ABCDE* by $\frac{2}{3}$. The resulting five image points *A'*, *B'*, *C'*, *D'*, and *E'* are connected below.

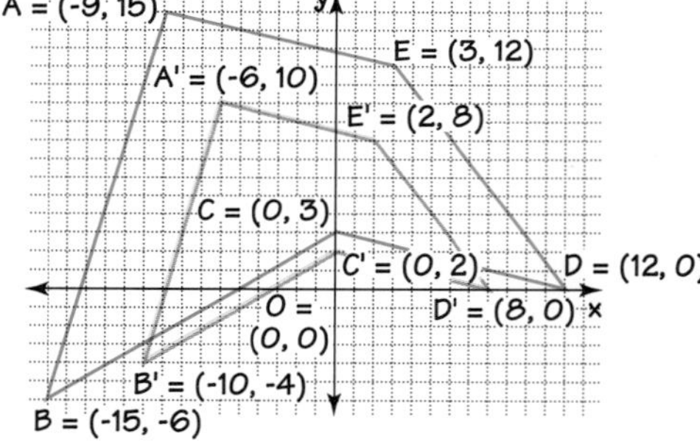

Lesson 12-1 Overview

Broad Goals This lesson introduces the transformation S_k that maps (*x*, *y*) onto (*kx*, *ky*).

Perspective Outside mathematics, there are two common paper-and-pencil methods for changing the size of a figure. One method is to draw a grid of squares over the figure; then, on a second grid of different-sized squares, redraw each part of the figure to the appropriate size, square by square. The second method is to project the first figure onto a flat surface and trace the image.

The work of this lesson is related to the first of these methods. However, instead of multiplying the size of the grid squares by the number of times you want to enlarge or reduce the figure, you multiply each coordinate of the figure by *k*. The transformation that maps (*x*, *y*) onto (*kx*, *ky*) is the size change of magnitude *k* with center (0, 0). In this lesson, though, it is not called a size change; it is called S_k, and students are asked to explore its properties.

The advantage of using S_k is the ease with which the size of a figure can be changed and the speed with which certain properties can be deduced. Proved in this lesson is the fact that under S_k, distances between image points are *k* times distances between their corresponding preimages. This is the

▶ To describe the result, examine the preimage and the image sides closely. You could write the following:

(1) Image and preimage sides seem to be parallel.

(2) Image sides appear to be $\frac{2}{3}$ as long as the preimage sides.

Closer examination gives something else.

(3) A point, its preimage, and the origin are collinear.

Do you see anything else?

The Example describes a transformation in which the image of (x, y) is $\left(\frac{2}{3}x, \frac{2}{3}y\right)$. This transformation is denoted $S_{\frac{2}{3}}$. To verify the first property of $S_{\frac{2}{3}}$ found in the Example, you can focus on a segment and its image, say $\overline{AE}$ and $\overline{A'E'}$. Using slopes, it is easy to show that $\overline{AE} \parallel \overline{A'E'}$.

$$\text{slope of } \overline{AE} = \frac{12-15}{3--9} = \frac{-3}{12} = -\frac{1}{4}$$
$$\text{slope of } \overline{A'E'} = \frac{8-10}{2--6} = \frac{-2}{8} = -\frac{1}{4}$$

Since the slopes are equal, $\overline{AE}$ and $\overline{A'E'}$ are parallel.

In the following Activity, the image of (x, y) is $(4x, 4y)$. The properties numbered (1) and (2) in the solution to the Example can be verified for this case.

Activity

On the coordinate plane below, $\overline{M'N'}$ is the image of $\overline{MN}$ under S_4.

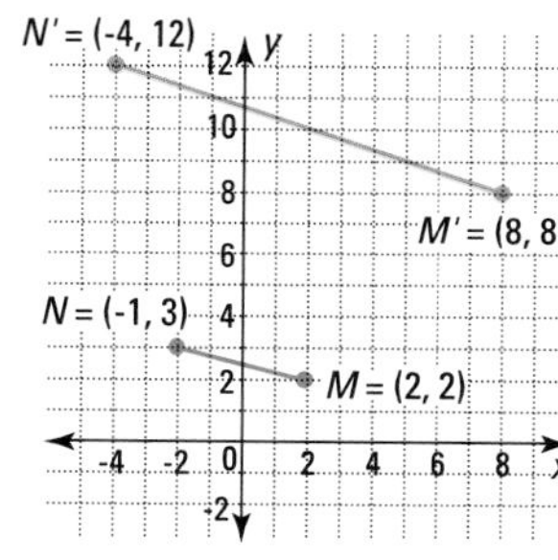

a. By calculating slopes, verify that $\overline{M'N'} \parallel \overline{MN}$.

b. By calculating distances, verify that $M'N' = 4 \cdot MN$.

Activity

a) slope of $\overline{M'N'} = \frac{12-8}{-4-8} = -\frac{1}{3}$; slope of $\overline{MN} = \frac{3-2}{-1-2} = -\frac{1}{3}$. Thus $\overline{M'N'} \parallel \overline{MN}$.

b) $M'N' = \sqrt{(12-8)^2 + (-4-8)^2} = 4\sqrt{10}$; $MN = \sqrt{(3-2)^2 + (-1-2)^2} = \sqrt{10}$. Thus, $M'N' = 4 \cdot MN$.

Properties of the Transformation S_k

In general, the transformation which maps (x, y) onto (kx, ky) is denoted by the symbol S_k. The number k is called the **magnitude** of S_k. Any number but zero can be the magnitude, but in this book $k > 0$ unless otherwise stated. (In Question 24, you are asked to explore what happens when k is negative.) The transformation S_k has many important properties, all of which can be proved using coordinate geometry.

Have students record the results of the **Activity** for use with **Question 4** on page 689.

This lesson uses coordinate methods from Chapter 11. The proof on page 688 is straightforward, but it may be difficult if students' algebra skills are rusty.

Additional Examples

1. In quadrilateral $RSTU$, $R = (-5, 3)$, $S = (4, 2)$, $T = (0, 0)$, and $U = (-1, -3)$. Describe the result when all coordinates of the points on this figure are multiplied by 2. Sample: (1) Image and preimage sides either are collinear or seem to be parallel. (2) Image sides appear to be twice as long as the preimage sides. (3) A point, its preimage, and the origin are collinear.
2. In $\triangle WXY$, $W = (3, 0)$, $X = (5, 0)$, and $Y = (-1, 2)$.
   a. Find the image of $\triangle WXY$ under S_3. $W' = (9, 0)$, $X' = (15, 0)$, $Y' = (-3, 6)$
   b. How many times as long as $\overline{XY}$ is $\overline{X'Y'}$? 3
   c. How many times as great as the area of $\triangle WXY$ is the area of $\triangle W'X'Y'$? 9
   d. Prove that $\overline{XY} \parallel \overline{X'Y'}$. The lines that contain $\overline{XY}$ and $\overline{X'Y'}$ each have slope $-\frac{1}{3}$, so the segments are parallel.

fundamental property of size changes, and S_k could be thought of as multiplying the lengths of sides of the squares in the grid by k. Also deduced is that a line is parallel to its image under S_k.

Students who have studied earlier UCSMP courses will have encountered S_k as a picture of multiplication by k. Beginning with a preimage on a coordinate plane, they will have multiplied the coordinates of key points by a nonzero number and graphed the image. Students have been shown graphically that multiplication by a negative reverses sign, as seen in cases where k is negative and the image is "upside-down" (rotated 180°). They will have learned the term *size change* as a name for this transformation.

Note that we cannot prove S_k is a size change until the next lesson, because a definition of size change is needed first.

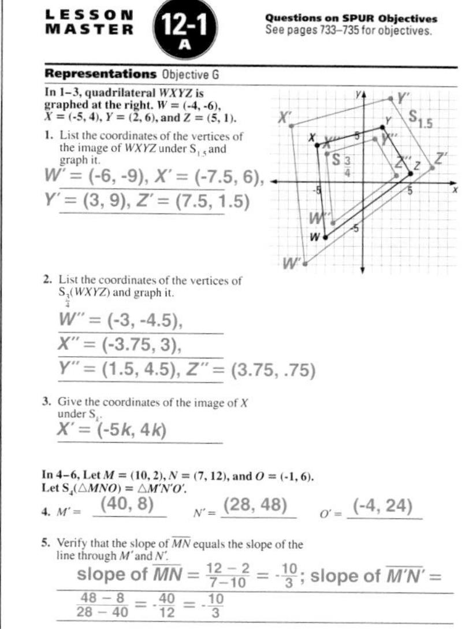

LESSON MASTER 12-1 A

Questions on SPUR Objectives
See pages 733–735 for objectives.

Representations Objective G

In 1–3, quadrilateral $WXYZ$ is graphed at the right. $W = (-4, -6)$, $X = (-5, 4)$, $Y = (2, 6)$, and $Z = (5, 1)$.

1. List the coordinates of the vertices of the image of $WXYZ$ under $S_{1.5}$ and graph it.
   $W' = (-6, -9)$, $X' = (-7.5, 6)$, $Y' = (3, 9)$, $Z' = (7.5, 1.5)$
2. List the coordinates of the vertices of $S_{\frac{3}{4}}(WXYZ)$ and graph it.
   $W'' = (-3, -4.5)$, $X'' = (-3.75, 3)$, $Y'' = (1.5, 4.5)$, $Z'' = (3.75, .75)$
3. Give the coordinates of the image of X under S_k.
   $X' = (-5k, 4k)$

In 4–6, Let $M = (10, 2)$, $N = (7, 12)$, and $O = (-1, 6)$. Let $S_4(\triangle MNO) = \triangle M'N'O'$.

4. $M' =$ (40, 8) $N' =$ (28, 48) $O' =$ (-4, 24)
5. Verify that the slope of $\overline{MN}$ equals the slope of the line through M' and N'.
   slope of $\overline{MN} = \frac{12-2}{7-10} = -\frac{10}{3}$; slope of $\overline{M'N'} = \frac{48-8}{28-40} = \frac{40}{-12} = -\frac{10}{3}$
6. Use the distance Formula to verify that $N'O' = 4 \cdot NO$.
   $NO = \sqrt{(7+1)^2 + (12-6)^2} = \sqrt{8^2 + 6^2} = 10$; $N'O' = \sqrt{(28+4)^2 + (48-24)^2} = \sqrt{32^2 + 24^2} = 40 = 4 \cdot 10 = 4 \cdot NO$

Notes on Questions

Question 11 Teaching Aid 160 contains this question. The idea of similarity is much more vivid with a complicated figure than with a simple figure like a triangle. Ask: The sides of the image are how many times as long as the sides of the preimage? [2 times] The area of the image is how many times as great as the area of the preimage? [4 times] How do the measures of corresponding angles compare? [They are equal.]

(Notes on Questions continue on page 690.)

Follow-up for Lesson 12-1

Practice

For more questions on SPUR Objectives, use **Lesson Master 12-1A** (shown on page 687) or **Lesson Master 12-1B** (shown on pages 688–689).

Assessment

Written Communication Have each student draw a polygon on a set of coordinate axes and identify a transformation S_k, where $k > 0$. Then have students graph their polygon under S_k and explain how the transformation was obtained. [Students graph a polygon under the transformation S_k.]

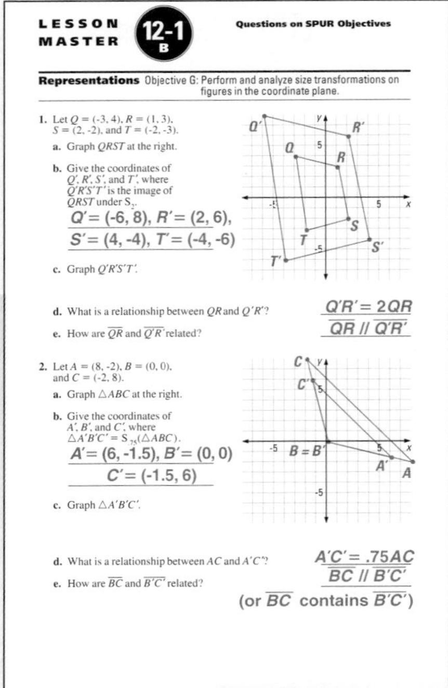

LESSON MASTER 12-1 B Questions on SPUR Objectives

Representations Objective G: Perform and analyze size transformations on figures in the coordinate plane.

1. Let $Q = (-3, 4)$, $R = (1, 3)$, $S = (2, -2)$, and $T = (-2, -3)$.
   a. Graph $QRST$ at the right.
   b. Give the coordinates of Q', R', S', and T', where $Q'R'S'T'$ is the image of $QRST$ under S_2.
      $Q' = (-6, 8)$, $R' = (2, 6)$, $S' = (4, -4)$, $T' = (-4, -6)$
   c. Graph $Q'R'S'T'$.
   d. What is a relationship between QR and $Q'R'$? $Q'R' = 2QR$
   e. How are $\overline{QR}$ and $\overline{Q'R'}$ related? $\overline{QR} \parallel \overline{Q'R'}$

2. Let $A = (8, -2)$, $B = (0, 0)$, and $C = (-2, 8)$.
   a. Graph $\triangle ABC$ at the right.
   b. Give the coordinates of A', B', and C', where $\triangle A'B'C' = S_{.75}(\triangle ABC)$.
      $A' = (6, -1.5)$, $B' = (0, 0)$, $C' = (-1.5, 6)$
   c. Graph $\triangle A'B'C'$.
   d. What is a relationship between AC and $A'C'$? $A'C' = .75AC$
   e. How are $\overline{BC}$ and $\overline{B'C'}$ related? $\overline{BC} \parallel \overline{B'C'}$ (or $\overline{BC}$ contains $\overline{B'C'}$)

Properties of S_k Theorem
Let S_k be the transformation mapping (x, y) onto (kx, ky). Then under S_k,
(1) a line and its image are parallel, and
(2) the distance between two image points is k times the distance between their preimages.

Proof

Given: $P = (a, b)$, $Q = (c, d)$,
$S_k(P) = P' = (ka, kb)$, and $S_k(Q) = Q' = (kc, kd)$.

To prove: (1) $\overleftrightarrow{PQ} \parallel \overleftrightarrow{P'Q'}$.
(2) $P'Q' = k \cdot PQ$.

Drawing:

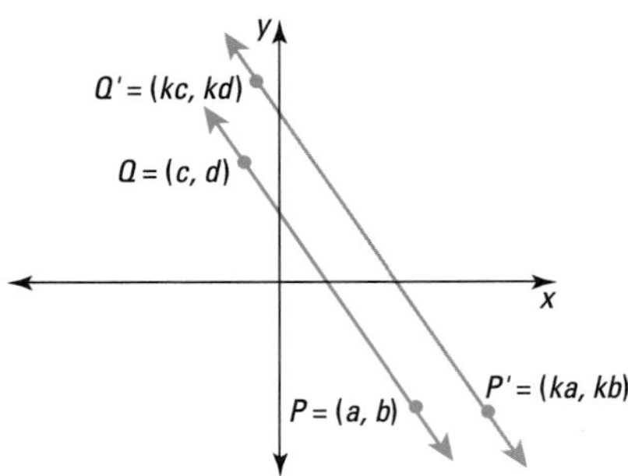

Argument:

(1) $\overleftrightarrow{P'Q'}$ is parallel to $\overleftrightarrow{PQ}$ if the slopes are the same.

slope of $\overleftrightarrow{P'Q'} = \frac{kd - kb}{kc - ka} = \frac{k(d - b)}{k(c - a)} = \frac{d - b}{c - a}$

slope of $\overleftrightarrow{PQ} = \frac{d - b}{c - a}$

Thus $\overleftrightarrow{PQ} \parallel \overleftrightarrow{P'Q'}$.

(2) The goal is to show that $P'Q' = k \cdot PQ$.
From the Distance Formula,

$$PQ = \sqrt{(c - a)^2 + (d - b)^2}.$$

Also from the Distance Formula,

$P'Q' = \sqrt{(kc - ka)^2 + (kd - kb)^2}$.	
$= \sqrt{(k(c - a))^2 + (k(d - b))^2}$	Distributive Property
$= \sqrt{k^2(c - a)^2 + k^2(d - b)^2}$	Power of a Product
$= \sqrt{k^2((c - a)^2 + (d - b)^2)}$	Distributive Property
$= \sqrt{k^2}\sqrt{(c - a)^2 + (d - b)^2}$	Square Root of a Product
$= k\sqrt{(c - a)^2 + (d - b)^2}$	Since $k > 0$, $\sqrt{k^2} = k$.
$= k \cdot PQ$	Substitution

Optional Activities

Writing

Materials: Graph paper or **Teaching Aid 105**

After you define S_k, have students perform other transformations. Have them draw polygons, each on a separate set of coordinate axes. Have them find the images of each polygon under S_k for $k = 1$, $k = 1.5$, and $k = .5$. Then have them write as many conjectures as they can about the results.

Adapting to Individual Needs

Challenge

Have students do the following.

1. Investigate $S_3 \circ T(F)$ and $T \circ S_3(F)$, where F is any figure and T is (a) a reflection over the x-axis, (b) a rotation of 90°, and (c) a translation 3 units up and 4 units right. [In the first two cases, $S_3 \circ T(F) \cong T \circ S_3(F)$]
2. Write a conjecture about the composition of size changes and isometries. [Conjectures will vary.]

3) $BC = \sqrt{(-15-0)^2 + (-6-3)^2} = 3\sqrt{34}$; $B'C' = \sqrt{(-10-0)^2 + (-4-2)^2} = 2\sqrt{34} = \frac{2}{3} \cdot BC$

4a) slope of $\overline{M'N'} = \frac{12-8}{-4-8} = -\frac{1}{3}$; slope of $\overline{MN} = \frac{3-2}{-1-2} = -\frac{1}{3}$. Thus, $\overline{M'N'} \parallel \overline{MN}$.

b) $M'N' = \sqrt{(12-8)^2 + (-4-8)^2} = 4\sqrt{10}$; $MN = \sqrt{(3-2)^2 + (-1-2)^2} = \sqrt{10}$. Thus, $M'N' = 4 \cdot MN$.

QUESTIONS

Covering the Reading

1. Name four occupations which use scale models.
   Samples: clothing designers, inventors, architects, city planners

In 2 and 3, refer to the Example.

2. Verify that $\overline{B'C'} \parallel \overline{BC}$ by finding their slopes.
   slope of $\overline{BC} = \frac{3}{5}$; slope of $\overline{B'C'} = \frac{3}{5}$
3. Verify that $B'C' = \frac{2}{3}BC$ by using the Distance Formula. See left.
4. Show your answers to the Activity in this lesson. See left.
5. Let $J = (5, -8)$, $K = (-6, 0)$, and $L = (-10, -4)$.
   a. Graph $\triangle JKL$ and its image under S_3. See margin.
   b. Describe what S_3 does to $\triangle JKL$. See margin.
6. a. S_k is the transformation which maps (x, y) onto __?__. (kx, ky)
   b. The number k is the __?__ of S_k. magnitude
7. Name two properties of S_k. A line and its image are parallel, and the distance between two image points is k times the distance between their preimages.
8. A segment has endpoints (ka, kb) and (kc, kd).
   a. What is its slope? $\frac{d-b}{c-a}$
   b. What is its length? $k\sqrt{(a-c)^2 + (b-d)^2}$

Applying the Mathematics

In 9 and 10, let O be the origin and A be the point $(-2, 7)$. Let $A' = S_3(A)$.

9. a. Give the coordinates of A'. $(-6, 21)$
   b. By calculating distances, show that $OA + AA' = OA'$. See margin.
   c. *True or false.* A is between O and A'. Justify your answer. See margin.
10. Justify the conclusion that $OA' = 3 \cdot OA$.
   $OA = \sqrt{53}$ and $OA' = 3\sqrt{53}$. By substitution, $OA' = 3 \cdot OA$.
11. An artist wished to draw the tiger beetle pictured on page 685 at double its actual size. So the artist drew an outline of the beetle at actual size onto graph paper as shown at the right. Then the coordinates of key points on the insect were multiplied by 2 and the image drawn. Repeat what the artist did, using your own paper. See margin.

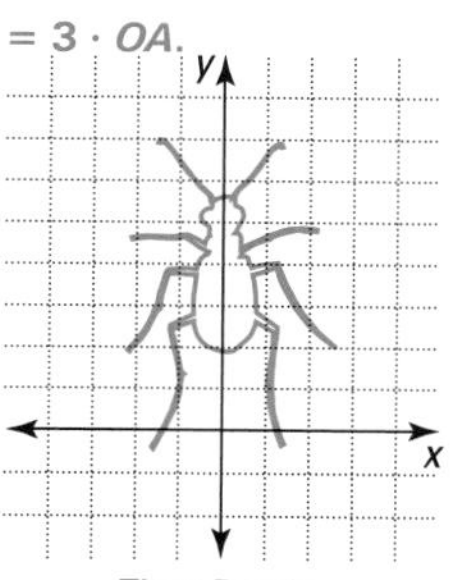

Tiger Beetle
actual size

12. a. Find $S_1(\triangle ABC)$, where $A = (4, -3)$, $B = (6, 1)$, and $C = (-2, 8)$. a) $\triangle ABC$
   b. What is the image of (x, y) under S_1? (x, y)
   c. Describe S_1. S_1 maps every preimage onto itself.

Project Update Project 3, *Models of Everyday Objects*, on page 729, relates to the content of this lesson.

Additional Answers, continued

11.

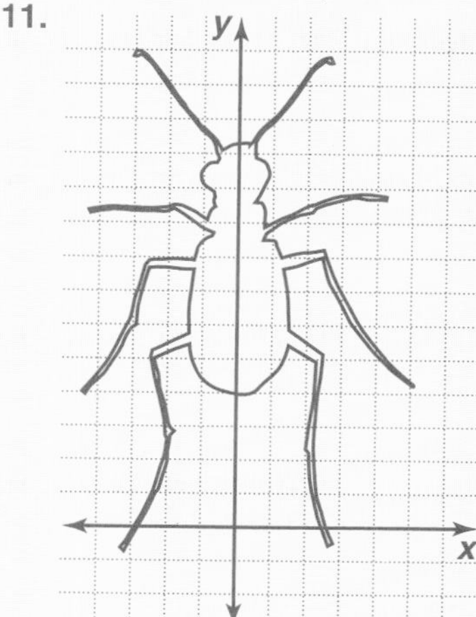

Additional Answers

5a.

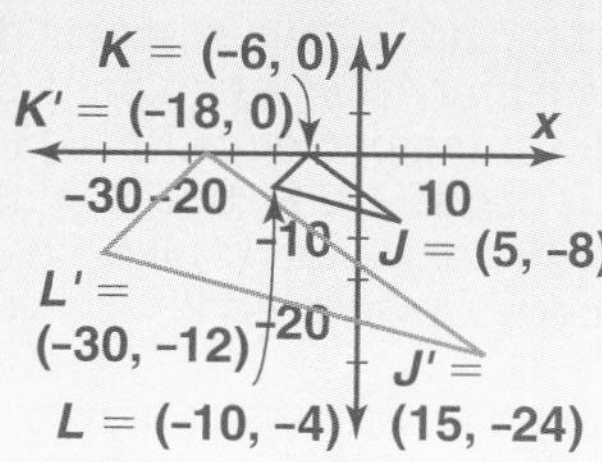

5b. The sides of $\triangle J'K'L'$ are parallel to and 3 times the length of the corresponding sides of $\triangle JKL$. Each preimage and its image are collinear with the origin.

9b. $OA = \sqrt{53}$, $AA' = 2\sqrt{53}$, $OA' = 3\sqrt{53}$. Thus, $OA + AA' = OA'$.

c. By the Properties of S_k Theorem, the slopes of $\overline{OA}$ and $\overline{OA'}$ are the same. Also, $OA' > OA$. Thus, A is between O and A'.

▶ **LESSON MASTER 12-1B** *page 2*

3. Let $H = (-2, -4)$, $K = (1, 3)$, and $W = (4, -4)$, and let $S_{2.5}(\triangle HKW) = H'K'W'$.
   a. Give the coordinates of H', K', and W'.
   $H' = (-5, -10)$, $K' = (2.5, 7.5)$, $W' = (10, -10)$
   b. What is a relationship between HW and $H'W'$? $H'W' = 2.5 \cdot HW$
   c. Use the Distance Formula to verify your answer to Part **b**.
   $HW = \sqrt{(-2-4)^2 + (-4+4)^2} = \sqrt{36} = 6$; $H'W' = \sqrt{(-5-10)^2 + (-10+10)^2} = \sqrt{225} = 15 = 2.5 \cdot HW$
   d. How are $\overline{KW}$ and $\overline{K'W'}$ related? $\overline{KW} \parallel \overline{K'W'}$
   e. Use slopes to verify your answer to Part **d**.
   slope of $\overline{KW} = \frac{3+4}{1-4} = -\frac{7}{3}$; slope of $\overline{K'W'} = \frac{7.5+10}{2.5-10} = -\frac{7}{3}$
   f. What is the image of (m, n) under $S_{2.5}$? $(2.5m, 2.5n)$
4. Let $E = (a, b)$ and $F = (p, q)$, and let $S_k(EF) = E'F'$.
   a. Give the coordinates of $E' = S_k(E)$ and $F' = S_k(F)$.
   $E' = (ka, kb)$; $F' = (kp, kq)$
   b. How do EF and $E'F'$ compare? $E'F' = k \cdot EF$
   c. Use the Distance Formula to verify your answer to Part **b**.
   $EF = \sqrt{(a-p)^2 + (b-q)^2}$;
   $E'F' = \sqrt{(ka-kp)^2 + (kb-kq)^2} = \sqrt{k^2(a-p)^2 + k^2(b-q)^2} = k \cdot EF$
   d. How are $\overline{EF}$ and $\overline{E'F'}$ related? $\overline{EF} \parallel \overline{E'F'}$
   e. Use slopes to verify your answer in Part **d**.
   slope of $\overline{EF} = \frac{b-q}{a-p}$; slope of $\overline{E'F'} = \frac{kb-kq}{ka-kp} = \frac{k(b-q)}{k(a-p)} = \frac{b-q}{a-p}$

Notes on Questions

Question 13 This is an important problem in calculating scaled values and should be discussed.

Question 16 This question is intended to help students make the connection between congruence and similarity.

Question 18 The analogous theorem for size transformations is found in Lesson 12-3.

Question 19 Music Connection Any combination of tones played simultaneously is a chord. The dominant-seventh chord is common in western music. It consists of a triad, that is, the first, third, and fifth notes of a given tonality, topped with a minor seventh. The first note is five notes up from the key in which the musician is playing. Thus, the dominant seventh of C major is G-B-D-F; G is five notes up from the keynote C, B and D are the other notes of the G major chord, and F is the dominant seventh.

Questions 21–22 These questions begin a three-day review of solving algebraic proportions, in preparation for Lesson 12-4.

Question 24 In general, S_{-k} is the composite of S_k and a rotation of 180°. Notice that both S_k and S_{-k} preserve orientation. Many students think that S_{-k} switches orientation.

Additional Answers

14c. $QP = \sqrt{(2 - -3)^2 + (-8 - 12)^2 + (0 - 4)^2}$
So $QP = 21$; $Q'P' = \sqrt{(10 - -15)^2 + (-40 - 60)^2 + (0 - 20)^2} = 105 = 5 \cdot QP$

16a. Sample argument:

Conclusions	Justifications
1. $\angle KLM \cong \angle GFM$	// Lines ⇒ AIA ≅ Thm.
2. $\angle LMK \cong \angle FMG$	Vertical Angles Thm.
3. $\overline{LM} \cong \overline{FM}$	def. of midpoint
4. $\triangle KLM \cong \triangle GFM$	ASA Congruence Thm. (steps 1, 2, 3)

b. Since $\triangle KLM \cong \triangle GFM$, by the CPCF Theorem, $MG = MK$.

17. Every isometry preserves angle measure, betweenness, collinearity (lines), and distance (lengths of segments).

13. At the right is a scale drawing of the side of a cabin. If each unit on the paper is $\frac{1}{8}$ inch and the drawing is $\frac{1}{96}$ actual size, what is the height of the actual cabin? 144 inches or 12 feet

14. In three dimensions, S_k is the transformation mapping (x, y, z) onto (kx, ky, kz).
 a. Find the image of $P = (-3, 12, 4)$ under S_5. Call this point P'. $P' = (-15, 60, 20)$
 b. Find the image of $Q = (2, -8, 0)$ under S_5. Call this point Q'. b) $Q' = (10, -40, 0)$
 c. Using the Three-Dimension Distance Formula, verify that $Q'P' = 5 \cdot QP$. See margin.

15. At the right is a convenient location for any triangle $\triangle PQR$. Find $S_2(\triangle PQR)$.
$P' = (0, 0)$, $R' = (2a, 0)$, $Q' = (2b, 2c)$

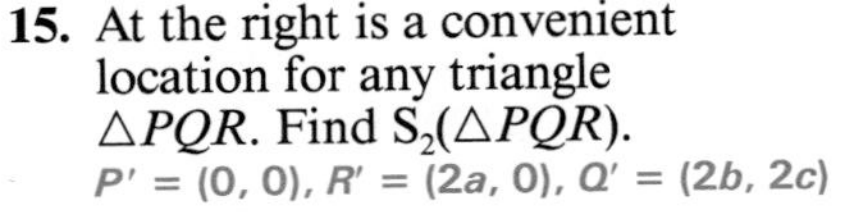

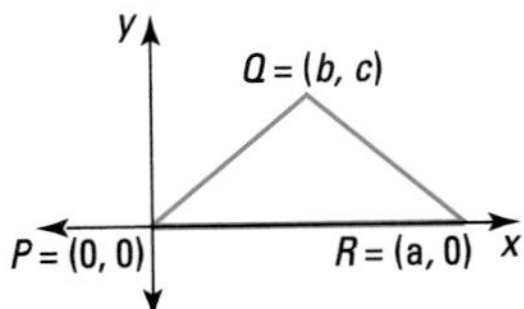

Review

16. In the figure at the left, $\overleftrightarrow{KL} \parallel \overleftrightarrow{FG}$ and M is the midpoint of $\overline{LF}$.
 a. Write a proof argument which shows that $\triangle KLM \cong \triangle GFM$.
 b. Write a proof argument which shows that $MG = MK$. *(Lesson 7-3)*
 a, b) See margin.

17. What are the *A-B-C-D* properties of isometries? *(Lesson 4-7)* See margin.

18. State the Figure Reflection Theorem. *(Lesson 4-2)* See margin.

19. The quadrilateral CEGB♭ at the left joins the four notes which make up the *dominant-7th chord* of the key of F. Rotate the quadrilateral to find the notes which make up the dominant-7th chord of the key of A. *(Lesson 3-2)* E, G♯, B, D

20. Draw this situation: B is between A and C and $AC = 5 \cdot AB$. *(Lesson 1-8)* See left.

In 21–23, solve. *(Previous course)*

21. $\frac{2}{9} = \frac{3}{x}$ $x = 13.5$

22. $\frac{2y - 5}{5} = \frac{3y + 14}{8}$ $y = 110$

23. $AB - 9 = \frac{3}{4} \cdot AB$ (Here, AB is the length of $\overline{AB}$.) $AB = 36$

20) A B C

Exploration

24. Use $\triangle JKL$ of Question 5.
 a. Find $S_k(\triangle JKL)$ where $k = -3$. $J' = (-15, 24)$, $K' = (18, 0)$, $L' = (30, 12)$
 b. Describe what S_{-3} does to $\triangle JKL$. See left.
 c. Repeat parts **a** and **b**, but let $k = -\frac{1}{2}$. See left.
 d. Write some conjectures about S_k when k is negative.
 S_k makes a figure whose sides are $-k$ times as long and rotated 180° about the origin.

24b) Its side measures are multiplied by 3, and it is rotated 180° about the origin.

c) $J' = (-\frac{5}{2}, 4)$, $K' = (3, 0)$, $L' = (5, 2)$. Its side measures are multiplied by $\frac{1}{2}$, and it is rotated 180° about the origin.

18. If a figure is determined by certain points, then its reflection image is the corresponding figure determined by the reflection images of those points.

Setting Up Lesson 12-2

Materials If you plan to have students do Activity 1 in *Optional Activities* on page 692, they will need to bring photographs to class along with their negatives. Rubber bands are needed for the explanation given in *English Language Development*.

Students will need an automatic drawer for **Question 26** on page 697.

Introducing Lesson 12-2

Drawing Size-Change Images

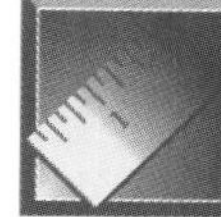

IN-CLASS ACTIVITY

Work on this activity with another student. Choose different centers. Both of you will need rulers.

Here is a way to change the size of a figure without using coordinates. At the right is a face made up of segments, arcs, and dots. Suppose you wish to draw a face like this one, but with corresponding lengths 3 times as long. Here is how to do this *size change of magnitude* 3.

To begin, trace the above figure or draw another like it. Now choose a point O in the plane to be the *center* of this size transformation. O can be anywhere in the plane, but here, for clarity, we select O above and to the left of the face. Then choose and label some key points on the figure. Key points are endpoints of segments and centers of arcs. We have chosen and labeled points A through I.

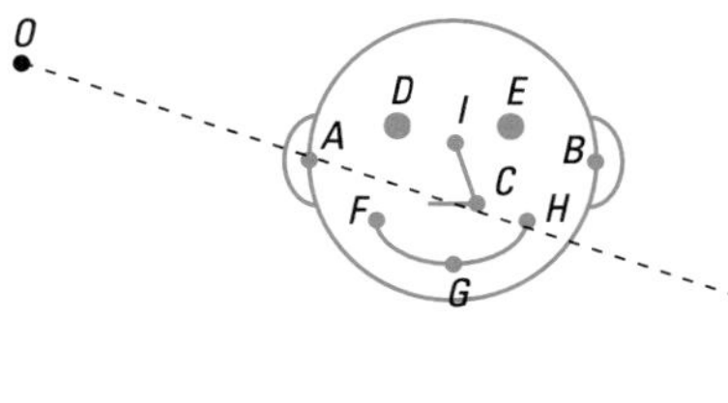

Find the image of each point. Here is how to find point A.

Step 1: Lightly draw ray $\overrightarrow{OA}$.
Step 2: Measure OA.
Step 3: Locate the point A' on $\overrightarrow{OA}$ so that $OA' = 3 \cdot OA$. That is, A' is 3 times as far from the center as A is. Point A' is the image of A.

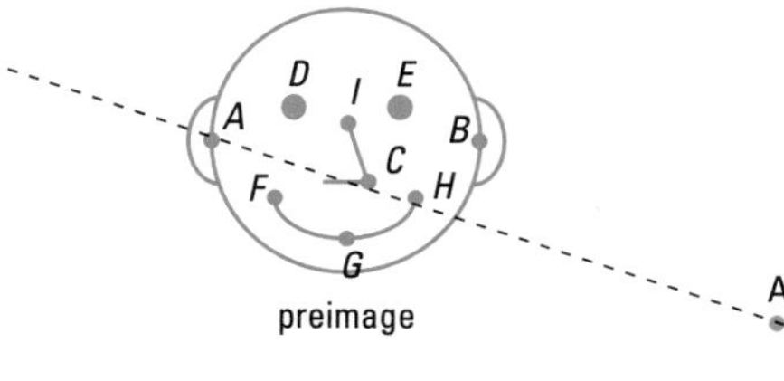

$OA' = 3 \cdot OA$

Repeat Steps 1–3 for the points B through I. Then connect the image points in the same way the preimages are connected. See margin.

In-class Activity

Resources

From the ***Teacher's Resource File***
- Answer Master 12-2
- Teaching Aid 161: Drawing Size-Change Images

Additional Resources
- Visual for Teaching Aid 161

This In-class Activity asks students to draw the size-change image of a figure without using coordinates.

In Step 3, some students may draw the image of A so that AA' (the distance between preimage and image) is 3 times OA. This results in an image under a size change of magnitude 4. Emphasize that all measurements to find images are taken from the center O of the size change.

Have students measure OA' and OA on this page so they see that OA' is in fact 3 times OA. **Teaching Aid 161** can be used in the explanation.

Have students record the results of In-class Activity for use with **Question 1** on page 694.

TEACHING AID 161
Lesson 12-2

Drawing Size-Change Images

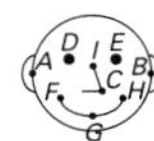

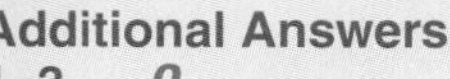

Additional Answers

1–3.

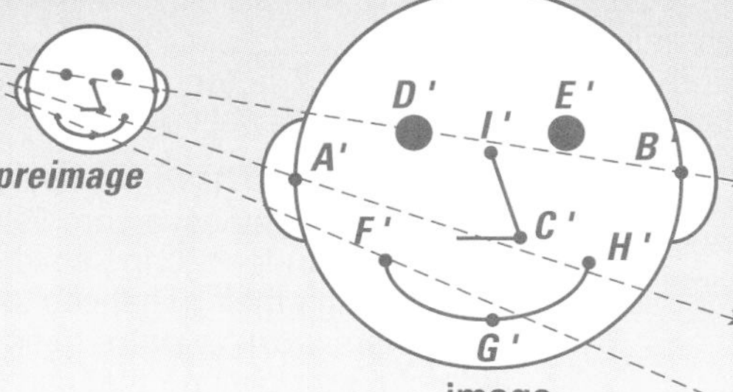

Lesson 12-2

Objectives
A Draw size-transformation images of figures.
C Recognize and apply properties of size transformations.

Resources
From the ***Teacher's Resource File***
- Lesson Master 12-2A or 12-2B
- Answer Master 12-2
- Teaching Aids
  157 Warm-up
  162 Additional Examples
  163 Questions 4–5, 10
  164 Questions 11–12, 19
- Technology Sourcebook, Computer Master 21

Additional Resources
- Visuals for Teaching Aids 157, 162–164
- GeoExplorer or other automatic drawers
- Photographs and their negatives
- Rubber bands

Teaching Lesson 12-2

Warm-up
Name as many professions as you can in which it might be useful to make enlargements or reductions of drawings or photographs. **Answers will vary.**

Notes on Reading
Students who have studied from UCSMP *Transition Mathematics* or UCSMP *Algebra* will have seen how to do a size transformation with coordinates but not without coordinates.

LESSON

12-2 *Size Changes*

Make a wish, any size. *Japanese Daruma dolls are made of papier-mâché and sold without eyes. When you make a wish, you draw one eye. If the wish comes true, you draw the other eye. The dolls shown are almost size-change images of each other.*

❶ In the In-class Activity, you were shown how to draw a figure 3 times as large as a given figure. Below is the same process for a magnitude of 2.25. Because the magnitude is greater than one, the image is larger than the preimage.

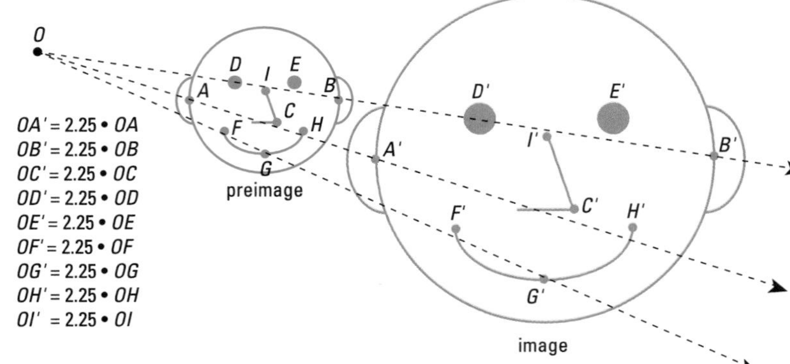

The same procedure can be used if the magnitude is less than or equal to one. Shown below is the face and its image when the magnitude is $\frac{1}{3}$ and the center is O. Notice OC'' is $\frac{1}{3}OC$. Now the image is smaller than the preimage.

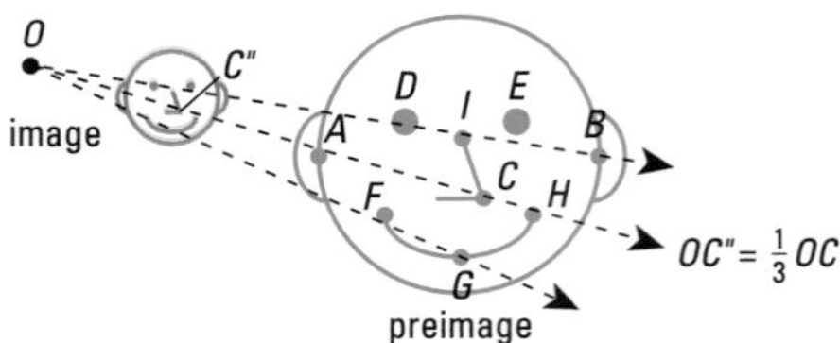

Lesson 12-2 Overview

Broad Goals The goal of this lesson is for students to draw and study size-change images of figures without using coordinates.

Perspective The disadvantage of using coordinates to make size changes is that figures often are not given on a coordinate plane. Thus, this lesson develops a synthetic formal definition of the size change with center *O* and magnitude *k*. Students are then expected to draw images of figures without the use of coordinates. Finally, it is proved that the transformation S_k, studied in the preceding lesson, is a size change. Since any point can be the origin of a coordinate system, the properties of S_k deduced in Lesson 12-1 apply to all size changes. This is verified in the drawings students make in the lesson.

Optional Activities

Activity 1
Materials: Photographs and their negatives

You may wish to have students do this activity after they have completed the lesson. Have students bring several photographs and their negatives to school. Have them **work in pairs** to find the magnitude of a size change that can map the negative onto the photograph.

The Definition of a Size Change

Because each preimage point has a unique image, this procedure defines a transformation. This transformation is called a *size transformation* or *size change.*

> **Definition**
> Let O be a point and k be a positive real number. For any point P, let $S(P) = P'$ be the point on $\overrightarrow{OP}$ with $OP' = k \cdot OP$. Then S is the **size change** or **size transformation** with **center** O and **magnitude** or **size-change factor** k.

When $k > 1$, S is called an **expansion.** When $0 < k < 1$, S is a **contraction.** When $k = 1$, S is called the **identity transformation** because each point coincides with its image and the figure keeps its identity. Pictured on the previous page are an expansion with magnitude 2.25 and a contraction with magnitude $\frac{1}{3}$.

When figures have the same shape and tilt, they are size-change images of each other. The center and magnitude of the size change can be found by drawing lines and measuring.

Example

EFGH is the image of *ABCD* under a size change. Find the center and magnitude of the size change.

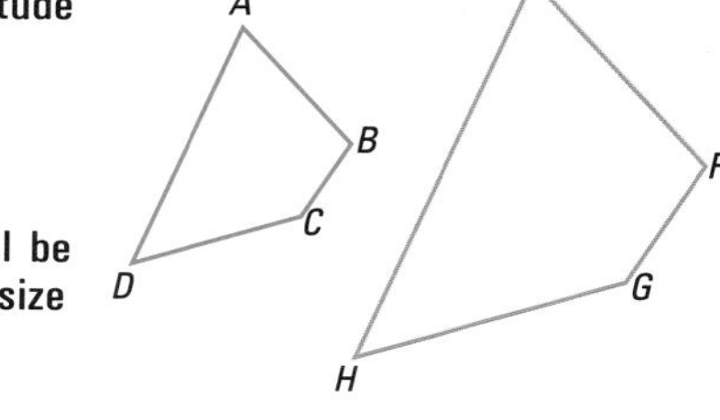

Solution

Draw lines through the pairs of corresponding points. The lines will be concurrent at O, the center of the size change.

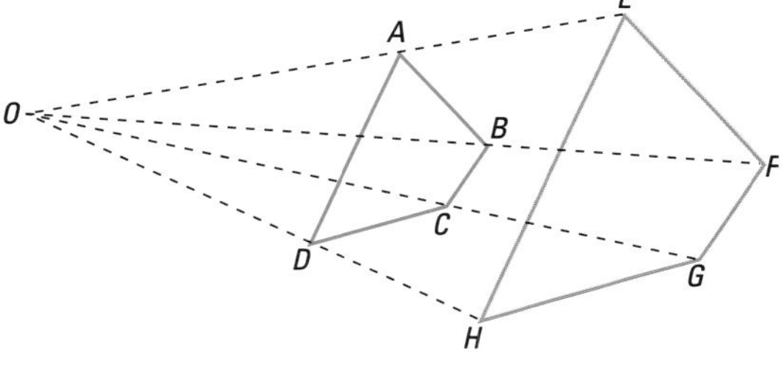

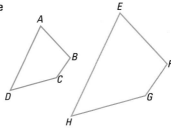

The magnitude k satisfies the equation $OE = k \cdot OA$. So measure OE and OA and solve for k. Here we find

OE = 64 mm and
OA = 40 mm. So
$64 = k \cdot 40$
$\frac{64}{40} = k$
$k = 1.6$

Check

Pick another point and its image. Does $OH = 1.6 \cdot OD$? We find $OH = 52$ mm and $OD = 32.5$ mm. So it checks.

❶ If students had difficulty with the In-class Activity, it may be helpful to begin the lesson by giving them two or three simple polygons and directions to find the size-change image given a magnitude and a specified point as center. **Questions 4–5 and 13** can be used for this purpose.

You might need to point out that certain synonyms are used interchangeably. That is, size change = size transformation, and magnitude = scale factor = size-change factor. In many books, particularly those of British origin, a size transformation is called a *dilation* or a *dilatation.*

Note that a description of a size change without coordinates needs to include the name of the center along with the magnitude.

Error Alert Some students may have difficulty finding the image points under a size transformation with center O and magnitude k because they start their measurements from the preimage points. Remind them that image points are located by measuring from the *center* of the transformation.

Multicultural Connection Folk dolls, like the Japanese Daruma dolls shown on page 692, can be found in most cultures. Folk dolls are usually made locally from materials available in the area—clay, cloth, corncobs, animal skins, flowers, nuts, straw, and wood. The Sioux Indians make dolls from deerskin and decorate them with beads and porcupine quills. In Africa, dolls are made of clay, feathers, and wood. Russians use pine cones, sticks, and dried moss to make dolls called "moss men." The Russian stacking dolls, or matreshka, are hollow wooden dolls. The Inuits of the Arctic region make dolls from sealskin, while people of the tropics weave dolls from palm leaves.

Optional Activities

Activity 2 Technology Connection
You may consider using *Technology Sourcebook, Computer Master 21,* with Lessons 12-2 and 12-3. In this activity, students apply size changes to polygons and examine how size changes affect distance and other properties.

Activity 3 Art Connection
After students have completed the lesson, have some students create a design by transforming a simple figure through one or more size changes. Have other students examine the completed designs to identify the center and magnitude k for each size change.

Adapting to Individual Needs

Extra Help
The sentence preceding the S_k Size-Change Theorem on page 694 refers to the size changes of this lesson as synthetic size changes. Some students may not understand the meaning of the word *synthetic.* Point out that synthetic size changes are those in which coordinates are not involved, as opposed to the transformation S_k studied in Lesson 12-1.

Additional Examples

These examples are also given on **Teaching Aid 162.**

1. *KITE* is the image of *PLAY* under a size change. Find the center and magnitude of the size change.

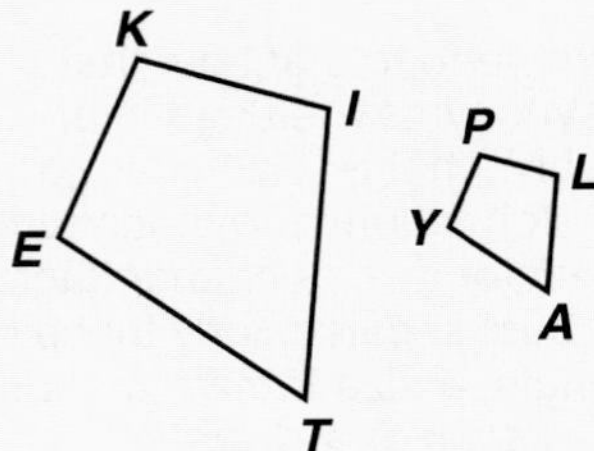

Center: point *O* (shown below); magnitude: 2.6

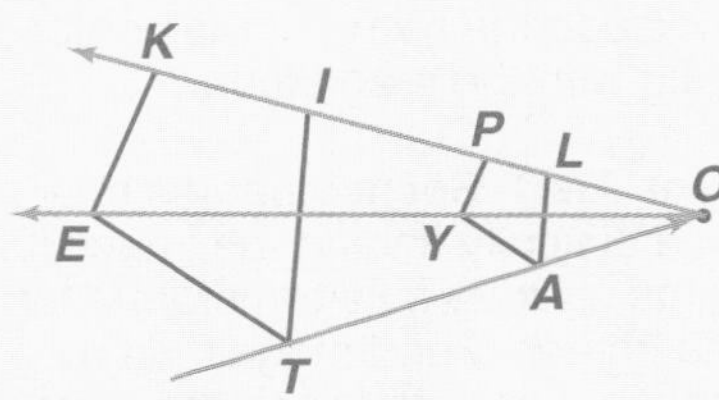

2. Trace the flag of **Questions 4–5.** Find its image under the size change with center *D* and magnitude 1.5.

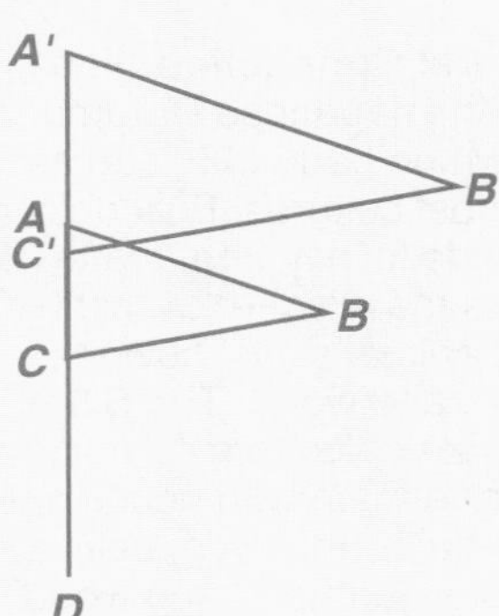

Proving That S_k Is a Size-Change Transformation

The next theorem relates the size changes of this lesson to the transformation S_k that was defined in Lesson 12-1.

S_k Size-Change Theorem
When $k > 0$, the transformation S_k, where $S_k(x, y) = (kx, ky)$, is the size change with center (0, 0) and magnitude k.

Proof
It must be shown that a point and its image under S_k satisfy the defining properties of a size change.

Given: $O = (0, 0)$, $P = (a, b)$, and $P' = S_k(P) = (ka, kb)$.

To prove: (1) P' lies on $\overrightarrow{OP}$.
(2) $OP' = k \cdot OP$.

Drawing:

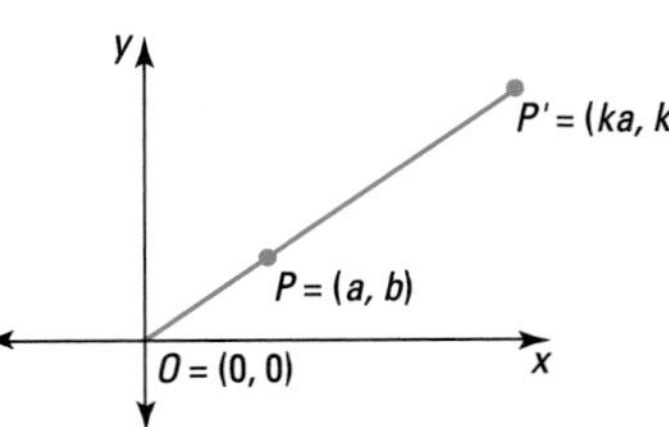

Argument:
First notice that $O' = S_k(O) = (k \cdot 0, k \cdot 0) = (0, 0) = O$.

(1) By part (a) of the Properties of S_k Theorem, $\overline{O'P'} \parallel \overline{OP}$. But there is only one line through O parallel to $\overrightarrow{OP}$. So, O, P, and P' must be on the same line. Thus P' lies on $\overrightarrow{OP}$.

(2) By part (b) of the Properties of S_k Theorem, $O'P' = k \cdot OP$. Since $O' = O$, then $O'P' = OP'$. By the Transitive Property of Equality, $OP' = k \cdot OP$.

The S_k Size-Change Theorem enables you to work with or without coordinates when doing size changes. In the next lesson, we apply the properties of S_k to deduce many properties of size changes.

QUESTIONS

Covering the Reading

1. Refer to the In-class Activity on page 691. Give the lengths of $\overline{OD}$ and $\overline{OD'}$. 3.1 cm, 9.3 cm

2. For the expansion of the face in this lesson, what are the center and magnitude? *O*, 2.25

3. For the contraction of the face in this lesson, what are the center and magnitude? *O*, $\frac{1}{3}$

Adapting to Individual Needs

English Language Development
Materials: Rubber bands

There are a number of new terms in this lesson. You can use a rubber band to demonstrate the meaning of *expansion* and *contraction* to students with limited English proficiency. Direct students' attention to page 731 and encourage them to place the new vocabulary into their notes.

Challenge
Have students draw square *ABCD*. Then have them do the following:

1. Locate a point O that is the center of a size change $S_{\frac{1}{2}}$ such that *ABCD* intersects $S_{\frac{1}{2}}(ABCD)$ in two points. [*O* must be located on $\overleftrightarrow{AC}$ or $\overleftrightarrow{BD}$, in the exterior of *ABCD*, with the distance to the nearest vertex half the length of a diagonal of the square.]
2. Locate a point *P* that is the center of size change S_4 such that *ABCD* intersects $S_4(ABCD)$ in exactly one point. [*P* must be located on $\overleftrightarrow{AC}$ or $\overleftrightarrow{BD}$ in the exterior of *ABCD*, with the distance to the nearest vertex $\frac{1}{3}$ the length of a diagonal of the square.]

In 4 and 5, trace the drawing below. Find the image of the flag under each transformation.

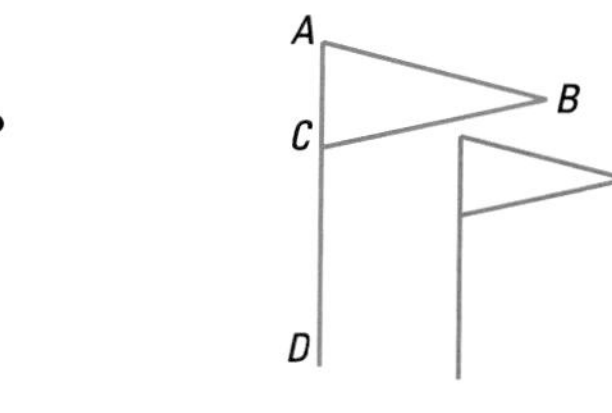

4. the size change with center O, magnitude 3 See margin.

5. the size change with center P, magnitude $\frac{3}{4}$ See above.

6. Let S be a size transformation with size-change factor 6 and center O. Let A be any point. Fill in the blanks.
   a. S(A) is _?_ times as far from O as A is. 6
   b. Points A, O, and S(A) are _?_. collinear

7. a. If k is the scale factor of an expansion, then _?_. $k > 1$
   b. If k is the scale factor of a contraction, then _?_. $0 < k < 1$

8. If k is the scale factor of the identity transformation, then _?_. $k = 1$

9. Consider the proof that the transformation S_k is a size change of magnitude k with center O.
   a. What is given? $O = (0, 0)$, $P = (a, b)$, $P' = S_k(P) = (ka, kb)$
   b. What two statements were proved? that P' lies on $\overrightarrow{OP}$ and that $OP' = k \cdot OP$

In 10–12, trace each figure. Use a ruler to determine the center and size-change factor k for the size transformation represented. (The figure is blue and the image is orange.)

$k = 1/3$

10. 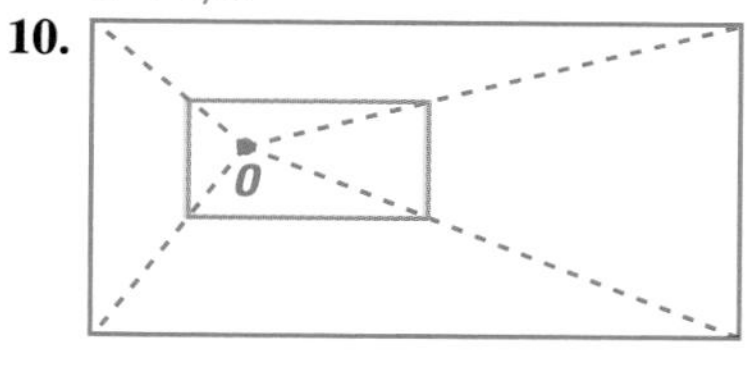

11. 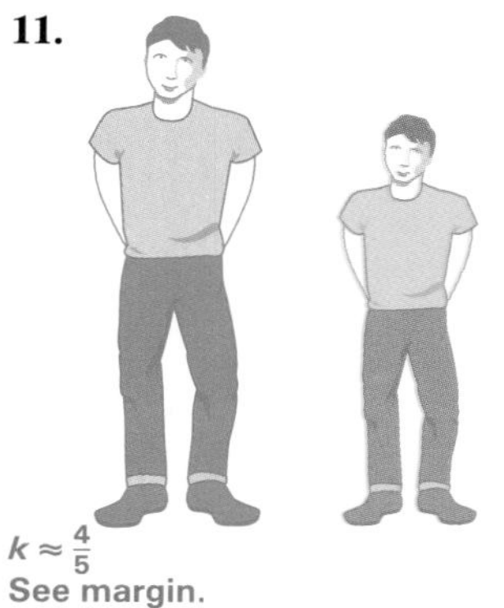

$k \approx \frac{4}{5}$
See margin.

12. 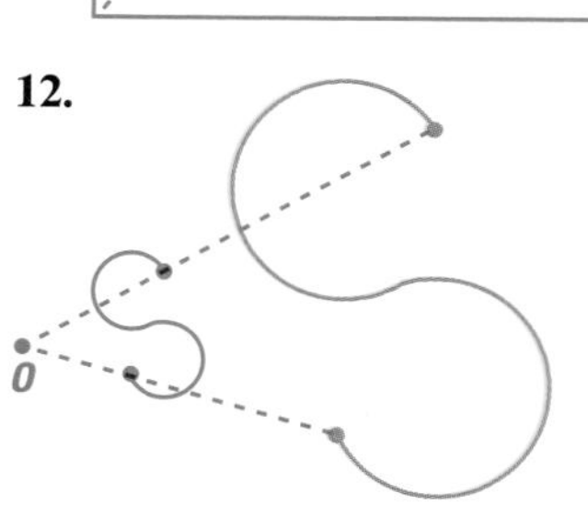

$k \approx 3$

Notes on Questions

Teaching Aid 163 contains the diagrams in **Questions 4–5 and 10.**

Question 6a Another way to ask this question is: $OA' =$ _?_ $\cdot OA$

Questions 7–8 If the magnitude k of a size change is allowed to be negative, then, when $|k| > 1$, the size change is an expansion. When $0 < |k| < 1$, the size change is a contraction. When $|k| = 1$, the size change is either the identity or a rotation of 180°.

Questions 10–12 Ask students if the following statement is always true: The intersection of the lines connecting the image points to the preimage points will be the center of the size transformation. [Yes]

Teaching Aid 164 contains the diagrams in **Questions 11–12 and 19.**

Additional Answers

4.

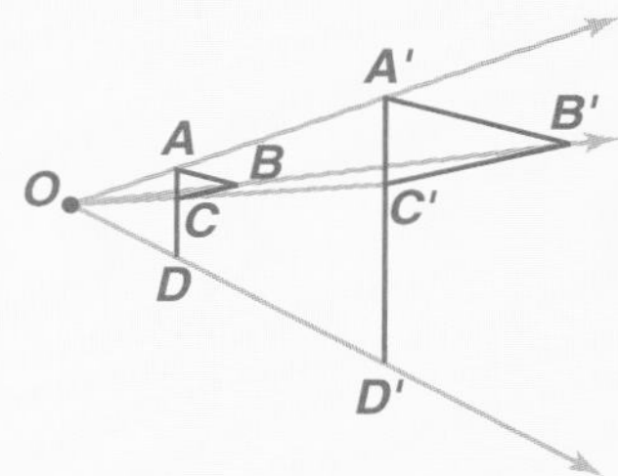

Additional Answers, continued

11.

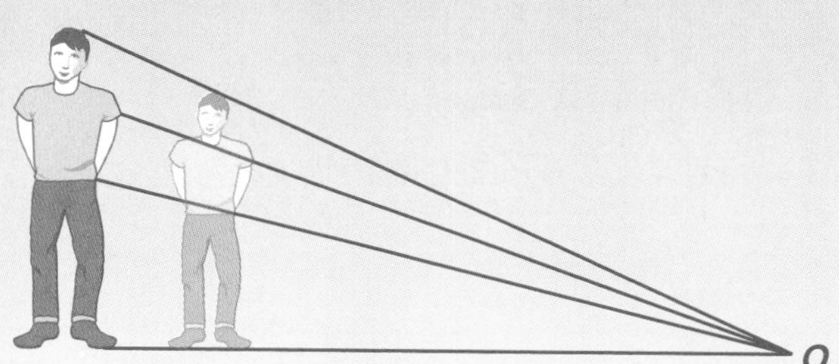

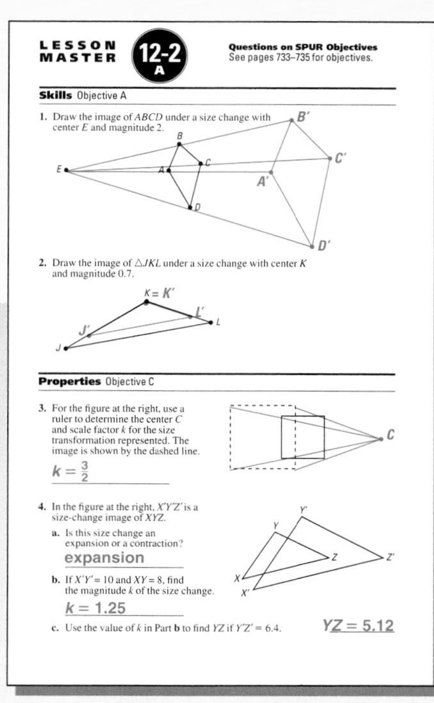
LESSON MASTER 12-2 A

Questions on SPUR Objectives
See pages 733–735 for objectives.

Skills Objective A

1. Draw the image of $ABCD$ under a size change with center E and magnitude 2.

2. Draw the image of $\triangle JKL$ under a size change with center K and magnitude 0.7.

Properties Objective C

3. For the figure at the right, use a ruler to determine the center C and scale factor k for the size transformation represented. The image is shown by the dashed line.
$k = \frac{3}{2}$

4. In the figure at the right, $X'Y'Z'$ is a size-change image of XYZ.
   a. Is this size change an expansion or a contraction? expansion
   b. If $X'Y' = 10$ and $XY = 8$, find the magnitude k of the size change. $k = 1.25$
   c. Use the value of k in Part **b** to find YZ if $Y'Z' = 6.4$. $YZ = 5.12$

Notes on Questions

Questions 14–16 The text states that "the figure is a guide and not necessarily accurate" because the same figure is used for a number of different questions. This is a very common occurrence in textbooks. However, remind students that for a particular problem, an answer could be checked by drawing a figure with accurate measurements.

Question 21 This question illustrates that S_4 preserves betweenness and collinearity. It is a natural lead-in to the next lesson.

Question 26 Many students think that the farther away the center is from the pentagon, the larger the image will be. The point of this exploration is to show that the size of an image depends only on the magnitude of the size change, not on the location of its center.

Follow-up for Lesson 12-2

Practice

For more questions on SPUR Objectives, use **Lesson Master 12-2A** (shown on page 695) or **Lesson Master 12-2B** (shown on pages 696–697).

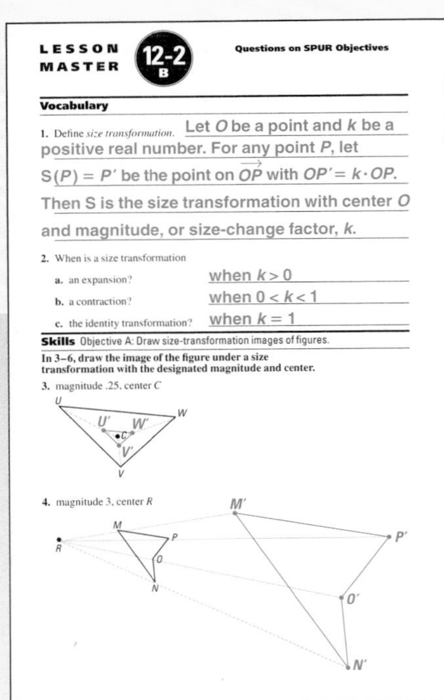

LESSON MASTER 12-2 B — Questions on SPUR Objectives

Vocabulary

1. Define *size transformation.* Let O be a point and k be a positive real number. For any point P, let $S(P) = P'$ be the point on $\overrightarrow{OP}$ with $OP' = k \cdot OP$. Then S is the size transformation with center O and magnitude, or size-change factor, k.

2. When is a size transformation
   a. an expansion? when $k > 0$
   b. a contraction? when $0 < k < 1$
   c. the identity transformation? when $k = 1$

Skills Objective A: Draw size-transformation images of figures.

In 3–6, draw the image of the figure under a size transformation with the designated magnitude and center.

3. magnitude .25, center C

4. magnitude 3, center R

Applying the Mathematics

13. In the figure at the right, $A'B'C'D'$ is the image of $ABCD$ under the size change with center O.
    a. Is this size change an expansion or a contraction? expansion
    b. If $OA = 10$ and $AA' = 4$, what is the magnitude of the size change? 1.4

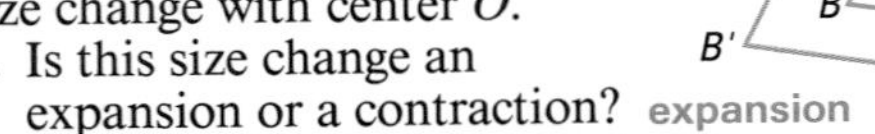

In 14–16, use the figure below. S is a size change with center O and $S(\triangle ABC) = \triangle A'B'C'$. The figure is a guide and not necessarily accurate.

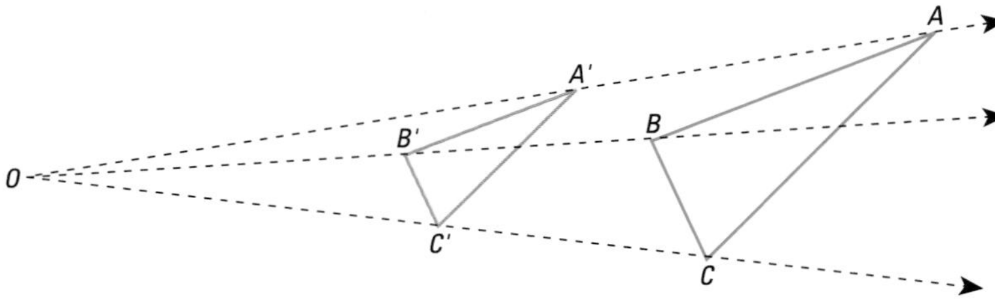

14. If $k = \frac{2}{3}$ and $OA = 9$, then $OA' =$ _?_ and $AA' =$ _?_. 6, 3

15. If $OB = 5$ and $OB' = 3$, then $k =$ _?_. $\frac{3}{5}$

16. If $\frac{OB'}{OB} = \frac{3}{4}$, then $k =$ _?_. $\frac{3}{4}$

17. In Question 11 of Lesson 12-1, you drew a size-change image of an insect. What are the center and magnitude of the size change? (0, 0), 2

18. Draw a figure whose linear dimensions are 1.5 times as large as those of the figure at the right. Use any method you wish. See left.

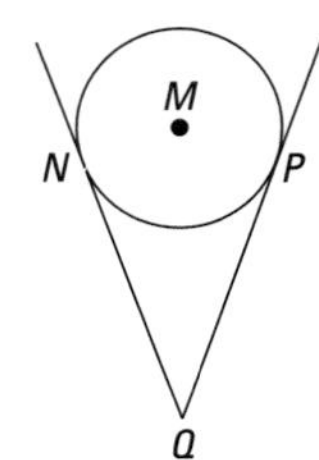

18)

M'
N'
P'
M
N
P
$Q = Q'$

19. Trace $\triangle ABC$ below and draw its image under a size change with center A and magnitude $\frac{4}{5}$.

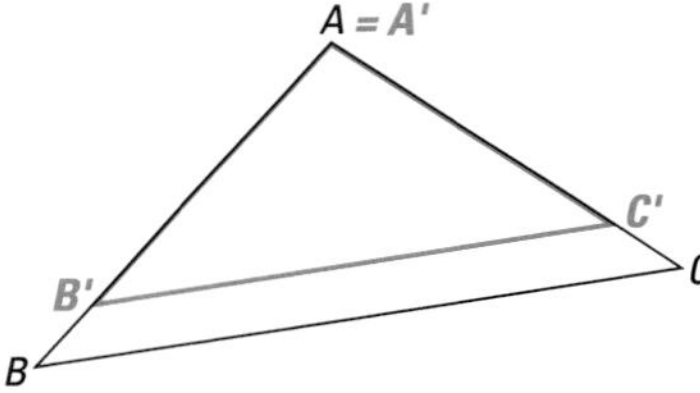

Additional Answers

21a. slope of $\overline{PQ} = \frac{8-2}{-4-9} = \frac{6}{-13} = -\frac{6}{13}$, slope of $\overline{QR} = \frac{-10-8}{35--4} = \frac{-18}{39} = -\frac{6}{13}$, so P, Q, and R are collinear since $\overline{PQ} \parallel \overline{QR}$ and they share Q.

b. $PQ = \sqrt{205}$; $QR = \sqrt{1845} = 3\sqrt{205}$; $PR = \sqrt{820} = 2\sqrt{205}$. Since $PQ + PR = QR$, P is between Q and R.

c. $P' = (36, 8)$, $Q' = (-16, 32)$, $R' = (140, -40)$

d. slope of $\overline{P'Q'} = \frac{32-8}{-16-36} = \frac{24}{-52} = -\frac{6}{13}$, $\overline{Q'R'} = \frac{-40-32}{140--16} = \frac{-72}{156} = -\frac{6}{13}$, so P', Q', and R' are collinear since $\overline{P'Q'} \parallel \overline{Q'R'}$ and they share Q'.

Review

20. Let $A = (0, -4)$, $B = \left(-13, \frac{1}{3}\right)$, and $C = (7, 11)$. Give the coordinates of the vertices of the image of $\triangle ABC$ under S_3. *(Lesson 12-1)*
$A' = (0, -12)$, $B' = (-39, 1)$, $C' = (21, 33)$

21. Given $P = (9, 2)$, $Q = (-4, 8)$, and $R = (35, -10)$. See margin.
a. Show that P, Q, and R are collinear.
b. Show that P is between Q and R.
c. Find the images P', Q', and R' of P, Q, and R under S_4.
d. Show that P', Q', and R' are collinear.
e. Show that P' is between Q' and R'. *(Lesson 12-1)*

22. The rectangular field $ABCD$ pictured below is 300′ by 400′. What is the perimeter of $\triangle ABC$? *(Lessons 8-1, 8-6)* 1200′

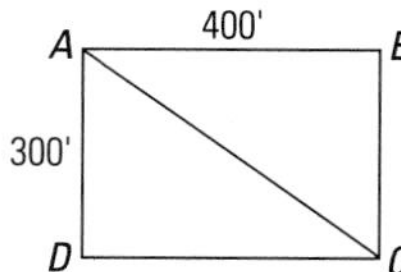

23. Is the figure of Question 22 traversable? If yes, give a path. If no, tell why not. *(Lesson 1-4)* Yes; A to D to C to A to B to C

24. a. How many inches are in a mile? 63,360
b. How many millimeters are in a kilometer? *(Previous course)* 1,000,000

25. Solve each equation. *(Previous course)*
a. $\frac{z+1}{2} = \frac{30}{40}$ $z = 0.5$
b. $\frac{M}{5} = \frac{6}{M}$ $M = \pm\sqrt{30} \approx \pm 5.48$

Exploration

26. On an automatic drawer, you can perform a size change on a figure by entering its center and magnitude. Draw a nonconvex pentagon using an automatic drawer. Show the image of this pentagon under a size change. (You pick the magnitude and the center.) Move the center so that it is inside, outside, and on the pentagon. How do the images compare?
Sample: Consider pentagon $RSTUV$. Let the magnitude of the size change be 1.5 and centers be P, Q, and R. The images are congruent. See left for graph.

26)

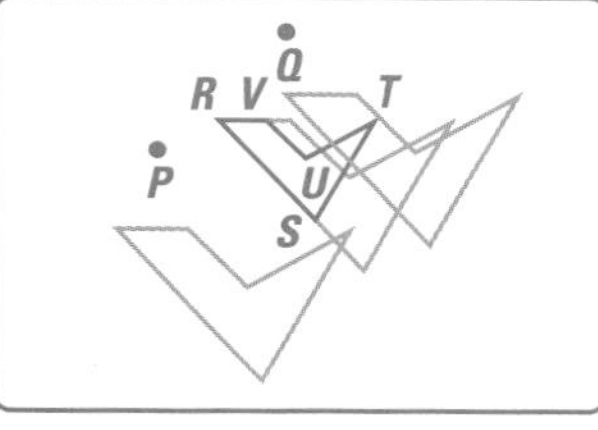

Assessment

Written Communication Have students write a paragraph explaining how to use the methods of this lesson to draw a size change for a simple figure of their own choosing. [Students explain the method for drawing a size change without using coordinates.]

Extension

A point that coincides with its image under a transformation is called a *fixed point.* If all points are fixed points—that is, if each point of a figure is mapped onto itself—the transformation is the *identity transformation.* In a size transformation, the center is always a fixed point. The size change with magnitude 1 is the identity, and any point may be considered its center. Have students determine the number of fixed points in other types of transformations they have studied in this course. [For transformations other than the identity transformation, the numbers of fixed points are as follows: rotation—one (the center); translation—none; reflection—infinitely many (any point on the symmetry line).]

Project Update Project 5, *Pantograph,* on page 730, relates to the content of this lesson.

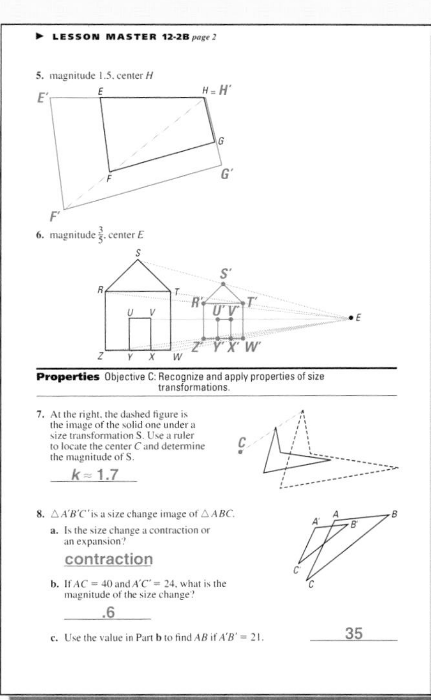
▸ LESSON MASTER 12-2B *page 2*

5. magnitude 1.5, center H

6. magnitude $\frac{3}{5}$, center E

Properties Objective C: Recognize and apply properties of size transformations.

7. At the right, the dashed figure is the image of the solid one under a size transformation S. Use a ruler to locate the center C and determine the magnitude of S.
$k = 1.7$

8. $\triangle A'B'C'$ is a size change image of $\triangle ABC$.
a. Is the size change a contraction or an expansion? contraction
b. If $AC = 40$ and $A'C' = 24$, what is the magnitude of the size change? .6
c. Use the value in Part **b** to find AB if $A'B' = 21$. 35

e. $P'Q' = \sqrt{3280} = 4\sqrt{205}$, $Q'R' = \sqrt{29520} = 12\sqrt{205}$, and $P'R' = \sqrt{13120} = 8\sqrt{205}$. Since $P'Q' + P'R' = Q'R'$, P' is between Q' and R'.

Setting Up Lesson 12-3

The discussion of **Question 21** will lead naturally into the more general properties of size changes studied in Lesson 12-3.

Materials For Activity 1 in *Optional Activities* in Lesson 12-3, you will need an overhead projector, pictures of shapes (such as cartoon characters), and transparencies. If you plan to use Activity 3, students will need an automatic drawer.

Lesson 12-3

Objectives

A Draw size-transformation images of figures.

C Recognize and apply properties of size transformations.

Resources

From the ***Teacher's Resource File***

- Lesson Master 12-3A or 12-3B
- Answer Master 12-3
- Teaching Aids
  105 Graph paper
  157 Warm-up
  165 Additional Examples
  166 Example and Question 1
  167 Questions 14–16
- Technology Sourcebook, Computer Master 21

Additional Resources

- Visuals for Teaching Aids 105, 157, 165–167
- GeoExplorer or other automatic drawers
- Pictures of shapes, overhead projector, transparencies

Teaching Lesson 12-3

Warm-up

1. State the A-B-C-D Theorem. **Every isometry preserves angle measure, betweenness, collinearity (lines), distance (lengths of segments).**
2. Point *D* is between points *E* and *F*. By the Additive Property of Distance, what can be concluded? *ED + DF = EF*

LESSON

12-3 *Properties of Size Changes*

You now have seen ways to find size changes with and without coordinates. You should be able to work without coordinates because figures are not always given on a coordinate plane. However, since coordinates enable some properties of size changes to be deduced rather easily, you should be able to work with coordinates. And, since any point can be the origin for a coordinate system, if a property of S_k can be deduced, then it holds for size changes with other centers.

Parallelism and Size Changes

For instance, the property that a line and its image under S_k are parallel can be used to draw images of polygons quickly.

Example

Let S be a size transformation with magnitude 0.6 and center *O*. Draw S(*ABCD*).

O •

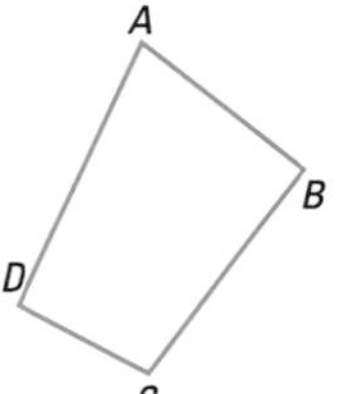

Lesson 12-3 Overview

Broad Goals In this lesson, the properties of size changes are deduced and students apply them to drawing images of figures.

Perspective In Chapter 4, students learned that reflections preserve the four properties we call the A-B-C-D properties. In Chapter 5, it was shown that translations, rotations, and all other isometries also preserve these properties. This lesson shows that size transformations preserve the A-B-C properties, but not the D property. That is, size transformations preserve angle measure, betweenness, and collinearity, but they do not preserve distance. Many students will understand what it means to "preserve" a property only after seeing some of the examples.

The Size-Change Distance Theorem demonstrates that size changes do not preserve distance. Many students find it surprising that size changes *do* preserve all the other properties that were preserved by reflections, namely angle measure, betweenness, and collinearity.

Students may wonder why we bother to prove theorems about size changes. Note that whereas the preservation properties of reflections were assumed, all the properties of size transformations can be proved.

Solution

$S(ABCD)$ is determined by the images of A, B, C, and D. Draw guide rays $\overrightarrow{OA}$, $\overrightarrow{OB}$, $\overrightarrow{OC}$, and $\overrightarrow{OD}$. Measuring, we find $OA \approx 56$ mm. So $OA' = 0.6 \cdot OA \approx 0.6 \cdot 56 \text{ mm} \approx 34$ mm. This locates A'. Since $\overline{A'B'} \parallel \overline{AB}$, we find B' by drawing a line through A' parallel to $\overleftrightarrow{AB}$. This line intersects $\overrightarrow{OB}$ at B'. Likewise, since $\overline{A'D'} \parallel \overline{AD}$, find D' by drawing a line parallel to $\overleftrightarrow{AD}$. This line intersects $\overrightarrow{OD}$ at D'. Continue this process until all the vertices of the image polygon are located.

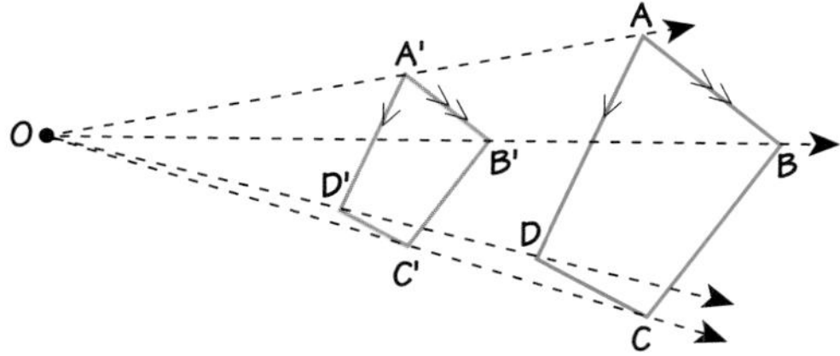

S(ABCD) = A'B'C'D'

How Do Size Changes Affect Distance?

In the Questions of the last two lessons, you have been asked to verify some of the properties of size changes. The property concerning distance is the most important property of size changes, and was proved in Lesson 12-1.

> **Size-Change Distance Theorem**
> Under a size change with magnitude $k > 0$, the distance between any two image points is k times the distance between their preimages.

Another way to think of this is that the *ratio* of the length of an image to the length of its preimage is k. That is, $A'B' = k \cdot AB$ implies that $\frac{A'B'}{AB} = k$.

Preservation Properties of Size Changes

Recall the A-B-C-D properties of reflections and other isometries. Size changes do not preserve distance, but they preserve the other three properties.

> **Size-Change Preservation Properties Theorem**
> Every size transformation preserves (1) angle measure, (2) betweenness, and (3) collinearity.

The proof of this theorem is given on the next page.

Notes on Reading

Cooperative Learning You might wish to begin this lesson by asking students to **work in groups** to make a list of as many properties of reflections as they can remember. After the list is written, ask whether each property of reflections is also a property of size transformations. Students should be able to name at least the Flip-Flop Theorem, the preservation properties, and the switching of orientation. Of these properties, the preservation of angle measure, betweenness, and collinearity are properties of size transformations; the Flip-Flop Theorem, the preservation of distance, and the switching of orientation are not.

You may wish to use **Teaching Aid 166** as you discuss the **Example** with your class.

Reading Mathematics You might need to read the proofs of the theorems on page 700 in detail with students. Emphasize that the proofs are algebraic, and that the problem-solving heuristic *try a simpler case* can be used to verify the theorems.

For an alternative discussion of the Size-Change Distance Theorem, see Activity 1 of *Optional Activities* on page 700.

Ask students why preserving betweenness means that the image of a segment is a segment, the image of a ray is a ray, and the image of an angle is an angle. [Each figure is defined in terms of betweenness and unions of sets.]

The formal argument that the size change image of a segment is a segment—that is, that size transformations preserve segments—is given below in *Lesson 12-3 Overview.* It is more formal than you should expect from your students.

Any transformation preserves the union of sets. That is, $T(A \cup B) = T(A) \cup T(B)$. From this, one can give a rigorous proof that if a transformation preserves betweenness, then the image of a segment is a segment. Suppose T is a size transformation with $T(A) = A'$ and $T(B) = B'$. Then:

$T(\overline{AB}) = T(A \cup B \cup$ set of points between A and $B)$	def. of segment
$= T(A) \cup T(B) \cup T($set of points between A and $B)$	All transformations preserve union
$= A' \cup B' \cup$ set of points between A' and B'	Given; T preserves betweenness
$= \overline{A'B'}$.	def. of segment

The proof that the image of an angle is an angle is analogous to the proof for a segment. The proof that the image of an angle *has the same measure as the original angle* requires an examination of cases. For instance, you must consider the case where O, B, and C are collinear.

Science Connection Creating greatly enlarged images of extremely small objects is called *photomicrography.* The apparatus used includes a compound microscope attached to a simple camera or achromatic lens, a film holder that resists all motion and vibration, and a special light and filter system to illuminate specimens which, thanks to their size, have a low range of luminance. The typical magnifying power of such an apparatus is about 2000x, but if an electron or x-ray microscope is used, a much greater level of magnification can be achieved.

Additional Examples

These examples are also given on **Teaching Aid 165.**

1. Let S be a size transformation with magnitude 1.75 and center O. Draw S(HAT).

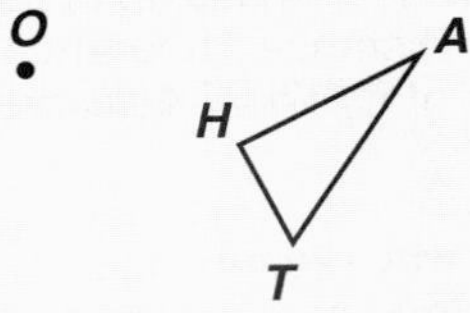

S(HAT) = $H'A'T'$, shown below.

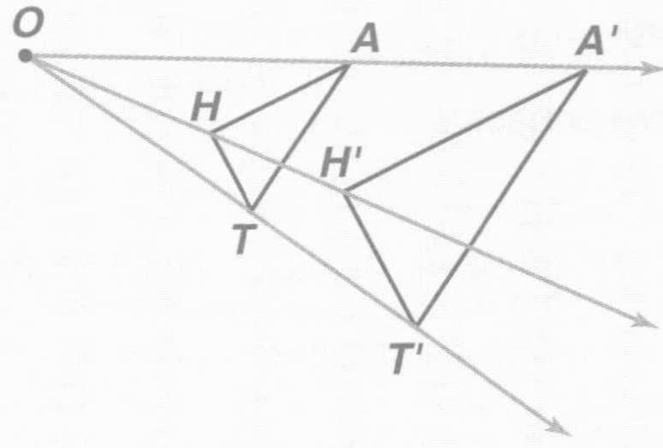

Proof

Given: S is a size transformation with center O. S(A) = A', S(B) = B', S(C) = C'.

To prove: (1) $m\angle ABC = m\angle A'B'C'$
(2) If B is between A and C, then B' is between A' and C'.
(3) If A, B and C are collinear, then A', B' and C' are collinear.

Drawing (1):

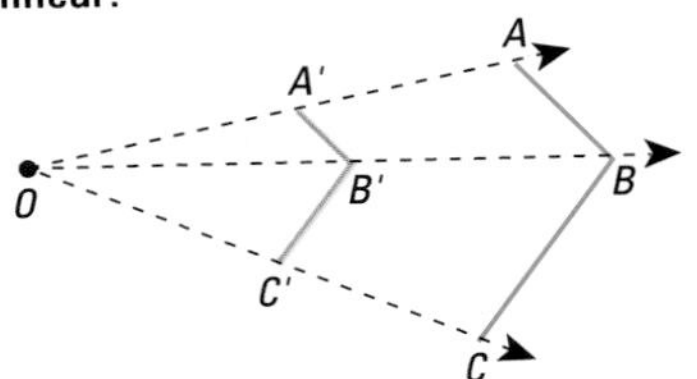

Argument (1):

Conclusions	Justifications
1. $\overleftrightarrow{BC} \parallel \overleftrightarrow{B'C'}$ $\overleftrightarrow{AB} \parallel \overleftrightarrow{A'B'}$	A line and its image under a size transformation are parallel.
2. $m\angle ABO = m\angle A'B'O$ $m\angle OBC = m\angle OB'C'$	// lines ⇒ corr. ∠s ≅
3. $m\angle ABO + m\angle OBC = m\angle A'B'O + m\angle OB'C'$	Addition Property of Equality
4. $m\angle ABO + m\angle OBC = m\angle ABC$ $m\angle A'B'O + m\angle OB'C' = m\angle A'B'C'$	Angle Addition Property
5. $m\angle ABC = m\angle A'B'C'$	Substitution (step 4 in step 3)

The following argument proves that size transformations preserve betweenness.

Drawing (2):

A' B' C'

A B C

Argument (2):

Conclusions	Justifications
0. B is between A and C.	Given
1. $AB + BC = AC$	definition of betweenness
2. $k \cdot (AB + BC) = k \cdot AC$	Multiplication Property of Equality
3. $k \cdot AB + k \cdot BC = k \cdot AC$	Distributive Property
4. $A'B' = k \cdot AB$ $B'C' = k \cdot BC$ $A'C' = k \cdot AC$	Size-Change Distance Theorem
5. $A'B' + B'C' = A'C'$	Substitution (step 4 into step 3)
6. B' is between A' and C'.	definition of betweenness

Argument (3):

Betweenness implies collinearity. So argument (2) also proves that collinearity is preserved.

Optional Activities

Activity 1 Alternate Approach

Materials: Pictures of shapes, overhead projector, transparencies

Demonstrate the Size-Change Distance Theorem by using an overhead projector, pictures of shapes, and transparencies of the shapes. Project the transparency onto the screen. Then place the original shape on top of its image on the screen to show that the image is similar to the preimage.

Activity 2 Writing

Materials: Graph paper or **Teaching Aid 105**

You can use this activity after students complete the lesson. Have students **work in pairs.** Tell each pair of students to draw a figure on graph paper. Have some pairs expand the figure by a given scale factor, and have others contract the figure. Then have students measure all the sides and angles of both the image and preimage. (If they use convenient points, students can calculate the lengths using the Distance Formula. Angles should be measured to the nearest degree with a protractor.) Have students write a summary of their conclusions. The conclusions can then be shared with the entire class.

1)

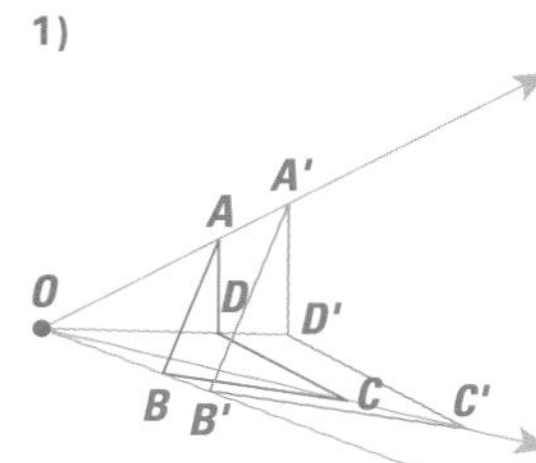

2) Divide the length of the image segment by the length of the preimage segment.

9)

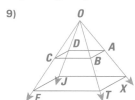

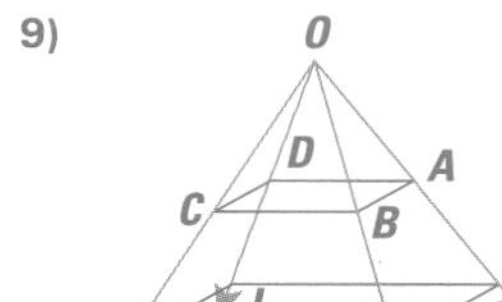

The preservation of angle measure, betweenness, and collinearity implies that images of figures are determined by images of key points. Because size changes preserve collinearity, the image of a line is a line. Because size changes preserve betweenness, the image of a segment is a segment and the image of a ray is a ray. So the image of an angle is an angle, the image of a triangle is a triangle, and so on.

Figure Size-Change Theorem
If a figure is determined by certain points, then its size-change image is the corresponding figure determined by the size-change images of those points.

The Figure Size-Change Theorem was applied as early as Lesson 12-1 to find the image of a pentagon.

QUESTIONS

Covering the Reading

1. Trace the figure below. Let S be the size transformation with magnitude 1.4 and center O. Draw S($ABCD$). See left.

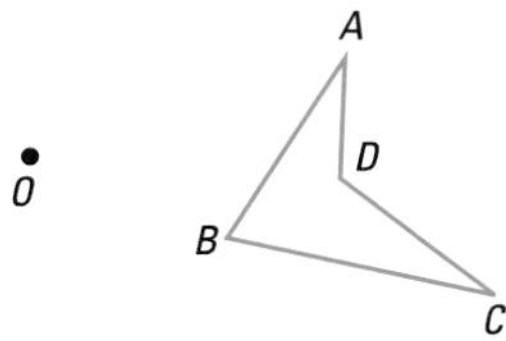

2. Suppose you know the lengths of a segment and its image under a size change. How can the magnitude of the size change be calculated? See left.

3. *True or false.* Size transformations preserve distance. False

4. Suppose a photograph of an insect is k times its actual size. If a leg on the picture is 3 cm long, how long is the actual leg? $\frac{3}{k}$ cm

5. Size transformations preserve _?_, _?_, and _?_. angle measure, betweenness, collinearity

In 6–8, S is a size transformation of magnitude 200.

6. If $S(\angle TJK) = \angle T'J'K'$ and $m\angle T'J'K' = 43$, find $m\angle TJK$. 43

7. Suppose $S(\overleftrightarrow{AB}) = \overleftrightarrow{CD}$. How are $\overleftrightarrow{AB}$ and $\overleftrightarrow{CD}$ related? $\overleftrightarrow{AB} \parallel \overleftrightarrow{CD}$

8. If $S(TINY) = HUGE$, then $S(N) =$ _?_. G

In 9–11, S is a size change with $S(A) = X$, $S(B) = T$, $S(C) = E$, and $S(D) = J$.

9. Draw a possible picture. See left.

10. $S(\angle BCD) =$ _?_. $\angle TEJ$

11. If $m\angle BAD = 73$, then $m\angle$ _?_ $= 73$. TXJ

Scareab. *A rhinoceros beetle can grow to 6 cm in length.*

2. Every size change maps any line onto a line that is parallel to it. Which, if any, isometries have this same property? All translations and those rotations with magnitude 180

3. Circle P has radius 5. Circle Q has radius 22. Is there a size change that maps circle P onto circle Q? If so, what is its magnitude? If not, why not? Yes. The magnitude is $\frac{22}{5}$.

Notes on Questions

Question 1 Teaching Aid 166 can be used with this question.

Question 5 Although the expected responses are given here, there are other correct answers: perpendicularity (if two lines are perpendicular, so are their size-transformation images), type of figure (the image of a triangle under a size transformation is a triangle), and so on.

Question 8 You might ask students the following question: Do the words *TINY* and *HUGE* indicate that S is an expansion? [Despite the words used, no information is given about the magnitude of S.]

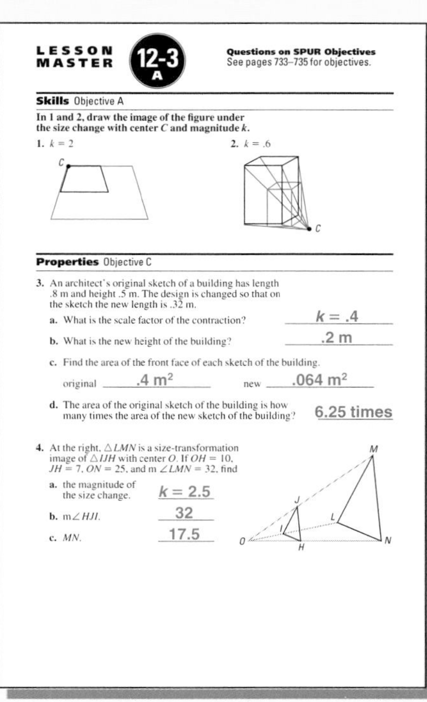

LESSON MASTER 12-3 A

Questions on SPUR Objectives
See pages 733–735 for objectives.

Skills Objective A

In 1 and 2, draw the image of the figure under the size change with center C and magnitude k.

1. $k = 2$

2. $k = .6$

Properties Objective C

3. An architect's original sketch of a building has length .8 m and height .5 m. The design is changed so that on the sketch the new length is .32 m.

a. What is the scale factor of the contraction? $k = .4$

b. What is the new height of the building? .2 m

c. Find the area of the front face of each sketch of the building.
original .4 m² new .064 m²

d. The area of the original sketch of the building is how many times the area of the new sketch of the building? 6.25 times

4. At the right, $\triangle LMN$ is a size-transformation image of $\triangle IJH$ with center O. If $OH = 10$, $JH = 7$, $ON = 25$, and $m\angle LMN = 32$, find

a. the magnitude of the size change. $k = 2.5$

b. $m\angle HJI$. 32

c. MN. 17.5

Optional Activities

Activity 3 Technology Connection
Materials: Automatic drawer

After you have discussed the **Example** with students, you may wish to have them use an automatic drawer to create a size transformation. Have them use the drawer to construct a polygon. They should also construct a point not on the polygon that will be the center of the size transformation. Then, using the *dilation* feature of the software, students should choose a scale factor such as 2 and have the drawer perform the size transformation. Now instruct students to grab the point that is the center of the transformation and move it to various locations on the screen. Have them describe the effect this has on the image polygon. [The image polygon changes position, but it does not change size.] You may wish to have students save their constructions on disk files for use in future lessons.

Notes on Questions

Question 12 You might ask students to prove that $\angle ABO \cong \angle DEO$. It is a nice two-step proof. [$\overline{AB} // \overline{DE}$ because of the Size-Change Theorem. Then the angles are corresponding angles and are congruent because of the Parallel Lines Postulate.]

Question 13a Ask students to identify the relationship between the answer to this question and the answer to the following related question: If T(*MICRO*) = *MEGAS*, what is the magnitude of T? [The magnitude is $\frac{8}{5}$, or 1.6. It is the reciprocal of $\frac{5}{8}$.]

Questions 14–16 You can use **Teaching Aid 167** with these questions. Many students believe that the farther the center of a size transformation is from the figure, the larger the image will be. These questions verify that the center determines the location of the image but does *not* determine its size. In the next lesson, students learn how the magnitude of the transformation affects the size.

Questions 17, 19–20 These questions address three real-world applications of size changes: photography **(Question 17),** scale drawings **(Question 19),** and map scales **(Question 20).** Although many of the questions in this lesson involve polygons, be sure to emphasize these broader and more realistic applications of size changes.

(Notes on Questions continue on page 704.)

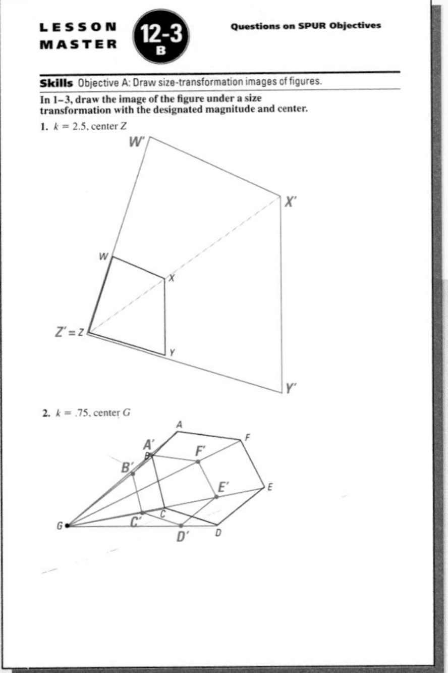

Applying the Mathematics

12. At the right, $\triangle DEF$ is a size-transformation image of $\triangle ABC$ with center O. $AB = 6$, $BC = 8$, $EF = 20$, and $DF = 30$. Find
    a. k, the magnitude of the size change. $\frac{5}{2} = 2.5$
    b. DE. 15 units
    c. AC. 12 units

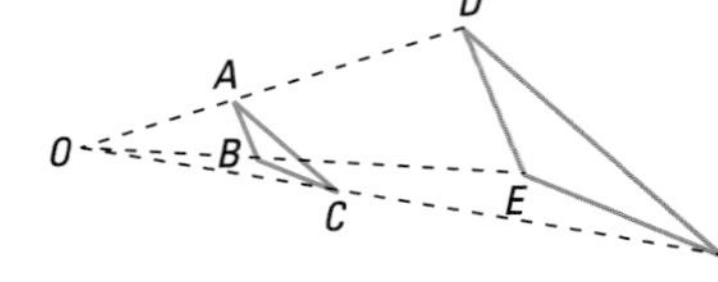

13. T is a size change with T(*MEGAS*) = *MICRO* and lengths as indicated at the right.
    a. What is the magnitude of T? $\frac{5}{8} = 0.625$
    b. What is the center of T? *M*
    c. Find *OR*. 7.5 units
    d. Find *ME*. 20.8 units

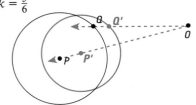

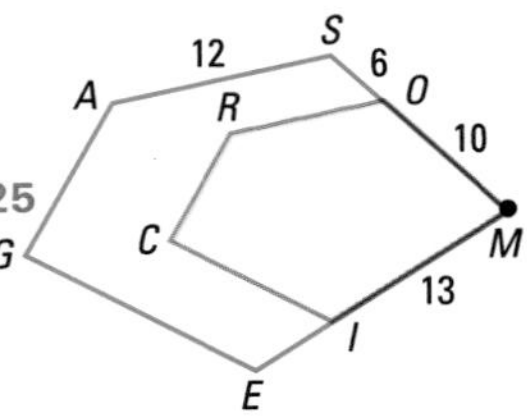

In 14–16, trace the figure. Use the Figure Size-Change Theorem to draw the image of the figure under the size change with center O and the given magnitude k.

14. $k = \frac{5}{6}$

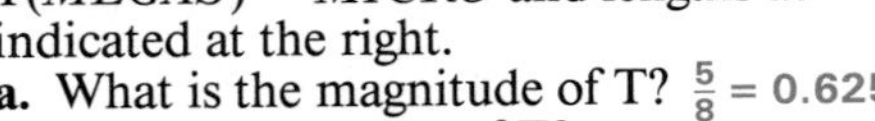

15. $k = \frac{5}{6}$

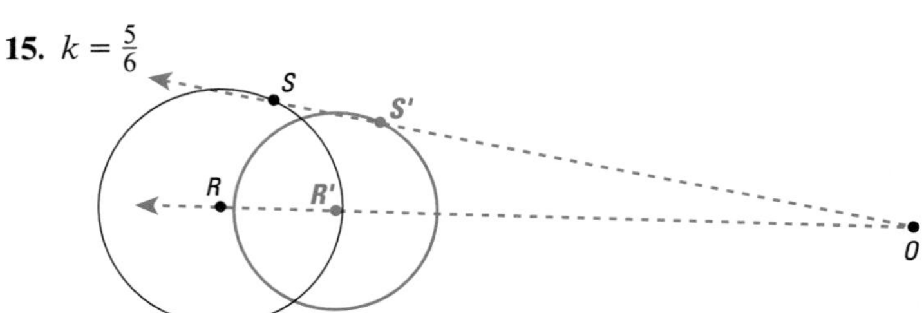

16. $k = 4$
    See margin.

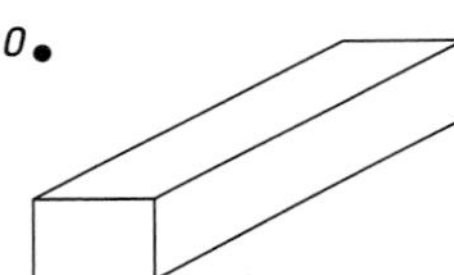

Adapting to Individual Needs

Extra Help
Point out to students that each image point in the **Example** could be determined by measuring, just as we did to find the image of *A*. However, the given method is more efficient and it applies the Properties of S_k Theorem from Lesson 12-1.

Additional Answers
16.

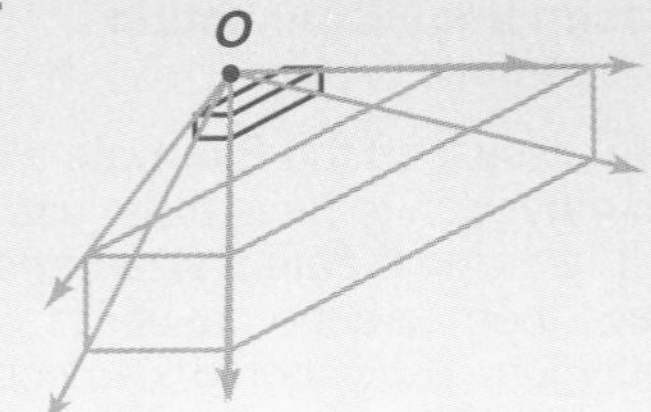

17. A photograph that has width 5 cm and length 12 cm is enlarged. The new width is 7 cm.
   a. Find the size-change factor of the enlargement. 1.4
   b. Find the length of the enlargement. 16.8 cm
   c. Find the areas of the photograph and its enlargement. 60 cm^2, 117.6 cm^2
   d. The area of the enlargement is how many times the area of the original? 1.96
   e. The perimeter of the enlargement is how many times the perimeter of the original? 1.4

18. Use the figure at the right.
   Given: $S(\triangle OAC) = \triangle OBD$. $OA = 6$, $AB = 1$, $BD = 4$, and $OC = 6.1$.
   Find the lengths of as many other segments as you can.
   $AC = \frac{24}{7} \approx 3.429$ units, $OD \approx 7.117$ units, $CD \approx 1.017$ units, $OB = 7$ units

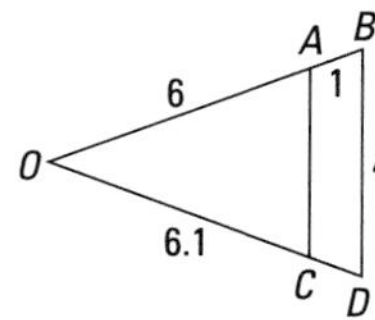

Review

19. Face A is a size-change image of face B. Trace the faces, and find the center and scale factor k. *(Lesson 12-2)* See margin.

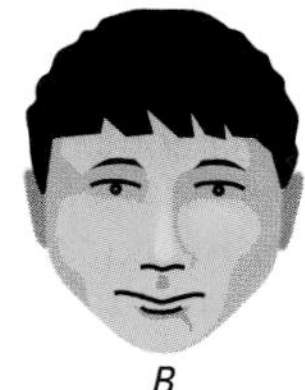

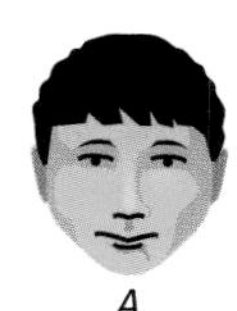

A Hopi hand-painted dance wand

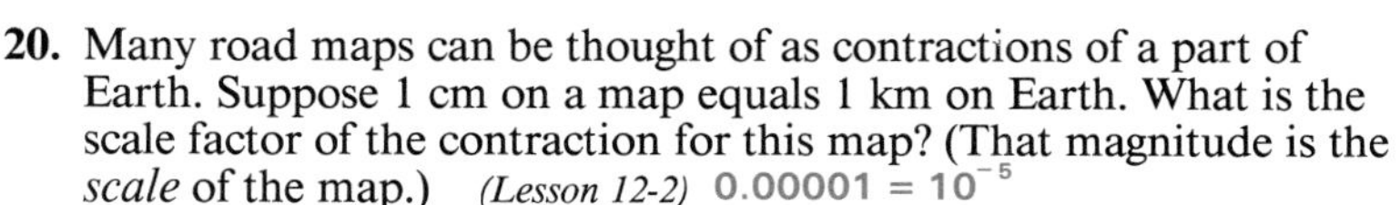

20. Many road maps can be thought of as contractions of a part of Earth. Suppose 1 cm on a map equals 1 km on Earth. What is the scale factor of the contraction for this map? (That magnitude is the *scale* of the map.) *(Lesson 12-2)* $0.00001 = 10^{-5}$

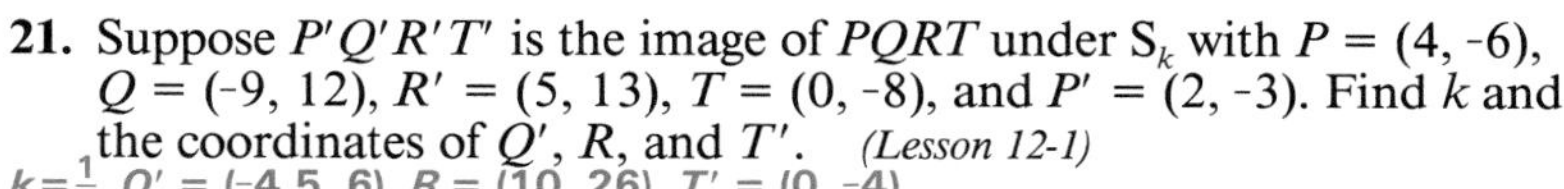

21. Suppose $P'Q'R'T'$ is the image of $PQRT$ under S_k with $P = (4, -6)$, $Q = (-9, 12)$, $R' = (5, 13)$, $T = (0, -8)$, and $P' = (2, -3)$. Find k and the coordinates of Q', R, and T'. *(Lesson 12-1)*
   $k = \frac{1}{2}$, $Q' = (-4.5, 6)$, $R = (10, 26)$, $T' = (0, -4)$

22. a. The Hopi design shown below represents clouds with rain. Draw it under a size change with magnitude 2. Then draw an enlargement of the image, using a size change of magnitude 1.5. *(Lesson 12-2)* Check students' drawings.
   b. How does the final design compare to the original? Its dimensions are 3 times those of the original.

Additional Answers

19. $k \approx 0.7$

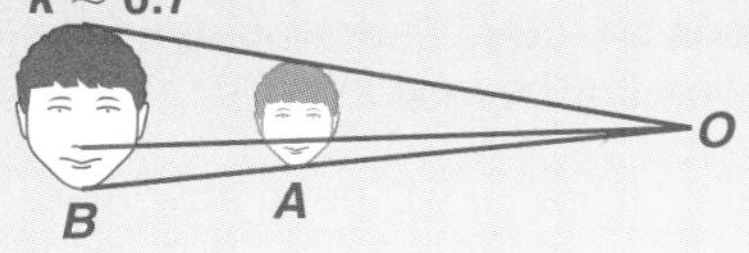

Practice

For more questions on SPUR Objectives, use **Lesson Master 12-3A** (shown on page 701) or **Lesson Master 12-3B** (shown on pages 702–703).

Assessment

Oral/Written Communication Refer students to **Questions 14–16.** Have each student draw the image of the figure in one of these questions using the same center O, but a different value for k. Then have them pick another question and draw the image of the given figure using the same value for k, but a different center. [Students provide correct size-change drawings of the type requested.]

Extension

As a follow-up to **Question 27,** ask students for the definition of S_k on a 3-dimensional coordinate system. [The image of (a, b, c) is (ka, kb, kc).] Does S_k in three dimensions multiply distances by k? [Yes; a proof is analogous to the proof in two dimensions.]

Project Update Project 5, *Pantograph,* on page 730, relates to the content of this lesson.

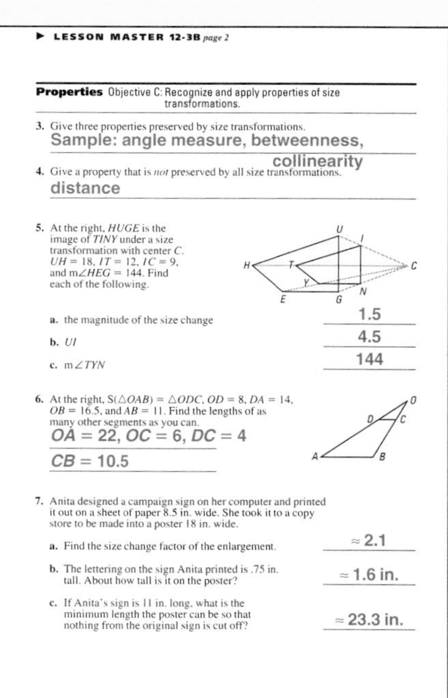

▶ LESSON MASTER 12-3B *page 2*

Properties Objective C: Recognize and apply properties of size transformations.

3. Give three properties preserved by size transformations.
   Sample: angle measure, betweenness, collinearity
4. Give a property that is *not* preserved by all size transformations.
   distance
5. At the right, $HUGE$ is the image of $TINY$ under a size transformation with center C. $UH = 18$, $IT = 12$, $IC = 9$, and $m\angle HEG = 144$. Find each of the following.
   a. the magnitude of the size change 1.5
   b. UI 4.5
   c. $m\angle TYN$ 144
6. At the right, $S(\triangle OAB) = \triangle ODC$, $OD = 8$, $DA = 14$, $OB = 16.5$, and $AB = 11$. Find the lengths of as many other segments as you can.
   $OA = 22$, $OC = 6$, $DC = 4$
   $CB = 10.5$
7. Anita designed a campaign sign on her computer and printed it out on a sheet of paper 8.5 in. wide. She took it to a copy store to be made into a poster 18 in. wide.
   a. Find the size change factor of the enlargement. ≈ 2.1
   b. The lettering on the sign Anita printed is .75 in. tall. About how tall is it on the poster? ≈ 1.6 in.
   c. If Anita's sign is 11 in. long, what is the minimum length the poster can be so that nothing from the original sign is cut off? ≈ 23.3 in.

Notes on Questions

Question 28 For some students, the answer may be obvious. To introduce a little "mystery" into the question, have them begin with a square whose sides are not horizontal and vertical.

23. Complete this hierarchy for isometries. *(Lesson 4-7)*

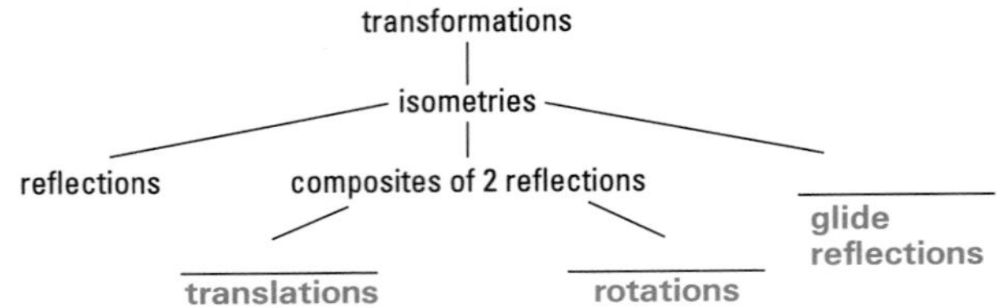

In 24 and 25, suppose $\frac{2x}{k} = \frac{b}{y}$. *(Previous course)*

24. Find k if $x = 9$, $b = 7$, and $y = 50$. $\frac{900}{7} \approx 128.57$

25. If $x = 1$ and $y = 1$, what can you say about the value of k? $k = \frac{2}{b}$

26. Solve for t: $\frac{t+3}{100} = \frac{t-5}{200}$. *(Previous course)*
$t = -11$

Exploration

27. **a.** Does the definition of size change given in Lesson 12-2 hold in three dimensions, or must it be modified? If so, how would you modify it? It holds in three dimensions.

b. What properties mentioned in this lesson are preserved by size changes in three dimensions? See left.

27b) angle measure, betweenness, collinearity, and parallelism of lines and their images

28. Consider this conjecture. If $MNOP$ is a square and S is a size change, then S($MNOP$) is a square.

a. Draw an instance of this conjecture. See left.

b. Is this conjecture true? If so, prove it. If not, draw a counterexample.
Yes; $MNOP$ has 4 equal sides and 4 right angles, by definition of a square. Since S_k multiplies distances by k, the sides of S_k ($MNOP$) are all equal, and since S_k preserves angle measure, the angles of S_k ($MNOP$) are all right angles. Therefore, S_k ($MNOP$) is also a square by definition of a square.

28a) Sample:

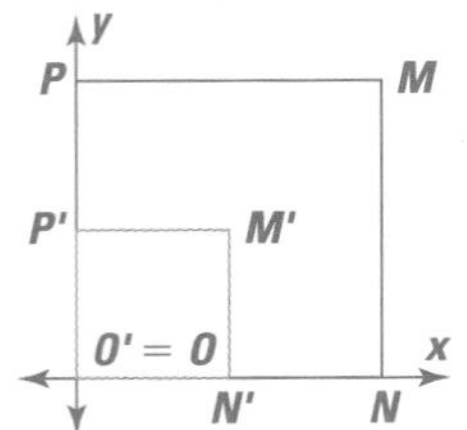

Adapting to Individual Needs

Challenge
Is rectangle $ABCD$ a size change image of rectangle $PQRS$? Explain why or why not.

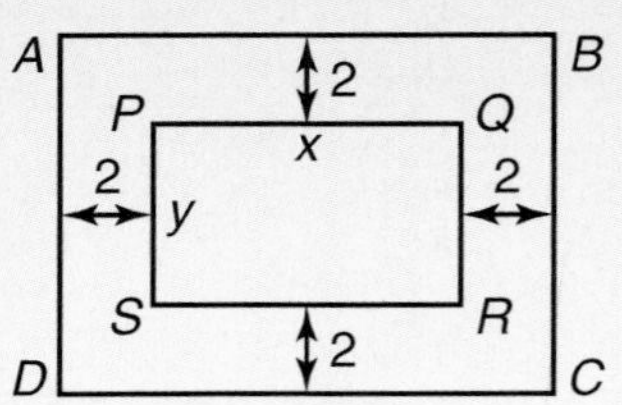

[No. Sample: Suppose $x = 5$ and $y = 3$. Then $\frac{AD}{PS} = \frac{7}{3}$ and $\frac{AB}{PQ} = \frac{9}{5}$. Since the ratio is not the same for these two sets of corresponding lengths, $ABCD$ is not a size change image of $PQRS$.]

Setting Up Lesson 12-4

Questions 24–26 review proportions in preparation for the next lesson.

Materials Students will need advertisements from a grocery store or drugstore for *Optional Activities* on page 706. Or, they will need to visit such stores to find data on prices for various sized containers of the same product.

LESSON

12-4

Proportions

Anchors aweigh. *This stock anchor, one of four common types of anchors, is heavy enough to keep the vessel from drifting.*

What Is a Ratio?

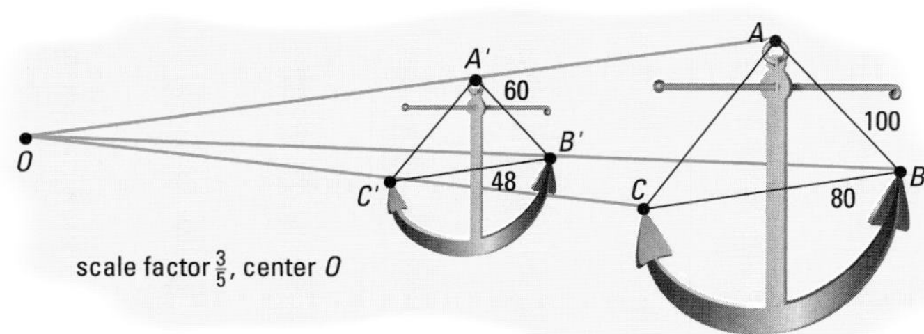

❶ A **ratio** is a quotient of two numbers, $\frac{m}{n}$, m/n, or $m : n$, where m and n are quantities of the same kind, such as lengths, populations, or areas. (If the quantities are of different kinds, $\frac{m}{n}$ is called a *rate*.)

Every size change involves equal ratios. For example, pictured above are a figure and its image under the size change with center O and magnitude $\frac{3}{5}$. Then, by the Size-Change Distance Theorem,

$$A'B' = \frac{3}{5} \cdot AB \quad \text{and} \quad B'C' = \frac{3}{5} \cdot BC.$$

$$\text{Consequently,} \quad \frac{A'B'}{AB} = \frac{3}{5} \quad \text{and} \quad \frac{B'C'}{BC} = \frac{3}{5}.$$

Thus in a size transformation, all ratios of image lengths to preimage lengths are equal. That is, $\frac{A'B'}{AB} = \frac{B'C'}{BC}$. This ratio is equal to the magnitude of the size change. The ratio is less than 1 if the size change is a contraction. It is greater than 1 if the size change is an expansion.

Lesson 12-4

Objectives

B Use proportions to find missing parts in similar figures.

E Identify and determine proportional lengths and distances in real situations.

Resources

From the ***Teacher's Resource File***

- Lesson Master 12-4A or 12-4B
- Answer Master 12-4
- Assessment Sourcebook: Quiz for Lessons 12-1 through 12-4
- Teaching Aids
  158 Warm-up
  168 Additional Examples

Additional Resources

- Visuals for Teaching Aids 158, 168
- Advertisements from a grocery store or drugstore and actual items in the ads

Teaching Lesson 12-4

Warm-up

One woman and 99 men are enrolled in a class. How many men would have to drop the class for the percent of men in the class to drop from 99% to 98%? **50 men**

Notes on Reading

❶ In general, this is a rather easy lesson. However, students may still be confused with the distinctions between *ratio, rate,* and *proportion.* You might wish to emphasize that a *ratio* is a quotient of two numbers with the same unit, while a *rate* is a

Lesson 12-4 Overview

Broad Goals This lesson is a review of the algebra needed to solve the proportions that arise in working with size changes and similar figures. The Means-Extremes Property is deduced.

Perspective The lesson begins with a discussion of the terminology that is necessary for later work with similar figures. Then the Means-Extremes Property is deduced, and an example is given.

In mathematics, a *ratio* is usually defined to be a quotient of two numbers, i.e., a fraction. The equality of two ratios or fractions is a *proportion.* This language is uniform in mathematics textbooks in the United States.

Outside the mathematics classroom, however, the word proportion often refers to a single fraction. In fact, that is the first definition given in most dictionaries. Consider, for instance, the sentence, "The proportion of women in the graduating class was $\frac{1}{3}$."

Students who are familiar with this common usage may need help in recognizing how it is different from the technical mathematical use. The Means-Extremes Property is discussed in UCSMP *Transition Mathematics* and UCSMP *Algebra,* so its name should be quite familiar to students who have had

(Overview continues on page 706.)

quotient of two numbers with different units. In a proportion, the two quotients can be either ratios or rates. **Questions 15 and 16** can be used to clarify these concepts.

We assume that students have seen the Means-Extremes Property before, though perhaps not with that name.

You may wish to spend some time discussing scale models, such as model airplanes, dolls, and so on. Because corresponding angles are congruent, scale models look like the "real thing." Given the length of segment on the model and the length of the corresponding segment on the real object, one can determine the scale of the model.

Multicultural Connection
Dollhouses are often built to scale, as illustrated in **Example 2** on page 708. Such dollhouses probably evolved in the 1500s from the medieval crèche and were popular in Holland, Germany, and Great Britain. The first such houses were built for wealthy families; they were furnished with replicas of the family's fine furniture, china, silver, and art. Dollhouses for children did not appear until the late 18th century.

Proportions and Size Changes

A statement that two quotients are equal is called a **proportion.** Each equation below is a proportion.

$$\frac{B'C'}{BC} = \frac{3}{5} \qquad \frac{2}{7} = \frac{x}{9} \qquad \frac{y+3}{5} = \frac{7}{y} \qquad \frac{A'B'}{AB} = \frac{B'C'}{BC}$$

Four numbers that form a true proportion are called **proportional.** The numbers 5, 3, 10, and 6, in that order, are proportional because $\frac{5}{3} = \frac{10}{6}$. The numbers 1, 2, 3, and 4 are not proportional because $\frac{1}{2} \neq \frac{3}{4}$.

Proportional numbers always occur when there is a size change. For instance, when $\triangle ABC$ is a size-transformation image of $\triangle XYZ$, you can say, "The sides of the triangles are proportional." This means the three ratios of the corresponding sides are equal.

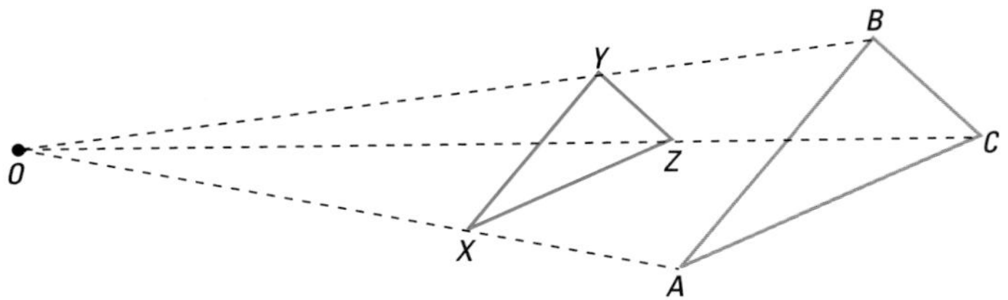

That is, $\frac{AB}{XY} = \frac{AC}{XZ} = \frac{BC}{YZ}$. Notice that in this proportion, *the numerators are lengths from one figure and the denominators are corresponding lengths in the other.* You can pick any two of these to form a true proportion.

$$\frac{AB}{XY} = \frac{AC}{XZ} \qquad \frac{AB}{XY} = \frac{BC}{YZ} \qquad \frac{AC}{XZ} = \frac{BC}{YZ}$$

Means and Extremes in a Proportion

The four terms in a proportion have two sets of names and are numbered in order. The 1st and 4th terms are the **extremes** and the 2nd and 3rd terms are the **means.**

1st term $\rightarrow a$, 2nd term $\rightarrow b$; $\frac{a}{b} = \frac{c}{d}$; $c \leftarrow$ 3rd term, $d \leftarrow$ 4th term

$\frac{a}{b} = \frac{c}{d}$ — extremes: a and d; means: b and c

In previous courses, you have learned that in any proportion, the product of the means equals the product of the extremes. This is the *Means-Extremes Property.*

> **Means-Extremes Property**
> If $\frac{a}{b} = \frac{c}{d}$, then $ad = bc$.

▶

Lesson 12-4 Overview, continued

these courses. However, all students should have some degree of familiarity with the property, since it is presented in all middle-school mathematics textbooks. Be aware that some students may know it as the "cross-multiplication" property.

Optional Activities

Consumer Connection
Materials: Advertisements from a grocery store or drugstore and actual items in the ads

You might use this activity as extra credit after students complete the lesson. Have students use newspaper advertisements from grocery stores or drug stores on various sizes of the same brand of merchandise. Have them determine the ratios of size change between the actual objects and their pictures in the newspaper. Which object is shrunk the most? Which object is expanded, the same size, or shrunk the least?

Proof

Given: $\frac{a}{b} = \frac{c}{d}$.

To prove: $ad = bc$.

Argument:

Multiply both sides of $\frac{a}{b} = \frac{c}{d}$ by bd.

$$bd \cdot \frac{a}{b} = bd \cdot \frac{c}{d}$$

$$b \cdot d \cdot a \cdot \frac{1}{b} = b \cdot d \cdot c \cdot \frac{1}{d}$$

Use the Commutative and Associative Properties of Multiplication.

$$\left(b \cdot \frac{1}{b}\right) \cdot a \cdot d = \left(d \cdot \frac{1}{d}\right) \cdot b \cdot c$$

Since the product of a number and its reciprocal is 1, these products can be simplified.

$$ad = bc$$

In geometry, a, b, c, and d are often lengths of segments.

Example 1

$\triangle QRS$ is the image of $\triangle TUV$ under a size change with center O. If $QR = 10$, $RS = 15$, and $TU = 25$, find UV.

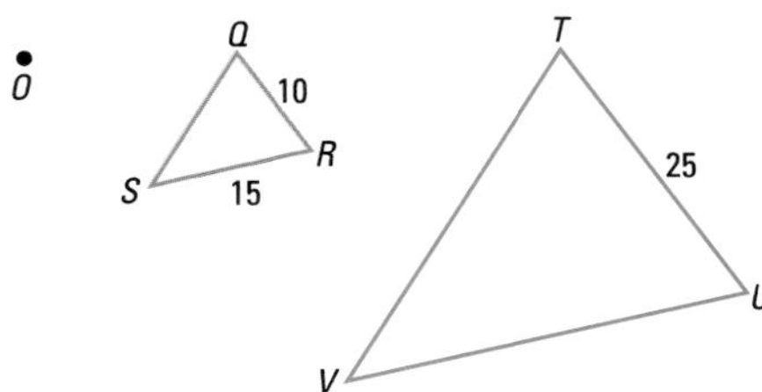

Solution 1

The sides of the triangles are proportional. Thus $\frac{TU}{QR} = \frac{UV}{RS}$.

Substituting,

$$\frac{25}{10} = \frac{UV}{15}.$$

Solve for UV, using the Means-Extremes Property:

$$25 \cdot 15 = 10 \cdot UV.$$

$$\frac{375}{10} = UV$$

$$UV = 37.5$$

Solution 2

The magnitude of the size change is $\frac{10}{25} = 0.4$.

So $0.4 \cdot UV = 15$, from which $UV = \frac{15}{0.4} = 37.5$.

Additional Examples

These examples are also given on **Teaching Aid 168.**

1. $\triangle DEF$ is the image of $\triangle ABC$ under a size change with center O. If $AB = 20$, $DE = 12$, and $DF = 16.5$, find AC.

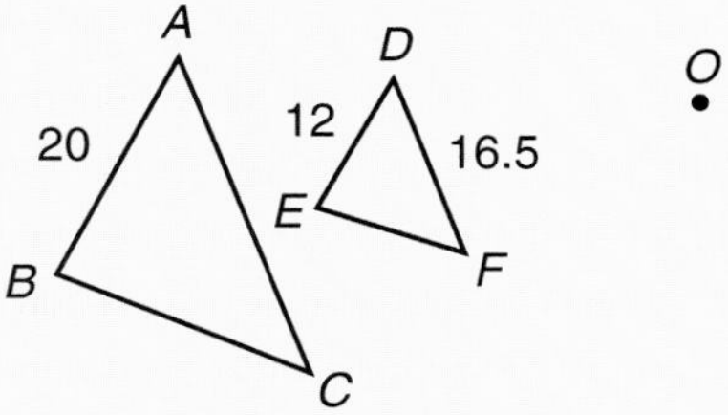

$AC = 27.5$

2. A toy train is $\frac{1}{48}$ actual size. If the locomotive of the train is $10\frac{7}{8}$" long and $2\frac{1}{4}$" high, how long and how high is the actual locomotive?
Length: 522", or $43\frac{1}{2}$'; Height: 108", or 9'

3. A Boeing 747 is about 70.5 meters long and has a wingspan of about 59.6 meters. The wingspan on a model of this plane is 40 centimeters. What will be the length of the model?
About 47.3 centimeters

Adapting to Individual Needs

Extra Help

Remind students that whenever they rename a fraction with a different denominator, they are using proportions. Point out that every fraction has an unlimited number of names, but only one name is in lowest terms. Also stress that the Means-Extremes Property applies only to proportions. Some students mistakenly try to apply the property in other situations, such as multiplication of fractions.

Challenge

Have students make scale drawings of one or more rooms in their homes, including the furniture. Students should be sure to identify the scale of their drawings. [Check students' drawings.]

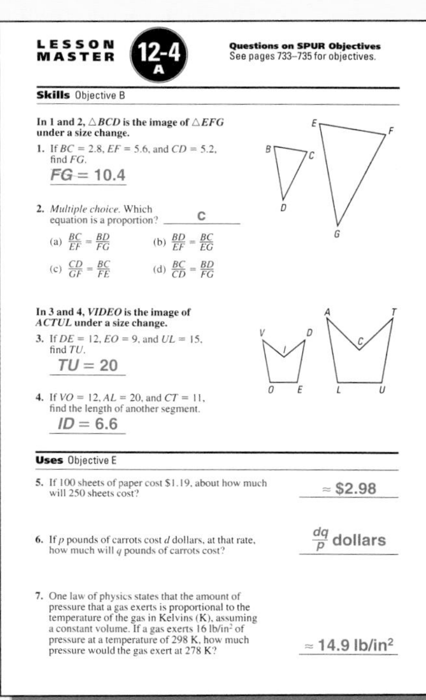

LESSON MASTER 12-4 A

Questions on SPUR Objectives
See pages 733–735 for objectives.

Skills Objective B

In 1 and 2, $\triangle BCD$ is the image of $\triangle EFG$ under a size change.

1. If $BC = 2.8$, $EF = 5.6$, and $CD = 5.2$, find FG.
$FG = 10.4$

2. *Multiple choice.* Which equation is a proportion? C
(a) $\frac{BC}{EF} = \frac{BD}{FG}$ (b) $\frac{BD}{EF} = \frac{BC}{EG}$
(c) $\frac{CD}{GF} = \frac{BC}{FE}$ (d) $\frac{BC}{CD} = \frac{BD}{FG}$

In 3 and 4, *VIDEO* is the image of *ACTUL* under a size change.

3. If $DE = 12$, $EO = 9$, and $UL = 15$, find TU.
$TU = 20$

4. If $VO = 12$, $AL = 20$, and $CT = 11$, find the length of another segment.
$ID = 6.6$

Uses Objective E

5. If 100 sheets of paper cost $1.19, about how much will 250 sheets cost? ≈ $2.98

6. If p pounds of carrots cost d dollars, at that rate, how much will q pounds of carrots cost? $\frac{dq}{p}$ dollars

7. One law of physics states that the amount of pressure that a gas exerts is proportional to the temperature of the gas in Kelvins (K), assuming a constant volume. If a gas exerts 16 lb/in^2 of pressure at a temperature of 298 K, how much pressure would the gas exert at 278 K? ≈ 14.9 lb/in^2

Notes on Questions

You may find it helpful to discuss all the questions in *Covering the Reading* quickly and in sequential order to ascertain that students know the terminology of the lesson.

Question 1 You might want to include the extended ratio in the discussion by asking students to describe a way to write the ratio 2 to 3 to 5. [2:3:5]

Questions 11–12 These questions indicate that the Side-Splitting Theorem of Lesson 13-3 could be deduced even now.

Question 13 Error Alert If students incorrectly answer $x = \frac{ab}{c}$, ask them to check their answers by substituting numbers for *a*, *b*, and *c* and solving the resulting equation for *x*. They should see that substituting the numbers in $\frac{ab}{c}$ will not give the same solution. However, substituting in $\frac{ac}{b}$ will give the same solution.

Questions 15–16 These questions should review material students have studied in algebra or other previous courses.

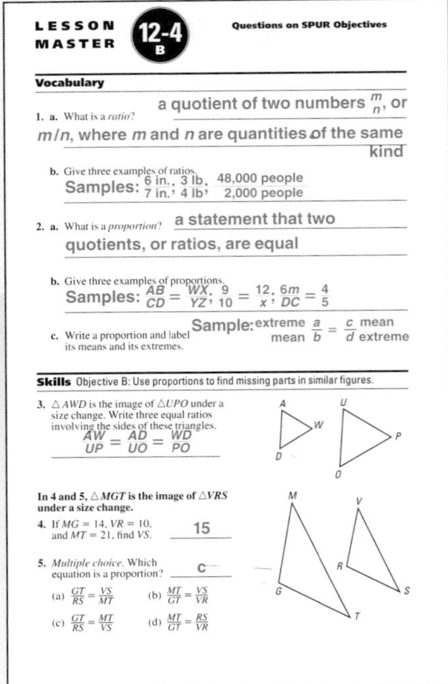

LESSON MASTER 12-4 B **Questions on SPUR Objectives**

Vocabulary

1\. a. What is a *ratio*? a quotient of two numbers $\frac{m}{n}$, or m/n, where m and n are quantities of the same kind

b. Give three examples of ratios. Samples: $\frac{6 \text{ in.}}{7 \text{ in.}}$, $\frac{3 \text{ lb}}{4 \text{ lb}}$, $\frac{48{,}000 \text{ people}}{2{,}000 \text{ people}}$

2\. a. What is a *proportion*? a statement that two quotients, or ratios, are equal

b. Give three examples of proportions. Samples: $\frac{AB}{CD} = \frac{WX}{YZ}$; $\frac{9}{10} = \frac{12}{x}$; $\frac{6m}{DC} = \frac{4}{5}$

c. Write a proportion and label its means and its extremes. Sample: extreme a, mean b, $\frac{a}{b} = \frac{c}{d}$, mean c, extreme d

Skills Objective B: Use proportions to find missing parts in similar figures.

3\. $\triangle AWD$ is the image of $\triangle UPO$ under a size change. Write three equal ratios involving the sides of these triangles. $\frac{AW}{UP} = \frac{AD}{UO} = \frac{WD}{PO}$

In 4 and 5, $\triangle MGT$ is the image of $\triangle VRS$ under a size change.

4\. If $MG = 14$, $VR = 10$, and $MT = 21$, find VS. 15

5\. *Multiple choice.* Which equation is a proportion? c

(a) $\frac{GT}{RS} = \frac{VS}{MT}$ (b) $\frac{MT}{GT} = \frac{VS}{VR}$

(c) $\frac{GT}{RS} = \frac{MT}{VS}$ (d) $\frac{MT}{GT} = \frac{RS}{VR}$

Proportions in Scale Models

Proportions occur in scale models, maps, and wherever else there are size changes.

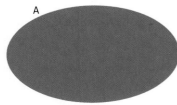

Dollhouse miniatures. *Accessories, such as the double boiler, the tea set, and the frying pan shown, are crafted to match the scale of the dollhouse.*

Example 2

A dollhouse is $\frac{1}{12}$ actual size. If a table in the dollhouse is an oval $6\frac{1}{2}''$ long and $4\frac{3}{8}''$ wide, how long and wide is the actual table it models?

Actual Table Dollhouse Table

Solution

Since corresponding lengths are proportional,

$$\frac{\text{dollhouse length}}{\text{actual length}} = \frac{1}{12} \text{ and } \frac{\text{dollhouse width}}{\text{actual width}} = \frac{1}{12}.$$

Substitute for the dollhouse table dimensions and let *L* and *W* be the actual length and width.

$$\frac{6\frac{1}{2}''}{L} = \frac{1}{12} \qquad \frac{4\frac{3}{8}''}{W} = \frac{1}{12}$$

Use the Means-Extremes Property.

$$1 \cdot L = 12 \cdot 6\frac{1}{2}'' \qquad 1 \cdot W = 12 \cdot 4\frac{3}{8}''$$

$$L = 78'' \qquad W = 52\frac{1}{2}''$$

Check

$\frac{78''}{6.5''} = 12$ and $\frac{52.5''}{4.375''} = 12$, so the measurements of the actual table are 12 times the measurements of the model.

QUESTIONS

Covering the Reading

1. *Multiple choice.* Which is *not* a way of writing the ratio of 7 to 9?
   (a) 7 : 9 (b) 7/9
   (c) $\frac{7}{9}$ (d) 7.9 d
2. A ratio is a __?__ of two numbers. quotient
3. A proportion is a statement that two __?__ are __?__. quotients, equal

708

Adapting to Individual Needs

English Language Development

To demonstrate *means* and *extremes* have four students stand in line facing the class. Ask the class to name the two middle students—*means* relates to *middle*. Have the class name the two end students—*extremes* relates to the *last* or *farthest*. Then relate these terms to the proportion $\frac{a}{b} = \frac{c}{d}$ when it is written as $a: b = c: d$ (*b* and *c* are the *means,* and *a* and *d* are the *extremes*). Have the first three students name numbers *a*, *b*, and *c*, and the last student give the value of *d* that makes a true proportion.

4) $\frac{2}{4} \neq \frac{6}{8}, \frac{2}{6} \neq \frac{4}{8}, \frac{2}{8} \neq \frac{4}{6}$

7) Sample: $\frac{SA}{BG} = \frac{SM}{BI} = \frac{AM}{GI}$

4. Why are the numbers 2, 4, 6, and 8 *not* proportional? See left.

5. Given $\frac{7}{x} = \frac{11}{y}$, name the

a. extremes. 7, y
b. means. x, 11
c. first term. 7
d. fourth term. y
e. third term. 11
f. second term. x

6. Suppose $\frac{r}{s} = \frac{t}{u}$. What conclusion is justified by the Means-Extremes Property? $ru = st$

7. In the figure at the right, $\triangle SMA$ is the image of $\triangle BIG$ under a size change. Write three equal ratios involving the sides of these triangles. See left.

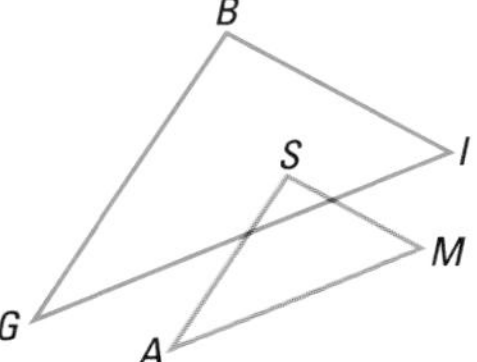

In 8 and 9, *ABCD* at the left is the image of *FGHE* under a size change with center *V*.

8. Fill in the missing length: $\frac{AB}{FG} = \frac{AD}{\square}$. FE

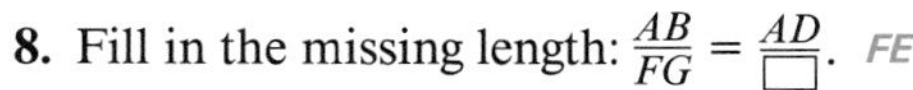

9. If $FG = 10$, $AB = 12$, and $BC = 15$, what is GH? 12.5

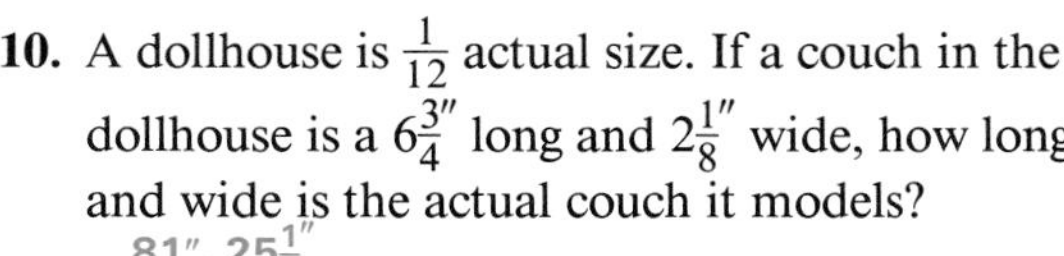

10. A dollhouse is $\frac{1}{12}$ actual size. If a couch in the dollhouse is a $6\frac{3}{4}''$ long and $2\frac{1}{8}''$ wide, how long and wide is the actual couch it models? 81″, $25\frac{1}{2}''$

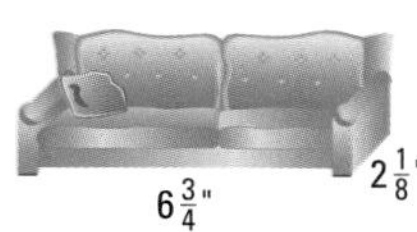

In 11 and 12, $\triangle GJK$ at the left is a size-change image of $\triangle GHI$.

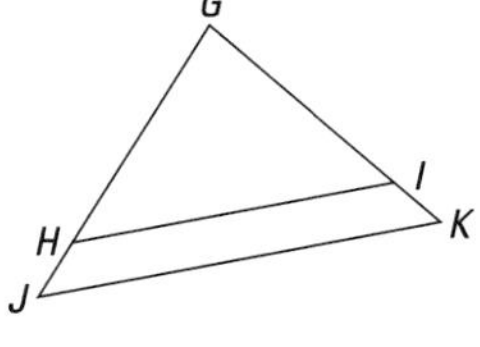

11. *True or false.* a) True b) True c) False

a. $\frac{GJ}{GH} = \frac{GK}{GI}$ **b.** $\frac{GH}{GJ} = \frac{GI}{GK}$ **c.** $\frac{JK}{HI} = \frac{GI}{GK}$

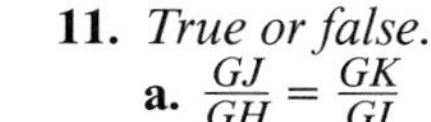

12. If $GH = 100$, $GJ = 130$, and $HI = 120$, then $JK =$ ___?___. 156

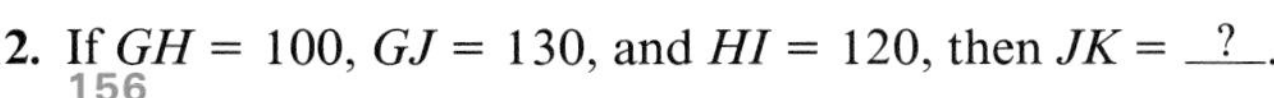

Applying the Mathematics

In 13 and 14, solve for *x*.

13. $\frac{a}{x} = \frac{b}{c}$ $x = \frac{ac}{b}$

14. $\frac{x}{x+3} = \frac{9}{10}$ $x = 27$

15. Weights and prices of fruit at a store usually are proportional. If 2.3 pounds of dates imported from Oman cost $2.39, what would 4 pounds of dates cost? ≈ $4.16

16. a. If you bike 13 miles in $1\frac{1}{2}$ hours, at that rate how many miles would you bike in $2\frac{1}{2}$ hours? $21\frac{2}{3} \approx 21.7$ miles

b. If you drive *m* miles in *h* hours, at that rate how many miles can you drive in *r* hours? $\frac{mr}{h}$ miles

17. A photograph measures 40 mm by 30 mm. It is enlarged so that the longer side measures 150 mm. What is the length of the shorter side of the enlargement? 112.5 mm

Question 16 Students could use the pattern of **part a** to do **part b.** Another method is to let *x* represent the unknown distance and use the following proportion:

$$\frac{m \text{ miles}}{h \text{ hours}} = \frac{x \text{ miles}}{r \text{ hours}}$$

Then they can solve this proportion to obtain $x = \frac{rm}{h}$. (Students who have studied previous UCSMP courses may think this way.)

(Notes on Questions continue on page 710.)

Follow-up for Lesson 12-4

Practice

For more questions on SPUR Objectives, use **Lesson Master 12-4A** (shown on page 707) or **Lesson Master 12-4B** (shown on pages 708–709).

Assessment

Quiz A quiz covering Lessons 12-1 through 12-4 is provided in the *Assessment Sourcebook.*

Group Assessment Ask students to explain how to solve for the fourth term in a proportion in which three of the terms are known. [Students correctly explain how to solve for an unknown term in a proportion.]

(Follow-up continues on page 710.)

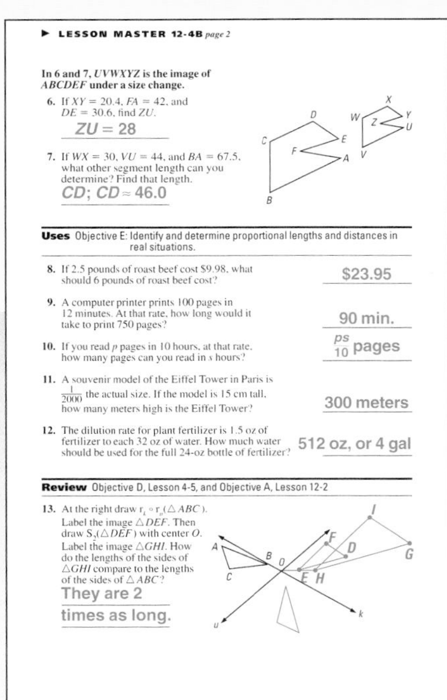

▶ LESSON MASTER 12-4B *page 2*

In 6 and 7, *UVWXYZ* is the image of *ABCDEF* under a size change.

6. If $XY = 20.4$, $FA = 42$, and $DE = 30.6$, find ZU. ZU = 28

7. If $WX = 30$, $VU = 44$, and $BA = 67.5$, what other segment length can you determine? Find that length. CD; CD = 46.0

Uses Objective E: Identify and determine proportional lengths and distances in real situations.

8. If 2.5 pounds of roast beef cost $9.98, what should 6 pounds of roast beef cost? $23.95

9. A computer printer prints 100 pages in 12 minutes. At that rate, how long would it take to print 750 pages? 90 min.

10. If you read *p* pages in 10 hours, at that rate, how many pages can you read in *s* hours? $\frac{ps}{10}$ pages

11. A souvenir model of the Eiffel Tower in Paris is $\frac{1}{2000}$ the actual size. If the model is 15 cm tall, how many meters high is the Eiffel Tower? 300 meters

12. The dilution rate for plant fertilizer is 1.5 oz of fertilizer to each 32 oz of water. How much water should be used for the full 24-oz bottle of fertilizer? 512 oz, or 4 gal

Review Objective D, Lesson 4-5, and Objective A, Lesson 12-2

13. At the right draw $r_x \circ r_y(\triangle ABC)$. Label the image $\triangle DEF$. Then draw $S_2(\triangle DEF)$ with center *O*. Label the image $\triangle GHI$. How do the lengths of the sides of $\triangle GHI$ compare to the lengths of the sides of $\triangle ABC$? They are 2 times as long.

Setting Up Lesson 12-5

The discussion of congruence in **Question 24** can be used as a lead-in to the definition of *similarity* in Lesson 12-5.

Materials Students answering **Question 25** in *Exploration* on page 716 will need scale models. Then, students should keep the model for **Question 22** in Lesson 12-6.

Extension

Have students prove this statement: The image of the midpoint of $\overline{AB}$ under a size change is the midpoint of $\overline{A'B'}$. [Sample: $AM = MB$ (definition of midpoint); $\frac{AM}{A'M'} = \frac{MB}{M'B'}$ (under a size change, corresponding distances are proportional); $\frac{AM}{A'M'} = \frac{AM}{M'B'}$ (Substitution Property of Equality); $AM \cdot M'B' = A'M' \cdot AM$ (Means-Extremes Property); $M'B' = A'M'$ (Multiplication Property of Equality); M' is the midpoint of $\overline{A'B'}$ (definition of midpoint)]

Project Update Project 2, *Golden Ratio,* and Project 5, *Pantograph,* on pages 729–730, relate to the content of this lesson.

Notes on Questions

Question 23 If the central polygon were a regular hexagon instead of a regular pentagon, the points F, G, H, and I would be collinear, and a tessellation of regular hexagons and equilateral triangles would be possible.

Question 24 This question is an appropriate lead-in for Lesson 12-5.

19) $S(A) = (8, -3)$, $S(B) = (5, 4)$, $AB = \sqrt{6^2 + 14^2} = \sqrt{232} = 2\sqrt{58}$; length of $S(\overline{AB}) = \sqrt{3^2 + 7^2} = \sqrt{58}$; $\sqrt{58} = \frac{1}{2} \cdot 2\sqrt{58}$

Review

18. Suppose S is a size change of magnitude 1.5, and $S(ABCDE) = UVWXY$. If $m\angle BDE = 47$ and $AE = 30$, find two other measures. *(Lessons 12-2, 12-3)* $m\angle VXY = 47$ and $UY = 45$

19. Let S be a size transformation of magnitude $\frac{1}{2}$ centered at the origin. If $A = (16, -6)$ and $B = (10, 8)$, verify that the distance between $S(A)$ and $S(B)$ is half the distance between A and B. *(Lessons 12-1, 12-3)* See left.

20. Trace the figure below. Draw the image of the figure under the size change with center H and magnitude $\frac{3}{5}$. *(Lesson 12-2)*

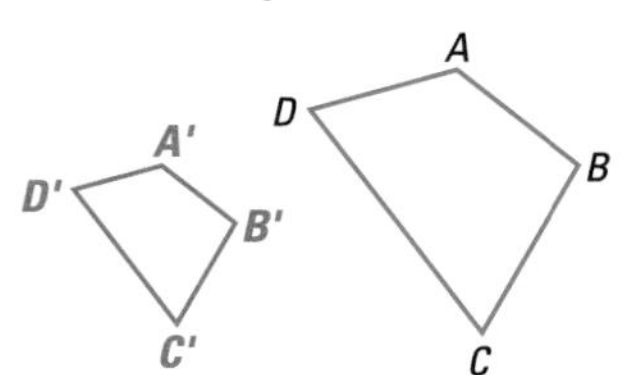

A photo enlarger projects an image from a negative onto photographic paper.

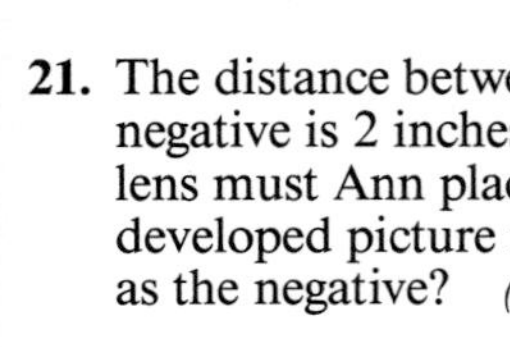

21. The distance between the lens and the negative is 2 inches. How far away from the lens must Ann place the photo paper if the developed picture is to be 5 times as large as the negative? *(Lesson 12-2)* 10 in.

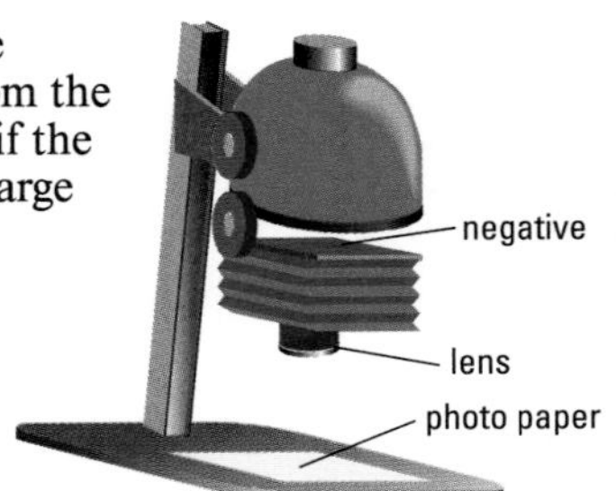

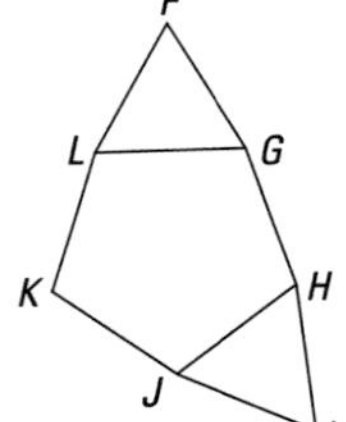

22) Sample: Choose $A = (0, 0)$, $B = (1, 1)$. Then $AB = \sqrt{1^2 + 1^2} = \sqrt{2}$. $T(A) = (0, 0)$. $T(B) = (2, 3)$. Length of $T(\overline{AB}) = \sqrt{2^2 + 3^2} = \sqrt{13}$. $\sqrt{13} \neq \sqrt{2}$. Thus T does not preserve distance.

22. Show that the transformation T with equation $T(x, y) = (2x, 3y)$ does not preserve distance. *(Lesson 12-1)* See left.

23. Given: FGL, $GHJKL$, and HIJ at the left are regular polygons.

a. Write an argument to prove that $\triangle FGL \cong \triangle HIJ$. See margin.

b. What is $m\angle GHI$? *(Lessons 6-7, 7-2)* 168

24. Finish this definition. Two figures α (alpha) and β (beta) are congruent, written $\alpha \cong \beta$, if and only if __?__. *(Lesson 5-1)*
β is the image of α under a reflection or composite of reflections.

Exploration

25. Draw a quadrilateral with sides of four different lengths. Next, draw a second quadrilateral with sides that are twice as long as those of the first quadrilateral. Must the corresponding angles of the two quadrilaterals be congruent? Explain why or why not. See margin.

Additional Answers

23a. Since $GHJKL$ is regular, $\overline{GL} \cong \overline{HJ}$. Since $\triangle FGL$ and $\triangle HIJ$ are regular polygons, they are equilateral (definition of regular polygon), and so $\overline{FG} \cong \overline{FL} \cong \overline{GL}$ and $\overline{HI} \cong \overline{JI} \cong \overline{HJ}$. Thus, by the Transitive Property of Congruence, all six of these segments are congruent. So, by the SSS Congruence Theorem, $\triangle FGL \cong \triangle HIJ$.

25. Sample:

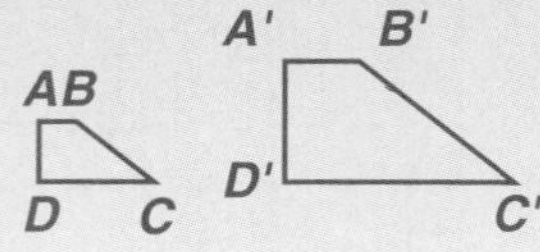

Corresponding angles are not necessarily congruent. Unlike triangles, the angles of a quadrilateral are not determined by the lengths of sides.

LESSON

12-5

Similar Figures

Model Plans. *Model enthusiasts often use detailed plans for constructing replicas of real-life objects.*

The word "congruent" refers to figures with the same size and shape. In Lesson 4-8, three terms relating to this idea were precisely defined:

congruent figures,
≅ (is congruent to), and
congruence transformation.

These precise definitions enable an in-depth study of figures with the same size and shape.

In this lesson, we define three corresponding terms for figures that have the same shape but not necessarily the same size:

similar figures,
~ (is similar to), and
similarity transformation.

A Precise Definition for Similar Figures

You have seen that under a size change, figures and their images have the same shape. So under any definition, these figures should be similar. But also, performing an isometry (reflection, rotation, translation, or glide reflection) on a figure does not change its shape. The definition of *similar figures* encompasses all of these possibilities.

Definition
Two figures F and G are similar, written $F \sim G$, if and only if there is a composite of size changes and reflections mapping one onto the other.

Lesson 12-5

Objectives

B Use proportions to find missing parts in similar figures.
E Identify and determine proportional lengths and distances in real situations.

Resources

From the ***Teacher's Resource File***
- Lesson Master 12-5A or 12-5B
- Answer Master 12-5
- Teaching Aids:
  158 Warm-up
  169 Additional Examples
- Activity Kit, Activity 25

Additional Resources
- Visuals for Teaching Aids 158, 169
- Protractors and rulers or **Geometry Template**
- Scale models

Teaching Lesson 12-5

Warm-up

Divide this figure into four congruent parts that each have the same shape as the original figure.

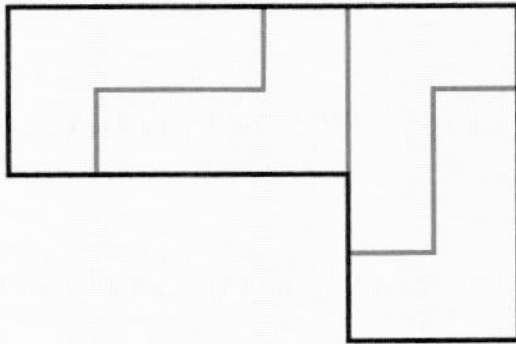

Lesson 12-5 Overview

Broad Goals This lesson covers the general definition of similar figures and its application to the process of finding missing lengths and angle measures.

Perspective Two figures are defined to be *similar* if one can be mapped onto the other by a composite of size transformations and reflections. This is a perfect analogue to the definition of congruent figures, and it is a definition that applies to all figures.

The properties of similar figures come immediately from the properties of size changes and reflections. In similar figures, corresponding distances are proportional and corresponding angles have the same measure. **Example 2** is much like those that students have seen in earlier lessons with size changes.

The transformation approach gives us a power that Euclid did not have. With standard approaches, one is forced to spend time proving individual theorems, such as *If two triangles are similar, then corresponding altitudes are in the same ratio as the ratio of similitude.* With transformations, all corresponding lengths are dealt with at the same time, which is the intuitive way.

Triangles ABC, PQR, SQT, and XYZ below are similar.

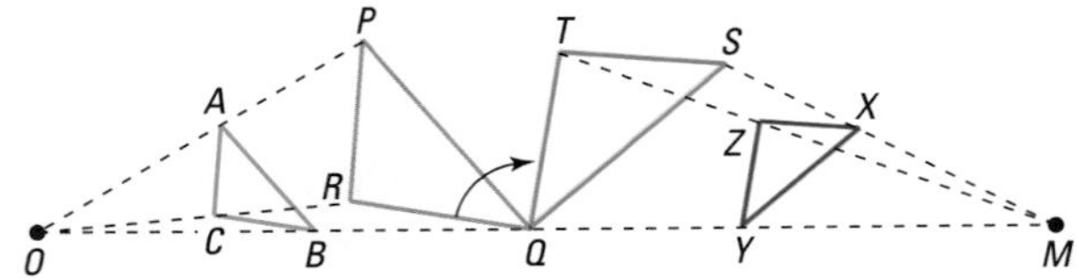

ΔPQR is a size-change image of ΔABC with center O and magnitude 1.8.
ΔSQT is a rotation image of ΔPQR with center Q and magnitude -90°.
ΔXYZ is a size-change image of ΔSQT with center M and magnitude $\frac{2}{3}$.

The symbol "~" is read "is similar to." Thus, in the figure below, you can write "$WXYZ \sim ABCD$" and say "Quadrilateral $WXYZ$ is similar to quadrilateral $ABCD$." As with congruence, corresponding vertices are written in corresponding order.

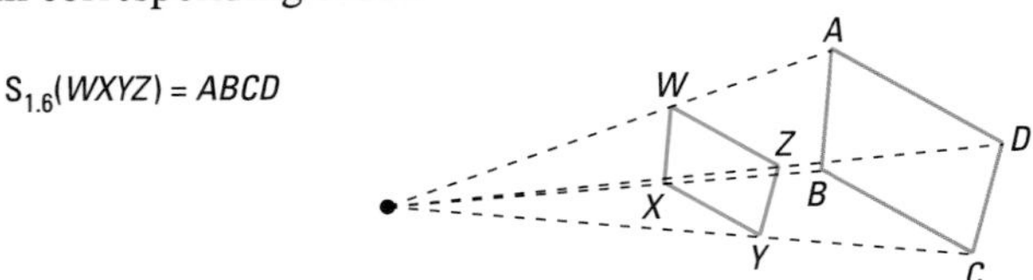

Which Transformations Are Similarity Transformations?

Transformations that give rise to similar figures are called *similarity transformations.*

> **Definition**
> A transformation is a **similarity transformation** if and only if it is the composite of size changes and reflections.

Recall that the size change S_1 with magnitude 1 is the identity transformation. It does nothing to a figure. Thus, all congruent figures are images of each other under a composite of reflections and S_1. So all congruent figures are similar figures.

Here is a hierarchy of transformations you have studied, with similarity transformations, size changes, and the identity transformation included.

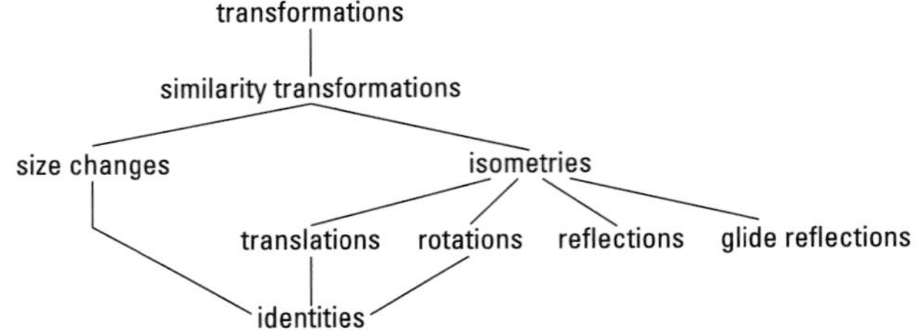

Properties of Similar Figures

The basic properties of similar figures come from preservation properties of similarity transformations. Compare these lists.

Notes on Reading

Reading Mathematics You may wish to read this lesson aloud with your students, placing an emphasis on the main ideas. Ask students what clues are given to help them remember the properties of similarity transformations. Also ask how these clues can be used to find the solutions to **Examples 1 and 2.**

Just as you may have begun the discussion of properties of size transformations by writing down the properties of reflections, you might begin the discussion of similar figures by writing down the definition of congruence. Then put parentheses around certain words and show replacements as indicated below in italics.

> Two figures F and G are (congruent) *similar,* written $F(\cong) \sim G$, if and only if there is a composite of (reflections) *reflections* and *size changes* mapping F onto G.

The Similar Figures Theorem is also analogous to a theorem of congruence. As shown below, only two words are different.

> If two figures are (congruent) *similar,* then:
> (a) corresponding angles are congruent;
> (b) corresponding lengths are (congruent) *proportional.*

The section on page 714, *The Ratio of Similitude,* introduces a convention that enables us to obtain a unique ratio of similitude between two figures. Notice that, when the ~ sign is used and one is asked for the ratio of similitude, the figure named first is considered the preimage; the image is second.

Error Alert Setting up the proportions used in **Examples 1 and 2** may be difficult for some students if they are not careful to match up the corresponding sides correctly. A good rule to remember is to put the corresponding sides of the same figure "all on the top" or "all on the bottom" of the proportion.

Optional Activities

Activity 1
In *Activity Kit, Activity 25,* students explore the notion that all parabolas are similar. This is a concept not easily accepted by students nor, in fact, by some teachers. It is recommended that this activity be used with your students as a follow-up to the lesson.

Preserved under reflections	Preserved under size transformations
Angle measure	Angle measure
Betweenness	Betweenness
Collinearity	Collinearity
Distance	

The properties common to both columns are preserved by similarity transformations. Thus similarity transformations have the A-B-C preservation properties, while distance is not preserved. Still, because size transformations are involved, similarity transformations multiply distance by a constant amount. Thus the ratios of image lengths to preimage lengths are equal.

Similar Figures Theorem
If two figures are similar, then
(1) corresponding angles are congruent, and
(2) corresponding lengths are proportional.

The Similar Figures Theorem allows lengths and angle measures in similar figures to be found.

Example 1

In the figure below, $r_\ell \circ S_{2.5}(ABCD) = WXYZ$, and the center of $S_{2.5}$ is O.

a. If $m\angle B = 85$, what angle in $WXYZ$ has measure 85?

b. If $CD = 12$, what length in $WXYZ$ can be determined, and what is it?

Solution

$ABCD \sim WXYZ$ because $r_\ell \circ S_{2.5}$ is a composite of a reflection and a size change.

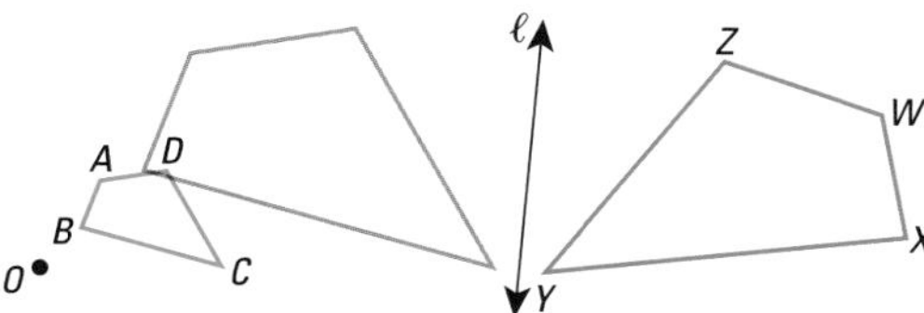

a. By the Similar Figures Theorem, corresponding angles are congruent. $\angle A \cong \angle W$, $\angle B \cong \angle X$, $\angle C \cong \angle Y$, and $\angle D \cong \angle Z$.
Since $m\angle B = 85$, so also $m\angle X = 85$.

b. By the Similar Figures Theorem, corresponding sides are proportional. These ratios equal 2.5, the magnitude of the size change.
$\frac{WX}{AB} = \frac{XY}{BC} = \frac{YZ}{CD} = \frac{ZW}{DA} = 2.5$. Since $CD = 12$, the length of the corresponding side YZ can be determined.

$$\frac{YZ}{12} = 2.5$$
$$YZ = 12 \cdot 2.5 = 30$$

Additional Examples

These examples are also given on **Teaching Aid 169.**

1. In the figure, $S_{1.25} \circ r_m(\triangle RST) = \triangle JLK$, and the center of $S_{1.25}$ is point O.

a. If $m\angle K = 67$, what angle in $\triangle RST$ has measure 67? $\angle T$

b. If $JK = 11$, what length in $\triangle RST$ can be determined, and what is this length? $RT = 8.8$

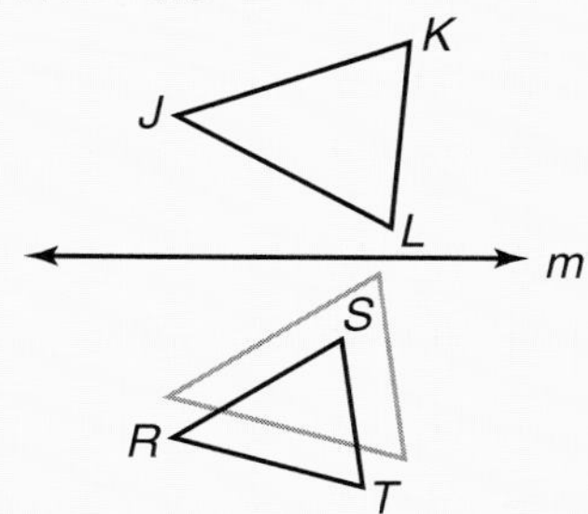

2. $\triangle NUT \sim \triangle SQR$, with angle measures and lengths as indicated. Find as many angle measures and lengths in $\triangle NUT$ as possible using the Similar Figures Theorem.

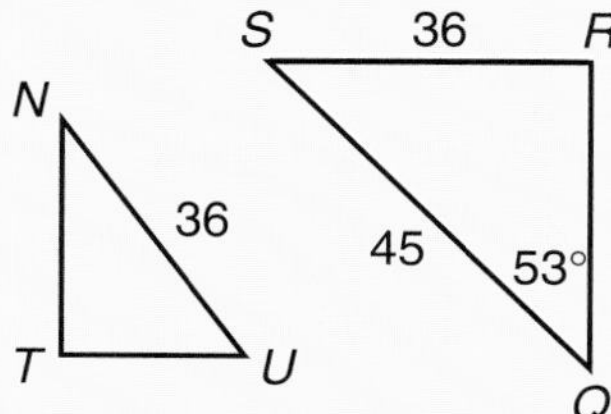

$m\angle U = 53$; $NT = 28.8$

(Additional Examples continue on page 714.)

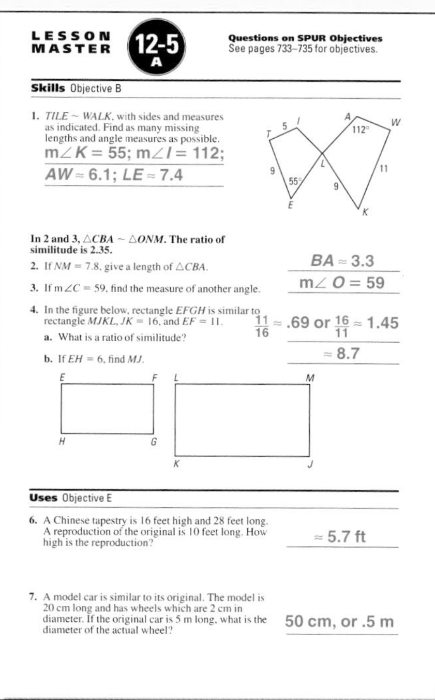

LESSON MASTER 12-5 A

Questions on SPUR Objectives
See pages 733–735 for objectives.

Skills Objective B

1. $TILE \sim WALK$, with sides and measures as indicated. Find as many missing lengths and angle measures as possible.
$m\angle K = 55$; $m\angle I = 112$;
$AW \approx 6.1$; $LE \approx 7.4$

In 2 and 3, $\triangle CBA \sim \triangle ONM$. The ratio of similitude is 2.35.

2. If $NM = 7.8$, give a length of $\triangle CBA$. $BA \approx 3.3$

3. If $m\angle C = 59$, find the measure of another angle. $m\angle O = 59$

4. In the figure below, rectangle $EFGH$ is similar to rectangle $MJKL$, $JK = 16$, and $EF = 11$.

a. What is a ratio of similitude? $\frac{11}{16} \approx .69$ or $\frac{16}{11} \approx 1.45$

b. If $EH = 6$, find MJ. ≈ 8.7

Uses Objective E

6. A Chinese tapestry is 16 feet high and 28 feet long. A reproduction of the original is 10 feet long. How high is the reproduction? ≈ 5.7 ft

7. A model car is similar to its original. The model is 20 cm long and has wheels which are 2 cm in diameter. If the original car is 5 m long, what is the diameter of the actual wheel? 50 cm, or .5 m

Optional Activities

Activity 2

After students complete the lesson, you might give them the figure at the right. Caution them not to assume that $ABCD$ is a square. Then tell them that $ABCD$ was rotated 90° about point O and then its image was transformed under the size change with center O, magnitude 1.98. Ask what angle in $EFGH$ has the same measure as $\angle D$. [$\angle G$] Ask what length in $EFGH$ can be determined if $AB = 4.62$ and have them give this length. [$EH = 9.1476$]

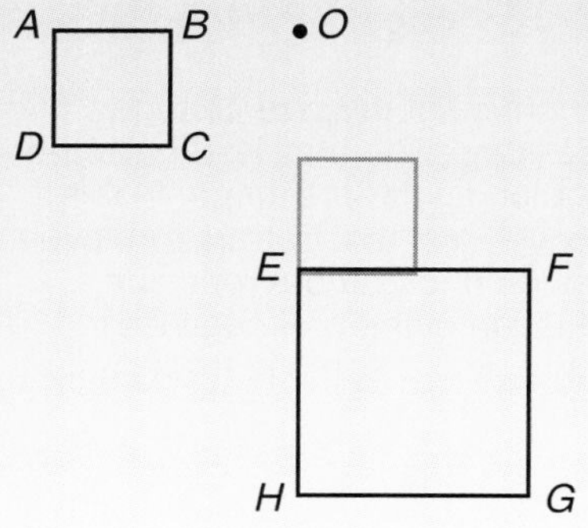

3. Suppose $\triangle ABC \sim \triangle XYZ$, with a ratio of similitude of 3.5. If $BC = 2$ and $m\angle Y = 15$, what other angle measures and lengths can be determined using the Similar Figures Theorem? $m\angle B = 15$; $YZ = 7$

Notes on Questions

Questions 1–3 Often the more complicated a figure is, the easier it is to see the similarity. Thus, students may find it easy to see the similarity in the figures used in these questions, whereas they may have some difficulty with the pentagons of **Questions 12–14.** In fact, students may have the greatest difficulty seeing the similarity in triangles, such as those on page 712 of this lesson.

Questions 9–11 Students may wonder whether there is any transformation that is *not* a similarity transformation. Refer them back to Lesson 4-8, in which examples of such transformations are given. [They do not preserve angle measure.]

Questions 12–14 You may wish to have students estimate some other angle measures and side lengths on one of these figures and have students calculate the corresponding angles and sides of the other figure.

(Notes on Questions continue on page 716.)

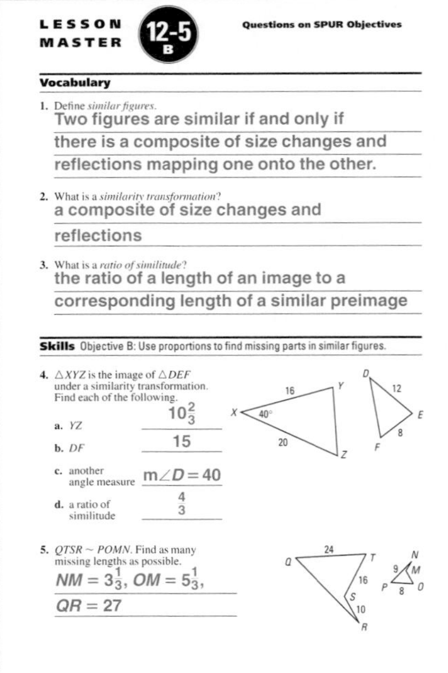
LESSON MASTER 12-5 B Questions on SPUR Objectives

Vocabulary

1. Define *similar figures.*
Two figures are similar if and only if there is a composite of size changes and reflections mapping one onto the other.

2. What is a *similarity transformation*?
a composite of size changes and reflections

3. What is a *ratio of similitude*?
the ratio of a length of an image to a corresponding length of a similar preimage

Skills Objective B: Use proportions to find missing parts in similar figures.

4. $\triangle XYZ$ is the image of $\triangle DEF$ under a similarity transformation. Find each of the following.
a. YZ $10\frac{2}{3}$
b. DF 15
c. another angle measure $m\angle D = 40$
d. a ratio of similitude $\frac{4}{3}$

5. $QTSR \sim POMN$. Find as many missing lengths as possible.
$NM = 3\frac{1}{3}$, $OM = 5\frac{1}{3}$, $QR = 27$

The Ratio of Similitude

The ratio of a length on an image to the corresponding length on a similar preimage is called the **ratio of similitude.** Unless otherwise specified, $F \sim G$, with *ratio of similitude k*, means that lengths in G divided by lengths in F equal k. The ratio of similitude is the product of the size-change factors of all the size transformations used in the similarity transformation. In Example 1 on page 713, the ratio of similitude is 2.5.

When examining similar figures, always look first for corresponding vertices. These give the pairs of congruent angles. Look next at corresponding sides.

Example 2

$\triangle ABC \sim \triangle RST$ with angle measures and lengths as indicated. Find as many angle measures and lengths in $\triangle RST$ as possible.

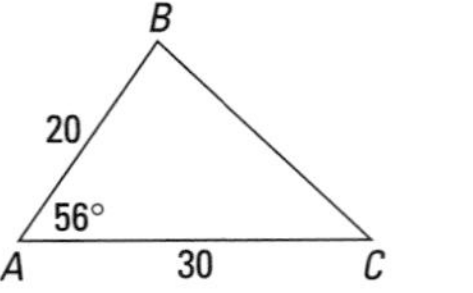

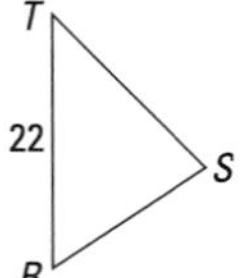

Solution

Angle measures: $\angle R$ corresponds to $\angle A$. In similar figures, corresponding angles are congruent. So $m\angle R = m\angle A = 56$.

Lengths: Since corresponding sides are proportional, $\frac{TR}{CA} = \frac{SR}{BA} = \frac{ST}{BC}$.

Any one of these ratios equals the ratio of similitude. Now substitute the three known lengths.

$$\frac{22}{30} = \frac{SR}{20} = \frac{ST}{BC}$$

Use the equality of the left and middle ratios.

$$\frac{22}{30} = \frac{SR}{20}$$

By the Means-Extremes Property,

$$30 \cdot SR = 440.$$

$$SR = \frac{440}{30} = 14\tfrac{2}{3} \approx 14.67$$

Neither BC nor ST nor the measures of the other four angles can be found using the Similar Figures Theorem.

In Example 2, the SAS condition is satisfied, so enough information is given to determine the measures of all sides and angle measures in each triangle. But to do this, a theorem from trigonometry (called the Law of Cosines) is needed. We do not cover that theorem in this book.

Adapting to Individual Needs

Extra Help

Remind students that the size-change images in Lessons 12-1 and 12-2 have the same orientation as the preimage. In this lesson, however, a similarity transformation also can include one or more reflections. So the orientation of the preimage and image may not be the same in a similarity transformation.

English Language Development

Before they read the lesson, you might want to review the following terms with students who have limited English proficiency: *similar, similarity, transformation, ratio,* and *similitude.*

QUESTIONS

Covering the Reading

In 1–3, use the sketch below. Figure III is the image of Figure I under $S \circ r_\ell$, where S is the size transformation with center C, magnitude 2.3.

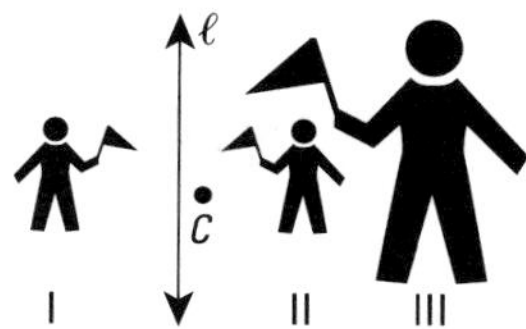

1. $S \circ r_\ell$ is what kind of transformation? a similarity transformation

2. Figures I and III are _?_. similar

3. Figures I and II are both _?_ and _?_. congruent, similar

4. Define *similar figures.* See left.

4) Two figures are similar if and only if there is a composite of size changes and reflections mapping one onto the other.

5. The symbol "~" is read _?_. is similar to

6. *True or false.* If two figures are congruent, then they are similar. True

7. *True or false.* If two figures are similar, then they are congruent. False

8. Tell whether the property is preserved by every similarity transformation.

a. angle measure Yes **b.** betweenness Yes
c. distance No **d.** orientation No

In 9–11, is the given transformation a similarity transformation?

9. a reflection Yes **10.** a size change with magnitude $\frac{1}{3}$ Yes

11. the composite of a rotation and a size change Yes

In 12–14, $ABCDE \sim FGHIJ$. The ratio of similitude is $\frac{4}{7}$.

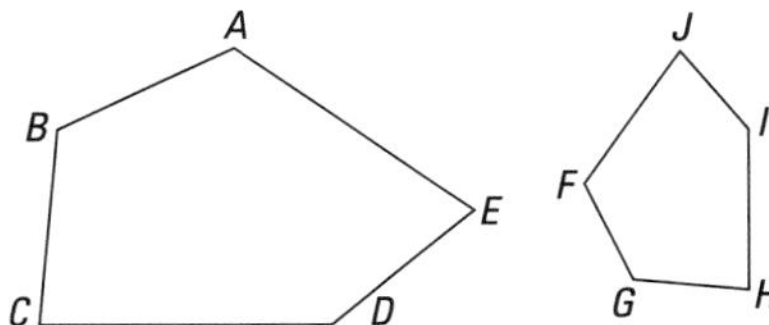

12. *True or false.* $m\angle I = \frac{4}{7} \cdot m\angle D$. False

13. Suppose $FJ = 10$.
a. Which other segment length can be determined? *AE*
b. What is that length? 17.5 units

14. If $DE = x$, then $IJ =$ _?_. $\frac{4x}{7}$

Follow-up for Lesson 12-5

Practice

For more questions on SPUR Objectives, use **Lesson Master 12-5A** (shown on page 713) or **Lesson Master 12-5B** (shown on pages 714–715).

Assessment

Written Communication Have students show a figure and its image under a similarity transformation that involves at least one size change and one reflection. [Students provide an example of the required type and include a suitable explanation and diagrams.]

Extension

Writing Have students determine whether each statement is true or false and give a convincing argument to support each answer. For any figure *F*, *G*, and *H*:

1. $F \sim F$.
2. if $F \sim G$, then $G \sim F$.
3. if $F \sim G$ and $G \sim H$, then $F \sim H$.

[All statements are true. Arguments will vary.]

Project Update Project 2, *Golden Ratio,* and Project 5, *Pantograph,* on pages 729–730, relate to the content of this lesson.

► **LESSON MASTER 12-5B** *page 2*

6. $\triangle GYT \sim \triangle UFZ$, with the ratio of similitude 4.5, $FZ = 31.5$, and $GT = 5$.
a. Find as many other segment lengths as possible. $YT = 7$, $UZ = 22.5$
b. If $m\angle Y = 62$ and $m\angle Z = 40$, find as many other angle measures as possible. $m\angle F = 62$, $m\angle T = 40$, $m\angle G = m\angle U = 78$

7. Parallelograms *ABCD* and *DEFG* are similar.
a. Complete the following. The ratio of similitude is _?_ or _?_. $\frac{7}{10}$ $\frac{10}{7}$
b. Find *BC*. 21
c. Find $m\angle A$. 105

28, B, A, C, D, E, 75°, 30, G, F, 40

Uses Objective E: Identify and determine proportional lengths and distances in real situations.

8. A slide measures 35 mm by 23 mm. The full picture is projected on a screen and measures 120 cm long. What is the width of the picture on the screen? ≈ 79 cm

9. Lucy is 5 ft 5 in. tall and her little sister Gwen is 4 ft 2 in. tall. In a photograph of the two sisters, Lucy is 6.25 in. tall. How tall is Gwen in the photograph? ≈ 4.81 in.

10. A scale model of the solar system shows Mercury 24 inches from the sun. The actual distance is about 36 million miles. Earth is about 93 million miles from the sun. In the model, how far should Earth be from the sun? ≈ 62 in.

11. On the 2-in.-by-2-in. photograph of a United States passport, the size of a person's face from the chin to the top of the head must not be less than 1 in. nor greater than $1\frac{3}{8}$ in. If a person's face measures 3.5 in. in a photograph, by what range of scale factors must the photograph be reduced for use on a passport? $\frac{2}{7}$ to $\frac{11}{28}$, or ≈ .29 to ≈ .39

Adapting to Individual Needs

Challenge
Ask students how many 3-by-5 rectangles can be cut from a 17-by-22 rectangular piece of paper? Have them sketch a solution.

[24 rectangles; a sample sketch is shown at the right.]

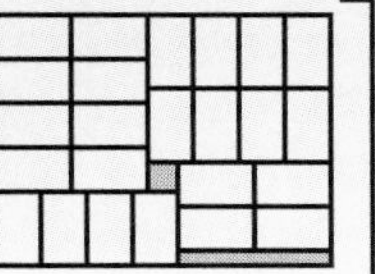

Notes on Questions

Question 17 History Connection The plane with the largest wingspan is the Hughes H.4 Hercules flying boat, more popularly known as the *Spruce Goose.* Built in 1947, it has a wingspan of 320 feet and a length of 218 feet 8 inches. It weighs 212 tons. It was flown only once, achieving an altitude of 70 feet and a distance of 3000 feet. Its pilot was also its builder, Howard Hughes.

Question 20 Although the cost is \$3.33 if rounded *to the nearest cent,* most stores round up.

Question 22 This question leads to solving the proportion $\frac{x}{x+5} = \frac{12}{16}$. This type of equation occurs often in Chapter 13 and should be discussed here.

Question 25 This question has a follow-up in **Question 22** of Lesson 12-6.

Question 26 The purpose of a question involving mathematics that students have not yet studied is to provoke interest. In this book, cosines are discussed in Lesson 13-7. The Law of Cosines can be found in any trigonometry book and in most advanced algebra and precalculus textbooks.

Additional Answers

19b. True, since if any two figures do not intersect, their images cannot intersect. (Here is a proof of the contrapositive: If their images intersected, then each point of intersection would have a preimage on both figures, so the preimages would have had to intersect.)

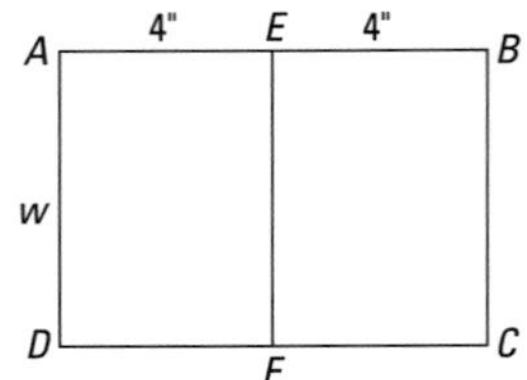

19a) False. For example, under a rotation other than 0°, 180°, or -180°, the image of a line intersects its preimage.

Applying the Mathematics

15. If $\triangle ABC \sim \triangle DEF$, $BC = 12$, $DE = 8$, and $EF = 16$, find AB. 6 units

16. Presto Printing makes folded cards which, when opened, have an outside boundary similar to that when they are folded. That is, in the figure at the left, $ABCD \sim ADFE$. Find the width w of the cards. $w = \sqrt{32} \approx 5.66$ in.

17. A model plane is similar to a real plane with ratio of similitude of $\frac{1}{45}$. If the wingspan of the model is 18″, what is the wingspan of the actual plane? 810″ or 67.5 ft

18. Let $P = (4, 7)$ and $Q = (-4, -8)$. Suppose $\overline{P'Q'} = S_6 \circ S_8(\overline{PQ})$. Find the length of $\overline{P'Q'}$. 816 units

19. Let S be a similarity transformation and let ℓ and m be lines. Tell whether the statement is true or false and justify your answer.

a. $S(\ell) \parallel \ell$ See left.

b. If $\ell \parallel m$, then $S(\ell) \parallel S(m)$. See margin.

Review

20. If 3 cans of tuna cost \$2.00, how much are 5 cans? *(Lesson 12-4)* \$3.34

21. Solve $\frac{5}{x} = \frac{11}{x+3}$ for x. *(Lesson 12-4, Previous course)* 2.5

22. In the figure at the right, $\triangle ABC$ is the image of $\triangle DBE$ under a size change with center B.

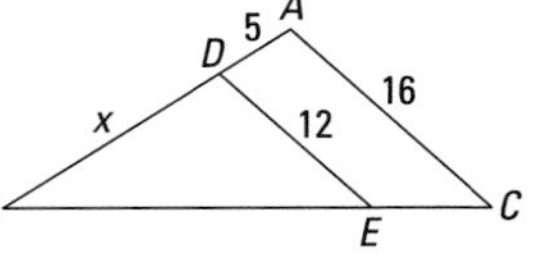

a. *True or false.* $\overleftrightarrow{DE} \parallel \overleftrightarrow{AC}$. True

b. *True or false.* $\frac{BD}{AB} = \frac{ED}{AC}$. True

c. Find x. *(Lessons 12-2, 12-3, 12-4)* $x = 15$

23. A spherical rubber ball has an outside diameter of 10 cm. The ball is hollow and the rubber is 1 cm thick. How much rubber is used in making the ball? *(Lesson 10-8)* $\frac{244\pi}{3} \approx 256$ cm^3

24. In triangles XYZ and APD, $\angle X \cong \angle A$, $\angle Y \cong \angle P$, and $\angle Z \cong \angle D$.

a. Is $\triangle XYZ$ necessarily congruent to $\triangle APD$? No

b. Justify your answer to part **a.** *(Lesson 7-1)* AAA is not a sufficient condition for congruent triangles. The triangles could be similar with a ratio of similitude not equal to 1.

Exploration

25. Scale models of objects are similar to objects that are larger or smaller than the models. Find a scale model.

a. For your scale model, what is the ratio of similitude?

b. A length of 1″ on the model corresponds to what length on the object it models? (Note: Save your scale model to do Question 22 of Lesson 12-6.) a, b) Answers will vary.

26)

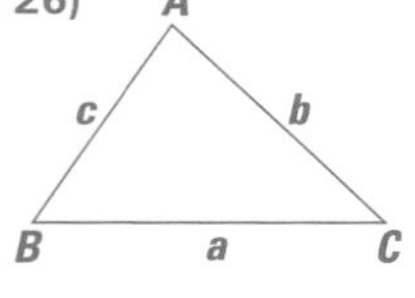

26. In Example 2, we noted that BC can be found by using a theorem called the Law of Cosines. Look in some other book to find out what this "law" is. In any triangle ABC, $c^2 = a^2 + b^2 - 2ab \cos C$.

Setting Up Lesson 12-6

Materials If possible, have models of similar figures available for Lesson 12-6—there is no better way to explain the ideas in the lesson than to use physical models. You will need a model of a regular square pyramid for *Extension* on page 723.

Students will need the models they used in **Question 25** above for **Question 22** in Lesson 12-6.

If you use Activity 1 in *Optional Activities* in Lesson 12-6, students will need scissors and tape. If you plan to use Activity 2, students will need an automatic drawer.

LESSON

12-6

The Fundamental Theorem of Similarity

Packaging nautical history. *Gil Charbonneau, a former sailor, constructs models of sailing ships for museums and collectors. See Example 3.*

Similar figures may be 2-dimensional or 3-dimensional because a similarity transformation can be done in three dimensions just as easily as in two. Any point can be the center of the size change and any real number, the scale factor. The Similar Figures Theorem holds for space figures—corresponding distances are multiplied by the scale factor, and corresponding angles are congruent.

A 3-Dimensional Example

In similar figures, perimeters, areas, and volumes satisfy a very important relationship, which is the subject of this lesson.

Activity

Below, Box I ~ Box II, with ratio of similitude 5. Find

a. the perimeter of the largest face of each box. 32 units, 160 units

b. the surface area of each box. 216 units^2, 5400 units^2

c. the volume of each box. 180 units^3, 22,500 units^3

3
6
10
Box I
Box II

Lesson 12-6

Objectives

D Use the Fundamental Theorem of Similarity to find lengths, perimeters, areas, and volumes in similar figures.

F Apply the Fundamental Theorem of Similarity in real situations.

Resources

From the ***Teacher's Resource File***

- Lesson Master 12-6A or 12-6B
- Answer Master 12-6
- Teaching Aids
  105 Graph paper
  159 Warm-up
  170 Additional Examples 1–3

Additional Resources

- Visuals for Teaching Aids 105, 159, 170
- Physical models of similar objects
- Model of a regular square pyramid
- Scissors and tape
- Scale models from Lesson 12-5
- Videodisc

Teaching Lesson 12-6

Warm-up

One cone has radius 4 cm and height 3 cm. Find its surface area and volume. A second cone has radius 28 cm and height 21 cm. Find its surface area and volume. Compare the surface areas and volumes of the two cones. **1st cone: S.A. = 36 π cm^2, $V = 16\pi$ cm^3; 2nd cone: S.A. = 1764π cm^2, $V = 5488\pi$ cm^3; the second cone has 7^2, or 49, times the surface area and 7^3, or 343, times the volume of the first cone.**

Lesson 12-6 Overview

Broad Goals This lesson discusses, proves, and applies the Fundamental Theorem of Similarity. That is, if two figures are similar with ratio of similitude k, then: (a) corresponding angle measures are equal, (b) corresponding lengths and distances are in the ratio k, (c) corresponding areas and surface areas are in the ratio k^2, and (d) corresponding volumes are in the ratio k^3.

Perspective In this lesson, we prove a general theorem for perimeter, area, and volume. Then the statement of that theorem is combined with the Similar Figures Theorem in a broader statement that we call the Fundamental Theorem of Similarity.

The proof of the General Theorem is not rigorous by today's mathematical standards. A rigorous proof would require notions of limits that are beyond the scope of this book.

Perhaps no theorem of geometry is more important than the Fundamental Theorem of Similarity. In fact, it could just as appropriately be called the "fundamental theorem of measurement." It is worth at least two days of class time; the second day is for Lesson 12-7, which *must* be discussed in order for students to realize the importance of the theorem.

(Overview continues on page 718.)

Notes on Reading

Reading Mathematics The reading in this lesson is packed with ideas. You may wish to go over it with students paragraph by paragraph, or even line by line.

There is no better way to explain the ideas of this lesson than to use physical models. Possible examples other than those mentioned in the lesson are basketballs of different sizes, souvenir statues of different sizes, and flags of different sizes.

We begin with a 3-dimensional example because students tend to have a greater intuitive sense about 3-dimensional figures.

Have students record the results of the **Activity** for use with **Question 2a** on page 721.

You may wish to restate the Fundamental Theorem of Similarity so that it is more like the general theorem that precedes it. That is, in similar figures with ratio of similitude k:

$$\frac{p'}{p} = k$$

$$\frac{A'}{A} = k^2$$

$$\frac{V'}{V} = k^3$$

Here's still another way. In similar figures with ratio of similitude k:

$$\frac{A'}{A} = \left(\frac{p'}{p}\right)^2 = \frac{p'^2}{p^2}$$

$$\frac{V'}{V} = \left(\frac{p'}{p}\right)^3 = \frac{p'^3}{p^3}$$

The questions in this lesson may be surprisingly difficult for some of your students. Students rarely do calculations involving area and volume of similar figures before taking geometry in high school, and so they lack intuition for the implications of the Fundamental Theorem of Similarity. Lesson 12-7 should help students develop a greater intuitive sense of these concepts.

In the Activity, you should have noticed that the face of Box II has 5 times the perimeter of the face of Box I, and that Box II has 25 times the surface area and 125 times the volume of Box I.

These answers could have been predicted without calculating any perimeters, surface areas, or volumes. The ratio of similitude of the boxes is 5. The ratio of corresponding lengths is 5, or 5^1. The ratio of corresponding surface areas is 25, or 5^2, because area involves the multiplication of 2 dimensions. The ratio of corresponding volumes is 125, or 5^3, because volume involves the multiplication of 3 dimensions.

A 2-Dimensional Example

Example 1

$\triangle ABC \sim \triangle DEF$. Give the ratios of the perimeters and areas of these triangles.

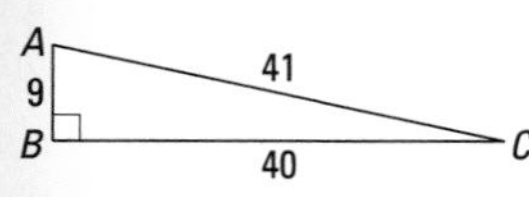

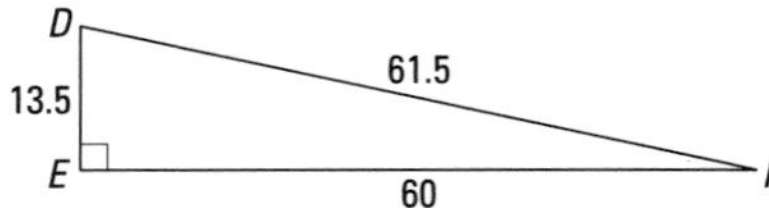

Solution

The perimeters and areas can be calculated directly.

For $\triangle ABC$:
Perimeter = 9 + 40 + 41 = 90 units
Area = $\frac{1}{2} \cdot 40 \cdot 9$ = 180 square units

For $\triangle DEF$:
Perimeter = 13.5 + 60 + 61.5 = 135 units
Area = $\frac{1}{2} \cdot 13.5 \cdot 60$ = 405 square units

Thus, the ratio of perimeters = $\frac{135}{90} = 1.5$
and the ratio of areas = $\frac{405}{180} = 2.25$.

The ratio of similitude is 1.5. The ratio of perimeters is 1.5^1, while the ratio of areas is 1.5^2.

The General Theorem

These examples are instances of the following theorem, which applies to all similar figures in 2 or 3 dimensions.

Theorem
If $G \sim G'$ and k is the ratio of similitude, then
(1) $\text{Perimeter}(G') = k \cdot \text{Perimeter}(G)$ or $\frac{\text{Perimeter}(G')}{\text{Perimeter}(G)} = k$,
(2) $\text{Area}(G') = k^2 \cdot \text{Area}(G)$ or $\frac{\text{Area}(G')}{\text{Area}(G)} = k^2$, and
(3) $\text{Volume}(G') = k^3 \cdot \text{Volume}(G)$ or $\frac{\text{Volume}(G')}{\text{Volume}(G)} = k^3$.

Lesson 12-6 Overview, continued

The Fundamental Theorem of Similarity is not covered in some geometry courses because it requires a knowledge of similarity, perimeter, area, and volume, all of which are topics that may not be encountered until late in the school year. We have tried to put it earlier, even before the triangle similarity theorems, which we feel are not as important.

Video

Wide World of Mathematics The segment, *Seeing with Your Hands,* focuses on fiberglass models of buildings in Washington, D.C., such as the White House and the Capitol. This segment may be used to lay the groundwork for students to apply the Fundamental Theorem of Similarity with scale models. Related questions and an investigation are provided in videodisc stills and in the Video Guide. A related CD-ROM activity is also available.

Videodisc Bar Codes

Search Chapter 59

Play

Proof

Argument (1):

Suppose lengths $a, b, c, d, e, \ldots$ make up the perimeter of G. Then lengths $ka, kb, kc, kd, ke, \ldots$ make up the perimeter of G'.

$$\begin{aligned}\text{Perimeter}(G') &= ka + kb + kc + \ldots \\ &= k(a + b + c + \ldots) \\ &= k \cdot \text{Perimeter}(G)\end{aligned}$$

Argument (2):

Let $A = \text{Area}(G)$. Then you could think of the area of G as the sum of the areas of A squares with sides of length 1 (unit squares). Then the area of G' is the sum of areas of A squares with sides of length k units. Since each square in G' has area k^2,

$$\text{Area}(G') = A \cdot k^2 = k^2 \cdot \text{Area}(G).$$

Argument (3):

The argument is much like that for the area. Let $V = \text{Volume}(G)$. Then the volume of G equals that of V cubes with edges of length 1 (unit cubes). The volume of G' is the sum of the volumes of V cubes each with edges of length k. Since each cube in G' has volume k^3,

$$\text{Volume}(G') = V \cdot k^3 = k^3 \cdot \text{Volume}(G).$$

Part (2) of the theorem can be seen in area formulas, such as $A = \pi r^2$ (circles), $A = \ell w$ (rectangles), $A = \frac{1}{2}h(b_1 + b_2)$ (trapezoids), L.A. $= ph$ (cylinders or prisms). Notice that each area formula involves the product of two lengths. (That's why the result is measured in square units.) So if each length is multiplied by k, the area is multiplied by k^2.

Volume formulas illustrate part (3) of the theorem. Consider some volume formulas: $V = \ell wh$ (boxes), $V = \frac{4}{3}\pi r^3$ (spheres), $V = \frac{1}{3}Bh$ (pyramids or cones). In each, there are three lengths multiplied. (For pyramids or cones, it looks as if there are only two quantities multiplied, but B is an area, so for B two lengths are multiplied.) Since each length is multiplied by k, the volume is multiplied by k^3.

The previous theorem and the Similar Figures Theorem combine to produce the most important theorem relating measures in similar figures.

Fundamental Theorem of Similarity

If two figures are similar with ratio of similitude k, then
(a) corresponding angle measures are equal;
(b) corresponding lengths and perimeters are in the ratio k;
(c) corresponding areas and surface areas are in the ratio k^2; and
(d) corresponding volumes are in the ratio k^3.

You might want to demonstrate the Fundamental Theorem of Similarity by setting up proportions using the ratio of similitude. For example, using the pyramids of **Question 13a,** the proportion would be $\left(\frac{8}{12}\right)^3 = \frac{100}{x}$. Students can then solve the proportion by the Means-Extremes Property.

Additional Examples

Examples 1–3 are also given on **Teaching Aid 170.**

1. *RSTU* ~ *WXYZ*. Give the ratios of the perimeters and the areas of these rectangles.

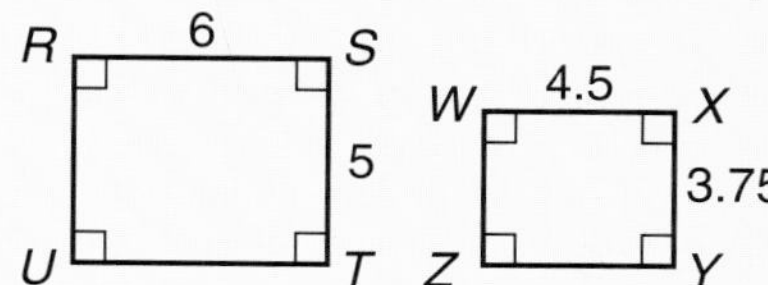

Ratio of perimeters $= \frac{3}{4} = .75$; **ratio of areas** $= \frac{9}{16} = .5625$

2. Hexagons *ABCDEF* and *UVWXYZ* are similar with ratio of similitude $\frac{4}{5}$. If *ABCDEF* has area 56 square units, what is the area of *UVWXYZ*?

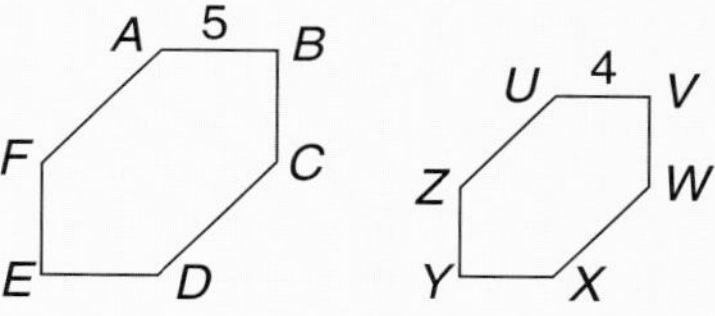

35.84 square units

(Additional Examples continue on page 720.)

Optional Activities

Activity 1

Materials: Graph paper or **Teaching Aid 105,** scissors, tape

After you have done the **Activity** at the beginning of the lesson, you may wish to have students make their own 3-dimensional models. On graph paper, have them draw nets for two different-sized cubes. (For example, at the right are nets for a 4 × 4 × 4 cube and a 6 × 6 × 6 cube.)

Have them cut out each net, fold it into a cube, and tape the edges. Then have students determine the ratios of similitude between the sides of their cubes. Have them use this ratio to predict the ratio of the surface areas, then count the unit blocks on the surface of each cube to verify their predictions. Also have them determine the ratio of the volumes of their cubes. If you wish, you could have them demonstrate the relationship between the volumes by filling each cube with a light-weight material—such as popcorn—and comparing the amounts that fit into the two cubes.

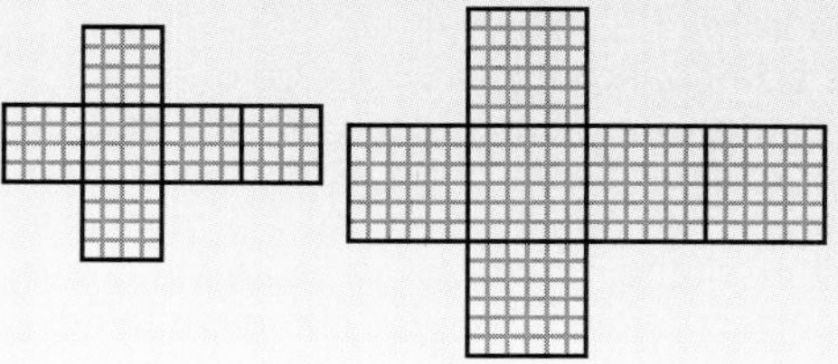

3. Two toy trucks are shown. Each is similar to the same type of truck, so they are similar to each other. The larger toy is 18 cm long, and the smaller is 6 cm long.

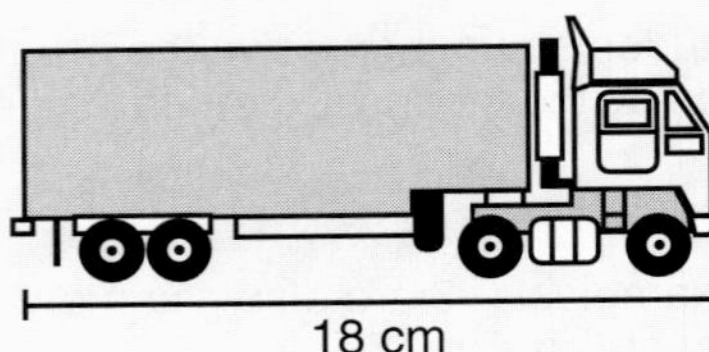

a. How do the heights of the toy trucks compare? The height of the larger toy is 3 times that of the smaller toy.

b. How do the areas of the floors of the holds (where the cargo is stored) compare? The area of the floor of the larger toy is 9 times that of the smaller toy.

c. How do the volumes of the holds compare? The volume of the hold of the larger toy is 27 times that of the smaller toy.

4. The lengths of the sides of $\triangle ABC$ are 12, 15, and 17. The length of the shortest side of a similar triangle, $\triangle DEF$, is 5.

a. What is the perimeter of $\triangle DEF$, the similar triangle? $18\frac{1}{3}$

b. How do the areas of the triangles compare? The area of $\triangle ABC$ is $\frac{144}{25}$, or 5.76, times the area of $\triangle DEF$.

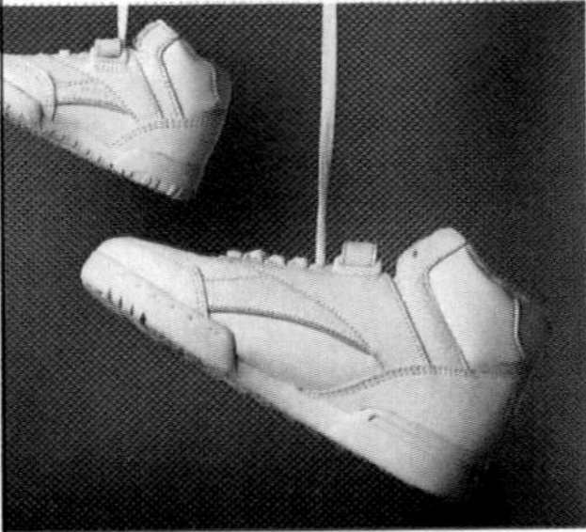

Similarity check. *Can you find similar pentagons on these two shoes?* The upper right regions are nearly pentagons and seem to be similar.

Example 2

Pentagons *ABCDE* and *FGHIJ* are similar with ratio of similitude $\frac{2}{3}$. If *FGHIJ* has area 50 square units, what is the area of *ABCDE*?

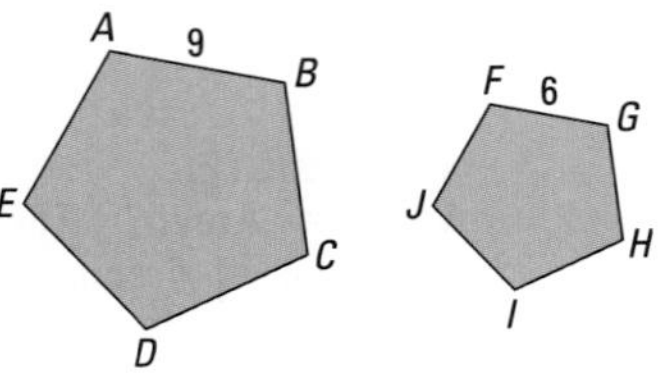

Solution

The ratio of areas is the square of the ratio of similitude.

$$\frac{\text{Area(FGHIJ)}}{\text{Area(ABCDE)}} = \left(\frac{2}{3}\right)^2 = \frac{4}{9}$$

Substituting,

$$\frac{50}{\text{Area(ABCDE)}} = \frac{4}{9}, \text{ from which}$$

$$\text{Area(ABCDE)} = \frac{450}{4} = 112.5 \text{ square units.}$$

Example 3

Two models of the same schooner (a boat with front and rear masts) are shown below. Each model is similar to the original, so they are similar to each other. The larger model is 120 cm long; the smaller, 30 cm long.

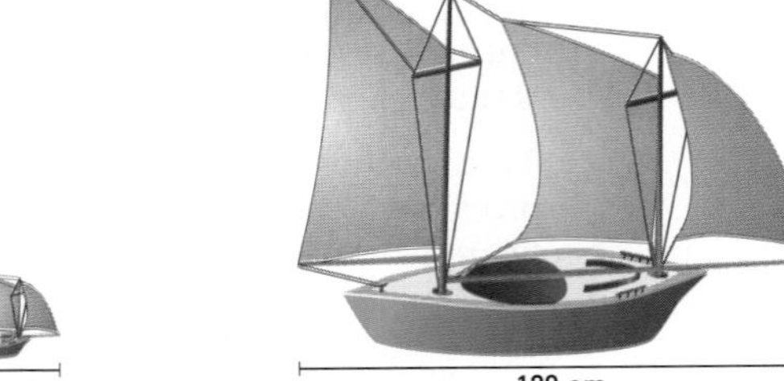

a. How do their heights compare?

b. How do the areas of their sails compare?

c. How do the volumes of their hulls (the bodies of the boats) compare?

Solution

First compute the ratio of similitude.

$$k = \frac{\text{length of large schooner}}{\text{length of small schooner}} = \frac{120 \text{ cm}}{30 \text{ cm}} = 4$$

Optional Activities

Activity 2 Technology Connection

Materials: Automatic drawer

After you have discussed the Fundamental Theorem of Similarity, have students use the size-change *dilation* feature of an automatic drawer to construct a triangle and its image under a size change of a given magnitude. They should then use the *measure* feature of the drawer to measure each pair of corresponding angles. Next have them use the measure and *calculate* features to measure the lengths of each pair of corresponding sides and the ratio between them, the perimeters of both triangles and the ratio between them, and the areas of both triangles and the ratio between them. Have students discuss how the results illustrate the Fundamental Theorem of Similarity.

a. The height is a length, so the ratio of the heights is k.

$$\frac{\text{height of large schooner}}{\text{height of small schooner}} = k = 4.$$

So the height of the large schooner is 4 times that of the small schooner.

b. The ratio of the areas of the sails is k^2.

$$\frac{\text{area of large sail}}{\text{area of small sail}} = k^2 = 16$$

The areas of sails in the large schooner are 16 times those of the small schooner.

c. To compare the volumes of their hulls, use k^3.

$$\frac{\text{volume of larger hull}}{\text{volume of smaller hull}} = k^3 = 64$$

The volume of the large hull is 64 times the volume of the small hull.

QUESTIONS

Covering the Reading

2a) 32 units and 160 units; 216 units^2 and 5400 units^2; 180 units^3 and 22,500 units^3

1. Can a similarity transformation be done in three dimensions? Yes

2. a. Give your results for the Activity in this lesson. See left.
   b. Give the ratios of the perimeters, surface areas, and volumes. 5, 25, 125

3. At the right, $\triangle ABC \sim \triangle DEF$. b) $\frac{5}{4} = 1.25$
   a. Give the ratio of similitude. $\frac{5}{4} = 1.25$
   b. Give the ratio of the perimeters.
   c. Give the ratio of the areas. $\frac{25}{16} = 1.5625$

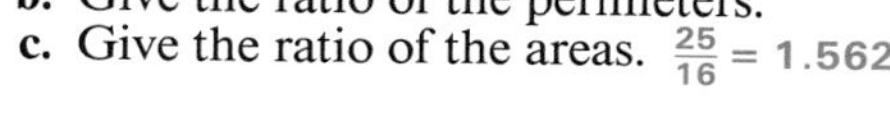

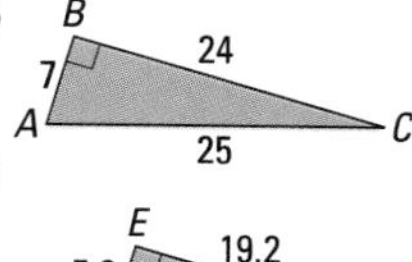

4. Area is the product of __?__ lengths. two

5. Volume is the product of __?__ lengths. three

6. The ratio of similitude of two figures is $\frac{5}{3}$. Find the ratio of their
   a. perimeters. $\frac{5}{3}$
   b. areas. $\frac{25}{9}$
   c. volumes. $\frac{125}{27}$
   d. corresponding sides. $\frac{5}{3}$

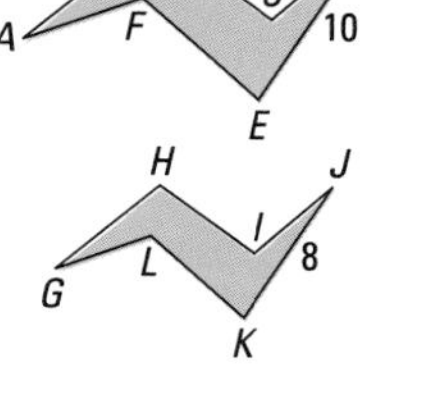

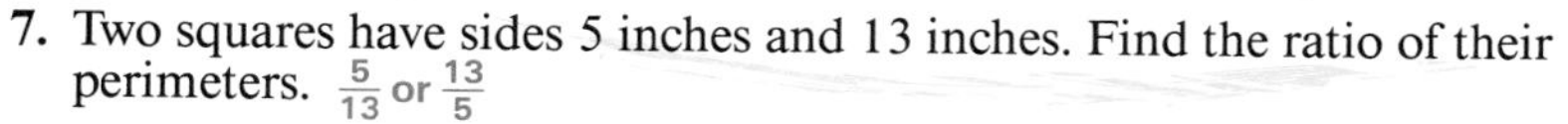

7. Two squares have sides 5 inches and 13 inches. Find the ratio of their perimeters. $\frac{5}{13}$ or $\frac{13}{5}$

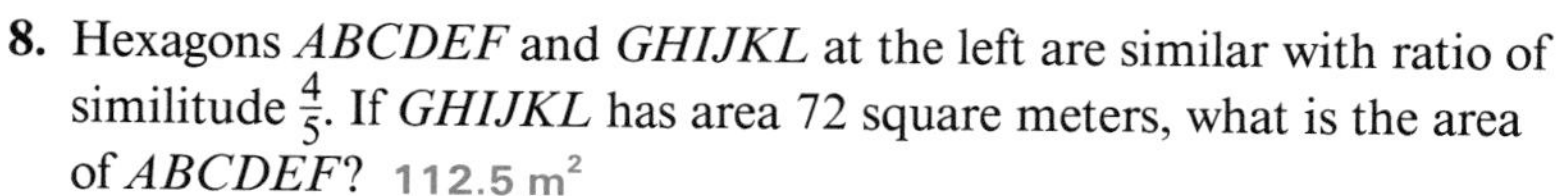

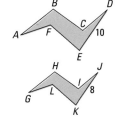

8. Hexagons $ABCDEF$ and $GHIJKL$ at the left are similar with ratio of similitude $\frac{4}{5}$. If $GHIJKL$ has area 72 square meters, what is the area of $ABCDEF$? 112.5 m^2

5. Before a wooden shed is built, a model of the shed is to be made. The size of the model is to be $\frac{1}{6}$ of the actual size.
   a. How does the total length of wood needed for the model compare to the total length of wood needed for the actual shed? The total length of wood needed for the model is $\frac{1}{6}$ the total length of wood needed for the actual shed.
   b. How does the inside volume of the model compare to the inside volume of the actual shed? The inside volume of the model is $\frac{1}{216}$ the inside volume of the actual shed.
   c. If the wood needed for the model weighs 5 pounds, what is the weight of the wood needed for the actual shed? 1080 pounds

Notes on Questions

Question 2 The answers can be found in two ways: (1) by calculating the quantities for each box and then dividing, or (2) by calculating each quantity for one box and then multiplying by a power of the ratio of similitude using the Fundamental Theorem of Similarity. Students can answer the questions either way. They can use one answer to check the other.

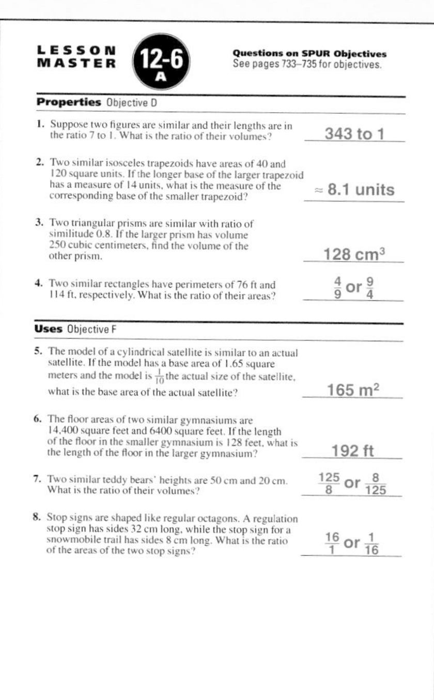

LESSON MASTER 12-6 A

Questions on SPUR Objectives
See pages 733–735 for objectives.

Properties Objective D

1. Suppose two figures are similar and their lengths are in the ratio 7 to 1. What is the ratio of their volumes? 343 to 1
2. Two similar isosceles trapezoids have areas of 40 and 120 square units. If the longer base of the larger trapezoid has a measure of 14 units, what is the measure of the corresponding base of the smaller trapezoid? ≈ 8.1 units
3. Two triangular prisms are similar with ratio of similitude 0.8. If the larger prism has volume 250 cubic centimeters, find the volume of the other prism. 128 cm^3
4. Two similar rectangles have perimeters of 76 ft and 114 ft, respectively. What is the ratio of their areas? $\frac{4}{9}$ or $\frac{9}{4}$

Uses Objective F

5. The model of a cylindrical satellite is similar to an actual satellite. If the model has a base area of 1.65 square meters and the model is $\frac{1}{10}$ the actual size of the satellite, what is the base area of the actual satellite? 165 m^2
6. The floor areas of two similar gymnasiums are 14,400 square feet and 6400 square feet. If the length of the floor in the smaller gymnasium is 128 feet, what is the length of the floor in the larger gymnasium? 192 ft
7. Two similar teddy bears' heights are 50 cm and 20 cm. What is the ratio of their volumes? $\frac{125}{8}$ or $\frac{8}{125}$
8. Stop signs are shaped like regular octagons. A regulation stop sign has sides 32 cm long, while the stop sign for a snowmobile trail has sides 8 cm long. What is the ratio of the areas of the two stop signs? $\frac{16}{1}$ or $\frac{1}{16}$

Adapting to Individual Needs

Extra Help

Stress that the Fundamental Theorem of Similarity is useful in comparing unknown perimeters, areas, and volumes even when the figures involved are irregular in shape. In **Example 3,** for instance, the two similar figures are 3-dimensional ship models. By simply measuring the length of each, we are able to compare the areas and the volumes as well.

English Language Development

As was mentioned in *Covering the Reading,* this lesson is packed with ideas. If you go over the reading, as suggested, paragraph by paragraph, pay attention to the special needs of students with limited English proficiency. If you do not go over the reading in this way, pair students with limited English proficiency with English-speaking students and assign them to go over the reading together.

Notes on Questions

Question 12 Point out that the lengths of the individual sides do not need to be known.

Question 14 In general, larger objects made from the same material as smaller objects are far heavier than one would think. (See Question 5c in *Additional Examples.*) This question is directly related to the next lesson.

Question 14 History Connection The legacy of Dr. Martin Luther King, Jr. (1929–1968) is, of course, recorded in film clips and reprints of his speeches, but often students are unaware of his significant writings. His first book, *Stride Toward Freedom,* written in 1958, chronicles the Montgomery bus boycott of 1955; that was his first action that grabbed major national attention. His 1963 work, entitled *Why We Can't Wait,* was written during the height of the desegregation movement in Birmingham, Alabama. One of his last works was *Where Do We Go from Here: Chaos or Community?,* which was written in 1967; it chronicles his musings on the use of nonviolence to enact social change.

LESSON MASTER 12-6 B Questions on SPUR Objectives

Properties Objective D: Use the Fundamental Theorem of Similarity to find lengths, perimeters, areas, and volumes in similar figures.

1. At the right, $ABCD \sim UVWX$.
   a. What is the ratio of similitude? $\frac{2}{3}$ or $\frac{3}{2}$
   b. What is the ratio of their perimeters? $\frac{2}{3}$ or $\frac{3}{2}$
   c. What is the ratio of their areas? $\frac{4}{9}$ or $\frac{9}{4}$

2. $EFGHIJ \sim ONMLKJ$ with a ratio of similitude of $\frac{3}{5}$. The area of $EFGHIJ$ is 32 square units and the perimeter of $OMNLKJ$ is 14 units.
   a. What is the area of $OMNLKJ$? 11.52 units²
   b. What is the perimeter of $EFGHIJ$? $23\frac{1}{3}$ units

3. Two figures are similar with a ratio of similitude of 4.2.
   a. What is the ratio of corresponding lengths? $\frac{4.2}{1}$
   b. What is the ratio of their perimeters? $\frac{4.2}{1}$
   c. What is the ratio of their areas? $\frac{17.64}{1}$
   d. What is the ratio of their volumes? $\frac{74.088}{1}$
   e. What is the ratio of corresponding angle measures? $\frac{1}{1}$

9. Two models of the same airplane are similar to each other. The larger model is 90 cm long, and the smaller is 30 cm long.
   a. How do their wingspans compare? The ratio is $\frac{1}{3}$.
   b. How do the areas of their tailpieces compare? The ratio is $\frac{1}{9}$.
   c. How do the volumes of their bodies compare? The ratio is $\frac{1}{27}$.

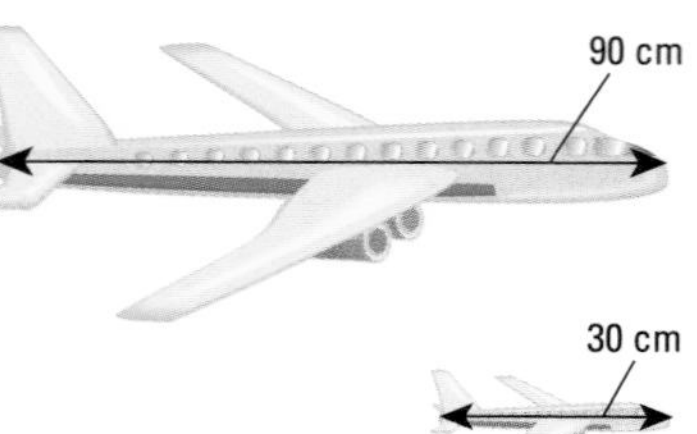

Applying the Mathematics

10. $R \sim R'$, $k = 4$, and Volume(R) = 34 cubic units. Find Volume(R'). 2176 units³

11. Right cylinder Q has height 25 and the radius of its base is 11.
    a. Find its volume and surface area. See left.
    b. Let cylinder Z be the image of cylinder Q under a size change with magnitude 3. Cylinder Z will have __?__ times the volume and __?__ times the surface area of cylinder Q. 27, 9
    c. Find the volume and the surface area of cylinder Z. $V = 81{,}675\pi$ units³; S.A. = 7128π units²

25
11
cylinder Q

11a) $V = 3025\pi$ units³; S.A. = 792π units²

12. Two similar nonregular 15-gons have perimeters of 20 ft and 28 ft. What is the ratio of the length of a side of the smaller to the length of the corresponding side of the larger? $\frac{20}{28} \approx 0.71$

13. Corresponding edges of two similar pyramids are 8 and 12 inches.
    a. Find the volume of the larger pyramid if the smaller has volume 100 cubic inches. 337.5 in³
    b. Find the volume of the smaller pyramid if the larger has volume 100 cubic inches. ≈ 29.63 in³

Martin Luther King, Jr. received the Nobel prize for peace in 1964.

14. On two similar solid brass statues of Martin Luther King, Jr., the lengths of the left ear are 3 cm and 5 cm.
    a. If the base area of the larger statue is 50 cm², find the base area of the smaller statue. 18 cm²
    b. The volume of brass in the smaller statue is 216 cm³. What volume of brass is in the larger statue? 1000 cm³

15. The volumes of two spheres are 288π mm³ and 7776π mm³.
    a. What is a ratio of similitude for these spheres? 3 or $\frac{1}{3}$
    b. What is a ratio of their surface areas? 9 or $\frac{1}{9}$

16. *Multiple choice.* The bases of two quadrangular prisms are similar with ratio of similitude 1.5, but the prisms have the same height. What is the ratio of their volumes? b

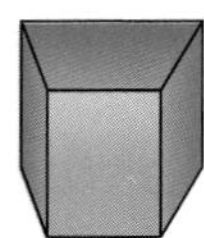
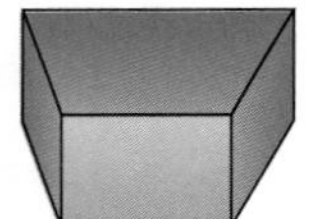

(a) 1.5 (b) 2.25 (c) 3 (d) 4.5
(e) cannot be determined from the given information

Review

17. Below, Figure $Q \sim$ Figure R. Determine the ratio of similitude. *(Lesson 12-5)* $\frac{3}{2}$

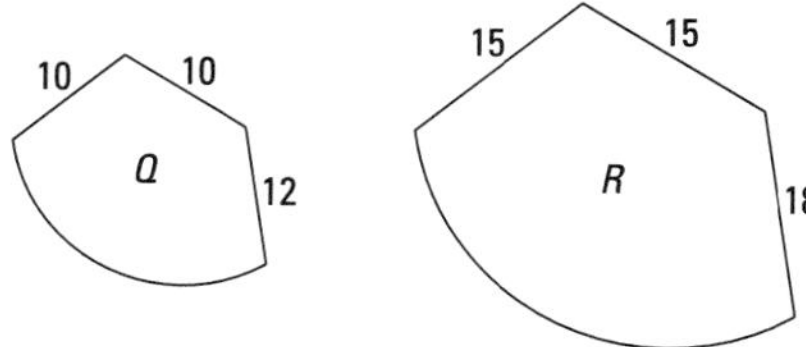

18. $\triangle ABC \sim \triangle DEF$ with ratio of similitude 2.5. If $AB = 3$, $BC = 5$, and $m\angle B = 135$, find as many lengths and angle measures in $\triangle DEF$ as you can. *(Lesson 12-5)* $DE = 7.5$; $EF = 12.5$; $m\angle E = 135$

19. A comic strip measures 6″ by 2″. The smaller sides of a reduction measure $\frac{1}{2}$″. What are the lengths of the larger sides of the reduction? *(Lesson 12-4)* $1\frac{1}{2}$″

20. A goal post and its shadow are shown below. The length of the shadow of each vertical post is 75 ft. The crossbar is 10 ft high and its shadow falls 24 ft from the base of the goal post. What is the height h of the goal post? *(Lesson 12-4)* 31.25 ft

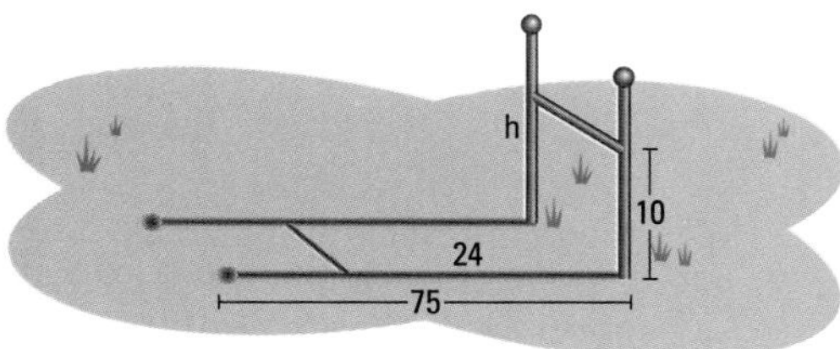

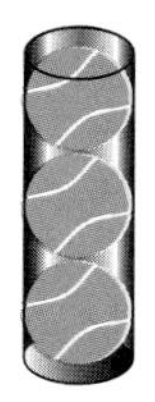

21. A can of tennis balls usually holds three balls, as pictured at the left. What percent of the volume of the can is not used by the balls? (Hint: Let r be the radius of the can and proceed from there.) *(Lessons 10-5, 10-8)* $33\frac{1}{3}\%$

Exploration

22. In Question 25 of Lesson 12-5, you were asked to find a scale model of an actual object. Weigh the scale model you found. If the actual object was made from the same materials, what would be its weight? Answers will vary.

Follow-up for Lesson 12-6

Practice

For more questions on SPUR Objectives, use **Lesson Master 12-6A** (shown on page 721) or **Lesson Master 12-6B** (shown on pages 722–723).

Assessment

Group Assessment Ask students to explain the relationship between the ratio of similitude of similar figures and perimeter, area, or volume of the figures. [Students explain such relationships using the General Theorem on page 718.]

Extension

History Connection The Great Pyramid of Cheops is a regular square pyramid. Originally it was 482 feet high, and each side of the base was 756 feet long. Give students a model of a regular square pyramid and have them determine if it is similar to the Cheops Pyramid. [Answers will vary.]

Project Update Project 1, *Finish This Story,* Project 3, *Models of Everyday Objects,* and Project 6, *Prices of Fruit Drinks,* on pages 729–730, relate to the content of this lesson.

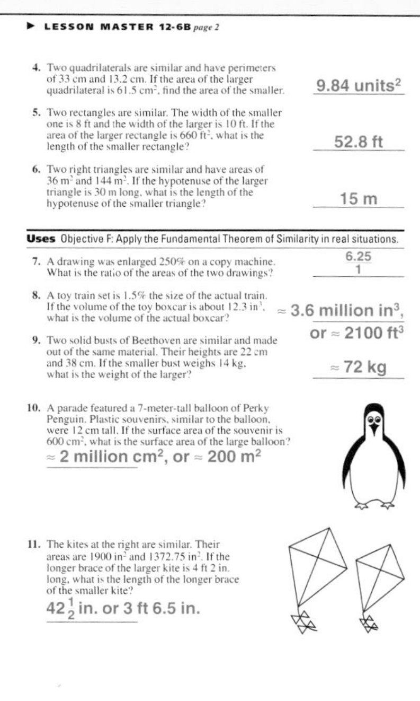

▶ **LESSON MASTER 12-6B** *page 2*

4. Two quadrilaterals are similar and have perimeters of 33 cm and 13.2 cm. If the area of the larger quadrilateral is 61.5 cm^2, find the area of the smaller. 9.84 $units^2$

5. Two rectangles are similar. The width of the smaller one is 8 ft and the width of the larger is 10 ft. If the area of the larger rectangle is 660 ft^2, what is the length of the smaller rectangle? 52.8 ft

6. Two right triangles are similar and have areas of 36 m^2 and 144 m^2. If the hypotenuse of the larger triangle is 30 m long, what is the length of the hypotenuse of the smaller triangle? 15 m

Uses Objective F: Apply the Fundamental Theorem of Similarity in real situations.

7. A drawing was enlarged 250% on a copy machine. What is the ratio of the areas of the two drawings? $\frac{6.25}{1}$

8. A toy train set is 1.5% the size of the actual train. If the volume of the toy boxcar is about 12.3 in^3, what is the volume of the actual boxcar? $\approx$ 3.6 million in^3, or $\approx$ 2100 ft^3

9. Two solid busts of Beethoven are similar and made out of the same material. Their heights are 22 cm and 38 cm. If the smaller bust weighs 14 kg, what is the weight of the larger? $\approx$ 72 kg

10. A parade featured a 7-meter-tall balloon of Perky Penguin. Plastic souvenirs, similar to the balloon, were 12 cm tall. If the surface area of the souvenir is 600 cm^2, what is the surface area of the large balloon? $\approx$ 2 million cm^2, or $\approx$ 200 m^2

11. The kites at the right are similar. Their areas are 1900 in^2 and 1372.75 in^2. If the longer brace of the larger kite is 4 ft 2 in. long, what is the length of the longer brace of the smaller kite? $42\frac{1}{2}$ in. or 3 ft 6.5 in.

Setting Up Lesson 12-7

Materials Students doing *Challenge* in Lesson 12-7 will need copies of *Gulliver's Travels.* They are asked to read Part II, "A Voyage to Brobdingnag," and write a report.

Lesson 12-7

Objectives

F Apply the Fundamental Theorem of Similarity in real situations.

Resources

From the ***Teacher's Resource File***

- Lesson Master 12-7A or 12-7B
- Answer Master 12-7
- Teaching Aid 159: Warm-up

Additional Resources

- Visual for Teaching Aid 159

Teaching Lesson 12-7

Warm-up

Name as many movies as you can in which humans or animals appear in either a giant size or a reduced size. **Samples: *Honey, I Shrunk the Kids; The Indian in the Cupboard;* and *King Kong***

Notes on Reading

The cartoons seen by young children violate many physical and biological laws. For instance, cartoon characters walk off cliffs and do not fall until they realize there is nothing under them. Often there are giant and miniature creatures with the same shape. Some people believe there could be giant humans. This lesson is designed to show why such beings cannot exist.

LESSON

12-7

Can There Be Giants?

Giants are common characters in children's stories; an example is the giant from *Jack and the Beanstalk.* Saturday morning cartoons often have giant creatures with human shapes. The tallest man on record was Robert Wadlow from Alton, Illinois. On June 27, 1940, at age 22, he was measured at 8 ft, 11.1 in. Wadlow was about 1.5 times the height of a typical male. Can humans be much taller? The Fundamental Theorem of Similarity provides the answer.

Measuring-up. *Tailor Sol Winkelman fits a suit for Robert Wadlow in 1936. At this time Wadlow was 8′5″ tall.*

Giants in *Gulliver's Travels*

Let's look at what the theorem reveals, using an example from a famous novel. In *Gulliver's Travels,* Jonathan Swift writes about a man named Gulliver who visits the land of Brobdingnag, where the Brobdingnagians are similar to us but 12 times as tall. Their volume, and thus their weight, would be 12^3 times ours. Since $12^3 = 1728$, they would weigh about 1728 times what we weigh. If you weigh 140 pounds, a similar Brobdingnagian would weigh 241,920 pounds! He or she would support this weight on feet covering a region whose area is only 12^2, or 144 times what you stand on. So each bone of a Brobdingnagian would have to carry 12 times as much weight as yours.

Even champion weight lifters seldom lift more than twice their body weight—and when they do, it is only for a few seconds. Imagine what lifting 12 times your weight would do. It would quickly break your bones!

Lesson 12-7 Overview

Broad Goals This lesson applies the Fundamental Theorem of Similarity to explain why there cannot be giants. It also explores related topics, such as costs of similar items.

Perspective When this material was first tested, it was discovered that students neither understood nor *believed* the effects of the Fundamental Theorem of Similarity until they read this lesson. One reason for their difficulty is that physical and biological instances of the Fundamental Theorem of Similarity often are misrepresented in books, television programs, and other places from which they obtain information. For instance, the fact that small birds eat many times their weight in food often is cited as if it indicates something special about birds that does not apply to humans. It is not special; small birds have more surface area for their volume than do larger animals. Larger birds, such as eagles and hawks, have less surface area in relation to their volume, and so they do not consume as many times their weight in food as do the smaller birds.

In the first part of the 20th century, many people tried to build heavier-than-air vehicles that would fly. They would build a small model and find that it could fly, much like the paper airplanes and toy gliders children

You might think that a giant body would find some way of dealing with the extra weight. But it can't. Wadlow had to wear a leg brace to support his weight. One day while getting out of a car (which was hard for him to do), the brace cut a deep wound in his leg, which became infected. Eighteen days after his height was measured, he died in Manistee, Michigan.

The Fundamental Theorem of Similarity in Nature

Animals have developed within the constraints imposed by the Fundamental Theorem of Similarity. Elephants have legs with large horizontal cross-sectional areas to support their great weight. Thoroughbred race horses have thin legs which enable them to run fast, but their legs are small for their bodies, and when a thoroughbred falls, its legs often break. Draft horses which pull wagons have thicker, stronger legs, but these horses are slow. A mosquito can walk on the surface of water without sinking. It is so light that it will not break the surface tension of the water. It also has thin legs which support its light body. But that body has a relatively large surface area. When a raindrop forces a mosquito's body into the water, the surface tension acts like glue on the body's surface, and the thin legs cannot pull the mosquito from the water.

Giants by Gully! *This sketch from a 1795 French edition of* Gulliver's Travels *shows Gulliver in the corn fields of Brobdingnag.*

Food and Clothing Needs

In general, the amount of food needed by an animal is proportional to its volume. The Brobdingnagians would need to consume 1728 times the food needed by Gulliver. A person Gulliver's size needs about 2500 calories a day to maintain body weight (about 16 calories per pound). A Brobdingnagian would require 1728 times 2500 calories a day. That's a lot of food.

Gulliver also visited the land of Lilliput, where people were $\frac{1}{12}$ his height. For Gulliver, as for us, a new shirt would require about two square yards of material. Clothing is related to surface area, so we multiply by the square of the ratio of similitude. The Lilliputians, being $\frac{1}{12}$ Gulliver's height, would require only $\left(\frac{1}{12}\right)^2$ or $\frac{1}{144}$ times the two square yards needed by Gulliver. The Brobdingnagians would require 12^2 or 144 times as much material. Thus, geometry answers questions about clothing and food needs as well as the properties of giants.

Example 1

A pizzeria sells 12″-diameter pizzas with cheese and one topping for $9.99 (plus tax). Suppose the price of a pizza is based on the amount of ingredients used to make the pizza, and that the pizzas have the same thickness. What would be the charge for a 14″-diameter pizza with cheese and one topping?

▶

Pacing Although there is a substantial amount of reading in this lesson, students find the material interesting and can read it on their own. However, be certain to discuss all the questions in *Covering the Reading.* This should be a day to relax a bit. You might engage students in an informal discussion on the subject of the lesson. Ask them what was new to them and what, if anything, was surprising.

Literature Connection *Gulliver's Travels,* written by Jonathan Swift and published in 1726, makes a very imaginative children's tale, but it was originally intended as social satire. In the book, Gulliver is a gullible, good-natured hero who is sent on a series of four voyages. Each of the races he encounters symbolically embodies a common human trait. In Lilliput, a society of tiny people is mired in mistrust and trivial disputes. In Brobdingnag, a race of giants is far more generous and large-hearted than he. On the third voyage he encounters several cultures where science and dreams of progress have ruined life for the citizens. In the fourth voyage, he meets the rational Houyhnhnms and the bestial, unreasoning Yahoos; in trying to define himself, Gulliver discovers that he—and the rest of us—have more in common with the Yahoos than we would care to acknowledge. He returns to England a much sadder, wiser man.

build today. Then they would use the same materials, only larger, for the actual plane. They did not consider that the weight of the model would be multiplied by the cube of the scale factor, but the surface area—which is critical to lift—would be multiplied by only the square of the scale factor. The actual planes seldom could fly, and they often collapsed.

As indicated in the lesson, Galileo was the first to realize that there could not be giants with the shape of normal humans because the strength of the human bone would not allow it. He discovered what is now taken as axiomatic by biologists, namely, that the shapes of animals often can be explained by mathematical arguments. The two most famous treatises on this subject are reprinted in *The World of Mathematics.* These are "On Growth and Form," by D'Arcy Wentworth Thompson, and "On Being the Right Size," by J.B.S. Haldane.

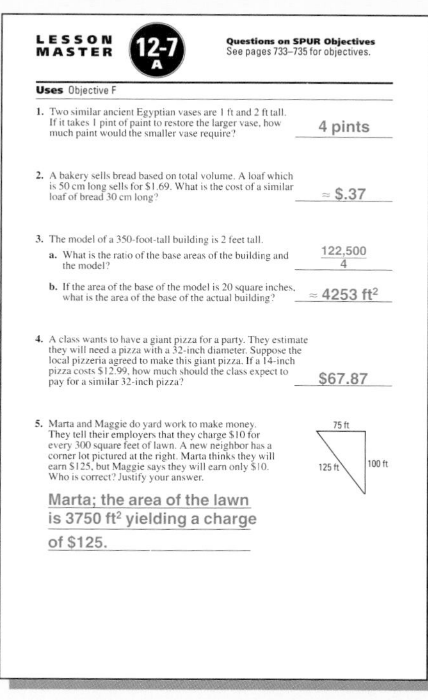

LESSON MASTER 12-7 A

Questions on SPUR Objectives
See pages 733–735 for objectives.

Uses Objective F

1. Two similar ancient Egyptian vases are 1 ft and 2 ft tall. If it takes 1 pint of paint to restore the larger vase, how much paint would the smaller vase require? **4 pints**

2. A bakery sells bread based on total volume. A loaf which is 50 cm long sells for $1.69. What is the cost of a similar loaf of bread 30 cm long? **≈ $.37**

3. The model of a 350-foot-tall building is 2 feet tall.
   a. What is the ratio of the base areas of the building and the model? $\frac{122{,}500}{4}$
   b. If the area of the base of the model is 20 square inches, what is the area of the base of the actual building? **≈ 4253 ft²**

4. A class wants to have a giant pizza for a party. They estimate they will need a pizza with a 32-inch diameter. Suppose the local pizzeria agreed to make this giant pizza. If a 14-inch pizza costs $12.99, how much should the class expect to pay for a similar 32-inch pizza? **$67.87**

5. Marta and Maggie do yard work to make money. They tell their employers that they charge $10 for every 300 square feet of lawn. A new neighbor has a corner lot pictured at the right. Marta thinks they will earn $125, but Maggie says they will earn only $10. Who is correct? Justify your answer.

Marta; the area of the lawn is 3750 ft² yielding a charge of $125.

Additional Examples

1. A manufacturer charges retailers \$129 for a rectangular area rug that measures 6 feet by 9 feet. Suppose the manufacturer bases prices on the amount of material used to make the rug. What would the manufacturer charge for a rug that is made of the same material and measures 8 feet by 12 feet? (Round to the nearest dollar.) \$229
2. At a movie theater, a small container holds 3 cups of popcorn. A similar container that is twice as tall also is available. Does the larger container hold an amount of popcorn that is suitable for one person? The larger container holds 24 cups of popcorn; most people would find this too much for one person to consume. Since the containers are similar, all dimensions of the larger container are twice that of the smaller container. Therefore, the volume of the larger container is 8 times greater than the smaller container and will hold 24 cups of popcorn.

Notes on Questions

Question 12 The thickness of the paint is assumed to be the same for both the scale model and the original object. If the thickness were proportional to the linear dimensions of the object, then the amount of paint needed would be proportional to the volume.

LESSON MASTER 12-7 B Questions on SPUR Objectives

Uses Objective F: Apply the Fundamental Theorem of Similarity in real situations.

In 1 and 2, consider Alice's assortment of size-changing pills from *Alice in Wonderland*. Suppose Alice is 5 ft tall, weighs 100 pounds, and drinks an 8-ounce glass of orange juice every day.

1. If Alice takes a pill that makes her 6 times as large,
   a. how tall would Alice be? 30 ft
   b. how much would Alice weigh? 21,600 lb
   c. how much orange juice would she drink every day? Give your answer to the nearest *gallon*. 13.5 gal
2. If Alice takes a pill that makes her $\frac{1}{6}$ as large,
   a. how tall would Alice be? 10 in.
   b. how much would Alice weigh? ≈ .46 lb, or 7.4 oz
   c. how much orange juice would she drink every day? ≈ .04 oz
3. Two similar American flags are 2 ft long and 6 ft long. If the area of the red fabric on the smaller flag is 124 in^2, what is the area of the red fabric on the larger one? 1116 in^2
4. If a 16-inch pizza costs \$13.50, about how much should a 10-inch pizza cost? \$5.27
5. If an 8-inch pizza serves 2 people, how many people can be served from a 16-inch pizza? 8 people
6. Two similar storage sheds are 3.8 m and 5.6 m tall.
   a. If the materials for a new roof on the smaller one cost \$850, what would the materials for a new roof on the larger one cost? \$1845.98
   b. The exhaust fan for the larger one moves twice as much air per minute as the fan for the smaller one. Will it do as good a job ventilating the shed? Explain your answer. No; the volume of the larger shed is ≈ 3.2 times that of the smaller, so the fan should move ≈ 3.2 times as much air.

Solution

Since the tops of both pizzas are circles, they are similar, with $k = \frac{14}{12} = \frac{7}{6}$. An immediate response is to charge $\frac{7}{6} \cdot \$9.99$. However, this is not correct because the crust and toppings are proportional to the *area*, not the linear dimensions. So we must multiply by $\left(\frac{7}{6}\right)^2$.

The price, based only on amount of ingredients, would be $\$9.99 \cdot \left(\frac{7}{6}\right)^2 = \$9.99 \cdot \frac{49}{36} \approx \$13.60$.

Usually the prices of pizzas are not based only on ingredients. Other factors, such as salaries, equipment, competition, and overhead must be taken into account.

This Mayan clay figurine was found in Campeche, Mexico, and dates from 700–1000 A.D.

Example 2

A solid clay figurine weighs 5 kilograms. A similar one, twice as tall, stands next to it. Could a 4-year-old child pick up the taller figurine?

Solution

Weight is proportional to volume. Thus the multiplying factor for weight is the cube of the ratio of similitude, in this case 2^3. The taller figurine weighs $2^3 \cdot 5 = 40$ kg (about 90 pounds).

A child of 4 would not be able to pick up the figurine, and many adults would be surprised at the weight of the figurine.

The Fundamental Theorem of Similarity was known to Euclid, but the structural applications were not recognized until over 1800 years later by the Italian scientist Galileo. He considered this discovery as important as his more famous discovery that when heavier-than-air objects of different weights are dropped from the same height, they fall to the ground at the same rate.

QUESTIONS

Covering the Reading

In 1–3, according to *Gulliver's Travels* and the Fundamental Theorem of Similarity,

1. Brobdingnagians are _?_ times the height of Gulliver, so they weigh _?_ times as much. 12, 1728
2. Lilliputians are _?_ times the height of Gulliver, so they weigh _?_ times as much. $\frac{1}{12}$, $\frac{1}{1728}$
3. Brobdingnagians are _?_ times the height of Lilliputians so they weigh _?_ times as much. 144, 144^3 or 2,985,984
4. Who was Robert Wadlow? the tallest man on record

Optional Activities

Activity 1 Writing

After they have completed the lesson, you might want students to research one of the persons or topics discussed in the lesson and write a report of their findings. Possible subjects are Robert Wadlow, weightlifting trends, or the pizza topic of **Question 25.**

Activity 2 Cooperative Learning

After completing the lesson, have students discuss these questions in small groups.

1. If two similar polygons have the same area, must they be congruent? [Yes]
2. If two similar polygons have the same perimeter, must they have the same area? [Yes]

Baby giant. *Only in pictures will you see a toddler this size. This scene is from* Honey, I Blew Up the Kid.

In 5–8, consider an imaginary female giant 27 feet tall, which is about 5 times the height of an average woman. If the giant and an average-height woman have similar shapes, how would the following quantities compare? 5–8) See left.

5. weights
6. nose lengths
7. areas of footprints
8. wrist circumferences

9. *True or false.* Champion weight lifters often lift weights five times their own weights. False

10. *True or false.* Prices of pizza are proportional to their diameters. False

11. Why does an elephant need thicker legs for its height than a mosquito needs for its height? See margin.

12. A scale model is $\frac{1}{15}$ actual size. If it is made from the same materials as the original object, then its weight will be ___?___ times the weight of the original. The amount of paint needed to cover the exterior will be ___?___ times the amount of paint used to cover the original. $\frac{1}{3375}$, $\frac{1}{225}$

5) The giant would weigh about 125 times the weight of the woman.

6) The giant's nose would be about 5 times as long as the woman's.

7) The giant's footprints would have an area about 25 times that of the woman's footprints.

8) The giant's wrist circumference would be about 5 times the woman's.

Applying the Mathematics

13. Two similar solid clay figurines are 40 cm and 50 cm tall. If the shorter one weighs 8 kg, how much will the taller one weigh? 15.625 kg

14. A pizza store manager calculates that the ingredients in a 16″ pizza cost the store \$1.50. At this rate, what do the ingredients cost in a 12″ pizza with the same thickness? ≈ \$0.84

15. A 90-cm-tall statue weighs 120 kg. If a similar statue weighs 40 kg, how tall (to the nearest centimeter) is it? ≈ 62 cm

16. The surface area of Earth is about 13 times that of the moon.
a. What is the ratio of their radii, considering them both to be spheres? $\sqrt{13} \approx 3.6$
b. What is the ratio of their volumes? $(\sqrt{13})^3 \approx 46.9$

17. When his height was measured at 8′11.1″, Robert Wadlow weighed 439 lbs. How much would a 5′10″ man weigh if he were similar in shape to Wadlow? ≈ 123 lb

18. Suppose two boxes have congruent bases, but one box is twice the height of the other.
a. Are the boxes similar? No
b. How do their volumes compare? The taller box has twice the volume of the shorter.
c. How do their surface areas compare? The taller box has more surface area, but the ratio of their areas cannot be determined.

Review

19. A hexagon has area 70 units². What is the area of its image under a size change of magnitude $\frac{2}{5}$? *(Lesson 12-6)* 11.2 units²

Question 14 Consumer Connection Students should note that pizza prices are not based solely on the cost of ingredients. There are fixed costs that the manager must consider, such as rent and lighting; these are the same regardless of the size or number of pizzas sold. There also are the cost of boxes and the cost of heating the oven; these have nothing to do with the ingredients, but do depend on the number of pizzas. The manager also must consider labor costs. All of these costs—and others—must be covered by the income from the pizzas sold, and all are used to determine the price charged.

(Notes on Questions continue on page 728.)

Follow-up for Lesson 12-7

Practice

For more questions on SPUR Objectives, use **Lesson Master 12-7A** (shown on page 725) or **Lesson Master 12-7B** (shown on pages 726–727).

(Follow-up continues on page 728.)

3. If two similar figures have the same surface area, must they have the same volume? [Yes]

For each question, students should make a conjecture and give reasons that justify it. After the groups have discussed all the statements, have them share their conjectures with the entire class.

Additional Answers

11. The weights of the animals increase as the cube of the heights; thus, to support this greater weight, the cross-section of the skeleton of the larger animal, which determines the strength of the skeleton, must be correspondingly larger.

► **LESSON MASTER 12-7B** *page 2*

7. Gilberto made a solid model of a volcano out of papier-maché. He used 8 sheets of newspaper for the papier-maché. Now he wants to make a similar volcano twice as tall.
a. How many sheets of newspaper will he need? 64 sheets
b. How will the area of the bases of the two volcanoes compare?
Area of larger will be 4 times area of smaller.

8. Mr. Crane picked two pumpkins from his garden. They appeared to be similar in shape. The larger one weighed 16 pounds and the smaller weighed 2 pounds. What was the ratio of their diameters? $\approx \frac{2}{1}$ or $\approx \frac{1}{2}$

9. Two aluminum cans are similar. The larger uses 1.8 times the aluminum as the smaller. If the larger holds 48 ounces, what is the capacity of the smaller? ≈ 19.9 oz

10. The areas of two similar ice skating rinks are 1200 ft² and 1728 ft². The fence surrounding each is the same height. If it takes 9 gallons of paint to paint the fence around the smaller rink, how much paint is needed for the fence around the larger rink? 10.8 gal

11. If it takes 1200 gallons to fill a cylindrical swimming pool, how much would it take to fill a similar swimming pool with double the radius? 9600 gal

12. A wooden crate has a volume of 2 m³. By what factor should each dimension be multiplied to make a similar crate with a volume of 54 m³? 3

Review Objective B, Lesson 12-5

13. $\triangle SDM \sim \triangle TGK$
a. Write three equal ratios involving the sides of these triangles.
$\frac{SD}{TG} = \frac{DM}{GK} = \frac{SM}{TK}$
b. Write three equations involving angle measures.
$m\angle S = m\angle T$ $m\angle D = m\angle G$ $m\angle M = m\angle K$

D S M K G T

Assessment

Written Communication Have students write a short paragraph describing a fictional situation involving giants or miniature people, other than the ones discussed in the lesson. They should choose a ratio of similitude for their characters different from 12 or $\frac{1}{12}$ and then give some examples comparing area and volume. [Students provide a fictional situation of the type required and apply the Fundamental Theorem of Similarity to determine areas and volumes that pertain to their fictional characters.]

Extension

Two jars of the same brand of crunchy peanut butter are on a shelf in a supermarket. The taller jar is twice as tall as the shorter, but its diameter is only half the diameter of the shorter jar. The taller jar costs $1.00 and the shorter jar costs $1.50. Which is the better buy? [The shorter jar]

Project Update Project 4, *Similar People,* on page 730, relates to the content of this lesson.

Notes on Questions

Question 23 This question involves the situation of the Side-Splitting Theorem, which will be discussed in Lesson 13-3.

Question 24 Sports Connection This exploration provides statistical confirmation of the concepts of the lesson. Students may be interested to know that, in the clean and jerk, the competitor must first lift the barbell to his chest (the clean), and then lift it above his head in one motion, standing with arms extended (the jerk). The jerk is done by squatting and extending the arms, then using leg power to rise. Thus, the weight lifter actually uses the full area of his body to lift the weight. The Turkish weight lifter Naim Suleymanoglu, called "the Pocket Hercules," was the first to lift three times his weight; he still holds the record for lifting the greatest weight in proportion to body weight.

21) Two figures are similar if and only if there is a composite of size changes and reflections mapping one onto the other.

22) Answer is shown in reduced size.

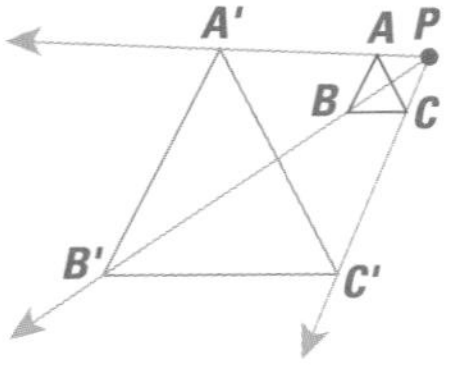

20. At the right, $\triangle PQR \sim \triangle MST$. Find as many missing lengths and angle measures as possible. *(Lessons 12-4, 12-5)* $m\angle R = 42$; $m\angle T = 42$; $m\angle S = 43$; $MT = 12.24$; $RQ \approx 29.8$

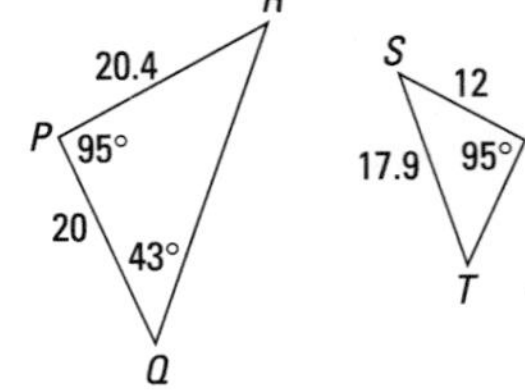

21. Define similar figures. *(Lesson 12-5)* See left.

22. Trace $\triangle ABC$ and point P at the right. Then draw the image of $\triangle ABC$ under a size change with center P, magnitude 4. *(Lesson 12-2)* See left.

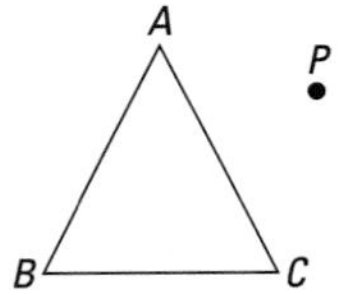

23. Write a proof argument using the given figure.
Given: K is the midpoint of $\overline{FJ}$. The segments $\overline{KI}$ and $\overline{KG}$ are drawn parallel to $\overline{FH}$ and $\overline{HJ}$.
To prove: $\triangle FGK \cong \triangle KIJ$. *(Lesson 7-3)*
See margin.

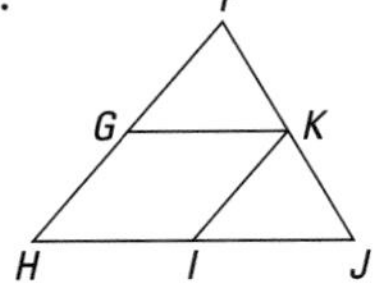

Pocket Hercules. *Breaking all records in his weight class at the 1996 Olympics, Turkey's Naim Suleymanoglu became the first weight lifter to win gold medals at three Olympics. At 141 lb and 4' 11", he lifted three times his body weight.*

Exploration

24. Below are the winning total amounts lifted in the men's weightlifting competition in the 1992 Olympic Games. "Weight Class" refers to the lifter's maximum allowable weight.

a. Calculate the ratios of weight lifted to weight lifter's maximum weight. See chart below.

b. What trends do you see? See left.

c. Give an explanation for any trends you find. See left.

Weight Class	Winner	Team	Total (2 lifts)	
52.0 kg	Ivan Ivanov	Bulgaria	265.0 kg	2.55
56.0 kg	Chun Byung Kwan	S. Korea	287.5 kg	2.57
60.0 kg	Naim Suleymanoglu	Turkey	320.0 kg	2.67
67.5 kg	Israel Militossian	Unified Team	337.5 kg	2.5
75.0 kg	Fedo Kassapu	Unified Team	357.5 kg	2.38
82.5 kg	Pyrros Dimas	Greece	370.0 kg	2.24
90.0 kg	Kakhi Kakhiaehvili	Unified Team	412.5 kg	2.29
100.0 kg	Victor Tregoubov	Unified Team	410.0 kg	2.05
110.0 kg	Ronny Weller	Germany	432.5 kg	1.97
Over 110.0 kg	Aleksandr Kourlovitch	Unified Team	450.0 kg	2.04

24b) In general, heavier men lift more absolute weight, but a smaller percentage of their own weight, than lighter men do.

c) Sample: The lighter men have more surface area relative to their weight than the heavier men do.

25. Find the costs of two different-size pizzas (with the same ingredients) at a local pizza parlor. Answers may vary.

a. What is the ratio of the diameters of the pizzas?

b. What is the ratio of the costs of the pizzas?

c. Are costs based on areas?

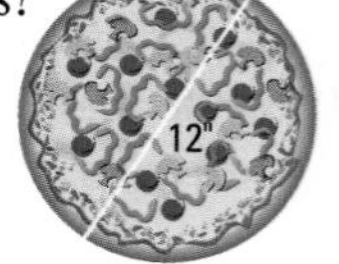

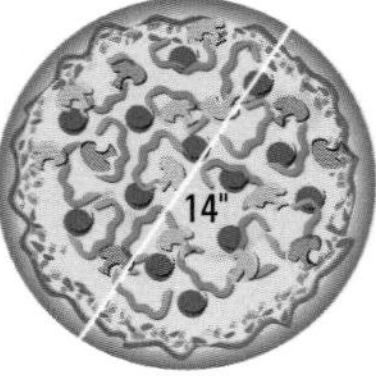

Adapting to Individual Needs

Challenge Writing

Materials: Copy of *Gulliver's Travels*

Have students read Part II of *Gulliver's Travels,* which is called "A Voyage to Brobdingnag," and write a report about some of the measurements found in Gulliver's descriptions.

Additional Answers

23.

Conclusions	Justifications
1. $\overline{FK} \cong \overline{KJ}$	def. of midpoint
2. $\angle FKG \cong \angle KJI$, $\angle KFG \cong \angle JKI$	// Lines ⇒ corresponding ∠s ≅
3. $\triangle FGK \cong \triangle KIJ$	ASA Congruence Thm. (steps 1 and 2)

A project presents an opportunity for you to extend your knowledge of a topic related to the material of this chapter. You should allow more time for a project than you do for typical homework questions.

1 Finish This Story

A pharaoh in ancient Egypt asked a goldsmith to make two statues, identical except for scale, of the pharaoh and his son. The statue of the pharaoh was to be six times the height of the statue of his son. The statue of the pharaoh required 60 pieces of gold, which the pharaoh supplied to the goldsmith. After that statue was completed, the goldsmith asked for 10 pieces of gold to make the statue for the son. The pharaoh gave the goldsmith the 10 pieces, the goldsmith made the statue, and the pharaoh was so pleased with the result that he rewarded the goldsmith with 5 gold pieces. Some time later, one of the pharaoh's advisors told him that the goldsmith had cheated him.

Write a conclusion to this story, which will answer the following questions: Was the pharaoh really cheated? If so, by how much? If not, why is the advisor wrong? If the goldsmith hired a lawyer to defend him, what might the lawyer say? If the advisor hired a lawyer to defend him, what would that lawyer say?

2 Golden Ratio

A rectangle known as the golden rectangle has the following property: If the square on its short side is cut off, then the remaining rectangle is similar to the original, as shown here.

(Diagram: rectangle with sides s and ℓ, square of side s marked off by dashed line.)

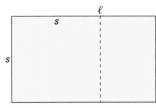

The ratio of the long side to the short side of the golden rectangle is called the golden ratio, and is often represented by the Greek letter ϕ (phi). (This is the same letter used to describe the empty set, but it is not related at all to that use.)

a. Research the golden rectangle and golden ratio and write a report on them. What are some of their properties and applications?

b. Use an automatic drawer or straightedge and compass to construct a golden rectangle. Write an explanation of how you did this, complete with sketches.

3 Models of Everyday Objects

Make a 3-dimensional scale model of a real object. Calculate the surface areas and volumes of the original object and your scale model. Write a report on how you built your model, including calculations.

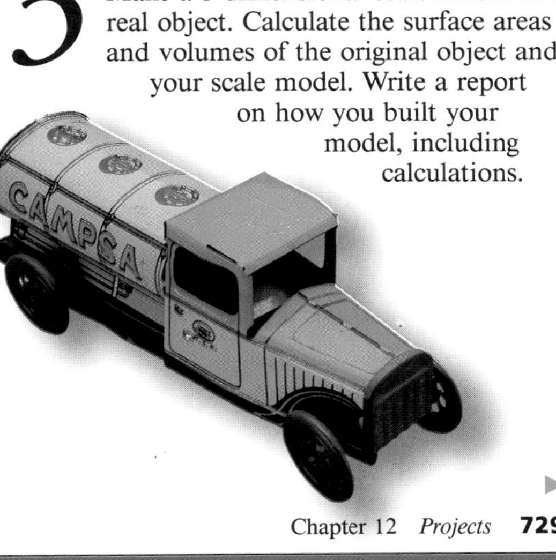

Chapter 12 Projects

The projects relate chiefly to the content of the lessons of this chapter as follows:

Project	Lesson(s)
1	12-6
2	12-4, 12-5
3	12-1, 12-6
4	12-7
5	12-2, 12-3, 12-4, 12-5
6	12-6

1 Finish This Story After students have written their conclusions to the story, you might extend the project by having them stage a courtroom trial in which the matter is litigated.

2 Golden Ratio It has often been written that, since the time of the ancient Greeks, the shape of the golden rectangle has been considered "the most aesthetically pleasing rectangular shape," but recent research does not back this up.

3 Models of Everyday Objects This project is fairly straightforward, but some students may become frustrated when a measurement on the model does not turn out to be as planned—measurement error and factors such as the thickness of construction materials may account for slight differences.

Possible responses

1. Responses will vary.

2a. By definition, a rectangle with length ℓ and width w is a golden rectangle if $\frac{\ell}{w} = \frac{\ell + w}{\ell}$, that is, if $\ell^2 = w + w^2$. For simplicity, let $\ell = 1$. Then $1 = w + w^2$. This equation has roots $\frac{1}{2}(1 \pm \sqrt{5})$. The positive root, $\frac{1}{2}(1 + \sqrt{5})$, is called the golden ratio. Its value is about 1.618. Studied by the Greeks as early as the fifth century B.C., the golden ratio is thought to have a pleasing shape. The Greeks used it in much of their architecture. The golden ratio also appears in nature, within the botanical phenomenon known as *phyllotaxis.* Certain natural arrangements—such as the whorls on a pine cone or pineapple, the seeds of a sunflower, and the branches on the stems of some plants, follow the sequence of Fibonacci numbers: 1, 1, 2, 3, 5, 8, 13, ... The nth term of this sequence, a_n, involves the golden ratio:

$$a_n = \frac{1}{\sqrt{5}}\left(\left(\frac{1+\sqrt{5}}{2}\right)^n - \left(\frac{1+\sqrt{5}}{2}\right)^n\right)$$

(Responses continue on page 730.)

4 Similar People For item ii and item iv of **part a,** students will need to calculate cube roots. In **part b,** a spreadsheet can be used to generate the chart quickly.

5 Pantograph The term *pantograph* refers not only to the drawing instrument described here, but also to any framework of this type. Students may have seen examples of the pantograph framework in use. The most common is a wooden safety gate.

6 Prices of Fruit Drinks Be sure students are aware of the measurements needed to determine if the cups are similar (top diameter, bottom diameter, slant height). Once they have these linear measures, some students may believe that they must use them in a formula to calculate the volume of the cup in cubic units. Lead them to see that the situation involves liquid capacity, and so an appropriate unit of volume is the fluid ounce or milliliter.

Additional responses, page 729

2b. To construct a golden rectangle using compass and straightedge, you can proceed as follows: (1) Construct a square several inches long and label it *ABCD*. Extend $\overleftrightarrow{AB}$ and $\overleftrightarrow{DC}$. (2) Locate the midpoint *E* of $\overline{DC}$. (3) Construct an arc with point *E* as center and $\overline{EB}$ as radius. Mark the point where the arc intersects $\overleftrightarrow{DC}$ as point *F*. (4) Construct a line perpendicular to $\overleftrightarrow{DC}$ at point *F*. Label the point where it intersects $\overleftrightarrow{AB}$ as point *G*. Rectangles *AGFD* and *BGFC* are both golden rectangles. The construction is shown below.

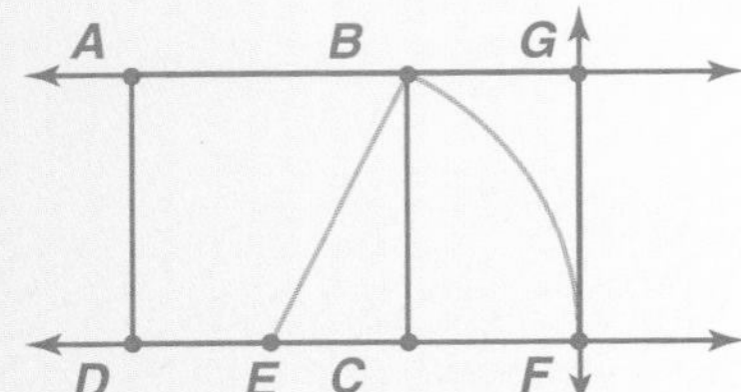

3. Responses will vary.

(continued)

4 Similar People

a. Record your height and weight, and use the method of Lesson 12-7 to determine:

(i) the weight of a similar person a foot (.3048 meter) taller than you are.

(ii) the height of a similar person 20 pounds (9.07 kg) lighter than you are.

(iii) the weight of a similar person 7 feet tall.

(iv) the height of a similar person who weighs 50 pounds.

b. Using your height and weight, create a chart to show the weights of people with similar shape, but taller or shorter, in two-inch intervals from 4′6″ to 6′6″.

c. Consult a chart which gives average male and female heights and weights. Do the average weights in this chart assume people are similar? Why or why not?

5 Pantograph

A pantograph is a mechanical device used for drawing similar figures. In the pantograph shown below, *P* is fixed. When *Q* traces a figure, *S* draws the image of the figure under a size change with magnitude $\frac{PC}{PA}$. Write a report on how a pantograph works, and how drawings can be enlarged or shrunk with it.

6 Prices of Fruit Drinks

Find a place where you can purchase fruit drinks in at least three sizes. For example, some places have small, medium, and large drinks. Some have extra-large drinks.

a. Are the containers similar? Support your answer by referring to the dimensions of the containers.

b. Calculate the volume of the container for each size drink.

c. Divide each volume by the cost of the drink for that container.

d. Which size has the lowest price per unit volume? Which size do you feel is the best buy, and why?

4a. Responses will vary. In general, the heights and weights of two similar persons, *A* and *B*, are related as follows:

$$\left(\frac{\text{height } A}{\text{height } B}\right)^3 = \frac{\text{weight } A}{\text{weight } B}$$

b. Responses will vary.

c. Responses will vary.

5. Sample information students might include: Pantographs are used for reducing or enlarging engineering drawings and maps and for guiding cutting tools over complex paths. Artists who make miniatures use them to achieve greater detail in their works.

6a. Responses will vary. Most likely the ratio $\frac{\text{bottom diameter}}{\text{slant height}}$ will not be the same for all four cups, so the cups will not be similar.

SUMMARY

In the coordinate plane, a size change centered at the origin can be achieved by multiplying coordinates of points by a given scale factor. Since a coordinate system can be created with any point as the origin, size transformations can be centered anywhere. Size transformations can occur in two or three dimensions.

Two figures are similar if and only if one can be mapped onto the other by a composite of reflections and size transformations. The ability to draw or construct similar figures is necessary in the making of scale drawings, toys or scale models, maps, blueprints, and other diagrams. In similar figures, angles and their images are congruent. Lengths of image segments are k times the lengths of preimage segments, where k is a positive number called the ratio of similitude. Areas of images are k^2 times the areas of their preimages. Volumes of images are k^3 times the volumes of their preimages. These relationships between two similar figures help explain why large animals need relatively thicker legs than small animals, and why there cannot be giants.

When one quantity is k times another, then the ratio of the quantities equals k. An equality of two ratios is called a proportion. Whenever there are similar figures, corresponding lengths are proportional. Solving proportions can help you determine unknown measurements.

VOCABULARY

Below are the most important terms and phrases for this chapter. For the starred (*) terms you should be able to give a definition of the term. For the other terms you should be able to give a general description and a specific example of each.

Lesson 12-1
S_k, magnitude
Properties of S_k Theorem

Lesson 12-2
*size change
*size transformation
*center of size transformation
*magnitude of size transformation
*size-change factor k
expansion
contraction
identity transformation
S_k Size-Change Theorem

Lesson 12-3
Size-Change Distance Theorem
Size-Change Preservation Properties Theorem
Figure Size-Change Theorem

Lesson 12-4
ratio
proportion, proportional
extremes, means
Means-Extremes Property

Lesson 12-5
*similar figures, $F \sim G$
*similarity transformation
Similar Figures Theorem
ratio of similitude

Lesson 12-6
Fundamental Theorem of Similarity

Summary

The Summary gives an overview of the entire chapter and provides an opportunity for students to consider the material as a whole. Thus, the Summary can be used to help students relate and unify the concepts presented in the chapter.

Vocabulary

Terms, symbols, and properties are listed by lesson to provide a checklist of concepts that students must know. Emphasize that students should read the vocabulary list carefully before starting the Progress Self-Test. If students do not understand the meaning of a term, they should refer back to the indicated lesson.

b. Responses will vary.
c. Responses will vary. Students' results may be slightly larger than the actual amount of liquid that will be put into the cup—for practical purposes, cups cannot be filled completely.
d. Reponses will vary. Students may note that many factors may determine what is the best buy for a particular individual. For instance, the large size might cost less per unit of liquid than a smaller size, but if a person is not able, or does not want, to drink a large amount, a smaller size would be a better buy for that person.

CHAPTER TWELVE

Progress Self-Test

For the development of mathematical competence, feedback and correction, along with the opportunity to practice, are necessary. The Progress Self-Test provides the opportunity for feedback and correction; the Chapter Review provides additional opportunities and practice. We cannot overemphasize the importance of these end-of-chapter materials. It is at this point that the material "gels" for many students, allowing them to solidify skills and understanding. In general, student performance should be markedly improved after these pages.

Assign the Progress Self-Test as a one-night assignment. Worked-out *solutions* for all questions are in the Selected Answers section of the student book. Encourage students to take the Progress Self-Test honestly, grade themselves, and then be prepared to discuss the test in class.

Advise students to pay special attention to those Chapter Review questions (pages 733–735) which correspond to the questions that they missed on the Progress Self-Test.

Additional Answers

1.

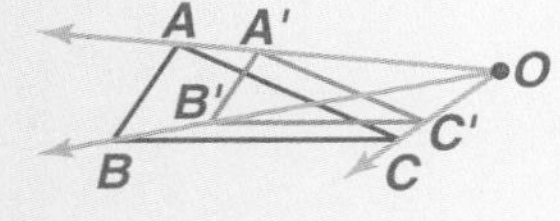

2.

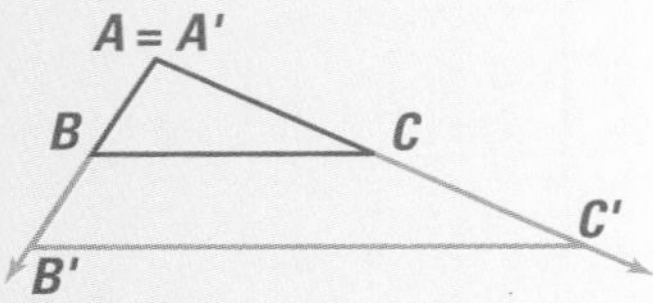

PROGRESS SELF-TEST

1–4, 9–11, 14, 15, 18–20) See margin.

Take this test as you would take a test in class. You will need a ruler and compass. Check your work with the solutions in the Selected Answers section in the back of the book.

In 1 and 2, trace the figure. Draw the image of $\triangle ABC$ under each size change.

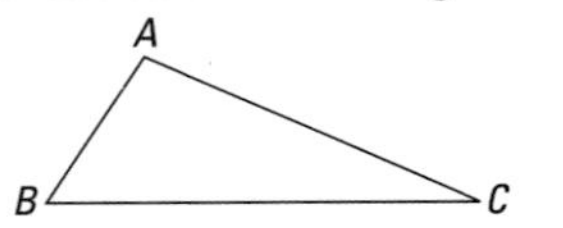

1. center O, magnitude $\frac{3}{4}$.
2. center A, magnitude 2.
3. Trace the figure at the right. Draw the image of $\odot E$ under a size change with center F, magnitude 1.5.

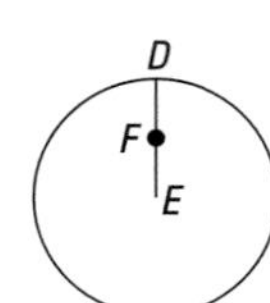

4. Trace the figure below in which the preimage is blue and the image is orange. Use a ruler to determine the center and size-change factor k for the size change represented.

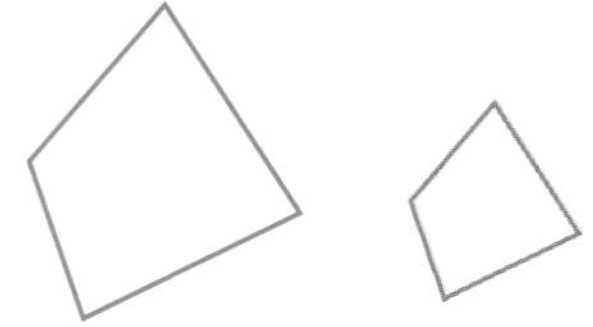

5. $QUAD \sim FOUR$ with side and angle measures as indicated at the right. Find as many missing lengths and angle measures as possible. $m\angle AUQ = 37$, $DA = 20.25$, $OU = 32$

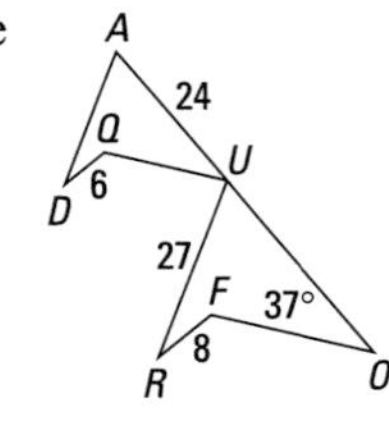

In 6 and 7, $S(\triangle VXZ) = \triangle WXY$ in the figure.

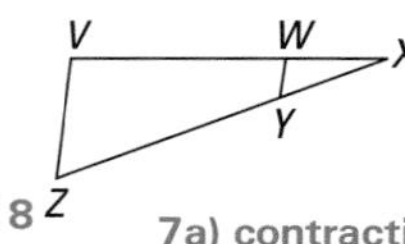

6. $VZ = 12$, $WY = 4$, and $WX = 6$. What is XV? 18
7. a. Is this S an expansion or a contraction? 7a) contraction

   b. What is the center of the size change? X

8. *Multiple choice.* Size changes preserve a

   (a) angle measure. (b) distance.

   (c) area. (d) volume.

9. Define similar figures.
10. $\triangle P'Q'R'$ is a size-change image of $\triangle PQR$ with a magnitude of 5. How do the areas of $\triangle P'Q'R'$ and $\triangle PQR$ compare?
11. A pyramid has volume 729 cm^3. What is the volume of a similar pyramid $\frac{1}{3}$ as high?
12. At the right, $\triangle QRS \sim \triangle VTU$.

    a. Find QS. $2y$

    b. Find TU. $6x$

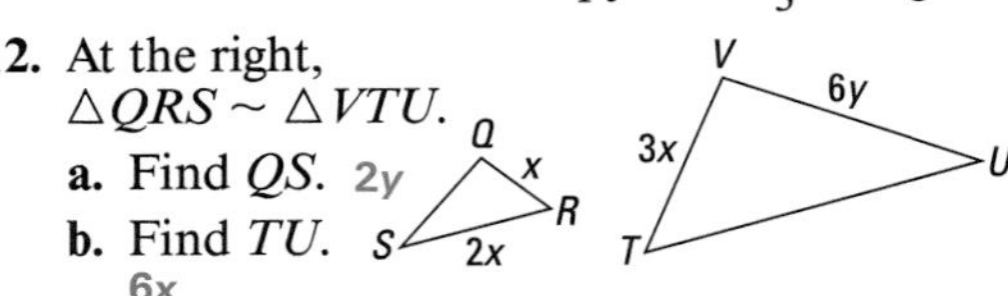

13. A photo slide measures 5 cm by 3 cm. If the shorter dimension of a similar print is 25 cm, what is its longer dimension? $41\frac{2}{3} \approx 41.7$ cm
14. A car can go 41 km in 28 minutes. At that rate, how long will it take to travel 100 km?
15. A solid figurine is 4″ tall and weighs 5 pounds. What will a similar solid figurine of the same material weigh if it is 12″ tall?
16. Suppose a person 2 meters tall has feet 33 cm long. If a person with similar physique were 0.4 meter tall, how long would this person's feet be? 6.6 cm
17. If there were a person 6 times as tall as you with a similar physique, the person would weigh __?__ times as much. This weight would be supported by about __?__ times the area. 6^3 or 216, 6^2 or 36
18. Graph $\triangle ABC$ and $S_{\frac{1}{3}}(\triangle ABC)$ if $A = (6, -6)$, $B = (9, 0)$, and $C = (-6, 10)$.
19. If $P = (5, -1)$ and $Q = (1, 2)$, verify that the distance between $S_8(P)$ and $S_8(Q)$ is $8 \cdot PQ$.
20. At the right, kite $KITE$ is conveniently located on a coordinate plane. Find the coordinates of the vertices of $S_4(KITE)$.

y-axis; x-axis; $K = (0, b)$; $(-a, 0) = E$; $I = (a, 0)$; $T = (0, -c)$

Additional Answers, continued

3.

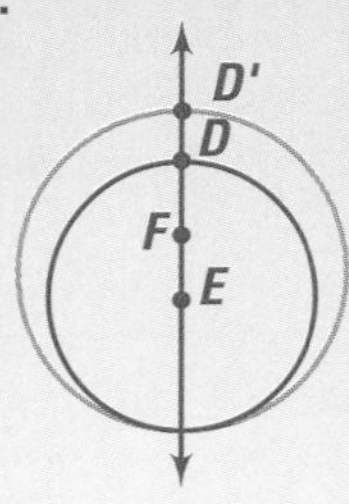

4.

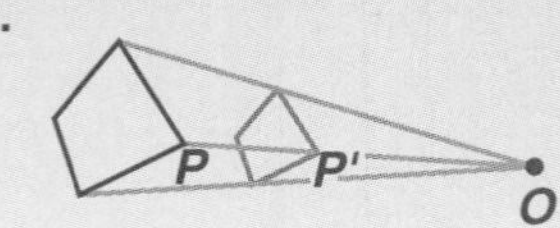

$OP = 5.6$ cm, $OP' = 3.4$ cm; so the magnitude is $\frac{3.4}{5.6} \approx 0.6$.

9. Two figures F and G are similar if and only if there is a composite of size changes and reflections mapping F onto G.

10. $\text{area}(\triangle P'Q'R') = 5^2 \cdot \text{area}(\triangle PQR) = 25 \cdot \text{area}(\triangle PQR)$
11. $\frac{V}{729} = (\frac{1}{3})^3$; $V = \frac{729}{27} = 27$ cm^3
14. ≈ 68 minutes
15. $w = 135$ lb
18. $S_{\frac{1}{3}}(A) = (2, -2)$, $S_{\frac{1}{3}}(B) = (3, 0)$, $S_{\frac{1}{3}}(C) = (-2, \frac{10}{3})$. Graph is shown at the right.

CHAPTER REVIEW

Questions on SPUR Objectives

SPUR stands for **S**kills, **P**roperties, **U**ses, and **R**epresentations. The Chapter Review questions are grouped according to the SPUR Objectives for this chapter.

SKILLS DEAL WITH THE PROCEDURES USED TO GET ANSWERS.

1, 2, 4, 5) See margin.

Objective A: *Draw size-transformation images of figures.* *(Lessons 12-2, 12-3)*

In 1–6, first trace the figure.

1. Draw the image of $\triangle ABC$ under a size change with center O, magnitude 1.5.

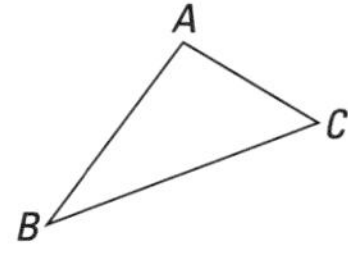

2. Draw the image of $\triangle ABC$ above under a size transformation with center A, magnitude 0.8.
3. Draw the image of $DEFG$ below under a size transformation with center I, scale factor $\frac{2}{3}$. See below.

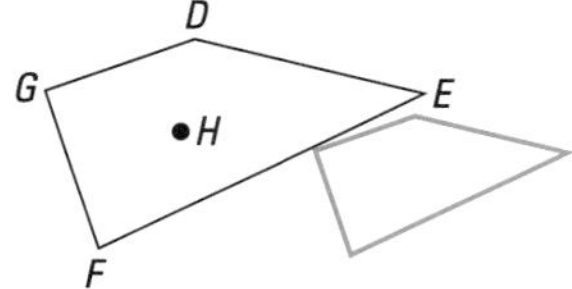

4. Draw the image of $DEFG$ above under a size change with scale factor $\frac{5}{3}$, center H.
5. Draw the image of $ABCDE$ under a size transformation with center O, magnitude 3.2.
6. Draw $A'B'C'D'E'$, the image of $ABCDE$, under a size change with center E, magnitude 1. The image is $ABCDE$ itself.

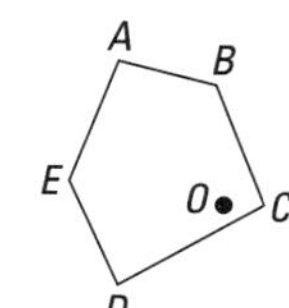

Objective B: *Use proportions to find missing parts in similar figures.* *(Lessons 12-4, 12-5)*

7. Below, $HOURS$ is the image of $PENTA$ under a size change. Some side and angle measures are indicated. Find as many missing lengths and angle measures as possible. (Be careful about which vertices correspond.)

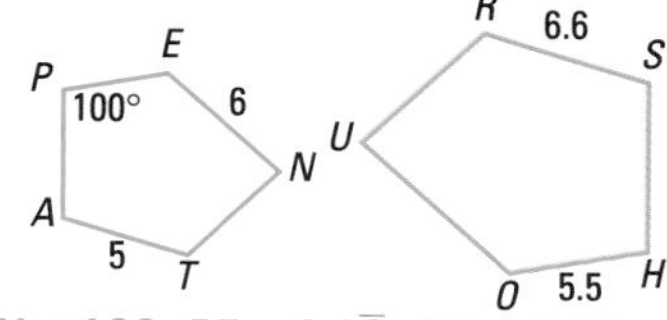

$m\angle H = 100$, $PE = 4.1\overline{6}$, $OU = 7.92$

8. Let S be a size transformation with $S(\triangle JKL) = \triangle JMN$, as pictured below.
   a. Find JN. 7.5
   b. Find LN. 2.5
   c. Find MN. 10.5

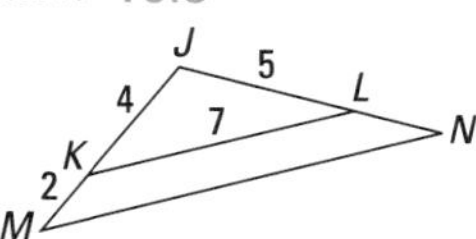

In 9 and 10, $\triangle TUV \sim \triangle WXV$.

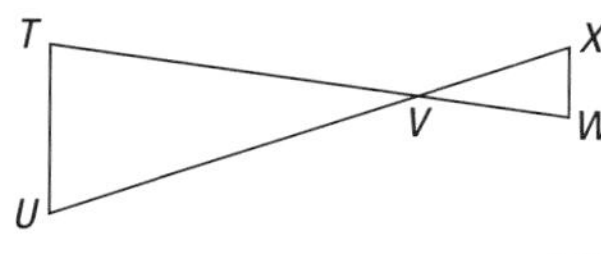

9. If $TV = 10$, $VW = 5$, and $VX = 6$, find VU. $VU = 12$ units
10. $TU = 70$, $XW = 42$, and $TV = 112.5$.
    a. What other length can be found? VW
    b. Find it. 67.5 units

Chapter 12 Review

Resources

From the ***Teacher's Resource File***

- Answer Master for Chapter 12 Review
- *Assessment Sourcebook:* Chapter 12 Test, Forms A–D Chapter 12 Test, Cumulative Form

Additional Resources

- Quiz and Test Writer

The main objectives for the chapter are organized in the Chapter Review under the four types of understanding this book promotes—Skills, Properties, Uses, and Representations.

(Continued on page 734.)

Additional Answers

1.

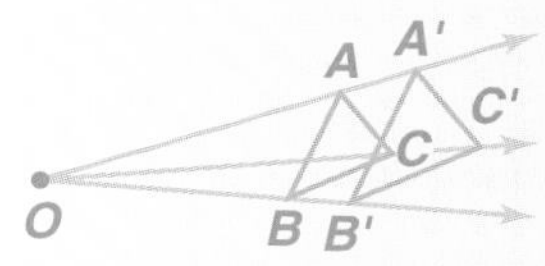

2.

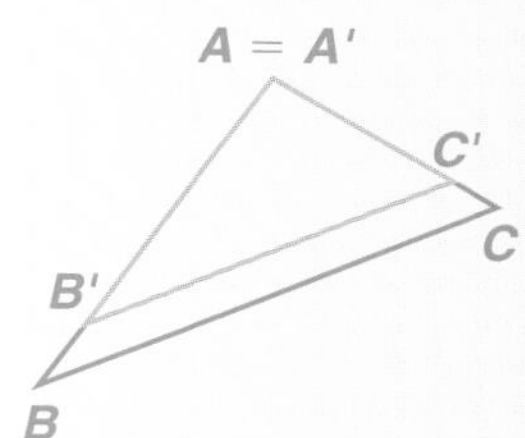

4.

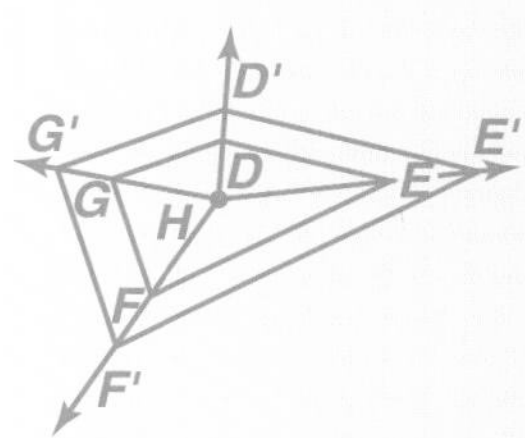

5.

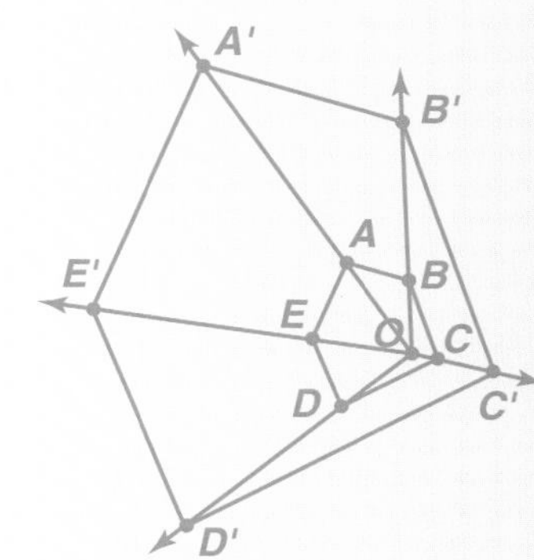

Additional Answers, page 732

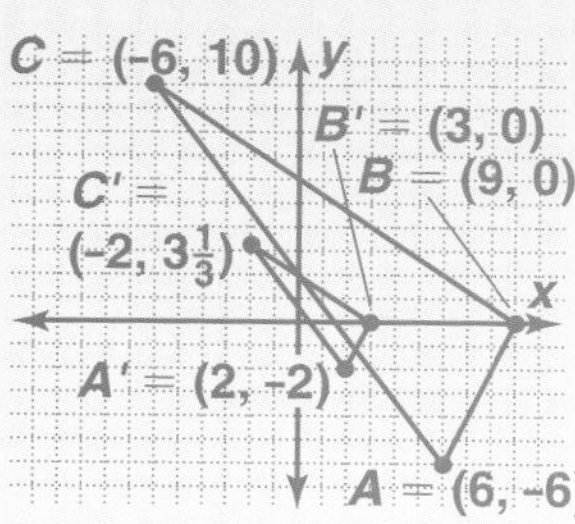

19. $S_8(P) = (40, -8)$, $S_8(Q) = (8, 16)$; The distance between $S_8(P)$ and $S_8(Q) = \sqrt{(40-8)^2 + (-8-16)^2} = \sqrt{32^2 + (-24)^2} = \sqrt{1600} = 40$; $PQ = \sqrt{(5-1)^2 + (2+1)^2} = \sqrt{4^2 + 3^2} = \sqrt{25} = 5$. Therefore, the distance between $S_8(P)$ and $S_8(Q)$ is $8 \cdot PQ$.
20. $K' = (0, 4b)$, $I' = (4a, 0)$, $T' = (0, -4c)$, $E' = (-4a, 0)$

Whereas end-of-chapter material may be considered optional in some texts, in UCSMP *Geometry* we have selected these objectives and questions with the expectation that they will be covered. Students should be able to answer these questions with about 85% accuracy after studying the chapter.

You may assign these questions over a single night to help students prepare for a test the next day, or you may assign the questions over a two-day period. If you work the questions over two days, then we recommend assigning the evens for homework the first night so that students get feedback in class the next day, then assigning the *odds* the night before the test because answers are provided to the odd-numbered questions.

It is effective to ask students which questions they still do not understand and use the day or days as a total class discussion of the material which the class finds most difficult.

Additional Answers

15.

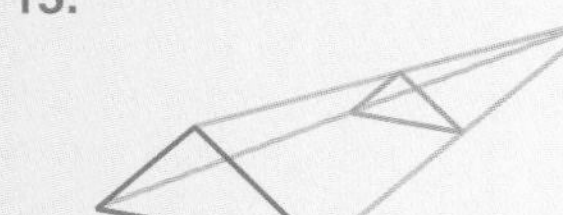

19. Area ($\triangle A'B'C'$) = 121 · area($\triangle ABC$)

20. If the ratio of similitude is k, the ratio of volumes is k^3.

11. $\triangle ABC \sim \triangle DEF$ in the figure at the right.

a. Find DF. $\frac{2}{3}y$

b. Find BC. $3z$

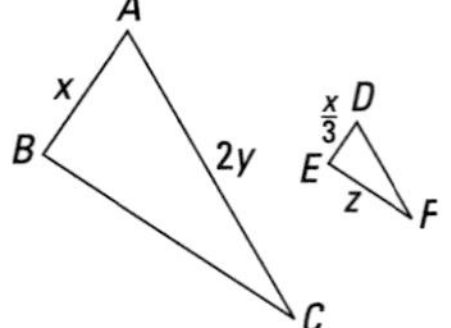

12. The two boxes below are similar. Find the other two dimensions of Box II. $7\frac{1}{3}$, $2\frac{2}{3}$

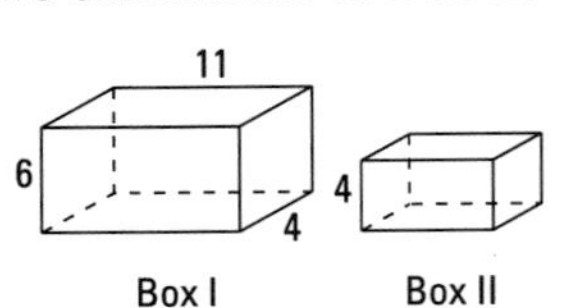

PROPERTIES DEAL WITH THE PRINCIPLES BEHIND THE MATHEMATICS.

15, 19, 20) See margin.

Objective C: *Recognize and apply properties of size transformations.* *(Lessons 12-2, 12-3)*

13. Suppose S is a size transformation of magnitude 4 and S($\triangle CAT$) = $\triangle FUN$.

a. S(T) = __?__. N

b. If m$\angle NUF$ = 71, find m$\angle CAT$. 71

c. If AC = 11, find UF. 44

14. *Multiple choice.* A size change of magnitude .5 does *not* preserve d

(a) angle measure. (b) betweenness.
(c) collinearity. (d) distance.

In 15 and 16, the preimage is blue and the image is orange. Trace the figure and then use a ruler to determine the center and size-change factor k for the size change represented.

15.

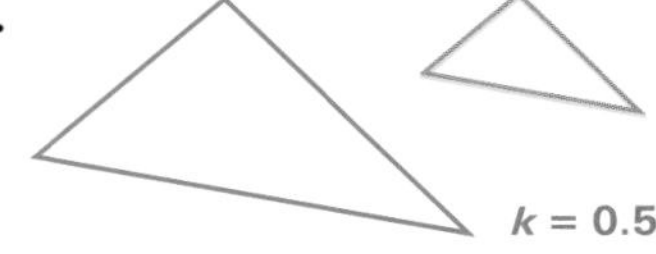

$k = 0.5$

16.

$k \approx 0.37$

In 17 and 18, $\triangle RST$ is the image of $\triangle OQP$ under a size change.

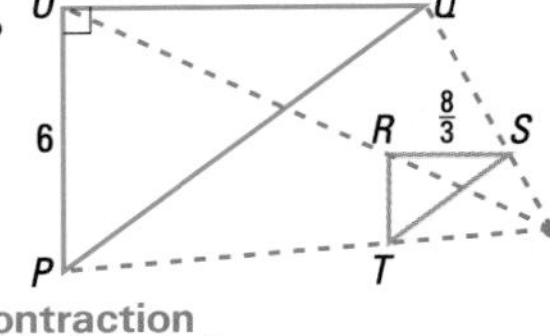

17. a. Is this size change an expansion or contraction? contraction

b. *True or false.* $\overleftrightarrow{PQ} \parallel \overleftrightarrow{ST}$ True

18. a. Trace the figure and locate the center of the size change. See above.

b. What is the magnitude of the size change?

c. Find the lengths of $\overline{PQ}$, $\overline{RT}$, and $\overline{ST}$.
10; 2; $\frac{10}{3}$ b) $\frac{1}{3}$

Objective D: *Use the Fundamental Theorem of Similarity to find lengths, perimeters, areas, and volumes in similar figures.* *(Lesson 12-6)*

19. If $\triangle A'B'C'$ is the image of $\triangle ABC$ under a size change of magnitude 11, how do the areas of $\triangle A'B'C'$ and $\triangle ABC$ compare?

20. How are the volumes of similar figures related to the ratio of similitude?

21. A hexagon has area 20 cm^2 and a shortest side with length 6 cm. A similar hexagon has a shortest side of length 8 cm. What is the area of this similar hexagon? $\approx$ 35.6 cm^2

22. A prism has volume 64 cubic meters. What is the volume of a similar prism $\frac{3}{4}$ as high? 27 cubic meters

USES DEAL WITH APPLICATIONS OF MATHEMATICS IN REAL SITUATIONS.

Objective E: *Identify and determine proportional lengths and distances in real situations.* *(Lessons 12-4, 12-5)*

23. A photograph is 5″ by 8″. If a similar photograph is 10″ in its longer dimension, what is its shorter dimension? 6.25″

24. A recipe for *sevyan*, a noodle pudding served on the holiday *Id Alfitr* by Indian and Pakistani Muslims, calls for seven ounces of sevyan noodles for five servings. How many ounces of sevyan noodles are needed for two servings? 2.8 ounces

Additional Answers, continued

35.

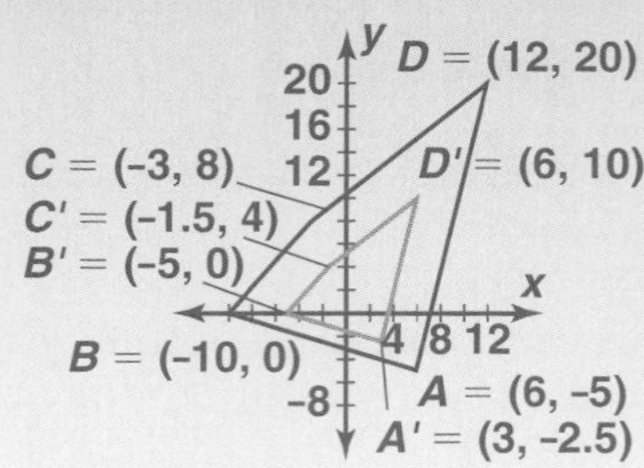

36.

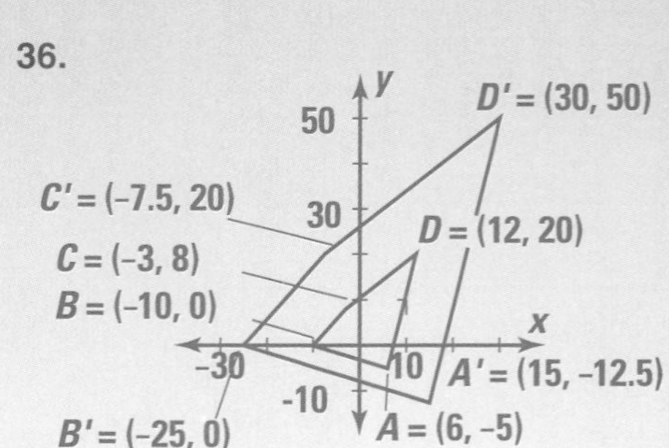

25. TV screens are nearly all similar. If a 9″ screen (measured along a diagonal) is 7″ wide, how wide is a 26″ screen? ≈ 20.2″

26. If a marathon runner covers 15 miles in 1 hour 45 minutes, at that rate how many miles can the runner cover in $2\frac{1}{2}$ hours?

27. A poster of a certain landscape is 15″ × 20″. If a similar photograph of the same landscape is 6″ × 8″, how tall will an 8″ spire in the poster appear in the photograph? 3.2″

28. A highway from Chicago to Milwaukee is 90 miles long and 6″ long on a map. If the actual highway from Chicago to St. Louis is 300 miles long, how long is this highway on the map? 20″

26) ≈ 21.43 miles

Objective F: *Apply the Fundamental Theorem of Similarity in real situations.* *(Lessons 12-6, 12-7)*

29. A solid figurine is 20 cm tall and weighs 3 kg. How much will a similar solid figurine of the same material weigh if it is 32 cm tall? ≈ 12.3 kg

CHAPTER TWELVE

30. If a 10-inch diameter pizza costs $5.89, and if cost is proportional to the quantity of ingredients used to make it, what should a 16-inch diameter pizza cost if it has the same kinds of ingredients and the same thickness? ≈ $15.08

31. Dolls are often $\frac{1}{12}$ actual size. The same cloth used for a real coat can be used to make how many doll coats? 144

32. An elephant 16 feet high can weigh 7 tons. (A ton is 2000 pounds.) If a similar elephant were 1 foot high, how many pounds would it weigh? ≈ 3.4 lb

33. If there were a person 8 times as tall as you and with your physique, the person would weigh __?__ times as much as you do. This weight would be supported by __?__ times the area that supports you. 512, 64

34. *True or false.* Larger animals need thicker legs to support their weight. True

REPRESENTATIONS DEAL WITH PICTURES, GRAPHS, OR OBJECTS THAT ILLUSTRATE CONCEPTS.

35–39) See margin.

Objective G: *Perform and analyze size transformations on figures in the coordinate plane.* *(Lesson 12-1)*

In 35–37, $A = (6, -5)$, $B = (-10, 0)$, $C = (-3, 8)$, $D = (12, 20)$.

35. Graph $ABCD$ and its image under $S_{\frac{1}{2}}$.

36. Graph $ABCD$ and its image under $S_{2.5}$.

37. List the coordinates of the image of $ABCD$ under S_k.

38. Let S be the size transformation of magnitude 5, center (0, 0).

y; 4; 2; 0; 4; x; -2; -4; -6; P = (1, 4); Q = (2, -1); R = (3, -6)

   a. Using the graph at the right, find S(P), S(Q), and S(R).

   b. Fill in the blank and then prove the statement. The distance between S(P) and S(Q) is __?__ times the distance between P and Q.

   c. Verify that the slope of $\overline{PQ}$ equals the slope of the line through S(P) and S(Q).

   d. Verify that S(P), S(Q), and S(R) are collinear.

   e. Verify that S(Q) is between S(P) and S(R).

In 39 and 40, refer to the figure $HEXAGO$ below. Let S be the size transformation of magnitude $\frac{1}{2}$, center (0, 0).

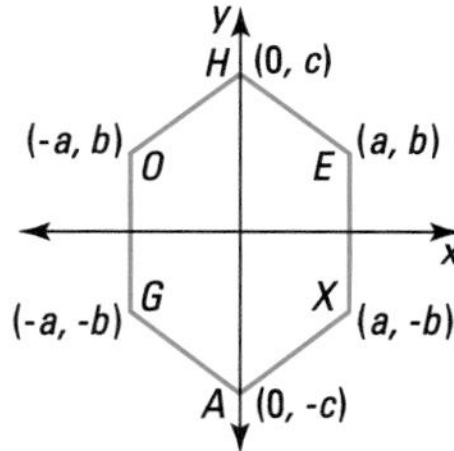

39. What are the coordinates of S(E), S(H), and S(G)?

40. Let S($HEXAGO$) = ($BCDFIJ$). What size transformation T could be applied to $BCDFIJ$ so that T($BCDFIJ$) = ($HEXAGO$)? T: magnitude 2 with same center as S

Assessment

Evaluation The *Assessment Sourcebook* provides five forms of the Chapter 12 Test. Forms A and B present parallel versions in a short-answer format. Forms C and D offer performance assessment. The fifth test is Chapter 12 Test, Cumulative Form. About 50% of this test covers Chapter 12; 25% covers Chapter 11, and 25% covers earlier chapters.

For information on grading, see General Teaching *Suggestions; Grading in the Professional Sourcebook* which begins on page T20 in Part 1 of the Teacher's Edition.

Feedback After students have taken the test for Chapter 12 and you have scored the results, return the tests to students for discussion. Class discussion on the questions that caused trouble for most students can be very effective in identifying and clarifying misunderstandings. You might want to have them write down the items they missed and work either in groups or at home to correct them. It is important for students to receive feedback on every chapter test, and we recommend that students see and correct their mistakes before proceeding too far into the next chapter.

37. $A' = (6k, -5k)$, $B' = (-10k, 0)$, $C' = (-3k, 8k)$, $D' = (12k, 20k)$

38a. $S(P) = (5, 20)$, $S(Q) = (10, -5)$, $S(R) = (15, -30)$

b. 5; $PQ = \sqrt{26}$; distance between S(P) and S(Q) $= \sqrt{650} = 5 \cdot \sqrt{26}$

c. slope of $\overline{PQ} = \frac{-1-4}{2-1} = \frac{-5}{1} = -5$, of images: $= \frac{-5-20}{10-5} = \frac{-25}{5} = -5$

d. slope of line through S(R) and S(Q) $= \frac{-30--5}{15-10} = \frac{-25}{5} = -5$, same as slope through S(P) and S(Q) as seen in part (c), and they share the point S(Q). Thus, they are collinear.

e. The distance from S(P) to S(Q) is $5\sqrt{26}$. The distance from S(Q) to S(R) is $5\sqrt{26}$. The distance from S(P) to S(R) is $10\sqrt{26}$. Since $5\sqrt{26} + 5\sqrt{26} = 10\sqrt{26}$, S(Q) is between S(P) and S(R).

39. $S(E) = (\frac{1}{2}a, \frac{1}{2}b)$, $S(H) = (0, \frac{1}{2}c)$, $S(G) = (-\frac{1}{2}a, -\frac{1}{2}b)$

Chapter 13 Planner

Adapting to Individual Needs

The student text is written for the vast majority of students. The chart at the right suggests two pacing plans to accommodate the needs of your students. Students in the Full Course should complete the entire text by the end of the year. Students in the Minimal Course will spend more time when there are quizzes and more time on the Chapter Review. Therefore, these students may not complete all of the chapters in the text.

Options are also presented to meet the needs of a variety of teaching and learning styles. For each lesson, the Teacher's Edition provides a section entitled *Adapting to Individual Needs.* This section regularly includes **Optional Activities, Challenge** problems, **English Language Development** suggestions, and suggestions for providing **Extra Help.** The Teacher's Edition also frequently includes an **Error Alert,** an **Extension,** and an **Assessment** alternative. The options available in Chapter 13 are summarized in the chart below.

Chapter 13 Pacing Chart

Day	Full Course	Minimal Course
1	13-1	13-1
2	13-2	13-2
3	13-3	13-3
4	Quiz*; 13-4	Quiz*; begin 13-4.
5	13-5	Finish 13-4.
6	13-6	13-5
7	Quiz*; 13-7	13-6
8	13-8	Quiz*; begin 13-7.
9	Self-Test	Finish 13-7.
10	Review	13-8
11	Test*	Self-Test
12		Review
13		Review
14		Test*

*in the Teacher's Resource File

Chapter 13 Block Schedule

Day	Recommended Pacing
1	Lessons 13-1, 13-2
2	Lesson 13-3
3	Lessons 13-4, 13-5
4	Lesson 13-6
5	Lessons 13-7
6	Lesson 13-8, Self-Test, Chapter Review
7	Chapter Review, Chapter Test or Comprehensive Test (Omit items 24 and 25.)

In the Teacher's Edition...

Lesson	Optional Activities	Extra Help	Challenge	English Language Development	Error Alert	Extension	Cooperative Learning	Ongoing Assessment
13-1	●	●	●	●		●	●	Written
13-2	●	●	●	●		●	●	Oral/Written
13-3	●	●	●	●	●	●	●	Oral/Written
13-4	●	●	●			●	●	Written
13-5	●	●	●	●	●	●	●	Oral/Written
13-6	●	●	●			●	●	Oral/Written
13-7	●	●	●	●	●	●		Oral/Written
13-8	●	●	●	●	●	●		Written

In the Additional Resources...

	In the Teacher's Resource File								
Lesson	Lesson Masters, A and B	Teaching Aids*	Activity Kit*	Answer Masters	Technology Sourcebook	Assessment Sourcebook	Visual Aids**	Technology	Video Segments
13-1	13-1	171, 174, 175		13-1	25		171, 174, 175, AM	GeoExplorer	
13-2	13-2	171	26	13-2	25		171, AM	GeoExplorer	
13-3	13-3	171, 176		13-3	26	Quiz	171, 176, AM	GeoExplorer	
In-class Activity				13-4					
13-4	13-4	172, 177, 178		13-4			172, 177, 178, AM		
13-5	13-5	172, 179	27	13-5	27		172, 179, AM	GeoExplorer	
In-class Activity				13-6					
13-6	13-6	172		13-6	27	Quiz	172, AM	GeoExplorer	
13-7	13-7	4, 173, 180	28	13-7			4, 173, 180, AM		13-7
13-8	13-8	105, 173		13-8			105, 173, AM		
End of Chapter				Review		Tests			

*Teaching Aids are pictured on pages 736C and 736D. The activities in the Activity Kit are pictured on page 736C.

**Visual Aids provide transparencies for all Teaching Aids and all Answer Masters.

Also available is the Study Skills Handbook which includes study-skill tips related to reading, note-taking, and comprehension.

Integrating Strands and Applications

	13-1	13-2	13-3	13-4	13-5	13-6	13-7	13-8
Mathematical Connections								
Number Sense	●	●	●		●	●	●	
Algebra	●	●	●	●	●	●	●	●
Geometry	●	●	●	●	●	●	●	●
Measurement	●	●	●	●	●	●	●	●
Logic and Reasoning	●	●	●	●	●	●	●	●
Statistics/DataAnalysis				●				
Patterns and Functions		●		●	●	●	●	●
Interdisciplinary and Other Connections								
Art								
Music		●						
Literature								
Science					●			●
Social Studies	●		●	●			●	●
Multicultural		●	●					
Technology	●		●	●			●	●
Career								
Consumer								
Sports					●			

Teaching and Assessing the Chapter Objectives

Chapter 13 Objectives (Organized into the SPUR categories—Skills, Properties, Uses, and Representations)	**Lessons**	**Progress Self-Test Questions**	**Chapter Review Questions**	**In the Teacher's Resource File: Chapter Test, Forms A and B**	**Chapter Test, Forms C**	**Chapter Test, Forms D**
Skills						
A: Find lengths in figures by applying the Side-Splitting Theorem and the Side-Splitting Converse Theorem.	13-3	3, 4	1–6	1, 2	1	
B: Calculate lengths using the Right Triangle Altitude Theorem.	13-4	1, 2	7–10	3, 13	2	
C: Calculate lengths of sides in isosceles right triangles and in 30-60-90 triangles.	13-5	5, 6	11–16	4, 5	3	✓
D: Determine sines, cosines, and tangents of angles and use the SAS Triangle Area Formula.	13-6, 13-7, 13-8	8, 13, 15	17–24	8–10		
E: Estimate or determine exact values of the trigonometric ratios.	13-6, 13-7	10, 11	25–30	6, 7	4	
Properties						
F: Determine whether or not triangles are similar using the AA, SAS, or SSS Similarity Theorems.	13-1, 13-2	7, 9	31–36	11, 12	5	
G: Know the definitions of sine, cosine, and tangent.	13-6, 13-7	12, 14	37–44	14, 15	4	✓
Uses						
H: Use the Triangle Similarity and Side-Splitting Theorems to find lengths and distances in real situations.	13-2, 13-3	16, 18	45–48	16, 17		✓
I: Use sines, cosines, and tangents to determine unknown lengths in real situations.	13-6, 13-7	17, 20	49–52	18	4	✓
J: Determine components of vectors in real situations.	13-8	19	53–54	19	6	
Representations There are no representation objectives for this chapter.						

Assessment Sourcebook
Quiz for Lessons 13-1 through 13-3
Quiz for Lessons 13-4 through 13-6
Chapter 13 Test, Forms A–D
Chapter 13 Test, Cumulative Form

Quiz and Test Writer

Activity Kit

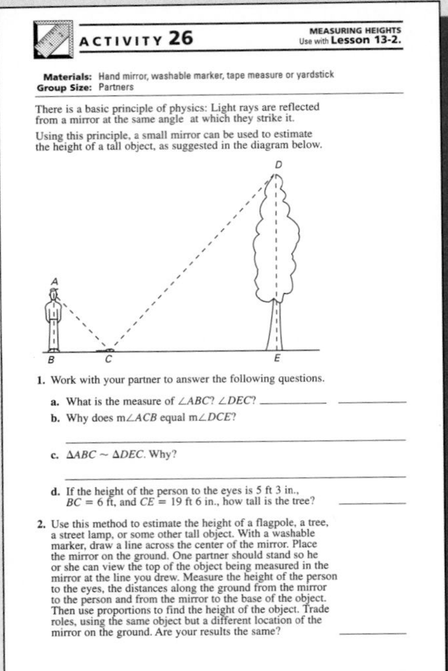
ACTIVITY 26 — MEASURING HEIGHTS — Use with Lesson 13-2.

Materials: Hand mirror, washable marker, tape measure or yardstick
Group Size: Partners

There is a basic principle of physics: Light rays are reflected from a mirror at the same angle at which they strike it.

Using this principle, a small mirror can be used to estimate the height of a tall object, as suggested in the diagram below.

1. Work with your partner to answer the following questions.
   a. What is the measure of $\angle ABC$? $\angle DEC$? ______ ______
   b. Why does $m\angle ACB$ equal $m\angle DCE$? ______
   c. $\triangle ABC \sim \triangle DEC$. Why? ______
   d. If the height of the person to the eyes is 5 ft 3 in., BC = 6 ft, and CE = 19 ft 6 in., how tall is the tree? ______
2. Use this method to estimate the height of a flagpole, a tree, a street lamp, or some other tall object. With a washable marker, draw a line across the center of the mirror. Place the mirror on the ground. One partner should stand so he or she can view the top of the object being measured in the mirror at the line you drew. Measure the height of the person to the eyes, the distances along the ground from the mirror to the person and from the mirror to the base of the object. Then use proportions to find the height of the object. Trade roles, using the same object but a different location of the mirror on the ground. Are your results the same? ______

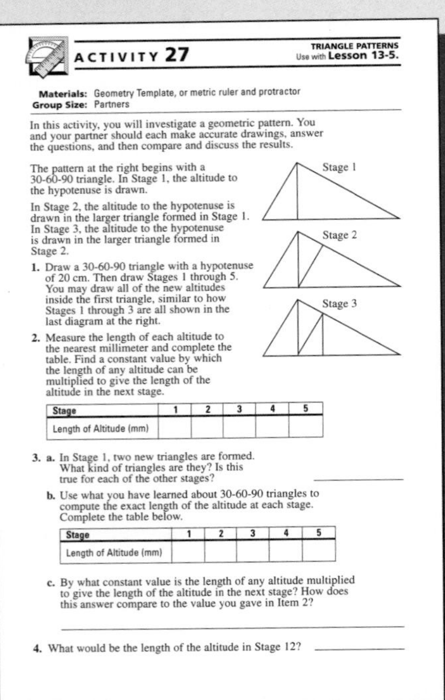
ACTIVITY 27 — TRIANGLE PATTERNS — Use with Lesson 13-5.

Materials: Geometry Template, or metric ruler and protractor
Group Size: Partners

In this activity, you will investigate a geometric pattern. You and your partner should each make accurate drawings, answer the questions, and then compare and discuss the results.

The pattern at the right begins with a 30-60-90 triangle. In Stage 1, the altitude to the hypotenuse is drawn.

In Stage 2, the altitude to the hypotenuse is drawn in the larger triangle formed in Stage 1. In Stage 3, the altitude to the hypotenuse is drawn in the larger triangle formed in Stage 2.

1. Draw a 30-60-90 triangle with a hypotenuse of 20 cm. Then draw Stages 1 through 5. You may draw all of the new altitudes inside the first triangle, similar to how Stages 1 through 3 are all shown in the last diagram at the right.
2. Measure the length of each altitude to the nearest millimeter and complete the table. Find a constant value by which the length of any altitude can be multiplied to give the length of the altitude in the next stage.

Stage	1	2	3	4	5
Length of Altitude (mm)					

3. a. In Stage 1, two new triangles are formed. What kind of triangles are they? Is this true for each of the other stages? ______
   b. Use what you have learned about 30-60-90 triangles to compute the exact length of the altitude at each stage. Complete the table below.

Stage	1	2	3	4	5
Length of Altitude (mm)					

   c. By what constant value is the length of any altitude multiplied to give the length of the altitude in the next stage? How does this answer compare to the value you gave in Item 2? ______
4. What would be the length of the altitude in Stage 12? ______

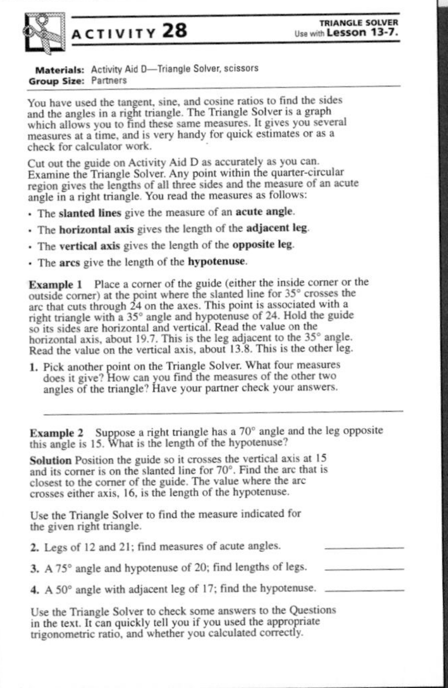
ACTIVITY 28 — TRIANGLE SOLVER — Use with Lesson 13-7.

Materials: Activity Aid D—Triangle Solver, scissors
Group Size: Partners

You have used the tangent, sine, and cosine ratios to find the sides and the angles in a right triangle. The Triangle Solver is a graph which allows you to find these same measures. It gives you several measures at a time, and is very handy for quick estimates or as a check for calculator work.

Cut out the guide on Activity Aid D as accurately as you can. Examine the Triangle Solver. Any point within the quarter-circular region gives the lengths of all three sides and the measure of an acute angle in a right triangle. You read the measures as follows:

- The **slanted lines** give the measure of an **acute angle**.
- The **horizontal axis** gives the length of the **adjacent leg**.
- The **vertical axis** gives the length of the **opposite leg**.
- The **arcs** give the length of the **hypotenuse**.

Example 1 Place a corner of the guide (either the inside corner or the outside corner) at the point where the slanted line for 35° crosses the arc that cuts through 24 on the axes. This point is associated with a right triangle with a 35° angle and hypotenuse of 24. Hold the guide so its sides are horizontal and vertical. Read the value on the horizontal axis, about 19.7. This is the leg adjacent to the 35° angle. Read the value on the vertical axis, about 13.8. This is the other leg.

1. Pick another point on the Triangle Solver. What four measures does it give? How can you find the measures of the other two angles of the triangle? Have your partner check your answers. ______

Example 2 Suppose a right triangle has a 70° angle and the leg opposite this angle is 15. What is the length of the hypotenuse?

Solution Position the guide so it crosses the vertical axis at 15 and its corner is on the slanted line for 70°. Find the arc that is closest to the corner of the guide. The value where the arc crosses either axis, 16, is the length of the hypotenuse.

Use the Triangle Solver to find the measure indicated for the given right triangle.

2. Legs of 12 and 21; find measures of acute angles. ______
3. A 75° angle and hypotenuse of 20; find lengths of legs. ______
4. A 50° angle with adjacent leg of 17; find the hypotenuse. ______

Use the Triangle Solver to check some answers to the Questions in the text. It can quickly tell you if you used the appropriate trigonometric ratio, and whether you calculated correctly.

Teaching Aids

Teaching Aid 4, Coordinate Plane (shown on page 4D), can be used with **Lesson 13-7.**
Teaching Aid 105, Graph Paper (shown on page 434C), can be used with **Lesson 13-8.**

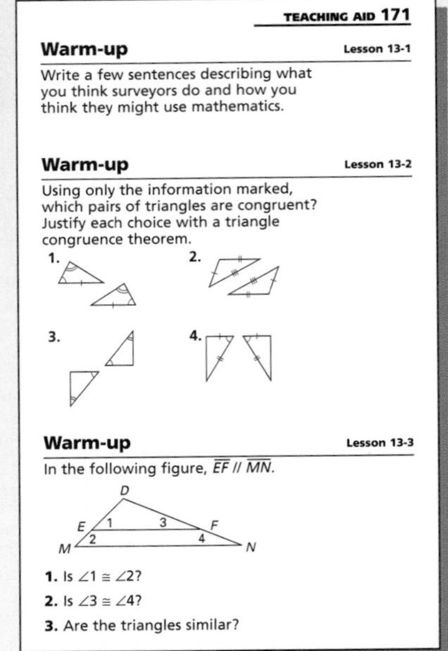
TEACHING AID 171

Warm-up Lesson 13-1

Write a few sentences describing what you think surveyors do and how you think they might use mathematics.

Warm-up Lesson 13-2

Using only the information marked, which pairs of triangles are congruent? Justify each choice with a triangle congruence theorem.

1. 2. 3. 4.

Warm-up Lesson 13-3

In the following figure, $\overline{EF} \parallel \overline{MN}$.

1. Is $\angle 1 \cong \angle 2$?
2. Is $\angle 3 \cong \angle 4$?
3. Are the triangles similar?

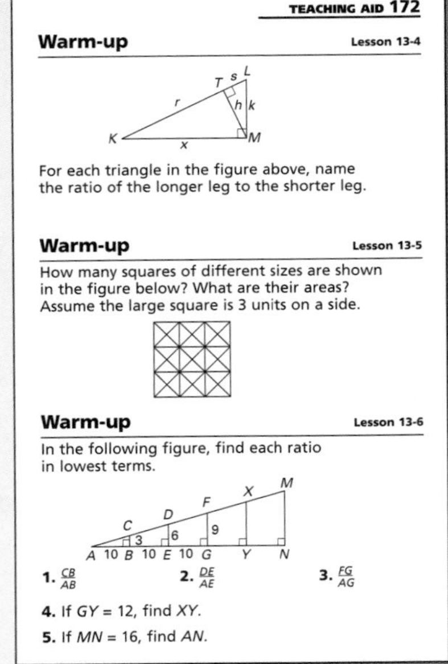
TEACHING AID 172

Warm-up Lesson 13-4

For each triangle in the figure above, name the ratio of the longer leg to the shorter leg.

Warm-up Lesson 13-5

How many squares of different sizes are shown in the figure below? What are their areas? Assume the large square is 3 units on a side.

Warm-up Lesson 13-6

In the following figure, find each ratio in lowest terms.

1. $\frac{CB}{AB}$ 2. $\frac{DE}{AE}$ 3. $\frac{FG}{AG}$
4. If GY = 12, find XY.
5. If MN = 16, find AN.

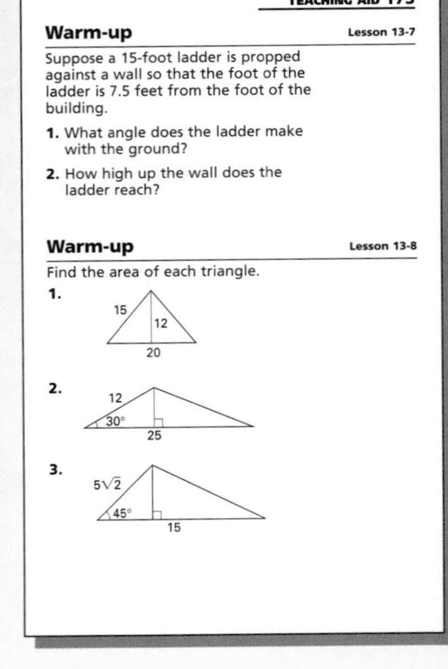
TEACHING AID 173

Warm-up Lesson 13-7

Suppose a 15-foot ladder is propped against a wall so that the foot of the ladder is 7.5 feet from the foot of the building.

1. What angle does the ladder make with the ground?
2. How high up the wall does the ladder reach?

Warm-up Lesson 13-8

Find the area of each triangle.

1.

2.

3.

TEACHING AID 174
Lesson 13-1

Additional Examples

1. *True or false* A triangle with sides 8, 12, and 16 is similar to a triangle with sides 12, 16, and 24.

2. $\triangle DEF$ has been drawn such that $\triangle ABC \sim \triangle DEF$ with ratio of similitude 2. But someone forgot to label the vertices and the lengths of the sides in the large triangle. Label the triangle correctly.

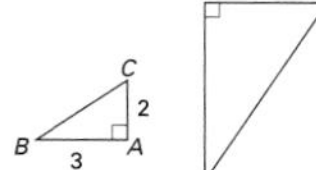

TEACHING AID 175
Lesson 13-1

Challenge

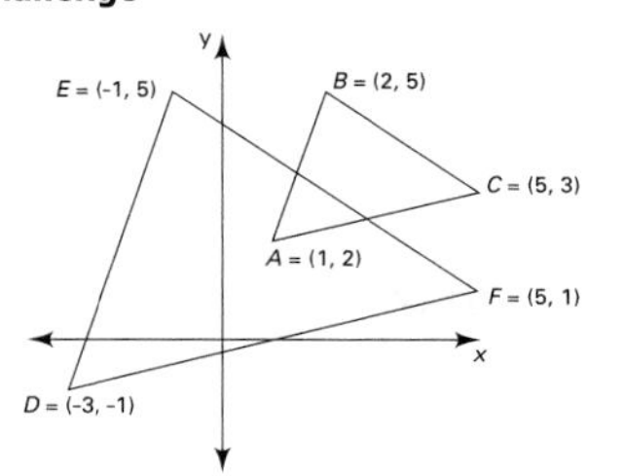

TEACHING AID 176
Lesson 13-3

Additional Examples

1. In $\triangle RIG$ below, $\overline{AN} \parallel \overline{RI}$. If $IN = 5$, what are the lengths of $\overline{NG}$ and $\overline{RI}$?

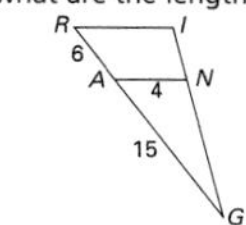

2. $\overline{BE}$ is a segment which splits two sides of $\triangle ACD$ as shown here. Is $\overline{BE} \parallel \overline{CD}$?

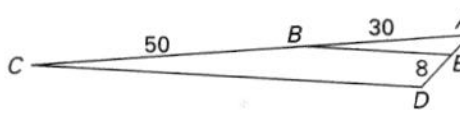

3. Fine *x*, *LM*, and *ON*.

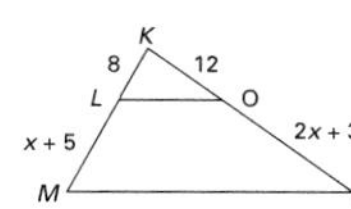

TEACHING AID 177
Lesson 13-4

Similar Triangles Within a Right Triangle

original triangle

$\triangle ABC$ is split into two similar triangles which are then reflected and rotated.

TEACHING AID 178
Lesson 13-4

Additional Examples

1. Find the difference between the geometric mean of 4 and 6 and the arithmetic mean of 4 and 6.

2. The altitude to the hypotenuse of a right triangle splits the hypotenuse into segments of lengths 6 and 7.

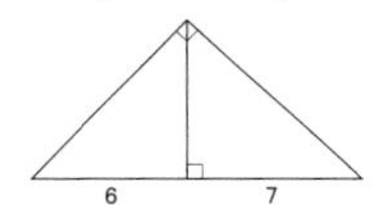

a. What are the lengths of the legs of the triangle?
b. What is the length of the altitude to the hypotenuse?

TEACHING AID 179
Lesson 13-5

Additional Examples

1. An airport is built on a piece of land approximately one mile square. Find the length of the longest runway that can be built on land that is one mile square. Give your answer to the nearest 50 feet.

2. Triangle *ABC* is an isosceles right triangle and $m\angle DAC = 30$. If $AC = 4$, what is *BD*?

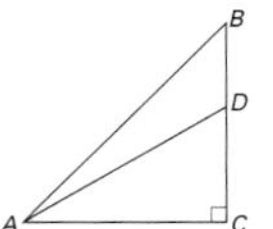

3. What are the lengths of the legs of a 30-60-90 right triangle whose hypotenuse has length 50?

4. Find the height of parallelogram *WXYZ*.

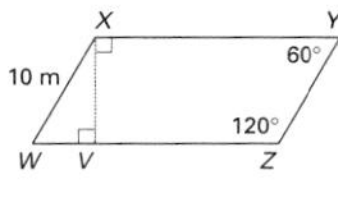

TEACHING AID 180
Lesson 13-7

Additional Examples

1. In right triangle *HUG*, find sin *U*, cos *U*, sin *G*, and cos *G*.

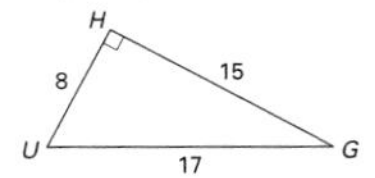

2. Which two of the following are equal: sin 45°, cos 45°, tan 45°?

3. A supporting wire 8 feet long is to extend from the top of a pole 6 feet high. What is the angle between the wire and the pole?

Chapter 13 Opener

Pacing

All lessons in this chapter are designed to be covered in one day. At the end of the chapter, you should plan to spend 1 day to review the Progress Self-Test, 1–2 days for the Chapter Review, and 1 day for a test. You may wish to spend a day on projects, and possibly a day is needed for quizzes. Therefore, this chapter should take 11–14 days.

Using Pages 736–737

Point out that surveyors try to determine lengths and angle measures directly whenever they can, but that there are often distances and angle measures that are inaccessible. In this chapter, students will begin to see how such inaccessible distances and angle measures can be determined with a great deal of precision.

History Connection The father of trigonometry is generally said to be Hipparchus of Nicaea (180–125 B.C.), although his work has been lost. Hipparchus arrived at many of his conclusions through his work in astronomy, trying to ascertain the relationships between stars in the celestial sphere. Ptolemy, the Alexandrian astronomer of the 2nd century A.D., continued Hipparchus' work and formulated detailed trigonometric tables in his *Almagest,* or "The Greatest." This work was very influential to later mathematicians.

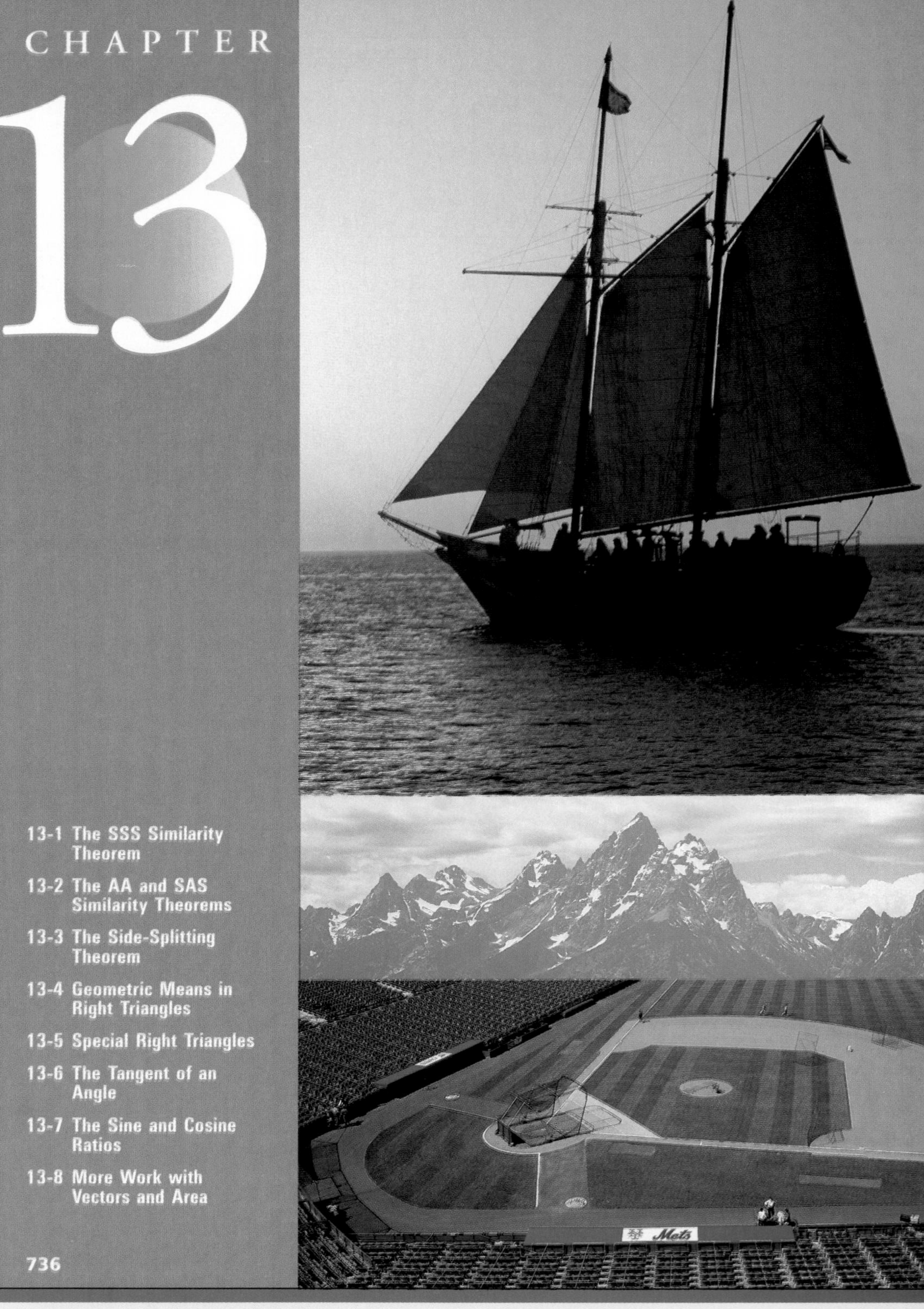
CHAPTER 13

736

Chapter 13 Overview

Under our definition of *similar figures,* there can be similar figures of any type. This chapter begins by developing criteria for two triangles to be similar. The SSS Similarity Theorem is deduced and used in Lesson 13-1, and the AA and SAS Similarity Theorems are discussed in Lesson 13-2. Students who have studied UCSMP *Transition Mathematics* or UCSMP *Algebra* should have studied proportions in similar triangles.

In Lesson 13-3, the AA Similarity Theorem is used to prove the Side-Splitting Theorem, which states that a line parallel to a side of a triangle splits the other two sides proportionally. Then, in Lesson 13-4, the AA Similarity Theorem is applied to prove that the triangles formed by the altitude to the hypotenuse of a right triangle are similar.

The last three lessons of this chapter cover the trigonometry ideas that we believe every student should know. Though most people in the mathematical sciences would agree that trigonometry is needed for the study of physics by college-bound students, many other students also can benefit from studying some basic trigonometry. Mathematics books for the trades (such as carpentry) tend to concentrate on applications of arithmetic, but also contain a reasonable amount of trigonometry. Most often, the content covered is the same as the

SIMILAR TRIANGLES AND TRIGONOMETRY

As you saw in Chapter 12, similarity is a powerful idea with many applications. One group of important applications not discussed in that chapter is the use of similarity to obtain the measures of lengths that are inaccessible or that are too large or too small to be measured directly.

Surveyors, pilots, navigators, and many other people estimate lengths or distances as part of their job. For this they often use trigonometry, which literally means "triangle measure." Trigonometry is based on simple properties of similar right triangles, yet it allows us to estimate the heights of buildings or mountains, the distances across lakes or rivers, the depths of craters on the moon, and even distances to stars.

In this chapter, you will first study the conditions under which triangles are similar. Then, after investigating properties of similar right triangles, you will learn about the sine, cosine, and tangent of an angle, which are the beginnings of trigonometry.

Photo Connections

The photo collage makes real-world connections to the content of the chapter: similarity and trigonometry.

The application of trigonometry to navigation and to surveying is historically very significant, for it was the only way that some distances and directions could be determined before satellites.

Sailboat While the people aboard this sailboat are enjoying a calm evening cruise, navigating the boat requires a knowledge of astronomy, physics, mathematics, and a variety of instruments. The speed and direction of the boat is called its velocity. As shown in Lesson 13-8, the velocity can be represented by a vector.

Transamerica Building This distinctive pyramid-shaped building in San Francisco is the home of the Transamerica Corporation. Trigonometry allows us to estimate the heights of such buildings. In lessons 13-6 and 13-7 students will learn three trigonometric ratios, the tangent, the sine, and the cosine.

Mountains Trigonometry also allows us to estimate the heights of mountains. These mountains, The Tetons in Wyoming, rise 7,000 feet above Jackson Hole Valley, providing breathtaking views from the valley. The highest peak, Grand Teton, is 13,700 feet above sea level.

Baseball Stadium A major league baseball diamond is a 90-foot square. In Lesson 13-5 students will use the Isosceles Right Triangle Theorem to find the diagonal distance from home plate to second base. Shea Stadium shown here is the home of the New York Mets. It was built in 1964 and holds over 55,500 people.

Airplane Sophisticated equipment and highly trained individuals keep large airplanes like this Airbus A320 flying. A knowledge of mathematics, such as vectors, plays a role in determining the location and velocity of the airplane.

Chapter 13 Projects

At this time you might want to have students look over the projects on pages 789–790.

trigonometry presented in this book—right triangle-trigonometry needed to find the lengths of sides given angle measures and a side, instruction on how to find angle measures, and many applications.

Right triangles provide the link between similar triangles and trigonometry. Lesson 13-5 includes a discussion of 30-60-90 and 45-45-90 triangles. We consider the tangent ratio first, since it is the easiest to understand and the one most closely related to slope. In Lesson 13-6, we examine the tangent of an angle. Lesson 13-7 covers the sine and cosine of an angle. Lesson 13-8 applies this trigonometry to the finding of components of vectors and areas of triangles.

Scientific calculators are essential in this chapter.

Lesson 13-1

Objectives

F Determine whether or not triangles are similar using the SSS Similarity Theorem.

Resources

From the ***Teacher's Resource File***

- Lesson Master 13-1A or 13-1B
- Answer Master 13-1
- Teaching Aids
  171 Warm-up
  174 Additional Examples
  175 Challenge
- Technology Sourcebook, Computer Master 22

Additional Resources

- Visuals for Teaching Aids 171, 174–175
- GeoExplorer or other automatic drawers

Teaching Lesson 13-1

Warm-up

Writing Write a few sentences describing what you think surveyors do and how you think they might use mathematics. **Sample: Surveyors for construction companies determine exactly where a street or building or other structure is to be placed so that it agrees with the plans that have been legally approved by the municipality. Surveyors also determine the legal boundaries of land necessary for determining who owns (and who can sell) fences, rights-of-way, natural resources, and so on.**

LESSON

13-1 *The SSS Similarity Theorem*

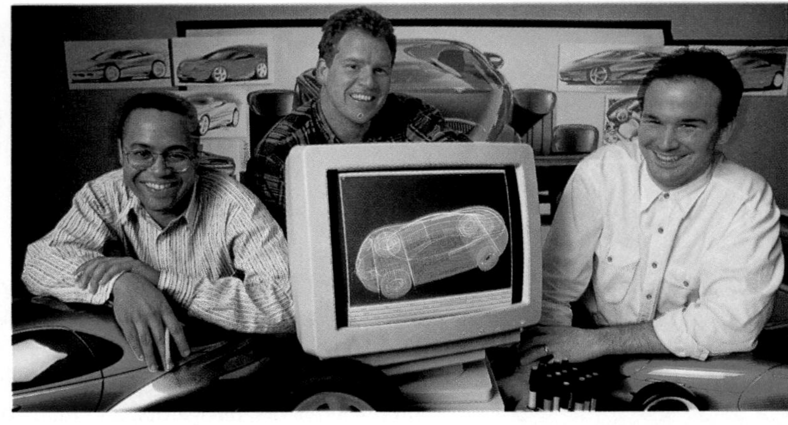

Model team. *Computer assisted design (CAD) and teamwork combine to produce a detailed prototype car of the future.*

❶ Imagine that you are the head of a design team. You ask all the team members to construct triangles with sides of lengths 2, 4, and 5. How will these triangles compare?

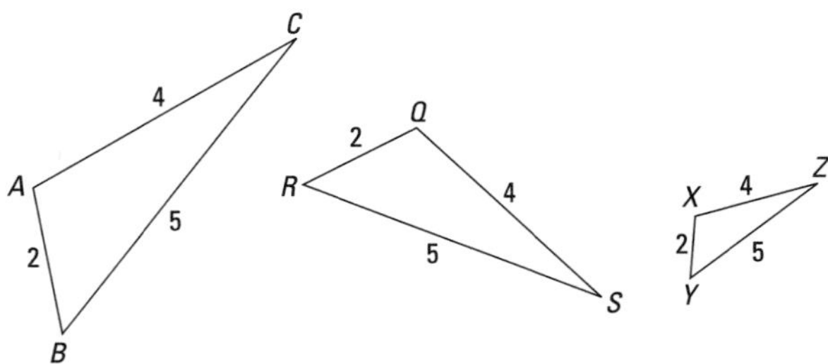

Three triangles that the team members might make are drawn above. Notice that because no unit was named, the triangles may not be congruent. Some people might use centimeters as a unit, others could use inches, and others could just use some arbitrary unit. However, the triangles do look similar.

Below, $\triangle QRS$ is measured using the same unit as $\triangle ABC$. Note that the ratios of the corresponding sides are equal. From this information, it can be proved that the triangles are similar.

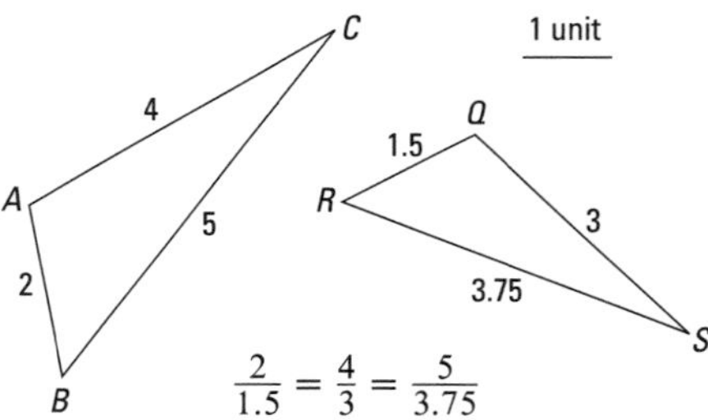

$$\frac{2}{1.5} = \frac{4}{3} = \frac{5}{3.75}$$

Lesson 13-1 Overview

Broad Goals This lesson introduces the SSS Similarity Theorem and begins a two-lesson sequence in which three triangle similarity theorems are presented. The proofs of the similarity theorems all employ the same strategy of applying a size change to one triangle and showing that its image is congruent to the other.

Perspective In the notes for Lesson 12-5, it was pointed out that determining similarity in triangles by sight is more difficult than determining similarity by sight in more complicated figures. Thus, it is particularly useful to have theorems indicating when triangles are similar.

In this and in the next lesson, the correspondences of triangle similarity theorems with triangle congruence theorems are more than analogies, because each congruence theorem is used to deduce its similarity counterpart. For instance, the SSS Congruence Theorem is critical in deducing the SSS Similarity Theorem.

Just apply a size change of magnitude $\frac{4}{3}$ to $\triangle QRS$. The resulting image $\triangle Q'R'S'$ (not drawn), has sides of the same length as $\triangle ABC$. So $\triangle Q'R'S' \cong \triangle ABC$ by the SSS Congruence Theorem. Since $\triangle ABC$ is the image of $\triangle QRS$ under a similarity transformation, $\triangle ABC \sim \triangle QRS$. This idea can be applied to any two triangles whose three pairs of sides are proportional. The result is called the SSS Similarity Theorem.

SSS Similarity Theorem
If three sides of one triangle are proportional to three sides of a second triangle, then the triangles are similar.

Proof

Given: $\frac{XY}{AB} = \frac{YZ}{BC} = \frac{XZ}{AC}$.

To prove: $\triangle ABC \sim \triangle XYZ$.

Drawing:

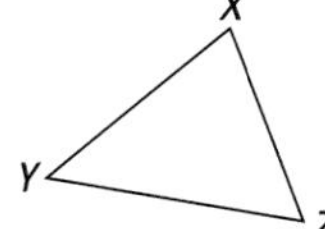

Argument:

Let $k = \frac{XY}{AB}$. Then, by the Transitive Property of Equality, $k = \frac{YZ}{BC}$ and $k = \frac{XZ}{AC}$. Apply any size transformation with magnitude k to $\triangle ABC$.

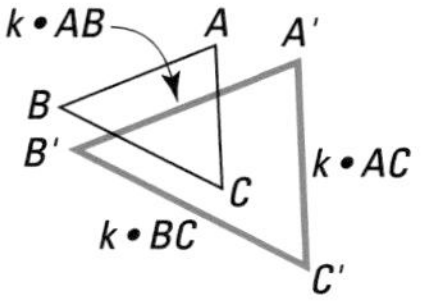

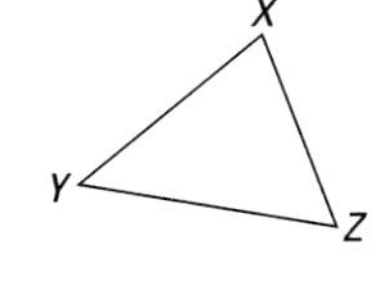

In the image $\triangle A'B'C'$, $A'B' = k \cdot AB$, $B'C' = k \cdot BC$, and $A'C' = k \cdot AC$.

But
$$k \cdot AB = \frac{XY}{AB} \cdot AB = XY$$
$$k \cdot BC = \frac{YZ}{BC} \cdot BC = YZ$$
$$k \cdot AC = \frac{XZ}{AC} \cdot AC = XZ.$$

Thus the three sides of $\triangle A'B'C'$ have the same lengths as the three sides of $\triangle XYZ$. So, by the SSS Congruence Theorem, $\triangle A'B'C' \cong \triangle XYZ$. The definition of congruence tells us there is an isometry mapping $\triangle A'B'C'$ onto $\triangle XYZ$. So there is a composite of a size change (the one we started with) and an isometry mapping $\triangle ABC$ onto $\triangle XYZ$. So, by the definition of similarity, $\triangle ABC \sim \triangle XYZ$.

Notes on Reading

You might want to use the suggestions in *Optional Activities* below to introduce this lesson.

❶ Go through in detail the material on page 738 and the proof of the SSS Similarity Theorem on this page.

Ask several students to state the SSS Congruence Theorem and use it to name the congruent sides and angles of two congruent triangles. Then you can change the wording to fit the SSS Similarity Theorem. Have students name the congruent angles and write the proportions which relate the sides.

Optional Activities

Activity 1

You can use this activity to introduce the lesson. Have students **work in small groups.** Tell students to draw a triangle with any convenient dimensions and then draw the triangle that would result from multiplying the length of each side of the triangle by 3. Have students compare the sizes and the shapes of the two triangles. Have them measure the angles. Ask these questions: Could the triangles be congruent? Why or why not? Then have students draw another triangle whose side lengths are $\frac{2}{3}$ of the original side lengths. Have them describe the three triangles. [The triangles should look alike but be of different sizes.]

Activity 2 Technology Connection

You might consider using *Technology Sourcebook, Computer Master 22,* with Lessons 13-1 and 13-2. In this activity, students use the definition of similar figures to establish which of four given conditions ensure similarity of triangles.

❷ As you go through **Example 1,** you might wish to discuss **Question 26.** It is important for students to realize that having lengths of corresponding sides in the same ratio ensures similarity for triangles but not for other polygons.

❸ The difficult part of **Example 2** is determining which vertices correspond. Two ways of doing this are given below—in each case, order the sides of each triangle by length.

(1) The intersections of the two longer sides in each triangle correspond, the intersections of the two shorter sides correspond, and the third vertices correspond.

(2) The vertices opposite the longest sides correspond, the vertices opposite the shortest sides correspond, and the vertices opposite the third sides correspond. Remind students of the Unequal Sides Theorem and the Unequal Angles Theorem from Lesson 7-9.

Applying the SSS Similarity Theorem

One way to tell whether two triangles are similar is to order the sides of each triangle by their lengths. Then compare the ratios formed by corresponding lengths.

❷ **Example 1**

True or false. A triangle with sides 3, 4, and 6 is similar to a triangle with sides 8, 6, and 12.

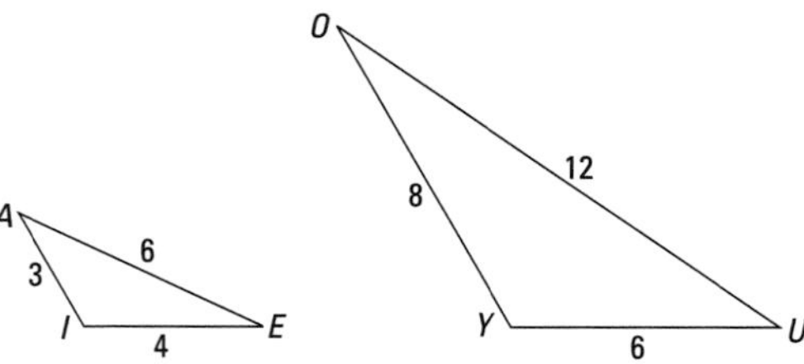

Solution

For each triangle put the sides in order from shortest to longest. Then form three ratios.

$$\frac{6}{3} \quad \frac{8}{4} \quad \frac{12}{6}$$

Since all the ratios are equal, the triangles are similar due to the SSS Similarity Theorem. The answer is **true**.

In Example 1, the ratio of similitude is either 2 or $\frac{1}{2}$, depending on which triangle is first. The corresponding sides tell you which vertices correspond. One way to write the similarity is $\triangle IEA \sim \triangle YOU$. This tells which corresponding angles are congruent. For instance, $\angle E \cong \angle O$.

❸ **Example 2**

Given $\triangle ABC$ and $\triangle XYZ$ below with sides and approximate angle measures as indicated.

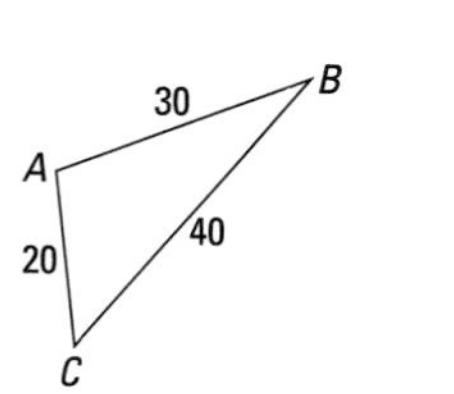

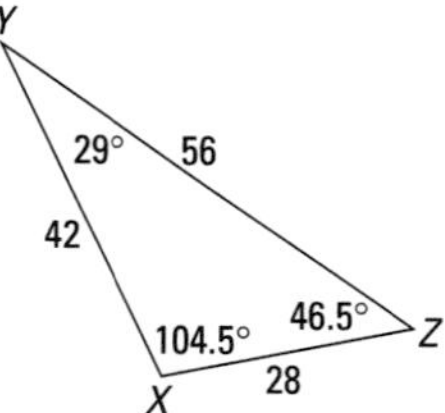

a. Ratios of which sides are equal?
b. Are the triangles similar?
c. $\triangle BAC \sim$ __?__
d. Find the measure of each angle of $\triangle ABC$.

Adapting to Individual Needs

Extra Help

In **Example 1** it is stated that one way to write the similarity is "$\triangle IEA \sim \triangle YOU$." Point out that there are actually five other ways the similarity could be stated since $\triangle IEA$ could also be named $\triangle IAE$, $\triangle EAI$, $\triangle EIA$, $\triangle AEI$, or $\triangle AIE$. However, once the name is chosen for the first triangle, the name for the second triangle must be chosen so that the corresponding angles are in the same order.

Solution

a. The shortest side of $\triangle ABC$ must correspond to the shortest side of $\triangle XYZ$. In general, the sides correspond in the order of their lengths. Write the extended proportion.

Is $\frac{28}{20} = \frac{42}{30} = \frac{56}{40}$?

Yes, since $\frac{28}{20} = 1.4$, $\frac{42}{30} = 1.4$, and $\frac{56}{40} = 1.4$.

Thus, $\frac{XZ}{AC} = \frac{XY}{AB} = \frac{YZ}{BC}$.

b. Since all three ratios of sides are equal, the triangles are similar due to the SSS Similarity Theorem.

c. The vertices of the congruent angles correspond, so $\triangle BAC \sim \triangle YXZ$.

d. The congruent angles are opposite the corresponding sides.
$\overline{BC}$ corresponds to $\overline{YZ}$, so $\angle A \cong \angle X$. $m\angle A = 104.5$.
$\overline{AC}$ corresponds to $\overline{XZ}$, so $\angle B \cong \angle Y$. $m\angle B = 29$.
$\overline{AB}$ corresponds to $\overline{XY}$, so $\angle C \cong \angle Z$. $m\angle C = 46.5$.

QUESTIONS

Covering the Reading

1. What is the literal meaning of *trigonometry*? triangle measure

2. Imagine that you are a teacher. You ask each of your students to draw a triangle with sides of lengths 7, 9, and 12. See left.
   a. Must all the triangles drawn be congruent? Why or why not?
   b. Must all the triangles drawn be similar? Why or why not?

3. One way to prove $\triangle ABC \sim \triangle DEF$ is to find a size-change image of $\triangle ABC$ that is _?_ to $\triangle DEF$. congruent

4. State the SSS Similarity Theorem. See left.

5. If $\triangle RST \sim \triangle UVW$, name two ratios equal to $\frac{RS}{UV}$. $\frac{ST}{VW}$, $\frac{TR}{WU}$

6. *True or false.* A right triangle with sides 5, 12, and 13 is similar to a right triangle with sides 60, 65, and 25. Justify your answer. See left.

7. *True or false.* A right triangle with sides 20, 21, and 29 is similar to a right triangle with sides 41, 9, and 40. Justify your answer.
   False; $20/9 \neq 21/40 \neq 29/41$, so the triangles are not similar.

8. Examine triangles ABC and DEF at the right.
   a. Ratios of which sides are equal? $\frac{AB}{ED} = \frac{AC}{EF} = \frac{BC}{DF}$
   b. Are the triangles similar? Yes
   c. Find the measure of each angle of $\triangle DEF$. $m\angle E = 37$, $m\angle D = 53$, $m\angle F = 90$
   d. $\triangle DEF \sim$ _?_ $\triangle BAC$

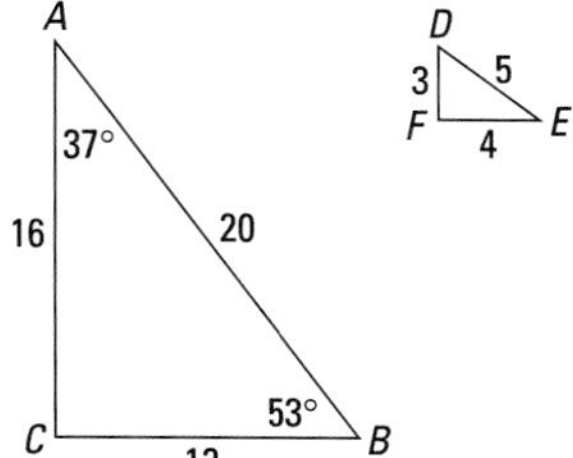

2a) No, because no unit was named. Students might use different units to draw triangles.

b) Yes. According to the SSS Similarity Theorem, they are similar because their sides are proportional.

4) If the three sides of one triangle are proportional to the three sides of a second triangle, then the triangles are similar.

6) True; $\frac{5}{25} = \frac{12}{60} = \frac{13}{65}$, so the triangles are similar by the SSS Similarity Theorem.

Additional Examples

These examples are also given on **Teaching Aid 174.**

1. *True or false* A triangle with sides 8, 12, and 16 is similar to a triangle with sides 12, 16, and 24. False, since not all of the ratios $\frac{8}{12}$, $\frac{12}{16}$, and $\frac{16}{24}$ are equal.

2. $\triangle DEF$ has been drawn such that $\triangle ABC \sim \triangle DEF$ with ratio of similitude 2. But someone forgot to label the vertices and the lengths of the sides in the large triangle. Label the triangle correctly.

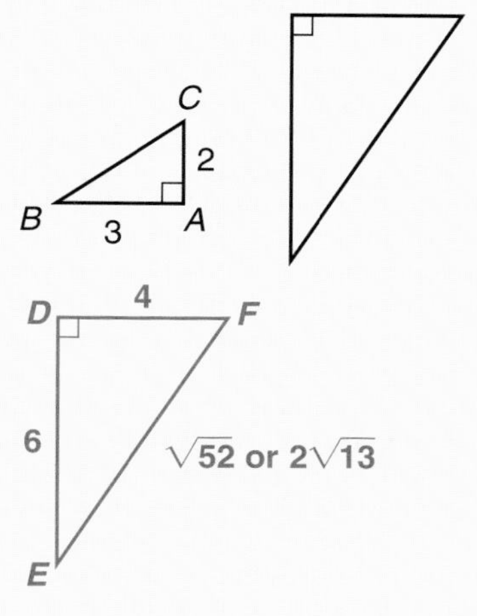

Adapting to Individual Needs

English Language Development

Before students with limited English proficiency begin reading this lesson, you might want to review the meanings of *congruence* and *similarity*. You might draw two congruent triangles on the overhead projector and show that they are the same size and shape. Then draw two similar triangles and note they are the same shape but not necessarily the same size.

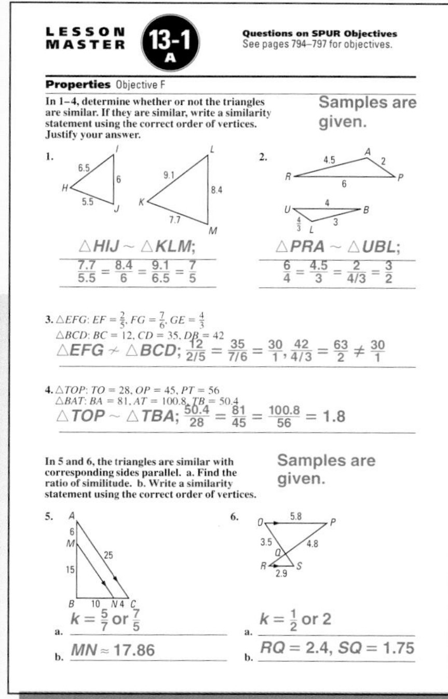

LESSON MASTER 13-1 A

Questions on SPUR Objectives
See pages 794–797 for objectives.

Properties Objective F

In 1–4, determine whether or not the triangles are similar. If they are similar, write a similarity statement using the correct order of vertices. Justify your answer. Samples are given.

1. $\triangle HIJ \sim \triangle KLM$; $\frac{7.7}{5.5} = \frac{8.4}{6} = \frac{9.1}{6.5} = \frac{7}{5}$

2. $\triangle PRA \sim \triangle UBL$; $\frac{6}{4} = \frac{4.5}{3} = \frac{2}{4/3} = \frac{3}{2}$

3. $\triangle EFG$: $EF = \frac{2}{5}$, $FG = \frac{7}{6}$, $GE = \frac{4}{3}$
$\triangle BCD$: $BC = 12$, $CD = 35$, $DB = 42$
$\triangle EFG \nsim \triangle BCD$; $\frac{12}{2/5} = \frac{35}{7/6} = \frac{30}{1}$, $\frac{42}{4/3} = \frac{63}{2} \neq \frac{30}{1}$

4. $\triangle TOP$: $TO = 28$, $OP = 45$, $PT = 56$
$\triangle BAT$: $BA = 81$, $AT = 100.8$, $TB = 50.4$
$\triangle TOP \sim \triangle TBA$; $\frac{50.4}{28} = \frac{81}{45} = \frac{100.8}{56} = 1.8$

In 5 and 6, the triangles are similar with corresponding sides parallel. a. Find the ratio of similitude. b. Write a similarity statement using the correct order of vertices. Samples are given.

5. a. $k = \frac{5}{7}$ or $\frac{7}{5}$
   b. $MN \approx 17.86$

6. a. $k = \frac{1}{2}$ or 2
   b. $RQ = 2.4$, $SQ = 1.75$

Notes on Questions

Question 10 This question helps to familiarize students with the situation of the Side-Splitting Theorem and thus helps to set up Lesson 13-3.

Question 13 **Example 2** of the next lesson is identical to this question.

Questions 16–20 You might extend these questions to include other formulas.

Question 24 This kind of algebraic simplification is utilized in the proof of the Side-Splitting Theorem in Lesson 13-3.

Question 26 If you discussed this question with **Example 1,** as suggested in the *Notes on Reading,* you might ask students to further consider the situation for quadrilaterals. Then ask for a general conclusion.

Follow-up for Lesson 13-1

Practice

For more questions on SPUR Objectives, use **Lesson Master 13-1A** (shown on page 741) or **Lesson Master 13-1B** (shown on pages 742–743).

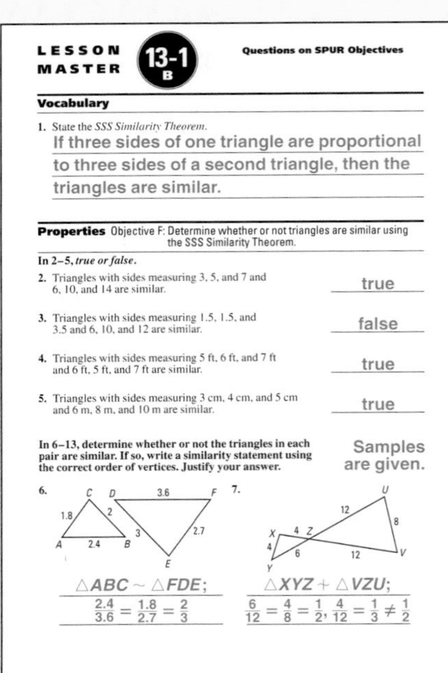

LESSON MASTER 13-1 B Questions on SPUR Objectives

Vocabulary

1. State the *SSS Similarity Theorem.* If three sides of one triangle are proportional to three sides of a second triangle, then the triangles are similar.

Properties Objective F: Determine whether or not triangles are similar using the SSS Similarity Theorem.

In 2–5, *true or false.*

2. Triangles with sides measuring 3, 5, and 7 and 6, 10, and 14 are similar. true
3. Triangles with sides measuring 1.5, 1.5, and 3.5 and 6, 10, and 12 are similar. false
4. Triangles with sides measuring 5 ft, 6 ft, and 7 ft and 6 ft, 5 ft, and 7 ft are similar. true
5. Triangles with sides measuring 3 cm, 4 cm, and 5 cm and 6 m, 8 m, and 10 m are similar. true

In 6–13, determine whether or not the triangles in each pair are similar. If so, write a similarity statement using the correct order of vertices. Justify your answer. Samples are given.

6. $\triangle ABC \sim \triangle FDE$; $\frac{2.4}{3.6} = \frac{1.8}{2.7} = \frac{2}{3}$

7. $\triangle XYZ \not\sim \triangle VZU$; $\frac{6}{12} = \frac{4}{8} = \frac{1}{2}, \frac{4}{12} = \frac{1}{3} \neq \frac{1}{2}$

Applying the Mathematics

In 9 and 10, the triangles are similar with corresponding sides parallel.
a. List the corresponding vertices.
b. Find a ratio of similitude.
c. Determine as many missing side lengths as possible.

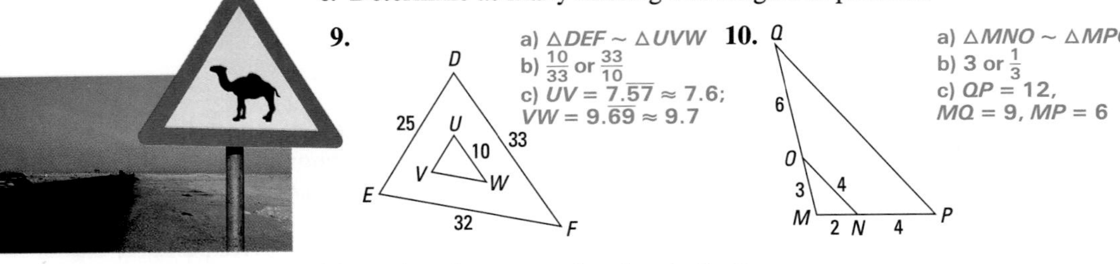

Camel-crossing signs are common in Saudi Arabia.

9. a) $\triangle DEF \sim \triangle UVW$ b) $\frac{10}{33}$ or $\frac{33}{10}$ c) $UV = 7.\overline{57} \approx 7.6$; $VW = 9.\overline{69} \approx 9.7$

10. a) $\triangle MNO \sim \triangle MPQ$ b) 3 or $\frac{1}{3}$ c) $QP = 12$, $MQ = 9$, $MP = 6$

11. a. Are these two triangles similar? Yes
b. Why or why not? Using the Pythagorean Theorem, $AC = 39$ and $DF = 32$. Since $\frac{24}{39} = \frac{32}{52} = \frac{40}{65}$, $\triangle ABC \sim \triangle EFD$ by the SSS Similarity Theorem.

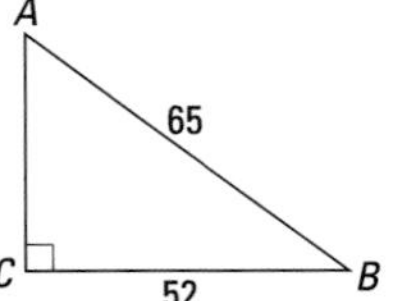

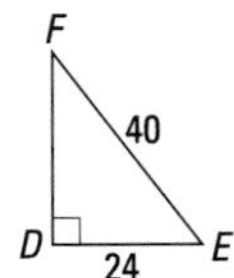

12. Are the two triangles at the right similar? If so, write the similarity with the vertices in the proper order. If not, explain why not. Yes; $\triangle PQR \sim \triangle TVU$

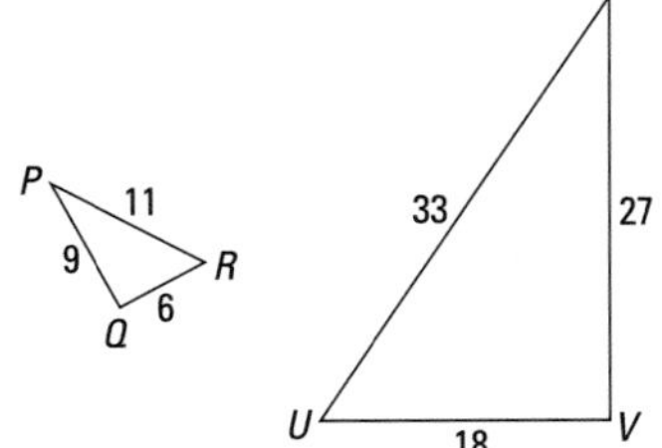

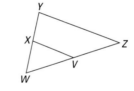

13. Use the figure at the right to write a proof argument. See margin.
Given: X is the midpoint of $\overline{WY}$. V is the midpoint of $\overline{WZ}$.
To prove: $\triangle WXV \sim \triangle WYZ$.

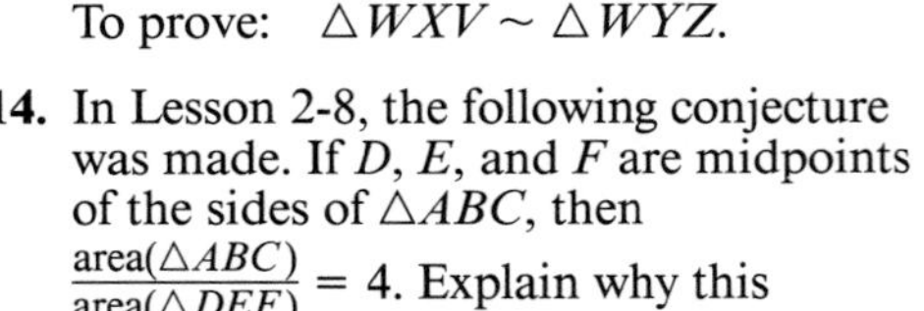

14. In Lesson 2-8, the following conjecture was made. If D, E, and F are midpoints of the sides of $\triangle ABC$, then $\frac{\text{area}(\triangle ABC)}{\text{area}(\triangle DEF)} = 4$. Explain why this conjecture is true.

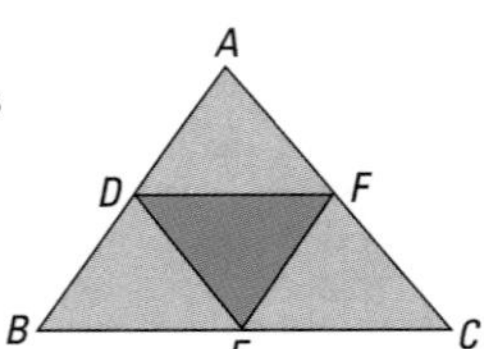

14) $\triangle DEF \sim \triangle CAB$, the ratio of similitude is 2. By the Fundamental Theorem of Similarity, the ratio of areas is the square of the ratio of similitude. Thus, $\frac{\text{area }(\triangle ABC)}{\text{area }(\triangle DEF)} = 4$

Adapting to Individual Needs

Challenge

Materials: **Teaching Aid 175**

Give students the figure at the right or **Teaching Aid 175.** Have them use the SSS Similarity Theorem to prove that $\triangle ABC$ is similar to $\triangle DEF$. [$AB = \sqrt{10}$; $DE = 2\sqrt{10}$; $BC = \sqrt{13}$; $EF = 2\sqrt{13}$; $AC = \sqrt{17}$; $DF = 2\sqrt{17}$. The lengths of corresponding sides are in the same ratio. Thus, the triangles are similar.]

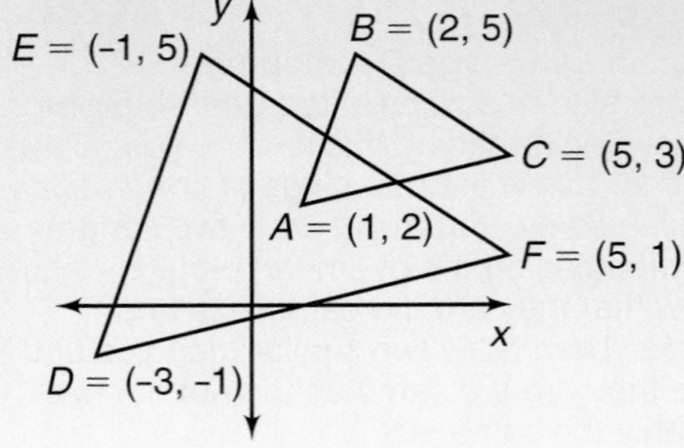

16) volume of a pyramid or a cone with height h and base of area B.

17) surface area of a box with sides ℓ, w, h

18) perimeter of a triangle with sides a, b, c

19) volume of a cylinder of height h and base of radius r

Review

15. Suppose that $\triangle DEF$ is the image of $\triangle ABC$ under a size change of magnitude 5. Then $\triangle ABC$ is the image of $\triangle DEF$ under a size change of magnitude __?__. *(Lesson 12-2)* $\frac{1}{5}$

In 16–20, the given formula finds what quantity in what figure? *(Lessons 10-5, 10-6, 10-7)* 16–19) See left.

16. $V = \frac{1}{3}Bh$ **17.** S.A. $= 2\ell w + 2wh + 2\ell h$

18. $p = a + b + c$ **19.** $V = \pi r^2 h$

20. L.A. $= \pi r\ell$
lateral area of a right cone with base of radius r and and slant height ℓ.

In 21 and 22, refer to the figure below in which $HG = 9$, $GI = 40$ and $HI = 41$

21. a. Find the area of $\triangle GHI$. 180
b. Find GJ, the length of the altitude to the hypotenuse. (Hint: use the area formula) *(Lesson 8-4)* $\frac{360}{41} \approx 8.78$

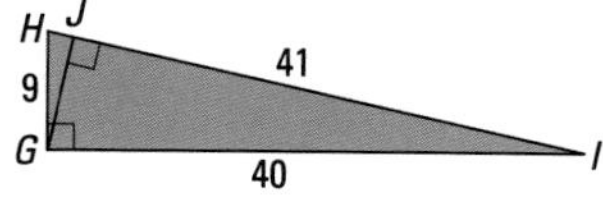

22. If $m\angle I = 13$, find as many other angle measures as you can. *(Lesson 5-7)* $m\angle H = m\angle JGI = 77$, $m\angle HGJ = 13$

23. *Multiple choice.* $\frac{2x + 10}{2} =$ __?__ *(Previous course)* b
(a) $\frac{x + 5}{2}$ (b) $x + 5$ (c) $x + 10$ (d) $2x + 5$

24. *Multiple choice.* $\frac{a + b}{b} =$ __?__ *(Previous course)* a
(a) $\frac{a}{b} + 1$ (b) $\frac{a}{b} + b$ (c) $a + 1$ (d) a

25. Solve for x. $\pm 10\sqrt{2}$
$\frac{10}{x} = \frac{x}{20}$ *(Previous course)*

26) No; for example, the two pentagons shown below have proportional sides, but they are not similar.

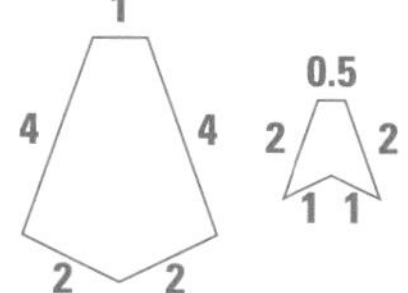

Exploration

26. Is there an SSSSS Similarity Theorem for pentagons? If so, how do you know? If not, draw a counterexample. See left.

Assessment

Written Communication Have students write a paragraph explaining how they could determine if two triangles are similar if none of the lengths or angle measures are given. [Students recognize that they could measure the sides, put the lengths of the sides in order, and then determine if the ratios of corresponding sides are equal. Some students may correctly observe that they could measure corresponding angles to see if they are congruent. This method is discussed in the following lesson.]

Extension

Give students this problem:
In the diagram below, $\angle C$ is a right angle and $\overline{AE} \parallel \overline{BD}$. Find AB, BD, and AE. [$AB = 1.\overline{6}$, $BD = 13$, $AE = 17.\overline{3}$]

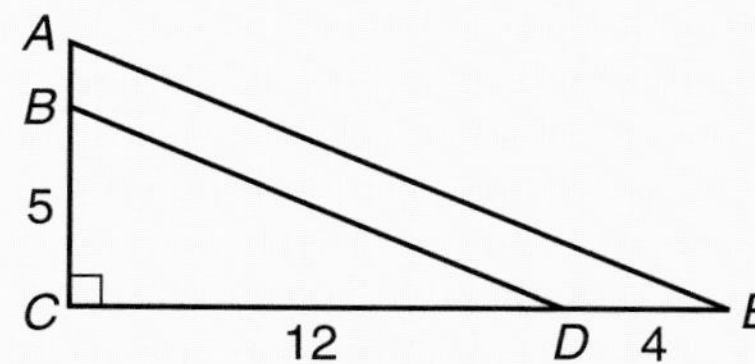

Project Update Project 5, *Oblique Triangles with Integer Sides and Integer Altitudes,* on page 790, relates to the content of this lesson.

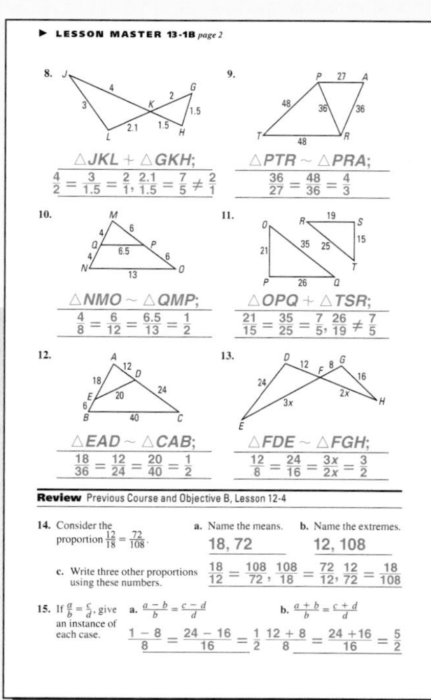

LESSON MASTER 13-1B *page 2*

8. $\triangle JKL \not\sim \triangle GKH$; $\frac{4}{2} = \frac{3}{1.5} = \frac{2}{1}$, $\frac{2.1}{1.5} = \frac{7}{5} \neq \frac{2}{1}$

9. $\triangle PTR \sim \triangle PRA$; $\frac{36}{27} = \frac{48}{36} = \frac{4}{3}$

10. $\triangle NMO \sim \triangle QMP$; $\frac{4}{8} = \frac{6}{12} = \frac{6.5}{13} = \frac{1}{2}$

11. $\triangle OPQ \not\sim \triangle TSR$; $\frac{21}{15} = \frac{35}{25} = \frac{7}{5}$, $\frac{26}{19} \neq \frac{7}{5}$

12. $\triangle EAD \sim \triangle CAB$; $\frac{18}{36} = \frac{12}{24} = \frac{20}{40} = \frac{1}{2}$

13. $\triangle FDE \sim \triangle FGH$; $\frac{12}{8} = \frac{24}{16} = \frac{3x}{2x} = \frac{3}{2}$

Review Previous Course and Objective B, Lesson 12-4

14. Consider the proportion $\frac{12}{18} = \frac{72}{108}$.
a. Name the means. 18, 72
b. Name the extremes. 12, 108
c. Write three other proportions using these numbers. $\frac{18}{12} = \frac{108}{72}$, $\frac{108}{18} = \frac{72}{12}$, $\frac{12}{72} = \frac{18}{108}$

15. If $\frac{a}{b} = \frac{c}{d}$, give an instance of each case.
a. $\frac{a - b}{b} = \frac{c - d}{d}$ $\frac{1 - 8}{8} = \frac{24 - 16}{16} = \frac{1}{2}$
b. $\frac{a + b}{b} = \frac{c + d}{d}$ $\frac{12 + 8}{8} = \frac{24 + 16}{16} = \frac{5}{2}$

Additional Answers

13.

Conclusions	Justifications
1. $WX = \frac{1}{2}WY$, $WV = \frac{1}{2}WZ$	def. of midpoint
2. $XV = \frac{1}{2}YZ$	Midpoint Connector Thm.
3. $\frac{WX}{WY} = \frac{1}{2}$, $\frac{WV}{WZ} = \frac{1}{2}$, $\frac{XV}{YZ} = \frac{1}{2}$	Multiplication Prop. of Equality
4. $\frac{WX}{WY} = \frac{WV}{WZ} = \frac{XV}{YZ}$	Transitive Prop. of Equality
5. $\triangle WXV \sim \triangle WYZ$	SSS Similarity Thm. (step 4)

Lesson 13-2

Objectives

F Determine whether or not triangles are similar using the AA and SAS Similarity Theorems.

H Use the Triangle Similarity Theorems to find lengths and distances in real situations.

Resources

From the ***Teacher's Resource File***
- Lesson Master 13-2A or 13-2B
- Answer Master 13-2
- Teaching Aid 171: Warm-up
- Activity Kit, Activity 26
- Technology Sourcebook, Computer Master 22

Additional Resources
- Visual for Teaching Aid 171
- GeoExplorer or other automatic drawers

Teaching Lesson 13-2

Warm-up

Using only the information marked, which pairs of triangles are congruent? Justify each choice with a triangle congruence theorem.
Pairs 1, 2, and 4 are congruent.

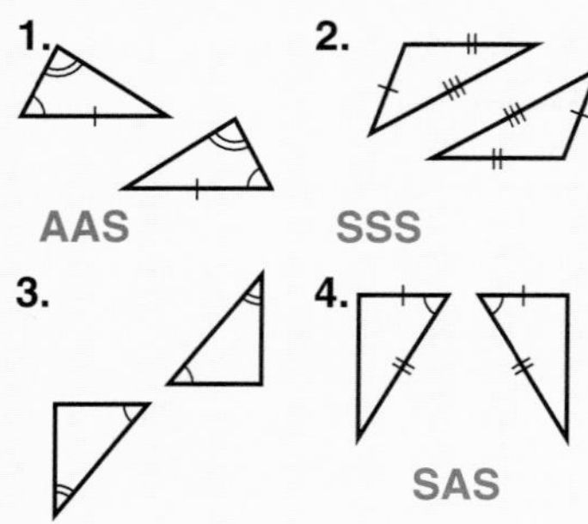

LESSON

13-2 *The AA and SAS Similarity Theorems*

Shaping music. *Many of the instruments used by the Orchestra of Russian Folk Music are similar in shape. See Question 8.*

Similarity Counterparts of the Triangle Congruence Theorems

For each triangle congruence theorem there is a counterpart triangle similarity theorem. In the triangle similarity theorems, the letter "A" still denotes a pair of congruent angles but "S" denotes a *ratio* of corresponding sides.

Three triangle similarity theorems are used more often than the others.

Triangle Congruence Theorem	Triangle Similarity Theorem
SSS →	SSS
SAS →	SAS
ASA →	AA
AAS →	AA

The strategy used in proving the AA and SAS Similarity Theorems is the same as that used in proving the SSS Similarity Theorem. A size change is applied to one triangle so that its image is congruent to the other triangle. The key decision in each proof is the choice of the magnitude k of the size change. Once k is chosen, the only other thing to do is identify the triangle congruence theorem to use. That theorem always turns out to be the corresponding triangle congruence theorem.

AA Similarity

Consider the two triangles at the top of the next page. Two angles in each are congruent. The lengths of the included sides are also shown.

Lesson 13-2 Overview

Broad Goals The goals of this lesson are to have students (1) realize that the proofs of the various triangle similarity theorems all follow the same idea; (2) determine whether two triangles are similar given various angle measures and side lengths; and (3) use the triangle similarity theorems in simple proofs.

Perspective There is a triangle similarity theorem corresponding to every triangle congruence theorem. In each case, the congruence theorem can be used in deducing the similarity theorem.

Congruence	Similarity
SSS	SSS
SAS	SAS
ASA or AAS	AA
HL	HL
SsA	SsA

Some geometry texts in the United States discuss only AA, the easiest to use in proofs. It's quite common for books to discuss SSS, SAS, and AA, and to ignore HL and SsA, just as we do. HL Similarity—if the hypotenuse and a leg of two right triangles are proportional, then the triangles are similar—can be deduced using the Pythagorean Theorem and SSS Similarity. The HL or SsA Similarity Theorems are not proved or discussed within the lesson

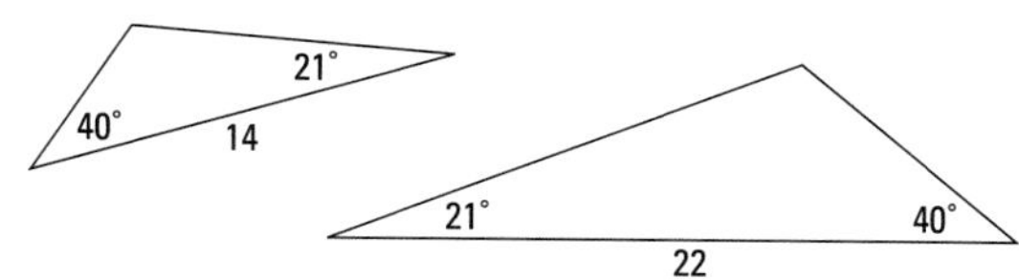

Under a size change of magnitude $\frac{22}{14}$, the image of the smaller triangle is a triangle with two angles of 40° and 21° and an included side of length $\frac{22}{14} \cdot 14$, or 22. So the image is congruent to the larger triangle by the ASA Congruence Theorem. This argument holds when any two angles of one triangle are congruent to two angles of another.

AA Similarity Theorem
If two angles of one triangle are congruent to two angles of another, then the triangles are similar.

Proof

Given: Triangles ABC and XYZ with $\angle A \cong \angle X$ and $\angle B \cong \angle Y$.
To prove: $\triangle ABC \sim \triangle XYZ$.

Drawing: The congruent angles signal the corresponding vertices. This indicates the corresponding sides and enables a picture to be drawn and marked.

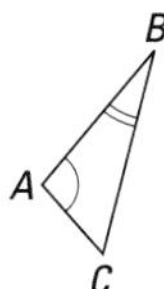

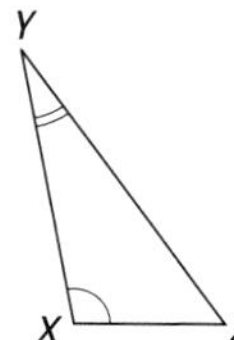

Argument:
X and A are corresponding vertices, as are Y and B. So $\overline{XY}$ and $\overline{AB}$ are corresponding sides, let $k = \frac{XY}{AB}$ be the magnitude of a size transformation applied to $\triangle ABC$.

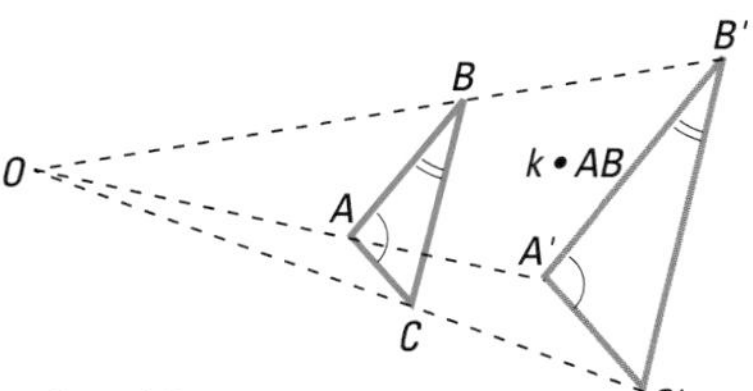

Then $A'B' = k \cdot AB$
$= \frac{XY}{AB} \cdot AB$
$= XY.$

Also, since size transformations preserve angle measure, $\angle A \cong \angle A'$ and $\angle B \cong \angle B'$. By the Transitive Property of Congruence, $\angle A' \cong \angle X$ and $\angle B' \cong \angle Y$. So $\triangle A'B'C' \cong \triangle XYZ$ by the ASA Congruence Theorem. Thus $\triangle ABC$ can be mapped onto $\triangle XYZ$ by a composite of size changes and reflections. So $\triangle ABC \sim \triangle XYZ$.

Notes on Reading

You might want to use Activity 1 in *Optional Activities* below to introduce this lesson.

Students often have difficulty knowing which triangle similarity theorem to use in a proof. Here is a way to help them remember:
- If 2 angles, use AA.
- If 1 angle, use SAS.
- If 0 angles, use SSS.

Students often wonder why there is no Similarity Theorem called ASA, AAS, or AAA. Explain the reason as follows: AA is enough to determine that two triangles are similar. ASA, AAS and AAA all include AA. The condition S in ASA and AAS and the third A in AAA are redundant and thus not necessary.

because neither theorem is needed for any future standard theorem. SSS, AA, and SAS are more important. (See **Question 26.**)

Optional Activities

Activity 1 Cooperative Learning
You might use this activity to introduce the lesson. Give each student three angle measures of a triangle. Make sure that more than one student has the same set of measures. Have each student draw a triangle with the given angle measures and measure the sides of his/her triangle. Finally, have groups of students that have the same angle measures compare the ratios of the sides of the triangles, and then discuss what they find. [The measures of the corresponding sides are proportional.]

Activity 2
You can use *Activity Kit, Activity 26,* after discussing the lesson. In this activity, students use a mirror and the concept of similar triangles to estimate the height of a tall object.

❶ **Multicultural Connection**
When discussing **Example 1,** you might mention that a sundial also relies on a shadow cast by the sun. The sundial is the earliest known timekeeping device used in human culture. The first sundial used was the gnomon, which consisted of a vertical stick or pillar which cast a shadow, the length and angle of which determined the time of day. The Egyptians improved on this device by placing a crosspiece on a flat base inscribed with specific time divisions. The Greeks, Romans, and Arabs all used various forms of the sundial at different times in history. With the advent of mechanical clocks in the 14th century, the sundial fell out of use and became a decorative object more than anything else.

❷ An alternate proof for **Example 2** is given in Activity 3 in *Optional Activities* below.

For instance, the triangles at the right have congruent angles as indicated. So $\triangle ABC \sim \triangle XYZ$ by the AA Similarity Theorem. One ratio of similitude is any of the equal ratios $\frac{XY}{AB} = \frac{YZ}{BC} = \frac{XZ}{AC}$. Substituting the given lengths into these ratios, $\frac{XY}{AB} = \frac{70}{20} = \frac{50}{AC}$. From this the ratio of similitude is $\frac{70}{20}$. Solving the proportion $\frac{70}{20} = \frac{50}{AC}$ gives $AC = 14\frac{2}{7}$.

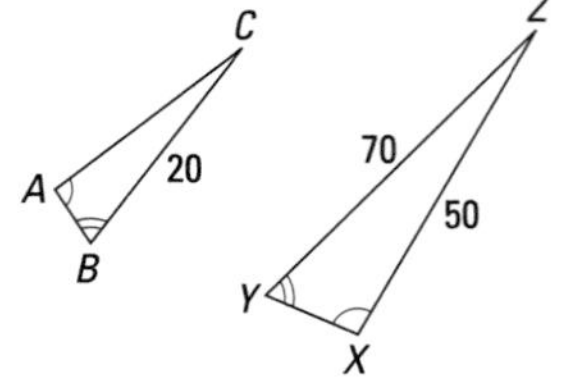

The AA Similarity Theorem justifies a method for determining the height of an object.

❶ **Example 1**

A meter stick casts a shadow 70 cm long at the same time that a tree casts a shadow 3.4 m long. How tall is the tree?

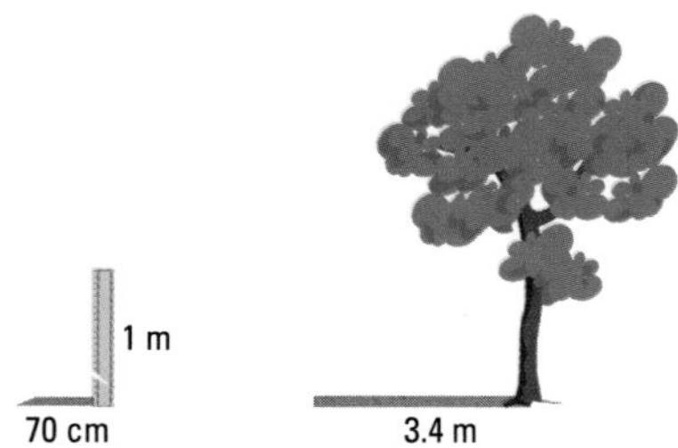

Solution
The key to the solution is that the sun is so far away that its rays can be considered to be parallel. Consequently, right triangles are formed with congruent acute angles.

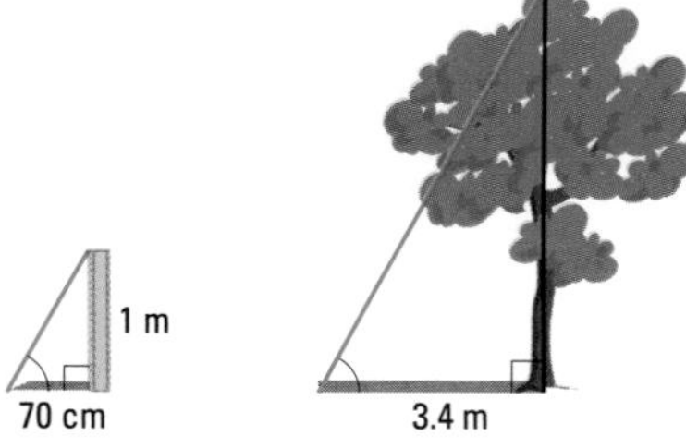

By the AA Similarity Theorem, the triangles are similar. So corresponding sides are proportional.

$$\frac{1\text{ m}}{70\text{ cm}} = \frac{h}{3.4\text{ m}}$$

Convert to the same units. We choose to convert to centimeters.

$$\frac{100\text{ cm}}{70\text{ cm}} = \frac{h}{340\text{ cm}}$$

Solve the proportion. $70h = 34{,}000$

$h \approx 486$ cm

The tree is about 490 cm, or 4.9 m tall.

746

Optional Activities

Activity 3 An alternate proof for **Example 2** is given below. Consider the size change C with center P and magnitude 2. By the definition of size change, $C(P) = P$, $C(T) = S$, and $C(Q) = R$, so $C(\triangle PTQ) = \triangle PSR$. Thus, by the definition of similarity, $\triangle PTQ \sim \triangle PSR$. In general, when figures are to be proved similar, there is always a proof that goes back to the definition of similarity.

Adapting to Individual Needs

Extra Help
You might discuss why there are four triangle congruence theorems, while there are only three counterpart triangle similarity theorems. Point out that as long as we know two angles of one triangle are congruent to two angles of another, we don't have to know anything about the sides. Since both the ASA and AAS cases involve two congruent angles, they both have the same counterpart similarity theorem.

English Language Development
You might want to review the meaning of the word reciprocal before students prove the Reciprocals Property in **Question 23.** Remind students that 3 and $\frac{1}{3}$ are reciprocals because $3 \cdot \frac{1}{3} = 1$, Similarly, $\frac{3}{2}$ and $\frac{2}{3}$ are reciprocals, and, in general, if $a \neq 0$ and $b \neq 0$, $\frac{a}{b}$ and $\frac{b}{a}$ are reciprocals.

SAS Similarity

The third important triangle similarity theorem is the *SAS Similarity Theorem.* You are asked to prove it in Question 16.

> **SAS Similarity Theorem**
> If, in two triangles, the ratios of two pairs of corresponding sides are equal and the included angles are congruent, then the triangles are similar.

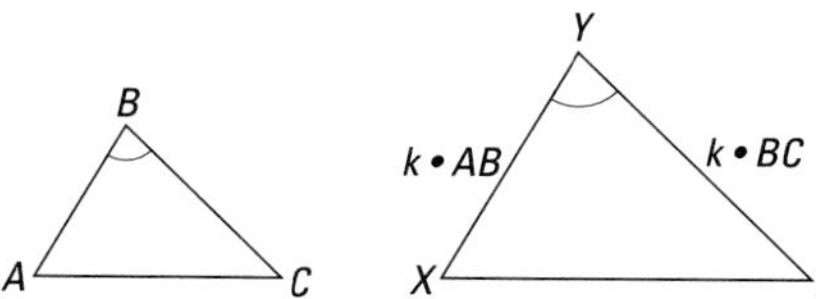

Specifically, if in two triangles ABC and XYZ, $\angle B \cong \angle Y$, and $\frac{AB}{XY} = \frac{BC}{YZ}$, then $\triangle ABC \sim \triangle XYZ$.

❷ **Example 2**

In the figure at the right, T is the midpoint of $\overline{PS}$, and Q is the midpoint of $\overline{PR}$. Write an argument which proves that $\triangle PTQ \sim \triangle PSR$.

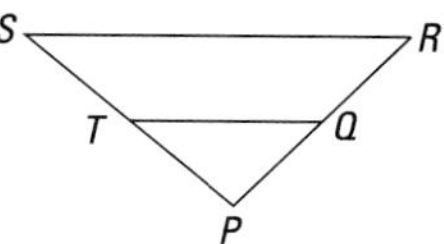

Solution 1

$\frac{PT}{PS} = \frac{PQ}{PR} = \frac{1}{2}$. $\angle P$, included by these sides, is in both triangles. So, by the SAS Similarity Theorem, $\triangle PTQ \sim \triangle PSR$.

Solution 2

By the Midpoint Connector Theorem, $\overline{QT} \parallel \overline{RS}$. Thus $\angle TQP \cong \angle R$ and $\angle PTQ \cong \angle S$, because // lines $\Rightarrow$ corr. $\angle$s $\cong$. Then $\triangle PTQ \sim \triangle PSR$ by the AA Similarity Theorem.

QUESTIONS

Covering the Reading

1. For each triangle similarity theorem, give the corresponding triangle congruence theorem(s).
   a. SSS Similarity Theorem SSS Congruence Theorem
   b. AA Similarity Theorem ASA or AAS Congruence Theorem
   c. SAS Similarity Theorem SAS Congruence Theorem
2. Describe the general strategy used to prove all three triangle similarity theorems.
   A size change is applied to one triangle so that its image is congruent to the other triangle.

Additional Examples

1. Two similar triangles each have a 37° angle. The sides including the 37° angle in one of the triangles have lengths 6 cm and 5 cm. One side including the 37° angle in the other triangle has length 15 cm. What must be the length of the other included side?
   Either 12.5 or 18, depending on whether it corresponds to the 6-cm or the 5-cm side.
2. Prove that at least two of the four triangles formed by the diagonals of a trapezoid are similar.
   Let the trapezoid be *ABCD* with $\overline{AB} \parallel \overline{CD}$ and diagonals intersecting at *E* as shown below. Then $\angle EAB \cong \angle ECD$ and $\angle EBA \cong \angle EDC$ because they are pairs of alternate interior angles formed by parallel lines. Thus, by the AA Similarity Theorem, $\triangle AEB \sim \triangle CED$.

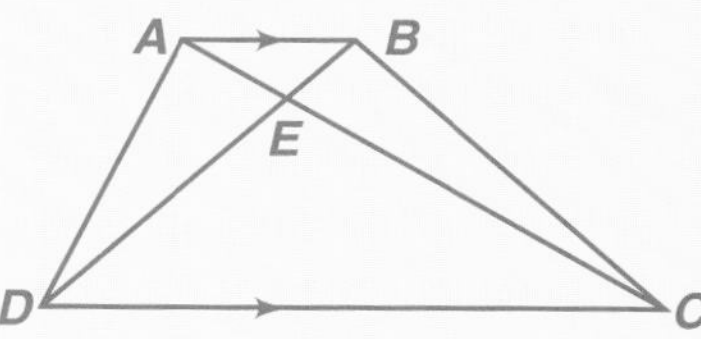

Notes on Questions

Question 1 You may want to have students write the complete statement of each theorem. But it is not advisable to do this more than once, except perhaps as a test item.

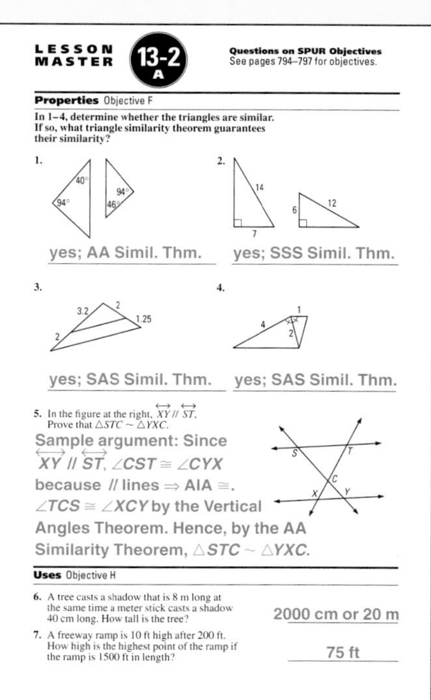

LESSON MASTER 13-2 A

Questions on SPUR Objectives
See pages 794–797 for objectives.

Properties Objective F

In 1–4, determine whether the triangles are similar. If so, what triangle similarity theorem guarantees their similarity?

1. 40° 94° 94° 46° yes; AA Simil. Thm.
2. 14 7 6 12 yes; SSS Simil. Thm.
3. 3.2 2 1.25 2 yes; SAS Simil. Thm.
4. 1 4 2 yes; SAS Simil. Thm.
5. In the figure at the right, $\overleftrightarrow{XY} \parallel \overleftrightarrow{ST}$. Prove that $\triangle STC \sim \triangle YXC$.
   Sample argument: Since $\overleftrightarrow{XY} \parallel \overleftrightarrow{ST}$, $\angle CST \cong \angle CYX$ because // lines $\Rightarrow$ AIA $\cong$. $\angle TCS \cong \angle XCY$ by the Vertical Angles Theorem. Hence, by the AA Similarity Theorem, $\triangle STC \sim \triangle YXC$.

Uses Objective H

6. A tree casts a shadow that is 8 m long at the same time a meter stick casts a shadow 40 cm long. How tall is the tree? 2000 cm or 20 m
7. A freeway ramp is 10 ft high after 200 ft. How high is the highest point of the ramp if the ramp is 1500 ft in length? 75 ft

Adapting to Individual Needs

Challenge

Give students the figure at the right. Explain that $\triangle ABC$ is isosceles. D and E are any points other than A and C on the legs. Have students prove that $\triangle ADF \sim \triangle CEG$. [Sample proof: $\angle A \cong \angle C$, since $\triangle ABC$ is isosceles. $\angle AFD \cong \angle CGE$, since both are right angles. Therefore, $\triangle ADF \sim \triangle CEG$ by the AA Similarity Theorem.]

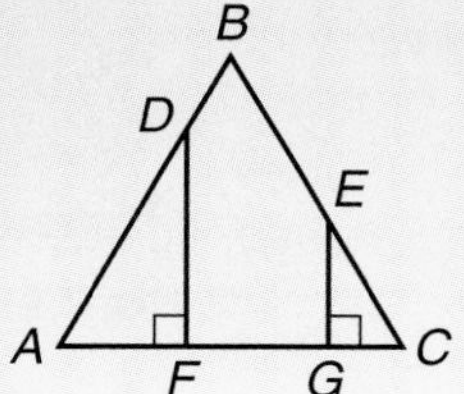

Notes on Questions

Question 7 The idea of shadows forming similar triangles is important for applications and for the work in trigonometry found in Lesson 13-6.

Question 8 This question exhibits a special case of the idea used to prove the SAS Similarity Theorem.

Question 16 Cooperative Learning You might want to put this problem on the chalkboard so that students can compare their answers. Emphasize how the steps of the proof are similar to the steps of the other two triangle similarity theorems.

Question 17 In general, the diagonals of a trapezoid form at least two similar triangles. (See *Additional Example 2.*)

(Notes on Questions continue on page 750.)

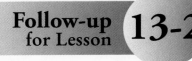

Follow-up for Lesson 13-2

Practice

For more questions on SPUR Objectives, use **Lesson Master 13-2A** (shown on page 747) or **Lesson Master 13-2B** (shown on pages 748–749).

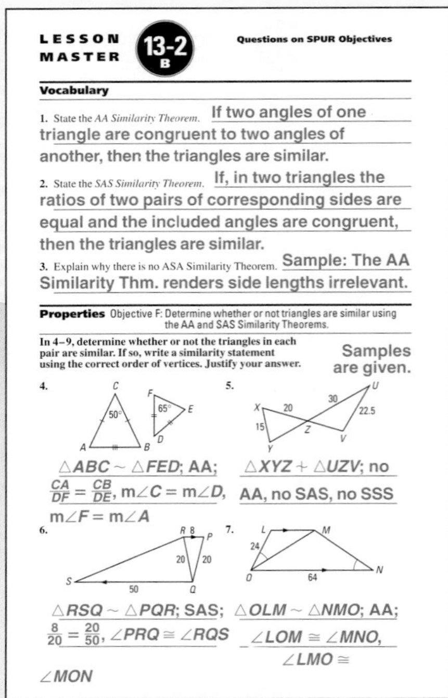

LESSON MASTER 13-2 B — Questions on SPUR Objectives

Vocabulary

1. State the *AA Similarity Theorem.* If two angles of one triangle are congruent to two angles of another, then the triangles are similar.

2. State the *SAS Similarity Theorem.* If, in two triangles the ratios of two pairs of corresponding sides are equal and the included angles are congruent, then the triangles are similar.

3. Explain why there is no ASA Similarity Theorem. Sample: The AA Similarity Thm. renders side lengths irrelevant.

Properties Objective F: Determine whether or not triangles are similar using the AA and SAS Similarity Theorems.

In 4–9, determine whether or not the triangles in each pair are similar. If so, write a similarity statement using the correct order of vertices. Justify your answer. Samples are given.

4. $\triangle ABC \sim \triangle FED$; AA; $\frac{CA}{DF} = \frac{CB}{DE}$, $m\angle C = m\angle D$, $m\angle F = m\angle A$

5. $\triangle XYZ \not\sim \triangle UZV$; no AA, no SAS, no SSS

6. $\triangle RSQ \sim \triangle PQR$; SAS; $\frac{8}{20} = \frac{20}{50}$, $\angle PRQ \cong \angle RQS$

7. $\triangle OLM \sim \triangle NMO$; AA; $\angle LOM \cong \angle MNO$, $\angle LMO \cong \angle MON$

3. Given: $\triangle ABC$ and $\triangle DEF$ below. What is the magnitude of a size change that can be applied to $\triangle ABC$ to produce an image congruent to $\triangle DEF$? $\frac{11}{18}$

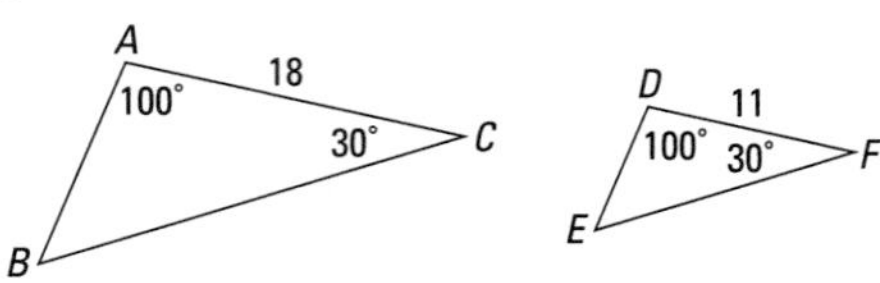

4. State the AA Similarity Theorem. If two angles of one triangle are congruent to two angles of another, then the triangles are similar.

5. What triangle congruence theorem is used in the proof of the AA Similarity Theorem? ASA Congruence Theorem

6. Suppose a person 5′6″ tall casts a shadow 3′ long at the same time that a flagpole casts a shadow 13′4″ long. To the nearest foot, how tall is the flagpole? 24′

7. A flat-roofed garage casts a shadow 5 meters long. At the same time, a meter stick casts a shadow 1.2 meters long. Determine the height of the garage. about 4.17 m

5 m
1 m
1.2 m

8. Russian *balalaika* orchestras consist of as many as six different sized balalaikas, long-necked lutes with triangular-faced soundboxes. The shapes of two balalaika soundboxes are shown below.

a. What is the magnitude of a size change applied to $\triangle PQR$ which would produce an image congruent to $\triangle XYZ$? 2.4

b. Which triangle congruence theorem is the justification that the image of the smaller triangle is congruent to the larger triangle? by the SAS Congruence Theorem

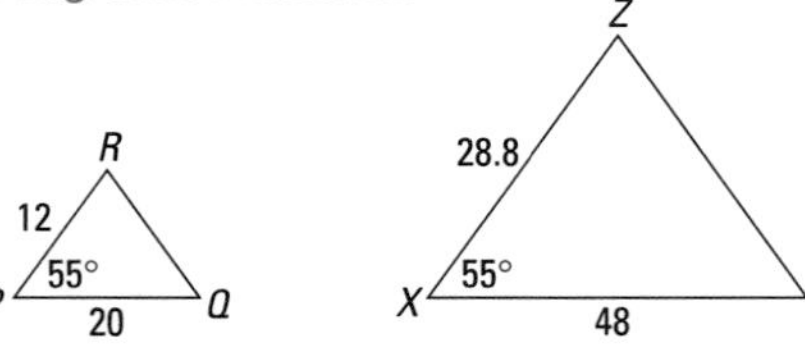

In 9 and 10, two triangles are given. See left.

a. Prove that the triangles are similar.

b. Find a ratio of similitude.

c. Determine as many missing angle measures or side lengths as possible using theorems you have had.

9a) $\frac{AB}{YX} = \frac{AC}{YZ} = 2$, $\angle A = \angle Y = 60$; by the SAS Similarity Theorem, $\triangle ABC \sim \triangle YXZ$
b) $\frac{1}{2}$ or 2
c) $BC = 5.9$

10a) $\angle G = \angle I = 115$, $\angle GHK = \angle IHJ = 24$; by the AA Similarity Theorem, $\triangle GHK \sim \triangle IHJ$.
b) $\frac{5}{9}$ or $\frac{9}{5}$
c) $m\angle K = 41$, $m\angle HJI = 41$, $GH = 144$, $JH = 111.25$

9.

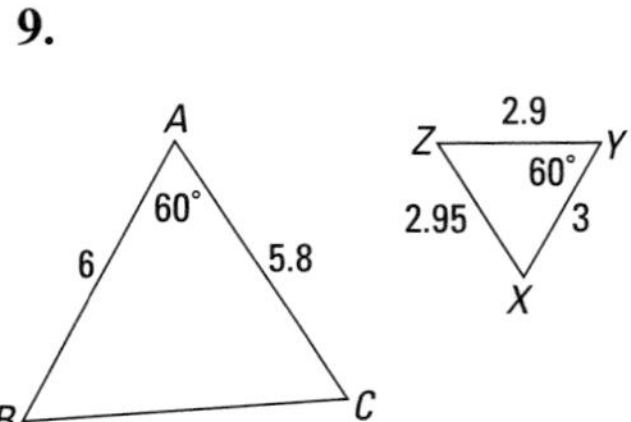

10.

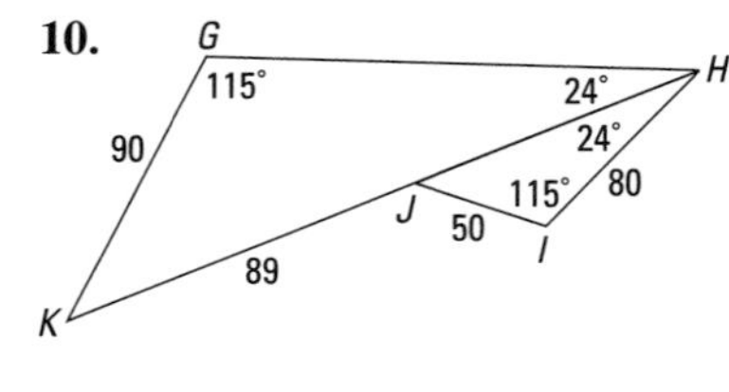

Additional Answers

11.

Conclusions	Justifications
1. $m\angle WYX = m\angle ZYV$	Vertical Angles Thm.
2. $\frac{WY}{VY} = 3$, $\frac{XY}{ZY} = 3$	Multiplication Prop. of Equality
3. $\frac{WY}{VY} = \frac{XY}{ZY}$	Transitive Prop. of Equality
4. $\triangle WXY \sim \triangle VZY$	SAS Similarity Thm. (steps 1 and 3)

11. Use the figure at the right.
Complete the proof. See margin.
Given: $WY = 3 \cdot VY$,
$XY = 3 \cdot YZ$.
To prove: $\triangle WXY \sim \triangle VZY$.

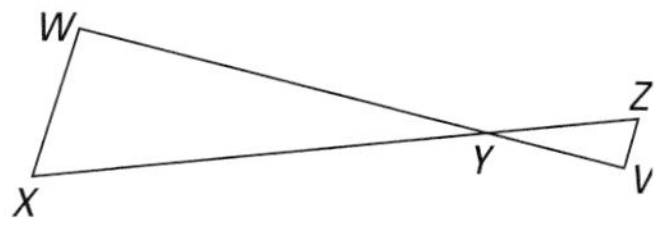

Applying the Mathematics

In 12–15, each figure contains at least two triangles.

a. Are two triangles similar?

b. If so, what triangle similarity theorem guarantees their similarity? If not, explain why not.

c. If the two triangles are similar, write the similarity with vertices in correct order.

12.

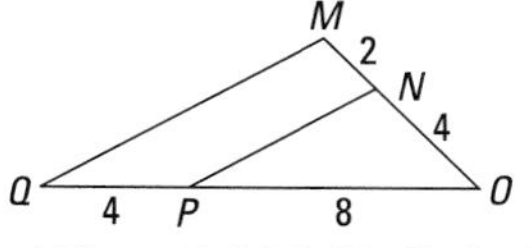

a) Yes b) SAS Similarity Theorem c) $\triangle ONP \sim \triangle OMQ$

13. a) No b) $\frac{12}{24} \neq \frac{5}{7} \neq \frac{13}{25}$

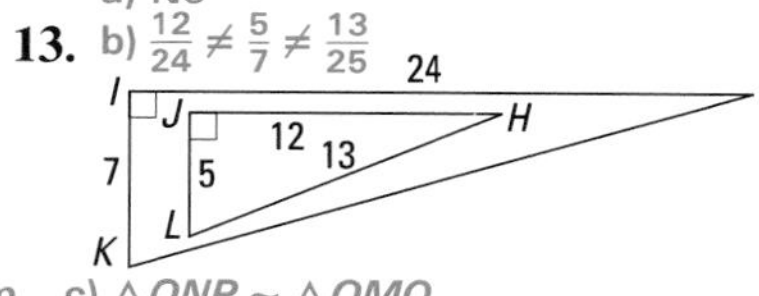

15a) Yes
b) SSS Similarity Theorem
c) $\triangle XVW \sim \triangle AZY$

14.

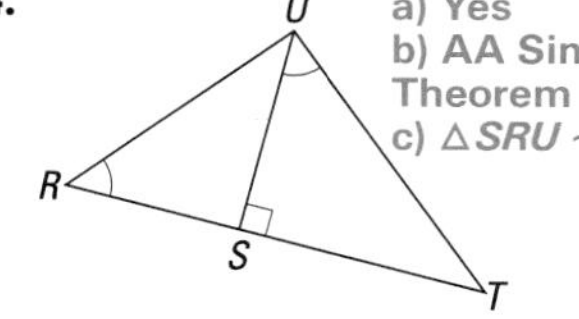

a) Yes
b) AA Similarity Theorem
c) $\triangle SRU \sim \triangle SUT$

15. See left.

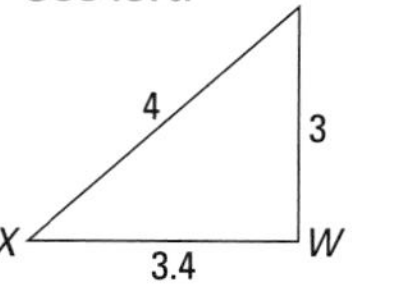

16. Write a proof argument to prove the SAS Similarity Theorem using the given figure.
Given: $\angle B \cong \angle Y$,
$\frac{XY}{AB} = \frac{YZ}{BC}$.
To prove: $\triangle ABC \sim \triangle XYZ$.
(Hint: Use the general idea of the proof of the AA Triangle Similarity Theorem.) See margin.

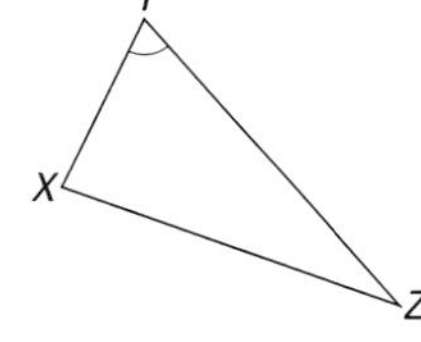

17) $\angle ABC \cong \angle EDC$, and $\angle BAC \cong \angle DEC$ from the // Lines ⇒ AIA ≅ Theorem. Thus, $\triangle CED \sim \triangle CAB$ by the AA Similarity Theorem.

17. In the director's chair pictured below, $\overline{AE}$ and $\overline{BD}$ intersect at C, and $\overleftrightarrow{AB} \parallel \overleftrightarrow{DE}$. Prove that $\triangle ABC$ and $\triangle EDC$ are similar. See left.

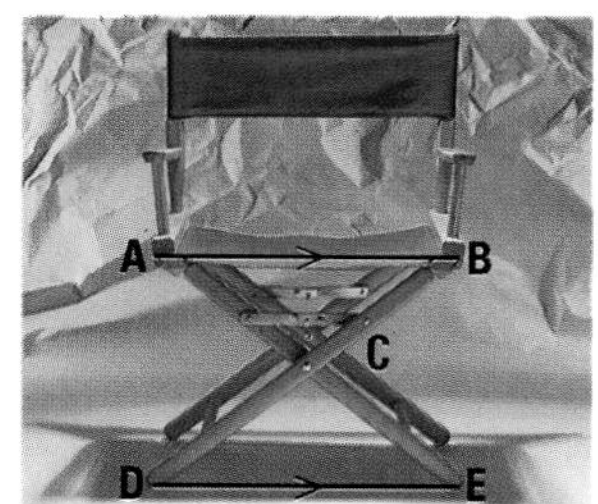

Assessment

Oral/Written Communication
Have students **work in pairs.** Have students select the SSS, AA, or SAS Similarity Theorem. Then each student should draw and label a pair of triangles which are similar by the theorem he/she selected. Students should exchange drawings with their partner and write a complete proof showing that the two triangles are similar. [Students write a correct proof using the SSS, AA, or SAS Similarity Theorem.]

Extension

Give students this problem. For a pair of triangles of each type given below, what information about the angles would be sufficient to prove that the triangles are similar?

1. Right triangles [Acute angle of one congruent to acute angle of the other]
2. Isosceles triangles [Vertex angles congruent or base angle of one congruent to base angle of the other]
3. Equilateral [Nothing else is necessary. All equilateral triangles are similar.]

Project Update Project 1, *Measuring with Shadows,* and Project 5, *Oblique Triangles with Integer Sides and Integer Altitudes* on pages 789–790, relate to the content of this lesson.

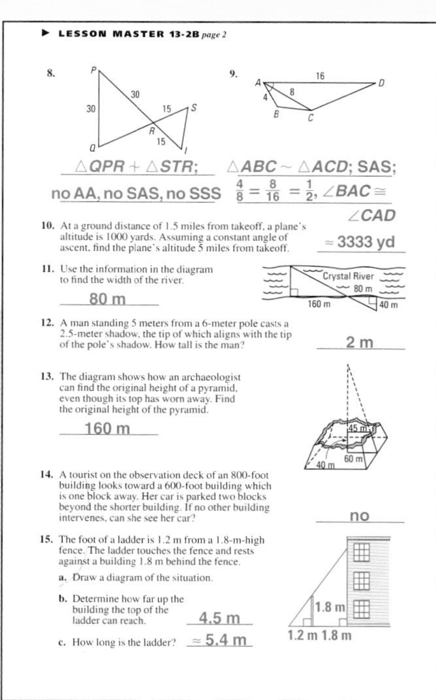

▶ **LESSON MASTER 13-2B** *page 2*

8. $\triangle QPR \not\sim \triangle STR$; no AA, no SAS, no SSS

9. $\triangle ABC \sim \triangle ACD$; SAS; $\frac{4}{8} = \frac{8}{16} = \frac{1}{2}$, $\angle BAC \cong \angle CAD$

10. At a ground distance of 1.5 miles from takeoff, a plane's altitude is 1000 yards. Assuming a constant angle of ascent, find the plane's altitude 5 miles from takeoff. $\approx$ 3333 yd

11. Use the information in the diagram to find the width of the river. 80 m

12. A man standing 5 meters from a 6-meter pole casts a 2.5-meter shadow, the tip of which aligns with the tip of the pole's shadow. How tall is the man? 2 m

13. The diagram shows how an archaeologist can find the original height of a pyramid, even though its top has worn away. Find the original height of the pyramid. 160 m

14. A tourist on the observation deck of an 800-foot building looks toward a 600-foot building which is one block away. Her car is parked two blocks beyond the shorter building. If no other building intervenes, can she see her car? no

15. The foot of a ladder is 1.2 m from a 1.8-m-high fence. The ladder touches the fence and rests against a building 1.8 m behind the fence.

a. Draw a diagram of the situation.

b. Determine how far up the building the top of the ladder can reach. 4.5 m

c. How long is the ladder? $\approx$ 5.4 m

16. Let $k = \frac{XY}{AB} = \frac{YZ}{BC}$. Then $XY = k \cdot AB$ and $YZ = k \cdot BC$. Let $\triangle A'B'C'$ be the image of $\triangle ABC$ under a size change of magnitude k. So $A'B' = k \cdot AB$ and $B'C' = k \cdot BC$. Also, since size transformations preserve angle measure, $\angle B' \cong \angle B$. With transitivity, $A'B' = XY$, $B'C' = YZ$, and $\angle B' \cong \angle Y$. So, $\triangle A'B'C' \cong \triangle XYZ$ by the SAS Congruence Theorem. Thus, $\triangle XYZ$ can be mapped onto $\triangle ABC$ by a composite of size changes and reflections. So $\triangle ABC \sim \triangle XYZ$.

Notes on Questions

Question 26 First ask students for the statements of the theorems.

(1) HL: If in two right triangles, the hypotenuse and one leg in one triangle are proportional to the hypotenuse and one leg in the other, then the triangles are similar. There is a reasonably easy proof of the HL Triangle Similarity Theorem. Suppose the hypotenuse and leg of one triangle are c and a, and of another are kc and ka. (That is, they are proportional.) Then, using the Pythagorean Theorem, the third side of one triangle is $\sqrt{c^2 - a^2}$, while the third side of the other triangle is $\sqrt{(kc)^2 - (ka)^2} = \sqrt{k^2(c^2 - a^2)} = k\sqrt{c^2 - a^2}$. Thus, all the sides are proportional and the triangles are similar by SSS Similarity.

(2) SsA: If two sides of one triangle are proportional to two sides of another triangle, and the angles opposite the longer sides are congruent, then the triangles are similar. A proof of the SsA Similarity Theorem utilizes the same ideas as those in the proofs of the AA, SSS, and SAS triangle similarity theorems.

Review

18. **a.** Are triangles LMN and PQR, pictured below, similar? No
b. If so, why? If not, why not? *(Lesson 13-1)* $\frac{12}{8} \neq \frac{16}{12} \neq \frac{20}{16}$

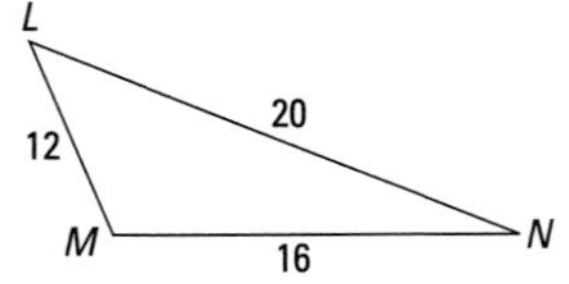

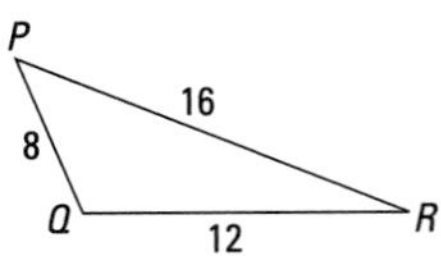

In 19–21, solve. *(Lesson 12-4)*

19. $\frac{AB}{4} + 1 = \frac{3}{8} + 1$ $AB = 1.5$ **20.** $\frac{d}{d+1} = \frac{3}{5}$ $d = 1.5$ **21.** $\frac{n}{12} = \frac{n-12}{9}$ $n = 48$

22. *True or false.* For all positive numbers x and y, $\frac{x+y}{y} = \frac{x}{y} + 1$. *(Previous course, Lesson 12-4)* True

23. Prove the following theorem, known as the **Reciprocals Property:** if $\frac{a}{b} = \frac{c}{d}$, and a, b, c, and d do not equal zero, then $\frac{b}{a} = \frac{d}{c}$. *(Lesson 12-4)* See margin.

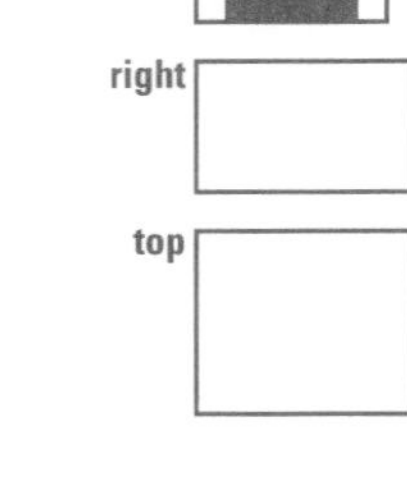

24. Refer to Question 7. Draw front, right, and top views of the garage. (Consider the door to be on the front side of the garage.) *(Lesson 9-7)* See left.

25. The diagonal of a square field is 50 meters long. What is the length of a side of the field? *(Lesson 8-6)* $25\sqrt{2} \approx 35.4$ meters

Exploration

26. Is there an HL Similarity Theorem and an SsA Similarity Theorem for triangles? If so, how do you know? If not, draw a counterexample. See margin.

Additional Answers

23.

Conclusions	Justifications
1. $ad = bc$; $\frac{d}{c} = \frac{b}{a}$	Multiplication Prop. of Equality
2. $\frac{b}{a} = \frac{d}{c}$	Symmetric Prop. of Equality

26. Yes, because there are HL and SsA Congruence Theorems. These theorems could be deduced using the same techniques used in this lesson to deduce the SAS and AA Similarity Theorems. (See the notes for this question.)

Setting Up Lesson 13-3

Questions 19–22 will help set up Lesson 13-3. In particular, a natural step in answering **Question 19** is to subtract 1 from each side of the equation; in Lesson 13-3, 1 is added to each side. The equation in **Question 22** involves adding 1 to a fraction.

LESSON

13-3

The Side-Splitting Theorem

A Proportion Within a Triangle

Pictured below is an asymmetric roof. Still, the parallel beams split the sides of the roof, forming similar triangles.

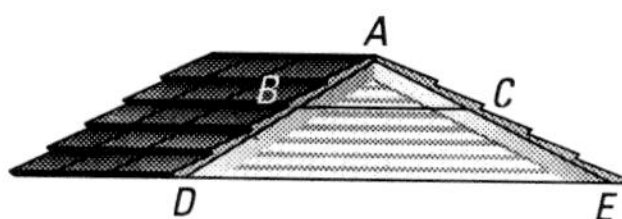

It turns out that the lengths AB, BD, AC, and CE are proportional. We call this result the *Side-Splitting Theorem.* Its proof depends on the AA Similarity Theorem and properties of algebra.

Side-Splitting Theorem
If a line is parallel to a side of a triangle and intersects the other two sides in distinct points, it splits these sides into proportional segments.

Proof:

Given: $\overleftrightarrow{PQ} \parallel \overleftrightarrow{BC}$.

To prove: $\frac{AP}{PB} = \frac{AQ}{QC}$.

Drawing:

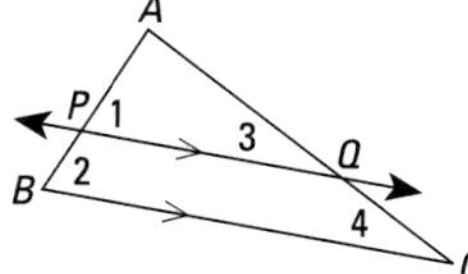

Argument:
$\angle 1 \cong \angle 2$ and $\angle 3 \cong \angle 4$ since // lines $\Rightarrow$ corr. $\angle$s $\cong$. Thus, by the AA Similarity Theorem, $\triangle APQ \sim \triangle ABC$. Now, in these triangles, corresponding sides are proportional.

$$\frac{AB}{AP} = \frac{AC}{AQ}$$

Now we split AB and AC into two parts using the Betweenness Theorem.

$$\frac{AP + PB}{AP} = \frac{AQ + QC}{AQ}$$

Write each side of the equation as the sum of two fractions.

$$\frac{AP}{AP} + \frac{PB}{AP} = \frac{AQ}{AQ} + \frac{QC}{AQ}$$

$$1 + \frac{PB}{AP} = 1 + \frac{QC}{AQ}$$

Subtract 1 from both sides. $\frac{PB}{AP} = \frac{QC}{AQ}$

Use the Reciprocals Property. $\frac{AP}{PB} = \frac{AQ}{QC}$

Lesson 13-3

Objectives

A Find lengths in figures by applying the Side-Splitting Theorem and the Side-Splitting Converse Theorem.

H Use the Side-Splitting Theorem to find lengths and distances in real situations.

Resources

From the ***Teacher's Resource File***
- Lesson Master 13-3A or 13-3B
- Answer Master 13-3
- Assessment Sourcebook: Quiz for Lessons 13-1 through 13-3
- Teaching Aids
  171 Warm-up
  176 Additional Examples
- Technology Sourcebook, Computer Master 23

Additional Resources
- Visuals for Teaching Aids 171, 176
- GeoExplorer or other automatic drawers

Teaching Lesson 13-3

Warm-up

In the following figure, $\overleftrightarrow{EF} \parallel \overleftrightarrow{MN}$.

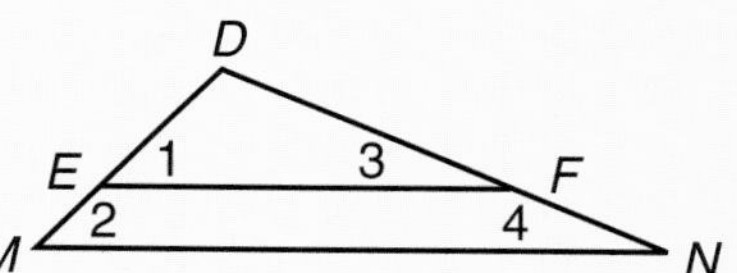

1. Is $\angle 1 \cong \angle 2$? **Yes, // lines $\Rightarrow$ Corresponding $\angle$s $\cong$**
2. Is $\angle 3 \cong \angle 4$? **Yes, // lines $\Rightarrow$ Corresponding $\angle$s $\cong$**
3. Are the triangles similar? **Yes, $\triangle DEF \sim \triangle DMN$ by AA Similarity**

Lesson 13-3 Overview

Broad Goals This lesson considers the proportional lengths formed by a line that is parallel to a side of a triangle.

Perspective The first theorem presented in this lesson states that if a line is parallel to a side of a triangle and intersects the other two sides in distinct points, it "splits" these sides into proportional segments. The proof of the theorem depends on similar triangles. The Side-Splitting Converse Theorem is also stated and proved in the lesson. The proofs of both theorems are difficult for most students to understand but should be presented in class and discussed thoroughly.

Notes on Reading

Reading Mathematics The Side-Splitting Theorem is an easy theorem to learn, but its proof on page 751 is not easy for most students to follow. Students have trouble with all the steps of the proof due to the reciprocals, the means exchange, the parts and the wholes, and the segments of the parallel lines. If students are confused, explain that there are only two things to remember: (1) the properties of size changes, under which ratios of lengths of images to preimages is constant (this takes care of the segments on the parallel lines as well as the parts to the wholes), and (2) the theorem itself.

You might want to use Activity 1 in *Optional Activities* below to introduce the Side-Splitting Converse Theorem.

The proof of the Side-Splitting Converse Theorem goes through the same steps as the proof of the Side-Splitting Theorem but in reverse order. Different letters are used so that the proofs will not be confusing, but you may wish to write the steps in reverse order and ask students for the reasons that lead from one step to the next. They will then have proved the converse.

You may wish to merge the two theorems in if-and-only-if language: A line which intersects two sides of a triangle in two distinct points is parallel to the third side if and only if it splits the two sides proportionally.

Note that the Midpoint Connector Theorem (Lesson 11-8) is a special case of the Side-Splitting Converse—one in which the ratio of the proportional segments is 1:1. The Midpoint Connector Theorem includes the bonus that the length of the segment is half of the third side. You may wish to mention that the ratio of the third sides is never equal to the ratio of the segments formed on the other two sides.

Have students record the results of the **Activity** for use with **Question 2** on page 754.

Activity
Samples: $AB \approx 3.4$ cm, $BC \approx 1.5$ cm, $AD \approx 2.9$ cm, $DE \approx 1.3$ cm; $\frac{AB}{BC} = \frac{AD}{DE}$

Activity

Measure *AB*, *BC*, *AD*, and *DE*. Form a true (or nearly true) proportion with these measurements.

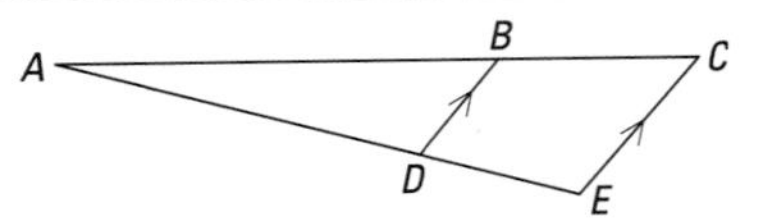

Example 1

Suppose beams $\overline{MN}$ and $\overline{ST}$ are parallel and split the sides of the roof into the lengths (in inches) as indicated.

a. Find *RN*.

b. Find *ST*.

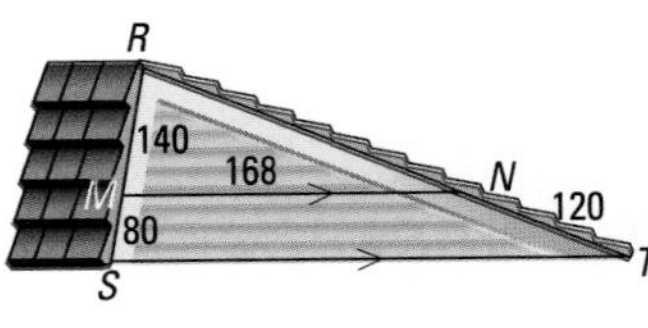

Solution

a. From the Side-Splitting Theorem,

$$\frac{RM}{MS} = \frac{RN}{NT}.$$

Substitute. $\frac{140}{80} = \frac{RN}{120}$

Solve for *RN*. $80 \cdot RN = 120 \cdot 140$

$RN = 210$ inches

b. $\triangle RMN \sim \triangle RST$. Thus $\frac{RM}{RS} = \frac{MN}{ST}$. Substituting, $\frac{140}{220} = \frac{168}{ST}$.

Thus $140 \cdot ST = 168 \cdot 220$ and $ST = 264$ inches.

The Converse of the Side-Splitting Theorem

The converse of the Side-Splitting Theorem is also true: If a line intersects two sides of a triangle and forms segments whose lengths are proportional, then the line is parallel to the third side.

Side-Splitting Converse Theorem
If a line intersects $\overline{OP}$ and $\overline{OQ}$ in distinct points *X* and *Y* so that $\frac{OX}{XP} = \frac{OY}{YQ}$, then $\overleftrightarrow{XY} \parallel \overleftrightarrow{PQ}$.

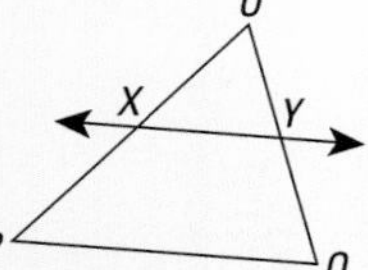

Proof:

Given: $\frac{OX}{XP} = \frac{OY}{YQ}$ in the figure above.

To prove: $\overleftrightarrow{XY} \parallel \overleftrightarrow{PQ}$.

Argument:
First we prove that the triangles are similar. Then corresponding angles are used to get the parallel lines. Using the Reciprocals Property,

Optional Activities

Activity 1 You can use this activity to introduce the Side-Splitting Converse Theorem. Have students **work in pairs.** One student should draw a triangle and a line within the triangle parallel to any side of the triangle. The other student should measure the sides of the triangle and the segments formed by the parallel line. They should set up ratios and verify the results of the theorem. Then students should reverse roles and repeat the activity using a different triangle.

Activity 2 Technology Connection
In *Technology Sourcebook, Computer Master 23,* students draw a triangle and a line parallel to one side of the triangle. By calculating various ratios, they verify the Side-Splitting Theorem. Then they explore the more general case of parallel lines cut by transversals.

$$\frac{XP}{OX} = \frac{YQ}{OY}.$$

Add 1 to both sides (in the form of $\frac{OX}{OX}$ on the left side, and $\frac{OY}{OY}$ on the right).

$$\frac{OX}{OX} + \frac{XP}{OX} = \frac{OY}{OY} + \frac{YQ}{OY}$$

Combine the fractions. $\frac{OX + XP}{OX} = \frac{OY + YQ}{OY}$

$OX + XP = OP$ and $OY + YQ = OQ$ by the Betweenness Theorem.
Substituting, $\frac{OP}{OX} = \frac{OQ}{OY}.$

Thus, two pairs of sides are proportional. By the Reflexive Property, $\angle XOY \cong \angle POQ$. So $\triangle OPQ \sim \triangle OXY$ by the SAS Similarity Theorem. The corresponding angles in the similar triangles are congruent, so $\angle OPQ \cong \angle OXY$. These are corresponding angles for $\overleftrightarrow{XY}$ and $\overleftrightarrow{PQ}$ with transversal $\overleftrightarrow{OP}$. Since corr. $\angle$s $\cong \Rightarrow$ // lines, $\overleftrightarrow{XY} \parallel \overleftrightarrow{PQ}$.

You may use the Side-Splitting Converse Theorem to conclude that lines are parallel.

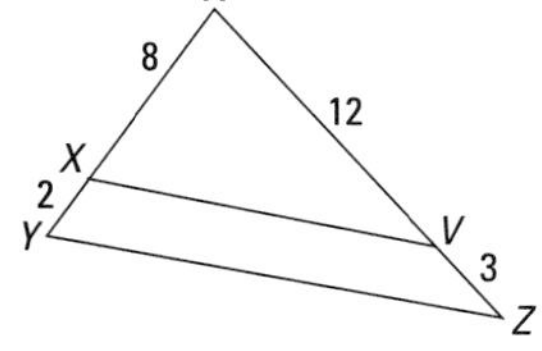

Example 2

Refer to the figure at the left. Is $\overline{XV} \parallel \overline{YZ}$? Why or why not?

Solution

Does $\frac{WX}{XY} = \frac{WV}{VZ}$? Yes, $\frac{8}{2} = \frac{12}{3}$.

So, by the Side-Splitting Converse Theorem, $\overline{XV} \parallel \overline{YZ}$.

An alternate way to solve Example 2 is to prove $\triangle WXV \sim \triangle WYZ$ by SAS Similarity and show $\overline{XV} \parallel \overline{YZ}$ using corresponding angles.

Example 3

The flag of Lesotho, a country in southern Africa, has a blue stripe with one edge of the stripe forming the diagonal $\overline{TE}$. The other edge $\overline{AB}$ of the blue stripe is parallel to $\overline{TE}$. If the dimensions of the flag are 40 cm by 60 cm, and AC is 42 cm, where is B located?

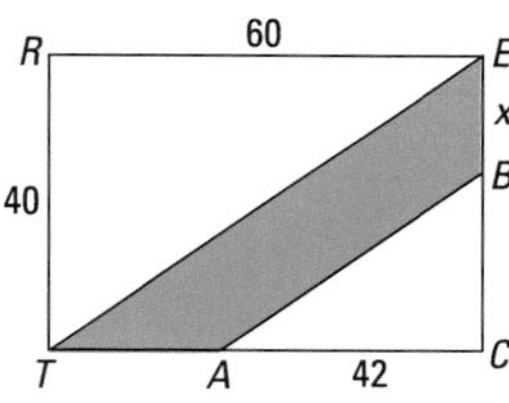

Lesotho is located in the east central part of South Africa. Its economy depends upon agriculture and production from diamond mines.

Solution

From the Side-Splitting Theorem, since $\overline{AB}$ is parallel to $\overline{TE}$,

$$\frac{CA}{AT} = \frac{CB}{BE}.$$

Let $BE = x$. Then $\frac{42}{18} = \frac{40 - x}{x}$

$$42x = 720 - 18x$$
$$60x = 720$$
$$x = 12$$

B should be located 12 cm from E.

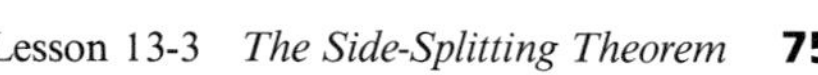

Additional Examples

These examples are also given on **Teaching Aid 176.**

1. In $\triangle RIG$ below, $\overline{AN} \parallel \overline{RI}$. If $IN = 5$, what are the lengths of $\overline{NG}$ and $\overline{RI}$?

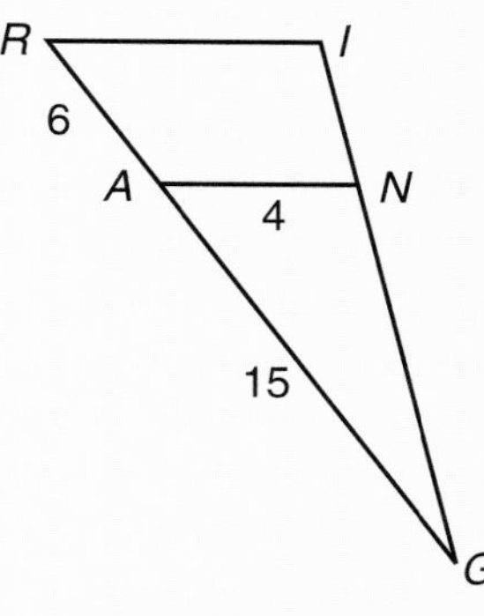

$NG = 12.5$, $RI = 5.6$

2. $\overline{BE}$ is a segment which splits two sides of $\triangle ACD$ as shown here. Is $\overline{BE} \parallel \overline{CD}$?

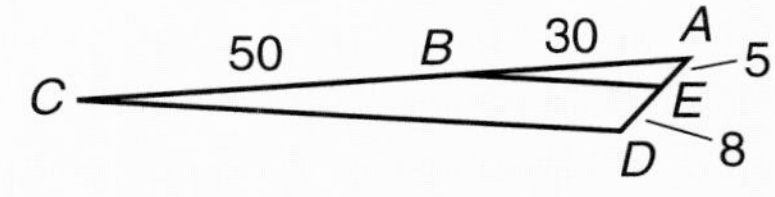

No. $\frac{30}{50} \neq \frac{5}{8}$

3.

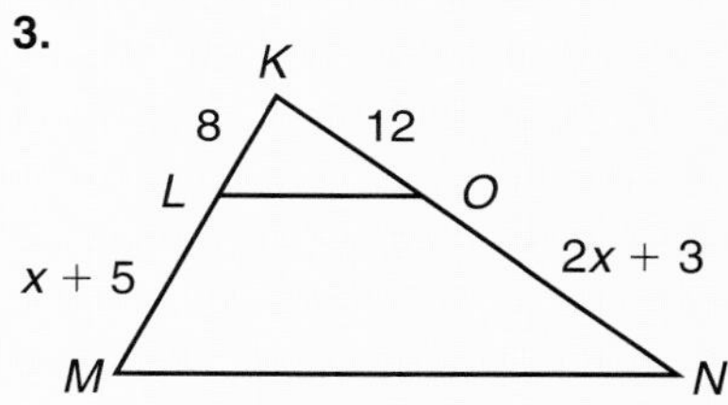

In $\triangle KNM$ above, $\overline{LO} \parallel \overline{MN}$. Find x, LM, and ON.
$x = 9$; $LM = 14$, $ON = 21$

Adapting to Individual Needs

Extra Help

In using the Side-Splitting Theorem, some students might set up one ratio involving a pair of segments from a "split side" and another from the base and the parallel segment. Stress that a proportion applying the Side-Splitting Theorem involves only the sides that are "split" by the parallel segment.

English Language Development

To illustrate the meaning of the term *splitting* for students with limited English proficiency, break or cut a pencil or similar object into two parts. Explain that you "split" the pencil into two parts. Then refer to the picture in the proof of the Side-Splitting Theorem and point out that line PQ splits (or cuts) both side AB and side AC into two parts.

Notes on Questions

Questions 12–14 The extension of the Side-Splitting Theorem (to cases in which there are more than two pairs of proportional segments, and in which the segments do not make up sides of a triangle) is particularly important for applications.

Question 14 Social Studies Connection The idea of laying out paved streets in major cities arose during the 12th and 13th centuries in Europe. Before then, most streets were little more than footpaths, spreading out concentrically from the village square. During the Renaissance, urban development became a more focused activity, partly for military purposes. The city had to be a fortress as well as a living space.

(Notes on Questions continue on page 756.)

Practice

For more questions on SPUR Objectives, use **Lesson Master 13-3A** (shown on page 755) or **Lesson Master 13-3B** (shown on pages 756–757).

Assessment

Quiz A quiz covering Lessons 13-1 through 13-3 is provided in the *Assessment Sourcebook*.

Oral/Written Communication Have students **work in groups** to make up two examples, one to illustrate the Side-Splitting Theorem and one to illustrate the Side-Splitting Converse Theorem. [Students provide correct examples.]

5) If a line intersects $\overline{OP}$ and $\overline{OQ}$ in distinct points X and Y so that $\frac{OX}{XP} = \frac{OY}{YQ}$, then $\overleftrightarrow{XY} // \overleftrightarrow{PQ}$.

QUESTIONS

Covering the Reading

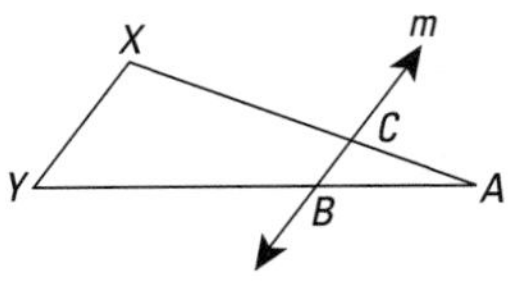

1. Given $m // \overleftrightarrow{XY}$, complete the proportions.
   a. $\frac{AC}{AX} = \underline{\ ?\ }$ $\frac{AB}{AY}$ or $\frac{CB}{XY}$
   b. $\frac{AB}{BY} = \underline{\ ?\ }$ $\frac{AC}{CX}$

2. Write the results you found from the Activity in this lesson. Sample: $\frac{AB}{BC} = \frac{AD}{DE}$

3. In the triangle below at the left, if $\overleftrightarrow{BC} // \overleftrightarrow{DE}$, then $CE = \underline{\ ?\ }$. 7.5

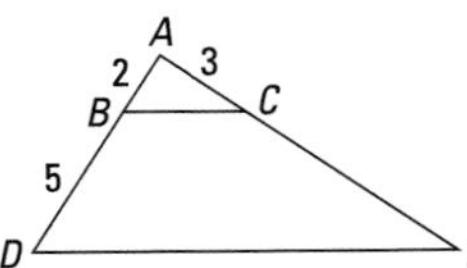

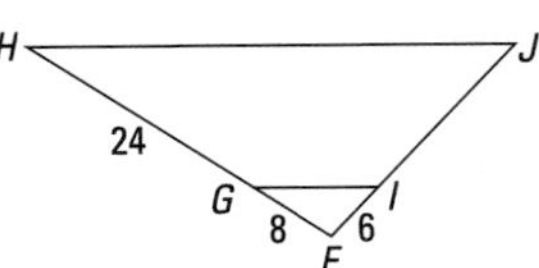

4. In the triangle above at the right, if $\overleftrightarrow{GI} // \overleftrightarrow{HJ}$, then $FJ = \underline{\ ?\ }$. 24

5. State the Side-Splitting Converse Theorem. See left.

In 6 and 7, use the figures below. Is $\overline{XV} // \overline{YZ}$? Why or why not?

6. No; because $\frac{1}{2} \neq \frac{3}{7}$

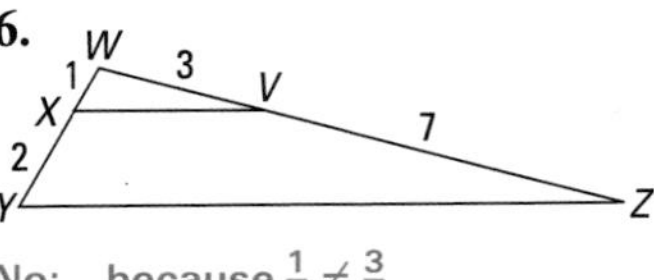

7. Yes; because $\frac{.75}{.5} = \frac{.6}{.4}$

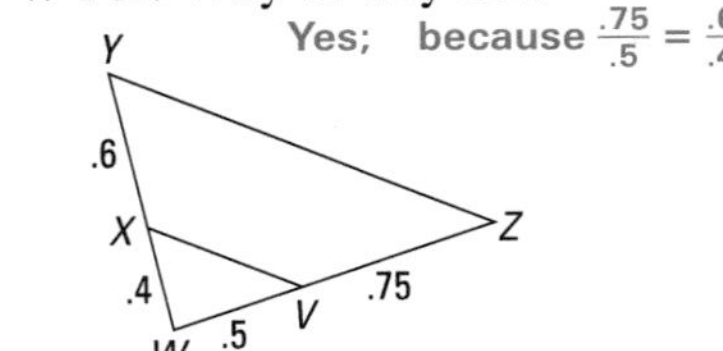

8. At the right, the beam $\overline{BC}$ splits the sides of this asymmetric roof. If $AB = 20$, $BD = 30$, $AE = 60$, and $\overline{BC} // \overline{DE}$, find AC and CE. $AC = 24$, $CE = 36$

9. In the drawing at the right, $\overleftrightarrow{MN} // \overleftrightarrow{PQ}$, $MP = 6$, $NQ = 5$, $ON = 30$, and $MN = 14$. Find each number.

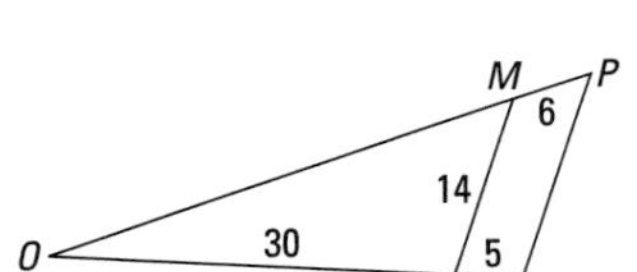

a. $\frac{NQ}{ON}$ $\frac{1}{6}$
b. $\frac{MP}{MO}$ $\frac{1}{6}$
c. MO 36
d. OP 42
e. $\frac{ON}{OQ}$ $\frac{6}{7}$
f. $\frac{OM}{OP}$ $\frac{6}{7}$
g. $\frac{MN}{PQ}$ $\frac{6}{7}$
h. PQ $\frac{98}{6} = 16\frac{1}{3}$

Adapting to Individual Needs

Challenge

Have students use the Side-Splitting Theorem to prove that the figure formed by connecting adjacent midpoints of the sides of any quadrilateral is a parallelogram. That is, given that *ABCD* is a quadrilateral and that *EFGH* is formed by connecting the midpoints of adjacent sides, prove that *EFGH* is a parallelogram.

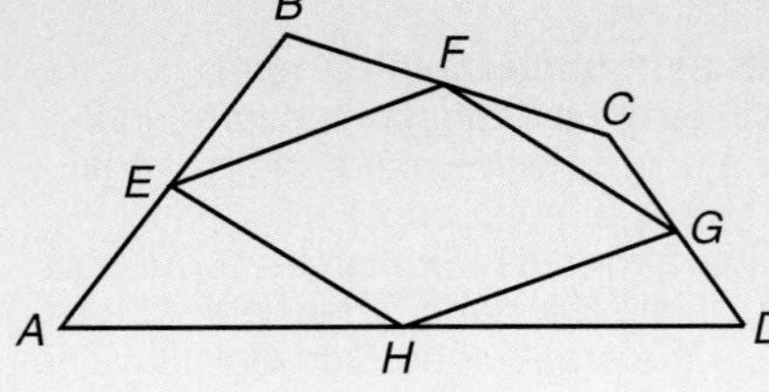

[Sample proof:
(1) $AE = EB$ and $AH = HD$, since E and H are midpoints. So $\frac{AE}{EB} = \frac{AH}{HD}$.
(2) Therefore, in $\triangle ABD$ (not shown) $\overline{EH} // \overline{BD}$, by the Side-Splitting Converse Theorem.
(3) Likewise, $BF = FC$ and $CG = GD$, since F and G are midpoints. So $\frac{BF}{FC} = \frac{GD}{CG}$.
(4) Therefore, in $\triangle CBD$ (not shown) $\overline{FG} // \overline{BD}$, by the Side-Splitting Converse Theorem.

Applying the Mathematics

10. In Question 9, what is the magnitude of the size change S with center O and S($\triangle MNO$) = $\triangle PQO$? $\frac{7}{6}$

11. Given: $\overleftrightarrow{DE} \parallel \overleftrightarrow{AC}$, $\overleftrightarrow{EF} \parallel \overleftrightarrow{AB}$, and lengths as indicated in the figure at the left.

a. Find DB. 7.5

b. Find FA. 9

c. $\angle A$ and $\angle AFE$ are __?__ angles. supplementary

d. Write a proportion using BD, DA, CF, and FA. $\frac{BD}{DA} = \frac{FA}{CF}$

12. Fill in the justifications for the proof argument of the following generalization of the Side-Splitting Theorem. If $m \parallel n \parallel p$, then $\frac{a}{b} = \frac{c}{d}$.

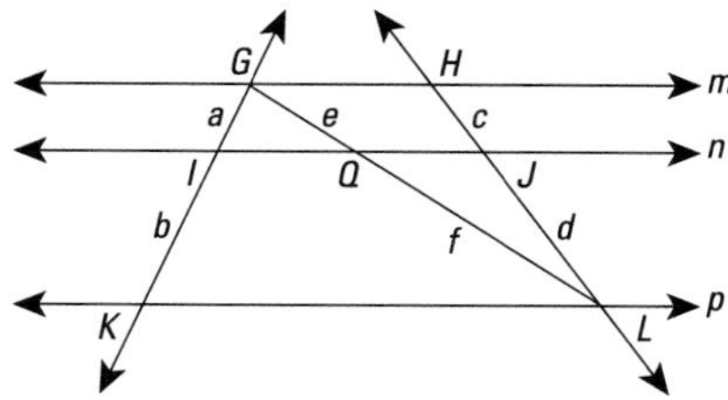

Argument:

Conclusions	Justifications
1. $\frac{a}{b} = \frac{e}{f}$	**a.** Side-Splitting Theorem
2. $\frac{e}{f} = \frac{c}{d}$	**b.** Side-Splitting Theorem
3. $\frac{a}{b} = \frac{c}{d}$	**c.** Transitive Property of Equality (steps 1 and 2)

In 13 and 14, use the map shown below. 8th, 9th, and 10th Streets are parallel. The distances along Rasci Road are as given.

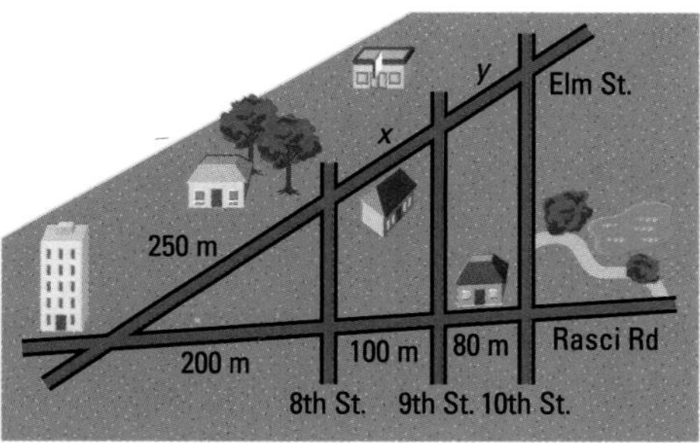

13. Find x and y, two distances along Elm Street. x = 125 m; y = 100 m

14. The city wants to replace curbs on 8th, 9th, and 10th Streets between Elm and Rasci. If it is 120 meters from Elm St. to Rasci Rd. along 8th St., how many meters of curbs will be needed for 9th and 10th Streets? (Remember that curbs go on both sides of the street.) 360 m; 456 m

Extension

Prove that if a ray bisects an angle of a triangle, then it divides the opposite side into segments proportional to the other two sides.

Given: $\triangle ABC$ with $\overrightarrow{BD}$ the bisector of $\angle ABC$ and D on $\overline{AC}$.

To prove: $\frac{AD}{DC} = \frac{AB}{BC}$

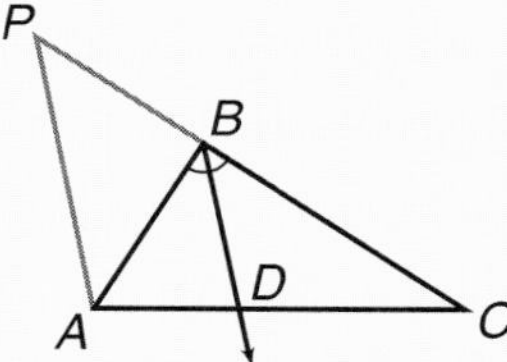

[Draw the line through A that is parallel to $\overrightarrow{BD}$. Let P be the point where this line intersects $\overleftrightarrow{BC}$.

Conclusions	Justifications
1. $\angle PAB \cong \angle ABD$	// lines ⇒ AIA ≅ Thm.
2. $\angle ABD \cong \angle DBC$	def. ∠ bisector
3. $\angle DBC \cong \angle APC$	// lines ⇒ Corr. ∠'s ≅
4. $\angle PAB \cong \angle APC$	Transitive Prop. of ≅
5. $AB = PB$	Isosceles △ Base Angles Converse Thm.
6. $\frac{PB}{BC} = \frac{AD}{DC}$	Side-Splitting Thm.
7. $\frac{AB}{BC} = \frac{AD}{DC}$	Substitution]

Project Update Project 1, *Measuring with Shadows,* and Project 2, *Splitting Sides of a Trapezoid,* on page 789, relate to the content of this lesson.

Steps 2 and 4 give $\overline{EH} \parallel \overline{FG}$, since both segments are parallel to $\overline{BD}$. In steps similar to 1–4, $\overline{EF}$ can be shown to be parallel to $\overline{HG}$. Therefore, $EFGH$ is a parallelogram, since both pairs of opposite sides are parallel.]

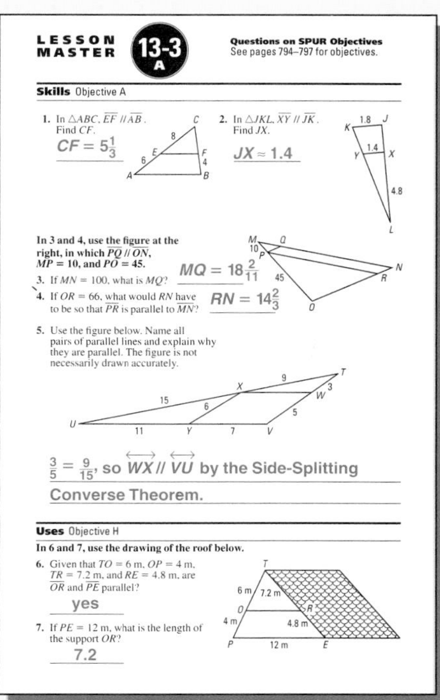

LESSON MASTER 13-3 A

Questions on SPUR Objectives
See pages 794–797 for objectives.

Skills Objective A

1. In $\triangle ABC$, $\overline{EF} \parallel \overline{AB}$. Find CF. $CF = 5\frac{1}{3}$

2. In $\triangle JKL$, $\overline{XY} \parallel \overline{JK}$. Find JX. $JX \approx 1.4$

In 3 and 4, use the figure at the right, in which $\overline{PQ} \parallel \overline{ON}$, $MP = 10$, and $PO = 45$.

3. If $MN = 100$, what is MQ? $MQ = 18\frac{2}{11}$

4. If $OR = 66$, what would RN have to be so that $\overline{PR}$ is parallel to $\overline{MN}$? $RN = 14\frac{2}{3}$

5. Use the figure below. Name all pairs of parallel lines and explain why they are parallel. The figure is not necessarily drawn accurately.

$\frac{3}{5} = \frac{9}{15}$, so $\overleftrightarrow{WX} \parallel \overleftrightarrow{VU}$ by the Side-Splitting Converse Theorem.

Uses Objective H

In 6 and 7, use the drawing of the roof below.

6. Given that TO = 6 m, OP = 4 m, TR = 7.2 m, and RE = 4.8 m, are $\overline{OR}$ and $\overline{PE}$ parallel? yes

7. If PE = 12 m, what is the length of the support OR? 7.2

Review

In 15–17, determine from the markings and other information whether the two triangles are similar. If so, indicate the corresponding vertices and state the theorem or definition that justifies your conclusion. *(Lessons 13-1, 13-2)*

15. No judgement can be made.

16. Yes. $\triangle PQR \sim \triangle TSU$ by the AA Similarity Theorem

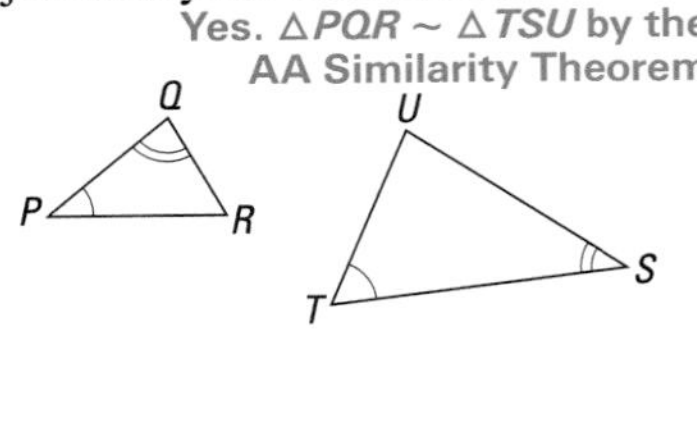

17. $\frac{ST}{XY} = \frac{TO}{YZ} = \frac{OS}{ZX}$ Yes. $\triangle STO \sim \triangle XYZ$ by the SSS Similarity Theorem.

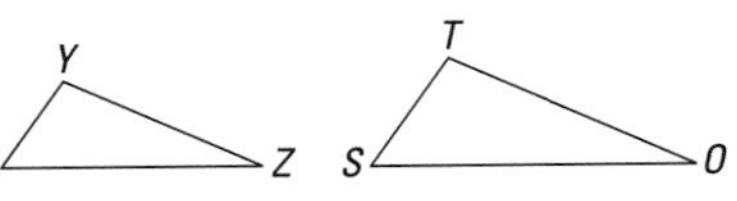

18. In Lesson 13-2, you saw one way to use similar triangles to find the height of a structure. Here is another. Place a mirror on the ground between you and the building. Move until you can see the top of the building in the mirror. Measure the distances d and e and the height h of your eyes from the ground.

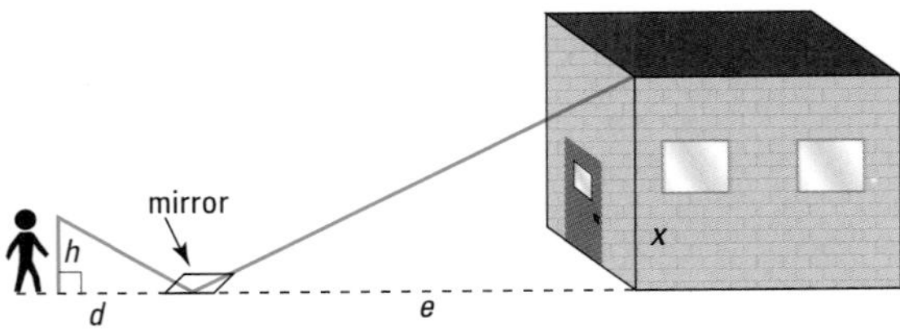

a. Explain why $\frac{x}{h} = \frac{e}{d}$. See left.

b. Henry's eyes are 5′8″ off the ground when he stands 4′3″ from a mirror and sees the top of the building in it. If the mirror is 15′6″ from the building, how tall is the building? *(Lesson 13-2)* 20′8″

18a) because the two triangles involved here are similar by the AA Similarity Theorem

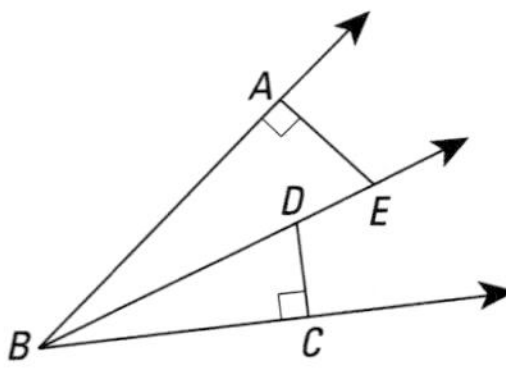

19. Refer to the figure at the left to complete the proof. See margin.

Given: $\overrightarrow{BE}$ bisects $\angle ABC$; $\overline{AE} \perp \overline{AB}$, $\overline{DC} \perp \overline{CB}$.

To prove: $\triangle ABE \sim \triangle CBD$. *(Lesson 13-2)*

20. The fraction $\frac{4}{\sqrt{3}}$ equals $\frac{4}{\sqrt{3}} \cdot \frac{\sqrt{3}}{\sqrt{3}}$, or $\frac{4\sqrt{3}}{3}$. This last form is easier to add to other multiples of $\sqrt{3}$, and is sometimes thought to be simpler. In this way, simplify the following. *(Previous course)*

a. $\frac{5}{\sqrt{3}}$ $\frac{5\sqrt{3}}{3}$

b. $\frac{1}{\sqrt{2}}$ $\frac{\sqrt{2}}{2}$

c. $\frac{3}{\sqrt{6}}$ $\frac{\sqrt{6}}{2}$

21. *Multiple choice.* $\sqrt{75} =$ __?__ a *(Previous course)*

(a) $5\sqrt{3}$ (b) $25\sqrt{3}$ (c) $3\sqrt{5}$ (d) $3\sqrt{25}$

22. *Multiple choice.* $\sqrt{16 + 16} =$ __?__ c *(Previous course)*

(a) $2\sqrt{16}$ (b) $16\sqrt{2}$ (c) $4\sqrt{2}$ (d) 8

Notes on Questions

Question 15 Error Alert Some students may determine that the triangles are not similar. Not enough information is given to make a conclusion.

Question 18 This question is referenced in Project 1 on page 789.

Question 20 What is called *simpler* may not be easier to work with or estimate. Calculators have changed the notion of simplification of square roots. It is now as easy to estimate with a radical in the denominator as with a radical in the numerator.

Questions 20–22 These questions provide a preparation for Lesson 13-5.

Question 23 Some people think this idea can be used to trisect an angle. By having students measure the angles, we show that it does not work.

LESSON MASTER 13-3 B Questions on SPUR Objectives

Vocabulary

In 1 and 2, complete the *Side-Splitting Theorem* and its converse.

1. If a line is __?__ to a side of a triangle and intersects the other two sides in distinct points, it splits these sides into __?__ segments. parallel proportional

2. If a line intersects $\overline{OP}$ and $\overline{OQ}$ in distinct points X and Y so that $\frac{OX}{XP} = \frac{OY}{YQ}$, then $\overline{XY}$ is parallel to $\overline{PQ}$.

3. At the right, draw a picture of the situation in Question 2. Sample: (O, 4, 5, X, Y, 8, 10, P, Q)

Skills Objective A: Find lengths in figures by applying the Side-Splitting Theorem and the Side-Splitting Converse Theorem.

4. Given $\triangle XYZ$ at the right, in which $RS \parallel YZ$, find each missing length.

a. $XR = 8$; $XS = 6$; $XZ = 15$; $XY =$ 20

b. $XS = 6$; $XR = 9$; $XY = 15$; $XZ =$ 10

c. $XS = 6$; $SZ = 4$; $XR = 8$; $RY =$ $5\frac{1}{3}$

d. $XR = 6n$; $RY = 2n$; $XS = 9$; $SZ =$ 3

5. In the diagram at the right, $h \parallel j \parallel k$. Find each missing length.

a. $AC = 9$; $BC = 6$; $DF = 15$; $EF =$ 10

b. $AB = 4$; $BC = 13$; $EF = 39$; $DE =$ 12

c. $AB = 5y$; $DE = 2y$; $EF = 12$; $BC =$ 30

6. Given $\triangle ADM$ at the right, in which $OP \parallel AD$, tell whether each statement is true.

a. $\frac{x}{y} = \frac{z}{w}$ yes

b. $\frac{x+y}{y} = \frac{z+w}{z}$ no

Additional Answers

19.

Conclusions	Justifications
1. $\angle ABE \cong \angle CBD$	def. of angle bisector
2. $\triangle ABE \sim \triangle CBD$	AA Similarity Thm. (step 1 and given)

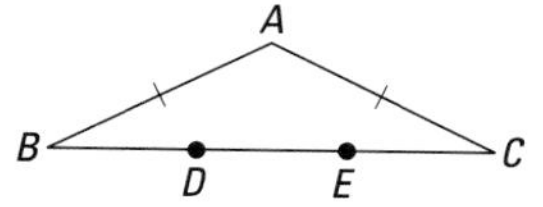

23. In the figure at the left, $AB = AC$ and D and E split $\overline{BC}$ into three congruent segments. Carefully trace the figure (or use an automatic drawer) and draw $\overline{AD}$ and $\overline{AE}$. Do they trisect $\angle BAC$? That is, do they split $\angle BAC$ into three angles of equal measure? Justify your answer.
No, the three angle measures are approximately 30, 70, and 30.

Exploration

24. Here is an algorithm to divide a line segment $\overline{AB}$ into n congruent parts. (The figures show the case $n = 5$.)

Step 1: Draw any ray $\overrightarrow{AC_1}$, that is not collinear with $\overrightarrow{AB}$. For convenience, make C_1 close to A

Step 2: On $\overrightarrow{AC_1}$ mark off n segments of lengths AC_1, so that $AC_1 = C_1C_2 = C_2C_3 = C_3C_4 = C_4C_5 \dots$

Step 3: Draw $\overline{BC_n}$ (here $n = 5$, so $\overline{BC_5}$ is drawn.)

Step 4: Draw parallels to $\overline{BC_n}$ through $C_1, C_2, C_3, \dots$ Let the parallels intersect $\overline{AB}$ at $B_1, B_2, B_3, \dots B_{n-1}$ thus $AB_1 = B_1B_2 = B_2B_3 = \dots = B_{n-1}B$. (In the figure below, $\overline{AB}$ has been divided into five congruent parts.)

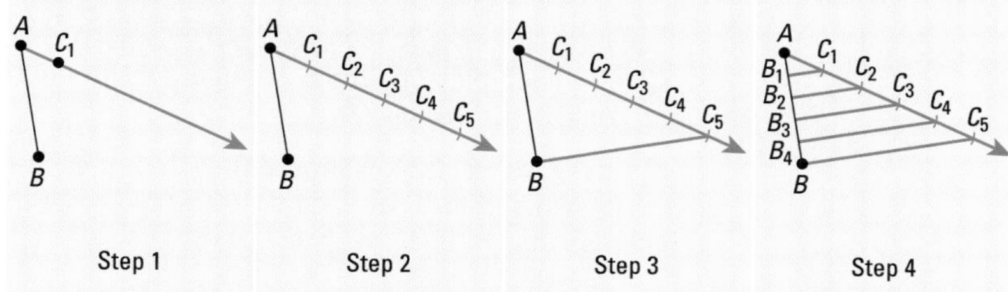

a. Trace $\overline{AB}$ below on a separate sheet of paper. Follow the algorithm to divide $\overline{AB}$ into 7 congruent parts. **See left.**

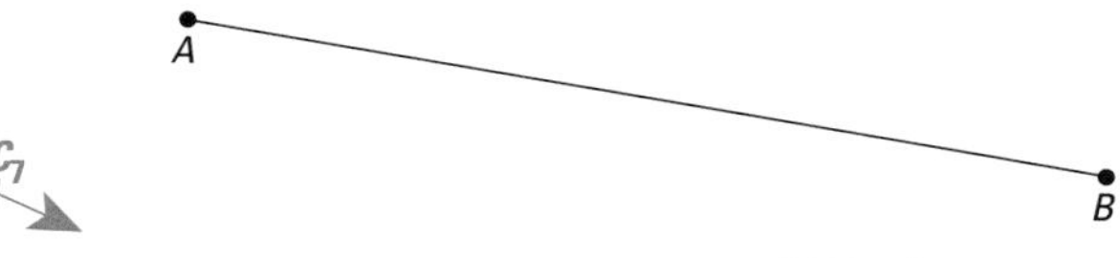

b. How do you know that each part of $\overline{AB}$ is $\frac{1}{7}$ of $\overline{AB}$?
$\frac{AB_1}{AB} = \frac{AC_1}{AC_7} = \frac{1}{7}$ from the AA Similarity Theorem. The other segments have length $\frac{1}{7} \cdot AB$ due to the Side-Splitting Theorem.

24a)

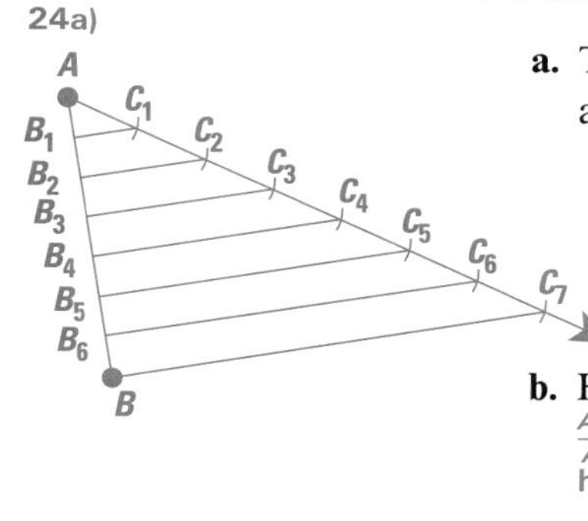

Question 24 This construction enables a person to trisect a *segment,* but the same idea does not work for angles, as **Question 23** shows. It is a standard construction with ruler and compass, but we strongly urge doing this as a drawing, not as a construction. Students know that parallels can be constructed because of the Corresponding Angles Postulate. To construct all of the parallel lines is very time consuming. (Making the corresponding angles congruent will ensure that the lines are parallel.)

Setting Up Lesson 13-4

Be certain to discuss **Questions 20–22.** They review some arithmetic that is useful when discussing special triangles.

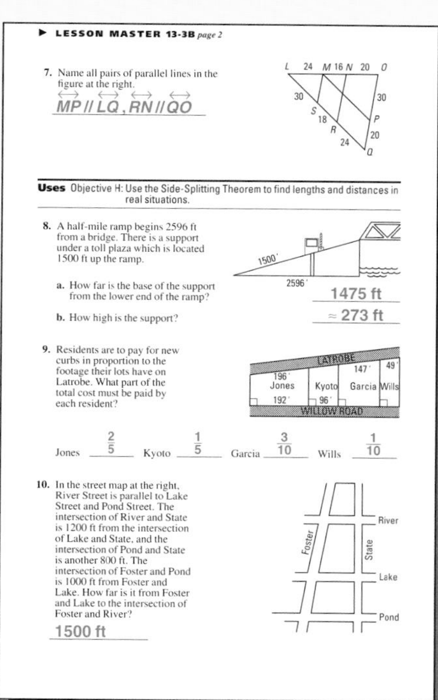

LESSON MASTER 13-3B *page 2*

7. Name all pairs of parallel lines in the figure at the right.
$\overleftrightarrow{MP} \parallel \overleftrightarrow{LQ}$, $\overleftrightarrow{RN} \parallel \overleftrightarrow{QO}$

Uses Objective H: Use the Side-Splitting Theorem to find lengths and distances in real situations.

8. A half-mile ramp begins 2596 ft from a bridge. There is a support under a toll plaza which is located 1500 ft up the ramp.

a. How far is the base of the support from the lower end of the ramp? 1475 ft

b. How high is the support? ≈ 273 ft

9. Residents are to pay for new curbs in proportion to the footage their lots have on Latrobe. What part of the total cost must be paid by each resident?

Jones $\frac{2}{5}$ Kyoto $\frac{1}{5}$ Garcia $\frac{3}{10}$ Wills $\frac{1}{10}$

10. In the street map at the right, River Street is parallel to Lake Street and Pond Street. The intersection of River and State is 1200 ft from the intersection of Lake and State, and the intersection of Pond and State is another 800 ft. The intersection of Foster and Pond is 1000 ft from Foster and Lake. How far is it from Foster and Lake to the intersection of Foster and River?
1500 ft

In-class Activity

Resources

From the ***Teacher's Resource File***

- Answer Master 13-4

This In-class Activity has students investigate the relationships among lengths in a right triangle when an altitude is drawn to the hypotenuse.

When an altitude is drawn from the largest angle in any triangle, it falls within the triangle. But it does not form two similar triangles unless the original triangle is isosceles and the angle is the vertex angle, in which case the two triangles formed are congruent. But these triangles are not similar to the original unless the original triangle is a right triangle. So the right triangle is truly special, and the fact that one gets similar triangles by drawing the altitude is not at all obvious.

You should have students measure to check that the ratios of sides that they identify in Step 5 are equal.

Have students record the results of this In-class Activity for use with **Question 1** on page 762.

Introducing Lesson 13-4

Similarity in Right Triangles

IN-CLASS ACTIVITY

Work with a partner. For this activity, both of you will need a ruler, protractor, and compass.

B, D, C, A

1 Trace right $\triangle ABC$ at the right or draw one like it. Measure $\angle A$ and $\angle B$. m$\angle A$ = 58 m$\angle B$ = 32

2 Draw $\overline{CD}$, the altitude to hypotenuse $\overline{AB}$. See right.

3 Use a protractor to determine these four angle measures.

a. m$\angle CDB$ 90 **b.** m$\angle CDA$ 90

c. m$\angle DCB$ 58 **d.** m$\angle DCA$ 32

4 There are three triangles in your figure. Which pairs of triangles are similar? For each pair write the similarity correspondences with the vertices in correct order. $\triangle CDA \sim \triangle BCA$, $\triangle BCA \sim \triangle BDC$, $\triangle CDA \sim \triangle BDC$

5 For each pair of similar triangles, write the three equal ratios of the sides. See below.

6 In Question 5, you should find that in each set of ratios, one side appears twice. For each set of ratios, write the proportion that includes that side. 5, 6) $\frac{CD}{BC} = \frac{DA}{CA} = \frac{CA}{BA}$; $\frac{DA}{CA} = \frac{CA}{BA}$. $\frac{BC}{BD} = \frac{BA}{BC} = \frac{CA}{DC}$; $\frac{BC}{BD} = \frac{BA}{BC}$. $\frac{CD}{BD} = \frac{DA}{DC} = \frac{CA}{BC}$; $\frac{CD}{BD} = \frac{DA}{DC}$.

LESSON

13-4

Geometric Means in Right Triangles

Right triangles mean stronger buildings. *These prefabricated house frames reduce the length of time it takes to build a house.*

You may recall that the average of two numbers is also called their **arithmetic mean.** It is the coordinate of the midpoint of two points on a number line. In this lesson, you will learn about another kind of mean, the *geometric mean.* The geometric mean appears in surprising places.

What Is the Geometric Mean?

It is possible for the two means in a proportion to be equal, as in

$$\frac{2}{10} = \frac{10}{50}.$$

When this happens, the number that appears twice is called a geometric mean of the other two numbers. In the proportion above, 10 is a geometric mean of 2 and 50. In this course, we are interested only in positive geometric means of positive numbers.

> **Definition**
> Let a, b, and g be positive numbers. g is the **geometric mean** of a and b if and only if
> $$\frac{a}{g} = \frac{g}{b}.$$

If g is the geometric mean of a and b, then $\frac{a}{g} = \frac{g}{b}$. Then by the Means-Extremes Property $g^2 = ab$. So $g = \pm\sqrt{ab}$. Thus $\sqrt{ab}$ is the positive geometric mean. This is a proof argument for the following theorem.

> **Geometric Mean Theorem**
> The positive geometric mean of the positive numbers a and b is $\sqrt{ab}$.

Lesson 13-4

Objectives

B Calculate lengths using the Right-Triangle Altitude Theorem.

Resources

From the ***Teacher's Resource File***

- Lesson Master 13-4A or 13-4B
- Answer Master 13-4
- Teaching Aids
  - 172 Warm-up
  - 177 Similar Triangles Within a Right Triangle
  - 178 Additional Examples

Additional Resources

- Visuals for Teaching Aids 172, 177–178

Teaching Lesson 13-4

Warm-up

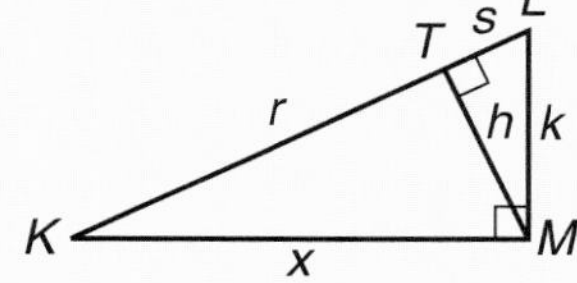

For each triangle in the figure above, name the ratio of the longer leg to the shorter leg.

$\triangle KML$: $\frac{x}{k}$; $\triangle KMT$: $\frac{r}{h}$; $\triangle MTL$: $\frac{h}{s}$

Notes on Reading

Students are asked to give a proof in *Challenge* on page 763 that the arithmetic mean A is larger than the geometric mean G unless the two given numbers are equal.

Lesson 13-4 Overview

Broad Goals This lesson considers the relationship of the altitude of a right triangle to the legs and segments of the hypotenuse.

Perspective The geometric mean is related to multiplication in the same way that the arithmetic mean is related to addition.

(1) If G is the geometric mean of x and y, then $G \cdot G = x \cdot y$. Analogously, if A is the arithmetic mean of a and b, then $A + A = a + b$.

(2) Take any three consecutive terms of a geometric (exponential) sequence, such as 6, 18, 54. Then the middle term is the geometric mean of the other two. Take any three consecutive terms of an arithmetic (linear) sequence, such as 6, 11, 16. Then the middle term is the arithmetic mean of the other two.

(3) The geometric mean of n positive numbers (not defined in the text) is the nth root of their product. The arithmetic mean of n numbers is their sum divided by n.

When the altitude to the hypotenuse of a right triangle is drawn, the resulting figure has two smaller triangles, each similar to the original and to each other. The result from this splitting is that segments have some very nice relationships, all involving geometric

(Overview continues on page 760.)

❶ Activity 2 in *Optional Activities* on page 761 relates to this section of the reading.

❷ If we draw a right triangle like the one in **Example 2,** it is easier to remember the relationships of the Right-Triangle Altitude Theorem. Any one of the three segments drawn from the vertex C can be the geometric mean of two other segments in the figure. In general, if the other endpoint of the geometric-mean segment is X, then the two other segments are those segments of the hypotenuse with endpoint X. For example, when X is D, then CD is the geometric mean of AD and BD. When X is A, then CA is the geometric mean of DA and BA.

Stress the similarity relationship between the triangles formed by the altitude to the hypotenuse of a right triangle, and show students how the proportions are derived. You may want to use **Teaching Aid 177** which contains the figures. The algebraic relationships in the Right-Triangle Altitude Theorem are based on these proportions.

Point out that geometric means have applications outside of geometry. That is, the geometric mean is the "middle of growth" in any exponential growth situation. For example, if a population is growing exponentially and is x in year t_1 and y in year t_2, then it is $\sqrt{xy}$ in year $\frac{t_1 + t_2}{2}$, the middle year. You might also connect this content with the product of square roots in algebra; the geometric mean application is one reason why the expression $\sqrt{xy}$ is important, and why one learns to simplify $\sqrt{xy}$ as $\sqrt{x}\sqrt{y}$. Students of UCSMP *Algebra* have seen both of these applications.

Example 1

Find the geometric mean of 7 and 12.

Solution

Let g be the geometric mean. Using the Geometric Mean Theorem,

$$g = \sqrt{7 \cdot 12}$$
$$= \sqrt{84}$$

The geometric mean of 7 and 12 is $\sqrt{84}$.

Check

Use the definition of geometric mean. $\sqrt{84}$ is about 9.17. Is $\frac{7}{9.17} \approx \frac{9.17}{12}$? Yes, $0.7634 \approx 0.7642$.

The arithmetic mean of a and b is exactly halfway between them. The geometric mean, $\sqrt{ab}$, is also always between a and b. But it is equal to the arithmetic mean of a and b only if $a = b$; otherwise, it is smaller than the arithmetic mean. Both arithmetic and geometric means have applications in arithmetic, algebra, and geometry.

❶ Similar Triangles Within a Right Triangle

The name "geometric mean" comes from relationships among lengths in any right triangle. These relationships were discovered by the ancient Greeks and are described in Euclid's *Elements*. The proofs of these relationships depend mainly on the AA Similarity Theorem.

$\triangle ABC$ below at the left is split into two triangles, CBD and ACD, by drawing $\overline{CD}$, the altitude to its hypotenuse, as in the In-class Activity. We use the small letters a and b for the lengths of the legs of right $\triangle ABC$, and c for its hypotenuse. The letter h is the altitude to the hypotenuse. The point where the altitude intersects the hypotenuse splits it into two lengths, x and y, so $x + y = c$.

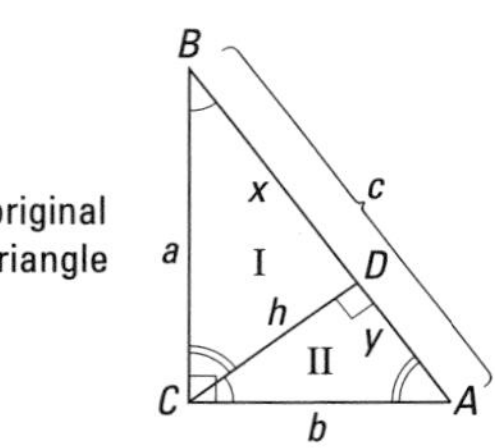

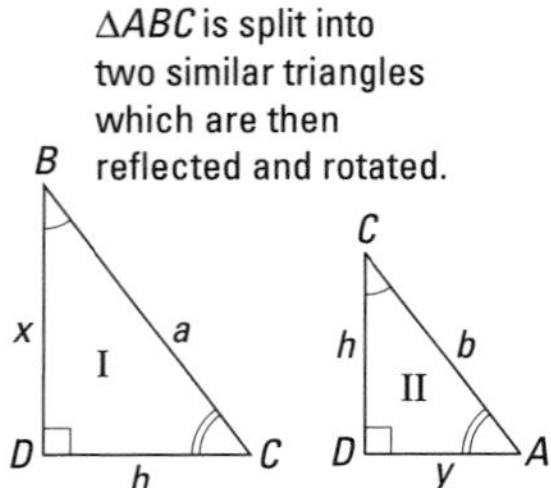

$m\angle A = m\angle BCD$, since both angles are complements of $\angle B$. So $\triangle$I, $\triangle$II, and $\triangle ABC$ are all right triangles, and each includes an angle equal in measure to $\angle A$. Thus, by the AA Similarity Theorem, all three triangles are similar: $\triangle ABC \sim \triangle CBD \sim \triangle ACD$. Since the triangles are similar, corresponding sides are proportional.

Lesson 13-4 Overview, continued

means and summarized in the Right-Triangle Altitude Theorem. This theorem has two parts but gives rise to three relationships in any triangle because there are two legs. The Right-Triangle Altitude Theorem also provides an alternate way to deduce the Pythagorean Theorem. Since the Pythagorean Theorem was proved in Chapter 8, the alternate proof is relegated to the questions.

Optional Activities

Activity 1 After discussing **Question 12,** you might show students how the Right-Triangle Altitude Theorem can be deduced from the Pythagorean Theorem. Use the figure above **Example 2** on page 761.

	Statement	Reason
(1)	$a^2 + b^2 = c^2$	(1–3) Pythagorean Theorem
(2)	$h^2 + x^2 = a^2$	
(3)	$h^2 + y^2 = b^2$	
(4)	$x + y = c$	Given
(5)	$x^2 + 2xy + y^2 = c^2$	Square (4).
(6)	$2h^2 + x^2 + y^2 = a^2 + b^2$	Add (2) and (3).
(7)	$2h^2 + x^2 + y^2 = c^2$	Substitute using (1).
(8)	$2h^2 + x^2 + y^2 = x^2 + 2xy + y^2$	Equate (5) and (7).
(9)	$2h^2 = 2xy$; $h^2 = xy$; $h = \sqrt{xy}$	Subtract $x^2 + y^2$ and solve for h. (Part 1 of Theorem)
(10)	$xy + x^2 = a^2$; $x(y + x) = a^2$; solve $xc = a^2$; $a = \sqrt{xc}$	Substitute xy for h^2 in (2), use (4), and solve for a. (Part 2 of Theorem)

Now look for proportions in which the same quantity appears twice. Consider $\triangle$I and $\triangle$II. Both have the side $\overline{CD}$ with length h.

$$\frac{BD}{CD} = \frac{CD}{AD}, \text{ or } \frac{x}{h} = \frac{h}{y}.$$

For $\triangle$I and $\triangle ABC$, $\overline{BC}$ is a side in both. $\frac{BD}{BC} = \frac{BC}{AB}$. For $\triangle$I and $\triangle ABC$, $\overline{AC}$ is a side in both. $\frac{AD}{AC} = \frac{AC}{AB}$. Thus,

$$\frac{x}{a} = \frac{a}{c} \quad \text{and} \quad \frac{y}{b} = \frac{b}{c}.$$

Thus in $\triangle ABC$, the altitude h and the legs a and b are geometric means of other lengths. This argument proves the following theorem:

Right-Triangle Altitude Theorem
In a right triangle,
(1) the altitude to the hypotenuse is the geometric mean of the segments into which it divides the hypotenuse, and
(2) each leg is the geometric mean of the hypotenuse and the segment of the hypotenuse adjacent to the leg.

Using the Geometric Mean Theorem, $h = \sqrt{xy}$, $a = \sqrt{cx}$, and $b = \sqrt{cy}$.

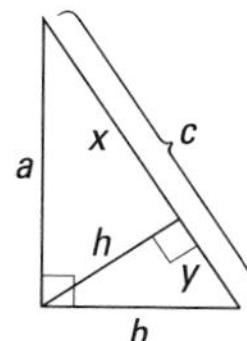

Notice the patterns of letters in these equations and in the solution to Example 2.

❷ Example 2

CD is the altitude to the hypotenuse of right triangle ABC, as shown below. If $AD = 3$ and $BD = 12$, find CD, CA, and CB.

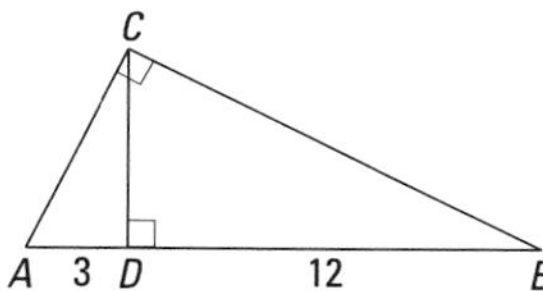

Solution

CD is the geometric mean of AD and BD.
So $CD = \sqrt{AD \cdot BD} = \sqrt{3 \cdot 12} = \sqrt{36} = 6$.
CA is the geometric mean of DA and BA.
So $CA = \sqrt{DA \cdot BA} = \sqrt{3 \cdot 15} = \sqrt{45} = 3\sqrt{5}$.
CB is the geometric mean of DB and AB.
So $CB = \sqrt{DB \cdot AB} = \sqrt{12 \cdot 15} = \sqrt{180} = 6\sqrt{5}$.

Likewise, the common average—the arithmetic mean—has applications in geometry. In Chapter 11, students saw that the coordinates of a segment's midpoint on a number line, in a plane, or in space is the arithmetic mean of the coordinates of the endpoints.

Additional Examples

These examples are also given on **Teaching Aid 178.**

1. Find the difference between the geometric mean of 4 and 6 and the arithmetic mean of 4 and 6.
   $5 - \sqrt{24}$, or about 0.101 (The arithmetic mean of two unequal numbers is always greater than the geometric mean.)
2. The altitude to the hypotenuse of a right triangle splits the hypotenuse into segments of lengths 6 and 7.

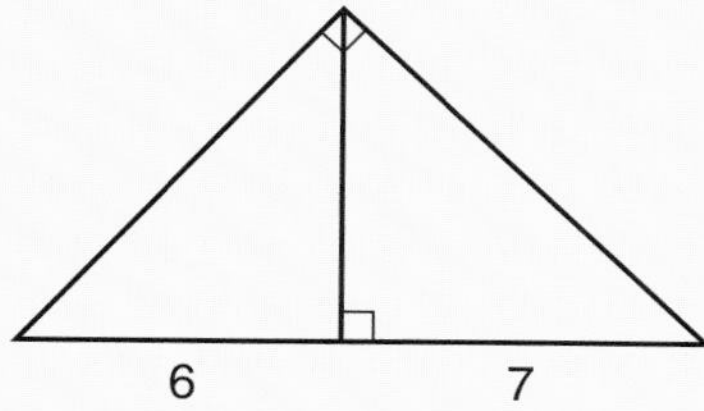

   a. What are the lengths of the legs of the triangle?
   $\sqrt{78}$ and $\sqrt{91}$
   b. What is the length of the altitude to the hypotenuse?
   $\sqrt{42}$

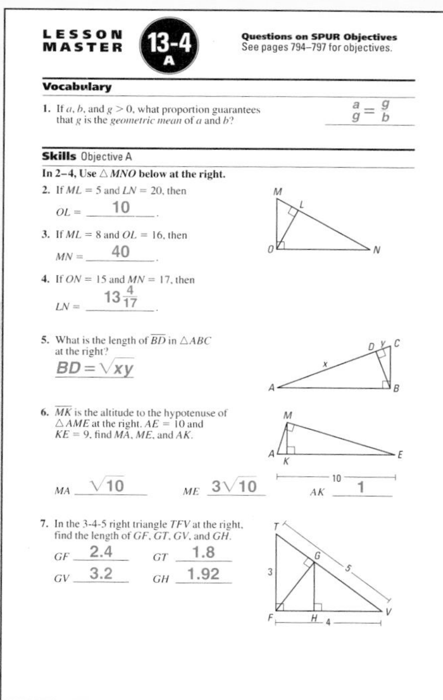

LESSON MASTER 13-4 A

Questions on SPUR Objectives
See pages 794–797 for objectives.

Vocabulary

1. If a, b, and $g > 0$, what proportion guarantees that g is the *geometric mean* of a and b? $\frac{a}{g} = \frac{g}{b}$

Skills Objective A

In 2–4, Use $\triangle MNO$ below at the right.

2. If $ML = 5$ and $LN = 20$, then $OL =$ 10.
3. If $ML = 8$ and $OL = 16$, then $MN =$ 40.
4. If $ON = 15$ and $MN = 17$, then $LN =$ $13\frac{4}{17}$.
5. What is the length of $\overline{BD}$ in $\triangle ABC$ at the right? $BD = \sqrt{xy}$
6. $\overline{MK}$ is the altitude to the hypotenuse of $\triangle AME$ at the right. $AE = 10$ and $KE = 9$, find MA, ME, and AK.
   MA $\sqrt{10}$ ME $3\sqrt{10}$ AK 1
7. In the 3-4-5 right triangle TFV at the right, find the length of GF, GT, GV, and GH.
   GF 2.4 GT 1.8
   GV 3.2 GH 1.92

Optional Activities

Activity 2

You might extend the section *Similar Triangles Within a Right Triangle* on page 760 by having students begin with right triangles of different sizes and shapes. Have them verify that the theorem applies to any right triangle. They should verify both parts of the Right-Triangle Altitude Theorem for their triangles.

Notes on Questions

Questions 5–7 Cooperative Learning You might want to have students go over these questions in a group. They should pay careful attention to the correspondences between vertices and then set up all the ratios using segments in the proportions.

Question 11 History Connection The boy scout and girl guide movements originated in England at the turn of the century by Lord Baden-Powell. The principles of Girl Guiding, as it was then called, were brought to the United States by Juliette Gordon Low of Savannah, Georgia. She organized the first troop on March 12, 1912. Today, with 3 million members, the Girl Scouts of the USA is the largest voluntary organization for girls in the world.

Question 12 Remind students that in this book the Pythagorean Theorem was first deduced in Chapter 8 from properties of area. The argument in this question using the Right-Triangle Altitude Theorem is a second common way by which the Pythagorean Theorem is deduced. Conversely, the Right-Triangle Altitude Theorem can be deduced from the Pythagorean Theorem as shown in Activity 1 in *Optional Activities,* on page 760.

(Notes on Questions continue on page 764.)

LESSON MASTER 13-4 B **Questions on SPUR Objectives**

Vocabulary

In 1 and 2, given the positive numbers a and b,

1. define the *geometric mean.* $g > 0$ such that $\frac{a}{g} = \frac{g}{b}$
2. define the *arithmetic mean.* $\frac{a + b}{2}$
3. For the set {4, 9}, find the
   a. arithmetic mean. 6.5 b. the geometric mean. 6
4. State the *Right-Triangle Altitude Theorem.* In a right △, the altitude to the hypotenuse is the geometric mean of the segments into which it divides the hypotenuse, and each leg is the geometric mean of the hypotenuse and the segment of the hypotenuse adjacent to the leg.

Skills Objective B: Calculate lengths using the Right-Triangle Altitude Theorem.

5. Given $\triangle MOP$ at the right, find each length.
   a. $MP = 3$; $MN = 12$; $MO =$ 6
   b. $PN = 4$; $MN = 9$; $ON =$ 6
   c. $PN = 28$; $PM = 7$; $OP =$ 14
   d. $OP = 8$; $MP = NP$; $MN =$ 16
6. Given the diagram at the right, find each length.
   a. $a = 30$; $c = 50$; $h =$ 24
   b. $h = 12$; $m = 9$; $b =$ 20
   c. $a = 24$; $m = 4$; $b =$ ≈ 142.0
   d. $b = 8$; $m = 12$; $c =$ 16
7. Find d in the diagram at the right.
   $d = 6\frac{2}{3}$

QUESTIONS

Covering the Reading

1) See page 758.

1. Give your answer to Parts 3–6 of the In-class Activity on page 758.

In 2 and 3, find the geometric mean of the given numbers to the nearest hundredth.

2. 2 and 50 10.00
3. 9 and 12 10.39

4. *True or false.* If g is the geometric mean of a and b, and $a < b$, then g is closer to a than to b. True

In 5–7, use the figure at the right.

5. a. $m\angle P = m\angle$ ___?___ QRS
   b. $\triangle PRQ \sim$ ___?___ $\sim$ ___?___ $\triangle RSQ$, $\triangle PSR$
   c. $\frac{QS}{RQ} = \frac{RQ}{?}$ PQ
   d. $\frac{QS}{?} = \frac{RS}{PS}$ RS
   e. RP is the geometric mean of ___?___ and ___?___. PQ, PS
   f. RS is the geometric mean of ___?___ and ___?___. PS, SQ
   g. RQ is the geometric mean of ___?___ and ___?___. PQ, SQ
6. If $RS = 6$ and $PS = 9$, then $QS =$ ___?___. 4
7. If $RS = 6$ and $SQ = 4$, then $QR =$ ___?___. $\sqrt{52} \approx 7.21$
8. Using the diagram at the right find each length.
   a. NC 13
   b. CE $\frac{25}{13} \approx 1.92$
   c. IE $\frac{60}{13} \approx 4.62$

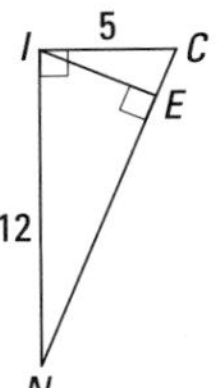

Applying the Mathematics

9) $x = \frac{16}{5} = 3.2$, $y = \frac{9}{5} = 1.8$, $h = \frac{12}{5} = 2.4$

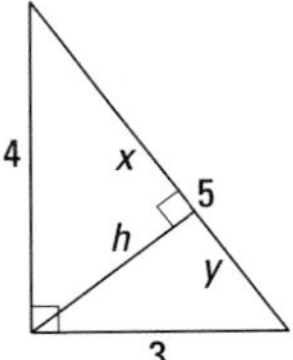

9. At the left is the famous 3-4-5 right triangle. The altitude to the hypotenuse has been drawn. Find the lengths of x, y, and h. See left.
10. *True or false.* Refer to the figure at the right.
    a. $\triangle QRT \sim \triangle RST$ True
    b. $m\angle QRS = 90$ True

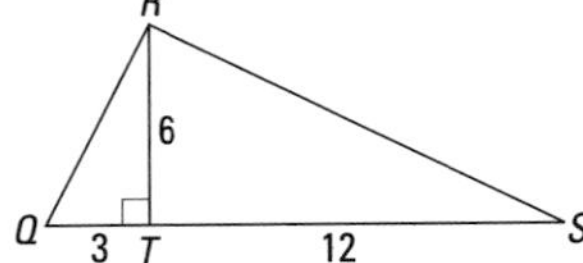

762

Adapting to Individual Needs

Extra Help

It may be confusing to some students that when $\triangle ABC \sim \triangle CBD \sim \triangle ACD$, the angle with vertex C is a different angle in each of the triangles. This becomes more obvious when each angle is named by three letters rather than just the vertex.

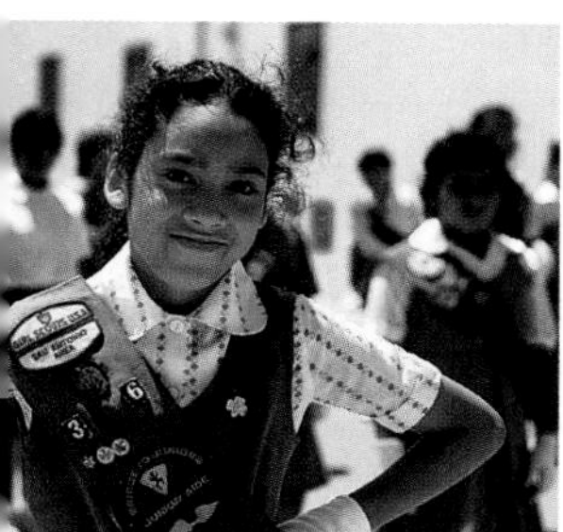

11. Nancy taught the members of Girl Scout Troop 36 that they could use a notebook to estimate distances. To show them how, she used the lifeguard tower at Henson Beach. She held the corner of her notebook near her eye (5 feet off the ground) and moved back from the tower until she could sight both the top and bottom of the tower along with two adjacent edges of the notebook. Then she asked her friend Amy to measure her (Nancy's) distance from the tower by pacing. Amy measured the distance as 8 feet.

a. Which part of the Right-Triangle Altitude Theorem could Nancy now use to estimate the height of the lifeguard tower? part (1)

b. How tall is the tower? ≈ 17.8 feet

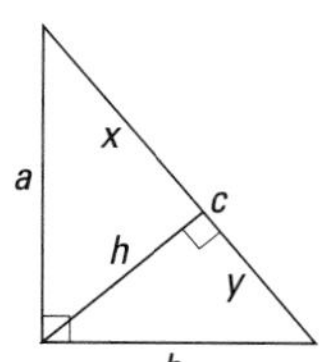

12. Provide the missing justifications in this argument proving the Pythagorean Theorem. See left.

Given: The right triangle at the left with lengths as indicated.

To prove: $a^2 + b^2 = c^2$.

Argument:

Conclusions	Justifications
1. a is the geometric mean of c and x; b is the geometric mean of c and y.	**a.**
2. $a = \sqrt{cx}$, $b = \sqrt{cy}$	**b.**
3. $a^2 = cx$, $b^2 = cy$	Multiplication Property of Equality
4. $a^2 + b^2 = cx + cy$	**c.**
5. $a^2 + b^2 = c(x + y)$	**d.**
6. $x + y = c$	Betweenness Theorem
7. $a^2 + b^2 = c^2$	**e.**

12a) Right Triangle Altitude Thm.
b) Geometric Mean Theorem
c) Addition Prop. of Equality
d) Distributive Property
e) Substitution Prop. of Equality

13. The altitude $\overline{CD}$ of right triangle ABC splits the hypotenuse into segments of lengths 6 and 9. Find the lengths of the altitude and the two legs.

$a = 3\sqrt{10}$, $b = 3\sqrt{15}$, $CD = 3\sqrt{6}$

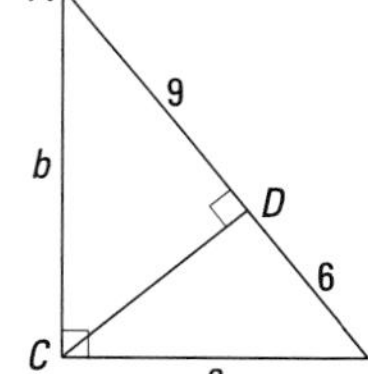

Follow-up for Lesson 13-4

Practice

For more questions on SPUR Objectives, use **Lesson Master 13-4A** (shown on page 761) or **Lesson Master 13-4B** (shown on pages 762–763).

Assessment

Written Communication Have students write a paragraph explaining how a geometric mean differs from an arithmetic mean and have them give an example of each. [Students give a clear explanation to differentiate the arithmetic mean and the geometric mean and then give a correct example of each type of mean.]

(Follow-up continues on page 764.)

Adapting to Individual Needs

Challenge

The geometric mean of two positive numbers is always less than the arithmetic mean, unless the two numbers are equal. Have students fill in the reasons in the proof.

Given: x and y are positive. To prove: $\frac{x+y}{2} \geq \sqrt{xy}$

Conclusions	Justifications
1. $(x - y)^2 \geq 0$	[Sq. of real nos. are not negative]
2. $x^2 - 2xy + y^2 \geq 0$	[Dist. Prop.]
3. $x^2 + 2xy + y^2 \geq 4xy$	[Add. Prop. of Equality]
4. $(x + y)^2 \geq 4xy$	[Dist. Prop. (Factoring)]
5. $\frac{(x+y)^2}{4} \geq xy$	[Mult. Prop. of Eq.]
6. $\sqrt{\frac{(x+y)^2}{4}} \geq \sqrt{xy}$	[If $a > b > 0$, then $\sqrt{a} > \sqrt{b}$]
7. $\frac{x+y}{2} \geq \sqrt{xy}$	[Def. of square root]

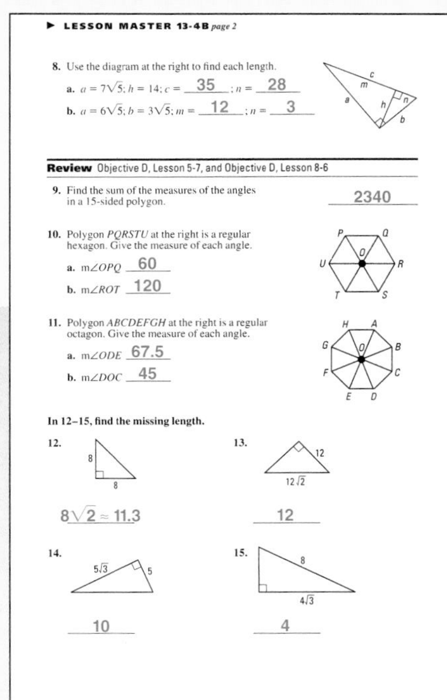

▶ LESSON MASTER 13-4B *page 2*

8. Use the diagram at the right to find each length.

a. $a = 7\sqrt{5}$; $h = 14$; $c =$ 35 ; $n =$ 28

b. $a = 6\sqrt{5}$; $b = 3\sqrt{5}$; $m =$ 12 ; $n =$ 3

Review Objective D, Lesson 5-7, and Objective D, Lesson 8-6

9. Find the sum of the measures of the angles in a 15-sided polygon. 2340

10. Polygon $PQRSTU$ at the right is a regular hexagon. Give the measure of each angle.

a. m∠OPQ 60

b. m∠ROT 120

11. Polygon $ABCDEFGH$ at the right is a regular octagon. Give the measure of each angle.

a. m∠ODE 67.5

b. m∠DOC 45

In 12–15, find the missing length.

12. $8\sqrt{2} \approx 11.3$

13. 12

14. 10

15. 4

Extension

After drawing the altitude to the hypotenuse of a right triangle, demonstrate that if an altitude is drawn to the hypotenuse of one of the *smaller* triangles, then the original triangle has been split into three similar triangles. Ask students how a right triangle can be split into any number of similar triangles. [Draw altitudes to the hypotenuse of the successively smaller triangles.]

All triangles can be split into four similar triangles by connecting the midpoints of the sides. Ask students how many similar triangles can be formed by connecting the midpoints of one of the smaller triangles. (The original triangle can be split into 7 similar triangles, and by continuing the process, one can get 10, 13, 16, . . . similar triangles.)

It can be proved that the only triangles that can be split into two or three triangles similar to themselves and the original are right triangles. The proof is not difficult but is by no means trivial; one must consider all possible ways in which a triangle can be split. There is only one triangle other than a right triangle that can be split into *five* triangles similar to itself, the 30-30-120 triangle. You might ask students if they can find out how to do the splitting. The answer is below.

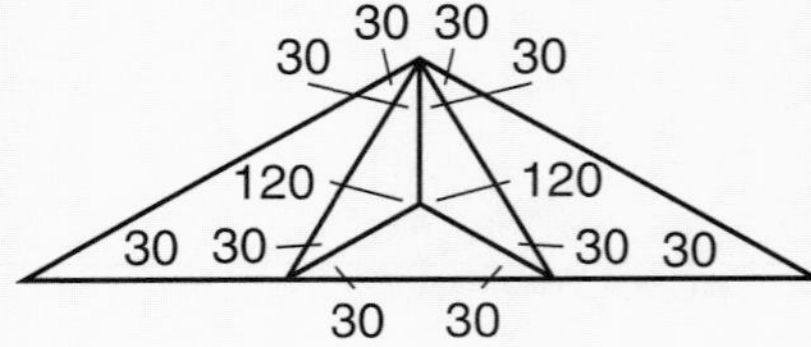

Notes on Questions

Question 23 In general, if x is positive, then $x^{\frac{a+b}{2}}$ is the positive geometric mean of x^a and x^b.

Question 24 Ask students to draw figures which can be used to compare with other students and to explain their conclusions.

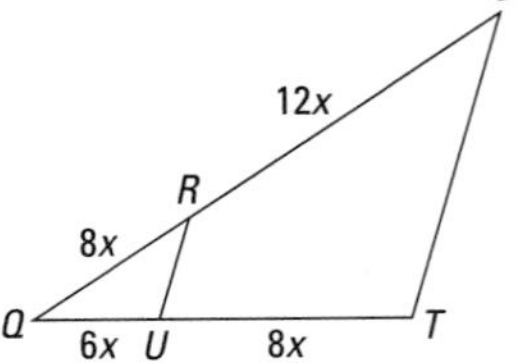

Review

14. Refer to the figure at the left. Is $\overline{RU} \parallel \overline{ST}$? Explain your answer. *(Lesson 13-3)* No; because $\frac{6x}{8x} \neq \frac{8x}{12x}$

15. Write the proof argument.
Given: $WXYZ$ at the right is a trapezoid with bases $\overline{WX}$ and $\overline{YZ}$.
To prove: $\triangle WXU \sim \triangle YZU$. *(Lesson 13-2)*
See margin.

In 16–18, each figure contains two triangles.
a. Are the triangles similar?
b. If so, which similarity theorem justifies their similarity?
c. Write the similarity with vertices in correct order. *(Lessons 13-1, 13-2)*

16.

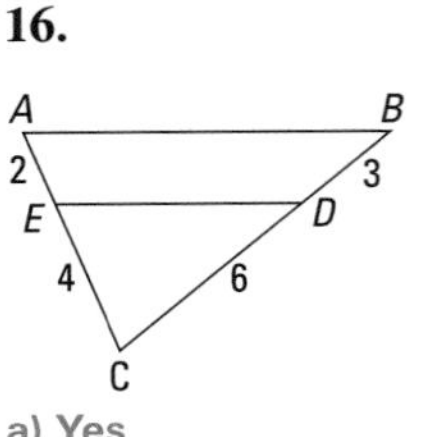

a) Yes
b) SAS Similarity Theorem
c) $\triangle CED \sim \triangle CAB$

17. a) No

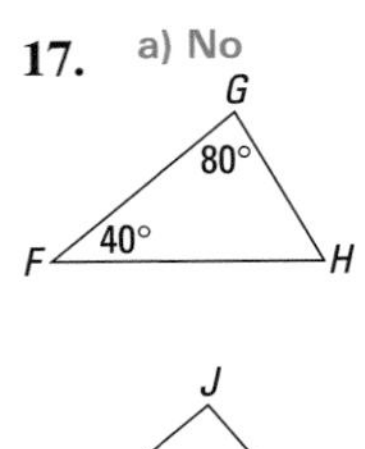

18.

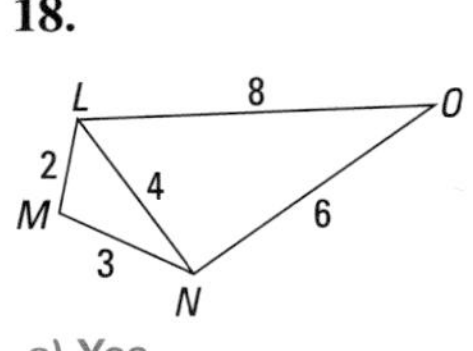

a) Yes
b) SSS Similarity Theorem
c) $\triangle LMN \sim \triangle LNO$

19. In the box at the left, suppose all the vertices are connected.
a. How many other segments have the same length as $\overline{AC}$? 3
b. How many other segments have the same length as $\overline{AG}$? 3
c. A 75-cm rod just fits in a carton whose inner dimensions are 60 cm by 40 cm by 24 cm. In how many positions will the rod fit? *(Lessons 9-2, 11-9)* 4

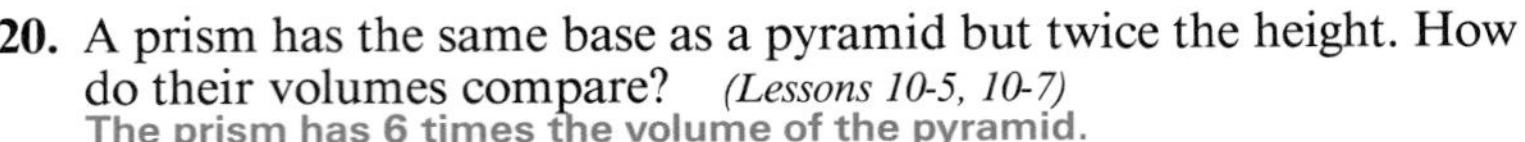

20. A prism has the same base as a pyramid but twice the height. How do their volumes compare? *(Lessons 10-5, 10-7)*
The prism has 6 times the volume of the pyramid.

21. In Question 12, why is it inappropriate to use the Pythagorean Theorem as the justification for Conclusion 7? *(Lesson 5-2)*
It is circular reasoning to use a theorem to prove itself.

22. a. Write a fraction equal to $\frac{1}{\sqrt{3}}$ with no radical sign in its denominator. $\frac{\sqrt{3}}{3}$
b. Round $\frac{1}{\sqrt{3}}$ to the nearest millionth. *(Previous course)* 0.577350

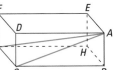

23a) Given the first ten positive integer powers of 2: 2, 4, 8, 16, 32, 64, 128, 256, 512, 1024, the powers 4, 8, 16, 32, 64, 128, 256, 512 are geometric means of other powers in the list.

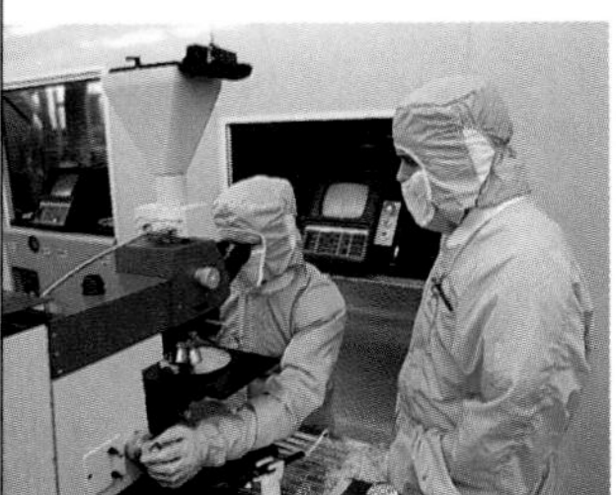

Two power. *Technicians in this "clean-room" dress as surgeons to prevent environmental contamination of computer chips. A computer's capacity for memory is expressed in powers of 2.*

Exploration

23. List the first ten positive integer powers of 2. a) See left.
a. Which of these are geometric means of other powers in your list.
b. Find a pattern which predicts when one power of a number is a geometric mean of other powers of that number.
Sample: a^n is a geometric mean of a^{n-1} and a^{n+1}.

24. Given: scalene $\triangle ABC$ such that $\angle C$ is *not* a right angle. Is it possible to find a point D on $\overline{AB}$ so that $\overline{CD}$ splits $\triangle ABC$ into 2 smaller similar triangles? Why or why not? See margin.

Additional Answers

15.

Conclusions	Justifications
1. $\overline{WX} \parallel \overline{ZY}$	def. of trapezoid
2. $\angle XWU \cong \angle ZYU$, $\angle WXU \cong \angle YZU$	// lines ⇒ AIA ≅ Thm.
3. $\triangle WXU \sim \triangle YZU$	AA Similarity Thm.

24. No, it is impossible, because if the two angles at D have different measures, then they must not be corresponding angles, and so their measures are the measures of two angles of each triangle. But these two measures add to 180, leaving no measure for the third angle.

LESSON

13-5

Special Right Triangles

Baseball Square. *Shown is Wrigley Field, home of the Chicago Cubs. See Example 1*

Certain right triangles have such relationships among their sides and angles that they are considered special.

Properties of Isosceles Right Triangles

By drawing the diagonals of a square, eight isosceles right triangles are formed. (Can you find all eight?) Notice that all isosceles right triangles are similar, because they all have the same angles: 45°, 45°, and 90°. Sometimes they are called **45-45-90 triangles.** In a 45-45-90 triangle, if you know the length of one side, you can find the lengths of the others. Suppose the congruent sides of one of these triangles have length x and the hypotenuse has length c, as in the triangle at the right below.

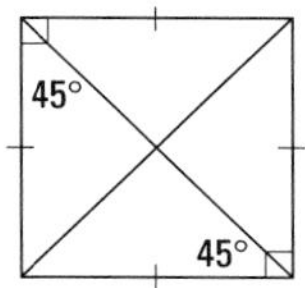

By the Pythagorean theorem $c^2 = x^2 + x^2$.
So $c^2 = 2x^2$.
Taking the positive square root, $c = x \cdot \sqrt{2}$.

The result is a relationship among the sides of any isosceles right triangle.

Isosceles Right Triangle Theorem
In an isosceles right triangle, if a leg is x, then the hypotenuse is $x\sqrt{2}$.

Lesson 13-5

Objectives

C Calculate lengths of sides in isosceles right triangles and in 30-60-90 triangles.

Resources

From the ***Teacher's Resource File***
- Lesson Master 13-5A or 13-5B
- Answer Master 13-5
- Teaching Aids
  172 Warm-up
  179 Additional Examples
- Activity Kit, Activity 27

Additional Resources
- Visuals for Teaching Aids 172, 179

Teaching Lesson 13-5

Warm-up

How many squares of different sizes are shown in the figure below? What are their areas? Assume the large square is 3 units on a side.

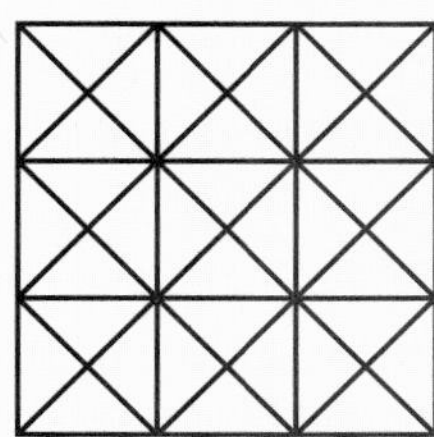

31; The smallest squares are the 12 with area $\frac{1}{2}$. Their sides are $\sqrt{\frac{1}{2}}$,

(Warm-up continues on page 766.)

Lesson 13-5 Overview

Broad Goals This lesson considers the ratios of lengths of sides in the 45-45-90 and 30-60-90 right triangles.

Perspective There are no precise characteristics for making a triangle special. Some triangles are special because of the ratios of the lengths of their sides. For instance, there are the 3-4-5 right triangles, with sides $3x$, $4x$, and $5x$. Some triangles are special because of the ratios of their angles.

The two special triangles in this lesson have angle ratios 1:2:3 (that is, 30-60-90) and 1:1:2 (that is, 45-45-90). The special triangle in **Question 25,** called the *heptagonal triangle,* has angles in the ratio 1:2:4.

The 30-60-90 and 45-45-90 triangles are special for at least two reasons. First, each occurs in conjunction with at least two regular polygons—the 30-60-90 triangle with the equilateral triangle and the regular hexagon, and the 45-45-90 triangle with the square and regular octagon. Second, the sines, cosines, and tangents of the acute angles in these triangles are either rational ($\frac{1}{2}$, or 1) or rational multiples of square roots of integers ($\frac{\sqrt{2}}{2}$, $\frac{\sqrt{3}}{2}$, $\frac{\sqrt{3}}{3}$, or $\sqrt{3}$); this fact is unique among acute angles with integral degree measures. The goal of the lesson is to determine the extended ratio of the sides in each of the special triangles.

which equals half of a diagonal of the unit square, or $\frac{\sqrt{2}}{2}$. There are 9 unit squares. The next larger size is the square whose area is 2, side length $\sqrt{2}$; there are five such squares. There are four squares whose area is 4, and there is one square whose area is 9.

Notes on Reading

You might want to use Activity 1 of *Optional Activities* below to introduce the lesson.

To emphasize the relationship between hexagons and equilateral triangles, show that a tessellation of equilateral triangles contains a tessellation of regular hexagons.

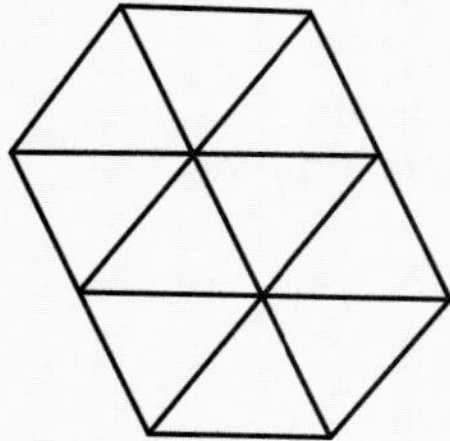

Another way of stating the Isosceles Right Triangle Theorem is as follows: The sides of an isosceles right triangle are in the extended ratio $1:1:\sqrt{2}$. Likewise, the 30-60-90 Triangle Theorem can be stated in the following way: The sides of a 30-60-90 triangle are in the extended ratio $1:\sqrt{3}: 2$.

Make sure students understand this new way of referring to a triangle, namely by using its angles or sides as a label, as is done for the 30-60-90 triangle, the 3-4-5 triangle, and other triangles in this lesson. Point out that although the new angle description uses the actual angle measures, the new description by sides uses the ratio of the side lengths, not the actual lengths of the sides.

Example 1

A major league baseball diamond is a 90-ft square. How far is it from home plate to second base, to the nearest tenth of a foot?

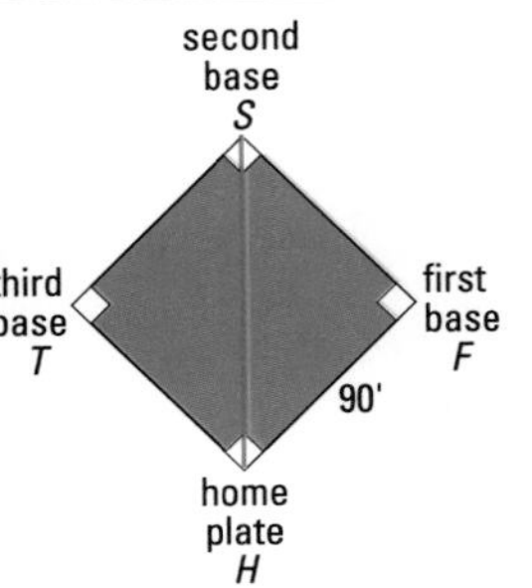

Solution

Triangle *HFS* is an isosceles right triangle with $\overline{HS}$ as its hypotenuse.

$$HS = 90\sqrt{2} \text{ feet}$$
$$\approx 127.3 \text{ feet}$$

In Example 1, a leg was known. In Example 2, a hypotenuse is known.

Example 2

At the right, a square *ABCD* is inscribed in a circle with diameter 12. What is an exact value for the length of a side of the square?

Solution

The word **inscribed** means that all vertices of the figure lie on the circle. Let $BC = x$. Then, by the Isosceles Right Triangle Theorem,

$$AC = x\sqrt{2}.$$

So $$12 = x\sqrt{2}.$$

So $$x = \frac{12}{\sqrt{2}}.$$

This is a perfectly good exact answer, but many people prefer fractions to have rational denominators. To rationalize the denominator, multiply both numerator and denominator by $\sqrt{2}$.

$$\frac{12}{\sqrt{2}} = \frac{12 \cdot \sqrt{2}}{\sqrt{2} \cdot \sqrt{2}} = \frac{12\sqrt{2}}{2} = 6\sqrt{2}$$

Check

You should check that $6\sqrt{2} = \frac{12}{\sqrt{2}}$ by finding decimal approximations on your calculator. Also check that the lengths satisfy the Pythagorean Theorem:

$$(6\sqrt{2})^2 + (6\sqrt{2})^2 = 12^2.$$

Properties of 30-60-90 Triangles

Another special right triangle is the **30-60-90 triangle.** All 30-60-90 triangles are similar. (Do you see why?) One way to form a 30-60-90 triangle is to draw any altitude of an equilateral triangle, as shown at the right.

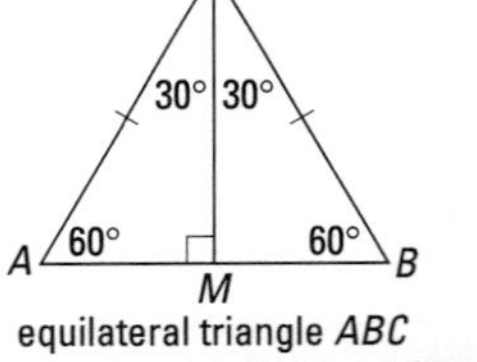

equilateral triangle *ABC*
30-60-90 triangles *CAM* and *CBM*

Again the lengths of all sides can be determined if one side length is known.

Optional Activities

Activity 1
You might use this activity to introduce the lesson. The activity will help students verify the Isosceles Right Triangle Theorem and the 30-60-90 Triangle Theorem. Have students **work in small groups.** Tell them to draw triangles given the angle measures 45, 45, 90 and 30, 60, 90. Have them measure the sides of the triangles and find the ratios of the sides. Discuss the results with the entire class.

Activity 2
You can use *Activity Kit, Activity 27,* as a follow-up to the lesson. In this activity, students explore a geometric pattern generated in a 30-60-90 triangle.

30-60-90 Triangle Theorem
In a 30-60-90 (right) triangle, if the shorter leg is x then the longer leg is $x\sqrt{3}$ and the hypotenuse is $2x$.

Proof

Given: $\triangle ABC$ with $m\angle A = 30$, $m\angle B = 60$, $m\angle C = 90$. The shorter leg is opposite the smaller acute angle, so let $BC = x$.

To prove: (1) $AB = 2x$;
(2) $AC = x\sqrt{3}$.

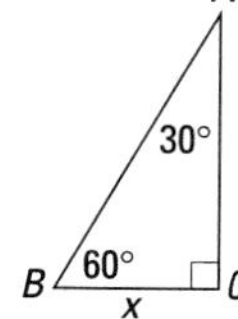

Argument:
The idea is to think of $\triangle ABC$ as half an equilateral triangle, and use the Pythagorean Theorem.

(1) Reflect $\triangle ABC$ over $\overleftrightarrow{AC}$. Let $D = r_{\overleftrightarrow{AC}}(B)$. By definition of congruence, $\triangle ABC \cong \triangle ADC$. Thus, $\triangle ADC$ is a 30-60-90 right triangle, with $CD = x$. Also, $m\angle BCD = 180$ so C lies on $\overleftrightarrow{BD}$ and ABD is a triangle. $\triangle ABD$ has three 60° angles, making it equilateral. Since $BD = 2x$, then $AB = 2x$.

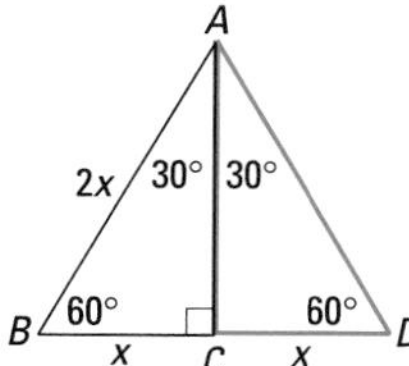

(2) Now apply the Pythagorean Theorem to $\triangle ABC$ to get AC.

$$AC^2 + BC^2 = AB^2$$
$$AC^2 + x^2 = (2x)^2$$
$$AC^2 + x^2 = 4x^2$$
$$AC^2 = 3x^2$$

Taking the positive square roots of each side:

$$AC = x\sqrt{3}.$$

Bee careful. *An apiary is a man-made home for bees consisting of thousands of hexagonal cells.*

Example 3

A natural beehive is a tessellation of regular hexagons. An apiarist measured a side of a large cell as 8.0 mm but forgot to measure the height h of each cell. Approximate the height to the nearest 0.1 mm.

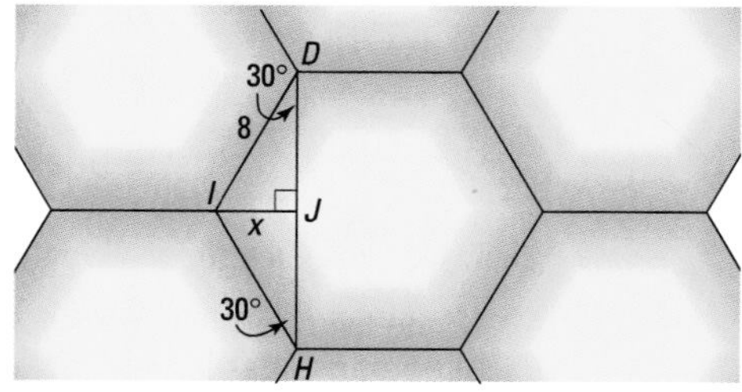

There are special triangles that are not right triangles. One example is the triangle in **Question 25** (see *Notes on Questions*); another is the 36-72-72 angle-measured isosceles triangle, which occurs when the diagonals of a regular pentagon are drawn.

To prepare students for the trigonometric ratios presented in future lessons, you might point out that 1.414 on their calculators is an approximation to $\sqrt{2}$, and that 1.732 is an approximation to $\sqrt{3}$. These approximations should be memorized by students. Mnemonic devices can be used to help students remember these approximations. Here is one example. George Washington, who was born in 1732, chopped down a cherry *three* with square roots. You may even mention the approximations 0.707 to $\frac{\sqrt{2}}{2}$ and 0.866 to $\frac{\sqrt{3}}{2}$.

Error Alert If they are not given the shorter leg of a triangle, some students will apply the ratio of the sides incorrectly when calculating the lengths of the sides of a right triangle. Stress that one multiplies by a number greater than 1 when "going from a shorter to a longer side" and divides when "going from a longer to a shorter side." For example, in a 30-60-90 triangle, one multiplies the shorter leg by $\sqrt{3}$ to get the longer leg, and one divides the longer leg by $\sqrt{3}$ to get the shorter leg.

Adapting to Individual Needs

Extra Help
In **Example 2** students are shown how to rationalize the denominator of $\frac{12}{\sqrt{2}}$. They may wonder why some people prefer the answer in the form $6\sqrt{2}$. Point out that if we replace $\sqrt{2}$ by a decimal approximation such as 1.414, the second answer would involve multiplication by a decimal, while the first one would involve division by a decimal. Now that calculators are so commonly used, either one is easy to compute. However, if one had to do the computation with paper and pencil, most people would prefer to multiply rather than divide by a decimal.

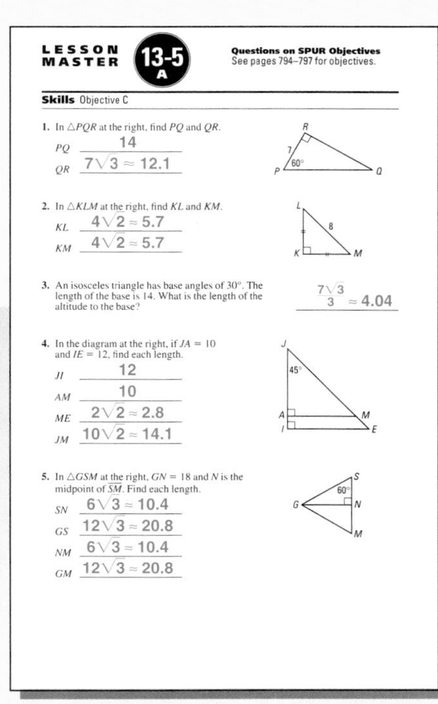
LESSON MASTER 13-5 A

Questions on SPUR Objectives
See pages 794–797 for objectives.

Skills Objective C

1. In $\triangle PQR$ at the right, find PQ and QR.
PQ 14
QR $7\sqrt{3} \approx 12.1$

2. In $\triangle KLM$ at the right, find KL and KM.
KL $4\sqrt{2} \approx 5.7$
KM $4\sqrt{2} \approx 5.7$

3. An isosceles triangle has base angles of 30°. The length of the base is 14. What is the length of the altitude to the base?
$\frac{7\sqrt{3}}{3} \approx 4.04$

4. In the diagram at the right, if $JA = 10$ and $IE = 12$, find each length.
JI 12
AM 10
ME $2\sqrt{2} \approx 2.8$
JM $10\sqrt{2} \approx 14.1$

5. In $\triangle GSM$ at the right, $GN = 18$ and N is the midpoint of $\overline{SM}$. Find each length.
SN $6\sqrt{3} \approx 10.4$
GS $12\sqrt{3} \approx 20.8$
NM $6\sqrt{3} \approx 10.4$
GM $12\sqrt{3} \approx 20.8$

Additional Examples

These examples are also given on **Teaching Aid 179.**

1. An airport is built on a piece of land approximately one mile square. Find the length of the longest runway that can be built on land that is one mile square. Give your answer to the nearest 50 feet. **$5280\sqrt{2} \approx 7450$ feet**
2. Triangle *ABC* is an isosceles right triangle and m∠*DAC* = 30. If *AC* = 4, what is *BD*?

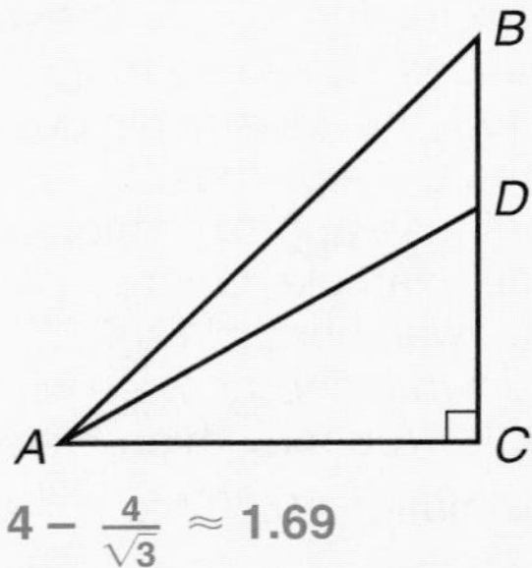

$4 - \frac{4}{\sqrt{3}} \approx 1.69$

3. What are the lengths of the legs of a 30-60-90 right triangle whose hypotenuse has length 50? **25 and $25\sqrt{3}$**
4. Find the height of parallelogram *WXYZ*.

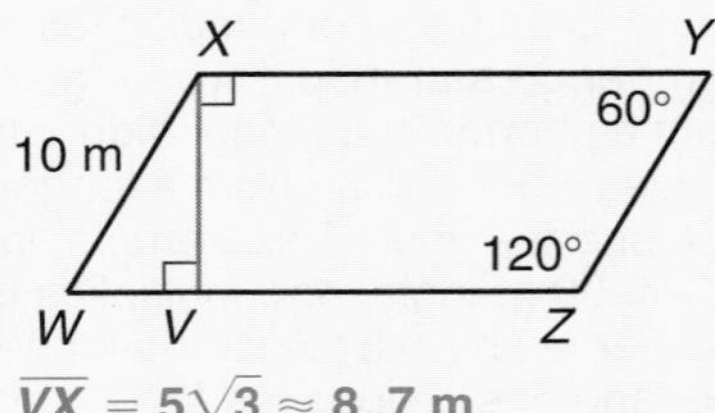

$\overline{VX} = 5\sqrt{3} \approx 8.7$ m

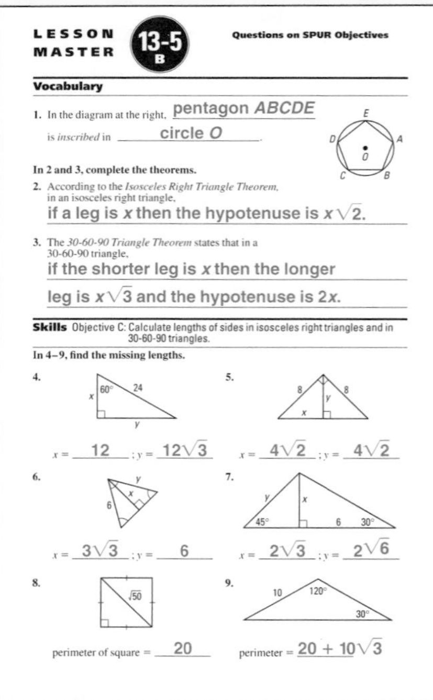

LESSON MASTER 13-5 B Questions on SPUR Objectives

Vocabulary

1. In the diagram at the right, pentagon *ABCDE* is *inscribed* in circle *O*.

In 2 and 3, complete the theorems.

2. According to the *Isosceles Right Triangle Theorem*, in an isosceles right triangle, if a leg is *x* then the hypotenuse is $x\sqrt{2}$.
3. The *30-60-90 Triangle Theorem* states that in a 30-60-90 triangle, if the shorter leg is *x* then the longer leg is $x\sqrt{3}$ and the hypotenuse is 2*x*.

Skills Objective C: Calculate lengths of sides in isosceles right triangles and in 30-60-90 triangles.

In 4–9, find the missing lengths.

4. $x =$ 12; $y =$ $12\sqrt{3}$
5. $x =$ $4\sqrt{2}$; $y =$ $4\sqrt{2}$
6. $x =$ $3\sqrt{3}$; $y =$ 6
7. $x =$ $2\sqrt{3}$; $y =$ $2\sqrt{6}$
8. perimeter of square = 20
9. perimeter = $20 + 10\sqrt{3}$

Solution

The figure on page 767 isolates one cell. *DH* is the desired height. From properties of a regular hexagon, m∠*DIH* = 120 and *DI* = *IH*. From the Isosceles △ Coincidence Theorem, altitude $\overline{IJ}$ bisects ∠*DIH* and so △*DIJ* is a 30-60-90 right triangle with hypotenuse 8.0 mm. Let *IJ*, the length of the shortest side, be *x*. Using the 30-60-90 Triangle Theorem, the hypotenuse DI = 2x = 8.0 mm, so x = 4.0 mm. The longer leg DJ = $x\sqrt{3} = 4\sqrt{3}$.

Now,
$$DH = 2 \cdot 4\sqrt{3} = 8\sqrt{3} \approx 13.9 \text{ mm.}$$

Applications to Other Triangles

With these theorems, lengths can be found in some non-right triangles that contain a 30°, 45°, or 60° angle.

Example 4

In △*XYZ* at the right, m∠*Z* = 45, m∠*Y* = 30, and *XY* = 8. Find *YZ* and *XZ*.

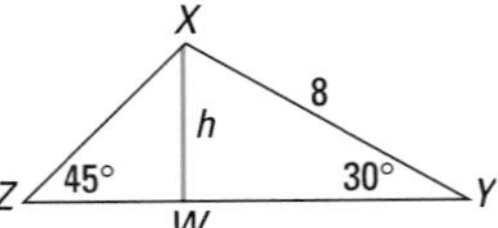

Solution

Right triangles are needed, so An auxiliary line is drawn, the altitude $\overline{XW}$ from X to $\overline{YZ}$. Let *XW* = *h*. This forms a 45-45-90 right triangle *XZW* and a 30-60-90 right triangle *XYW*. Now apply the theorems of this lesson. The side $\overline{XW}$, opposite the 30° angle in △XYW, is half of 8, so h = 4. Also, YW = $h\sqrt{3} = 4\sqrt{3}$. Since △XZW is isosceles, ZW = h = 4. Adding, YZ = ZW + YW = $4 + 4\sqrt{3} \approx 10.93$.
XZ = $h \cdot \sqrt{2} = 4\sqrt{2} \approx 5.66$.

Check

An accurate picture verifies these lengths.

Of course, you could always measure to get approximate lengths and angle measures in a triangle. One advantage of having the theorems of this lesson is that for these common triangles you do not have to measure. Another advantage is that they give exact values.

QUESTIONS

Covering the Reading

1. In an isosceles right triangle, the acute angles each measure __?__. **45**
2. If one leg of an isosceles right triangle has length 10 cm, the hypotenuse has length __?__. **$10\sqrt{2} \approx 14.14$ cm**

Adapting to Individual Needs

English Language Development

Before discussing **Example 2** you might want to review the meaning of *inscribed* (and the related term *circumscribed*). Write inscribed on the board and show that a square inscribed in a circle is inside the circle. In contrast, show that a square that is circumscribed about a circle is outside the circle.

3. On a Major League baseball field, how far is it from first base to third base? $90\sqrt{2} \approx 127.3$ ft

4. *True or false.*
   a. All right triangles are similar. False
   b. All right triangles with a 60° angle are similar. True
   c. All isosceles right triangles are similar. True

5. In a right triangle with a 30° angle, the _?_ has double the length of the _?_ leg. hypotenuse, short

In 6–9, find each missing length.

6. $a = 6\sqrt{2} \approx 8.49$

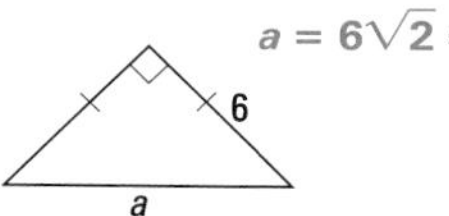

7. $\frac{15\sqrt{2}}{2} \approx 10.61$

b
15

8. $d = \frac{10\sqrt{3}}{3} \approx 5.77$, $c = \frac{20\sqrt{3}}{3} \approx 11.55$

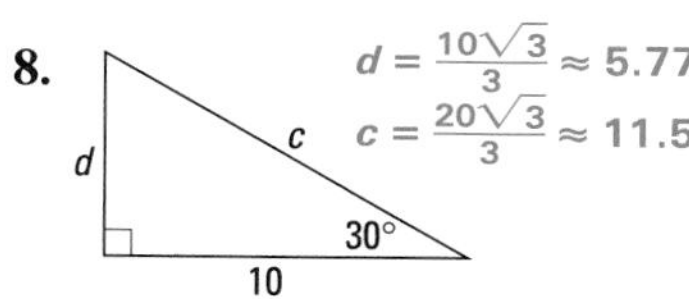

9. $f = \frac{25}{2} = 12.5$, $e = 12.5 \cdot \sqrt{3} \approx 21.65$

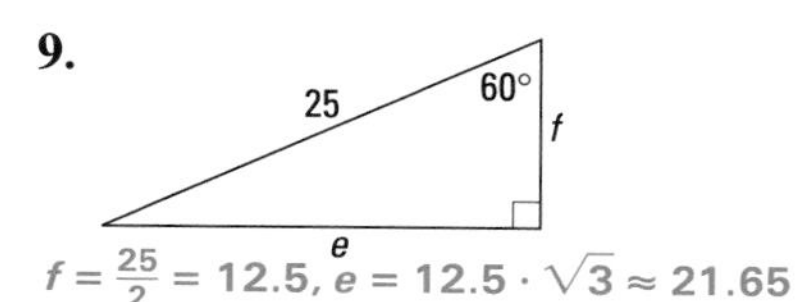

10. If the shortest side of a 30-60-90 triangle is 6 cm, what are the lengths of the other two sides (to the nearest 0.1 cm)? 10.4 cm, 12.0 cm

11. Refer to Example 3. Suppose the cell of a natural beehive is a regular hexagon with a side of length 5 mm. What is the height of each cell? $5\sqrt{3} \approx 8.66$ mm

12. In Example 4, what is $m\angle ZXY$? 105

13. In Example 4, what is the perimeter of $\triangle XYZ$? $12 + 4\sqrt{2} + 4\sqrt{3} \approx 24.59$ units

Applying the Mathematics

14. A square has side s. What is the length of its diagonals? $s\sqrt{2}$ units

15. What is the length of one of the altitudes of an equilateral triangle with a side of length 14? $7\sqrt{3} \approx 12.12$

16. Use the figure below. If $OL = h$, find the perimeter of $\triangle BLT$ in terms of h. $3h + h\sqrt{2} + h\sqrt{3} \approx 6.15h$

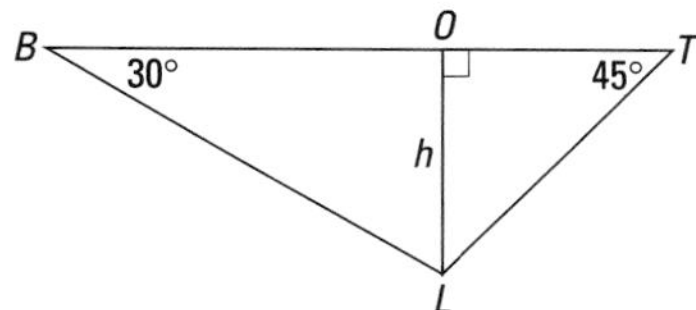

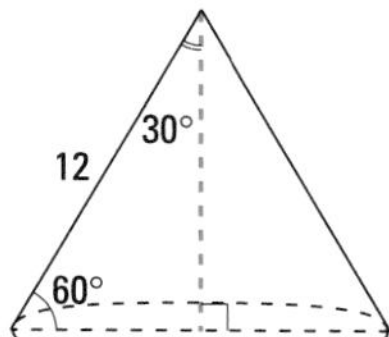

17. How many 30-60-90 triangles are formed when all the diagonals of a regular hexagon are drawn? 60

18. Find the total surface area and volume to the nearest tenth of the right cone at the left. $108\pi \approx 339.3$ units^2; $72\pi\sqrt{3} \approx 391.8$ units^3

Notes on Questions

Question 2 Review with students when an exact answer is required and when an approximate answer is more appropriate. Real-world examples almost always require estimates of answers that contain radicals. However, when one is calculating the length of a side of a triangle, in a non-applied situation, an exact answer usually is best.

Question 3 Remind students that since the diagonals of a rectangle are congruent, the answer must be the same as that in **Example 1.**

Question 16 For ease of computation, the answer can be factored into $(3 + \sqrt{2} + \sqrt{3})h$. To check if the answer is correct, you can use it to find the answer to **Question 13** with $h = 4$. However, do not ask students to consider it as a formula that needs to be memorized.

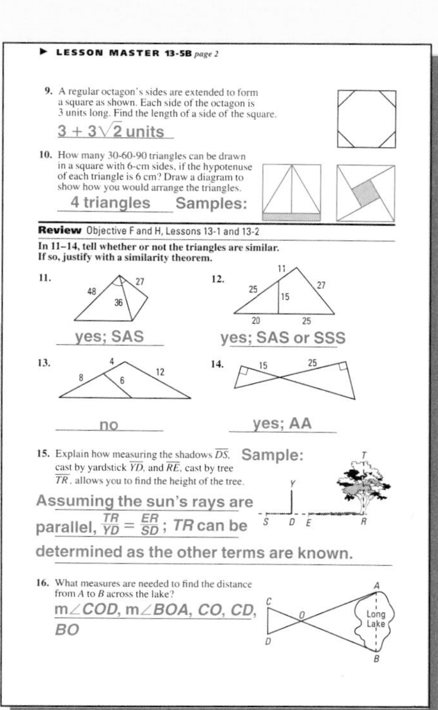

▶ **LESSON MASTER 13-5B** *page 2*

9. A regular octagon's sides are extended to form a square as shown. Each side of the octagon is 3 units long. Find the length of a side of the square. $3 + 3\sqrt{2}$ units

10. How many 30-60-90 triangles can be drawn in a square with 6-cm sides, if the hypotenuse of each triangle is 6 cm? Draw a diagram to show how you would arrange the triangles. 4 triangles Samples:

Review Objective F and H, Lessons 13-1 and 13-2

In 11–14, tell whether or not the triangles are similar. If so, justify with a similarity theorem.

11. yes; SAS

12. yes; SAS or SSS

13. no

14. yes; AA

15. Explain how measuring the shadows $\overline{DS}$, cast by yardstick $\overline{YD}$, and $\overline{RE}$, cast by tree $\overline{TR}$, allows you to find the height of the tree. Sample: Assuming the sun's rays are parallel, $\frac{TR}{YD} = \frac{ER}{SD}$; TR can be determined as the other terms are known.

16. What measures are needed to find the distance from A to B across the lake? $m\angle COD$, $m\angle BOA$, CO, CD, BO

Adapting to Individual Needs

Challenge

The 30-60-90 Triangle Theorem gives the lengths of the sides in terms of the shorter leg. Have students find the lengths of the sides in terms of the hypotenuse and in terms of the longer leg.

1. Hypotenuse [Let c be the length of the hypotenuse. The length of the shorter leg is $\frac{c}{2}$, and the length of the longer leg is $\frac{c\sqrt{3}}{2}$.]
2. Longer leg [Let b be the length of the longer leg. The length of the shorter leg is $\frac{b}{\sqrt{3}}$, and the length of the hypotenuse is $\frac{2b}{\sqrt{3}}$.]

Notes on Questions

Question 25 "The Heptagonal Triangle," an article in the January 1973 issue of *Mathematics Magazine,* was devoted to the extraordinary properties of this triangle. Another property is that $(\frac{a}{c})^2 + (\frac{c}{b})^2 + (\frac{b}{a})^2 = 5$.

Follow-up for Lesson 13-5

Practice

For more questions on SPUR Objectives, use **Lesson Master 13-5A** (shown on page 767) or **Lesson Master 13-5B** (shown on pages 768–769).

Assessment

Oral/Written Communication
Have students **work in pairs.** Each student should draw an isosceles right triangle and a 30-60-90 triangle. Each triangle should have the length of one of the three sides labeled. Then have students exchange diagrams and find the lengths of the remaining sides of each triangle. [Students correctly determine the missing lengths in isosceles right triangles and in 30-60-90 triangles.]

Extension

Ask students to answer the following questions.

1. Find the perimeter of an equilateral triangle if the length of an altitude is 3.5 units.

   [$7\sqrt{3}$ units or $\approx$ 12.1 units]

2.

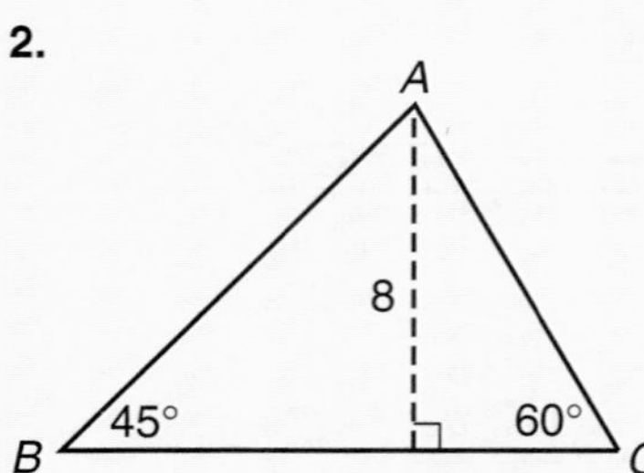

Find the perimeter of $\triangle ABC$.

[$8\sqrt{3} + 8\sqrt{2} + 8 \approx 33.2$]

Project Update Project 4, *Regular Polygons and Unit Circles,* and Project 5, *Oblique Triangles with Integer Sides and Integer Altitudes,* on page 790, relate to the content of this lesson.

Review

In 19 and 20, use the drawing at the right. *(Lesson 13-4)*

19. If $NO = 2$ and $MO = 3$, find OP. $OP = 4.5$

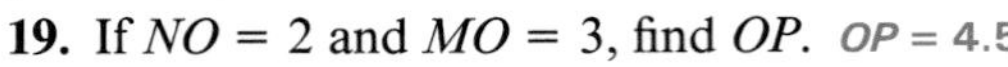

20. If $NO = 5$ and $OP = 10$, find MO.
$MO = \sqrt{50} \approx 7.07$

21. Find x and y in the figure at the left. *(Lesson 13-3)* $y = 9$; $x = \sqrt{80} \approx 8.94$

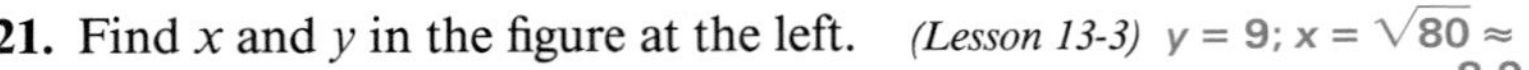

22. At the right $\overleftrightarrow{AB} \parallel \overleftrightarrow{CD} \parallel \overleftrightarrow{EF}$, $AX = 5$, $XD = 7$, and other lengths are as indicated. Find XB, BD, and CE. *(Lesson 13-3)*
$XB = 4\frac{3}{8} = 4.375$; $BD = 2\frac{5}{8} = 2.625$;
$CE = \frac{32}{7} = 4\frac{4}{7} \approx 4.57$

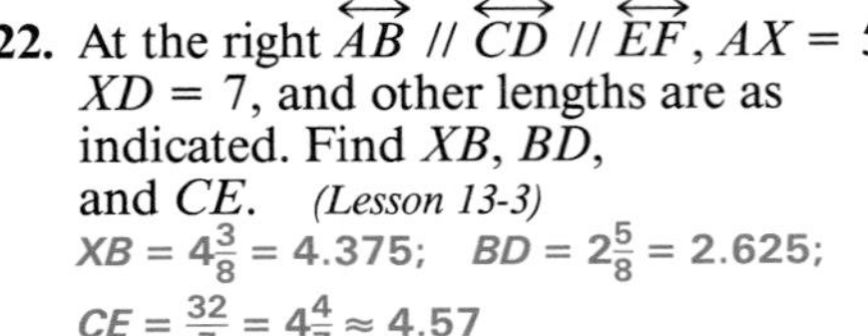

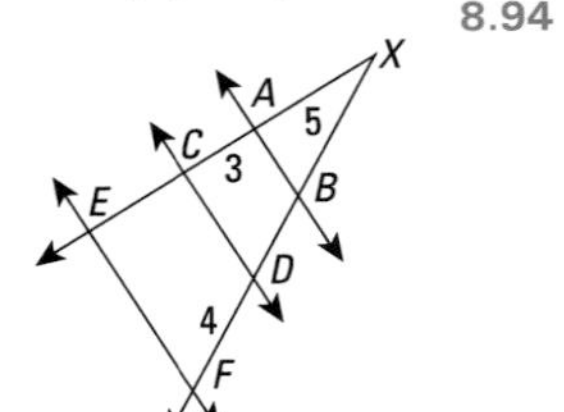

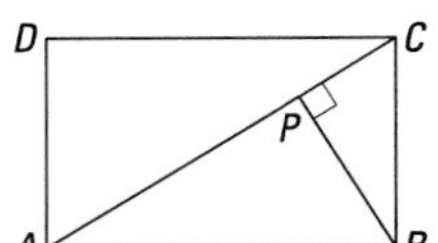

23. $\overline{BP} \perp \overline{AC}$ in rectangle $ABCD$ at the left. Name all triangles in the figure which are similar to $\triangle ADC$. Be sure to list them with their vertices in the correct order. *(Lessons 13-1, 13-2)*
$\triangle CBA$, $\triangle BPA$, $\triangle CPB$ (and also $\triangle ADC$)

24. A square and a circle each have area 400 square meters. Which has the larger perimeter? *(Lessons 8-1, 8-2, 8-7, 8-8)* square

Exploration

25. There are many triangles that could be considered special. One such triangle is formed in a regular heptagon by a side, a shorter diagonal, and a longer diagonal. a) Check students' drawings.

a. Use an accurate drawing tool to draw a regular heptagon. (One way is to draw seven equally spaced points on a circle, as has been done at the right.)

b. Measure a, b, and c.
Calculate $\left(\frac{c}{a}\right)^2 + \left(\frac{a}{b}\right)^2 + \left(\frac{b}{c}\right)^2$.
Your answer should be very close to a whole number.
Which whole number? 6

c. Measure the three angles of this triangle. How do they seem to be related?
The angles have measures x, $2x$, and $4x$, where $x = \frac{180}{7}$.

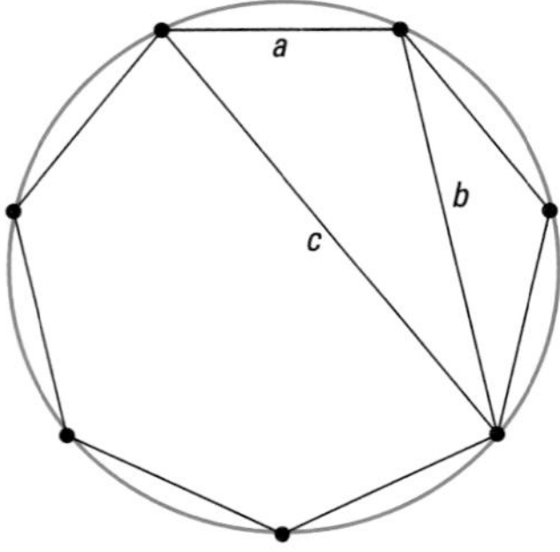

Setting Up Lesson 13-6

Have students **work in pairs** to do the In-class Activity on page 771 before assigning Lesson 13-6. It is recommended that students do the activity using automatic drawers, but if drawers are not available, students still can do the activity with paper and pencil.

Introducing Lesson 13-6

Ratios of Legs in Right Triangles

IN-CLASS ACTIVITY

Work with a partner. You will need a ruler and protractor, or an automatic drawer.

In right triangle ABC below, $m\angle A = 26$ and $\overline{B_1C_1} // \overline{B_2C_2} // \overline{B_3C_3} // \overline{BC}$.

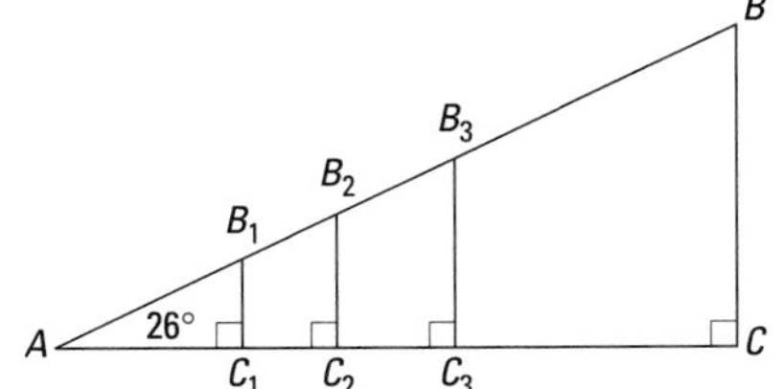

1) $B_1C_1 \approx 7$ mm
$AC_1 \approx 15$ mm
$\frac{B_1C_1}{AC_1} \approx 0.47$

Trace the figure above, or draw one of your own by hand or on an automatic drawer.

1 Measure B_1C_1 and AC_1 to the nearest millimeter and estimate $\frac{B_1C_1}{AC_1}$ to two decimal places. See above.

2 Do the same for B_2C_2 and AC_2, B_3C_3 and AC_3, and BC and AC. See margin.

3 How close to each other are the ratios $\frac{BC}{AC}$, $\frac{B_1C_1}{AC_1}$, $\frac{B_2C_2}{AC_2}$, and $\frac{B_3C_3}{AC_3}$? See margin.

4 Calculate the average of the four ratios in Step 3. ≈ 0.47

5 Each of the ratios in Step 3 is an estimate of the *tangent* of 26°. To get a calculator estimate of this value, make certain your calculator is in degree mode. Then press tan 26 ENTER if your calculator is a graphing calculator, 26 tan if you are using a scientific calculator. ≈ 0.49

6 How close to each other are your values from Steps 4 and 5? They should be nearly the same.

7 Draw another right triangle ABC with a 26° angle at A and a right angle at C, where $\overline{AC}$ and $\overline{BC}$ are neither horizontal nor vertical. Calculate $\frac{BC}{AC}$ for this triangle. See margin.

8 How does your value from Step 7 compare with your values from Steps 4 and 5? They should be nearly the same.

In-class Activity

Resources

From the ***Teacher's Resource File***

- Answer Master 13-6

This In-class Activity asks students to calculate the ratios of legs in right triangles and gives students concrete examples of the tangent of an angle.

If possible, you might wish to ask students to use automatic drawers to do this activity so they can get more precise values of the lengths of the segments and the ratios. If no such automatic drawers are available, students still can do the activity with pencil and paper. However, it is to be expected that they might get slightly different lengths and ratios. Ask them to do it in pairs so that each student has someone with whom to compare his/her work.

Whether you use technology or not, remind students that the results in this activity are approximations. The results can suggest that the ratios are equal but the mathematical proof needs the AA Similarity Theorem. A proof is given in the next lesson.

Have students record the results of this In-class Activity for use with **Question 1** on page 775.

Additional Answers

2. $B_2C_2 \approx 11$ mm, $AC_2 \approx 23$ mm, $B_3C_3 \approx 15$ mm, $AC_3 \approx 32$ mm, $BC \approx 26$ mm, $AC \approx 55$ mm
3. $\frac{BC}{AC} \approx 0.47$, $\frac{B_1C_1}{AC_1} \approx 0.47$, $\frac{B_2C_2}{AC_2} \approx 0.48$, $\frac{B_3C_3}{AC_3} \approx 0.47$; they should be very close.

7. $\frac{BC}{AC} \approx \frac{1.4}{2.8} = 0.5$

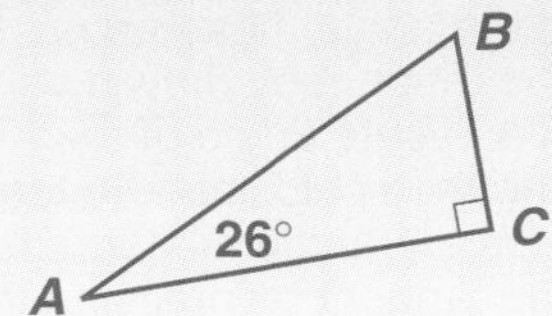

Lesson 13-6

Objectives

D Determine tangents of angles.
E Estimate or determine exact values of tangent ratios.
G Know the definition of tangent.
I Use tangents to determine unknown lengths in real situations.

Resources

From the ***Teacher's Resource File***

- Lesson Master 13-6A or 13-6B
- Answer Master 13-6
- Assessment Sourcebook: Quiz for Lessons 13-4 through 13-6
- Teaching Aid 172: Warm-up

Additional Resources

- Visual for Teaching Aid 172

Teaching Lesson 13-6

Warm-up

In the following figure, find each ratio in lowest terms.

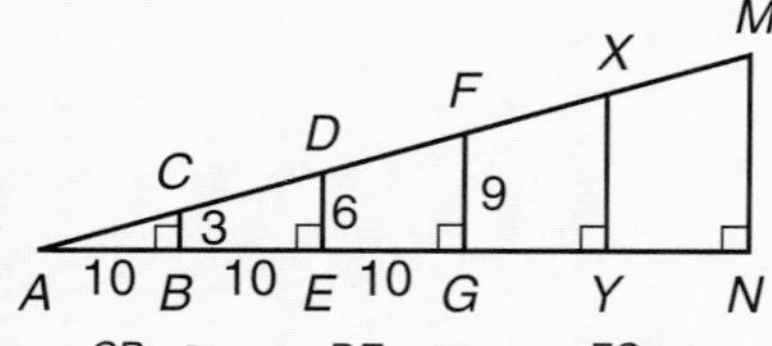

1. $\frac{CB}{AB}$ $\frac{3}{10}$ **2.** $\frac{DE}{AE}$ $\frac{3}{10}$ **3.** $\frac{FG}{AG}$ $\frac{3}{10}$

4. If $GY = 12$, find XY. 12.6

5. If $MN = 16$, find AN. $\frac{160}{3} = 53.\overline{3}$

LESSON

13-6 The Tangent of an Angle

If you know two sides of a right triangle, you can always find the third side by using the Pythagorean Theorem. In Lesson 13-5, you learned that if you know one side and one acute angle of a 30-60-90 or 45-45-90 triangle, you can find the other two sides. But most triangles do not contain these angles. In this lesson and the next lesson, you will learn how you can use one side and one acute angle of *any* right triangle to find the lengths of the other two sides.

Ratios of Legs in Right Triangles

Consider two right triangles ABC and XYZ with congruent acute angles. The triangles might be formed by figures and shadows at the same time of day. The triangles are similar because of the AA Similarity Theorem.

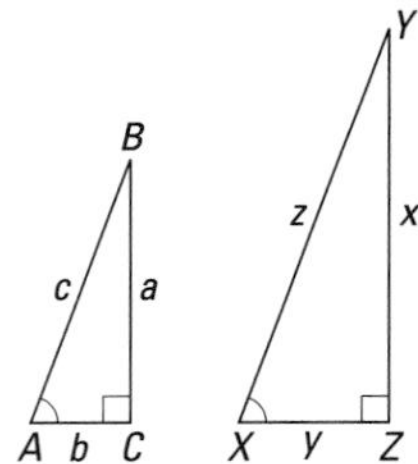

The drawing at the right follows custom by using a to represent the side opposite angle A, b to represent the side opposite angle B, and so on. (You should be careful to write small letters so they are different from capital letters.) Since corresponding sides are proportional,

$$\frac{a}{x} = \frac{b}{y}.$$

Multiplying both sides by $\frac{x}{b}$, yields a ratio of legs in each triangle.

$$\frac{a}{x} \cdot \frac{x}{b} = \frac{b}{y} \cdot \frac{x}{b}$$
$$\frac{a}{b} = \frac{x}{y}$$

The ratios of the legs are equal.

Lesson 13-6 Overview

Broad Goals This lesson introduces the definition of the tangent of an angle and gives various ways of determining its value.

Perspective After showing that the ratio of the opposite side to the adjacent side is constant for an acute angle of fixed measure in a right triangle (the In-class Activity on page 771 and a more formal argument in this lesson) and then defining the tangent as that ratio, Lesson 13-6 provides three ways to calculate or estimate tangents of angles: (1) When the angle measure is given, estimate the tangent by drawing a right triangle with an acute angle of the given measure and then calculate the tangent ratio. (2) When the angle measure is given, estimate the tangent by pressing the appropriate keys on a scientific or graphics calculator. (3) When the lengths of the sides in a right triangle are given or can be determined, the tangent can be calculated by dividing one length by another. Students should be able to use all three methods.

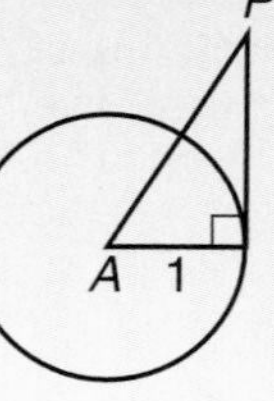

The origin of the name *tangent* used in trigonometry is found in the unit circle at the right. The length of the tangent segment from point P to the unit circle is tan A.

The Tangent Ratio

The legs a and x are **opposite** the congruent angles A and X. The legs b and y are **adjacent to** angles A and X. This argument proves that in a right triangle, the ratio

$$\frac{\text{leg opposite angle } A}{\text{leg adjacent to angle } A}$$

is the same for any angle congruent to A. This ratio is called the *tangent of angle A*.

Definition
In right triangle *ABC* with right angle *C*, the tangent of $\angle A$, written tan *A*, is

$$\frac{\text{leg opposite } \angle A}{\text{leg adjacent to } \angle A}.$$

In the In-class Activity on page 771, you were asked to calculate ratios for tan 26°.

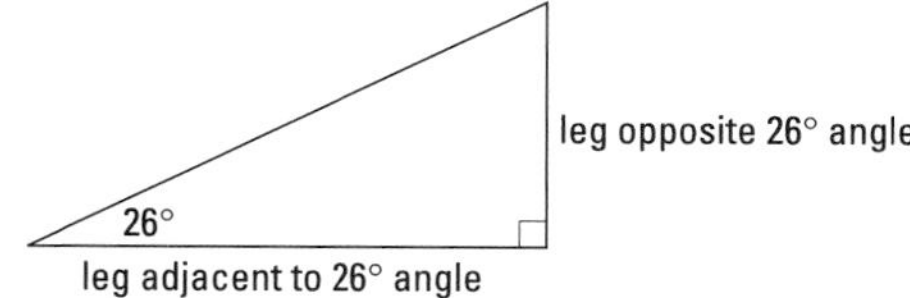

$$\tan 26° = \frac{\text{leg opposite } 26° \text{ angle}}{\text{leg adjacent to } 26° \text{ angle}}$$

But estimating using a drawing is tedious and not very precise. Today, most people use calculators to approximate values of tangents. Every scientific or graphics calculator contains a tan key. To use a tan key, make sure your calculator is measuring angles in degree mode (there are other modes, but we do not discuss them in this book). Your calculator may display 0.4877325886. That means tan 26° ≈ 0.4877325886.

Using Tangents to Find Lengths

When the measure of an angle and one leg in a right triangle are known, the tangent can help to find the length of the other leg.

Example 1

At a location 50 m from the base of a tree, the *angle of elevation* of the tree top is 33°. Determine the height of the tree to the nearest meter.

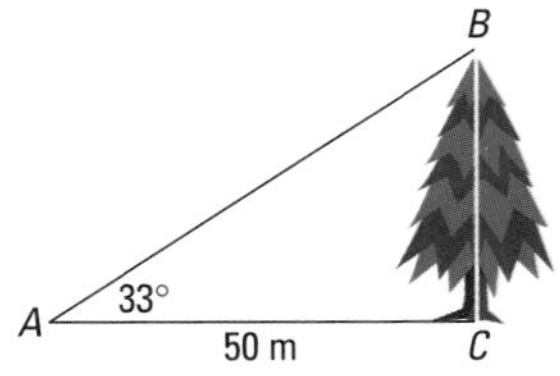

▶

Notes on Reading

You might want to use *Optional Activities* below to introduce this lesson.

Earlier in this chapter, students calculated the height of an object by using shadows and proportions in similar triangles. They may wonder why anyone would use the tangent ratio. Note that sometimes the measure of an angle needs to be calculated when no shadow or similar triangle is available.

Students should be able to estimate tangents using a drawing (In-class Activity) and to estimate tangents and angle measures using a calculator **(Examples 1 and 2).** For the special triangles, they should be able to get exact values knowing only the angle measures **(Example 3).** In reviewing **Example 2,** be certain students know how to use the 2nd function or Inverse keys on their calculator to find the acute angles of a right triangle with given side lengths. You should emphasize that knowing the trigonometric ratios will allow them to find the measures of *all* angles and *all* sides in a right triangle from the length of one side and the measure of one acute angle.

Make sure that students' calculators are in the degree mode before they press the tangent key. In lessons of this book where trigonometry is involved, the degree symbol is used when identifying angle measures in order to emphasize the degree mode.

LESSON MASTER 13-6 A

Questions on SPUR Objectives
See pages 794–797 for objectives.

Skills Objective D

1. Draw a right triangle with legs measuring 8 units and 15 units. Use this triangle to estimate $\angle G$ if $\tan G = \frac{8}{15}$.
   $m\angle G \approx 28$
   Sample: G, 8, 15

2. Use $\triangle AMC$ at the right. Find each ratio. (M, A, C, 5, 13)
   a. tan M $\frac{12}{5}$
   b. tan C $\frac{5}{12}$

Skills Objective E

3. In $\triangle JES$, use a protractor to determine $m\angle E$ to the nearest degree, and then calculate tan E to the nearest hundredth.
   $m\angle E \approx 25$, $\tan E = .47$

Properties Objective G

In 4 and 5, use $\triangle QRS$ at the right. Do *not* measure.

4. What is the tangent of $\angle Q$? $\frac{SR}{QR}$

5. $\frac{QR}{RS}$ is the tangent of which angle? $\angle S$

Uses Objective I

6. Gertie the gopher is looking at a tree that is 100 feet away from her hole. If the angle of elevation between Gertie's hole and the top of the tree is 23°, how tall is the tree? 42.4 ft

An application of tangents that is not covered in this book is the slope of lines. Specifically, the slope of an oblique line in the coordinate plane is the tangent of the angle that the upper part of the line makes with the positive ray of the *x*-axis. This application is found in the last chapter of UCSMP *Algebra*.

Optional Activities

You might use this activity to introduce the lesson. Have students select an angle measure for a non-right angle in a right triangle, draw the triangle, and measure the sides. Then have them find the ratio of the side opposite the angle selected to the side adjacent to the angle. Have them repeat the activity with right triangles with the same angle measures but sides of different lengths. Students should discover that the tangent ratio remains constant.

Additional Examples

1. George sighted a balloon directly overhead at the same time that Martha, who was 2.2 km away, saw it at an angle of 35° above the horizon. How high was the balloon at the time? **2.2 tan 35° ≈ 1.54 km, so the balloon was about 1.54 km above ground.**
2. In a right triangle with sides 20, 21, and 29, find the tangent of the smallest angle. **The smallest angle is opposite the shortest side. Its tangent is $\frac{20}{21} \approx .952$.**
3. By drawing, estimate tan 72°. **Sample drawing. A good estimate is a little more than 3.**

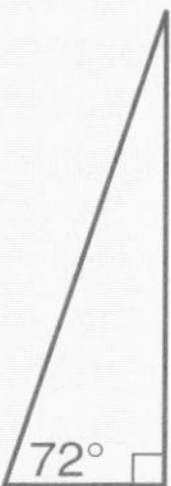

Notes on Questions

Question 2 A good estimate is within 5%, that is, between about .80 and .88. Remind students that larger drawings tend to yield better estimates, and it is easier to divide with lengths in metric units.

Questions 5–6 In general, the tangents of complementary angles are reciprocals, as these questions show.

LESSON MASTER 13-6 B — Questions on SPUR Objectives

Skills

In 1–3, use the figure at the right.

1. Which side is adjacent to $\angle C$? $\overline{AC}$ or $\overline{BC}$
2. Which side is opposite $\angle B$? $\overline{AC}$
3. Which angle is opposite $\overline{AB}$? $\angle C$
4. *Trigonometry* literally means angle measure.

Skills Objective D: Determine tangents of angles.

5. Consider $\triangle ABC$ at the right.
   a. Give tan *B*. $\frac{8}{12} = \frac{2}{3}$
   b. Give tan *A*. $\frac{12}{8} = \frac{3}{2}$
   c. From tan *B*, estimate $m\angle B$. ≈ 33.7
   d. From tan *A*, estimate $m\angle A$. ≈ 56.3

Skills Objective E: Estimate or determine exact values of the tangent ratio.

In 6–8, give exact values.

6. tan 30° $\frac{\sqrt{3}}{3}$ 7. tan 45° 1 8. tan 60° $\sqrt{3}$

In 9–14, estimate to the nearest thousandth.

9. tan 40° .839 10. tan 72° 3.078
11. tan 25° .466 12. tan 58° 1.600
13. tan 33.24° .655 14. tan 16.7° .300

In 15 and 16, use $\triangle KLM$ at the right. a. Estimate the tangent of the given angle to the nearest hundredth. b. Determine the measure of the angle.

15. a. tan *K* $\frac{1.75''}{2.5''}$
    b. $m\angle K$ 35
16. a. tan *M* $\frac{2.5''}{1.75''}$
    b. $m\angle M$ 55

Solution

The angle of elevation is $\angle A$ in the figure on page 773.

$$\tan 33° = \frac{\text{leg opposite } \angle A}{\text{leg adjacent to } \angle A}$$

$$\tan 33° = \frac{BC}{50}$$

Multiplying both sides by 50,

$BC = 50 \cdot \tan 33°$

= 50 [×] 33 [tan] [=] or 50 [×] [tan] 33 [ENTER]

≈ 32.47038

≈ 32 meters.

The exact value of a tangent of an acute angle can be determined if you know the lengths of the two legs in a right triangle with that angle. This value can then be used to determine the measure of the angle.

Example 2

In the right triangle at the left, find $m\angle D$.

Solution

$$\tan D = \frac{\text{leg opposite } \angle D}{\text{leg adjacent } \angle D} = \frac{EF}{ED} = \frac{5}{12}$$

To find $m\angle D$, use the $\tan^{-1}$ key, the inverse tangent function, on your calculator. $\tan^{-1} x$ is the angle whose tangent is *x*. Key in [$\tan^{-1}$] [(] 5 [÷] 12 [)] [ENTER] or 5 [÷] 12 [=] [$\tan^{-1}$]. Our calculator shows 22.61986495, which means $m\angle D \approx 22.62$.

Exact Values of the Tangent Ratio

You can use special triangles to find exact values of some tangents.

Example 3

Give an exact value for tan 60°.

Solution

Draw a 30-60-90 triangle. In $\triangle GHI$, $\tan 60° = \tan G = \frac{\text{leg opposite } \angle G}{\text{leg adjacent } \angle G} = \frac{HI}{GH}$. $\overline{GH}$ is the shorter leg. Call its length x. Then $HI = x\sqrt{3}$. Substituting, $\tan 60° = \frac{x\sqrt{3}}{x} = \sqrt{3}$.

Check

On your calculator, find tan 60° ≈ 1.732050808 ≈ $\sqrt{3}$.

The tangent of an angle is an example of a **trigonometric ratio.** You will study two other trigonometric ratios in the next lesson. With these ratios, you can find all sides and angles of a right triangle whenever you have enough information to satisfy any one of the triangle congruence conditions.

Adapting to Individual Needs

Extra Help

Point out to students that the tangent ratio is practical in determining measures that would be difficult to measure otherwise. In **Example 1** on pages 773–774, it is easy to measure the length along the ground, but difficult to measure the height of the tree. Mention that special instruments are available to measure angles of elevation.

Challenge

Give students these problems.

1. Use a calculator to investigate how, for an acute $\angle A$, the value of tan *A* changes
   a. as $m\angle A$ approaches 0°.
   b. as $m\angle A$ approaches 90°.
   [For 0°, tan *A* gets closer and closer to 0 as $m\angle A$ approaches 0°. For 90°, tan *A* increases without bound as $m\angle A$ approaches 90°.]

2) 30 mm, 40°, 36 mm

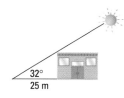

Sample: $\tan 40° \approx \frac{30}{36} = .8\overline{3}$

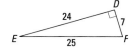

QUESTIONS

Covering the Reading

1. Refer to the In-class Activity on page 771.
   a. What average value did you get in Step 4? ≈ 0.48
   b. How close was this value to a calculator value for tan 26°? They are nearly the same.
2. Draw a right triangle with a 40° angle. Measure the sides, and use those measurements to estimate tan 40°. See left.
3. Use a calculator to estimate tan 73° to the nearest thousandth. 3.271
4. When the sun is 32° up from the horizon, the wall of a store casts a shadow 25 meters long. How high is the wall? $25 \tan 32° \approx 15.62$ meters

32°, 25 m

In 5 and 6, use $\triangle DEF$ at the right. Give the exact value of

D, E, F, 24, 7, 25

5. $\tan E$. $\frac{7}{24}$
6. $\tan F$. $\frac{24}{7}$
7. tan 30°. $1/\sqrt{3}$ or $\sqrt{3}/3$
8. tan 45°. 1
9. Draw a right triangle with legs of 4 units and 6 units. Use your triangle to estimate answers to the following questions. See left for sample.
   a. What is $m\angle A$ if $\tan A = \frac{2}{3}$? $\approx 34°$
   b. What is $m\angle A$ if $\tan A = \frac{3}{2}$? $\approx 56°$
   c. Check your answers to parts **a** and **b** with a calculator. $\tan^{-1}\left(\frac{2}{3}\right) \approx 33.7°$, $\tan^{-1}\left(\frac{3}{2}\right) \approx 56.3°$

9)

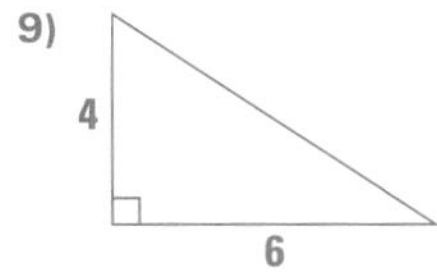

Applying the Mathematics

10. Suppose a person whose eye level is 5′ off the ground and who is 20′ away from a flagpole has to look up at a 40° angle to see the top of the pole. How high is the pole? $5 + 20 \tan 40° \approx 21.8$ ft

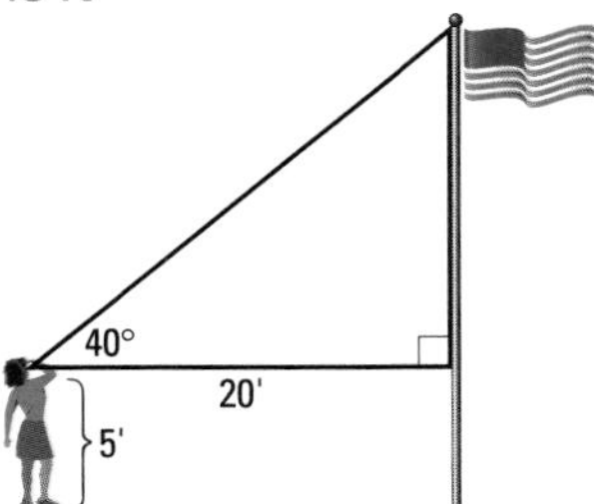

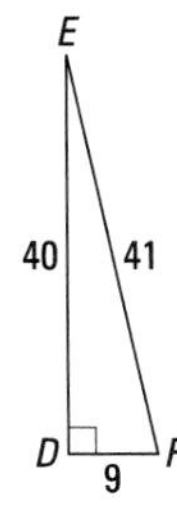

11. A size change of magnitude 3.5 is applied to $\triangle DEF$ at the left, resulting in $\triangle D'E'F'$ (not drawn). What is $\tan E'$? $\frac{9}{40} = .225$
12. Refer to $\triangle ABC$ and $\triangle XYZ$ at the beginning of this lesson. Prove that $\frac{a}{c} = \frac{x}{z}$. See margin.

Question 12 $\frac{a}{c}\left(= \frac{x}{z}\right)$ is the sine of $\angle A$, which is introduced in the next lesson.

(Notes on Questions continue on page 776.)

Follow-up for Lesson 13-6

Practice

For more questions on SPUR Objectives, use **Lesson Master 13-6A** (shown on page 773) or **Lesson Master 13-6B** (shown on pages 774–775).

Assessment

Quiz A quiz covering Lessons 13-4 through 13-6 is provided in the *Assessment Sourcebook.*

Oral/Written Communication
Have students **work in pairs.** First, have each student draw a right triangle with lengths of all three sides labeled correctly. Students may have to use the Pythagorean Theorem to determine the three lengths. Then have students exchange triangles and determine the tangent of each acute angle. [Students draw a right triangle with all three sides of correct length and then correctly determine the tangent for each acute angle.]

(Follow-up continues on page 776.)

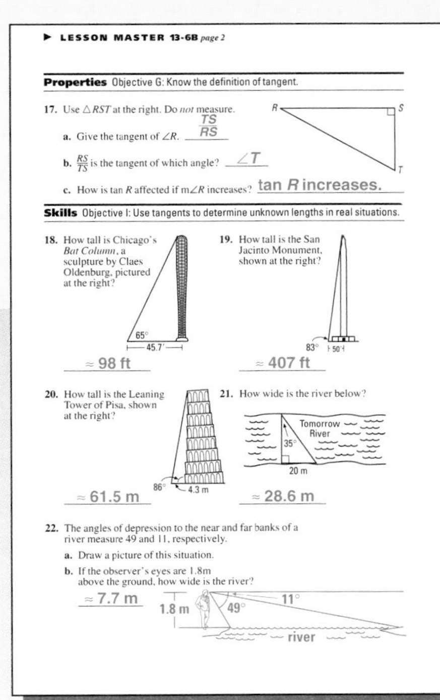

► **LESSON MASTER 13-6B** *page 2*

Properties Objective G: Know the definition of tangent.

17. Use $\triangle RST$ at the right. Do *not* measure.
   a. Give the tangent of $\angle R$. $\frac{TS}{RS}$
   b. $\frac{RS}{TS}$ is the tangent of which angle? $\angle T$
   c. How is tan R affected if $m\angle R$ increases? tan R increases.

Skills Objective I: Use tangents to determine unknown lengths in real situations.

18. How tall is Chicago's *Bat Column*, a sculpture by Claes Oldenburg, pictured at the right? ≈ 98 ft
   (65°, 45.7′)
19. How tall is the San Jacinto Monument, shown at the right? ≈ 407 ft
   (83°, 50′)
20. How tall is the Leaning Tower of Pisa, shown at the right? ≈ 61.5 m
   (86°, 4.3 m)
21. How wide is the river below? ≈ 28.6 m
   (Tomorrow River, 35°, 20 m)
22. The angles of depression to the near and far banks of a river measure 49 and 11, respectively.
   a. Draw a picture of this situation.
   b. If the observer's eyes are 1.8m above the ground, how wide is the river? ≈ 7.7 m
   (1.8 m, 49°, 11°, river)

2. Let A be an acute angle. Explain why
   a. $\tan A < 1$, if $m\angle A < 45°$.
   b. $\tan A = 1$, if $m\angle A = 45°$.
   c. $\tan A > 1$, if $m\angle A > 45°$.
   [Form a right triangle with $\angle A$ as one of the acute angles. The leg opposite $\angle A$ will be the shorter leg if $m\angle A$ is less than 45°, and the longer leg if $m\angle A$ is greater than 45°. The two legs will be the same in length if $m\angle A$ is exactly 45°.]

Additional Answers

12. $\triangle ABC$ and $\triangle XYZ$ are similar because of the AA Similarity Theorem; so $\frac{a}{x} = \frac{c}{z}$. (Corresponding sides are proportional.) By multiplying both sides by $\frac{x}{c}$, $\frac{a}{c} = \frac{x}{z}$.

Extension

You might give students the diagram below and this problem. One portion of a wide staircase has 6 steps. Each step goes up 18 cm for every change of 28 cm horizontally. The sides of the staircase are to be trimmed with a triangular oak panel. What is the measure of $\angle ABC$ at which the oak panel should be cut? [About 32.7°]

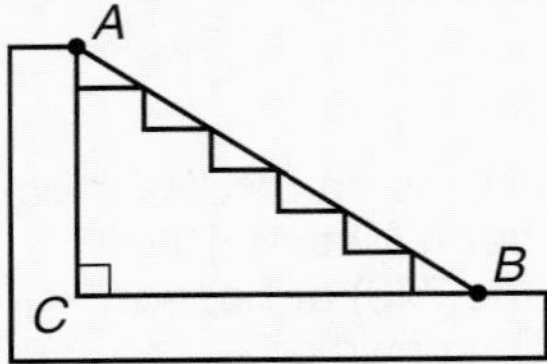

Project Update Project 1, *Measuring with Shadows,* and Project 4, *Regular Polygons and Unit Circles,* on pages 789–790, relate to the content of this lesson.

Notes on Questions

Questions 13–14 You might want to have students use their calculators to make some conjectures about the values of tangents.

Question 23 This question allows students to practice calculating tangents with a calculator. It also demonstrates an amazing theorem that is not well known: In any $\triangle ABC$ which is not a right triangle, $\tan A \cdot \tan B \cdot \tan C = \tan A + \tan B + \tan C$. The proof requires the identity for $\tan(A + B)$ and is beyond the scope of this course.

Additional Answers

14. Sample: In the figure below, $\tan 75° = \frac{a}{b}$ and $\tan 74° = \frac{a}{c}$. Since $c > b$, $\tan 75° > \tan 74°$.

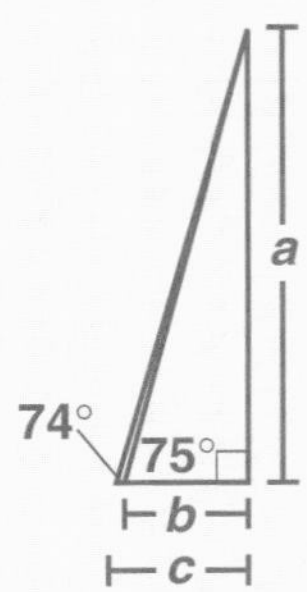

19a. No. Suppose a trapezoid is as the one at the right, where no two sides of AB, BC, DC, and AD are congruent. Therefore, no two of the triangles are congruent.

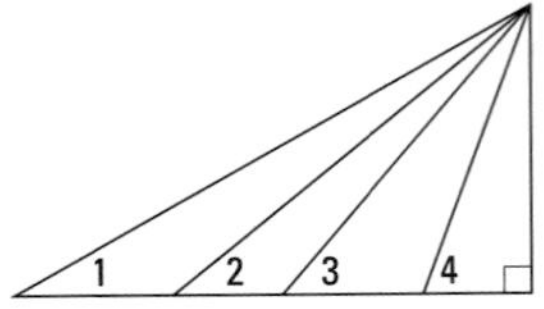

13. Use the figure at the left. Consider angles 1, 2, 3, and 4.
 a. Which has the largest tangent? $\angle 4$
 b. Which has the smallest tangent? $\angle 1$

14. Without calculating, explain why $\tan 75° > \tan 74°$. See margin.

Review

15a) $\frac{600}{\sqrt{3}} \approx 346.41$ units
b) $\frac{10{,}000}{\sqrt{3}} \approx 5773.50$ units^2

21)

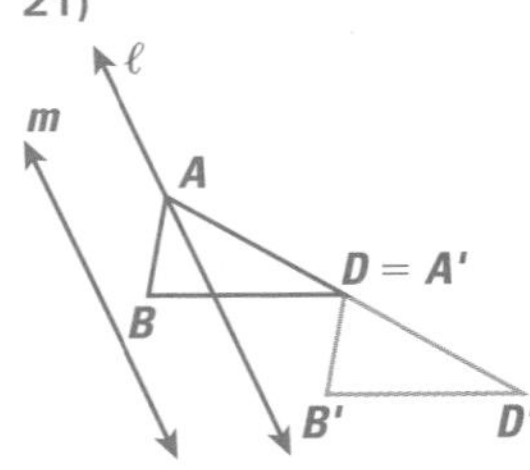

15. An altitude of an equilateral triangle has length 100. **a.** What is the perimeter of the triangle? **b.** What is the triangle's area? *(Lessons 8-4, 13-5)* See left.

16. Find the area of trapezoid $ZONK$ if $m\angle Z = m\angle O = 45$, $ZO = 24$, and $NK = 9$. *(Lessons 8-5, 13-5)* 123.75 units^2

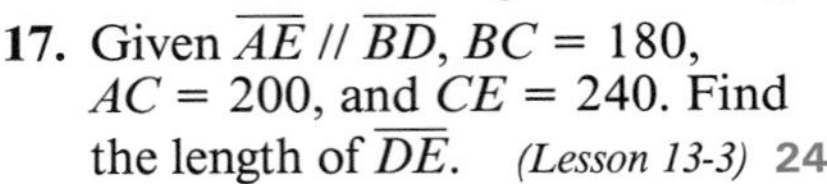

In 17 and 18, use the figure at the right.

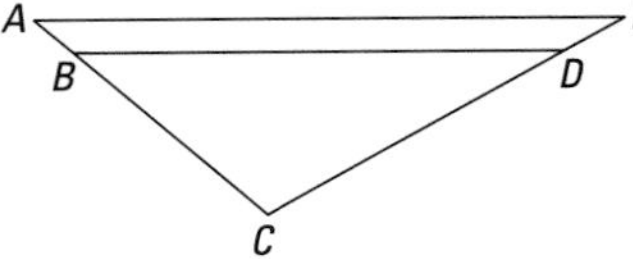

17. Given $\overline{AE} \parallel \overline{BD}$, $BC = 180$, $AC = 200$, and $CE = 240$. Find the length of $\overline{DE}$. *(Lesson 13-3)* 24

18. Suppose $BC = 13$, $AB = 0.8$, $ED = 0.9$, and $CD = 14$. Is $\overline{AE} \parallel \overline{BD}$? Why or why not? *(Lesson 13-3)*
No; because $0.8/13 \neq 0.9/14$.

19. The diagonals of any trapezoid split the trapezoid into four nonoverlapping triangles. See margin.
 a. Must two of these triangles be congruent? Justify your answer.
 b. Must two of these triangles be similar? Justify your answer.
 (Lesson 13-2)

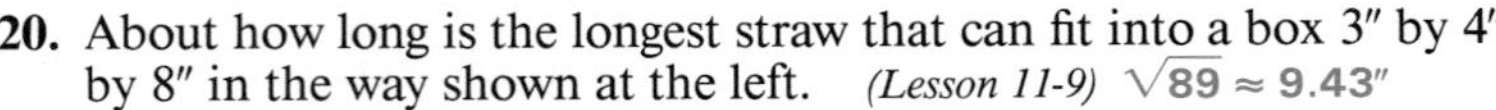

8" 4" 3"

20. About how long is the longest straw that can fit into a box 3″ by 4″ by 8″ in the way shown at the left. *(Lesson 11-9)* $\sqrt{89} \approx 9.43''$

In 21 and 22, trace the figure at the right, in which $\ell \parallel m$.

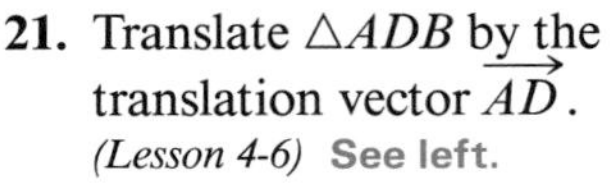

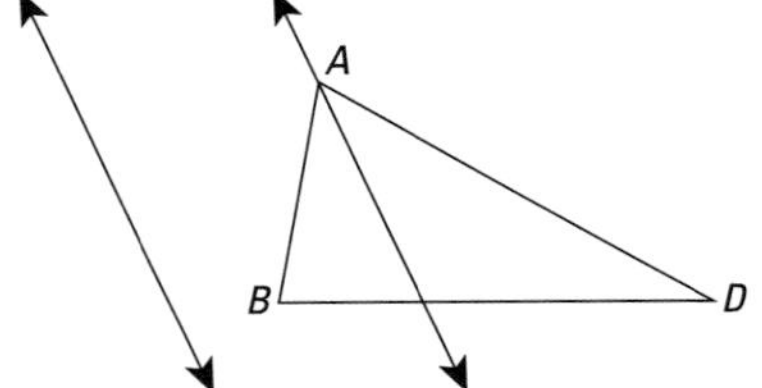

21. Translate $\triangle ADB$ by the translation vector $\overrightarrow{AD}$. *(Lesson 4-6)* See left.

22. Draw $r_\ell \circ r_m(DAB)$. Describe this transformation. *(Lesson 4-4)* See margin.

Exploration

23. Choose three angle measures (other than 90) whose sum is 180. (For example, you could choose 27, 97, and 56.) See left.
 a. Use a calculator to find the sum of the tangents of the numbers you have chosen. ≈ -6.1523
 b. Calculate the product of the tangents of the numbers you have chosen. ≈ -6.1523
 c. Repeat parts **a** and **b** with a different set of three angle measures.
 d. Make a conjecture based on your results. See left.
 Sample: If $m\angle A + m\angle B + m\angle C = 180$, then $\tan A + \tan B + \tan C = \tan A \cdot \tan B \cdot \tan C$.

23) Sample: Let $m\angle A = 27$, $m\angle B = 97$, and $m\angle C = 56$.
c) Let $m\angle A = 41$, $m\angle B = 24$, and $m\angle C = 115$. The sum of the tangents is about $-.830$. The product of the tangents is also about $-.830$.

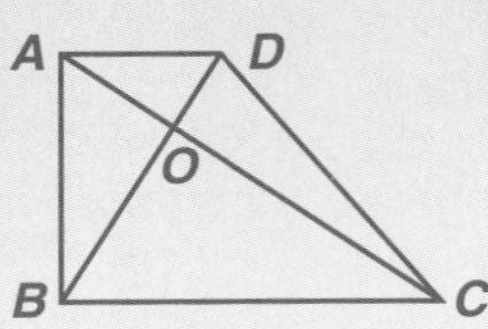

b. Yes. Use the trapezoid in part a. Because $\overline{AD} \parallel \overline{BC}$, $\angle DAO \cong \angle BCO$ and $\angle ADO \cong \angle CBO$ (// Lines ⇒ AIA ≅ Theorem). Therefore, by the AA Similarity Theorem, $\triangle ADO \sim \triangle CBO$.

22. It is a translation in the direction from m to ℓ perpendicular to m and ℓ, and twice the distance from m to ℓ.

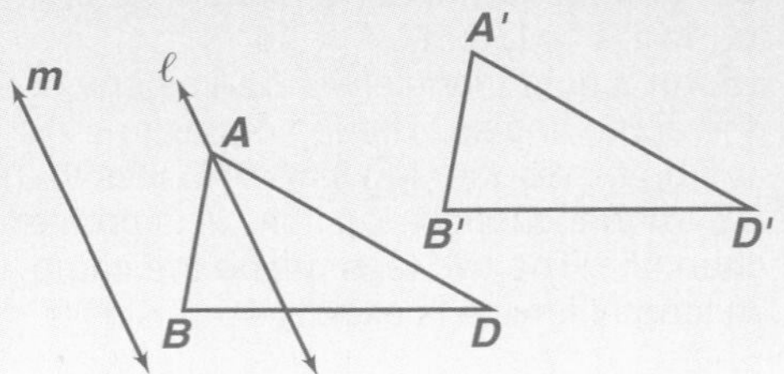

LESSON

13-7

The Sine and Cosine Ratios

Seaing the way. *Before radio communication, sailors needed to use a sextant to determine their position at sea. Sextants measure the angle between the horizon and a celestial body such as a star or the sun.*

The tangent is the ratio of the lengths of two legs in a right triangle. When a leg is compared to the hypotenuse, the *sine* or *cosine* ratio results.

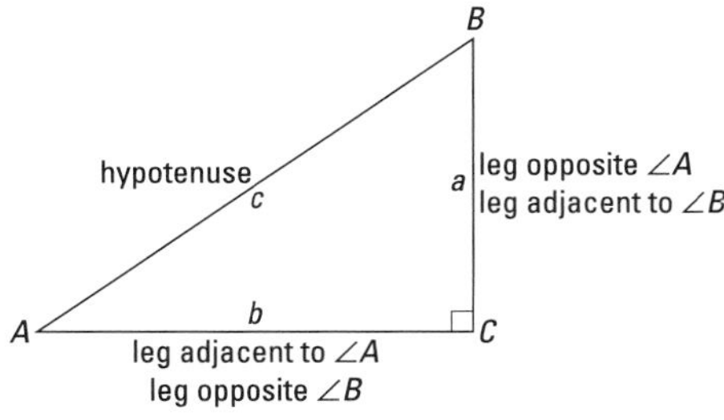

Definition
In right triangle ABC with right angle C,
the **sine of** $\angle A$**,** written **sin** A**,** is $\frac{\text{leg opposite } \angle A}{\text{hypotenuse}}$;
the **cosine of** $\angle A$**,** written **cos** A**,** is $\frac{\text{leg adjacent to } \angle A}{\text{hypotenuse}}$.

In the above triangle, $\sin A = \frac{a}{c}$ and $\cos A = \frac{b}{c}$. In any other right triangle with an acute angle congruent to $\angle A$, the sine and cosine of that angle will have these same values because of the AA Similarity Theorem.

Lesson 13-7

Objectives
D Determine sines and cosines of angles.
E Estimate or determine exact values of sine and cosine ratios.
G Know the definitions of sine and cosine.
I Use sines and cosines to determine unknown lengths in real situations.

Resources
From the ***Teacher's Resource File***
- Lesson Master 13-7A or 13-7B
- Answer Master 13-7
- Teaching Aids
  4 Coordinate Plane
  173 Warm-up
  180 Additional Examples
- Activity Kit, Activity 28
- Technology Sourcebook, Calculator Master 4

Additional Resources
- Visuals for Teaching Aids 4, 173, 180
- Videodisc

Teaching Lesson 13-7

Warm-up
Suppose a 15-foot ladder is propped against a wall so that the foot of the ladder is 7.5 feet from the foot of the building.
1. What angle does the ladder make with the ground? 60°
2. How high up the wall does the ladder reach? $7.5\sqrt{3}$ feet

Lesson 13-7 Overview

Broad Goals This lesson contains a standard treatment of the sine and cosine ratios. Students are expected to calculate the ratios and to use them to calculate unknown lengths in right triangles.

Perspective You may have found in the last lesson that understanding the keys on a calculator is a great motivator for learning mathematical ideas. This lesson should be even more motivating, because two keys are explained and because the words *sine* and *cosine* are associated exclusively with trigonometry.

You may also wish to motivate the further study of trigonometry by indicating that lengths of sides in *any* triangle can be determined by using sines and cosines if enough information is given, and that sound waves and many other phenomena can be described using these numbers.

Notes on Reading

As with tangents, students should be able to obtain exact or approximate values of sines and cosines: given sides of a right triangle **(Example 1),** in special triangles **(Example 2),** and by using a calculator or by drawing **(Example 3).** Nothing is better for concept development than an actual drawing.

❶ You may wish to give your students ways of checking values of sines and cosines like those found in **Example 1.** For any angles A and B:

(1) *Complements Property:* If $m\angle A + m\angle B = 90°$, then $\sin A = \cos B$ and $\cos A = \sin B$.

(2) *Pythagorean Identity:* $(\sin A)^2 + (\cos A)^2 = 1$. Students may discover this pattern in **Question 24.**

(3) *Tangent, Sine, Cosine Relationship*: $\tan A = \frac{\sin A}{\cos A}$.

Error Alert Students sometimes make errors in application problems involving the trigonometric ratios because they use the incorrect ratio. Stress that definitions must be applied correctly and are given for the acute angles only.

❷ **History Connection** Regiomontanus was a pseudonym of Johann Muller, a 15th century German mathematician from Königsberg. He created the name from the Latinization of Königsberg, which means "King's Mountain" in German. In the 1450s and 1460s he learned Greek in order to translate the works of Ptolemy, particularly the *Almagest,* in which the principles of trigonometry are stated. In 1464, he wrote the *Five Books of Triangles of All Kinds* based on Ptolemy's work, and thereby introduced trigonometry to the people of his time.

Example 1

Right triangle ABC has side lengths as indicated below. Find each value.

a. $\sin A$
b. $\cos A$
c. $\sin B$
d. $\cos B$

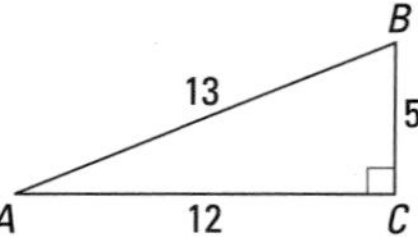

Solution

a. $\sin A = \frac{\text{leg opposite } \angle A}{\text{hypotenuse}} = \frac{5}{13} \approx 0.3846$

b. $\cos A = \frac{\text{leg adjacent to } \angle A}{\text{hypotenuse}} = \frac{12}{13} \approx 0.9231$

c. $\sin B = \frac{\text{leg opposite } \angle B}{\text{hypotenuse}} = \frac{12}{13} \approx 0.9231$

d. $\cos B = \frac{\text{leg adjacent to } \angle B}{\text{hypotenuse}} = \frac{5}{13} \approx 0.3846$

❶ In Example 1, the reason that $\sin A = \cos B$ is that each is equal to $\frac{BC}{AB}$. Also $\sin B = \cos A$ since both equal $\frac{AC}{AB}$. This is because the leg opposite one acute angle is the leg adjacent to the other. Also recall that angles A and B are complementary. This is the origin of the term "cosine"; *cosine* is short for *co*mplement's *sine.*

Estimating Sines and Cosines

As with tangents, you can estimate values of sines and cosines with drawings or a calculator. To approximate sin 54° or cos 54°, you can draw a right triangle with a 54° angle, as shown at the left. Measuring the sides of this triangle, we find lengths (to the nearest mm) of 21 mm, 29 mm, and 36 mm.

From these measurements, $\sin 54° = \frac{BC}{AB} \approx \frac{29}{36} \approx 0.81$ and $\cos 54° = \frac{AC}{AB} \approx \frac{21}{36} \approx 0.58$. A calculator gives greater accuracy. For sin 54°, press

54 [sin] or [sin] 54 [ENTER].

An 8-digit display will show 0.80901699 so $\sin 54° \approx 0.8090$. For cos 54°, press

54 [cos] or [cos] 54 [ENTER].

The display may show 0.58778525 so $\cos 54° \approx 0.5878$.

Exact Values of Sines and Cosines

Drawings and calculators usually give approximations to sines and cosines. When the lengths of sides are known exactly, as in special triangles, you can find exact values for the sine and cosine ratios.

Video

Wide World of Mathematics The segment, *The Leaning Tower of Pisa,* discusses the closing of the tower to visitors because the building is leaning more and more each year. The segment may be used to introduce or extend this lesson on the sine and cosine. Related questions and an investigation are provided in videodisc stills and in the Video Guide. A related CD-ROM activity is also available.

Videodisc Bar Codes

Search Chapter 64

Play

Example 2

Find exact values of sin 30° and cos 30°.

Solution

Sketch a 30-60-90 triangle as shown at the right. The legs have lengths x and $x\sqrt{3}$, and the hypotenuse has length $2x$.

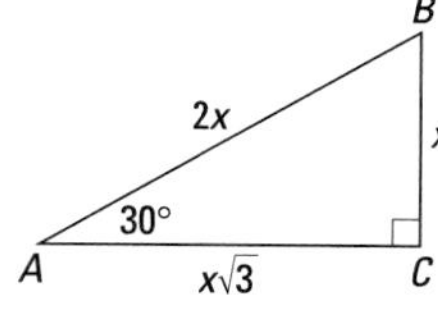

$\sin 30° = \frac{x}{2x} = \frac{1}{2}$

$\cos 30° = \frac{x\sqrt{3}}{2x} = \frac{\sqrt{3}}{2}$

Check

A calculator shows sin 30° = .5 and cos 30° ≈ .8660254. These decimal values agree with the exact values found in the solution.

An artist's rendering of Ptolemy.

Applications of Sines and Cosines

Sines and cosines have a great number and variety of applications, and a long history. The ancient Babylonians and Greeks measured the sides and angles of triangles carefully, needing such measurements for navigation, surveying, and astronomy. The first table of trigonometric values was constructed by Claudius Ptolemy in the second century A.D. Values like our present-day sine, cosine, and tangent values were first
2 obtained by the German astronomer Regiomontanus (1436–1476). The abbreviations *sin*, *cos*, and *tan* were first used by Euler.

Example 3

A particular 30-foot extension ladder is safe if the angle it makes with the ground is between 65° and 80°.

a. What is the farthest up on a vertical wall that a 30-foot ladder of this type can reach and still be safe?

b. How far, at a minimum, should the foot of the ladder be placed from the base of the wall?

Solution

First draw a picture. To reach the maximum height, use m∠A = 80. In the figure drawn, BC is the height for part **a** and AC is the horizontal distance for part **b**.

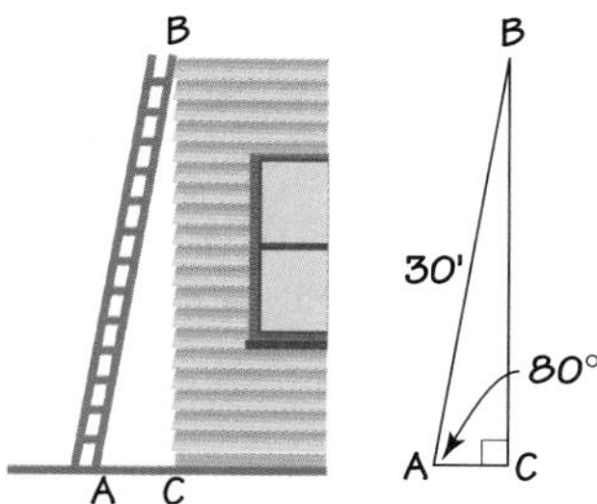

▶

A mnemonic you can present to help students remember the trigonometric ratios is "SOHCAHTOA" (a variant of "sock it to you"), which is short for "Sine is Opposite over Hypotenuse; Cosine is Adjacent over Hypotenuse; and Tangent is Opposite over Adjacent."

Additional Examples

These examples are also given on **Teaching Aid 180.**

1. In right triangle *HUG*, find sin *U*, cos *U*, sin *G*, and cos *G*.

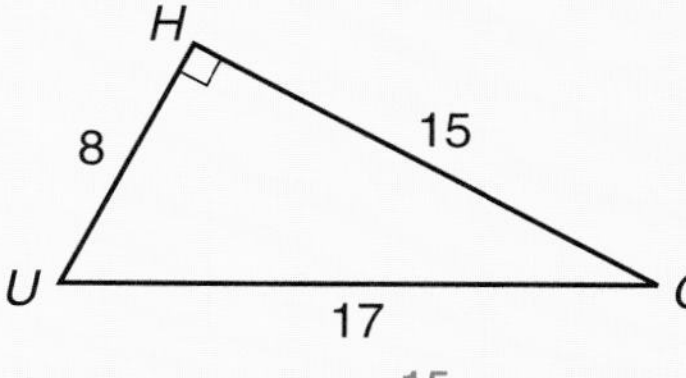

sin U = cos G = $\frac{15}{17}$ ≈ .882
sin G = cos U = $\frac{8}{17}$ ≈ .471

2. Which two of the following are equal: sin 45°, cos 45°, tan 45°? sin 45° and cos 45°

3. A supporting wire 8 feet long is to extend from the top of a pole 6 feet high. What is the angle between the wire and the pole? Let the angle be A. cos A = .75, from which m∠A ≈ 41.

Optional Activities

Activity 1 Technology Connection In *Technology Sourcebook, Calculator Master 4*, students measure right triangles and use their scientific calculator to estimate the sine and cosine ratios. Students then explore an interesting relationship between the sine and cosine of an angle.

Notes on Questions

Questions 4–5 When they are asked to find exact values, students should not use their calculators (unless they want to check calculations). Answers should be reduced ratios.

Question 6 Ask students first to use the lengths of the sides to obtain the ratios by division, and then to use their calculators to find the trigonometric values required and to check the decimal values of the ratios obtained by division.

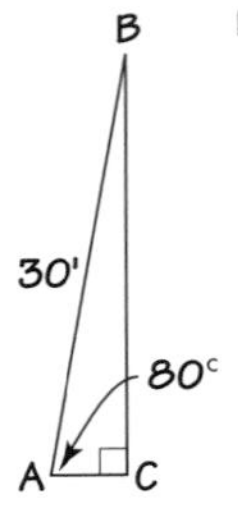

a. $\overline{BC}$ is the leg opposite the 80° angle. Since the hypotenuse is known, the sine should be used.

$$\sin 80^\circ = \frac{\text{leg opposite } 80^\circ \text{ angle}}{\text{hypotenuse}}$$

A calculator shows $\sin 80^\circ \approx 0.985$. Substituting,

$$0.985 \approx \frac{BC}{30}.$$

Solve for BC. $BC \approx 30 \cdot 0.985 \approx 29.6$ feet

The ladder can safely reach about 29.6 feet high on the wall.

b. $\overline{AC}$ is the leg adjacent to the 80° angle. This suggests using the cosine.

$$\cos 80^\circ = \frac{\text{leg adjacent to } 80^\circ \text{ angle}}{\text{hypotenuse}}$$

A calculator shows $\cos 80^\circ \approx 0.174$. Substituting,

$$0.174 \approx \frac{AC}{30}.$$

Solve for AC. $AC \approx 30 \cdot 0.174 \approx 5.2$ feet.

5.2 feet = 5 feet, 2.4 inches. If the ladder is placed less than 5.2 feet away it is too steep to be used safely.

Check

The Pythagorean Theorem can check both answers at once.

Does $AC^2 + BC^2 = AB^2$?

$$(5.2)^2 + (29.6)^2 = 30^2$$

The left side is 903.2, the right side is 900. This is close enough, given the approximations used for sin 80° and cos 80° and the rounding done to get 5.2 and 29.6.

The measure of an acute angle can be found if its sine or cosine is known, as the following example shows.

Example 4

Suppose the bottom of the ladder in Example 3 is placed 6 feet from the wall.

a. What angle does the ladder make with the ground?

b. Explain whether this is a safe position for the ladder.

Solution

a. Draw a picture, as at the right. The side adjacent to $\angle A$ and the hypotenuse are known. So the cosine should be used.

$\cos A = \frac{6}{30} = 0.2$

From this, $m\angle A =$ [cos⁻¹] $.2 \approx 78.5°$.

b. 78.5° is between 65° and 80°, so it is a safe position for the ladder.

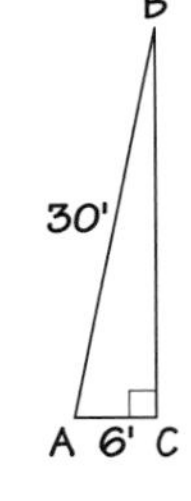

Optional Activities

Activity 2

Materials: Graph paper or **Teaching Aid 4**

You may use this activity to introduce the lesson. Have the students **work in groups.** Each group will need a scientific or graphics calculator and graph paper or **Teaching Aid 4.** Tell students that for each of the following angles, 15°, 30°, 45°, 60°, 75°, they should use the sine of the angle as the y-coordinate and the cosine of the angle as the x-coordinate and graph the point (x, y) in the coordinate plane. Tell them to find the sines and cosines on their calculators to the nearest hundredth. Also advise them to label the axes in tenths. Ask them to describe the resulting graph. [All points lie on the unit circle.]

Activity 3

You may use *Activity Kit, Activity 28,* as a follow-up to the lesson. In this activity, students use a graph called a Triangle Solver to find missing parts in right triangles.

QUESTIONS

Covering the Reading

M, O, N

1. In $\triangle MNO$ at the left, identify each segment.
   a. leg opposite $\angle N$ $\overline{MO}$ b. hypotenuse $\overline{MN}$
   c. leg adjacent to $\angle M$ $\overline{MO}$ d. leg adjacent to $\angle N$ $\overline{NO}$

2. In right $\triangle ABC$ with right angle C, what are $\cos A$ and $\sin A$? See left.

3. In $\triangle FGH$ at the right, find See left.
   a. $\sin F$.
   b. $\cos F$.
   c. $\tan G$.
   d. $\sin G$.

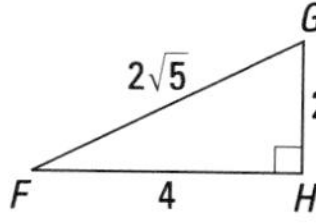

4. Give an exact value for: **a.** $\sin 60°$. **b.** $\cos 60°$. **c.** $\tan 60°$. See left.
5. Give an exact value for: **a.** $\sin 45°$. **b.** $\cos 45°$. **c.** $\tan 45°$. See left.
6. The figure at the right shows the approximate lengths of the sides in a right triangle with angles of 42° and 48° and hypotenuse 15. Use these lengths to fill in the blanks.

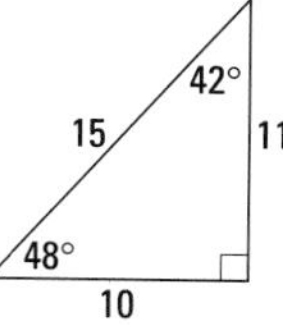

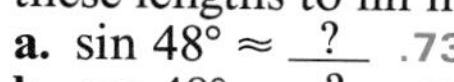

   a. $\sin 48° \approx$ _?_ .73
   b. $\cos 48° \approx$ _?_ .67
   c. $\tan 42° \approx$ _?_ .91
   d. $\cos 42° \approx$ _?_ .73

7. Estimate to the nearest thousandth. **a.** $\sin 13.2°$ **b.** $\cos 13.2°$ a) .228; b) .974
8. **a.** In Examples 3 and 4 what is the greatest safe distance between the base of the ladder and the wall? $\approx$ 12.7 ft
   b. How high will it reach at that distance? $\approx$ 27.2 ft.

In 9–11, consider a 20′ ladder with the same safety restrictions as in Example 3.

9. How far up on a vertical wall can the ladder safely reach? $\approx$ 19.7 ft
10. How far, at minimum, should the bottom of the ladder be from the wall? $\approx$ 3.5 ft
11. Is it safe to place the base of this ladder 6 feet from the wall? Yes

Applying the Mathematics

12. **a.** Use your calculator to estimate $\sin 89°$ to the nearest ten-thousandth. .9998
    b. Use a triangle to explain why the value is so near 1. See left.
13. In the triangles at the right, $\angle B \cong \angle B'$. See left.
    a. By measuring lengths of sides, estimate $\sin B$ and $\sin B'$.
    b. Do your results agree with what you expected?

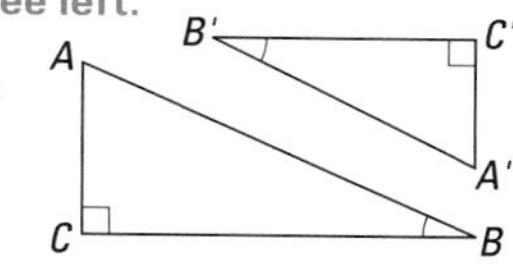

2) $\cos A = \frac{AC}{AB}$; $\sin A = \frac{BC}{AB}$

3a) $\frac{2}{2\sqrt{5}} = \frac{1}{\sqrt{5}} \approx .447$
b) $\frac{4}{2\sqrt{5}} = \frac{2}{\sqrt{5}} \approx .894$
c) 2
d) $\frac{4}{2\sqrt{5}} = \frac{2}{\sqrt{5}} \approx .894$

4a) $\frac{\sqrt{3}}{2}$ b) $\frac{1}{2}$ c) $\sqrt{3}$

5a) $\frac{1}{\sqrt{2}}$ or $\frac{\sqrt{2}}{2}$
b) $\frac{1}{\sqrt{2}}$ or $\frac{\sqrt{2}}{2}$ c) 1

12b) A right triangle with an 89° angle is close to isosceles (because the 89° angle is nearly the measure of the right angle), so the length of the leg opposite the 89° angle is almost the same as the hypotenuse.

13a) Sample: $\sin B \approx \frac{14}{34} \approx .412$; $\sin B' \approx \frac{10}{24} \approx .417$
b) Yes; they probably will not be equal, due to measurement error, but very close.

Adapting to Individual Needs

Extra Help

Remind students that the sine or cosine of an angle is never greater than 1 because the hypotenuse is the longest side in a right triangle and the hypotenuse appears in the denominator of both the sine and cosine ratios.

English Language Development

Before discussing **Question 16,** you might want to discuss the meaning of *depression* with students with limited English proficiency. Draw a figure on the board with a "hollow" in it. Explain that this low point is a depression. Similarly, a person who is feeling depressed is feeling "low" in spirits. Then explain that an angle of depression refers to the relationship between a person's eye to some object lower than the line of his or her eye.

LESSON MASTER 13-7 A — Questions on SPUR Objectives. See pages 794–797 for objectives.

Skills Objective D

In 1–3, use $\triangle JKL$ at the right. Find the indicated ratio.

1. sin K .6
2. cos K .8
3. cos J .6

Skills Objective E

4. Estimate sin 68° to the nearest hundredth. .93

In 5 and 6, give exact values.

5. cos 45° $\frac{\sqrt{2}}{2}$ 6. sin 60° $\frac{\sqrt{3}}{2}$

Properties Objective G

7. Define cos A. $\cos A = \frac{\text{leg adjacent to } \angle A}{\text{hypotenuse}}$

In 8 and 9, use $\triangle HIL$ at the right.

8. $\frac{IL}{HI}$ is the sine of angle H.
9. Write a ratio for cos H. $\frac{HL}{HI}$

Uses Objective I

10. What is the measure of the angle x made by a 200-ft supporting cable with a 150-ft-tall radio tower? 41.4
11. How far up on the side of a building can a 15-m ladder reach if the measure of the angle it makes with the ground may not exceed 72°? 14.3 m

Notes on Questions

Question 16 Ask students why the angle of depression from the top of the building has the same measure as the angle of elevation from the bottom of the building. [If parallel lines are cut by a transversal, then alternate interior angles have the same measure.]

Question 24 Many patterns can be seen in this table. For instance, as angle measures increase, the sine increases, but the cosine decreases. Also, the cosine of an angle equals the sine of its complement.

Follow-up for Lesson 13-7

Practice

For more questions on SPUR Objectives, use **Lesson Master 13-7A** (shown on page 781) or **Lesson Master 13-7B** (shown on pages 782–783).

Assessment

Oral/Written Communication
Follow the directions in the *Assessment* for Lesson 13-6, but now have the students find the sine and cosine of each acute angle. [Students draw a right triangle with all three sides of correct length and then correctly determine the sine and cosine for each acute angle.]

LESSON MASTER 13-7 B **Questions on SPUR Objectives**

Skills Objective D: Determine sines and cosines of angles.

1. Use $\triangle ABC$ at the right.

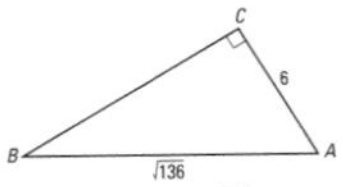

a. Find BC. 10
b. Find $\sin B$. $\frac{3\sqrt{34}}{34}$
c. Find $\sin A$. $\frac{5\sqrt{34}}{34}$
d. Find $\cos B$. $\frac{5\sqrt{34}}{34}$ e. Find $\cos A$. $\frac{3\sqrt{34}}{34}$
f. Estimate $m\angle B$. ≈ 31 g. Estimate $m\angle A$. ≈ 59

Skills Objective E: Estimate or determine exact values of sine and cosine ratios.

In 2–7, give exact values.

2. $\sin 30°$ $\frac{1}{2}$ 3. $\sin 45°$ $\frac{\sqrt{2}}{2}$ 4. $\sin 60°$ $\frac{\sqrt{3}}{2}$
5. $\cos 30°$ $\frac{\sqrt{3}}{2}$ 6. $\cos 45°$ $\frac{\sqrt{2}}{2}$ 7. $\cos 60°$ $\frac{1}{2}$

In 8–15, estimate to the nearest thousandth.

8. $\sin 40°$ .643 9. $\cos 40°$ .766
10. $\cos 65°$ .423 11. $\sin 83°$ .993
12. $\sin 47.8°$ .741 13. $\cos 56.1°$ .558
14. $\sin 70.5°$ .943 15. $\cos 29.6°$ .869

In 16–18, use $\triangle DEF$ at the right. Do *not* use a protractor.

16. Determine the approximate measure of each angle.
a. $m\angle D$ 40 b. $m\angle F$ 50

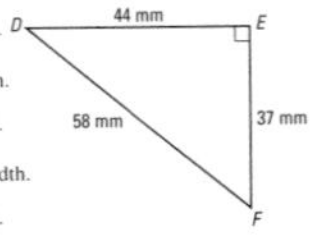

17. Calculate each sine to the nearest hundredth.
a. $\sin D$ $\approx .64$ b. $\sin F$ $\approx .76$

18. Calculate each cosine to the nearest hundredth.
a. $\cos D$ $\approx .76$ b. $\cos F$ $\approx .64$

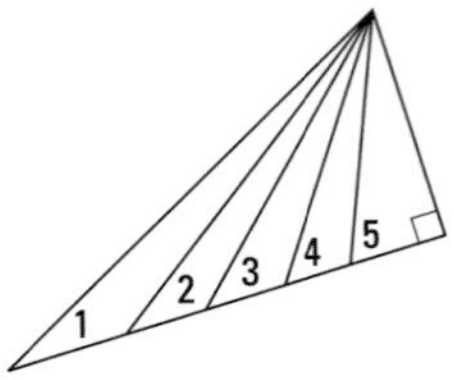

14. a. Of angles 1, 2, 3, 4 and 5 pictured at the left, which angle has the largest sine? $\angle 5$
b. Which angle has the largest cosine? $\angle 1$

15. What length wire is needed as a brace from the top of a 20-foot pole, if the brace is to make an angle of 85° with the ground? $\approx$ 20.1 ft

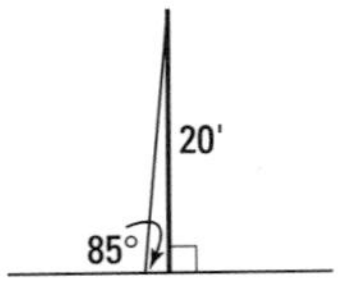

16. From the top of a building you look down at an object on the ground. If your eyes are 55 feet above the ground, and the angle of sight, called the *angle of depression*, is 50° below the horizontal, how far is the object from you? $\approx$ 72 ft

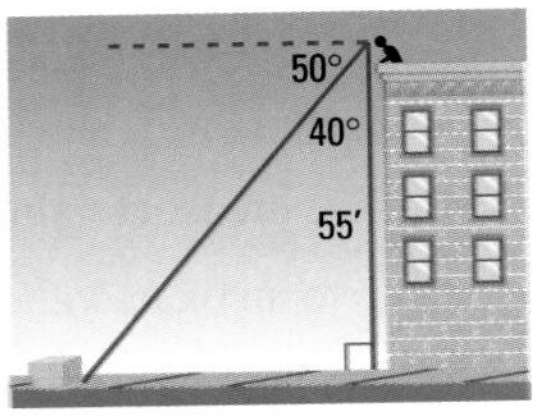

Review

17. When the sun is 25° up from the horizon, a tree casts a shadow 14.5 feet long. How tall is the tree? *(Lesson 13-6)* $\approx$ 6.76 feet

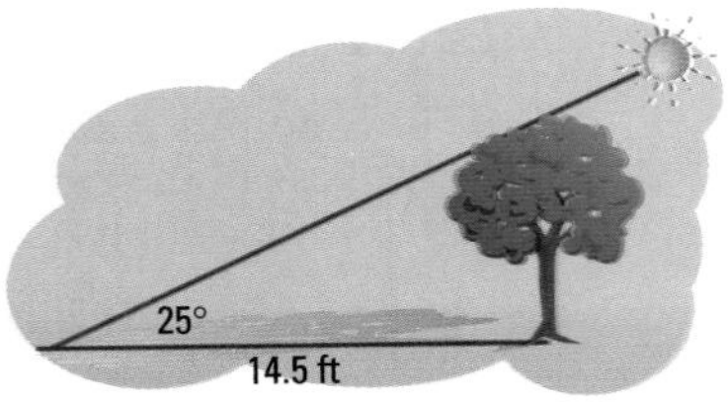

18. From eye level, 160 cm off the ground, about 440 meters away from a skyscraper, a person has to look up at an angle of 30° to see the top of the building. About how high (in meters) is the building? *(Lesson 13-6)* $\approx$ 255.6 m

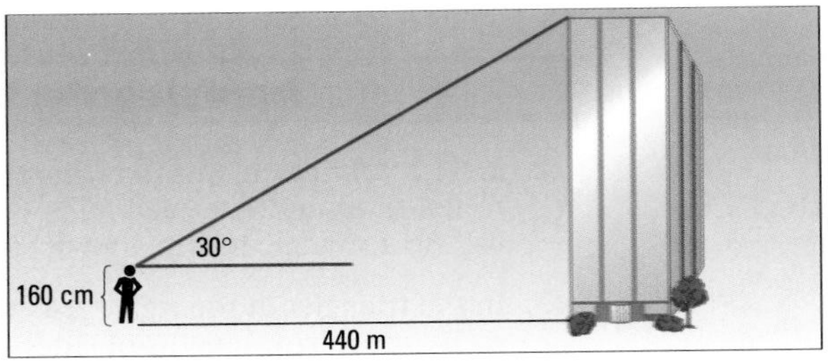

Adapting to Individual Needs

Challenge
Tell students to draw any right triangle *ABC* in which $\angle C$ is the right angle. Then have them use the definitions given in this lesson to prove the following results.

1. $(\sin A)^2 + (\cos A)^2 = 1$
$[(\sin A)^2 + (\cos A)^2 =$
$(\frac{a}{h})^2 + (\frac{b}{h})^2 = \frac{a^2 + b^2}{h^2} = \frac{h^2}{h^2} = 1$

2. $\tan A = \frac{\sin A}{\cos A}$ $[\frac{\sin A}{\cos A} = \frac{a/h}{b/h} = \frac{a}{b} = \tan A]$

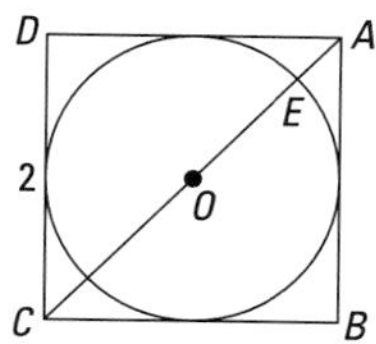
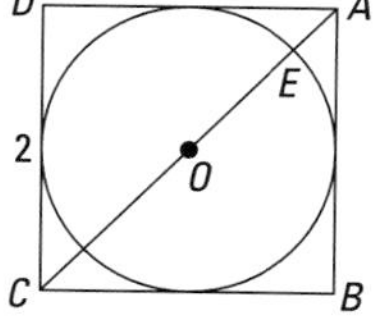

19. At the left, circle O is inscribed in the square. Find AE. *(Lesson 13-5)* $\sqrt{2} - 1 \approx 0.414$

20. Are the two triangles in the figure at the right similar? Explain why or why not. *(Lesson 13-2)* See left.

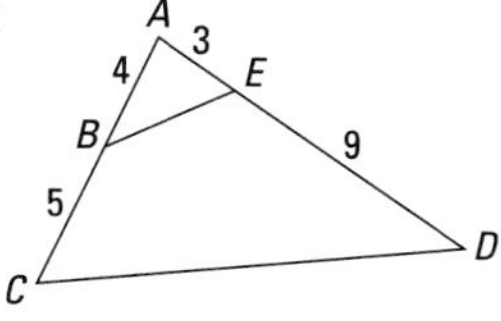

21. a. Write the converse, the inverse, and the contrapositive of the following statement: If $\triangle ABC \sim \triangle DEF$, then $m\angle ABC = m\angle DEF$.

b. Which of the statements you wrote in part **a** are true? *(Lessons 11-2, 13-2)* See left.

22. Isosceles $\triangle ABC$ has vertex angle A. If its sides are 7, 7, and 12, find the length of the altitude from A. *(Lessons 6-2, 8-6)* $\sqrt{13} \approx 3.6$ units

23. Trace the figure at the right. Then draw the image of $ABCD$ under the translation described by the vector $\overrightarrow{EF}$. *(Lesson 4-6)* See left.

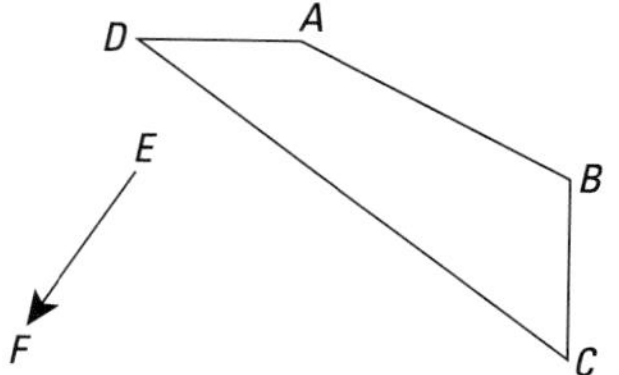

Exploration

24. a. Use a calculator to fill in this table of sine and cosine values.

x	sin x	cos x
5	.087	.996
10	.174	.985
15	.259	.966
20	.342	.940
25	.423	.906
30	.5	.866
35	.574	.819
40	.643	.766
45	.707	.707

x	sin x	cos x
50	.766	.643
55	.819	.574
60	.866	.5
65	.906	.423
70	.940	.342
75	.966	.259
80	.985	.174
85	.996	.087

b. For which of these values of x does $(\sin x)^2 + (\cos x)^2 = 1$? all

c. Generalize part **b.** For any value of x, $(\sin x)^2 + (\cos x)^2 = 1$

20) Yes, because $\angle BAE \cong \angle DAC$, $\frac{AE}{AB} = \frac{AC}{AD}$ $\left(\frac{3}{4} = \frac{9}{12}\right)$. $\triangle ADC \sim \triangle ABE$ (SAS Similarity Theorem)

21a) Converse: If $m\angle ABC = m\angle DEF$, then $\triangle ABC \sim \triangle DEF$.
Inverse: If $\triangle ABC$ is not similar to $\triangle DEF$ with vertices in that order, then $m\angle ABC \neq m\angle DEF$.
Contrapositive: If $m\angle ABC \neq m\angle DEF$, then $\triangle ABC$ is not similar to $\triangle DEF$ with vertices in that order.
b) The contrapositive is true.

23)

D A B A' D' B' C C'

Extension

Writing You might want to use the table of values calculated in **Question 24** to ask students to make some generalizations about the value of the sine and cosine function as the angle increases or decreases. Ask the following questions:

1. What happens to the value of the sine as the angle increases? [The sine increases from a number near 0 to a number near 1.]
2. What happens to the value of the cosine in the same interval? [The value of the cosine decreases from a number near 1 to a number near 0.]
3. What appears to be the maximum value for the sine or cosine? [1]
4. Justify your answer to Question 3 by considering the possible lengths of the sides of a right triangle. [Since the hypotenuse is the longest side and is the denominator, the ratios are always less than 1. But the side opposite an acute angle approaches the hypotenuse as the measure of the acute angle approaches 90°.]

Project Update Project 4, *Regular Polygons and Unit Circles,* on page 790, relates to the content of this lesson.

Setting Up Lesson 13-8

Review **Question 24** as a lead-in to Lesson 13-8.

▸ **LESSON MASTER 13-7B** *page 2*

Properties Objective G: Know the definitions of sine and cosine.

19. Define *sin A*. Sample: Sin A is the ratio of the side opposite ∠A to the hypotenuse.

In 20–23, use △*RST* at the right.

20. Write a ratio for each function.
a. sin R $\frac{ST}{RT}$ **b.** cos R $\frac{RS}{RT}$

21. $\frac{RS}{RT}$ is the sine of which angle? ∠T

22. $\frac{TS}{RT}$ is the cosine of which angle? ∠T

23. How is sin R affected if $m\angle R$ increases? s in R increases.

S T R

Uses Objective I: Use sines and cosines to determine unknown lengths in real situations.

24. From a point at the foot of a hill, the angle of elevation of the top is 15°. The distance from the foot of the hill to the top is 150 meters. Find the height of the hill. ≈ 38.8 m

25. A 30-foot ladder leans against a building making an angle of 72° with the ground.
a. How high on the building does the ladder reach? ≈ 28.5 ft
b. How far from the building is the end of the ladder? ≈ 9.3 ft

26. The tailgate of a tractor-trailer rig is 1 m off the ground. The greatest incline for efficiently loading the truck is 10°. How long should the ramp be for a 10° incline? ≈ 5.7 m

27. A plane takes off at an angle of 24° with the ground.
a. How far has it traveled in a horizontal distance after it has traveled 3 miles? ≈ 2.74 mi
b. How high, in feet, is the plane after it has traveled 3 miles? ≈ 6442 ft

28. A biker pedaled up a slope of 6° for 150 meters and then another 100 meters at a slope of 9°.
a. How far did the biker travel in a horizontal distance? ≈ 248 m
b. How far did the biker climb vertically? ≈ 31 m

Lesson 13-8

Objectives

D Use the SAS area formula.
J Determine components of vectors in real situations.

Resources

From the ***Teacher's Resource File***
- Lesson Master 13-8A or 13-8B
- Answer Master 13-8
- Teaching Aids
  105 Graph Paper
  173 Warm-up

Additional Resources
- Visuals for Teaching Aids 105, 173

Teaching Lesson 13-8

Warm-up

Find the area of each triangle.

1. 15, 12, 20
120 units²

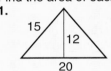

2. 12, 30°, 25
75 units²

3. $5\sqrt{2}$, 45°, 15
37.5 units²

LESSON

13-8 More Work with Vectors and Area

Go the distance. *The Panama Canal lies on a vector about 40° north of west. Its use shortens a ship's journey between the east and west coasts of the United States by 8000 nautical miles.*

A few lessons are not enough to show all the applications of sines and cosines. Sometimes entire books are devoted to trigonometry. In this lesson, we give applications that result directly from the definitions of the sine and cosine. The first application is to vectors, the second to area.

Finding Components of a Vector

Recall from Lesson 4-6 that a vector is a quantity that can be characterized by its direction and magnitude. Consider a ship that is moving at 25 miles per hour in a direction 30° south of east. This speed and direction is called its **velocity.** The velocity can be represented by the vector $\overrightarrow{OA}$ below. The magnitude of $\overrightarrow{OA}$ is 25 and the direction of $\overrightarrow{OA}$ is 30° clockwise from the positive x-axis. The velocity can be broken down into its eastern component and its southern component using sines and cosines.

Example 1

Find the eastern and southern components of the velocity of a ship moving at 25 miles per hour in a direction 30° south of east.

Solution

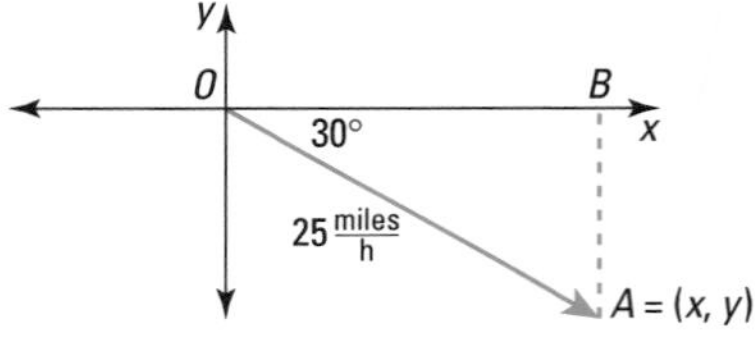

Lesson 13-8 Overview

Broad Goals This lesson covers two useful applications of trigonometry: finding components and directions of vectors and finding the area of a triangle given the SAS condition.

Perspective This lesson consists of two applications of the three trigonometric functions studied in previous lessons. The first application is to vectors. **Example 1** shows how to find the components of a vector using sines and cosines when its direction and length are known. **Example 2** reverses the process; from the components of a vector, its direction and length are found. This requires the tangent function.

The second application is to area. The SAS Triangle Area Formula, is deduced from the formula $A = \frac{1}{2}hb$ for the area of a triangle. Recall that Heron's Formula, finds the area of a triangle given the SSS condition. There is no simple formula for the area of a triangle given the ASA or AAS conditions.

The material in this lesson will be quite helpful for students who later will study physics. Often physics teachers introduce the trigonometric functions very early in the year, before mathematics teachers have covered them.

The eastern component is $\overrightarrow{OB}$. The southern component is $\overrightarrow{BA}$.

Since $\frac{OB}{OA} = \cos 30°$,

$$\begin{aligned} OB &= OA \cos 30° \\ &= 25 \cos 30° \\ &\approx 25 \cdot 0.866 = 21.65 \text{ miles/hr.} \end{aligned}$$

Similarly, because $\frac{BA}{OA} = \sin 30°$,

$$\begin{aligned} BA &= OA \sin 30° \\ &= 25 \sin 30° \\ &= 25 \cdot 0.5 = 12.5 \text{ miles/hr.} \end{aligned}$$

So the position of the ship is changing by about 21.65 miles/hr to the east and 12.5 miles/hr to the south.

In Example 1, one component was found using the sine of the given angle. The other component was found using the cosine. However, you do not have to memorize which is which. It is usually safer to draw a picture each time and use the definitions of the sine and cosine.

Finding the Direction of a Vector From Its Components

To find the direction of a vector from its components, the tangent is required.

Example 2

An airplane has to fly to a location 60 km east and 100 km north of its present location.

a. In what direction should it fly?

b. How far will it travel?

Solution

Again, draw a picture. A sample is shown at the right.

a. The direction can be found from m∠*FOE*. We know that

$$\tan \angle FOE = \frac{100}{60}.$$

So $m\angle FOE = \tan^{-1} \frac{100}{60}$. You can key in

100 ÷ 60 = INV tan or INV tan (100 ÷ 60) ENTER.

You should see 59.0362 . . . displayed. This means that $m\angle FOE \approx 59°$.

The direction the plane should fly is about 59° north of east.

You could also say that the plane should fly about 31° east of north.

b. *OF* can be found using the Pythagorean Theorem.

$$OF = \sqrt{60^2 + 100^2} = \sqrt{13600} \approx 116.6$$

The plane will travel about 117 km.

Notes on Reading

You might want to use *Optional Activities* below to introduce this lesson.

The first key idea in this lesson is that the trigonometric functions provide a way of using the measures of angles in triangles to obtain side lengths. This is applied to find the components of a vector. You might wish to use the following drawing to help students generalize the idea.

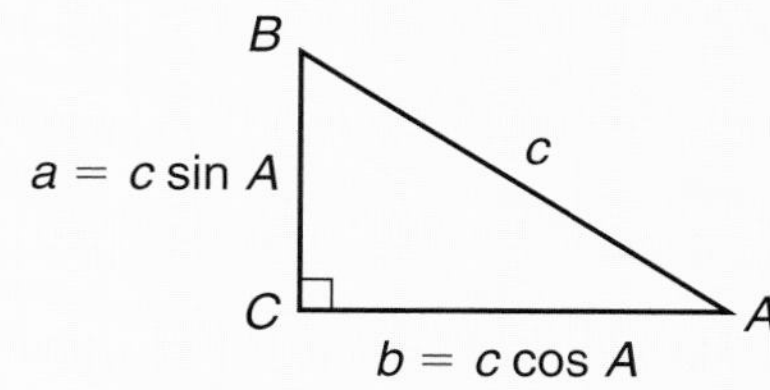

The second key idea is that, by going in the reverse direction, one can find the angle measures from the sides. The third key idea is that, with knowledge of the sides, we can obtain the area of a triangle. The specific instance of this in **Example 3** is followed by the general SAS Triangle Area Formula theorem.

Since the SAS area formula is the first formula that students have had which involves the trigonometric functions, make certain students understand how to evaluate it.

Optional Activities

Materials: Graph Paper or **Teaching Aid 105**

You can use this activity to introduce the lesson. Have students draw several triangles on graph paper. Tell them to place each triangle in a convenient location so they know the length of the altitude and the base without measuring. Then have them compute the area by first using the formula $A = \frac{1}{2}bh$ and then by using the SAS Triangle Area Formula. They should verify that the methods yield the same area.

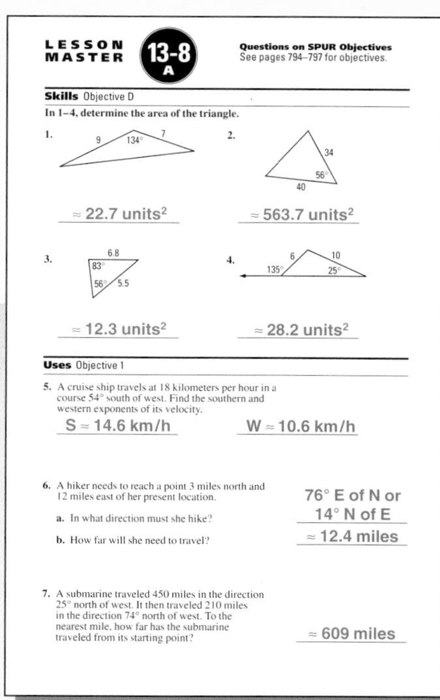

LESSON MASTER 13-8 A

Questions on SPUR Objectives
See pages 794–797 for objectives.

Skills Objective D

In 1–4, determine the area of the triangle.

1. ≈ 22.7 units²

2. ≈ 563.7 units²

3. ≈ 12.3 units²

4. ≈ 28.2 units²

Uses Objective 1

5. A cruise ship travels at 18 kilometers per hour in a course 54° south of west. Find the southern and western exponents of its velocity.
S ≈ 14.6 km/h W ≈ 10.6 km/h

6. A hiker needs to reach a point 3 miles north and 12 miles east of her present location.
   a. In what direction must she hike? 76° E of N or 14° N of E
   b. How far will she need to travel? ≈ 12.4 miles

7. A submarine traveled 450 miles in the direction 25° north of west. It then traveled 210 miles in the direction 74° north of west. To the nearest mile, how far has the submarine traveled from its starting point? ≈ 609 miles

Additional Examples

1. A segment 10 units long has one endpoint at the origin and goes in a direction 22° west of south. Give the coordinates of its other endpoint, to the nearest hundredth. (-10 sin 22°, -10 cos 22°) ≈ (-3.75, -9.27)
2. Willie travels 3.3 miles east and 2.4 miles south to get to school. From his house, Willie sees smoke in a direction 36° south of east. Is it possible that the smoke is from a fire originating at the school? The school is in the direction tan $\frac{2.4}{3.3}$, or about 36° south of east. So it is possible that the smoke is originating at the school.
3. What is the area of a triangular plot of land with two sides of lengths 150 meters and 173 meters, and an 83° angle between them? ≈ 12,900 square meters

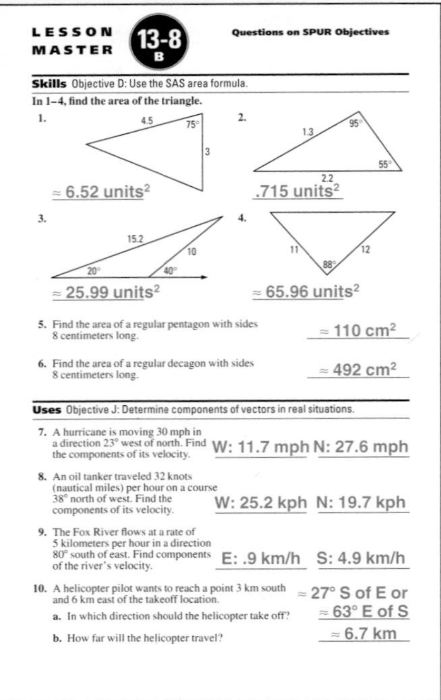

LESSON MASTER 13-8 B — Questions on SPUR Objectives

Skills Objective D: Use the SAS area formula.

In 1–4, find the area of the triangle.

1. ≈ 6.52 units²
2. .715 units²
3. ≈ 25.99 units²
4. ≈ 65.96 units²
5. Find the area of a regular pentagon with sides 8 centimeters long. ≈ 110 cm²
6. Find the area of a regular decagon with sides 8 centimeters long. ≈ 492 cm²

Uses Objective J: Determine components of vectors in real situations.

7. A hurricane is moving 30 mph in a direction 23° west of north. Find the components of its velocity. W: 11.7 mph N: 27.6 mph
8. An oil tanker traveled 32 knots (nautical miles) per hour on a course 38° north of west. Find the components of its velocity. W: 25.2 kph N: 19.7 kph
9. The Fox River flows at a rate of 5 kilometers per hour in a direction 80° south of east. Find components of the river's velocity. E: .9 km/h S: 4.9 km/h
10. A helicopter pilot wants to reach a point 3 km south and 6 km east of the takeoff location.
    a. In which direction should the helicopter take off? ≈ 27° S of E or ≈ 63° E of S
    b. How far will the helicopter travel? ≈ 6.7 km

Another Triangle Area Formula

The same idea that was applied in Example 1 can be used to find the area of a triangle if you know two sides and the included angle.

Example 3

In $\triangle PQR$, $PQ = 12$, $PR = 30$, and $m\angle P = 41°$. What is the area of $\triangle PQR$?

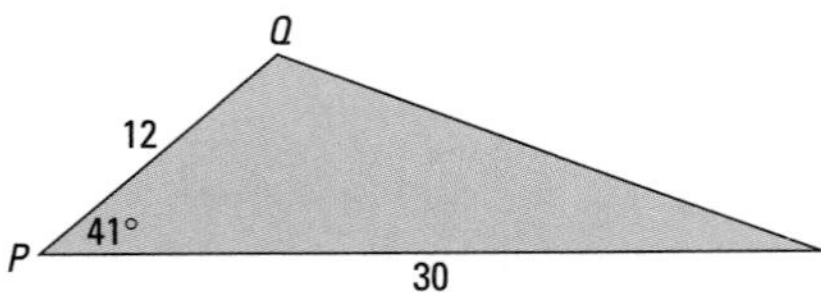

Solution

The area is given by the formula $A = \frac{1}{2}hb$, where h is the altitude to a base b. We let the longer side $\overline{PR}$ be the base, and draw the altitude from Q to that side, intersecting $\overline{PR}$ at T. $\triangle PQT$ is a right triangle. We need to find h.

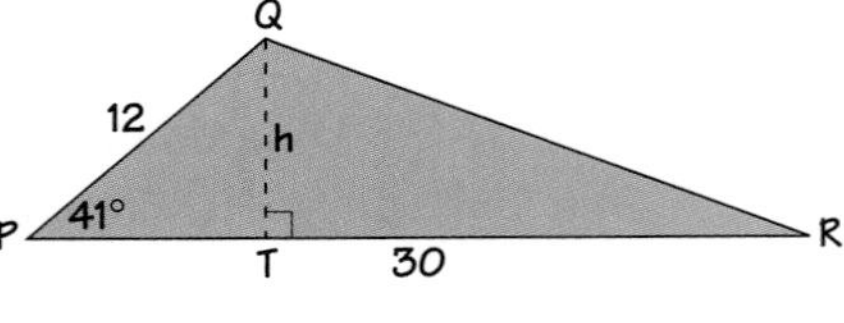

$$\sin P = \frac{h}{12}$$

So,

$$h = 12 \sin P$$
$$= 12 \sin 41°$$
$$\approx 7.87.$$

So, the area $A = \frac{1}{2}hb \approx \frac{1}{2} \cdot 7.87 \cdot 30 \approx 118.05$ square units.

The process that was used in Example 3 can be generalized to give the following elegant formula. The proof is left for you as Question 10.

SAS Triangle Area Formula
In any $\triangle ABC$, area($\triangle ABC$) $= \frac{1}{2}ab \sin C$.

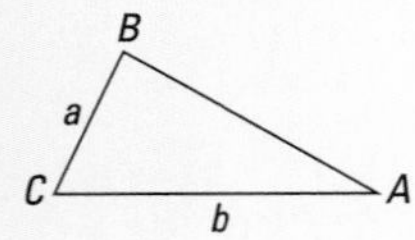

1)

340 mph
15°
y
x
0

2) Because $\triangle XYZ$ is a right triangle and $m\angle X = 90°$, $\sin Z = \frac{XY}{ZY}$. Therefore, $XY = YZ \cdot \sin Z$.

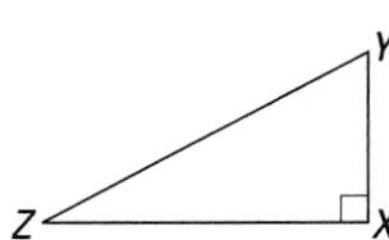

QUESTIONS

Covering the Reading

1. Consider a plane traveling at 340 mph in a direction 15° north of west. Picture this with a vector. See left.
2. In $\triangle XYZ$ at the left, explain why $XY = YZ \cdot \sin Z$. See left.

Funnel cloud. *Paths of tornadoes average 16 miles long and can be several hundred yards wide. They travel from 30 to 40 mph with winds as high as 500 mph.*

In 3–5, find the indicated side of the right triangle.

3.

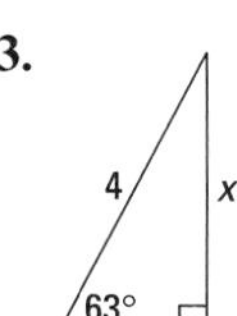
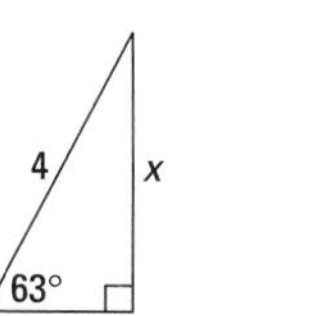

$x = 4 \sin 63° \approx 3.56$

4.

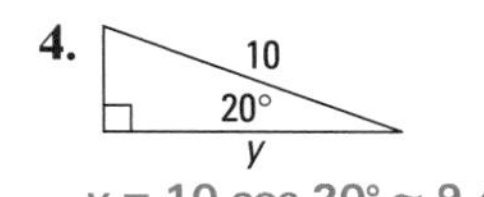

$y = 10 \cos 20° \approx 9.40$

5.

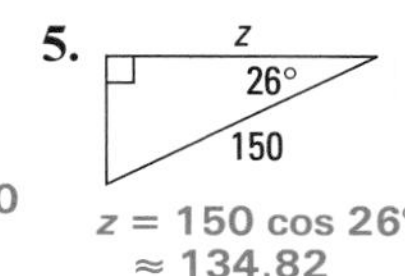

$z = 150 \cos 26° \approx 134.82$

6. Give the northern and eastern components of the velocity of a tornado moving at 20 mph in a direction 15° north of east. See left.

7. An airplane is to fly 200 km south and 40 km west of its present location. See left.

a. In what direction should it fly?

b. How far will it travel?

In 8 and 9, give the area of the triangle.

8. ≈ 2462.55 units^2

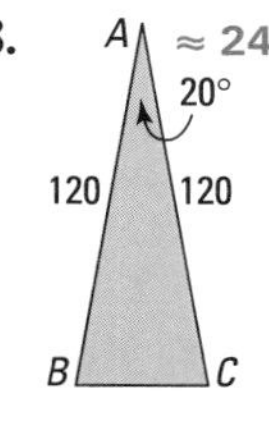

9. ≈ 50.2 units^2

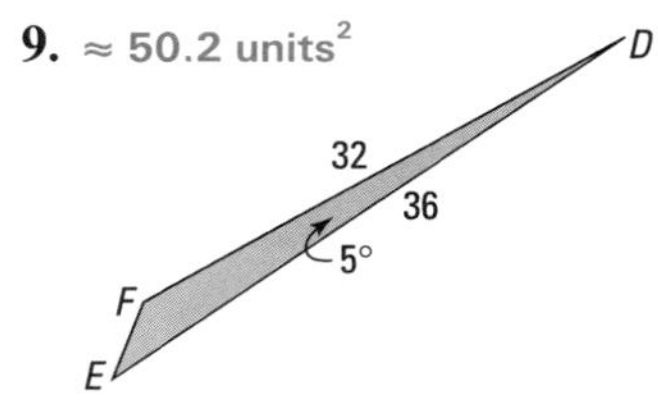

6) east component = $20 \cos 15° \approx 19.32$ mph; north component = $20 \sin 15° \approx 5.18$ mph

7a) $\approx 11°$ west of south, or 79° south of west
b) $\sqrt{41{,}600} = 40\sqrt{26}$ km ≈ 203.96 km

10)

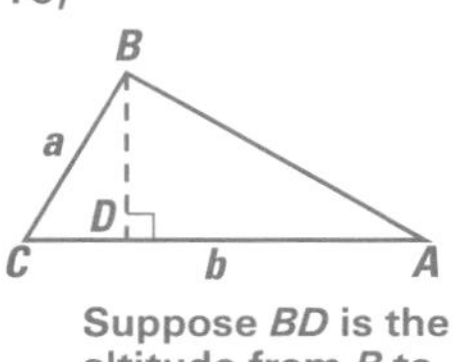

Suppose BD is the altitude from B to side $\overline{AC}$.

$\text{Area}(\triangle ABC) = \frac{1}{2} \cdot AC \cdot BD = \frac{1}{2} \cdot AC(BC \cdot \sin C) = \frac{1}{2} \cdot AC \cdot BC \cdot \sin C = \frac{1}{2} ba \sin C$

Applying the Mathematics

10. Prove the SAS Triangle Area Formula, Area $\triangle ABC = \frac{1}{2} ab \sin C$, when C is an acute angle. (Hint: Use the figure on page 786. Draw in the altitude from B to side $\overline{AC}$). See left.

11. A regular pentagon is cut from a disk of metal of radius 5 cm.

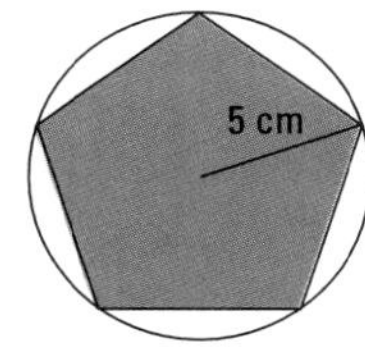

a. Find the area of the pentagon. ≈ 59.44 cm^2

b. How much material is cut off, to the nearest cm^2? ≈ 19 cm^2

12. What is the area of $\triangle STU$ below? ≈ 91 units^2

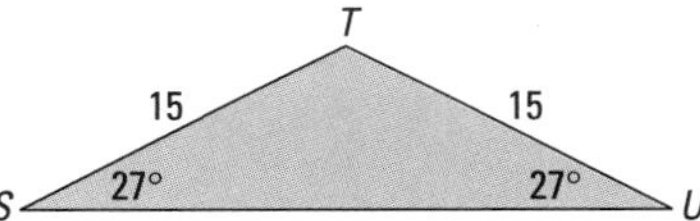

13. A trade triangle was formed between Johor, Malaysia; Singapore; and Batam Island, Indonesia in the 1960s to promote economic growth. Suppose a ship traveled 20 km on a trade route from Johor on a course 9° east of south to Singapore. Then it traveled 50 km on a course 24° south of east to Batam Island. How far (to the nearest km) is Johor from Batam Island? 63 km

Notes on Questions

Question 1 Error Alert Caution students that a direction 15° north of west and a direction 15° west of north are different

Questions 2–9 These questions should be covered in order.

Question 11 In general, the area of any regular polygon can be found from the radius of the circumscribed circle, using the SAS Triangle Area Formula. Project 4, on page 790, covers this generalization.

Question 12 Discuss the various ways this can be found. Here are two methods: (1) After finding $m\angle T$, the SAS Triangle Area Formula can be used. (2) The length of the altitude from T can be found using right triangle trigonometry. Then SU can be found using the Pythagorean Theorem. Finally, the area can be found using the formula $A = \frac{1}{2}hb$.

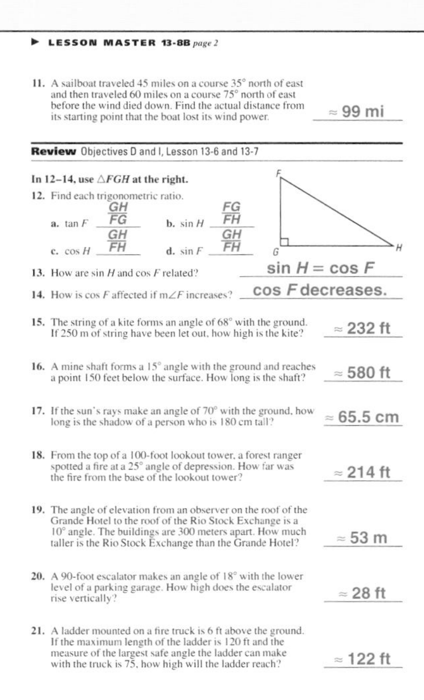

▶ **LESSON MASTER 13-8B** *page 2*

11. A sailboat traveled 45 miles on a course 35° north of east and then traveled 60 miles on a course 75° north of east before the wind died down. Find the actual distance from its starting point that the boat lost its wind power. ≈ 99 mi

Review Objectives D and I, Lesson 13-6 and 13-7

In 12–14, use $\triangle FGH$ at the right.

12. Find each trigonometric ratio.

a. $\tan F$ $\frac{GH}{FG}$ **b.** $\sin H$ $\frac{FG}{FH}$

c. $\cos H$ $\frac{GH}{FH}$ **d.** $\sin F$ $\frac{GH}{FH}$

13. How are $\sin H$ and $\cos F$ related? $\sin H = \cos F$

14. How is $\cos F$ affected if $m\angle F$ increases? $\cos F$ decreases.

15. The string of a kite forms an angle of 68° with the ground. If 250 m of string have been let out, how high is the kite? ≈ 232 ft

16. A mine shaft forms a 15° angle with the ground and reaches a point 150 feet below the surface. How long is the shaft? ≈ 580 ft

17. If the sun's rays make an angle of 70° with the ground, how long is the shadow of a person who is 180 cm tall? ≈ 65.5 cm

18. From the top of a 100-foot lookout tower, a forest ranger spotted a fire at a 25° angle of depression. How far was the fire from the base of the lookout tower? ≈ 214 ft

19. The angle of elevation from an observer on the roof of the Grande Hotel to the roof of the Rio Stock Exchange is a 10° angle. The buildings are 300 meters apart. How much taller is the Rio Stock Exchange than the Grande Hotel? ≈ 53 m

20. A 90-foot escalator makes an angle of 18° with the lower level of a parking garage. How high does the escalator rise vertically? ≈ 28 ft

21. A ladder mounted on a fire truck is 6 ft above the ground. If the maximum length of the ladder is 120 ft and the measure of the largest safe angle the ladder can make with the truck is 75, how high will the ladder reach? ≈ 122 ft

Adapting to Individual Needs

Extra Help

Point out that the SAS Triangle Area Formula applies only to triangles in which two known sides and the *included* angle are given. In other words, the formula does not apply when two sides and the angle opposite one of them are known.

English Language Development

You might want to discuss the meaning of the word *component* with students who have limited English proficiency. Explain that component means "one of the parts that make up a whole." A vector has a horizontal component and a vertical component.

Notes on Questions

Questions 14–15 There are two main ways to get the answers. The first way is by using the Pythagorean Theorem to find *AB* and then using the definitions of the trigonometric functions. The second is by first getting tan *A* (tan *B* in **Question 15**), then using the value of tan *A* to find the measure of angle *A*, and finally using a calculator to find sin *A* and cos *A*. Note that sin *B* = cos *A*, cos *B* = sin *A*, and tan $B = \frac{1}{\tan A}$.

Question 18a Error Alert Some students may know that the triangles are congruent, but then forget that congruent triangles are also similar.

Follow-up for Lesson 13-8

Practice

For more questions on SPUR Objectives, use **Lesson Master 13-8A** (shown on page 785) or **Lesson Master 13-8B** (shown on page 786–787).

Assessment

Written Communication Have students write three new examples similar to the ones given in the lesson. Each example should include the solution. [Students provide examples and solutions that are correct and that parallel those given in the book.]

Extension

Give students this problem: A plane leaves an airport and travels at 375 miles per hour in a direction 53.13° east of north. It suddenly encounters a wind that is blowing in a northerly direction at a speed of 45 miles per hour. How does the wind affect the direction of the plane? [The direction changes to about 48° east of north.]

Project Update Project 3, *Combining Forces,* and Project 4, *Regular Polygons and Unit Circles,* on page 790, relate to the content of this lesson.

14) $\sin A = \frac{7}{\sqrt{170}}$; $\cos A = \frac{11}{\sqrt{170}}$; $\tan A = \frac{7}{11}$

15) $\sin B = \frac{11}{\sqrt{170}}$; $\cos B = \frac{7}{\sqrt{170}}$; $\tan B = \frac{11}{7}$

18a) Yes, the two triangles are congruent by the SSS Congruence Theorem, so they are similar.

b) No, $\frac{12}{14} \neq \frac{13}{120} \neq \frac{14}{130}$

c) No, $\frac{12}{14} \neq \frac{13}{15} \neq \frac{14}{16}$

20a) It is a sphere with the same center and radius as circle *C*.

21) Sample: If 0° < α ≤ 90° then the area of triangle with fixed sides 7 and 10 increases as α increases. If 90° < α < 180° then the area of the triangle with fixed sides 7 and 10 decreases as α increases.

Review

In 14 and 15, consider △*ABC* at the right. *(Lessons 13-6, 13-7)* See left.

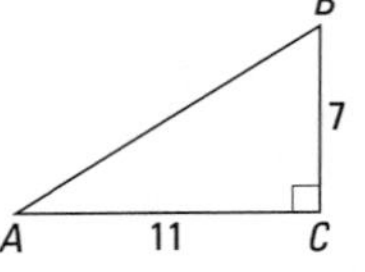

14. Give exact values of sin *A*, cos *A*, and tan *A*.

15. Give exact values of sin *B*, cos *B*, and tan *B*.

16. In regular hexagon *GHIDEF*, each side has length 10. Find the length of $\overline{GI}$. (Hint: Find the measures of the angles of △*GHI*.) *(Lessons 6-7, 13-5)* ≈ 17.32 units

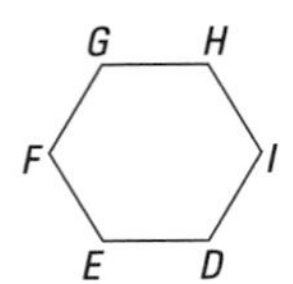

17. In a 5-12-13 right triangle, find the length of the altitude to the hypotenuse and the lengths of the segments into which the altitude splits the hypotenuse. *(Lesson 13-4)* $\frac{60}{13}$, $\frac{144}{13}$, $\frac{25}{13}$

18. A triangle has sides of 12, 13, and 14. Tell whether or not it is similar to each triangle. Explain why or why not. See left.

a. a triangle with sides of 13, 14, and 12

b. a triangle with sides of 120, 130, 14

c. a triangle with sides of 14, 15, and 16 *(Lesson 13-1)*

19. Make a conclusion using all of the following statements.

a. No *x* is a *y*.

b. If an animal is not a *y*, then the animal is not a *z*.

c. Rudolph is a *z*. *(Lesson 11-4)*

Rudolph is both a *y* and *z*, but not an *x*.

20. a. Refer to the figures at the right. Describe the figure formed by rotating circle *C* in space about line ℓ. See left.

b. Describe the figure formed by rotating circle *A* in space about line ℓ. *(Lesson 9-5)*
It is a doughnut (torus).

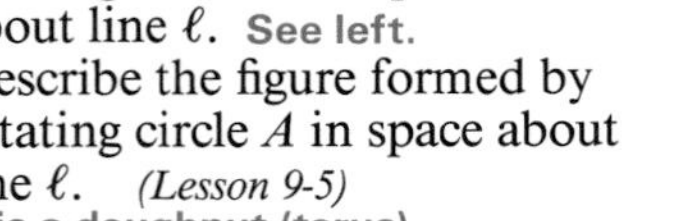

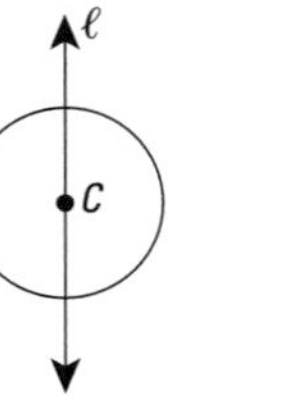

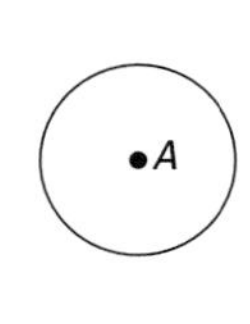

Exploration

21. The three triangles below have two congruent sides.

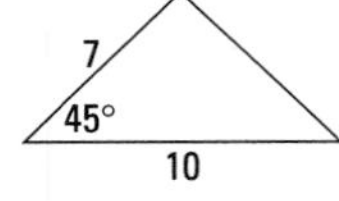

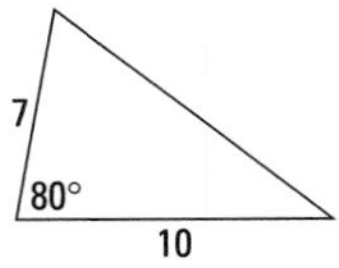

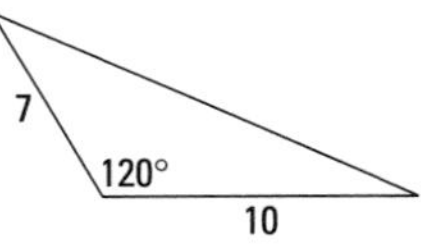

Explore what happens to the area of these triangles as the angle between the two sides increases from 0° to 180°. Write your explanation. See left.

Adapting to Individual Needs

Challenge

Let *v* be the vector whose initial point is the origin and whose endpoint is (*a*, *b*). Suppose (*a*, *b*) is in quadrant I.

1. Find the following in terms of *a* and *b*.

a. the magnitude (length) *r* of *v* [$r = \sqrt{a^2 + b^2}$]

b. the angle θ that *v* makes with the positive portion of the *x*-axis [$\theta = \tan^{-1} \frac{b}{a}$]

2. Suppose *v* has magnitude *r* and makes an angle θ with the positive portion of the *x*-axis. Give the horizontal and vertical components of *v*. [horizontal component: *r* cos θ, vertical component: *r* sin θ]

A project presents an opportunity for you to extend your knowledge of a topic related to the material of this chapter. You should allow more time for a project than you do for typical homework questions.

1 Measuring with Shadows

Four methods are given in this chapter for estimating heights of tall objects. They are found in Example 1 of Lesson 13-2, in Question 18 of Lesson 13-3, in Question 11 of Lesson 13-4, and in Example 1 of Lesson 13-6. Use at least three of these methods to estimate the height of at least three tall objects. Describe the methods you used and what you found.

2 Splitting Sides of a Trapezoid

Suppose you know the lengths of the four sides of a trapezoid $ABCD$ with bases $\overline{AB}$ and $\overline{CD}$ as pictured here. Further, suppose that you split the trapezoid by a segment $\overline{EF}$ parallel to the bases. Explain how, if you know the length of $\overline{AE}$, you can find

a. the lengths of $\overline{BF}$ and $\overline{FC}$, and

b. the length of $\overline{EF}$. If you cannot give a general process, answer the question for a number of special cases.

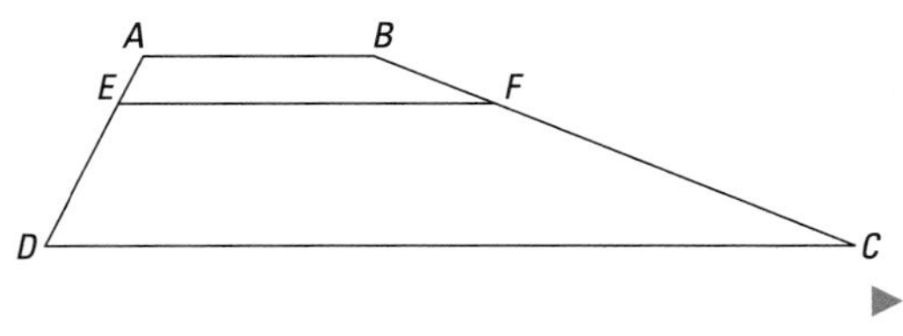

Chapter 13 Projects

The projects relate chiefly to the content of the lessons of this chapter as follows:

Project	Lesson(s)
1	13-2, 13-3, 13-6
2	13-3
3	13-8
4	13-5, 13-6, 13-7 13-8
5	13-1, 13-2, 13-5

1 Measuring with Shadows The four methods include (1) using similar triangles and the AA Similarity Theorem with shadows, (2) using similar triangles and the AA Similarity Theorem with reflections and mirrors, (3) using similar triangles and the geometric mean where the line of sight is common to both right triangles, and (4) using trigonometry.

2 Splitting Sides of a Trapezoid The main argument of the proof for **part a** is outlined in **Question 12** of Lesson 13-3.

Possible responses

1. Answers will vary. Students should describe at least three of the four methods of this chapter.
2. Given: Trapezoid $ABCD$ with $\overline{EF} \parallel \overline{DC}$. Prove: $\frac{AE}{ED} = \frac{BF}{FC}$.

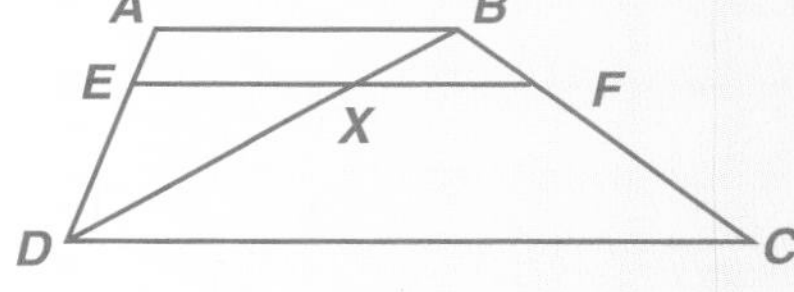

Additional responses

2a. We are given trapezoid $ABDC$ with $\overline{EF} \parallel \overline{AB} \parallel \overline{DC}$. Draw diagonal $\overline{BD}$, and label the intersection of $\overline{BD}$ and $\overline{EF}$ as X. Now consider $\triangle ABD$. By the Side-Splitting Theorem, $\frac{AE}{ED} = \frac{BX}{XD}$. By a similar argument, consider $\triangle BCD$. Again by the Side-Splitting Theorem, $\frac{BX}{XD} = \frac{BF}{FC}$. So, by the Transitive Property of Equality, $\frac{AE}{ED} = \frac{BF}{FC}$. Now $ED = AD - AE$. Let $BF = x$. Then $FC = BC - x$. By solving the proportion $\frac{AE}{ED} = \frac{x}{BC - x}$ for x, FC and BF can be found.

2b. Consider the pairs of triangles $\triangle DAB$ and $\triangle DEX$ and $\triangle BDC$ and $\triangle BXF$. Since $\overline{EF} \parallel \overline{AB} \parallel \overline{DC}$, it can be shown that $\triangle DAB \sim \triangle DEX$ and $\triangle BDC \sim \triangle BXF$ using the AA Similarity Theorem. Therefore, the sides of the respective similar triangles are in proportion, yielding $\frac{AD}{ED} = \frac{AB}{EX}$. So $EX = \frac{ED \cdot AB}{AD}$. Additionally, $\frac{CD}{FX} = \frac{CB}{FB}$ So $FX = \frac{CD \cdot FB}{CB}$. Lastly, $EF = EX + FX$.

(Responses continue on page 790.)

3 Combining Forces If vectors have components which go in the same direction, then those components are added. If vectors have components which go in different directions, then the smaller component is subtracted from the larger. The angle is determined using the inverse tangent function, and the length of the resultant vector is determined using the Pythagorean Theorem.

4 Regular Polygons and Unit Circles Remind students that in a regular polygon all sides and angles are congruent. The sum of the angle measures of a regular polygon is $180(n-2)$, where n is the number of angles (or sides) in the polygon.

5 Oblique Triangles with Integer, Sides and Integer Altitudes We begin with the figure shown below with a, b, c, d, and e integers. One possible way to expand the triangles is to multiply a, b, c, d, and e by the product ce. Then the values of m and n are computed as follows:

$$m = \frac{bce(ace + dce)}{c \cdot ce} = be(a + d),$$

$$n = \frac{bce(ace + dce)}{e \cdot ce} = bc(a + d).$$

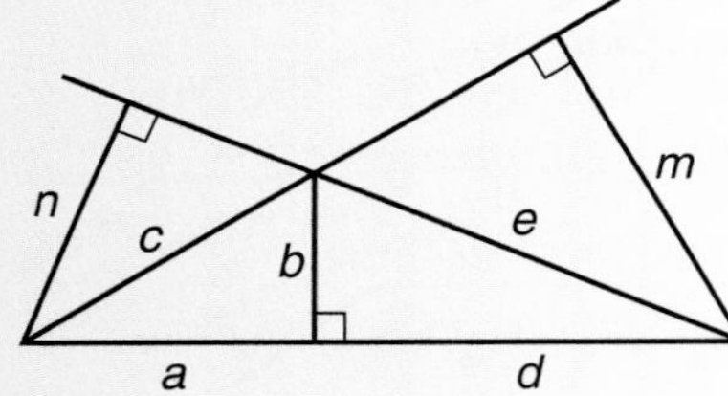

Another method, which will produce a similar set of figures, is to multiply all of a, b, c, d, and e by some multiple of ce.

(continued)

3 Combining Forces

By adding components of vectors, you can determine the result of two forces acting on an object. For instance, suppose a plane is flying at a speed and direction which, in still air, would be 550 mph, 25° north of west. Also, suppose there is a wind of 80 mph, 10° south of east. What is the resulting ground speed and direction of the plane in this wind condition? Answer this question and make up and answer at least two other questions using similar ideas.

4 Regular Polygons and Unit Circles

Each circle below has radius 1 unit. The regular polygon at the left is said to be circumscribed about the circle. The circle is inscribed in the polygon. The regular polygon below it is said to be inscribed in the circle. The circle is circumscribed about the polygon. There are formulas for the area and perimeter of these polygons in terms of the tangent and sine.

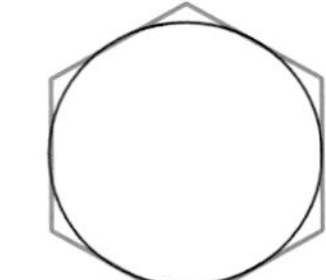

circumscribed regular hexagon

Perimeter $= 2n \cdot \tan\left(\frac{180°}{n}\right)$ units

Area $= n \cdot \tan\left(\frac{180°}{n}\right)$ square units

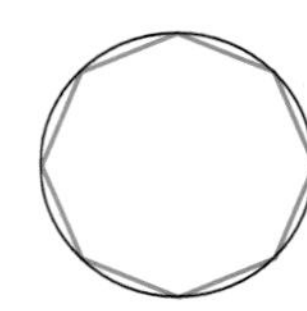

inscribed regular octagon

Perimeter $= 2n \cdot \sin\left(\frac{180°}{n}\right)$ units

Area $= n \cdot \sin\left(\frac{180°}{n}\right) \cdot \cos\left(\frac{180°}{n}\right)$ square units

a. Show that these formulas work when the regular n-gon is a square.

b. Prove any two of the formulas.

5 Oblique Triangles with Integer Sides and Integer Altitudes

The special triangles of this chapter do not have sides that are all integers. But you have seen many right triangles with sides that are all integers. For example, there are the 3-4-5 and 8-15-17 right triangles. We took two triangles of these types and put them together. $\triangle ALC$ below is a 3-4-5 triangle. $\triangle ABL$ is an 8-15-17 triangle. By expanding the triangles, we formed an oblique triangle whose sides are all integers and whose altitudes are also integers. Form two other oblique triangles whose three sides and three altitudes are all integers. Describe how you formed the triangles and how you determined the lengths of the altitudes.

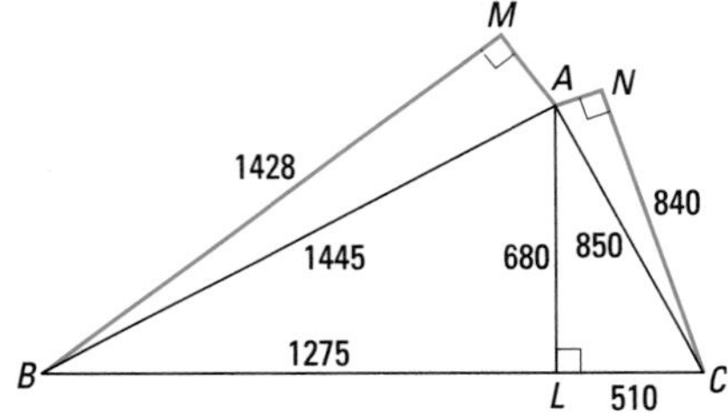

$\triangle ABC$ with sides $AB = 1445$, $AC = 850$, and $BC = 1785$, and altitudes $AL = 680$, $BM = 1428$, and $CN = 840$

Additional responses

3. In order to find the resulting speed, the components of each vector must be accounted for. With air speed of 550 mph 25° north of west, the north-south vector is $550 \cdot \sin 25°$ and the east-west vector is $-550 \cdot \cos 25°$. With wind speed of 80 mph 10° south of east, the north-south vector is $-80 \cdot \sin 10°$ and the east-west vector is $80 \cdot \cos 10°$.
north-south: $550 \cdot \sin 25° + (-80 \cdot \sin 10°)$ mph
east-west: $-550 \cdot \cos 25° + (80 \cdot \cos 10°)$ mph
The resulting vector formed is:
$\sqrt{(550 \cdot \sin 25° + (-80 \cdot \sin 10°))^2 + (-550 \cdot \cos 25° + (80 \cdot \cos 10°))^2} \approx$ 473.2 mph. The resulting angle formed is found by
$\tan x = \frac{550 \cdot \sin 25° + (-80 \cdot \sin 10°)}{-550 \cdot \cos 25° + (80 \cdot \cos 10°)}$; $x \approx 27.5°$ north of west.
The other problems that the students make up will vary.

SUMMARY

When triangles are similar, corresponding angles are congruent and corresponding sides form equal ratios. For triangles, the conditions guaranteeing similarity correspond to those for congruence. There are SSS, AA, and SAS Similarity Theorems, where A indicates corresponding congruent angles and S indicates equal ratios of corresponding sides.

Any line parallel to one side of a triangle and intersecting the other two sides forms similar triangles, and so splits these sides into proportional segments. The converse of this Side-Splitting Theorem is also true. When the altitude to the hypotenuse of a right triangle is drawn, two triangles are formed, each similar to the original. Three of the resulting proportions involve a geometric mean, as one length appears as both means in the proportion. The altitude itself is the geometric mean of the segments into which it divides the hypotenuse. Either leg is the geometric mean of the hypotenuse and the segment of the hypotenuse closest to it.

Right triangles are important because any triangle and thus any polygon can be split up into them, and because from knowing only one acute angle and one side, all lengths can be determined. Certain right triangles occur so often they are special. Any square can be split into two isosceles right triangles, with angles of 45°, 45°, and 90° and sides of lengths x, x, and $x\sqrt{2}$. Any equilateral triangle can be split into two right triangles with angles of 30°, 60°, and 90° and sides of lengths x, $x\sqrt{3}$, and $2x$.

When right triangles have congruent angles, the triangles are similar, and the ratios of corresponding sides within the triangles are equal. These are the trigonometric ratios. Three of the ratios are the tangent, sine, and cosine. The trigonometric ratios can be estimated using an accurate drawing or a scientific calculator, or calculated exactly if you are given lengths of sides in the triangle or are dealing with one of the special triangles.

Lengths in right triangles can be described in terms of sines and cosines. These descriptions give rise to the formula Area $= \frac{1}{2}ab \sin C$ for the area of any triangle. Sines and cosines also enable horizontal and vertical components of vectors to be described.

VOCABULARY

Below are the most important terms and phrases for this chapter. For the starred (*) terms you should be able to give a definition of the term. For the other terms you should be able to give a general description and a specific example of each.

Lesson 13-1
SSS Similarity Theorem

Lesson 13-2
AA Similarity Theorem
SAS Similarity Theorem
Reciprocals Property

Lesson 13-3
Side-Splitting Theorem
Side-Splitting Converse Theorem

Lesson 13-4
arithmetic mean
*geometric mean
Geometric Mean Theorem
Right-Triangle Altitude Theorem

Lesson 13-5
45-45-90 triangle
Isosceles Right Triangle Theorem
inscribed figure
30-60-90 triangle
30-60-90 Triangle Theorem

Lesson 13-6
leg opposite an angle
leg adjacent to an angle
*tangent of an angle A, *tan A
$\tan^{-1} x$
trigonometric ratio

Lesson 13-7
*sine of an angle A, *sin A
*cosine of an angle A, *cos A

Lesson 13-8
velocity
SAS Triangle Area Formula

Projects
Polygon circumscribed about a circle
Circle inscribed in a polygon
Polygon inscribed in a circle
Circle circumscribed about a polygon

Summary

The Summary gives an overview of the entire chapter and provides an opportunity for students to consider the material as a whole. Thus, the Summary can be used to help students relate and unify the concepts presented in the chapter.

Vocabulary

Terms, symbols, and properties are listed by lesson to provide a checklist of concepts a student must know. Emphasize to students that they should read the vocabulary list carefully before starting the Progress Self-Test. If students do not understand the meaning of a term, they should refer back to the indicated lesson.

4a. Begin with a unit circle with radius 1 unit. Then a circumscribed square will have sides of length 2 units, perimeter of 8 units, and area of 4 square units. According to the formulas: Perimeter $= 2(4) \cdot \tan\left(\frac{180°}{4}\right) = 8 \cdot \tan 45° = 8 \cdot 1 =$ 8 units. Yes, it checks. Area $= 4 \cdot \tan\left(\frac{180°}{4}\right) = 4 \cdot \tan 45° = 4 \cdot 1 = 4$ square units. Yes, it checks.

An inscribed square will have diagonal length 2 units, sides of length $\sqrt{2}$ units, perimeter of $4\sqrt{2}$ units, and area of 2 square units. According to the formulas, Perimeter $= 2(4) \cdot \sin\left(\frac{180°}{4}\right) = 8 \cdot \sin 45° = 8 \cdot \frac{\sqrt{2}}{2} = 4\sqrt{2}$ units. Yes, it checks. Area $= 4 \cdot \sin\left(\frac{180°}{4}\right) \cdot \cos\left(\frac{180°}{4}\right) = 4 \cdot \sin 45° \cdot \cos 45° =$ $4 \cdot \frac{\sqrt{2}}{2} \cdot \frac{\sqrt{2}}{2} = 2$ square units. Yes, it checks.

(Responses continue on page 792.)

Progress Self-Test

For the development of mathematical competence, feedback and correction, along with the opportunity to practice, are necessary. The Progress Self-Test provides the opportunity for feedback and correction; the Chapter Review provides additional opportunities and practice. We cannot overemphasize the importance of these end-of-chapter materials. It is at this point that the material "gels" for many students, allowing them to solidify skills and understanding. In general, student performance should be markedly improved after these pages.

Assign the Progress Self-Test as a one-night assignment. Answers to all questions are in the Selected Answers section of the student book. Encourage students to take the Progress Self-Test honestly, grade themselves, and then be prepared to discuss the test in class.

Advise students to pay special attention to those Chapter Review questions (pages 794–797) which correspond to questions missed on the Progress Self-Test.

PROGRESS SELF-TEST

Directions: Take this test as you would take a test in class. You will need a calculator with trigonometric functions. Check your work with the solutions in the Selected Answers section in the back of the book.

1. Use the figure at the right. If $BC = 6$ and $BD = 2$, find AB. $AB = 18$

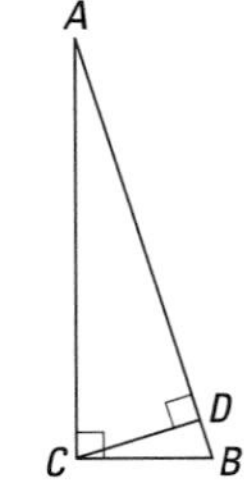

2. Refer to the figure at the right. If $XY = 60$ and $YZ = 75$, find WZ. $WZ = 27$

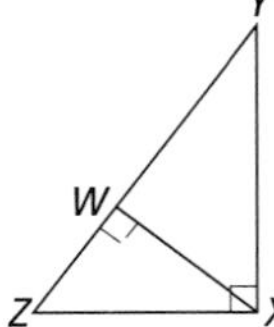

3) $VX = 13.75$

In 3 and 4, use the figure at the right, in which $\overleftrightarrow{WX} \parallel \overleftrightarrow{YZ}$.

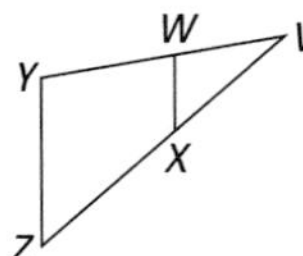

3. If $VW = 11$, $WY = 13$, and $VZ = 30$, what is VX?

4. If $WX = 8$, $YZ = 20$, and $WY = 15$, find VW. $VW = 10$

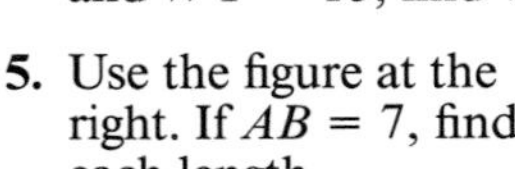
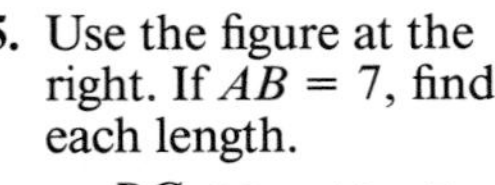

5. Use the figure at the right. If $AB = 7$, find each length.

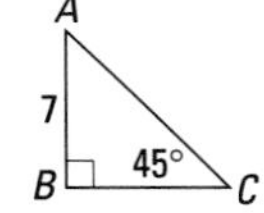

a. BC $BC = AB = 7$

b. AC $AC = 7\sqrt{2}$

6. An equilateral triangle has sides of length 30. Find the length of an altitude. $h = 15\sqrt{3} \approx 25.98$

9) Since $\overleftrightarrow{AB} \parallel \overleftrightarrow{DE}$, $\angle A \cong \angle E$, $\angle B \cong \angle D$ because of the // lines ⇒ AIA ≅ Thm. Therefore, $\triangle ABC \sim \triangle EDC$ by the AA Similarity Theorem.

9) See below left.

7. Refer to the triangles below. Are the triangles similar? Why or why not? See below.

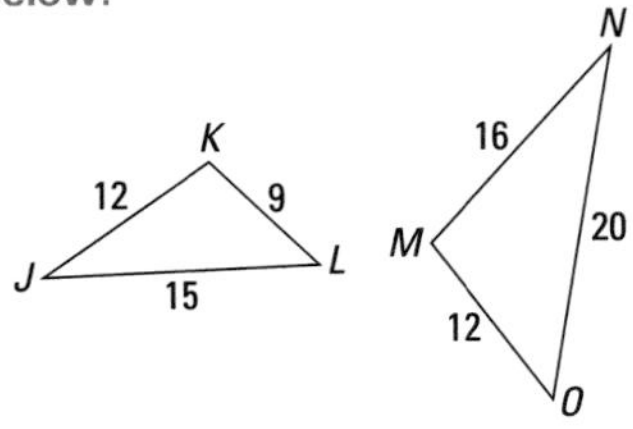

8. In $\triangle TRI$, $TR = 36$, $RI = 11$, and $m\angle TRI = 55$. What is the area of the triangle? ≈ 162 units^2

9. Write a proof argument.

Given: $\overleftrightarrow{AB} \parallel \overleftrightarrow{DE}$ and $\overline{AE}$ intersects $\overline{BD}$ at C in the figure below.

To prove: $\triangle ABC \sim \triangle EDC$.

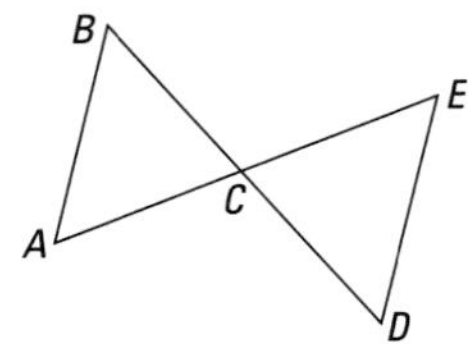

10. Estimate cos 31.2° to the nearest thousandth. ≈ 0.855

11. Give the exact value of sin 60°. $\frac{\sqrt{3}}{2}$

12. Define tan B for $\triangle ABC$ with right angle C. See below.

13. Refer to the figure below. Of the numbered angles, which has the smallest tangent? $\angle 3$

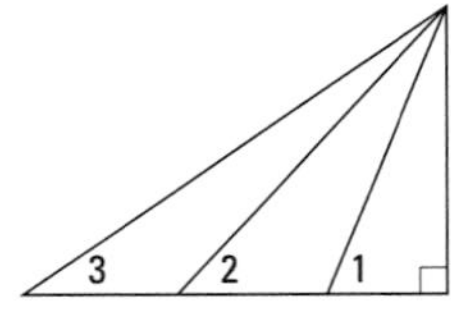

7) Yes, because $\frac{9}{12} = \frac{12}{16} = \frac{15}{20}$, the triangles are similar by the SSS Similarity Theorem.

12) $\tan B = \frac{AC}{BC}$

Additional responses, page 790

4b. Consider any regular n-gon.

For a circumscribed polygon, show that $P = 2n \cdot \tan(\frac{180°}{n})$: The perimeter of the circumscribed n-gon is n times the length of a side, or $n \cdot 2x$ units. To find x, recall that $\tan a = \tan(\frac{180°}{n}) = \frac{x}{1} = x$. So, $2x = 2 \cdot \tan(\frac{180°}{n})$ units is the length of one side, and $2 \cdot n \cdot \tan(\frac{180°}{n})$ units is the perimeter.

Show that $A = n \cdot (\frac{180°}{n})$: The area of the circumscribed n-gon is n times the area of one of the n isosceles triangles, which is $\frac{1}{2}(2x)(1) = x$ square units. From the above we know that $x = \tan(\frac{180°}{n})$. So the area of the n-gon is $n \cdot \tan(\frac{180°}{n})$ square units.

PROGRESS SELF-TEST

14. In right triangle ABC below, if $\sin B = \frac{9}{11}$, find $\cos A$. $\cos A = \frac{AC}{AB} = \sin B = \frac{9}{11}$

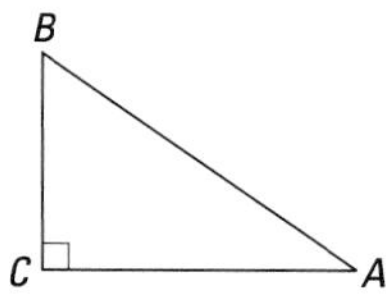

15. In triangle DEF below, find $\sin E$.
$\sin E = .280$

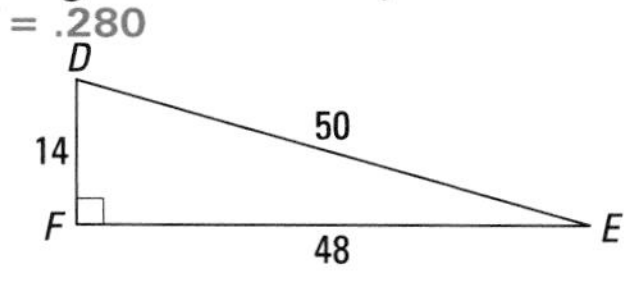

16. Washington, Adams, and Jefferson streets are parallel. Given the distances as indicated below, find x the length on Abigail Avenue between Washington and Adams. 220 m

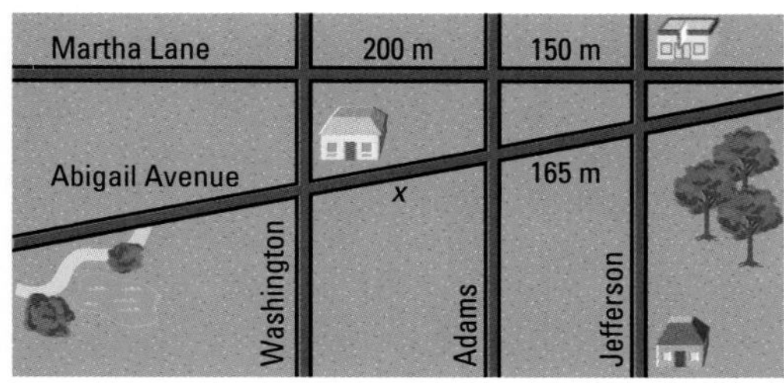

17. How far up on a vertical wall can a 15-foot ladder reach if the angle it makes with the ground is 80°? $\approx$ 14.8 ft

18. As of 1997, Nation's Bank Tower in Atlanta was the tallest building in the southern United States. At noon on some days, it casts a shadow 67 m long at the same time a vertical meter stick casts a shadow 21 cm long. About how tall, in meters, is Nation's Bank Tower? $\approx$ 319 m

19. A boat has to travel to a spot 6.2 km west and 4.8 km north of its present location.

a. In what direction should it go? See below.

b. How far will it travel? $\approx$ 7.84 km

20. From eye level 5 ft above the ground, a person has to look up at an angle of 35° to see the top of a tree 40 ft away. How tall is the tree? $\approx$ 33 ft

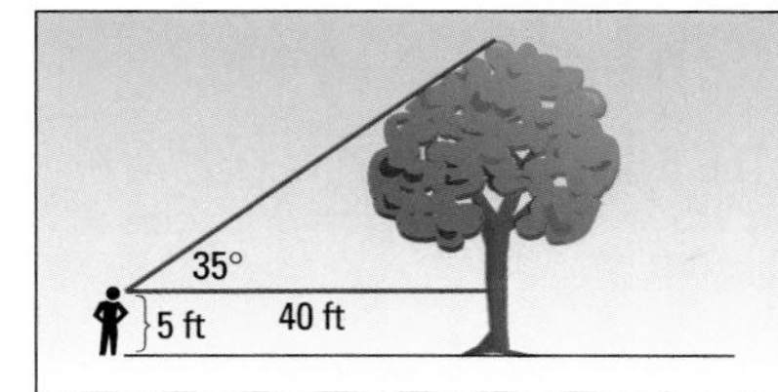

19a) about 38 ° north of west

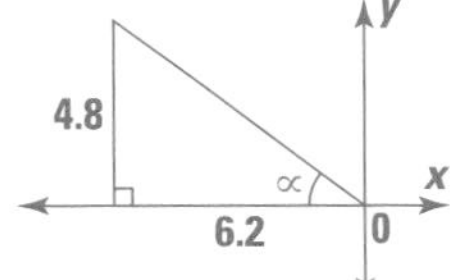

For an inscribed polygon, show that $P = 2n \cdot \sin\left(\frac{180°}{n}\right)$: The perimeter of the inscribed n-gon is n times the length of $2x$ units, or the length of the side of the n-gon. To find x, recall that $\sin a = \sin\left(\frac{180°}{n}\right) = \frac{x}{1}$. So $2x$ has length $2 \cdot \sin\left(\frac{180°}{n}\right)$ units and the perimeter is $2n \cdot \sin\left(\frac{180°}{n}\right)$ units.

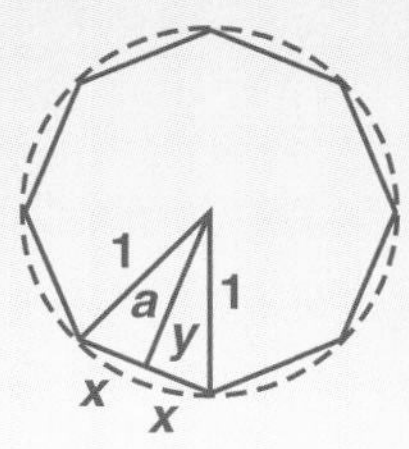

Show that $A = n \cdot \sin\left(\frac{180°}{n}\right) \cdot \cos\left(\frac{180°}{n}\right)$: The area of the inscribed n-gon is n times the area of one of the n isosceles triangles, which is xy square units. From above, we know that $x = \sin\left(\frac{180°}{n}\right)$. Note that $y = \cos\left(\frac{180°}{n}\right)$. The area of one isosceles triangle is $\sin\left(\frac{180°}{n}\right) \cdot \cos\left(\frac{180°}{n}\right)$ square units, and the area of the n-gon is $n \cdot \sin\left(\frac{180°}{n}\right) \cdot \cos\left(\frac{180°}{n}\right)$ square units.

(Responses continue on page 794.)

 CHAPTER THIRTEEN

Chapter 13 Review

Resources

From the ***Teacher's Resource File***
- Answer Master for Chapter 13 Review
- Assessment Sourcebook: Chapter 13 Test, Forms A–D Chapter 13 Test, Cumulative Form

Additional Resources
- Quiz and Test Writer

The main objectives for the chapter are organized in the Chapter Review under the four types of understanding this book promotes—Skills, Properties, Uses, and Representations.

Whereas end-of-chapter material may be considered optional in some texts, in UCSMP *Geometry* we have selected these objectives and questions with the expectation that they will be covered. Students should be able to answer these questions with about 85% accuracy after studying the chapter.

You may assign these questions over a single night to help students prepare for a test the next day, or you may assign the questions over a two-day period. If you work the questions over two days, then we recommend assigning the *evens* for homework the first night so that students get feedback in class the next day, then assigning the *odds* the night before the test, because answers are provided to the odd-numbered questions.

It is effective to ask students which questions they still do not understand and use the day or days as a total class discussion of the material which the class finds most difficult.

CHAPTER REVIEW

Questions on SPUR Objectives

SPUR stands for **S**kills, **P**roperties, **U**ses, and **R**epresentations. The Chapter Review questions are grouped according to the SPUR Objectives for this chapter.

SKILLS DEAL WITH THE PROCEDURES USED TO GET ANSWERS.

Objective A: *Find lengths in figures by applying the Side-Splitting Theorem and the Side-Splitting Converse Theorem.* (Lesson 13-3)

1. In $\triangle JMN$ below, $\overline{KL} \parallel \overline{MN}$. Find each length.

a. MN 10.5

b. LN 2.5

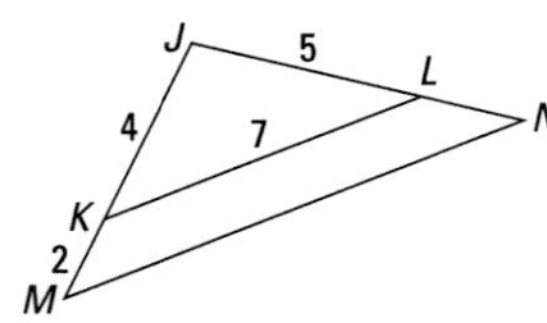

2. In the figure below, $\overleftrightarrow{NP} \parallel \overleftrightarrow{QS}$, $MP = 30$, and $PS = 120$. If $MQ = 90$, then $MN = \underline{\ ?\ }$. 18

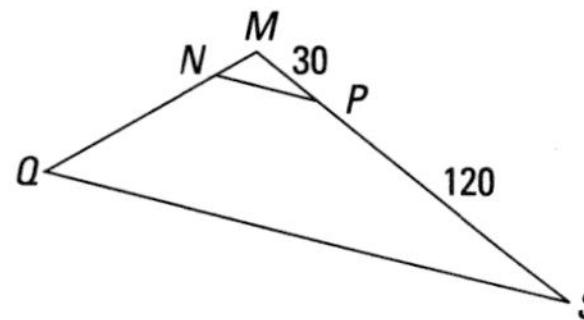

In 3 and 4, use the figures below. Is $\overline{UV} \parallel \overline{YZ}$? Why or why not?

3.

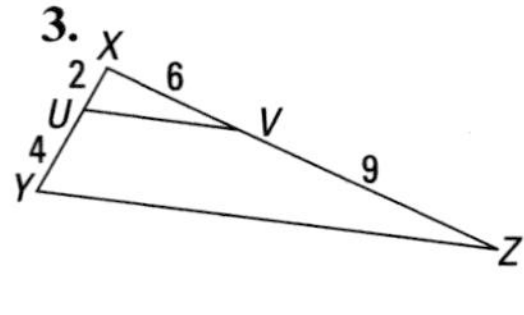

No; since $\frac{2}{4} \neq \frac{6}{9}$.

4.

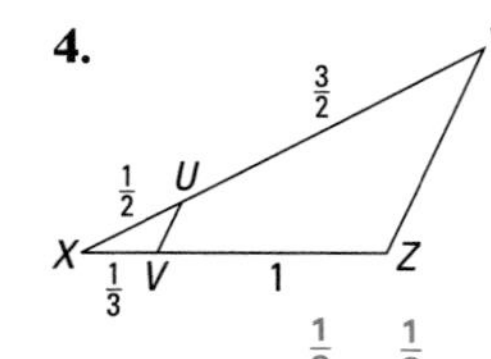

Yes; since $\frac{\frac{1}{3}}{1} = \frac{\frac{1}{2}}{\frac{3}{2}}$

5. If $\overline{AB} \parallel \overline{CD}$ in the figure below, find DE. 8

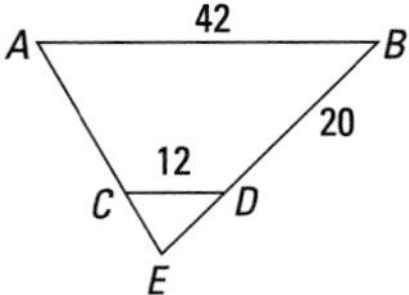

6. If $\overleftrightarrow{WV} \parallel \overleftrightarrow{UT}$ in the figure below, what is SW? 22

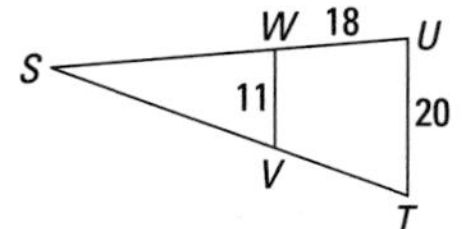

Objective B: *Calculate lengths using the Right-Triangle Altitude Theorem.* (Lesson 13-4)

In 7–9, refer to the figure below.

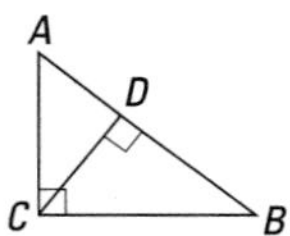

7. If $AD = 9$ and $DB = 4$, then $CD = \underline{\ ?\ }$. 6

8. If $AC = 7$ and $AB = 12$, then $AD = \underline{\ ?\ }$. ≈ 4.

9. If $DC = 12$ and $AD = 18$, then $BC = \underline{\ ?\ }$. ≈ 14.42

Additional responses, page 790

5. Sample values for *a, b, c, d, e, m,* and *n,* as shown in the diagram at the right, are:
   (1) a 3-4-5 (9-12-15) triangle and a 5-12-13 triangle; $ce = 195$: $a = 1755$, $b = 2340$, $c = 2925$, $d = 975$, $e = 2535$, $m = 2184$, $n = 2520$;
   (2) a 3-4-5 (12-16-20) triangle and a 5-12-13 triangle; $ce = 260$:

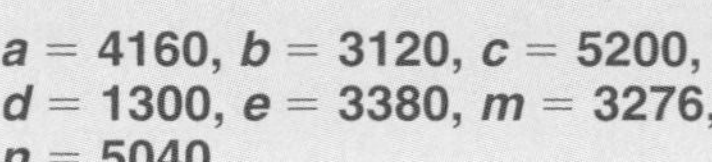
$a = 4160$, $b = 3120$, $c = 5200$, $d = 1300$, $e = 3380$, $m = 3276$, $n = 5040$

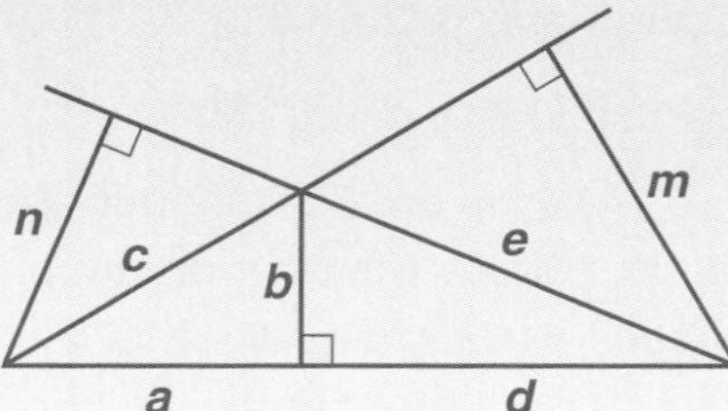

10. In $\triangle RQS$ below, $\overline{QR} \perp \overline{RS}$ and $\overline{RT} \perp \overline{QS}$. If $RT = 4$ and $TS = 8$, find each length.

a. QT 2 **b.** QR ≈ 4.47 **c.** RS ≈ 8.94 **d.** QS 10

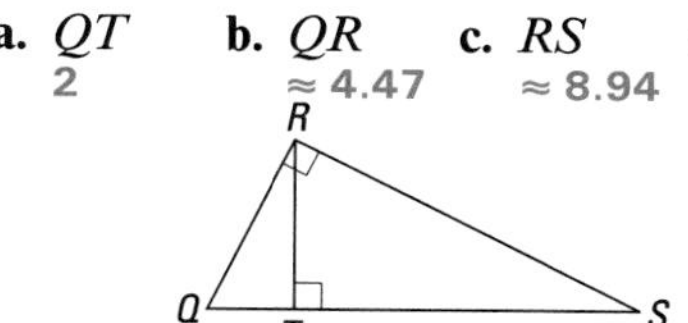

Objective C: *Calculate lengths of sides in isosceles right triangles and in 30-60-90 triangles.* *(Lesson 13-5)*

11. In $\triangle ABC$ below, find AC and BC.
$AC = 4\sqrt{3} \approx 6.93$
$BC = 8$

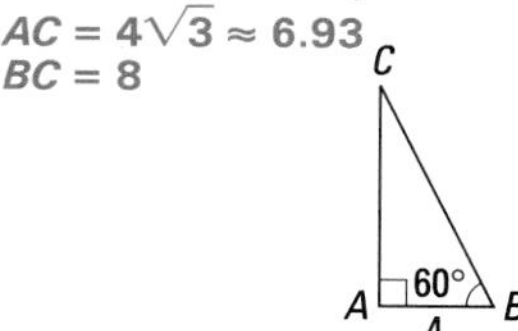

12. In $\triangle DEF$ below, find DE and EF.
$DE = 16$
$EF = 16\sqrt{2} \approx 22.63$

D
16
45°
E
F

13. An equilateral triangle has sides of length 12. Find the length of an altitude. $6\sqrt{3} \approx 10.39$

14. A square has sides of length q. What is the length of a diagonal? $q\sqrt{2}$

In 15 and 16, use the figure below.

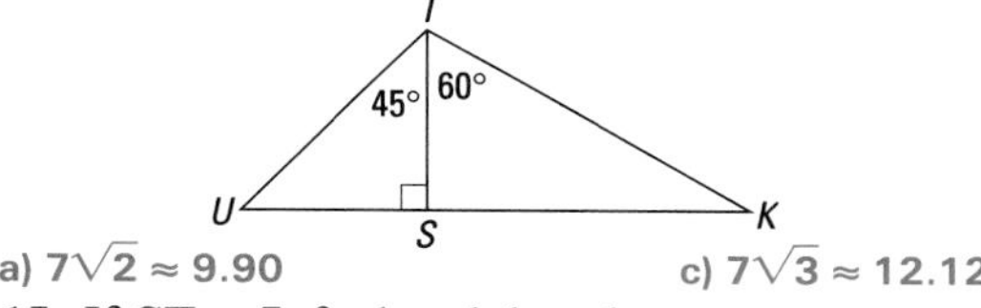

a) $7\sqrt{2} \approx 9.90$ c) $7\sqrt{3} \approx 12.12$

15. If $ST = 7$, find each length.

a. TU **b.** US 7 **c.** SK **d.** TK 14

16. If $SK = 13$, find each length.

a. ST ≈ 7.51 **b.** SU ≈ 7.51 **c.** TK ≈ 15.01

Objective D: *Determine sines, cosines, and tangents of angles and use the SAS Triangle Area Formula.* *(Lessons 13-6, 13-7, 13-8)*

17. Refer to $\triangle ABC$ below. By measuring, determine $m\angle A$ (to the nearest degree), and $\tan A$, $\sin A$, and $\cos A$ (to the nearest hundredth). Sample: $m\angle A \approx 35$, $\tan A \approx .69$, $\sin A \approx .60$, and $\cos A \approx .82$

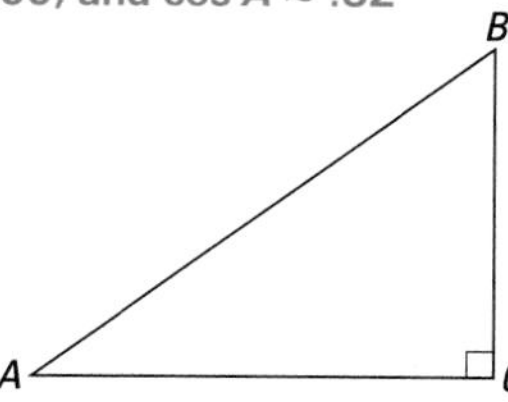

In 18 and 19, use the figure below. Choose from the numbered angles.

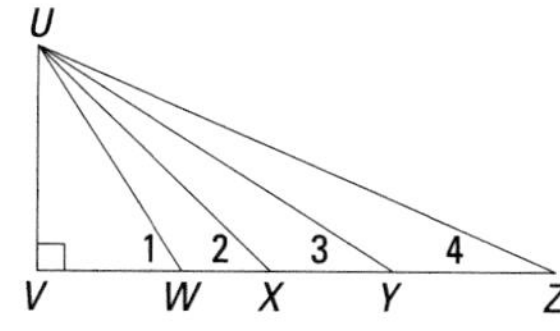

18. Which angle has the largest tangent? $\angle 1$

19. Which angle has the largest sine? $\angle 1$

In 20–22, use $\triangle ABC$ below. Give exact values for each.

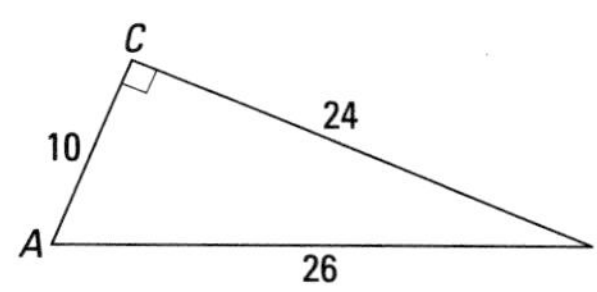

20. $\sin A$ $\frac{24}{26} = \frac{12}{13}$

21. $\cos B$ $\frac{24}{26} = \frac{12}{13}$

22. $\tan B$ $\frac{10}{24} = \frac{5}{12}$

In 23 and 24, determine the area of the triangle.

23. **24.**

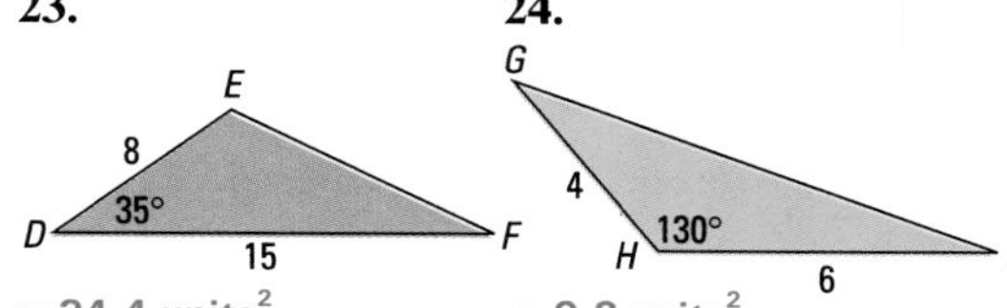

23. ≈ 34.4 units^2 24. ≈ 9.2 units^2

Assessment

Evaluation The *Assessment Sourcebook* provides five forms of the Chapter 13 Test. Forms A and B present parallel versions in a short-answer format. Forms C and D offer performance assessment. The fifth test is Chapter 13 Test, Cumulative Form. About 50% of this test covers Chapter 13; 25% of it covers Chapter 12, and 25% covers earlier chapters.

For information on grading, see *General Teaching Suggestions; Grading* in the *Professional Sourcebook,* which begins on page T20 in this Teacher's Edition.

Feedback After students have taken the test for Chapter 13 and you have scored the results, return the tests to students for discussion. Class discussion of the questions that caused trouble for the most students can be very effective in identifying and clarifying misunderstandings. You might want to have them write down the items they missed and work, either in groups or at home, to correct them. It is important for students to receive feedback on every chapter test, and we recommend that students see and correct their mistakes before proceeding too far into the next chapter.

CHAPTER THIRTEEN

Objective E: *Estimate or determine exact values of the trigonometric ratios.* *(Lessons 13-6, 13-7)*

In 25 and 26, estimate to the nearest thousandth.

25. sin 57.5° .843

26. tan 22.1° .406

In 27–30, give exact values.

27. sin 30° $\frac{1}{2}$

28. tan 60° $\sqrt{3}$

29. tan 45° 1

30. cos 45° $\frac{1}{\sqrt{2}} = \frac{\sqrt{2}}{2}$

PROPERTIES DEAL WITH THE PRINCIPLES BEHIND THE MATHEMATICS.

31b) by the SSS Similarity Theorem

Objective F: *Determine whether or not triangles are similar using the AA, SAS, or SSS Similarity Theorems.* *(Lessons 13-1, 13-2)*

31. One triangle has sides 40, 45, and 50.

a. Is this triangle similar to a second triangle with sides 10, 9, and 8? Yes

b. If so, why? If not, why not?

32. *True or false.* All equilateral triangles are similar. Explain your answer. See margin.

In 33 and 34, are the triangles similar? If so, why? If not, why not?

Yes, by the AA Similarity Theorem

33.

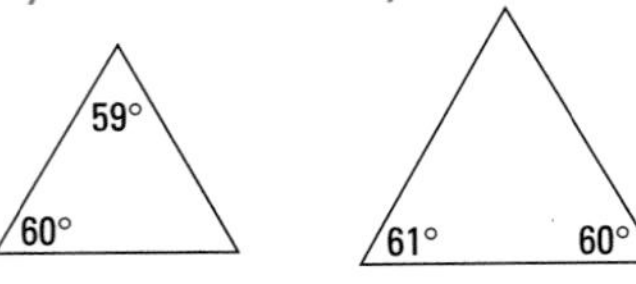

34.

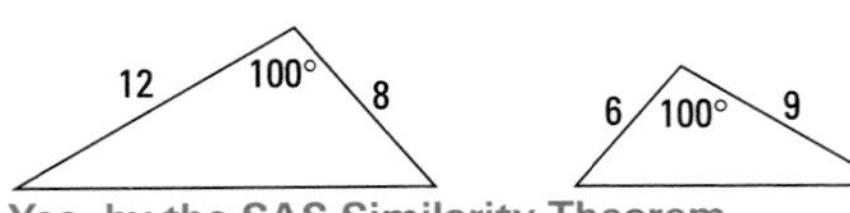

Yes, by the SAS Similarity Theorem

35. Write a proof argument.

Given: $ABCD$ is a trapezoid with $\overleftrightarrow{AB} \parallel \overleftrightarrow{CD}$ and diagonals intersecting at E.

To prove: $\triangle ABE \sim \triangle CDE$. See margin.

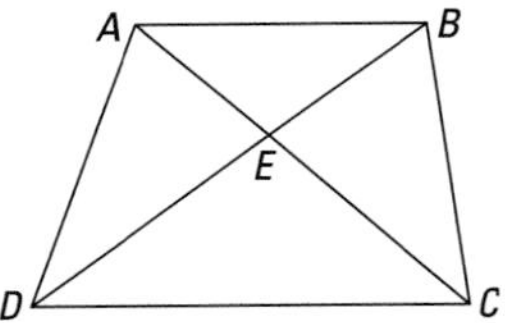

36. Write a proof argument.

Given: $\overline{AC} \perp \overline{CD}$, $BC = x$, $AC = 2x$, and $DC = 4x$.

To prove: $\triangle ABC \sim \triangle DAC$. See margin.

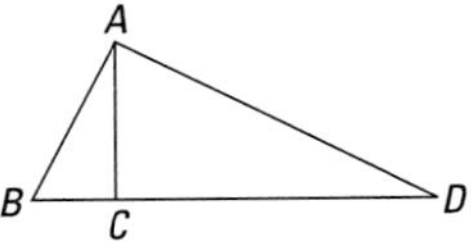

Objective G: *Know the definitions of sine, cosine, and tangent.* *(Lessons 13-6, 13-7)*

In 37–39, define for $\triangle ABC$ with right angle C.

37. cos A $\frac{AC}{AB}$ **38.** sin A $\frac{BC}{AB}$ **39.** tan A $\frac{BC}{AC}$

In 40–42, use the figure below.

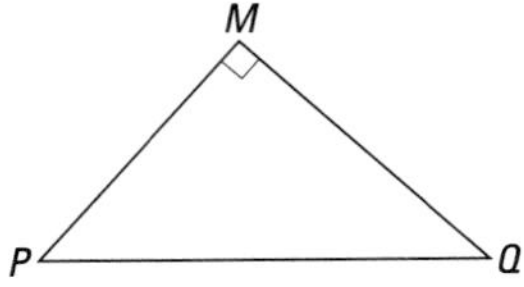

40. $\frac{MP}{MQ}$ is the tangent of which angle? Q

41. $\frac{MQ}{PQ}$ is the __?__ of angle P. sine

42. Give the cosine of angle Q. $\frac{MQ}{PQ}$

In 43 and 44, use right triangle $\triangle ABC$ below.

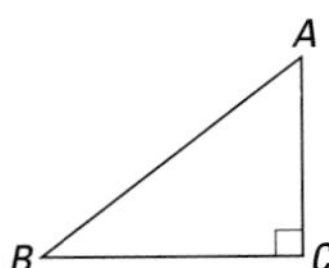

43. Write a ratio for tan B. $\frac{AC}{BC}$

44. If cos $A = x$, find sin B. x

Additional Answers

32. True; all angles in equilateral triangles measure 60; thus all equilateral triangles are similar by the AA Similarity Theorem.

35.

Conclusions	Justifications
1. $\angle BAE \cong \angle DCE$, $\angle ABE \cong \angle CDE$	// Lines ⇒ AIA ≅ Thm.
2. $\triangle ABE \sim \triangle CDE$	AA Similarity Thm. (step 1)

36.

Conclusions	Justifications
1. $\frac{BC}{AC} = \frac{x}{2x} = \frac{1}{2}$, $\frac{AC}{DC} = \frac{2x}{4x} = \frac{1}{2}$	def. of ratio
2. $\frac{BC}{AC} = \frac{AC}{DC}$	Transitive Prop. of Equality
3. $\triangle ABC \sim \triangle DAC$	SAS Similarity Thm. (step 2 and given)

USES DEAL WITH APPLICATIONS OF MATHEMATICS IN REAL SITUATIONS.

45) 15 m 47) See margin.

Objective H: *Use the Triangle Similarity and Side-Splitting Theorems to find lengths and distances in real situations.* *(Lessons 13-2, 13-3)*

45. A tree casts a shadow 9 meters long. At the same time, a vertical meter stick casts a shadow 60 cm long. How tall is the tree?

46. The height of a ramp at a point 1.5 meters from its bottom is 1.3 m. If the ramp runs for 4 m along the ground, what is its height at its highest point? (Round your answer to the nearest 0.1 m.) 3.5 m

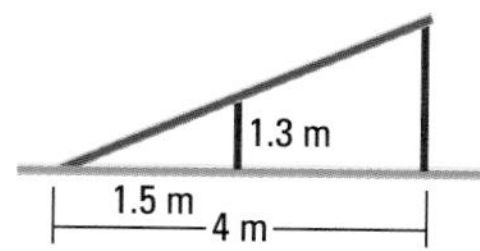

47. The beam $\overline{BC}$ is parallel to $\overline{DE}$ and splits the sides of the asymmetric roof. In the drawing below, if $AD = 50$, $AE = 70$, $BC = 25$, and $DE = 75$, find

a. AB. **b.** CE. See margin.

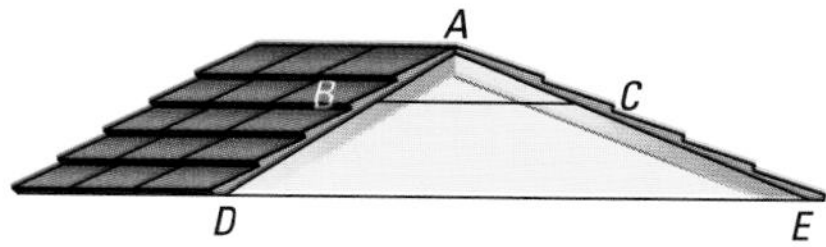

48. First Street runs north and south. Elm, Maple, and Pine run east and west. Distances between them are as indicated below. There is 2000 ft of frontage on Slant Street between Elm and Maple. How much frontage is there on Slant Street between Maple and Pine?
3,000 ft

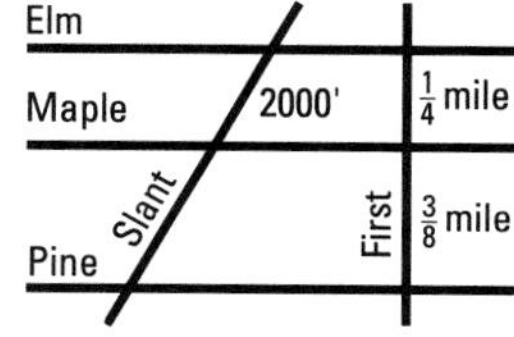

Objective I: *Use sines, cosines, and tangents to determine unknown lengths in real situations.* *(Lessons 13-6, 13-7)*

49. The tallest tree in the world (as of 1991) is a sequoia in Humboldt Redwoods State Park, California. When the sun is 57° up from the horizon, the tree casts a shadow 237 feet long. About how tall is this tree? ≈ 365 feet

50. How far up a vertical wall can a 4-meter ladder reach if the angle it makes with the ground is 75°? ≈ 3.86 meters

51. From eye level 2 meters off the ground and 25 meters from a sculpture, a sightseer on a bus has to look up at an angle of 20° to see the top of the sculpture. How high is the sculpture? ≈ 11.1 meters

52. From the window of a building you look down at a clown in a parade. If your eyes are 60 feet above the clown, and the angle of sight, measured from the building, is 25°, how far is the clown from you?
≈ 66 feet

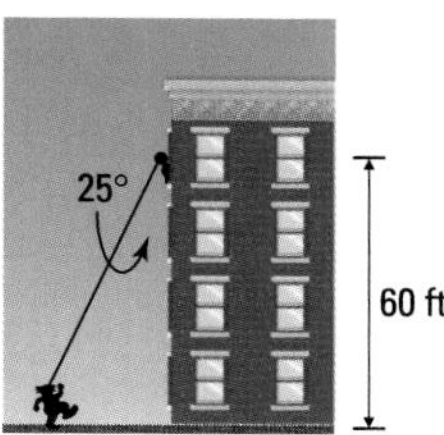

Objective J: *Determine components of vectors in real situations.* *(Lesson 13-8)*

53. A boat is moving at 60 knots on a course 72° north of east. Find the northern and eastern components of its velocity. See below.

54. A helicopter has to fly to a place 15 km west and 7 km south of its present location.

a. In what direction should it fly? 25° south of west

b. How far will it travel? ≈ 16.55 km

REPRESENTATIONS DEAL WITH PICTURES, GRAPHS, OR OBJECTS THAT ILLUSTRATE CONCEPTS.

There are no representation objectives for this chapter.

53) northern component: ≈ 57 knots; eastern component: ≈ 18.5 knots

Additional Answers

47a. $\frac{50}{3} \approx 16.67$ units

b. $70 - \frac{70}{3} \approx 46.67$ units

Chapter 14 Planner

Adapting to Individual Needs

The student text is written for the vast majority of students. The chart at the right suggests two pacing plans to accommodate the needs of your students. Students in the Full Course should complete the entire text by the end of the year. Students in the Minimal Course will spend more time when there are quizzes and more time on the Chapter Review. Therefore, these students may not complete all of the chapters in the text.

Options are also presented to meet the needs of a variety of teaching and learning styles. For each lesson, the Teacher's Edition provides a section entitled *Adapting to Individual Needs.* This section regularly includes **Optional Activities, Challenge** problems, **English Language Development** suggestions, and suggestions for providing **Extra Help.** The Teacher's Edition also frequently includes an **Error Alert,** an **Extension,** and an **Assessment** alternative. The options available in Chapter 14 are summarized in the chart below.

Chapter 14 Pacing Chart

Day	Full Course	Minimal Course
1	14-1	14-1
2	14-2	14-2
3	14-3	14-3
4	Quiz*; 14-4	Quiz*; begin 14-4.
5	14-5	Finish 14-4.
6	14-6	14-5
7	Quiz*; 14-7	14-6
8	14-8	Quiz*; begin 14-7.
9	14-9	Finish 14-7.
10	Self-Test	14-8
11	Review	14-9
12	Test*	Self-Test
13	Comprehensive	Review
14	Test*	Review
15		Test*
16		Comprehensive
17		Test*

*in the Teacher's Resource File

In the Teacher's Edition...

Lesson	Optional Activities	Extra Help	Challenge	English Language Development	Error Alert	Extension	Cooperative Learning	Ongoing Assessment
14-1	●	●	●			●	●	Oral/Written
14-2	●	●	●	●	●	●	●	Group
14-3	●	●	●			●	●	Oral/Written
14-4	●		●			●	●	Oral/Written
14-5	●	●	●	●		●	●	Oral/Written
14-6	●		●			●	●	Oral/Written
14-7	●	●	●	●		●	●	Oral/Written
14-8	●	●	●		●	●	●	Written
14-9	●		●	●		●		Written

In the Additional Resources...

	In the Teacher's Resource File								
Lesson	**Lesson Masters, A and B**	**Teaching Aids***	**Activity Kit***	**Answer Masters**	**Technology Sourcebook**	**Assessment Sourcebook**	**Visual Aids****	**Technology**	**Video Segments**
14-1	14-1	181		14-1	Comp 24		181, AM	GeoExplorer	
14-2	14-2	181, 185		14-2			181, 185, AM		
14-3	14-3	182, 186		14-3		Quiz	182, 186, AM		
14-4	14-4	182, 187		14-4			182, 187, AM		
14-5	14-5	182	29	14-5			182, AM		
14-6	14-6	183, 188	30	14-6	Comp 25	Quiz	183, 188, AM	GeoExplorer	14-6
In-class Activity		189		14-7			189, AM		
14-7	14-7	183, 190		14-7			183, 190, AM		
14-8	14-8	184		14-8			184, AM		
14-9	14-9	184		14-9			184, AM		
End of Chapter				Review		Tests			

*Teaching Aids are pictured on pages 798C and 798D. The activities in the Activity Kit are pictured on page 798C. Teaching Aid 189 which accompanies the In-class Activity preceding Lesson 14-7 is pictured with the lesson notes on page 835.

**Visual Aids provide transparencies for all Teaching Aids and all Answer Masters.

Also available is the Study Skills Handbook which includes study-skill tips related to reading, note-taking, and comprehension.

Integrating Strands and Applications

	14-1	14-2	14-3	14-4	14-5	14-6	14-7	14-8	14-9
Mathematical Connections									
Number Sense	●	●			●		●	●	●
Algebra		●		●		●	●	●	●
Geometry	●	●	●	●	●	●	●	●	●
Measurement	●	●	●	●	●	●	●	●	●
Logic and Reasoning	●	●	●	●	●	●	●	●	●
Patterns and Functions	●	●	●	●	●	●	●	●	●
Discrete Ma thematics			●						
Interdisciplinary and Other Connections									
Art						●			
Music					●				
Science		●			●	●	●		●
Social Studies	●		●				●		●
Multicultural								●	●
Technology	●			●		●			
Career		●	●						
Consumer									●
Sports	●		●					●	

Teaching and Assessing the Chapter Objectives

Chapter 14 Objectives (Organized into the SPUR categories—Skills, Properties, Uses, and Representations)	**Lessons**	**Progress Self-Test Questions**	**Chapter Review Questions**	**In the Teacher's Resource File: Chapter Test, Forms A and B**	**Chapter Test, Forms C**	**Chapter Test, Forms D**
Skills						
A: Calculate lengths of chords and arcs.	14-1	1, 3	1–6	1, 3	2	✓
B: Calculate measures of inscribed angles from measures of intercepted arcs, and vice versa.	14-2	4	7–10	2	1	✓
C: Calculate measures of angles between chords, secants, or tangents from measures of intercepted arcs, and vice versa.	14-2, 14-4, 14-6	5, 6, 11	11–16	5, 6	1	✓
D: Locate the center of a circle given sufficient information.	14-3	2	17–20	7	4	
E: Apply the Secant Length Theorem and the Tangent Square Theorem.	14-7	7, 8	21–24	8, 9	3	
Properties						
F: Make deductions from properties of radii, chords, and tangents, and know sufficient conditions for radii to be perpendicular to them.	14-1, 14-5, 14-6	9, 10	25–30	10		✓
G: Make deductions from properties of angles formed by chords, tangents, or secants.	14-2, 14-4, 14-6	12	31–34	4, 10		✓
H: Apply the Isoperimetric Theorems and the Isoperimetric Inequality to determine which figures have the greatest or least area, perimeter, or volume.	14-8, 14-9	14	35–40	11		
Uses						
I: Given the angle width of a lens and the width of an object, determine the set of points from which the object just fits in the picture.	14-3	15	41–42	12		
J: Determine the maximum distance that can be seen from a particular elevation.	14-5	16	43–46	13		
K: Apply the Isoperimetric Theorems and the Isoperimetric Inequality in real situations.	14-8, 14-9	13	47–50	14	5	
Representations There are no representation objectives for this chapter.						

Assessment Sourcebook
Quiz for Lessons 14-1 through 14-3
Quiz for Lessons 14-4 through 14-6
Chapter 14 Test, Forms A–D
Chapter 14 Test, Cumulative Form
Comprehensive Test, Chapters 1–14

Quiz and Test Writer

Activity Kit

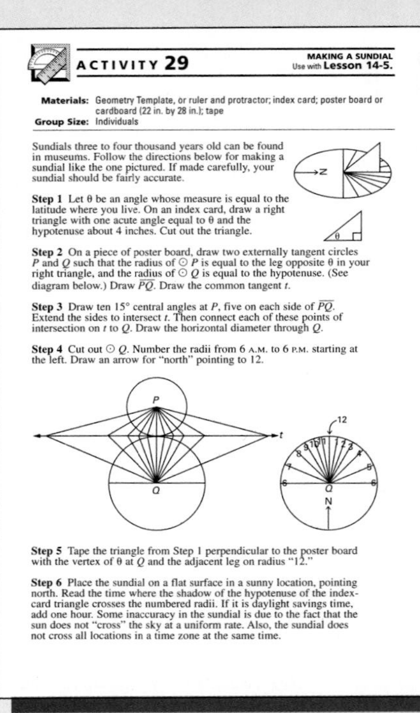

ACTIVITY 29

MAKING A SUNDIAL
Use with **Lesson 14-5.**

Materials: Geometry Template, or ruler and protractor; index card; poster board or cardboard (22 in. by 28 in.); tape
Group Size: Individuals

Sundials three to four thousand years old can be found in museums. Follow the directions below for making a sundial like the one pictured. If made carefully, your sundial should be fairly accurate.

Step 1 Let θ be an angle whose measure is equal to the latitude where you live. On an index card, draw a right triangle with one acute angle equal to θ and the hypotenuse about 4 inches. Cut out the triangle.

Step 2 On a piece of poster board, draw two externally tangent circles *P* and *Q* such that the radius of ⊙ *P* is equal to the leg opposite θ in your right triangle, and the radius of ⊙ *Q* is equal to the hypotenuse. (See diagram below.) Draw $\overline{PQ}$. Draw the common tangent *t*.

Step 3 Draw ten 15° central angles at *P*, five on each side of $\overline{PQ}$. Extend the sides to intersect *t*. Then connect each of these points of intersection on *t* to *Q*. Draw the horizontal diameter through *Q*.

Step 4 Cut out ⊙ *Q*. Number the radii from 6 A.M. to 6 P.M. starting at the left. Draw an arrow for "north" pointing to 12.

Step 5 Tape the triangle from Step 1 perpendicular to the poster board with the vertex of θ at *Q* and the adjacent leg on radius "12."

Step 6 Place the sundial on a flat surface in a sunny location, pointing north. Read the time where the shadow of the hypotenuse of the index-card triangle crosses the numbered radii. If it is daylight savings time, add one hour. Some inaccuracy in the sundial is due to the fact that the sun does not "cross" the sky at a uniform rate. Also, the sundial does not cross all locations in a time zone at the same time.

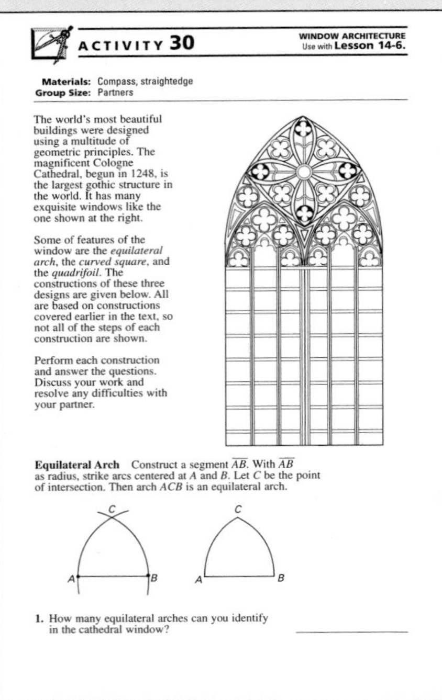

ACTIVITY 30

WINDOW ARCHITECTURE
Use with **Lesson 14-6.**

Materials: Compass, straightedge
Group Size: Partners

The world's most beautiful buildings were designed using a multitude of geometric principles. The magnificent Cologne Cathedral, begun in 1248, is the largest gothic structure in the world. It has many exquisite windows like the one shown at the right.

Some of features of the window are the *equilateral arch*, the *curved square*, and the *quadrifoil*. The constructions of these three designs are given below. All are based on constructions covered earlier in the text, so not all of the steps of each construction are shown.

Perform each construction and answer the questions. Discuss your work and resolve any difficulties with your partner.

Equilateral Arch Construct a segment $\overline{AB}$. With $\overline{AB}$ as radius, strike arcs centered at *A* and *B*. Let *C* be the point of intersection. Then arch *ACB* is an equilateral arch.

1. How many equilateral arches can you identify in the cathedral window? ____________

▶ **ACTIVITY 30** page 2

Curved Square Construct a square *WXYZ*. With $\overline{WX}$ as radius, strike arcs centered at *W*, *X*, *Y*, and *Z*. Let the points of intersection be *A*, *B*, *C*, and *D*. Then the figure *ABCD* is a curved square.

2. Mark the curved square in the cathedral window.

Quadrifoil Construct a square *WXYZ*. Construct the perpendicular bisectors of the sides to locate midpoint *M*, *N*, *O*, and *P*. Draw the diagonals of the square. In each of the four isosceles triangles formed, construct the bisectors of the base angles. Let them intersect at *A*, *B*, *C*, and *D*.

With radius *AM*, draw circles centered at *A*, *B*, *C*, and *D*. Let the points of tangency between the circles be *E*, *F*, *G*, and *H*. Then the union of major arcs *EF*, *FG*, *GH*, and *HE* is a quadrifoil.

3. How many full quadrifoils are shown in the window? How many partial-quadrifoils? ________ ________

4. With your partner, find and write about some other geometric ideas illustrated in the cathedral window.

____

____

5. Use only a compass and straightedge to design a window using equilateral arches, curved squares, and quadrifoils. Explain to your partner any other geometric ideas found in your window.

____

____

Teaching Aids

TEACHING AID 181

Warm-up Lesson 14-1

In Questions 1–9, draw a circle and identify the terms.

1. A radius of the circle
2. The radius of the circle
3. A diameter of the circle
4. The diameter of the circle
5. A chord of the circle
6. A central angle
7. An arc of the circle
8. Measure of an arc of the circle
9. A semicircle
10. Define *circle*.

Warm-up Lesson 14-2

1. On a large sheet of paper use a compass to draw a circle with a radius of 3 inches. Using the same compass opening, mark six equally spaced points on the circle. Then connect all the points with line segments. Be sure all possible segments are drawn. Describe the figure that is formed.
2. Pick any two adjacent segments from the same point on the circle. Measure the angle between the segments. What do you notice?

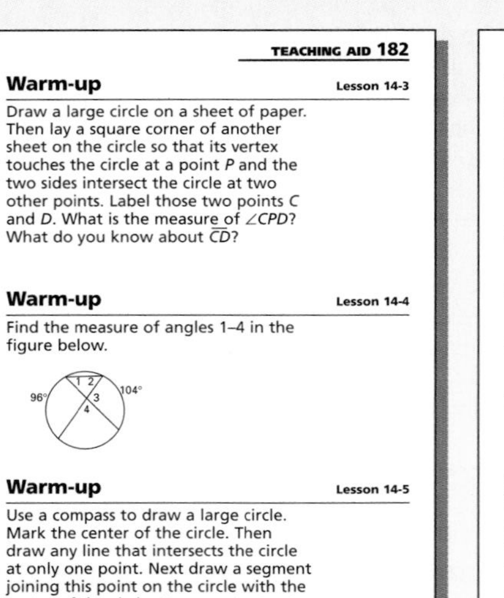

TEACHING AID 182

Warm-up Lesson 14-3

Draw a large circle on a sheet of paper. Then lay a square corner of another sheet on the circle so that its vertex touches the circle at a point *P* and the two sides intersect the circle at two other points. Label those two points *C* and *D*. What is the measure of ∠*CPD*? What do you know about $\overset{\frown}{CD}$?

Warm-up Lesson 14-4

Find the measure of angles 1–4 in the figure below.

Warm-up Lesson 14-5

Use a compass to draw a large circle. Mark the center of the circle. Then draw any line that intersects the circle at only one point. Next draw a segment joining this point on the circle with the center of the circle. Use a protractor to measure the angle that this segment makes with the first line that you drew. Repeat the process. What do you discover?

TEACHING AID 183

Warm-up Lesson 14-6

For each of Questions 1-7, draw a diagram to illustrate the situation.

1. A circle with a central angle
2. A circle with an inscribed angle
3. A circle with an angle formed by two chords intersecting inside the circle
4. A circle with an angle formed by two secants intersecting outside the circle
5. A circle with an angle formed by a tangent and a chord with one endpoint at the point of tangency
6. A circle with an angle formed by a tangent and a secant with the vertex of the angle outside the circle
7. A circle with an angle formed by two tangents

Warm-up Lesson 14-7

Find the geometric mean of each pair of numbers. Round to the nearest hundredth.

1. 4 and 25
2. 6 and 10

Solve each quadratic equation.

3. $x(x + 3) = 10$
4. $x^2 - 5x + 1 = 0$
5. $3x^2 - 2x = 4$

TEACHING AID 184

Warm-up

Lesson 14-8

1. Find all the possible different quadrilaterals that can be formed by connecting four of the eight equally spaced points on a circle. (Note: quadrilaterals that are formed by rotating a given quadrilateral do not count as different quadrilaterals.)

2. Which quadrilateral that you drew seems to have the greatest area?

Warm-up

Lesson 14-9

Find the surface area of a cube whose volume is 125 cubic feet.

TEACHING AID 185
Lesson 14-2

Additional Examples

1. The three angles of $\triangle ABC$ have measures 40, 60, and 80. If the circle through *A*, *B*, and *C* is drawn, what are the measures of the three minor arcs formed by the points?

2. *ABCDEF* is a regular hexagon. Find m∠*BFE*.

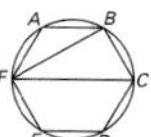

TEACHING AID 186
Lesson 14-3

Additional Examples

1. Trace the bottom of a drinking glass or a tin can to draw a circle. Then locate the center by using the right-angle method.

2. Trace the drawing of the building shown below. Diagram all the places where you could stand so that the front of the building, $\overline{EF}$, just fits into your picture if you use a camera with a 54° field of vision.

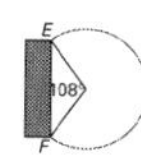

3. If the building in the diagram in Question 2 is 60 meters long, how far from the center of the circle is the building?

4. Explain how to locate the center of an arc you know to be a semicircle.

TEACHING AID 187
Lesson 14-4

Additional Examples

1. *ABCDEFHGH* is a regular octagon. What is the measure of the acute angles formed by $\overleftrightarrow{BG}$ and $\overleftrightarrow{AE}$?

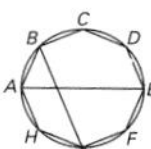

2. Use the diagram below. Find m$\overset{\frown}{BD}$.

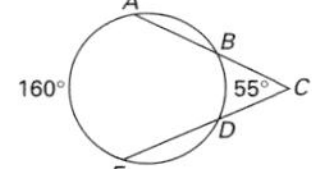

TEACHING AID 188
Lesson 14-6

Additional Examples

1. A chord $\overline{AB}$ in a circle forms an angle of 65° with the tangent to the circle at *A*. Draw a possible situation and determine the measures of the major and minor arcs with endpoints *A* and *B*.

2. In the diagram below, $\overleftrightarrow{LM}$ is tangent to the circle at *M* and m$\overset{\frown}{MK}$ = 48°. Find the m∠*L*.

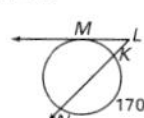

3. The measure of the major arc *DFE* is 290°. $\overrightarrow{CD}$ and $\overrightarrow{CE}$ are tangents to the circle. What is m∠*C*?

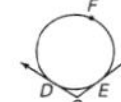

TEACHING AID 190
Lesson 14-7

Additional Examples

1. Three of the segments formed by two intersecting chords have lengths 4, 5, and 7 as shown below. What is the length of the fourth segment?

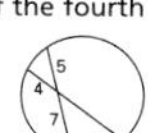

2. Given secants $\overrightarrow{RS}$ and $\overrightarrow{UV}$ intersecting at *T*, with lengths as shown, find *UV*.

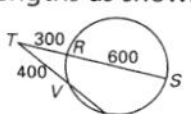

3. $\overleftrightarrow{QW}$ is tangent to the circle at *W*. If *QW* = 10 and *QE* = 5, find *QD* and *DE*.

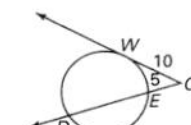

4. Given: *PA* = 6 and $\overline{PA}$ is tangent to the circle at *A*. If *BC* = 7, find *PB*.

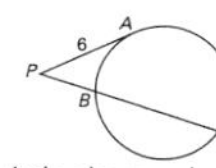

5. In the circle above, what is the power of point *P*?

Chapter Opener 14

Pacing

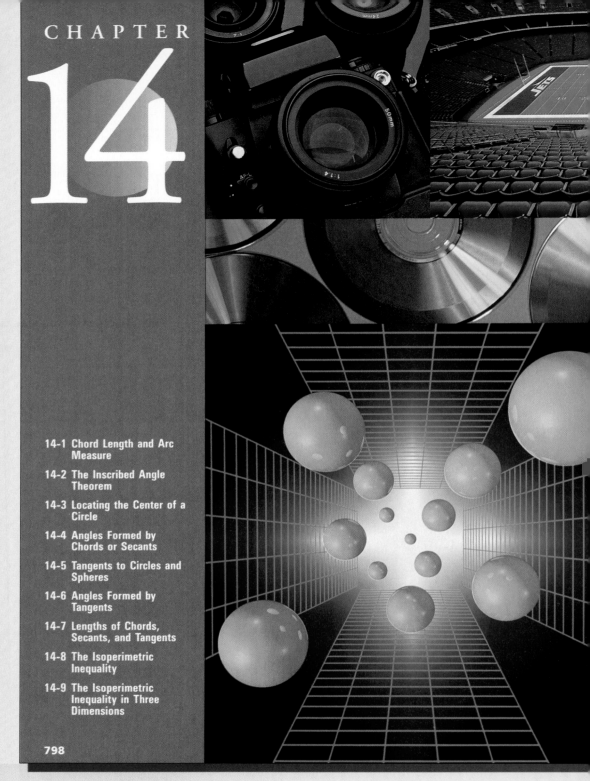

All lessons in this chapter are designed to be covered in one day. At the end of the chapter, you should plan to spend 1 day to review the Progress Self-Test, 1–2 days for the Chapter Review, and 1 day for a test. You may wish to spend a day on projects, and possibly a day is needed for quizzes. Therefore, this chapter should take 12–15 days.

Using Pages 798–799

The underlying belief of Galileo's quote is that *every* physical object is geometric, because every physical object has a shape. Thus, an understanding of the object's geometry is necessary to understand its physical characteristics.

Students have been familiar with circles from the time they were very young, so instances of circles do not need to be reviewed. Five sources for the origin of circles are given along with the pictures on this page. A sixth source of circles is found in wheels or cylinders that support a rolling object. A circle is not the only figure with constant width, but it is the most common such figure.

It might surprise your students that the word "circle" could be defined in any one of these five ways. That is, we could define a circle as a cross section of a particular figure, as a limit of polygons, as a shortest path on a sphere, or as a set of points on a coordinate plane. All the definitions are different from (but equivalent to) the standard definition as a set of points in a plane at a given distance from a point in that plane.

CHAPTER 14

Chapter 14 Overview

This chapter brings together ideas from many earlier chapters of the book. Measurement of arcs and relationships with central angles and chord length are discussed in Lesson 14-1. In Lesson 14-2, the relationship of an inscribed angle to its intercepted arc is proved, and this relationship is applied in Lesson 14-3 to show another way of finding the center of a circle. Trigonometry helps to locate the distance of the center from an object.

Lessons 14-4 through 14-7 present the beautiful theorems that relate the lengths of chords, secants, and tangents in circles, and the elegant theorems that relate the measures of angles formed by these segments with the arcs they intercept. Lessons 14-8 and 14-9 discuss the Isoperimetric Theorems and Inequalities. These cannot be proved with the mathematics at our disposal here, as the proofs require advanced calculus, but they are important results that should be learned by all students.

As the chapter-opener pages indicate, circles have a variety of applications. One interesting and useful application studied in this chapter is locating the position for a photographer so that an entire object lies in the field of vision. This kind of application may be used by students, and should be studied in detail.

Further Work With Circles

The great Italian scientist Galileo Galilei wrote in 1623:

. . . the universe . . . is written in the language of mathematics, and its characters are triangles, circles, and other geometrical figures, without which it is humanly impossible to understand a single word of it; without these, one is wandering about in a dark labyrinth.

Galileo's views have been mirrored in cultures around the world. The ancient Greeks believed that the sun, planets, and other celestial objects went around Earth in circles. The ancient Chinese believed that two forces, yin and yang, represented in the drawing below at the left, worked to create all that is. Today's Olympic Games symbol consists of five interlocking circles.

Circles involve ideas from many of the previous chapters of this book, so the study of circles is especially appropriate as a last chapter. You have seen circles arise from a variety of sources.

as cross-sections of cylinders, cones, and other 3-dimensional surfaces;

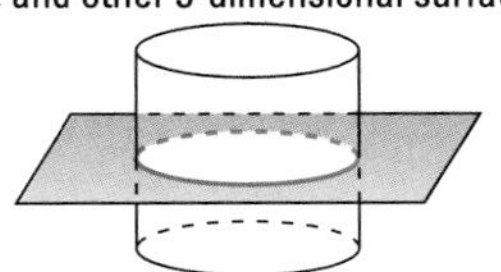

as limits of regular polygons;

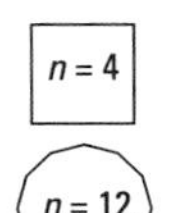

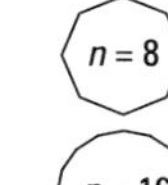

as shortest paths on the surface of a sphere;

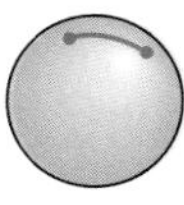

as a set of points at a fixed distance from a center;

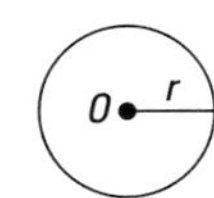

and as the graph of the solutions (x, y) to $(x - h)^2 + (y - k)^2 = r^2$.

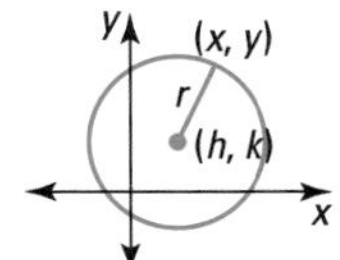

This chapter examines arcs of circles, and segments and angles associated with circles. The results are fascinating and often quite surprising; they are not obvious, yet not difficult to prove.

Multicultural Connection Circles have always played a vital role in religious thought around the world. One very popular circular symbol in Eastern thought is the yin-yang shown on this page. It consists of two interlocking halves of a circle, one light and one dark. The ancient Chinese believed that two forces, yin and yang, worked to create all that comes to be through contrasting elements or opposites. Yin is symbolically earth-related, dark, passive, and associated with even numbers. Yang is heavenly, light, active, and present in odd numbers. The constant interplay of the two forces constitutes the cyclical working of the universe. The yin-yang was probably conceived of in China well over two millennia ago, but has since spread throughout Eastern thought and religion.

Photo Connection

The photo collage makes real-world connections to the content of the chapter: circles.

Camera: In Lesson 14-2 students learn about picture angles and where they must stand to get an entire image in a picture.

Stadium: A football field is rectangular but many football stadiums are circular. In Lesson 14-8 students will find out why. Giant's Stadium, home of the New York Jets, is shown here.

CD-ROMS: Imagine an entire book, including pictures, sound tracks, and even motion, on a disc that is less than 5 inches in diameter. A **C**ompact **D**isc **R**ead-**O**nly **M**emory disc can store thousands of pages of information.

3-D Spheres Graphic: A sphere plays the same role in the 3-dimensional relationship between surface and volume (Lesson 14-9) as a circle does in the 2-dimensional relationship between perimeter and area (Lesson 14-8).

Movie Film: Movie film is usually described by its width—the greater the width the greater the detail obtained. Most movie theaters use film that is 35 mm wide and film used for television is 16 mm wide. Film is usually stored in circular canisters.

Chapter 14 Projects

At this time you might want to have students look over the projects on pages 853–854.

Pacing At this point in the year, many, if not most, classes are searching for extra days. The least important content of the chapter is that involving measures of angles formed by chords, secants, and tangents. These theorems have few applications in even later work in geometry and are not needed in any later high school or college mathematics course. In addition, they are seldom found on any college entrance exams. So, they can be deleted without affecting future course work in mathematics. Next least in importance are the theorems relating lengths of chords, tangents, and secants. Thus, a minimal run through the chapter should cover Lessons 14-1, 14-2, 14-3, and 14-5.

It is advisable for students to have compasses available for every lesson in this chapter. They will need protractors for some of the activities.

Lesson 14-1

Objectives

A Calculate lengths of chords and arcs.

F Make deductions from properties of radii and chords, and know sufficient conditions for radii to be perpendicular to them.

Resources

From the ***Teacher's Resource File***

- Lesson Master 14-1A or 14-1B
- Answer Master 14-1
- Teaching Aid 181: Warm-up
- Technology Sourcebook, Computer Master 24

Additional Resources

- Visual for Teaching Aid 181
- GeoExplorer or other automatic drawers

Teaching Lesson 14-1

Warm-up

In Questions 1–9, draw a circle and identify the terms. **Sample answers are given using the figure below.**

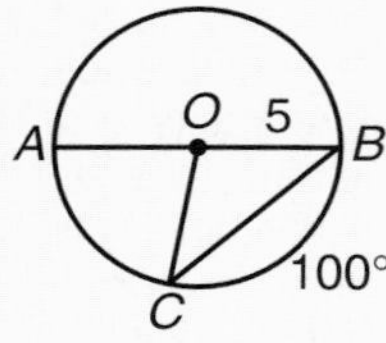

1. A radius of the circle $\overline{OA}$
2. The radius of the circle 5
3. A diameter of the circle $\overline{AB}$
4. The diameter of the circle 10
5. A chord of the circle $\overline{CB}$
6. A central angle $\angle COB$

LESSON

14-1 *Chord Length and Arc Measure*

Heads up! *Arcs, central angles, and sectors abound in this stained-glass panel in the roof of Penn Station in Baltimore, Maryland.*

Reviewing Central Angles, Chords, and Arcs

Recall some names of figures related to circles. An angle with its vertex at the center of a circle is a *central angle* of the circle. The arc of the circle in the interior of the angle is said to be **intercepted** by the angle. The *measure of the intercepted arc* is defined as the measure of its central angle.

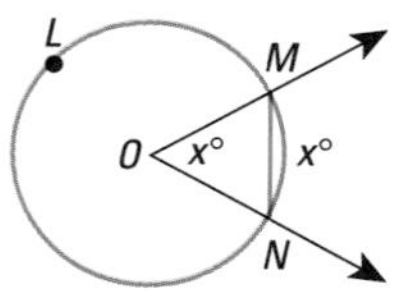

central angle MON
chord $\overline{MN}$
arc $\overset{\frown}{MN}$
$m\angle MON = x$
$m\overset{\frown}{MN} = x°$

In the drawing above, $m\angle MON$ seems to be about 45, thus arc $\overset{\frown}{MN}$ also measures 45°. $\overset{\frown}{MN}$ is a minor arc because its measure is less than 180°. The *major arc* $\overset{\frown}{MLN}$ has measure 360° − 45°, or 315°. An arc with measure 180° is a *semicircle*. If $\overset{\frown}{MN}$ is an arc of a circle, the segment $\overline{MN}$ is called the *chord of arc* $\overset{\frown}{MN}$.

Congruent Circles and Congruent Arcs

If two circles $\odot X$ and $\odot Y$ have equal radii, then $\odot X$ can be mapped onto $\odot Y$ by the translation vector $\overrightarrow{XY}$. So $\odot X$ and $\odot Y$ are congruent.

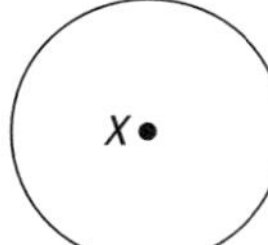

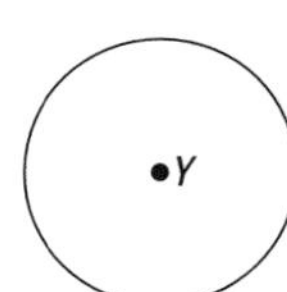

Lesson 14-1 Overview

Broad Goals This lesson covers a variety of relationships between arcs and chords in a circle.

Perspective The conclusions of this lesson result from three general notions: every circle has infinite reflection and rotation symmetry; all circles are similar; and all circles with the same radius are congruent.

The Arc-Chord Congruence Theorem can ultimately be traced back to the rotation symmetry of the circle. **Part 1** of the theorem is proved in the lesson. **Part 2** is left as an exercise in **Question 15.** It can be proved by noting that if two chords of the same length are in the same circle, then they are the same distance from the center, so one can be rotated into the other by rotating the perpendicular from the center to the first chord onto the perpendicular from the center to the second chord.

You might wish to restate the conclusions here as a third theorem of the lesson, namely: if two arcs have the same measure, then they are similar. The converse of this statement is also true, because arcs are measured by central angles, and measures of angles are not changed in similar figures.

If the two circles do not have equal radii, no isometry will map one onto the other, since isometries preserve distance. These arguments prove that *circles are congruent if and only if they have equal radii.*

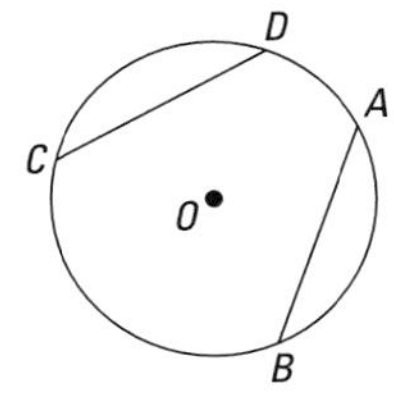

Suppose two arcs $\overset{\frown}{AB}$ and $\overset{\frown}{CD}$ have the same measure, as in the circle at the right. Then you can rotate $\overset{\frown}{AB}$ about O by the measure of $\angle AOC$ to the position of $\overset{\frown}{CD}$. Then the chord $\overline{AB}$ rotates to $\overline{CD}$, and $\overline{AB} \cong \overline{CD}$. Thus, in a circle, arcs of the same measure are congruent and have congruent chords. This proves part (1) of the next theorem for arcs in the same circle. The proof of part (2) is left for you as Question 15.

Arc-Chord Congruence Theorem
In a circle or in congruent circles,
(1) if two arcs have the same measure, they are congruent and their chords are congruent.
(2) if two chords have the same length, their minor arcs have the same measure.

In circles with *different* radii, however, arcs of the same measure are not congruent, nor are their chords congruent. This is pictured below. Arcs with the same measure are similar, though, because one can be mapped onto the other by a composite of a translation, a size change, and a rotation. See left.

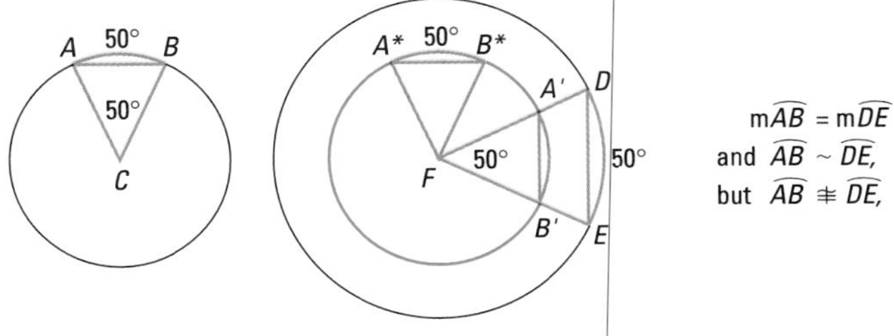

Translation (T): the direction is $\overrightarrow{CF}$; the magnitude is CF. Rotation (R): the center is F; the magnitude is $-m\angle A^*FD$, where A^* is the image of A under the translation T. Size Change (S): the center is F; the magnitude is $\frac{DF}{A'F}$ where $A' = R \circ T(A)$.

Curlers on ice. *Four concentric circles form the target in the sport of curling.*

Activity

Refer to the figure above. Describe a translation, rotation, and size change whose composite maps $\overset{\frown}{AB}$ onto $\overset{\frown}{DE}$. See above left.

Properties of Chords

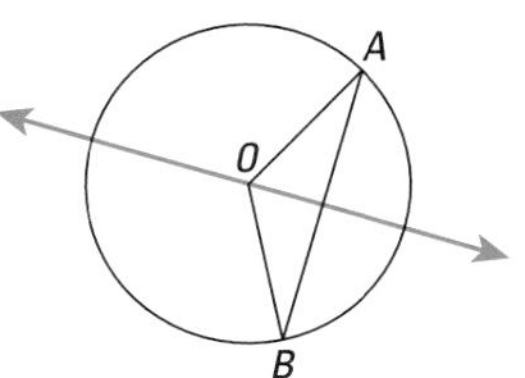

As shown in $\odot O$ at the left, when $\overset{\frown}{AB}$ is not a semicircle, $\triangle ABO$ is isosceles. You have learned that in an isosceles triangle, the bisector of the vertex angle, the perpendicular bisector of the base, the altitude from the vertex, and the median from the vertex all lie on the same line. (Recall the Isosceles Triangle Coincidence Theorem in Lesson 6-2.) In the language of circles and chords, this leads to the following theorem.

7. An arc of the circle $\overset{\frown}{CB}$
8. Measure of an arc of the circle 100°
9. A semicircle $\overset{\frown}{ACB}$
10. Define *circle.* The set of all points in a plane at a certain distance (its radius) from a certain point (its center)

Notes on Reading

You might begin this lesson by writing down the four parts of the Chord-Center Theorem. Have students complete the statements in the proof. (This is **Question 10.**)

Throughout this chapter, angles, chords, and arcs in circles are drawn with various tilts. This can be done because in a circle all directions are the same. The Arc-Chord Congruence Theorem can be thought of as a restatement of this property.

The properties of chords can help students distinguish between arc length and arc measure. Whereas two arcs with measure $x°$ in the same circle or in circles with the same radius are congruent, two arcs with measure $x°$ in circles with different radii are similar. If the central angle of the arc does not change, the arc's *length* changes if the radius of the circle changes, but its *measure* stays the same.

An alternate way of showing the various properties of circles, chords, and arcs is given in *Optional Activities* on page 802. The following procedure shows a general way to find the length of a chord of any arc. Draw the figure below on the board.

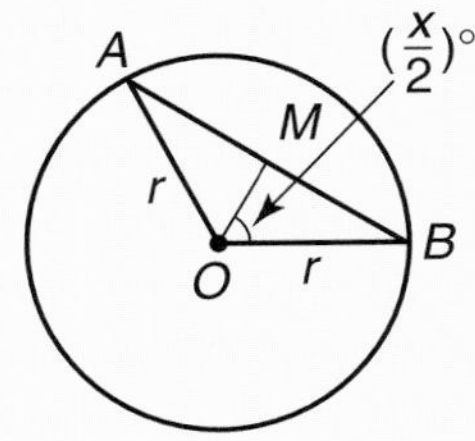

Since the endpoints of a chord and the center of its circle form the vertices of an isosceles triangle, certain properties of the isosceles triangle can be restated in terms of chords and circles. Recall that these properties were deduced from the reflection symmetry of the isosceles triangle. These properties are summarized in the Chord-Center Theorem.

Example 1 shows how students can calculate the length of a chord using trigonometry if the radius of the circle is known. **Example 2** shows how, using properties of special triangles, students can calculate lengths of chords for arcs of 60°, 90°, and 120°. These are the only arcs whose chord lengths can be determined easily without trigonometry.

Optional Activities

Activity 1 Technology Connection
In *Technology Sourcebook, Computer Master 24,* students draw circles and investigate properties of chords and arcs. You may want to use Questions 1 and 2 of the Activity to introduce the lesson. Question 3, an extension, involves an interesting relationship involving concentric circles.

Suppose the arc has measure $x°$, and $\overline{AB}$ is its chord, as drawn here. Then its central angle has measure x. Draw the radii to the endpoints of the arc, and draw the perpendicular bisector of the chord (which contains the center of the circle). Now, $m\angle AOM = \frac{x}{2}$, so $AM = r \sin \frac{x}{2}$. Thus, $AB = 2r \sin \frac{x}{2}$.

History Connection The application of sines to chords was the first historical use of sines. The Greek mathematician Ptolemy calculated lengths of chords using sines. The word sine comes from the Latin *sinus*, meaning *bridge*.

Review the notations used for chords, arcs, central angles, and major versus minor arcs. Chords are segments and use the same segment notation that we have used throughout this book, but arcs are used to designate the arc connecting the chord between two points. Central angles are named as angles normally are, but notice the use of three points to name a major arc. Arcs named with two letters are minor arcs unless the word "major" is included in the description.

The term *inscribed polygon* is important to discuss because it will be used in later lessons.

Have students record the results of the **Activity** for use with **Question 5** on page 804.

Chord-Center Theorem

(1) The line that contains the center of a circle and is perpendicular to a chord bisects the chord.
(2) The line that contains the center of a circle and the midpoint of a chord bisects the central angle of the chord.
(3) The bisector of the central angle of a chord is the perpendicular bisector of the chord.
(4) The perpendicular bisector of a chord of a circle contains the center of the circle.

Proof

Each part is only a restatement of a property of isosceles triangles. You are asked in Question 10 to fill in the blanks in the proof below.
(1) This says the altitude of an isosceles triangle is also the median.
(2) This says the __?__ of an isosceles triangle is also a(n) __?__.
(3) This says the __?__ of an isosceles triangle is also a(n) __?__.
(4) This says the __?__ of an isosceles triangle is also a(n) __?__.

How to Find the Length of a Chord

Given the measure of an arc, can the length of its chord be found? This can always be done using trigonometry if the radius of the circle is known. In fact, this was the kind of problem that first led to trigonometry.

Example 1

Find the length of a chord of a 103° arc in a circle of radius 20 cm.

Solution

A picture is drawn at the left. The length of $\overline{AB}$ is desired. $\triangle PAB$ is isosceles with vertex angle P. Let M be the midpoint of $\overline{AB}$. Then $\overline{PM}$ bisects $\angle APB$ and $\overline{PM} \perp \overline{AB}$. Thus $\triangle APM$ is a right triangle and $m\angle APM = \frac{103}{2} = 51.5$.

To find AM, use trigonometry.

$$\sin 51.5° = \frac{AM}{20}$$

$$AM = 20 \cdot \sin 51.5° \approx 15.65$$

Since M is a midpoint, $AB = 2 \cdot AM \approx 31.30$ cm.

If an arc in a circle has a measure of 60°, 90°, or 120°, its length can be found without trigonometry.

Example 2

A circle has radius 10″. Find the length of a chord of
a. a 60° arc. **b.** a 90° arc. **c.** a 120° arc.

Optional Activities

Activity 2 Alternate Approach
Another way to show some properties of circles, chords, and arcs is to draw a set of concentric circles, their radii, and chords as shown at the right. These circles illustrate the following properties when the circles are *not congruent*: (1) the arcs have the same degree measure; (2) the arcs have different lengths; and (3) the chords made by the arcs have different lengths.

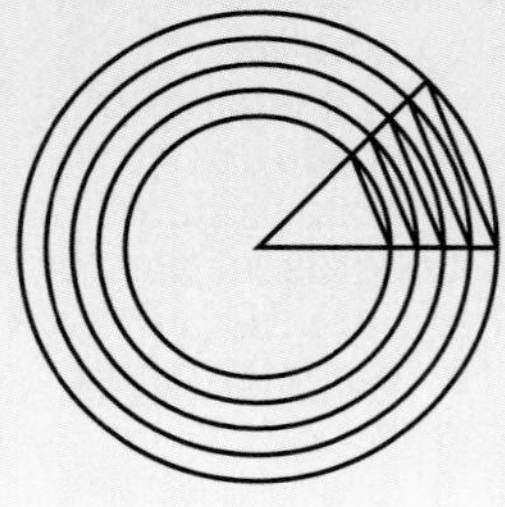

Adapting to Individual Needs

Extra Help
Some students will still confuse arc length with arc measure. Draw two different-sized wheels on the board, each with a 45° central angle. Point out that the arc on the smaller wheel has the same measure as the arc on the larger wheel. Yet if each wheel turns through an angle of 45°, the larger wheel will travel farther because the length of its 45° arc is greater than the length of the 45° arc on the smaller wheel.

▶ **Solution**

For each situation, draw a picture.

a. $\triangle AOB$ is an isosceles triangle with a $60°$ vertex angle, so it is equilateral. AB = 10".

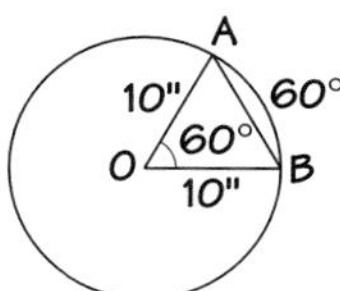

b. Since $m\angle COD = 90$, $\triangle COD$ is an isosceles right triangle. So $CD = \sqrt{2} \cdot 10" \approx 14.14"$.

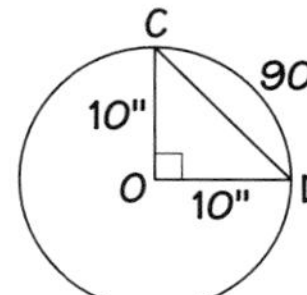

c. Since $m\angle FOE = 120$, $m\angle F = 30$ and $m\angle E = 30$. Draw altitude $\overline{OG}$ to the base of $\triangle OEF$. The two triangles formed are 30-60-90 triangles.
$OE = 2 \cdot OG$, so $OG = 5"$.
$GE = \sqrt{3} \cdot OG$, so $GE = 5\sqrt{3}"$. Therefore,
$FE = 2 \cdot GE = 10\sqrt{3}" \approx 17.32"$.

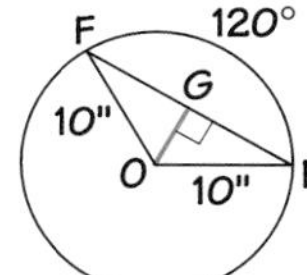

Recall that a polygon whose vertices lie on a given circle is called an inscribed polygon. So Example 2 provides a way of finding the length of a side of an inscribed regular hexagon, square, or equilateral triangle if you know the radius of the circle. The center of the inscribed regular polygon is the center of the circle.

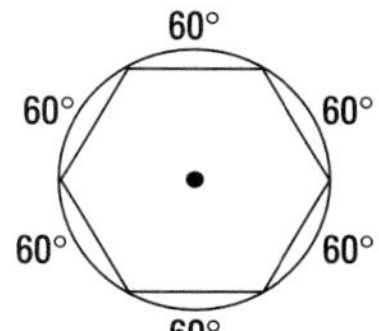

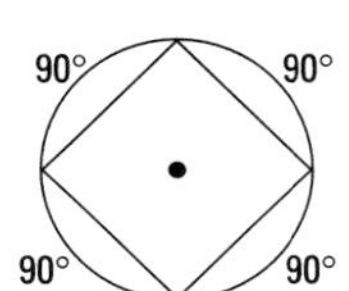

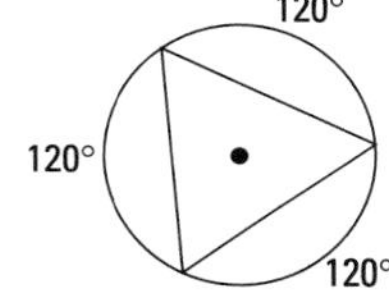

QUESTIONS

Covering the Reading

1. The measure of a minor arc of a circle is between _?_ and _?_.
0°, 180°
2. The measure of a major arc of a circle is between _?_ and _?_.
180°, 360°
3. *Multiple choice.* Two circles are congruent if and only if their radii are c
(a) parallel. (b) perpendicular.
(c) equal in length. (d) none of these.

Additional Examples

1. Find the length of a chord of a 90° arc in a circle with radius *r*.
$r\sqrt{2}$
2. Find the length of a chord of a 120° arc in a circle with radius 7.
$7\sqrt{3}$
3. Find the length of a chord of a 44° arc in a circle with diameter 14. **$14 \sin 22° \approx 5.24$**
4. People talk about drilling holes through the center of the earth and coming out in China. This is not true if the hole is drilled from the U.S. (the Indian Ocean is on the opposite side of most of the U.S.), but the length of a hole from one place on the earth to another can be calculated. The radius of the earth is about 3960 miles, and its circumference is about 24,880 miles. What would be the length of a hole through the earth from Washington D.C. directly to Beijing? By air along a great circle route, it is about 6950 miles from Washington to Beijing. **The arc measures about 100.6°; its chord is about 6090 miles long.**

Notes on Questions

Questions 1–2 As with segments, the phrase "between ___ and ___" is used when the endpoints of an arc are excluded, and "from ___ to ___" when the endpoints are included.

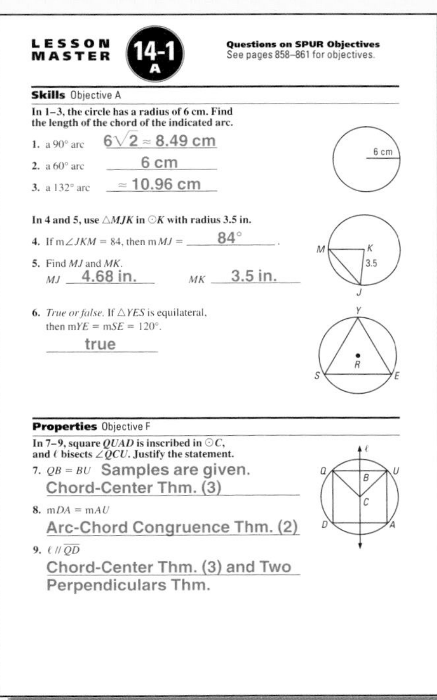

LESSON MASTER 14-1 A

Questions on SPUR Objectives
See pages 858–861 for objectives.

Skills Objective A

In 1–3, the circle has a radius of 6 cm. Find the length of the chord of the indicated arc.

1. a 90° arc $6\sqrt{2} \approx 8.49$ cm
2. a 60° arc 6 cm
3. a 132° arc ≈ 10.96 cm

In 4 and 5, use $\triangle MJK$ in $\odot K$ with radius 3.5 in.

4. If $m\angle JKM = 84$, then $m\overset{\frown}{MJ}$ = 84°.
5. Find *MJ* and *MK*.
MJ 4.68 in. *MK* 3.5 in.
6. *True or false.* If $\triangle YES$ is equilateral, then $m\overset{\frown}{YE} = m\overset{\frown}{SE} = 120°$.
true

Properties Objective F

In 7–9, square *QUAD* is inscribed in $\odot C$, and ℓ bisects $\angle QCU$. Justify the statement.

7. $QB = BU$ Samples are given.
Chord-Center Thm. (3)
8. $m\overset{\frown}{DA} = m\overset{\frown}{AU}$
Arc-Chord Congruence Thm. (2)
9. $\ell \parallel \overline{QD}$
Chord-Center Thm. (3) and Two Perpendiculars Thm.

Adapting to Individual Needs

Challenge

Have students generalize the following examples and questions from Lesson 14-1.

1. **Example 1:** Find a formula for the length of a chord of an $x°$ arc, in a circle of radius *r*. $[2r \sin \frac{x}{2}]$
2. **Example 2:** Find a simplified formula for the length of a chord, in a circle of radius *r*, for the special cases of:
   a. a 60° arc. [*r*]
   b. a 90° arc. $[r\sqrt{2}]$
   c. a 120° arc. $[r\sqrt{3}]$
3. **Question 18:** Find the length of a side of the square inscribed in a circle of radius *r* and find the area of the region that is inside the circle but outside the square. [Length: $r\sqrt{2}$; area: $(\pi - 2)r^2$]

Notes on Questions

Question 4 The drawings of the circles confirm the answers, but some students may not realize that.

Questions 11–14 Encourage students to begin their work on problems like these by drawing a picture.

Question 16 This question presents difficulties for many students. But the idea does not need to be mastered here. There will be other questions like it in review sets later in the chapter.

Practice

For more questions on SPUR Objectives, use **Lesson Master 14-1A** (shown on page 803) or **Lesson Master 14-1B** (shown on pages 804–805).

Assessment

Oral/Written Communication Have students **work in pairs.** First, have each student draw a circle with the length of a radius given, as well as the degree measure of an arc. Then have them exchange circles and determine the length of the chord which subtends the given arc. [Students determine the length of a chord when given the radius of the circle and the degree measure of the arc subtended by the chord.]

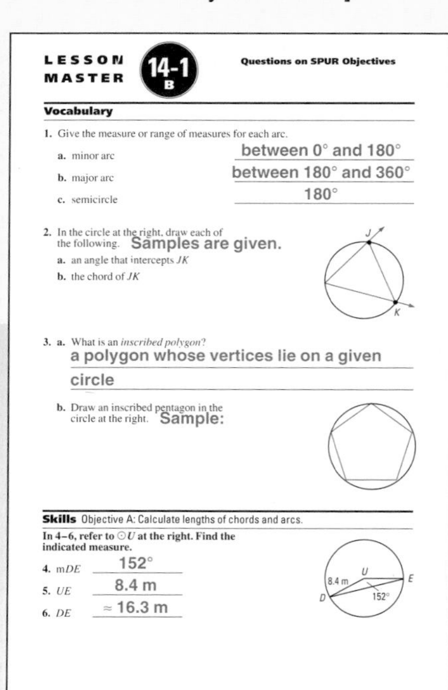

LESSON MASTER 14-1 B — Questions on SPUR Objectives

Vocabulary

1. Give the measure or range of measures for each arc.
   a. minor arc — between 0° and 180°
   b. major arc — between 180° and 360°
   c. semicircle — 180°

2. In the circle at the right, draw each of the following. Samples are given.
   a. an angle that intercepts JK
   b. the chord of JK

3. a. What is an *inscribed polygon*? a polygon whose vertices lie on a given circle
   b. Draw an inscribed pentagon in the circle at the right. Sample:

Skills Objective A: Calculate lengths of chords and arcs.

In 4–6, refer to $\odot U$ at the right. Find the indicated measure.

4. mDE — 152°
5. UE — 8.4 m
6. DE — ≈ 16.3 m

4. *True or false.* In $\odot Z$ and $\odot A$ below, $m\angle Z = m\angle A$ and $ZY > AC$.
   a. $m\widehat{XY} = m\widehat{BC}$ True
   b. $\widehat{XY} \sim \widehat{BC}$ True
   c. $\widehat{XY} \cong \widehat{BC}$ False

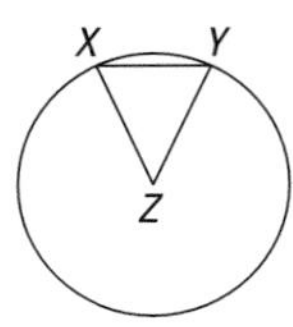

5. Give the results you found in the Activity in this lesson. See page 801.

In 6–9, use $\odot O$ pictured at the right.

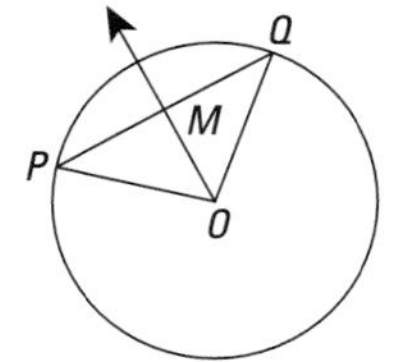

6. If $m\angle POQ = 98$, then $m\widehat{PQ}$ = __?__. 98°
7. Explain why $\triangle OPQ$ is isosceles. See left.

7) $OP = OQ$ by the definition of circle, and $\triangle OPQ$ is isosceles by the definition of isosceles triangle

8. If $\overrightarrow{OM} \perp \overline{PQ}$ then $\overrightarrow{OM}$ __?__ $\overline{PQ}$. bisects
9. If $\overrightarrow{OM}$ bisects $\angle POQ$, then $\overrightarrow{OM}$ __?__ $\overline{PQ}$. is the ⊥ bisector of

10. Fill in the blanks in the proof of the Chord-Center Theorem. See margin.

In 11–14, use $\odot O$ with radius 25 m shown at the left. Find the length of a chord of

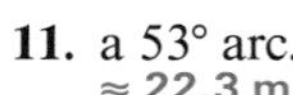

11. a 53° arc. ≈ 22.3 m
12. a 60° arc. 25 m
13. a 90° arc. $25\sqrt{2} \approx 35.4$ m
14. a 120° arc. $25\sqrt{3} \approx 43.3$ m

Applying the Mathematics

15. Use the figure at the right to complete this proof of part (2) of the Arc-Chord Congruence Theorem.
   Given: $AB = CD$.
   To prove: $m\widehat{AB} = m\widehat{CD}$.
   (Hint: The measure of an arc equals the measure of its central angle.) See margin.

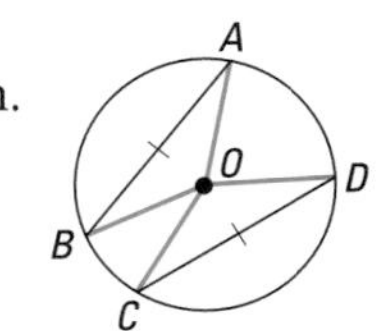

16. The circular hole with center Q shown at the right has radius 3 feet. A 5-foot board $\overline{XY}$ is to be wedged into the hole. What will be the distance from Q to $\overline{XY}$? (Hint: Draw some auxiliary radii and a perpendicular.) $\sqrt{2.75} \approx 1.66$ ft

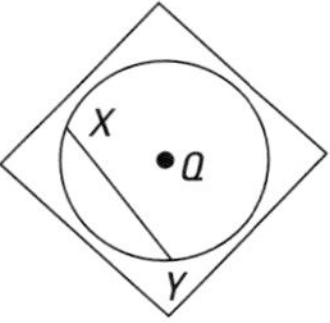

Notice the circular windows with square frames on the Lampoon Building similar to the situation in Question 16.

17. Trace the circle through points B, I, and G, or draw one like it by hand or with an automatic drawer.
   a. Draw the ⊥ bisector of $\overline{BI}$.
   b. Draw the ⊥ bisector of $\overline{IG}$.
   c. At what point do the lines of parts **a** and **b** intersect?
   d. Which part of which theorem justifies your answer to part **c**? Chord-Center Theorem (part 4)

   c) at the center of the circle

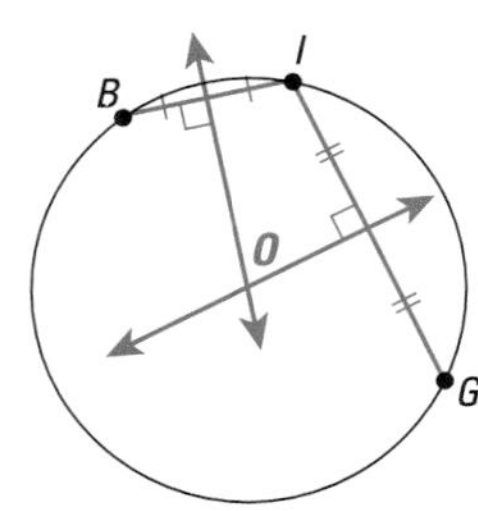

Additional Answers

10. Part 2: median to the base; bisector of the vertex ∠; Part 3: bisector of the vertex ∠; ⊥ bisector of the base; Part 4: ⊥ bisector of the base; altitude of the triangle

15.

Conclusions	Justifications
1. $OB = OC$, $OA = OD$	def. of circle
2. $\triangle AOB \cong \triangle DOC$	SSS Congruence Thm. (step 1 and given)
3. $m\angle AOB = m\angle DOC$	*CPCF* Theorem
4. $m\angle AOB = m\widehat{AB}$, $m\angle DOC = m\widehat{CD}$	def. of arc measure
5. $m\widehat{AB} = m\widehat{CD}$	Transitive Property of Equality

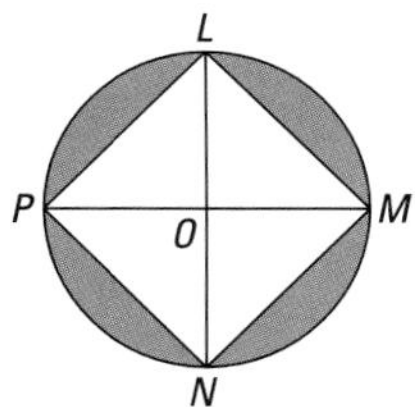

18. At the left, $LMNP$ is a square inscribed in $\odot O$. Suppose the radius of the circle is 1.

a. Find the length of a side of the square. $\sqrt{2}$ units

b. Find the area of the shaded region. $\pi - 2 \approx 1.14$ units^2

19. a. A regular hexagon is inscribed in a circle of radius 1. What is its perimeter? 6 units

b. A regular hexagon is inscribed in a circle of radius x. What is its perimeter? $6x$ units

Review

20. The diagonals of trapezoid $ABCD$ intersect at point E, as pictured below. Is $\triangle ABE \sim \triangle CDE$? Explain why or why not. *(Lesson 13-2)* See margin.

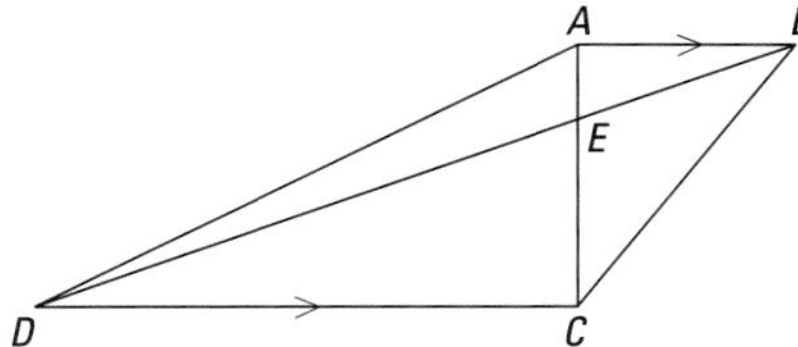

21. What is the volume of a square pyramid with base sides 2 m and height 1.4 m? *(Lesson 10-7)* ≈ 1.87 m^3

22. In the figure at the left, find $m\angle A$. *(Lesson 5-7)* 94

A
$2x°$
$x°$
$141°$
B C D

In 23 and 24, use $\odot Q$ at the right. *(Lesson 3-2)*

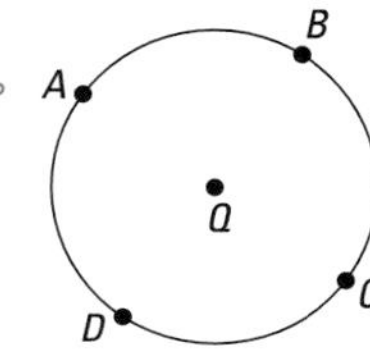

23. If $m\widehat{ABC} = 178°$ and $m\widehat{BC} = 94°$, find $m\widehat{AB}$. 84°

24. $m\widehat{BA} + m\widehat{BC} + m\widehat{CD} + m\widehat{AD} =$ __?__ 360°

Exploration

25. This question extends Question 18 to polygons of more than 4 sides.

a. Suppose a regular octagon is inscribed in a circle of radius 1. What is the area of the region between the circle and the octagon? (Hint: use the SAS Area Theorem.) $\pi - 2\sqrt{2} \approx 0.31$ units^2

b. Select any regular polygon with more than 8 sides and inscribe it in a circle of radius 1. Find the area between the regular polygon and the circle. See margin.

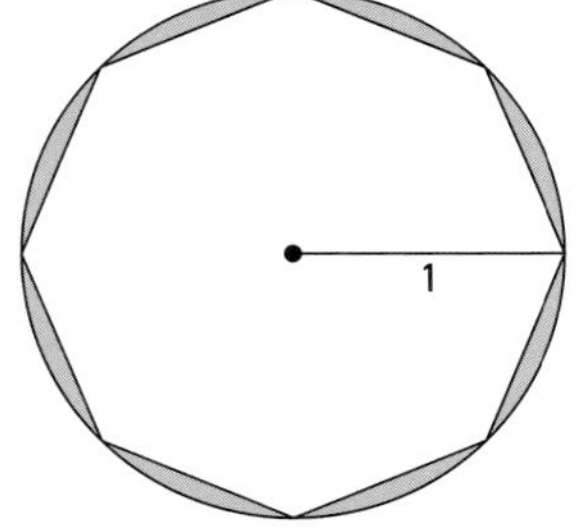

Extension

Writing If two arcs have the same measure, then they are similar. Ask students to describe the similarity transformation that maps one of the arcs onto the other. [The transformation is like that found in the proofs of the triangle similarity theorems. If the radii of the circles of the arcs are a and b, apply a size change to the circle with radius a by magnitude $\frac{b}{a}$. The image of the arc will have the same measure, since the measure of the central angle is preserved under a size change. Then the image circle will be congruent to the other circle. So the image arc and the arc in the circle of radius b are congruent. Therefore, one arc can be mapped onto the other by the composite of an isometry and a size change, and they are similar.]

Project Update Project 1, *Cutting Down on Waste,* Project 2, *Picture Angles,* and Project 4, *The Universe,* on page 853, relate to the content of this lesson.

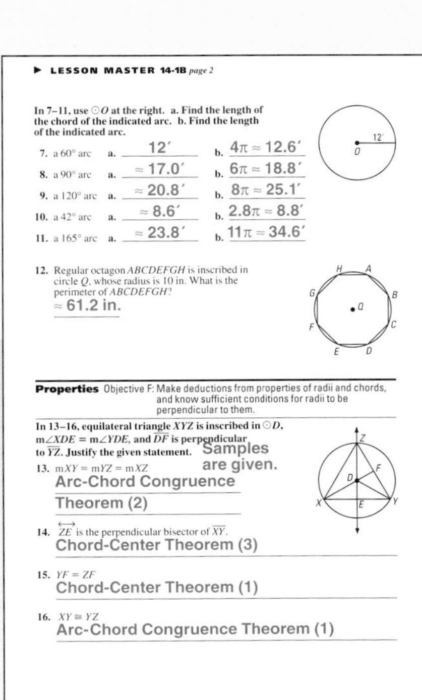

▶ **LESSON MASTER 14-1B** *page 2*

In 7–11, use $\odot O$ at the right. a. Find the length of the chord of the indicated arc. b. Find the length of the indicated arc.

		a.		b.
7.	a 60° arc	12′		$4\pi \approx 12.6'$
8.	a 90° arc	$\approx 17.0'$		$6\pi \approx 18.8'$
9.	a 120° arc	$\approx 20.8'$		$8\pi \approx 25.1'$
10.	a 42° arc	$\approx 8.6'$		$2.8\pi \approx 8.8'$
11.	a 165° arc	$\approx 23.8'$		$11\pi \approx 34.6'$

12. Regular octagon $ABCDEFGH$ is inscribed in circle Q, whose radius is 10 in. What is the perimeter of $ABCDEFGH$?
≈ 61.2 in.

Properties Objective F: Make deductions from properties of radii and chords, and know sufficient conditions for radii to be perpendicular to them.

In 13–16, equilateral triangle XYZ is inscribed in $\odot D$, $m\angle XDE = m\angle YDE$, and $\overline{DF}$ is perpendicular to $\overline{YZ}$. Justify the given statement. Samples are given.

13. $m\widehat{XY} = m\widehat{YZ} = m\widehat{XZ}$
Arc-Chord Congruence Theorem (2)

14. $\overleftrightarrow{ZE}$ is the perpendicular bisector of $\overline{XY}$.
Chord-Center Theorem (3)

15. $YF = ZF$
Chord-Center Theorem (1)

16. $\widehat{XY} \cong \widehat{YZ}$
Arc-Chord Congruence Theorem (1)

20. Yes; since $\overline{AB} \parallel \overline{CD}$ as indicated in the figure, $\angle EAB \cong \angle ECD$ and $\angle EBA \cong \angle EDC$ by the $\parallel$ Lines $\Rightarrow$ AIA $\cong$ Theorem. Therefore, $\triangle ABE \sim \triangle CDE$, by the AA Similarity Theorem.

25b. Sample: If the polygon is a regular decagon, the area of the region between it and a circumscribed circle of radius r is $0.20r^2$ units^2. In general, for a regular n-gon, the area of the region between it and a circumscribed circle is $(\pi - \frac{n}{2}\sin\frac{360°}{n})r^2$ units^2.

Lesson 14-2

Objectives

B Calculate measures of inscribed angles from measures of intercepted arcs, and vice versa.

C Calculate measures of angles between chords from measures of intercepted arcs, and vice versa.

G Make deductions from properties of angles formed by chords.

Resources

From the ***Teacher's Resource File***

- Lesson Master 14-2A or 14-2B
- Answer Master 14-2
- Teaching Aids
  181 Warm-up
  185 Additional Examples

Additional Resources

- Visuals for Teaching Aids 181, 185

Teaching Lesson 14-2

Warm-up

1. On a large sheet of paper use a compass to draw a circle with a radius of 3 inches. Using the same compass opening, mark six equally spaced points on the circle. Then connect all the points with line segments. Be sure all possible segments are drawn. Describe the figure that is formed. **A regular hexagon and all its diagonals**

LESSON

14-2 *The Inscribed Angle Theorem*

Picture perfect. *Sometimes in order to fit an entire building in a picture, the photographer must be located in a hard-to-reach place.*

A Situation Leading to Inscribed Angles

The **picture angle** of a camera lens is a measure indicating how wide a field of vision can be captured in one photo. A normal camera lens in a 35-mm camera has a picture angle of 62°. A wide-angle lens may have a picture angle as large as 118°. A telephoto lens has a smaller picture angle, perhaps 18°.

Here is a situation in photography. You want to take a picture of a building, and you want to get the entire front of the building in your picture. (Assume the height of the building is not a problem.) Suppose your camera has only one normal lens with a 62° field. The diagram at the right pictures the situation as seen from above.

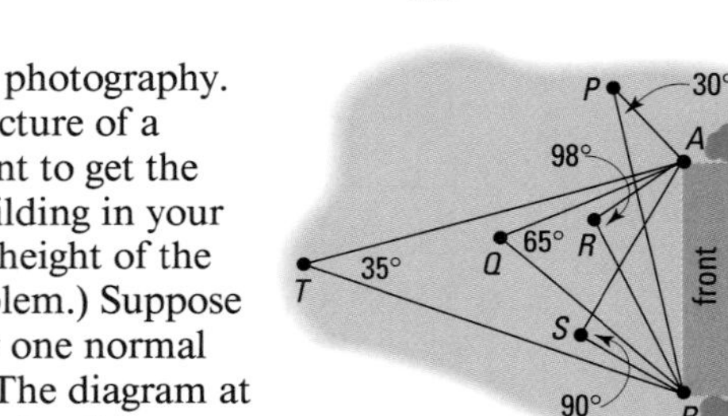

Let A and B be the endpoints of the building. If you stand at Q, $m\angle AQB$ is larger than 62, so the picture cannot include the entire front of the building. The same is true for points R and S. But at points P and T, the whole building easily fits in the picture. There is a natural question: where are all the points that are the vertex of a 62° angle through points A and B? The answer is surprising. It is found by considering *inscribed angles* in a circle.

806

Lesson 14-2 Overview

Broad Goals This lesson discusses the theorem that the measure of an inscribed angle is half the measure of its intercepted arc and applies it to angles inscribed in a semicircle.

Perspective The Inscribed Angle Theorem is motivated by the problem of deciding where a photographer can stand in order to fit an entire building in a picture. This application is continued in Lesson 14-3, where drawing the possible locations of the photographer is treated. The proof argument for this theorem is the standard one involving consideration of three cases.

There is a proof argument of the Inscribed Angle Theorem that does not involve three cases; it uses the Two-Reflection Theorem for Rotations. However, a rigorous proof of that theorem has more than three cases. The proof follows.

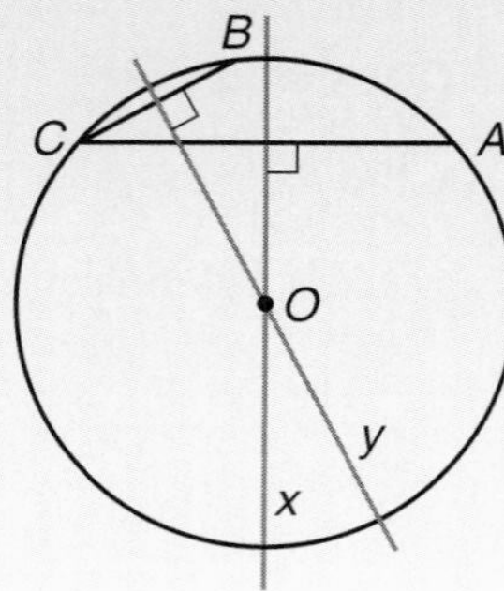

What Are Inscribed Angles?

Definition
An angle is an **inscribed angle** in a circle if and only if
a. the vertex of the angle is on the circle, and
b. each side of the angle intersects the circle at a point other than the vertex.

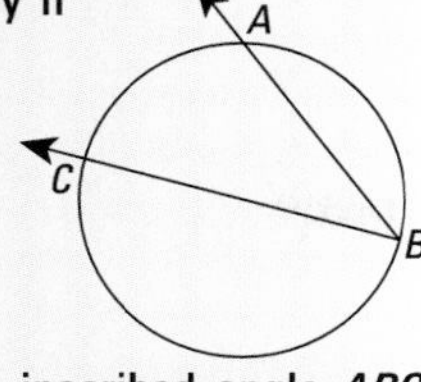

inscribed angle ABC

Activity
a) $m\angle A = m\angle B = m\angle C = 48$; $m\angle MON = 96$; $m\widehat{MN} = 96°$
b) Answers may vary; however, it is always true that $m\angle MCN = \frac{1}{2} m\widehat{MN}$.

❶ **Activity**

a. Below, inscribed angles A, B, and C intercept the same arc $\widehat{MN}$. Use a protractor to measure these angles. (You will need to extend sides.) Then measure $\angle MON$ to determine $m\widehat{MN}$.

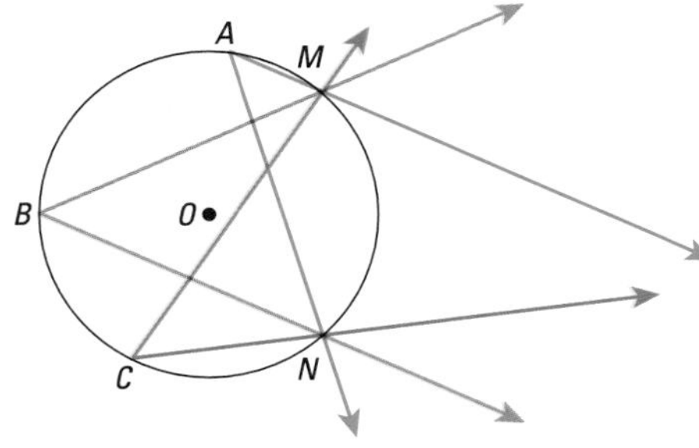

b. If you have access to dynamic software, create points A and B on circle O. Choose a point C on circle O but not on minor arc $\widehat{MN}$. Measure $\angle MCN$ and minor arc $\widehat{MN}$. Move point C around the major arc $\widehat{MN}$. What happens to $m\angle MCN$?

In the Activity above, you should find that all the inscribed angles have the same measure, and that the intercepted arc has twice that measure. This is true of all inscribed angles and their intercepted arcs.

Inscribed Angle Theorem
In a circle, the measure of an inscribed angle is one-half the measure of its intercepted arc.

Proof:
The steps of the argument depend on the position of the circle's center O relative to the inscribed $\angle ABC$. There are three possibilities. They are referred to as Case I, Case II, and Case III.

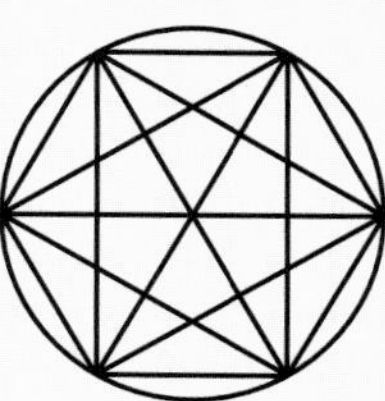

2. Pick any two adjacent segments from the same point on the circle. Measure the angle between the segments. What do you notice? The angle measures 30.

Notes on Reading

❶ To review this activity, draw a circle and three angles A, B, and C that inscribe the same arc.

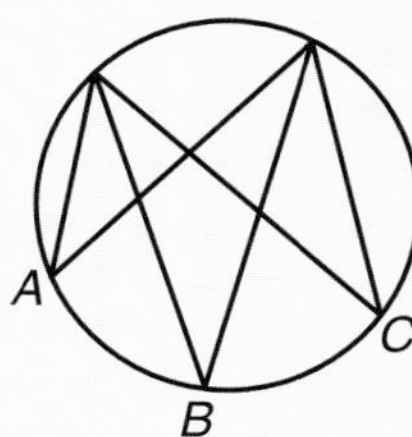

The angles do not look congruent because the shown parts of their side lengths are not the same. If you look near the vertices, however, the openings are the same. This suggests the angles are congruent.

Cooperative Learning The proof of the Inscribed Angle Theorem may be difficult for students to grasp because it is done in cases. You might want to go through the proof with the class. Point out that a proof is not complete until all possibilities are considered.

Consider the rotation R with center O and $R(A) = B$. What is its magnitude n? By the definition of rotation, $n = m\widehat{AB}$. Now note that $R = r_y \circ r_x$ where x and y are the perpendicular bisectors of chords $\overline{AC}$ and $\overline{BC}$. The proof of this is as follows: First, $r_y \circ r_x$ is a rotation because it is the composite of two reflections over intersecting lines. Since the lines are perpendicular bisectors of the chords, they both pass through the center of the circle. Thus they intersect at O. Now, from the definition of reflection, $r_y \circ r_x(A) = r_y(C) = B$. Then, by the Two-Reflection Theorem, the magnitude of this rotation is twice the measure of the angle between the reflecting lines. Therefore, $n = 2 \cdot m\angle O$.

The two triangles in the figure contain a pair of vertical angles, and each has a right angle. Thus, their third angles have the same measure, so $m\angle C = m\angle O$. Thus $n = 2 \cdot m\angle C$. So $2 \cdot m\angle C = m\widehat{AB}$.

Error Alert Some students may be bothered that the result of Case I is used in the arguments for Cases II and III; they may wonder if this is using a theorem in its own proof. Explain that once a result has been proved, it can be used immediately, even in the next line of a proof. The result in Case I is not the entire theorem, but only a part of the whole theorem.

Have students record the results of the **Activity** for use with **Question 5** on page 810.

Additional Examples

These examples are also given on **Teaching Aid 185.**

1. The three angles of $\triangle ABC$ have measures 40, 60, and 80. If the circle through A, B, and C is drawn, what are the measures of the three minor arcs formed by the points? **80°, 120°, and 160°; The check is that they add to 360°.**
2. $ABCDEF$ is a regular hexagon. Find $m\angle BFE$.

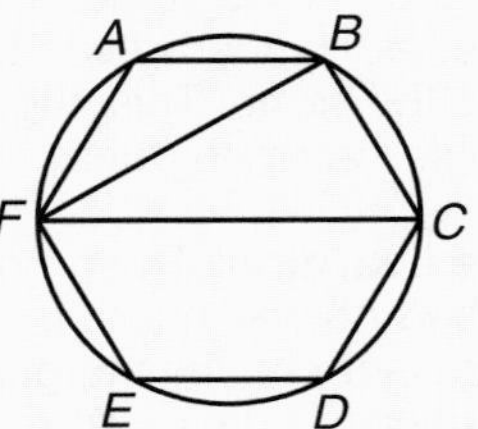

Inscribe the regular hexagon in a circle. $\angle BFE$ intercepts an arc of 180°, so it is a right angle.

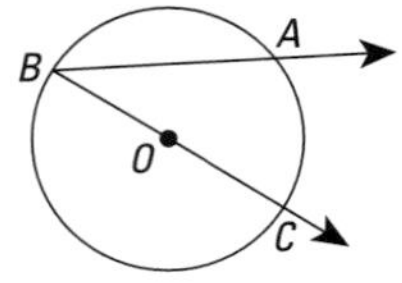

Case I: O lies on a side of $\angle ABC$.

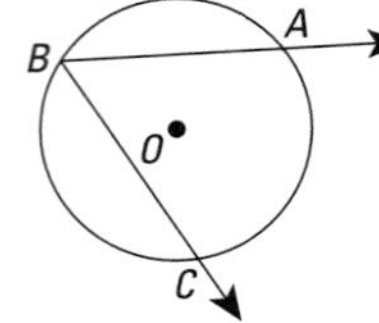

Case II: O is in the interior of $\angle ABC$.

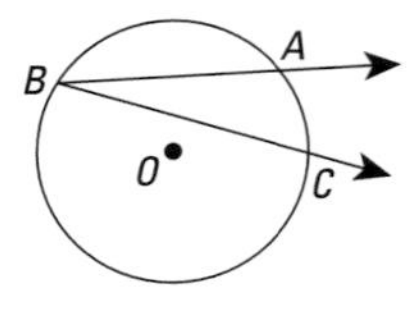

Case III: O is in the exterior of $\angle ABC$.

For all three cases what is given and what is to prove are the same.

Given: $\angle ABC$ inscribed in $\odot O$.

To prove: $m\angle ABC = \frac{1}{2} \cdot m\widehat{AC}$.

Argument:

Case I: Draw the auxiliary segment $\overline{OA}$. Since $\triangle AOB$ is isosceles, $m\angle B = m\angle A$. Call this measure x. By the Exterior Angle Theorem, $m\angle AOC = 2x$.

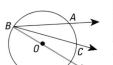

Because the measure of an arc equals the measure of its central angle, $m\widehat{AC} = 2x = 2 \cdot m\angle B$. Solving for $m\angle B$, $m\angle B = \frac{1}{2}m\widehat{AC}$.

Case I proves that $m\angle B = \frac{1}{2}m\widehat{AC}$ when one side of $\angle B$ contains the center of the circle. This fact is used in the proofs of the other cases.

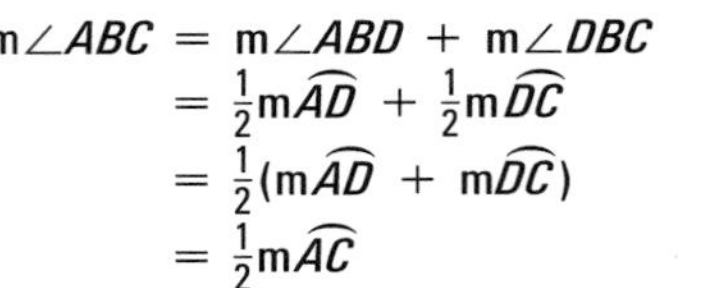

Case II: The auxiliary ray $\overrightarrow{BO}$ is needed.

$m\angle ABC = m\angle ABD + m\angle DBC$	Angle Addition Property
$= \frac{1}{2}m\widehat{AD} + \frac{1}{2}m\widehat{DC}$	by the result in Case I
$= \frac{1}{2}(m\widehat{AD} + m\widehat{DC})$	Distributive Property
$= \frac{1}{2}m\widehat{AC}$	Arc Addition

Case III: The proof is like the proof of Case II. Here $m\angle ABC = m\angle ABD - m\angle CBD$.

You are asked to complete the proof in Question 7.

Using the Inscribed Angle Theorem

Example 1

Four points A, B, C, and D split a circle into arcs with measures as shown. Find the measures of the angles of $ABCD$.

Solution

$m\angle A = \frac{1}{2}m\widehat{BCD} = \frac{1}{2}(100° + 148°) = 124°$

$m\angle B = \frac{1}{2}m\widehat{ADC} = \frac{1}{2}(62° + 148°) = 105°$

$m\angle C = \frac{1}{2}m\widehat{DAB} = \frac{1}{2}(62° + 50°) = 56°$

$m\angle D = \frac{1}{2}m\widehat{ABC} = \frac{1}{2}(50° + 100°) = 75°$

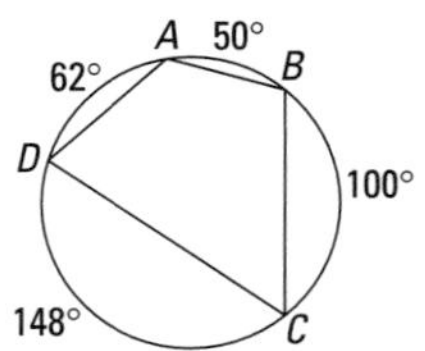

Optional Activities

As you discuss each theorem in the lesson, have students verify the theorem by actually measuring angles with a protractor. Remind them that they can determine the degree measure of an arc by measuring the central angle subtended by the arc.

Adapting to Individual Needs

Extra Help

The Inscribed Angle Theorem is not obvious to most students. If shown a picture like the one at the right, most students at first glance would not guess that $\angle RAS$, $\angle RBS$, and $\angle RCS$ have the same measure. They may need to be reminded that the sides of an angle are rays that extend infinitely. Since it is impossible to draw a side of infinite length, we extend them as far as is convenient. Therefore, we could extend all the segments in the figure to have the same length. Then it may be more apparent that the inscribed angles have the same measure.

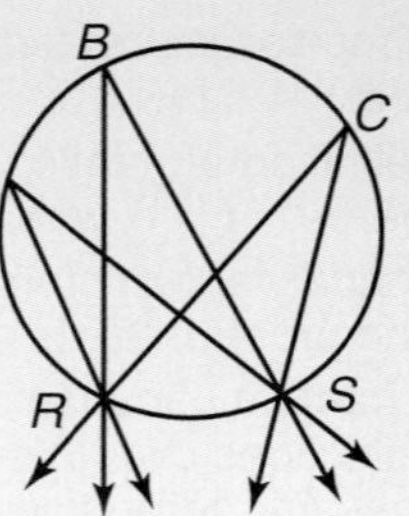

Check

The four angle measures add to 360° as they should. Furthermore, the measures look correct.

The next example demonstrates a surprising and useful consequence of the Inscribed Angle Theorem.

How many semicircles can you find in this Boston scene?

Example 2

Let $\widehat{PQR}$ be a semicircle. Find $m\angle PQR$.

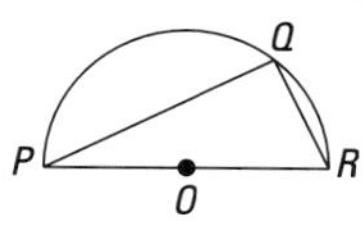

Solution

Complete the circle.

From the Inscribed Angle Theorem, $\angle PQR = \frac{1}{2}m\widehat{PSR}$. Since $\widehat{PSR}$ is a semicircle, $m\widehat{PSR} = 180°$. Thus $m\angle PQR = \frac{1}{2} \cdot 180 = 90$.

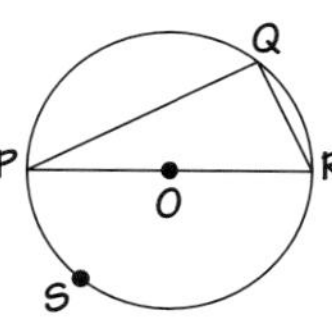

Example 2 proves the following.

Theorem

An angle inscribed in a semicircle is a right angle.

What about the camera problem stated at the beginning of this lesson? The answer is given in Example 2 of the next lesson.

QUESTIONS

Covering the Reading

1. What is the *picture angle* of a camera lens? See left.

1) measure indicating how wide a field of vision can be captured in one photo

2. Use the diagram at the right. A person stands at point P to take a picture of the house. Will the entire front of the house be in the picture
   a. if the person uses a normal camera lens? Yes
   b. if the person uses a telephoto lens? No
   c. if the person uses a wide-angle lens? Yes

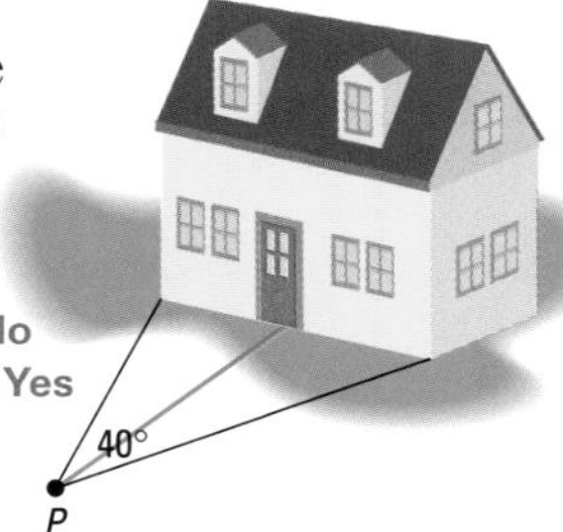

Notes on Questions

Question 2 This question may lead to interesting discussions of examples from students who have tried to take pictures of large objects.

Adapting to Individual Needs

English Language Development

If students with limited English proficiency have difficulties understanding the definitions and theorems, pair them with students who are proficient in English. Suggest that each pair carefully review the diagrams that accompany the statement of the theorems and definitions. Then have the student with limited English proficiency restate the definitions or theorems in his or her own words.

Challenge

Give students these problems.

1. Find a formula for the length of a chord formed by an inscribed angle measuring x, in a circle of radius r. $[2r \sin x°]$
2. If an equilateral triangle is inscribed in a circle of radius r, give a formula for the length s of a side of the triangle in terms of r. $[s = r\sqrt{3}]$

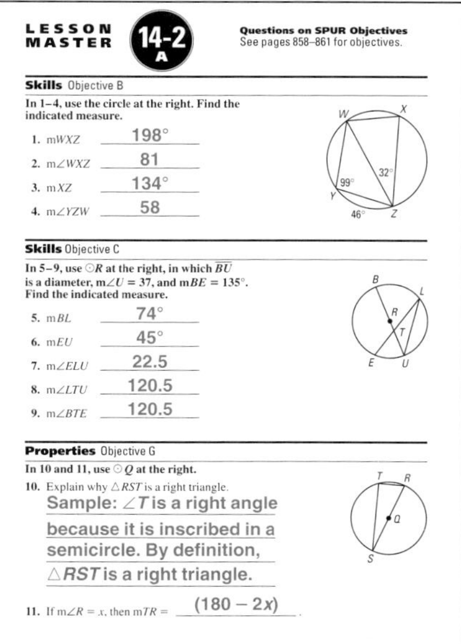

LESSON MASTER 14-2 A

Questions on SPUR Objectives
See pages 858–861 for objectives.

Skills Objective B

In 1–4, use the circle at the right. Find the indicated measure.

1. $m\widehat{WXZ}$ 198°
2. $m\angle WXZ$ 81
3. $m\widehat{XZ}$ 134°
4. $m\angle YZW$ 58

Skills Objective C

In 5–9, use ⊙R at the right, in which $\overline{BU}$ is a diameter, $m\angle U = 37$, and $m\widehat{BE} = 135°$. Find the indicated measure.

5. $m\widehat{BL}$ 74°
6. $m\widehat{EU}$ 45°
7. $m\angle ELU$ 22.5
8. $m\angle LTU$ 120.5
9. $m\angle BTE$ 120.5

Properties Objective G

In 10 and 11, use ⊙Q at the right.

10. Explain why $\triangle RST$ is a right triangle.
    Sample: $\angle T$ is a right angle because it is inscribed in a semicircle. By definition, $\triangle RST$ is a right triangle.
11. If $m\angle R = x$, then $m\widehat{TR} =$ $(180 - 2x)$.

Notes on Questions

Question 8 Have students check the answer by pointing out that the four angles should add to 360. Then ask: Do you need to know all four arc measures to do this question? [No, from three arc measures the fourth could be calculated.] Then ask students: Does either diagonal contain the center of the circle? Why or why not? [$\overline{BD}$ contains the center because $\widehat{BD}$ is a semicircle. $\overline{AC}$ does not contain the center.]

Question 13 You can use this question to ask students to make a generalization about the relationship between an inscribed angle and a central angle which intercept the same arc. [The measure of the inscribed angle is half the measure of the central angle.]

Question 14 A good review of the special triangle relationships involves this problem: Suppose the radius of the circle is x. Determine as many lengths of sides of these triangles as you can. [They can all be determined. $CD = x$, $AD = x\sqrt{3}$, $AB = BC = x\sqrt{2}$, $AC = 2x$.]

Question 16 This theorem is used later in the chapter in the proof of the Secant Length Theorem of Lesson 14-7, and should be discussed.

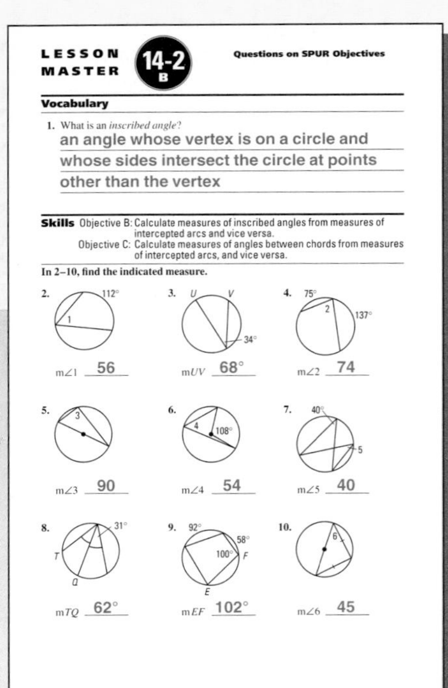
LESSON MASTER 14-2 B Questions on SPUR Objectives

Vocabulary

1. What is an *inscribed angle*? an angle whose vertex is on a circle and whose sides intersect the circle at points other than the vertex

Skills Objective B: Calculate measures of inscribed angles from measures of intercepted arcs and vice versa.
Objective C: Calculate measures of angles between chords from measures of intercepted arcs, and vice versa.

In 2–10, find the indicated measure.

2. m∠1 56
3. m$\widehat{UV}$ 68°
4. m∠2 74
5. m∠3 90
6. m∠4 54
7. m∠5 40
8. m$\widehat{TQ}$ 62°
9. m$\widehat{EF}$ 102°
10. m∠6 45

3. Use the circle below at the left. What is m∠*ABC*? 48.5

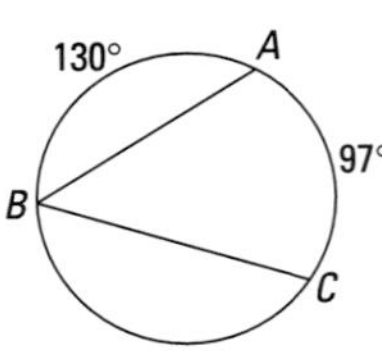

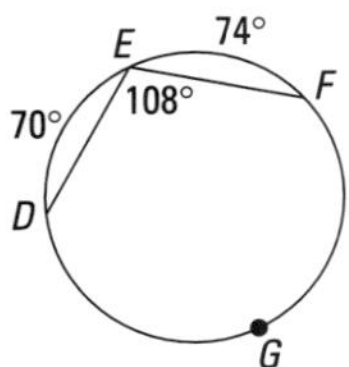

4. In the circle above at the right, what is m$\widehat{DGF}$? 216°

5. Give the measurements of the angles and arcs you found in the Activity of this lesson. See page 807.

6. The proof of the Inscribed Angle Theorem has three cases. How do the cases differ?
The center is either on, interior to, or exterior to the angle.

7. Finish this proof of Case III of the Inscribed Angle Theorem.

7b) Case I of the Inscribed Angle Theorem

Conclusions	Justifications
$m\angle ABC = m\angle ABD - m\angle CBD$	a. Angle Addition Property.
$= \frac{1}{2}m\widehat{AD} - \frac{1}{2}m\widehat{CD}$	b. See left.
$=$ c. $\frac{1}{2}(m\widehat{AD} - m\widehat{CD})$	Distributive Property
$= \frac{1}{2}m\widehat{AC}$	Arc Addition

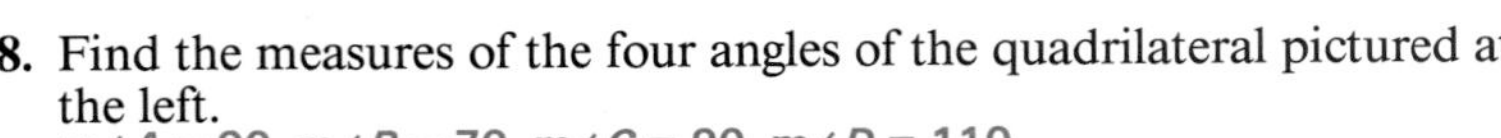

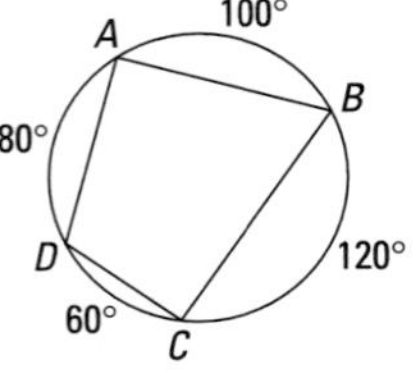

8. Find the measures of the four angles of the quadrilateral pictured at the left.
m∠A = 90, m∠B = 70, m∠C = 90, m∠D = 110

9. An angle inscribed in a semicircle has what measure? 90

In 10 and 11, $\overline{MN}$ is a diameter of ⊙*O*, as pictured below.

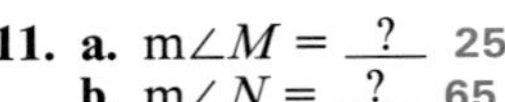

10. a. m$\widehat{ML}$ = ? 130°
b. m$\widehat{MPN}$ = ? 180°

11. a. m∠*M* = ? 25
b. m∠*N* = ? 65
c. m∠*L* = ? 90
d. △*LMN* is a(n) ? triangle. right

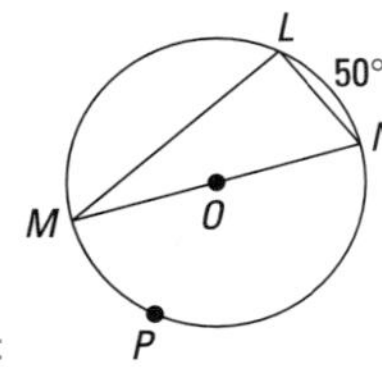

Applying the Mathematics

12. Use the figure at the right.
a. △*TUV* is ? in the circle.
b. m∠*U* = ? 127.5
a) inscribed

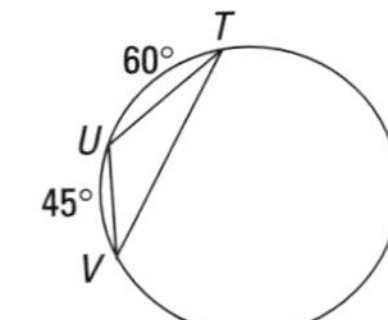

13. In the figure below, $\overline{YW}$ and $\overline{XZ}$ are diameters.
a. m$\angle WOZ$ = __?__ n
b. m$\angle Y$ = __?__ $\frac{n}{2}$

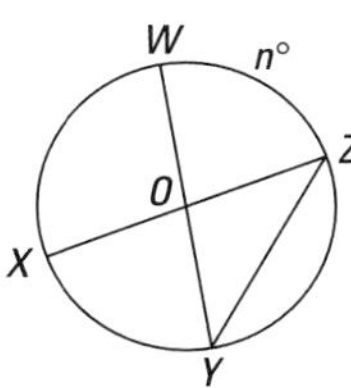

14. $\overline{AC}$ contains the center of the circle below. Calculate the measures of as many angles as you can. m$\angle D$ = 90, m$\angle DCA$ = 60, m$\angle ACB$ = 45, m$\angle B$ = 90, m$\angle DCB$ = 105, m$\angle BAC$ = 45, m$\angle BAD$ = 75

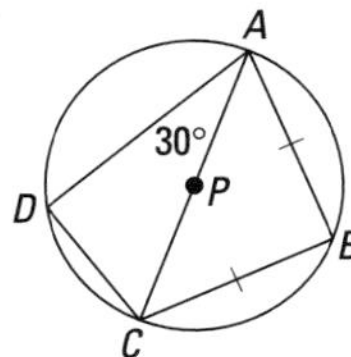

15. In ⊙O below, m$\angle M$ = 35 and m$\angle P$ = 92. If $MP = NQ$, find m$\widehat{MP}$. 53°

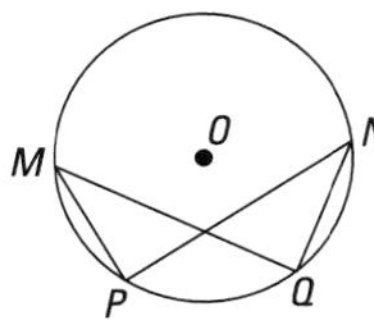

16. Fill in the justifications in this proof of the following theorem.

> **Theorem**
> **In a circle, if two inscribed angles intercept the same arc, then they have the same measure.**

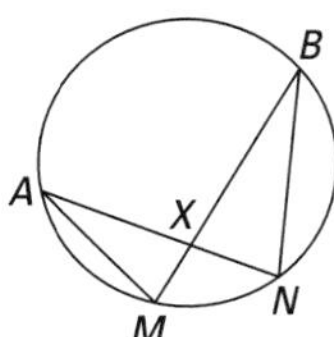

Given: Inscribed angles AMB and ANB.
To prove: m$\angle AMB$ = m$\angle ANB$.

Argument: c) Transitive Property of Equality (steps 1 and 2)

	Conclusions	Justifications
1.	m$\angle AMB = \frac{1}{2}$m$\widehat{AB}$	a. Inscribed Ang. Thm.
2.	m$\angle ANB = \frac{1}{2}$m$\widehat{AB}$	b. Inscribed Ang. Thm.
3.	m$\angle AMB$ = m$\angle ANB$	c. See above.

17. Use the given of Question 16 to prove that $\triangle AXM \sim \triangle BXN$.
See margin.

Additional Answers

17.

Conclusions	Justifications
1. m$\angle AXM$ = m$\angle BXN$	Vertical Angles Theorem
2. m$\angle AMB$ = m$\angle ANB$	If two inscribed angles intercept the same arc, then they have the same measure.
3. $\triangle AXM \sim \triangle BXN$	AA Similarity Thm. (steps 1 and 2)

LESSON MASTER 14-2B *page 2*

11. Find the measures of as many arcs and angles of the figure as you can.
m$\angle SCO$=m$\angle CSO$=31; m$\angle COM$=62; m$\angle MCO$=m$\angle CMO$=59; m$\angle SCM$=90; mCS=118°; mCM=62°; mMCS=mMGS=180°

12. Find the measures of the following arcs and angles of ⊙C.
a. HR 114°
b. m$\angle H$ 33
c. m$\angle HCR$ 114
d. JH 180°

Properties Objective G: Make deductions from properties of angles formed by chords.

13. Refer to the circle at the right.
a. Find m$\angle R$. n
b. Justify your answer to Part **a.**
Sample: By the Inscribed Angle Thm., m$\angle S = \frac{1}{2}$mPQ and m$\angle R = \frac{1}{2}$mPQ, so m$\angle R$ = m$\angle S$ = n.

14. The diagonals of quadrilateral $ABCD$ are diameters of ⊙O. Explain why $ABCD$ is a rectangle.
Sample: Since the angles of $ABCD$ are all inscribed in a semicircle, they are all right angles. By definition, $ABCD$ is a rectangle.

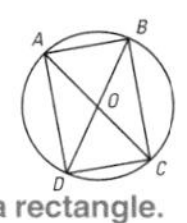

Notes on Questions

Question 19 With the Inscribed Angle Theorem, students now have a second way to determine measures of angles in regular n-gons. Begin by inscribing the regular n-gon in a circle. Each angle intercepts an an arc which covers $\frac{n-2}{n}$ of the 360° of the circle. So its measure is $\frac{1}{2} \cdot 360° \cdot \frac{n-2}{n}$, which simplifies to $\frac{180(n-2)}{n}$, the formula derived in an earlier chapter.

Question 20 Geography Connection The region involved in this question is in the suburbs of Chicago, quite near the editorial offices of ScottForesman.

Practice

For more questions on SPUR Objectives, use **Lesson Master 14-2A** (shown on page 809) or **Lesson Master 14-2B** (shown on pages 810–811).

Assessment

Group Assessment Have students explain why the measure of an inscribed angle is one-half the measure of its intercepted arc. [Students justify this statment by explaining each of the three positions of the circle's center relative to the respective inscribed angle.]

Extension

Writing You might want students to write a proof for another interesting result of the Inscribed Angle Theorem: If a quadrilateral is inscribed in a circle, its opposite angles are supplementary. [Since the opposite angles of a quadrilateral intercept the total circle between them, their sum is equal to half a circle, or 180.]

Project Update Project 2, *Picture Angles,* on page 853, relates to the content of this lesson.

Review

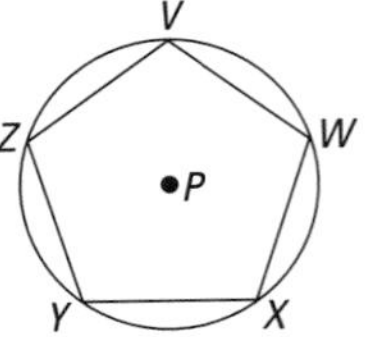

18. Find the perimeter of an equilateral triangle inscribed in a circle of radius 24. *(Lesson 14-1)* $72\sqrt{3} \approx 124.71$ units

19. Regular pentagon $VWXYZ$ is inscribed in $\odot P$ at the left.

a. What is $m\widehat{WX}$? 72°

b. If $PW = 50$, find the perimeter of the pentagon. *(Lesson 14-1)* $500 \sin 36° \approx 294$ units

20. Willow, Lake, and Central are east-west streets. Greenwood and Landwehr are north-south streets. Milwaukee is oblique to east-west streets. The distance on Milwaukee from Willow to Milwaukee and Central is 3 miles. What is the distance on Milwaukee from Lake to Willow? *(Lesson 13-3)* 1.8 miles

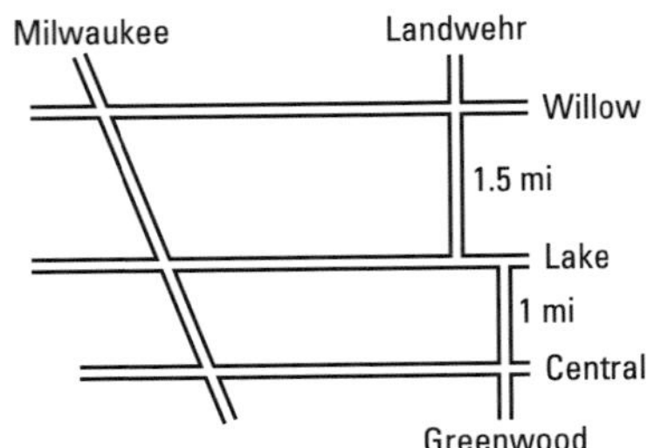

21. The length of a ballroom is twice its width, and its area is 280 square yards. How long is it from one corner of the ballroom to the opposite corner? *(Lessons 8-2, 8-6)* $\sqrt{700} \approx 26.46$ yards

22. Refer to the figure at the right. $LOGARITHM$ is a regular nonagon. L is the midpoint of $\overline{NO}$. What is $m\angle MLN$? *(Lesson 6-7)* 40

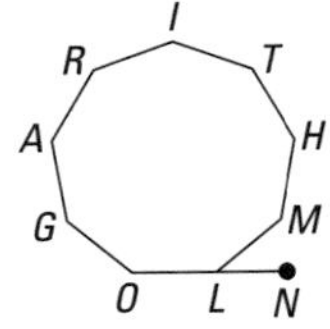

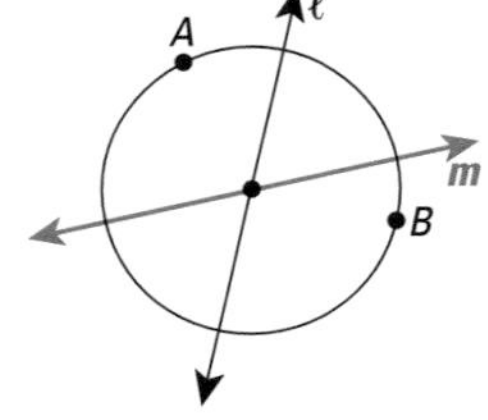

23. Trace the drawing at the left. Then draw line m so that $r_m \circ r_\ell(A) = B$. *(Lesson 4-5)* See left.

24. The circle with center C and radius r is defined to be the set of all points whose distance from C is equal to r. Give a good definition of the *interior* of this circle. *(Lesson 2-4)* See left.

25. Solve for x: $100n - 200 + x = 100n$. *(Previous course)* 200

23) line m is the $\perp$ bis. of the segment with endpoints B and $r_\ell(A)$.

24) The interior of a circle with center C and radius r is the set of all points whose distance from C is less than r.

Exploration

26. Examine a camera in your household or in a store. What is its normal picture angle? (You may need to refer to the instruction manual.) Answers may vary.

Setting Up Lesson 14-3

The "picture angle" application that begins in Lesson 14-2 continues into Lesson 14-3. In Lesson 14-2, enough information is given to know that the solution to the question in the third paragraph on page 806 is an arc of a circle C such that $m\angle AQB = 124$, that is, twice 62. In Lesson 14-3, students learn how to locate that center.

Materials If you have students do *Optional Activities* in Lesson 14-3, they will need circular objects that they can trace around, such as drinking cups, glasses, or aluminum cans.

LESSON

14-3

Locating the Center of a Circle

Suppose you bought a circular coffee-table top and wished to place it on a revolving pedestal base so that it rotates evenly. To do this you need to match the center of the base and the center of the table. In Lesson 3-8 you learned how to draw perpendicular bisectors of segments. If two segments are chords of the same circle, and are not parallel, then the intersection of their perpendicular bisectors is the center of the circle. That method for locating the center of a circle is called the *perpendicular bisector method.*

The Right-Angle Method

A second method relies on a theorem proved in the previous lesson: If an inscribed angle is a right angle, then its intercepted arc is a semicircle. So the segment connecting the endpoints of the intercepted arc is a diameter. Draw two diameters and you have the center. We call this the *right-angle method* for locating the center of the circle.

Example 1

Locate the center of the circle drawn at the right.

Solution

Step 1:

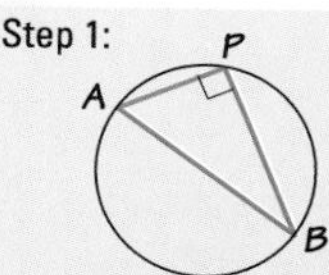

Choose a point P on the circle. Draw a right angle at P. $\overline{AB}$ is a diameter.

Step 2:

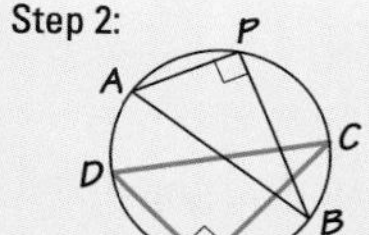

Choose a second point Q. Draw a right angle at Q. $\overline{CD}$ is a diameter.

Step 3:

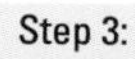

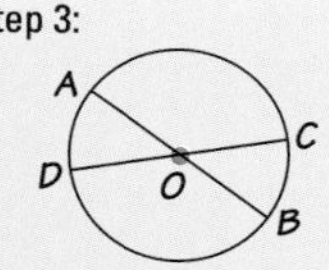

The diameters $\overline{AB}$ and $\overline{CD}$ intersect at the center of the circle.

This method is often used by people in drafting; the right angles are drawn with stiff metal instruments called *T-squares* or *ells.* You can use the corner of an index card or a piece of duplicating paper.

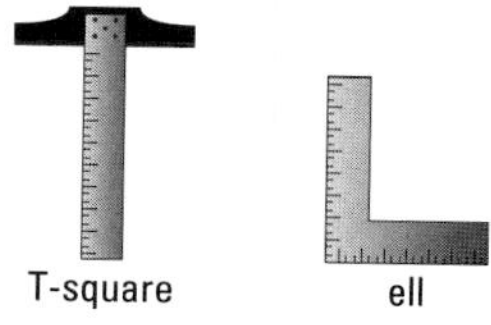

Lesson 14-3

Objectives

D Locate the center of a circle given sufficient information.

I Given the angle width of a lens and the width of an object, determine the set of points from which the object just fits in the picture.

Resources

From the ***Teacher's Resource File***

- Lesson Master 14-3A or 14-3B
- Answer Master 14-3
- Assessment Sourcebook: Quiz for Lessons 14-1 through 14-3
- Teaching Aids
  182 Warm-up
  186 Additional Examples

Additional Resources

- Visuals for Teaching Aids 182, 186
- Circular objects

Teaching Lesson 14-3

Warm-up

Draw a large circle on a sheet of paper. Then lay a square corner of another sheet on the circle so that its vertex touches the circle at a point P and the two sides intersect the circle at two other points. Label those two points C and D. What is the measure of $\angle CPD$? What do you know about $\overline{CD}$? **90; it is a diameter of the circle.**

Notes on Reading

When there are two methods for solving a problem, the good problem solver should wonder when one

Lesson 14-3 Overview

Broad Goals Two methods resulting from the Inscribed Angle Theorem for finding the center of a circle are shown in this lesson, and the photographer's problem from Lesson 14-2 is solved.

Perspective In Lesson 3-8, students learned how to draw a circle through any three given points. The method used to do this, namely the perpendicular bisector method, has the advantage of not requiring an entire circle. One can find the center of an arc, or the circle through just three points. The method is justified by using the theorem that the perpendicular bisector of a chord contains the center of a circle.

In this lesson, two other methods for locating the center of a circle, the right-angle method and the inscribed angle method, are described and justified. Carpenters use the right-angle method —it requires drawing a few lines and does not require a compass. The inscribed angle method enables one to locate the center if a protractor is available.

The photographer's problem in Lesson 14-2 can now be solved both in theory and in practice. That is, the set of points where the photographer can stand to fit an object in the picture is an arc. The center of that arc can be located, and the distance from the object to the center can be calculated.

method is to be preferred over the other. Some questions you might ask students about methods in this lesson are outlined in *Optional Activities*.

❶ Although the example of a photographer is given, in practice a photographer would usually back up until the building is in the field of vision. The ideas of the lesson would more likely be used by a motion-picture team, because the location of the camera (a more complicated piece of equipment) is often mapped out in advance and away from the set.

Additional Examples

These examples are also given on **Teaching Aid 186.**

1. Trace the bottom of a drinking glass or a tin can to draw a circle. Then locate the center by using the right-angle method. **Drawings will vary.**
2. Trace the drawing of the building shown below. Diagram all the places where you could stand so that the front of the building, $\overline{EF}$, just fits into your picture if you use a camera with a 54° field of vision. **You can stand anywhere on $\overset{\frown}{EGF}$.**

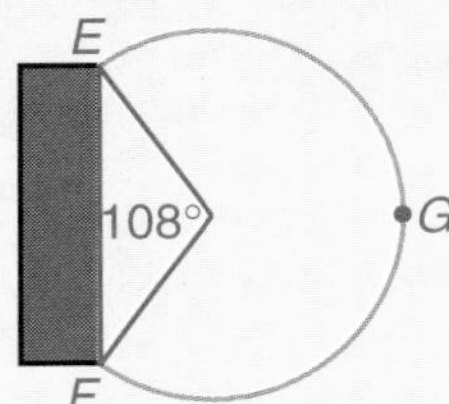

3. If the building in the diagram in Question 2 is 60 meters long, how far from the center of the circle is the building? $\frac{30}{\tan 54°} \approx$ **22 m**
4. Explain how to locate the center of an arc you know to be a semicircle. **Find the perpendicular bisector of the segment joining the endpoints of the arc.**

(Notes on Questions begin on page 816.)

Eagle eye. *Photographer Margaret Bourke White on the Chrysler Building, New York.*

Using the Inscribed Angle Theorem

A third method also uses the Inscribed Angle Theorem. This method is shown in Example 2.

Example 2

A camera has a 46° field of vision. Where are all the places a person could stand so the front of the building just fills the picture?

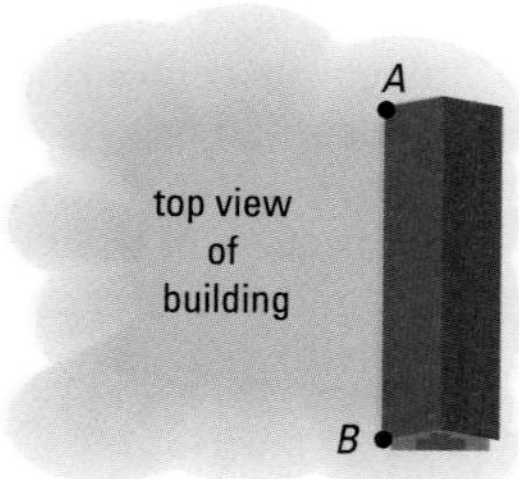

Solution

Consider a point P so that $m\angle APB = 46$. The front of the building will just fit in the picture if you stand at point P. There is one circle that contains points P, A, and B. $\overline{AB}$ is a chord in that circle.

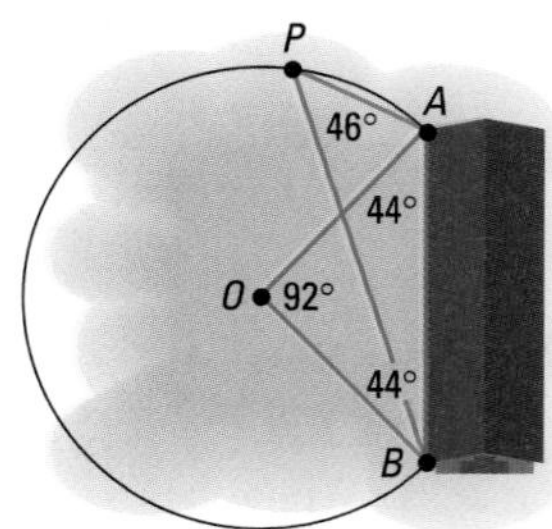

Step 1: Determine $m\overset{\frown}{AB}$. Since $m\angle P = \frac{1}{2}m\overset{\frown}{AB}$, $m\overset{\frown}{AB} = 2 \cdot m\angle P = 92°$.

Step 2: Find the center O of the circle containing $\overset{\frown}{AB}$ such that $m\angle AOB = 92$. Since $\triangle AOB$ is isosceles, $m\angle OAB = m\angle OBA = 44$. Draw the 44° angles at A and B. Their sides intersect at O.

Step 3: Draw $\odot O$ with radius OA. Any point P on the major arc $\overset{\frown}{APB}$ of the circle will satisfy $m\angle APB = 46$.

From anywhere on major arc $\overset{\frown}{APB}$, the front of the building will just fit the picture. Inside the circle you will get only part of the building in your picture. Outside the circle you will see more than the building in your picture.

You can use trigonometry to determine the distance from certain positions of point P to the building.

Optional Activities

✎ **Writing** After discussing the lesson, you might have students **work in groups** to write an answer for each question you might ask them about methods for locating the center of the circle. Then have students discuss their answers.

1. When would the right-angle method be preferred? [Students recognize that if a circle is already drawn and a right angle is available, this method is faster.]
2. When would the perpendicular bisector method be preferred? [Students recognize that if only a part of a circle is given, or if only three points are given, then this is the preferred method.]
3. When would the inscribed angle method be preferred? [Students recognize that the inscribed angle method is the preferred method for finding the center of a circle containing a chord only if that chord and the degree measure of its arc are known.]

Adapting to Individual Needs

Extra Help

In **Example 1**, some students may correctly notice that by drawing only one inscribed right angle, they can draw a diameter of the given circle and thus locate the center by bisecting the diameter. Point out, however, that it is quicker in most cases to simply inscribe the second right angle and find the point where two diameters intersect.

1 **Example 3**

A photographer wishes to photograph a building 130′ long with a lens that has an 80° field of vision. The picture is to be taken directly in front of the middle of the building. At least how far from the building will the photographer need to stand?

Solution

Let $\overline{QS}$ be the front of the building, as shown at the right. R is the midpoint of $\overline{QS}$. With the 80° lens the photographer needs to stand at a point P on the perpendicular bisector of $\overline{QS}$.

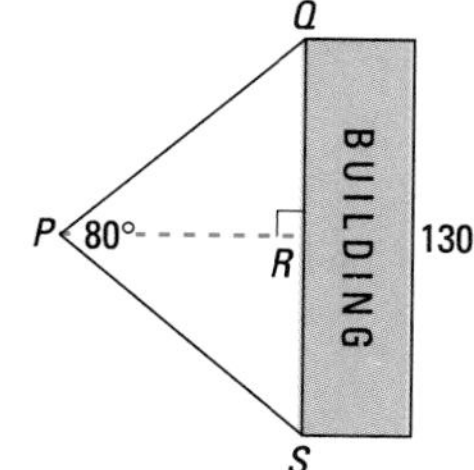

$QR = \frac{1}{2}QS = 65'$ and $PQ = PS$.

$\triangle PQS$ is isosceles and $\overrightarrow{PR}$ bisects $\angle QPS$. So $m\angle RPQ = 40$.

Now use trigonometry with right $\triangle PQR$.

$$\frac{65}{PR} = \tan 40°$$
$$65 = PR \cdot \tan 40°$$
$$\frac{65}{\tan 40°} = PR$$
$$77.5' \approx PR$$

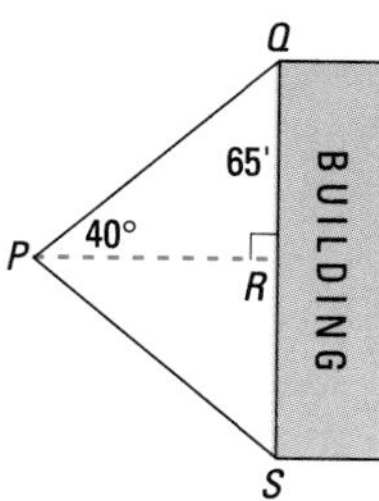

If the photographer stands on $\overrightarrow{RP}$ 77.5' or more from the building, the entire front of the building will be in the picture.

Check

We know from right $\triangle PQR$ that $m\angle PQR = 50°$. From the solution, $\tan\angle PQR = \frac{PR}{RQ} \approx \frac{77.5}{65} \approx 1.19$. From a calculator, $\tan 50° \approx 1.19$. So the value of PR checks.

QUESTIONS

Covering the Reading

1. Trace the circle at the left below. Find its center using the right-angle method.

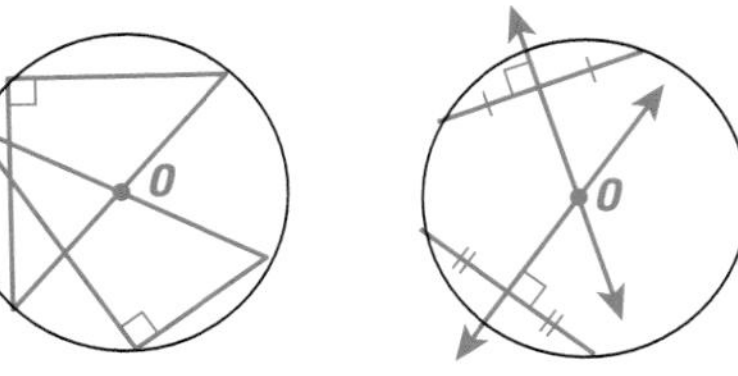

2. Trace the circle at the right above. Construct its center using the perpendicular bisector method.

Follow-up for Lesson 14-3

Practice

For more questions on SPUR Objectives, use **Lesson Master 14-3A** (shown on page 815) or **Lesson Master 14-3B** (shown on pages 816–817).

Assessment

Quiz A quiz covering Lessons 14-1 through 14-3 is provided in the *Assessment Sourcebook*.

Oral/Written Communication Have students **work in groups.** Give each group a circular object and have them use it to trace two circles. Then have them describe two different methods to find the center of the circle. [Students find the center of the circle using the methods described in this lesson.]

Extension

With paper circles there is a fourth way to find the center. Ask students to try to find it. [Fold the circle onto itself over two different diameters. The intersection of the diameters is the center.]

Project Update Project 2, *Picture Angles,* and Project 3, *Circles Associated with Triangles,* on page 853, relate to the content of this lesson.

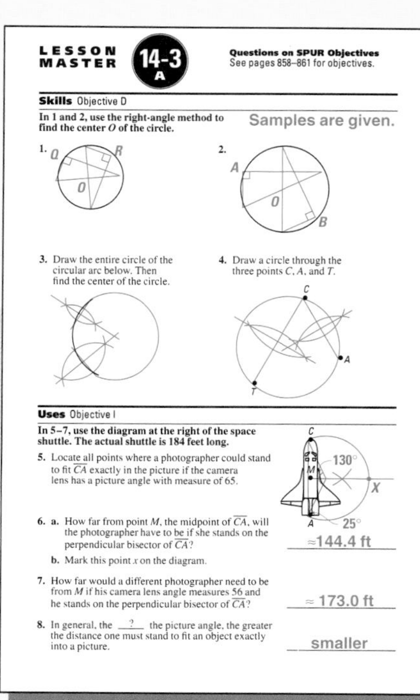

LESSON MASTER 14-3 A

Questions on SPUR Objectives
See pages 858–861 for objectives.

Skills Objective D

In 1 and 2, use the right-angle method to find the center O of the circle. Samples are given.

1. Q R O

2. A O B

3. Draw the entire circle of the circular arc below. Then find the center of the circle.

4. Draw a circle through the three points C, A, and T.

Uses Objective I

In 5–7, use the diagram at the right of the space shuttle. The actual shuttle is 184 feet long.

5. Locate all points where a photographer could stand to fit $\overline{CA}$ exactly in the picture if the camera lens has a picture angle with measure of 65.

6. a. How far from point M, the midpoint of $\overline{CA}$, will the photographer have to be if she stands on the perpendicular bisector of $\overline{CA}$? ≈144.4 ft

b. Mark this point x on the diagram.

7. How far would a different photographer need to be from M if his camera lens angle measures 56 and he stands on the perpendicular bisector of $\overline{CA}$? ≈ 173.0 ft

8. In general, the __?__ the picture angle, the greater the distance one must stand to fit an object exactly into a picture. smaller

Adapting to Individual Needs

Challenge

1. Tell students to let ABC be any triangle. Draw the circle through A, B, and C. Under the following conditions, where will the center of that circle be located?
   a. The triangle is acute. [Inside the triangle]
   b. The triangle is a right triangle. [At the midpoint of the hypotenuse]
   c. The triangle is obtuse. [Outside the triangle]
2. What is the area of the shaded region below? [$2\pi rR$]

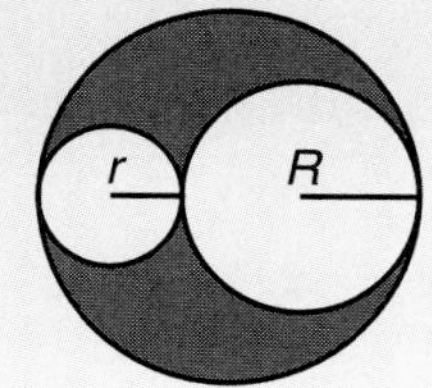

Notes on Questions

Question 5 Because the photographer has a lens with such a large angle, he or she can stand quite close to the steps and the entire building will still be in the picture. To draw the circle, if C is the center of the circle and A and B the ends of the steps, $m\angle ACB = 176$. So begin with 2° angles at A and B. Since there are wide-angle lenses with even wider picture angles (up to 118° in one catalog which we located), there is a natural question regarding what to do with such a camera. In such cases, the center of the circle is behind the front of the steps. For instance, with a 118° angle, $\angle ABC$ would be a 28° angle into the steps.

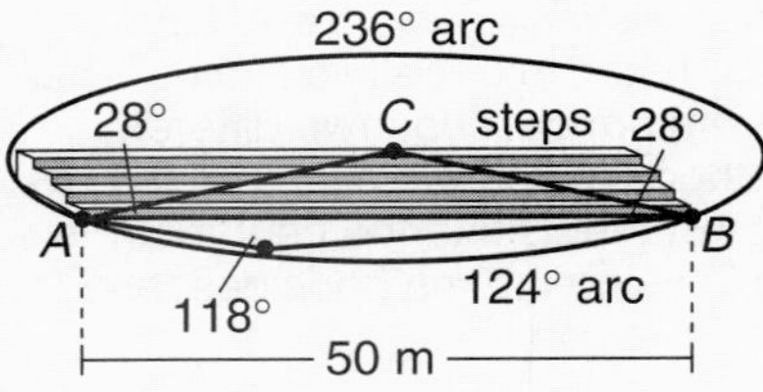

History Connection Emmy Noether, a German mathematician born in 1882, was perhaps the most creative abstract algebraist in modern times. She broke many barriers as a woman in the German university system by writing seminal works on non-commutative algebras—algebras whose answers are affected by the order in which numbers are multiplied. She was at the heart of a flurry of mathematical activity in Germany

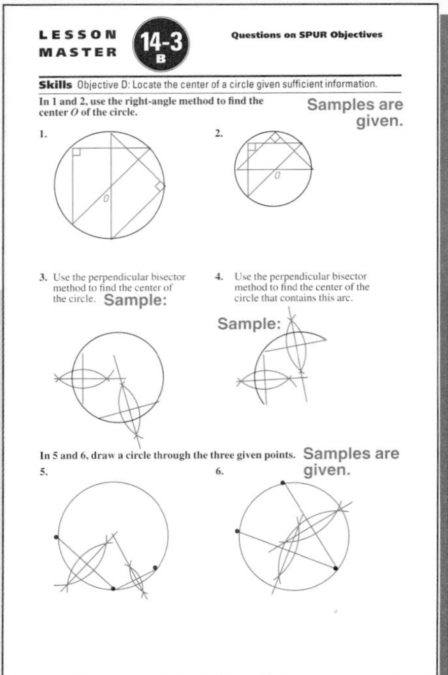
LESSON MASTER 14-3 B

Questions on SPUR Objectives

Skills Objective D: Locate the center of a circle given sufficient information.

In 1 and 2, use the right-angle method to find the center O of the circle. Samples are given.

1. 2.

3. Use the perpendicular bisector method to find the center of the circle. Sample:

4. Use the perpendicular bisector method to find the center of the circle that contains this arc. Sample:

In 5 and 6, draw a circle through the three given points. Samples are given.

5. 6.

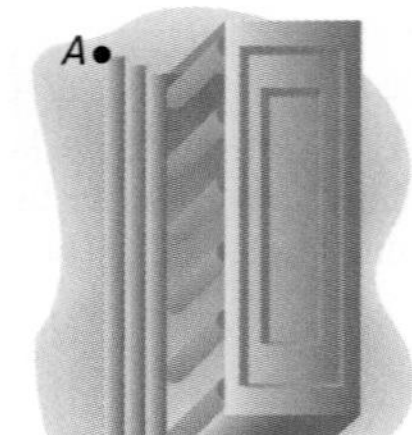

In 3 and 4, suppose you have a camera with a lens having a 56° field of vision.

3. Trace the monument at the left and diagram all the places where you could stand so that $\overline{AB}$, the monument's front, just fits into your picture. See left. You can stand anywhere on $\overset{\frown}{ACB}$.

4. Assume $AB = 60$ yards. If you wanted to stand in front of the middle of the monument and fit the entire monument into your picture, at least how far from the monument would you need to stand? $\approx$ 56.4 yards

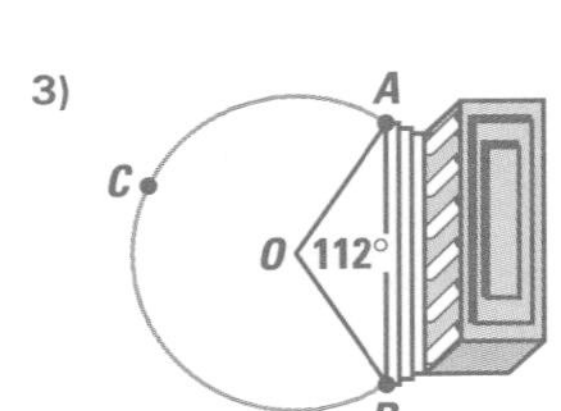

5. Each year, the classes at Emmy Noether High School take class pictures on the steps to the main entrance. The steps are 50 meters across.
   a. A photographer has an 88° wide-angle lens and wants to stand in front of the middle of the steps, as close to the students as possible. Where should the photographer stand? See margin.
   b. At the same time, parents of class members want to take pictures of the class. If they all have 88° wide-angle lenses and want the steps to fill the picture, where can they stand? They can stand anywhere on $\overset{\frown}{APB}$.

Applying the Mathematics

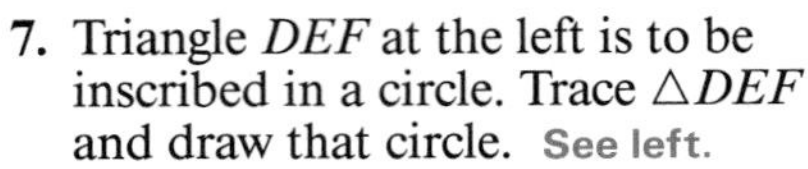

6. Trace points A, B, and C at the right. Use any method to draw the circle through points A, B, and C. See margin.

7. Triangle DEF at the left is to be inscribed in a circle. Trace $\triangle DEF$ and draw that circle. See left.

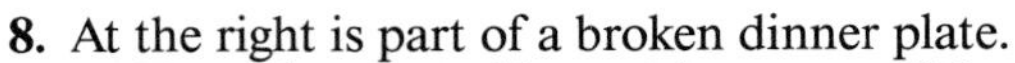

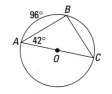

8. At the right is part of a broken dinner plate.
   a. Trace the arc and locate the center of the plate.
   b. When the plate was whole, what was its radius? approximately 1.5 cm

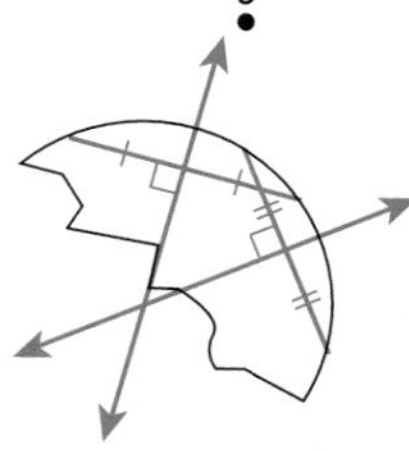

9. Draw a circle using the bottom of a can or bottle. Find the center of the circle using a sheet of paper and the right-angle method. See margin.

Review

10. $\overline{AC}$ is a diameter of $\odot O$ at the left. Find each measure.
   a. $m\angle C$ 48
   b. $m\overset{\frown}{BC}$ 84°
   c. $m\overset{\frown}{AC}$ 180° *(Lesson 14-2)*

11. *BEHIVS* is a regular hexagon. The diagonals from V are drawn.
   a. Find the measures of the numbered angles.
   b. *True or false.* $\triangle BEV$ is a right triangle. *(Lesson 14-2)* True

   a) All have measure 30°.

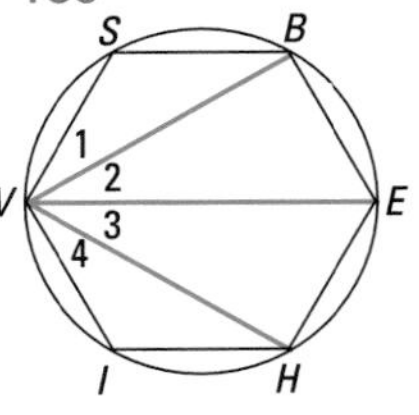

Additional Answers

5a. The photographer should stand at point P, which is about 25.9 m from the steps.

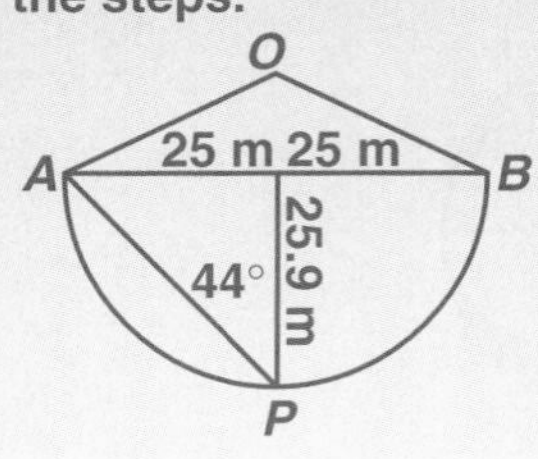

6. Sample:

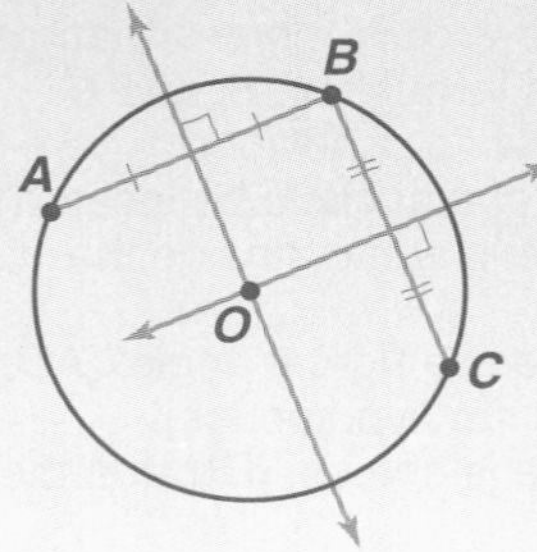

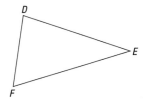

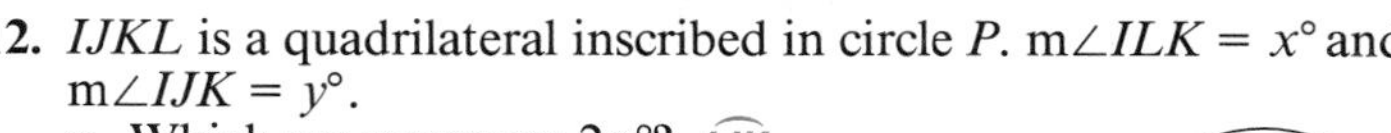
12. $IJKL$ is a quadrilateral inscribed in circle P. $m\angle ILK = x°$ and $m\angle IJK = y°$.
   a. Which arc measures $2x°$? $\overset{\frown}{IJK}$
   b. Which arc measures $2y°$? $\overset{\frown}{ILK}$
   c. What number does $2x + 2y$ equal? 360
   d. What is the sum of the measures of angles ILK and IJK? 180
   e. What is the sum of the measures of angles LIJ and LKJ? 180
   f. What does this prove about opposite angles in an inscribed quadrilateral? *(Lesson 14-2)* They are supplementary.

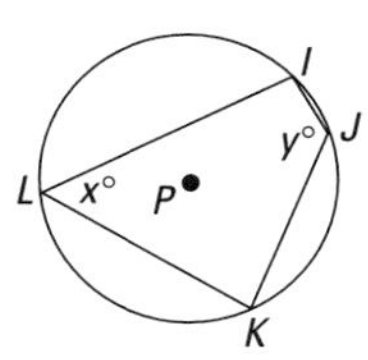

13a) $m\angle A = m\angle CDA = 30$, $m\angle ACD = 120$, $m\angle ADB = 90$, $m\angle BCD = m\angle BDC = m\angle CBD = 60$

13. In the figure at the right, $\overline{AB}$ is a diameter of $\odot C$, and $\triangle BCD$ is equilateral. a) See left.
   a. Find the measures of as many angles as you can.
   b. If $BD = x$, then what is the length of $\overline{AC}$? x units
   c. If $BD = 7$, what is the length of $\overline{AD}$? $7\sqrt{3} \approx 12.12$ units *(Lessons 5-7, 6-8, 13-5, 14-2)*

In 14 and 15, $\overline{PQ}$ is a chord of $\odot O$.

14. a. If M is the midpoint of $\overline{PQ}$, then __?__. $\overline{OM} \perp \overline{PQ}$
   b. If $\overline{OM} \perp \overline{PQ}$, then __?__. $PM = MQ$
   c. If $\overline{OM}$ bisects $\angle POQ$, then __?__. *(Lesson 14-1)* $\overline{OM} \perp \overline{PQ}$ and $\overline{OM}$ bisects $\overline{PQ}$.

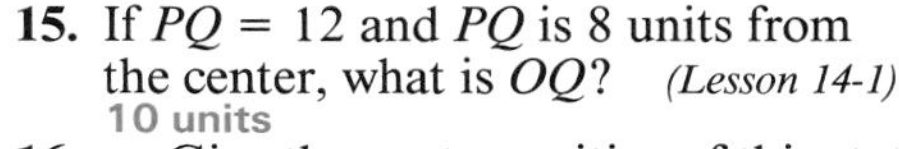
15. If $PQ = 12$ and PQ is 8 units from the center, what is OQ? *(Lesson 14-1)* 10 units

16a) If the diagonals of a figure are not congruent, then it is not a rectangle.

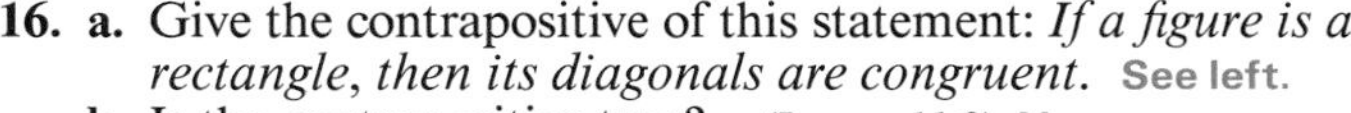
16. a. Give the contrapositive of this statement: *If a figure is a rectangle, then its diagonals are congruent.* See left.
   b. Is the contrapositive true? *(Lesson 11-2)* Yes

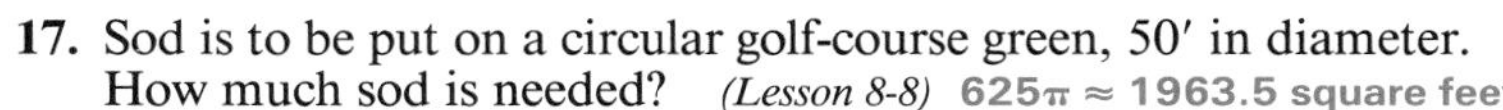
17. Sod is to be put on a circular golf-course green, 50′ in diameter. How much sod is needed? *(Lesson 8-8)* $625\pi \approx 1963.5$ square feet

Saint-Faustin golf course in Laurentides, Quebec, Canada.

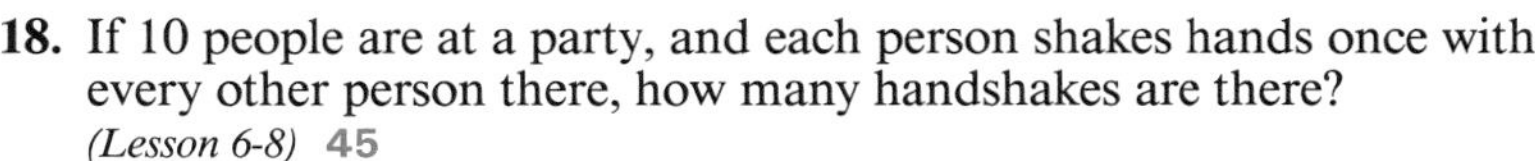
18. If 10 people are at a party, and each person shakes hands once with every other person there, how many handshakes are there? *(Lesson 6-8)* 45

Exploration

19. Each of the three circles at the right overlaps the other two. The three chords common to each pair of circles are drawn. They seem to have a point in common. Using a compass and ruler or an automatic drawer show other examples of this situation and decide whether the chords will always have a point in common. Answers may vary. (It is always true.)

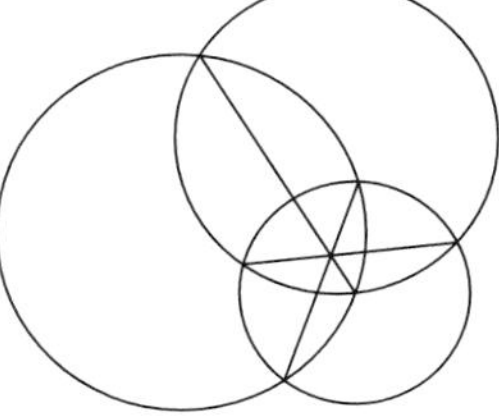

between the World Wars. When Hitler dismissed her and all Jewish university professors in the country in 1933, she emigrated to America, where she taught at Bryn Mawr College in Pennsylvania. She died in 1935.

Questions 7–8 The perpendicular bisector method is more appropriate for these questions, which demonstrate the weakness of the right-angle method.

Question 8b Students can measure their drawings to estimate the answer.

Question 11 It may surprise students that all the measured angles are congruent. This result can be generalized to any regular polygon.

Question 12 Have students explain orally why a parallelogram inscribed in a circle must be a rectangle. [The measures of opposite angles add to 180. Since the angles are congruent, they must be right angles.] Then go through all the special quadrilaterals and ask which ones can be inscribed and which ones cannot. [One general theorem is that an inscribed trapezoid must be an isosceles trapezoid.]

9. Sample:

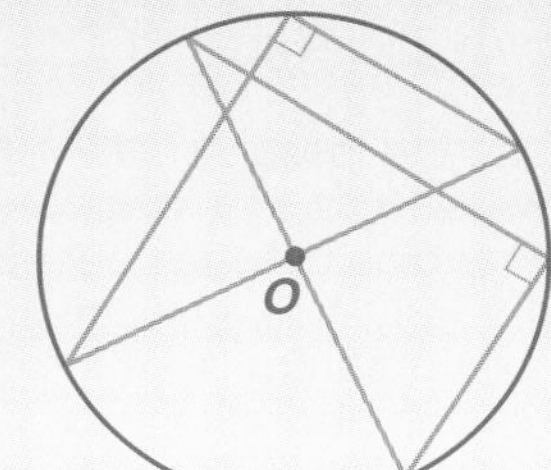

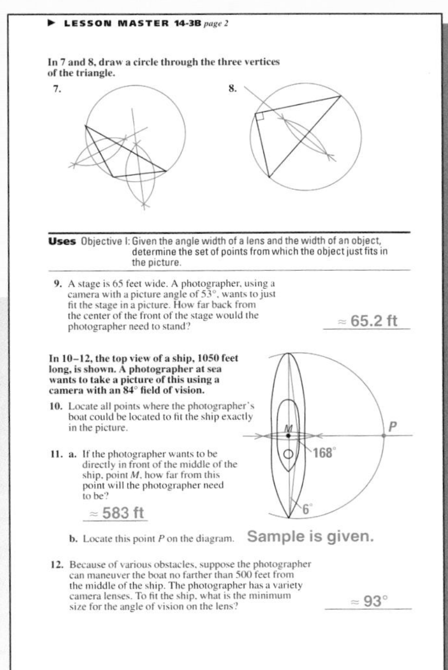
▶ LESSON MASTER 14-3B *page 2*

In 7 and 8, draw a circle through the three vertices of the triangle.

7.

8.

Uses Objective I: Given the angle width of a lens and the width of an object, determine the set of points from which the object just fits in the picture.

9. A stage is 65 feet wide. A photographer, using a camera with a picture angle of 53°, wants to just fit the stage in a picture. How far back from the center of the front of the stage would the photographer need to stand? ≈ 65.2 ft

In 10–12, the top view of a ship, 1050 feet long, is shown. A photographer at sea wants to take a picture of this using a camera with an 84° field of vision.

10. Locate all points where the photographer's boat could be located to fit the ship exactly in the picture.

11. a. If the photographer wants to be directly in front of the middle of the ship, point M, how far from this point will the photographer need to be? ≈ 583 ft
   b. Locate this point P on the diagram. Sample is given.

12. Because of various obstacles, suppose the photographer can maneuver the boat no farther than 500 feet from the middle of the ship. The photographer has a variety camera lenses. To fit the ship, what is the minimum size for the angle of vision on the lens? ≈ 93°

Lesson 14-4

Objectives

C Calculate measures of angles between chords or secants from measures of intercepted arcs, and vice versa.

G Make deductions from properties of angles formed by chords or secants.

Resources

From the ***Teacher's Resource File***

- Lesson Master 14-4A or 14-4B
- Answer Master 14-4
- Teaching Aids
  182 Warm-up
  187 Additional Examples

Additional Resources

- Visuals for Teaching Aids 182, 187

Teaching Lesson 14-4

Warm-up

Find the measures of angles 1–4 in the figure below.

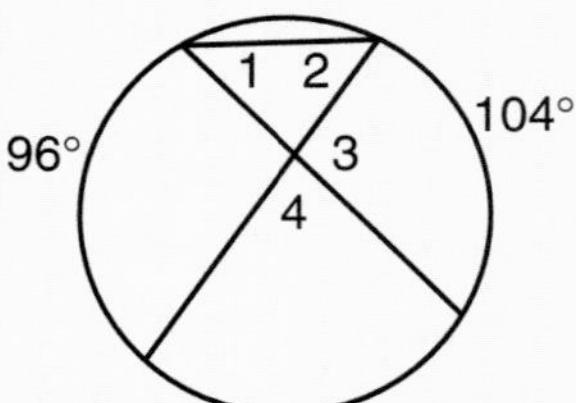

m∠1 = 52, m∠2 = 48,
m∠3 = 100, m∠4 = 80

LESSON

14-4

Angles Formed by Chords or Secants

Capital circularity. *Circular intersections as well as cross streets and diagonal avenues were part of the plans of Pierre-Charles L'Enfant, designer of Washington, D.C.*

Each side of a central angle or an inscribed angle intersects the circle in which it is found. In this lesson and the next one, other angles for which both sides intersect a circle will be discussed. The Inscribed Angle Theorem enables measures of these angles to be determined.

Angles Formed by Chords

First, consider an angle whose vertex is in the interior of a circle. For instance, consider the situation pictured at the right, where two chords $\overline{AB}$ and $\overline{CD}$ intersect at E. Given $m\widehat{AD} = x°$ and $m\widehat{BC} = y°$, what is $m\angle CEB$?

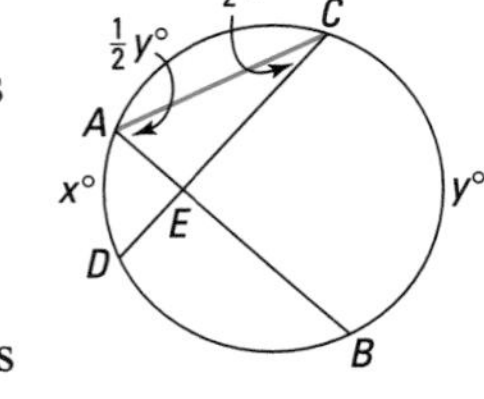

To find $m\angle CEB$, draw the auxiliary segment $\overline{AC}$. Now $\angle BAC$ and $\angle ACD$ are inscribed angles whose measures are half their intercepted arcs. So $m\angle BAC = \frac{1}{2}y$ and $m\angle ACD = \frac{1}{2}x$. $\angle CEB$ is an exterior angle of $\triangle ACE$. Its measure is the sum of the measures of $\angle BAC$ and $\angle ACD$.

Thus, $$m\angle CEB = \frac{1}{2}x + \frac{1}{2}y, \text{ or } \frac{1}{2}(x + y).$$

This argument proves the following startling theorem.

> **Angle-Chord Theorem**
> **The measure of an angle formed by two intersecting chords is one-half the sum of the measures of the arcs intercepted by it and its vertical angle.**

Lesson 14-4 Overview

Broad Goals This lesson discusses how to find the measure of an angle formed by two chords or two secants to a circle if the measure of the arcs they intercept is known.

Perspective The two theorems in this lesson, the Angle-Chord Theorem and the Angle-Secant Theorem, can be viewed as special cases of one general theorem. Think of standing at the vertex of an angle and simultaneously looking down its interior and back at its vertical angle. Suppose there is a single circle that has two arcs passing through this interior. Measure an arc as positive if you are inside it and negative if you are outside it. Then the measure of your angle is the average of the measures of the two arcs.

The importance of these theorems is as an application of the Inscribed Angle Theorem. Since the theorems are seldom applied outside of secondary school geometry, the lesson can be skipped if time is short.

So why do we include the lesson at all? After all, time is *always* short. However, finding measures of angles between chords or secants is a particularly nice application of the Inscribed Angle Theorem, showing its power. And there is an opportunity to review similar triangles. Also, we see again the advantage of drawing auxiliary lines.

Example 1

In $\odot O$ below, $m\overset{\frown}{XRY} = 200°$ and $m\overset{\frown}{VW} = 60°$. Find $m\angle XQY$.

Solution

$$m\angle XQY = \frac{1}{2}(m\overset{\frown}{XRY} + m\overset{\frown}{VW})$$
$$= \frac{1}{2}(200 + 60)$$
$$= \frac{1}{2}(260)$$
$$= 130$$

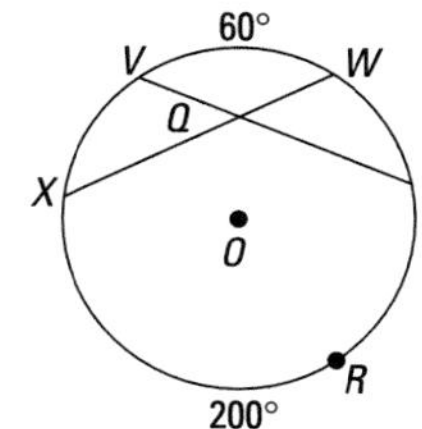

Activity

In Example 1, explain why the given information does not uniquely determine $m\overset{\frown}{WY}$.

Activity) Sample:

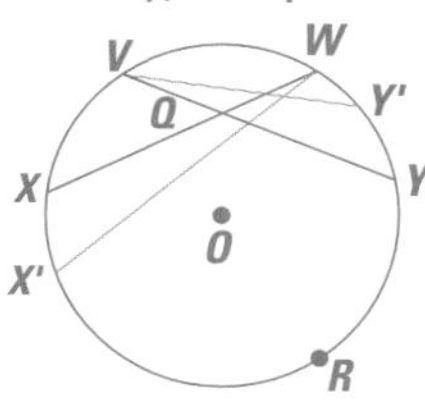

$m\overset{\frown}{XRY} = m\overset{\frown}{X'RY'} = 200°$, $m\overset{\frown}{VW} = m\overset{\frown}{VW} = 60°$, but $m\overset{\frown}{WY} \neq m\overset{\frown}{WY'}$

Angles Formed by Secants

The measure of an angle between chords can be found even when the lines containing the chords intersect in the exterior of the circle. Such lines are called *secants.*

Definition
A secant to a circle is a line that intersects the circle in two points.

Here is one way to find the measure of an angle formed by secants to the same circle. Below at the left, $\angle AEC$ is formed by two secants and intercepts the two arcs $\overset{\frown}{AC}$ and $\overset{\frown}{BD}$ with measures 84° and 26°. To find $m\angle E$, draw $\overline{AD}$, as pictured below at the right.

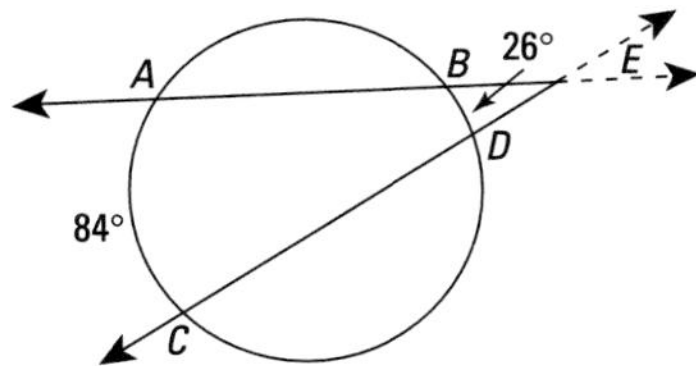

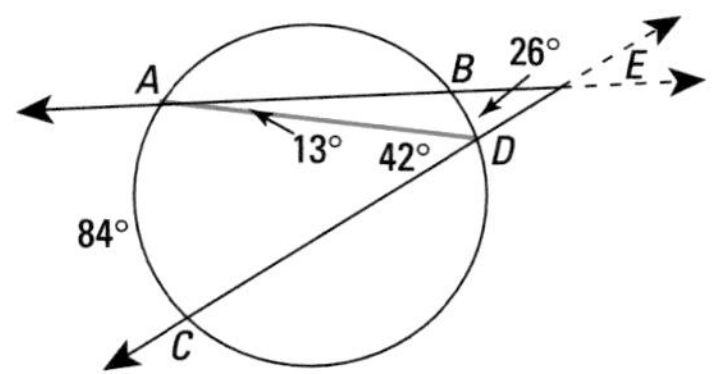

Again there are two inscribed angles. One of them is $\angle ADC$, an exterior angle to $\triangle ADE$. By the Exterior Angle Theorem,

$$m\angle DAE + m\angle E = m\angle ADC.$$

Solve for $m\angle E$.

$$m\angle E = m\angle ADC - m\angle DAE$$
$$m\angle E = \frac{1}{2}m\overset{\frown}{AC} - \frac{1}{2}m\overset{\frown}{BD}$$

Substitute the given measures.

$$= \frac{1}{2} \cdot 84 - \frac{1}{2} \cdot 26$$
$$= 42 - 13$$

So $m\angle E = 29$.

In solving for $m\angle E$, we have proved the following theorem.

Notes on Reading

You might want to begin the lesson with a concrete example, as suggested in *Optional Activities* below.

As you are discussing this lesson, point out that the Angle-Secant Theorem on page 820 is generalized from an example rather than being proved first. In similar fashion, **Question 1** is a special case of a general procedure for finding the measure of an angle formed by two intersecting chords. The generalization of the procedure is the proof of the Angle-Chord Theorem. Stress that much of mathematics is developed this way. That is, conjectures are made from observed results; then they are generalized and proved.

Additional Examples

These examples are also given on **Teaching Aid 187.**

1. *ABCDEFGH* is a regular octagon. What is the measure of the acute angles formed by $\overleftrightarrow{BG}$ and $\overleftrightarrow{AE}$?
   67.5

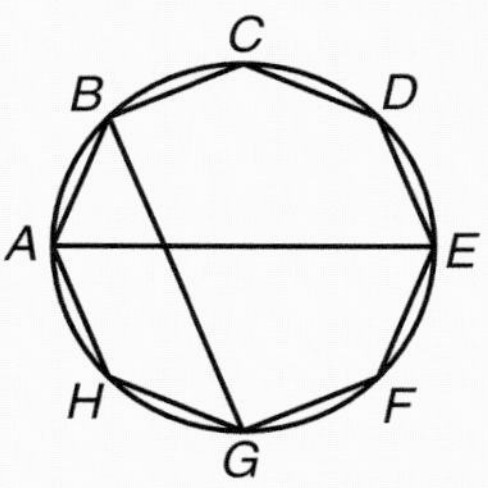

(Additional Examples continue on page 820.)

LESSON MASTER 14-4 A — **Questions on SPUR Objectives** See pages 858–861 for objectives.

Skills Objective C

In 1–3, use the circle at the right.

1. If $m\angle GHI = 52$ and $mGI = 44°$, what other arc measure can be determined? What is its measure? $mFJ = 60°$
2. If $m\,FG = 130°$ and $m\,IJ = 120°$, what is $m\angle IHJ$? 125
3. If $m\,FG = 133°$ and $m\,IJ = 117°$, what is $m\angle GHI$? 55

In 4–6, use $\odot Q$ at the right. Assume that $mNO = 30°$ and $mRS = 70°$.

4. What is $m\angle M$? 20
5. What is $m\angle RPS$? 50
6. List all other angle measures that you can.
   $m\angle RNS = m\angle ROS = 35$; $m\angle NSO = m\angle NRO = 15$; $m\angle NPR = m\angle OPS = 130$; $m\angle NPO = 50$

Properties Objective G

7. Write an argument to complete the proof.
   Given: $\odot A$ with segments and measures as given at the right.
   To prove: $\triangle OYC$ is an isosceles right triangle.

   Sample argument: By the Angle-Chord Thm., $m\angle OYC = \frac{1}{2}(165 + 15) = 90$. Since $m\angle OR = m\angle CK = x°$, $\overline{OR} \cong \overline{CK}$ by the Arc-Chord $\cong$ Thm. Then, $m\angle ROK = \frac{1}{2} \cdot 15$ and $m\angle KCR = \frac{1}{2} \cdot 15$, so $\angle ROK \cong \angle KCR$. By the Vertical Angles Thm., $\angle OYR \cong \angle CYK$, and $\triangle ORY \cong \triangle CKY$ by the AAS $\cong$ Thm. So, $\overline{OY} \cong \overline{CY}$ and $\triangle OYC$ is an isosceles right triangle by definition.

Optional Activities

You might use this activity to introduce the lesson. Have students draw regular hexagon *ABCDEF* inscribed in a circle. Note that each side of the polygon is a chord of a 60° arc. Now connect $\overline{AE}$ and $\overline{FC}$, as shown at the right. These segments are perpendicular as a result of reflection symmetry of the polygon to $\overleftrightarrow{CF}$. But notice that $m\overset{\frown}{AF} = 60°$ and $m\overset{\frown}{CE} = 120°$. Thus, the measure of the angle formed by the two intersecting chords is the average of the measures of the arcs intercepted by the angle and the vertical angle.

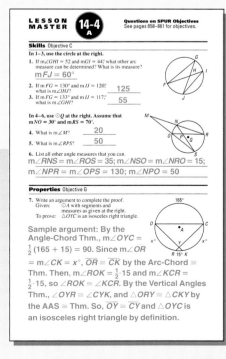

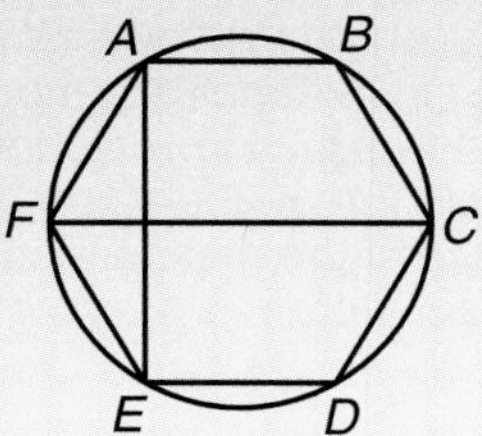

(Optional Activities continue on page 820.)

2. Use the diagram below. Find $m\overset{\frown}{BD}$. 50°

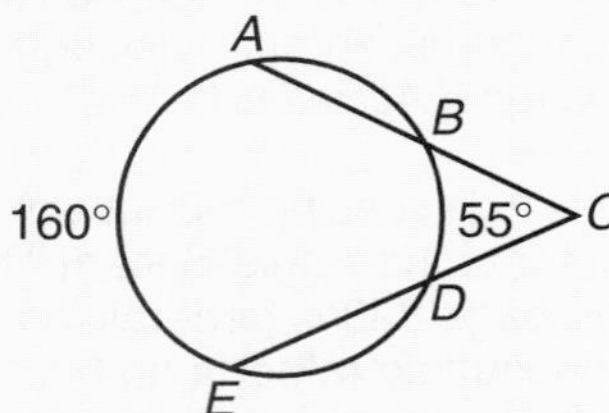

Notes on Questions

Question 3 $m\overset{\frown}{GH}$ allows $m\angle FJI$ to be found in one step; finding $m\overset{\frown}{FG}$ requires an additional step.

Question 6 The measure of every angle in this drawing can be found, and it is instructive to do so. You might then ask: Are any triangles in this drawing similar? [Yes, $\triangle QML \sim \triangle QOP$; $\triangle LON \sim \triangle PMN$]

Question 10 There is a short proof that Z is the center of the circle: $\angle VWX$ is a right angle, so $\overline{VX}$ is a diameter; $\angle YVW$ is a right angle, so $\overline{YW}$ is a diameter. The two diameters intersect at the center. The proof is analogous to the right-angle method for finding the center of a circle.

(Notes on Questions continue on page 822.)

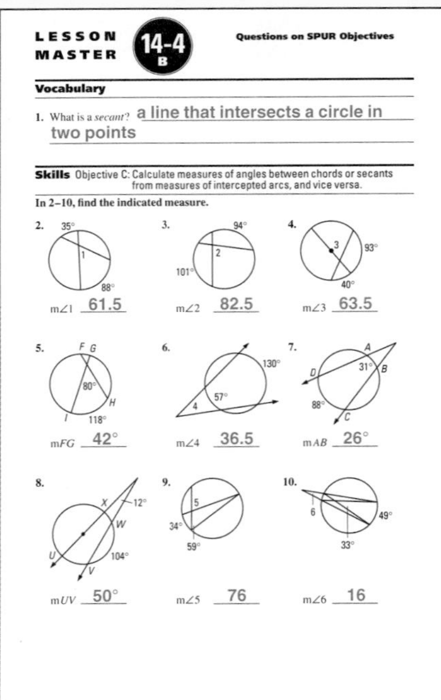
LESSON MASTER 14-4 B

Questions on SPUR Objectives

Vocabulary

1. What is a *secant*? a line that intersects a circle in two points

Skills Objective C: Calculate measures of angles between chords or secants from measures of intercepted arcs, and vice versa.

In 2–10, find the indicated measure.

2. $m\angle 1$ 61.5
3. $m\angle 2$ 82.5
4. $m\angle 3$ 63.5
5. $m\overset{\frown}{FG}$ 42°
6. $m\angle 4$ 36.5
7. $m\overset{\frown}{AB}$ 26°
8. $m\overset{\frown}{UV}$ 50°
9. $m\angle 5$ 76
10. $m\angle 6$ 16

> **Angle-Secant Theorem**
> The measure of an angle formed by two secants intersecting outside a circle is half the difference of the arcs intercepted by the angle.

Example 2

In $\odot R$ below, $m\overset{\frown}{KTM} = 195°$ and $m\overset{\frown}{JL} = 51°$. Find $m\angle P$.

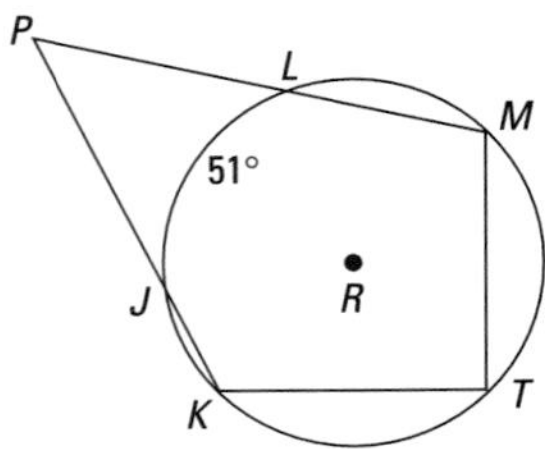

Solution

First, sort out which arcs are needed. $\angle P$ intercepts arcs $\angle\overset{\frown}{KTM}$ and $\overset{\frown}{JL}$. From the Angle-Secant Theorem,

$$\begin{aligned} m\angle P &= \tfrac{1}{2}(m\overset{\frown}{KTM} - m\overset{\frown}{JL}) \\ &= \tfrac{1}{2}(195 - 51) \\ &= \tfrac{1}{2} \cdot 144 \\ &= 72. \end{aligned}$$

In finding measures of angles formed by chords or secants you have a choice between drawing an auxiliary segment and calculating, or applying a theorem. You should be able to do both.

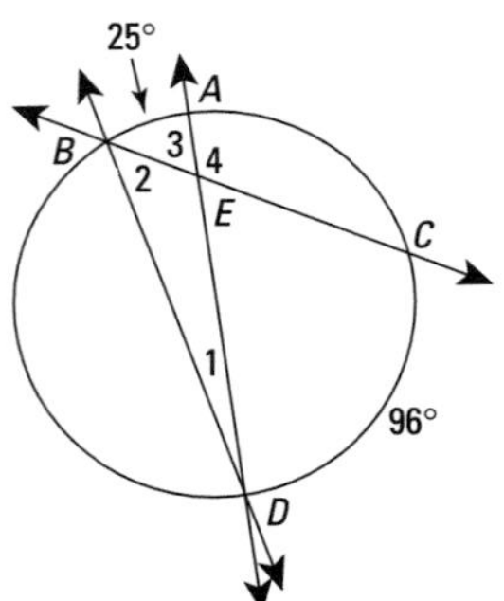

QUESTIONS

Covering the Reading

1. Use the figure at the left. Find each measure.
   a. $m\angle 1$ 12.5
   b. $m\angle 2$ 48
   c. $m\angle 3$ 60.5
   d. $m\angle 4$ 119.5

2. Use the figure at the right. Give the measure of the angle in terms of the measures of the arcs.
   a. $m\angle 5$ $\frac{x}{2}$ b. $\frac{z}{2}$
   b. $m\angle 6$
   c. $m\angle 7$ $\frac{x+z}{2}$ d. $\frac{x-z}{2}$
   d. $m\angle 8$

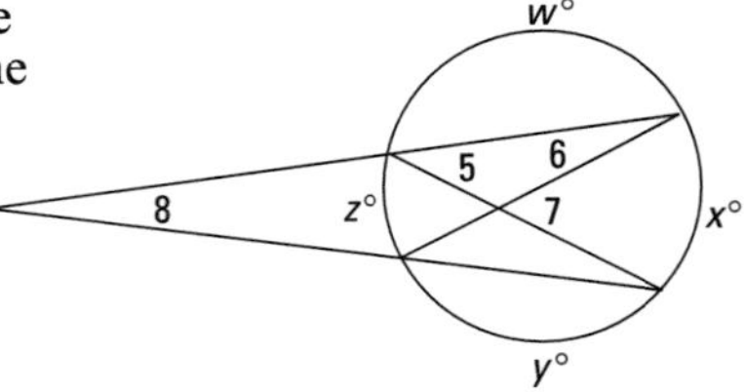

The chords $\overline{AC}$ and $\overline{EF}$ in the same figure can be extended to meet at H, as shown at the right. Have students verify that the measure of angle H is 30, half the difference of the measures of the arcs. The general theorem is the Angle-Secant Theorem.

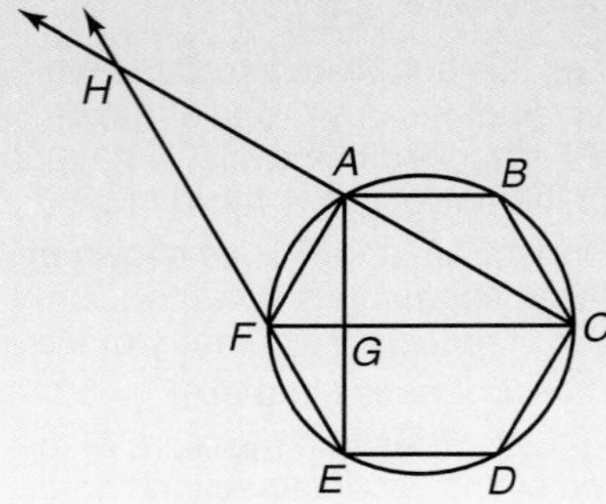

In 3 and 4, use the figure at the left.

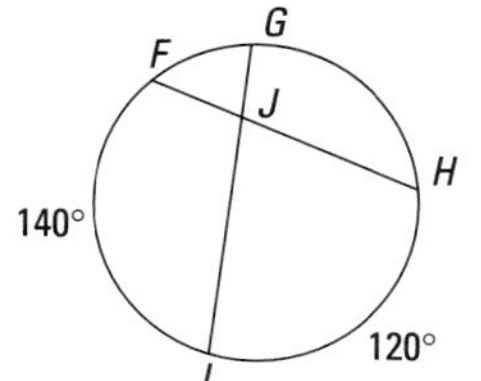

3. Which additional arc measure(s) do you need in order to find m∠*FJI*? m$\widehat{GH}$

4. Suppose $\overline{GI}$ is a diameter. Find m∠*FJI*. 100

5. Answer the question in the Activity of this Lesson. See page 819.

6. In the figure at the right, m$\widehat{LP}$ = 80° and m$\widehat{MO}$ = 50°. Find each measure.

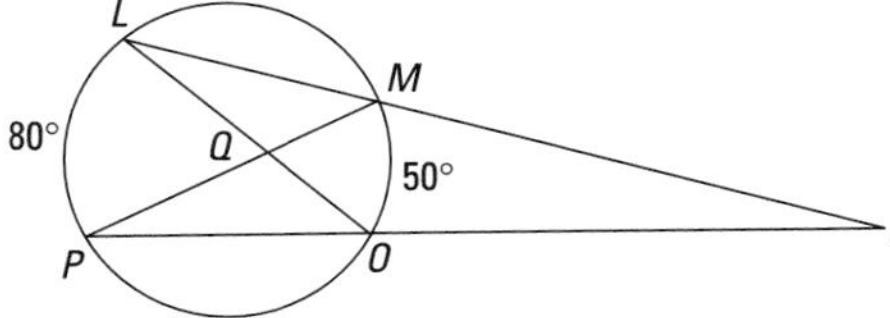

a. m∠*MQO* 65

b. m∠*N* 15

7. Define *secant*.
A secant to a circle is a line that intersects a circle in two points.

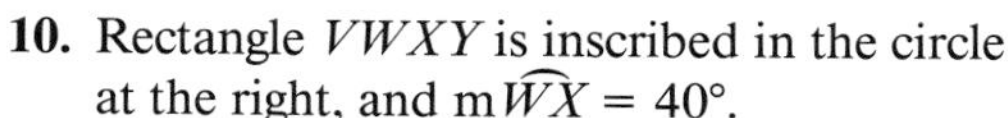

Applying the Mathematics

8. A point *P* is outside ⊙*O*. How many secants of ⊙*O* contain *P*? infinitely many

9. In the circle at the left, m$\widehat{RU}$ = 101° and $\overline{RS} \perp \overline{TU}$. Find m$\widehat{ST}$. 79°

10. Rectangle *VWXY* is inscribed in the circle at the right, and m$\widehat{WX}$ = 40°.

a. What is the measure of each acute angle formed by the intersection of the diagonals? 40

b. What is m∠*VYW*? 70

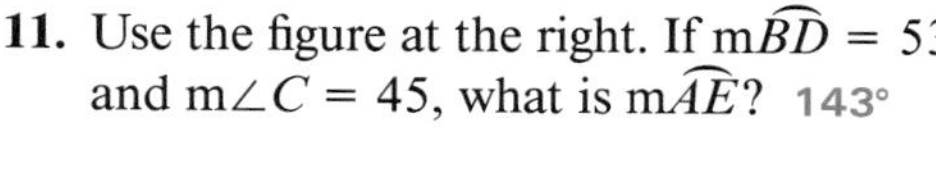

11. Use the figure at the right. If m$\widehat{BD}$ = 53° and m∠*C* = 45, what is m$\widehat{AE}$? 143°

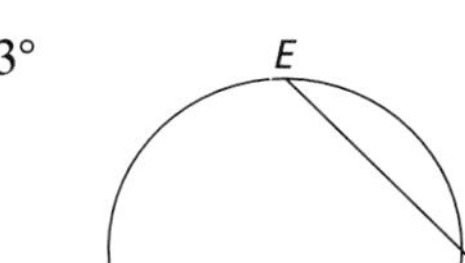

Review

12. Trace or copy the circular arc at the right. Then find its center to complete the whole circle. *(Lesson 14-3)*
See margin.

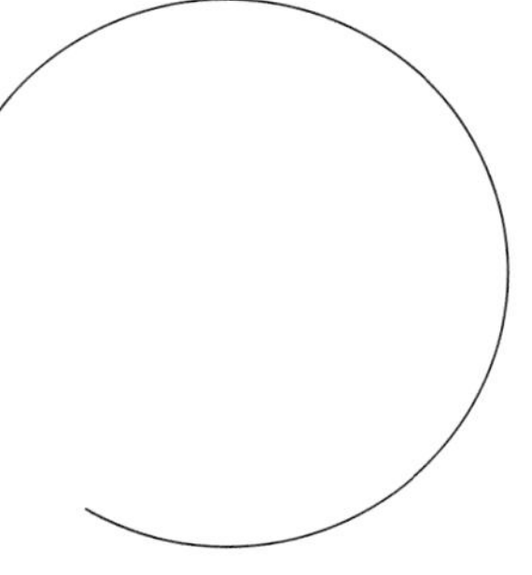

Follow-up for Lesson 14-4

Practice

For more questions on SPUR Objectives, use **Lesson Master 14-4A** (shown on page 819) or **Lesson Master 14-4B** (shown on pages 820–821).

Assessment

Oral/Written Communication
Have students **work in pairs.** Each student should make up two questions, one to apply each theorem introduced in this lesson. Then have students exchange questions and solve. [Students provide questions that can be solved by applying the Angle-Chord Theorem and the Angle-Secant Theorem, and then answer the questions correctly.]

Extension

Give students the following diagram or **Teaching Aid 187.**

Have them find m$\widehat{CD}$. [52°]

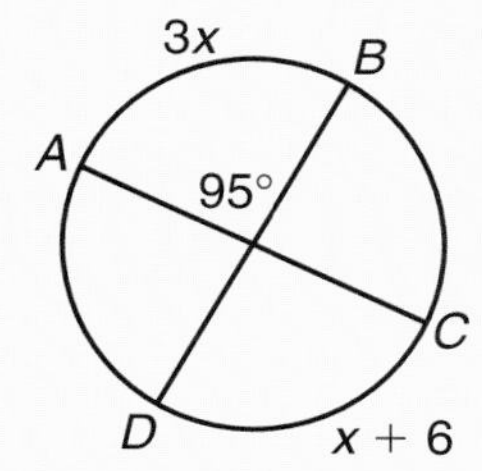

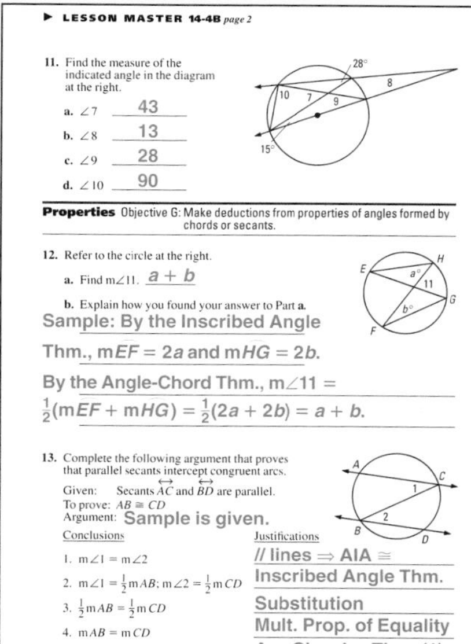

▶ **LESSON MASTER 14-4B** *page 2*

11. Find the measure of the indicated angle in the diagram at the right.

a. ∠7 43

b. ∠8 13

c. ∠9 28

d. ∠10 90

Properties Objective G: Make deductions from properties of angles formed by chords or secants.

12. Refer to the circle at the right.

a. Find m∠11. $a + b$

b. Explain how you found your answer to Part **a.**
Sample: By the Inscribed Angle Thm., m$\widehat{EF}$ = 2*a* and m$\widehat{HG}$ = 2*b*. By the Angle-Chord Thm., m∠11 = $\frac{1}{2}$(m$\widehat{EF}$ + m$\widehat{HG}$) = $\frac{1}{2}$(2*a* + 2*b*) = *a* + *b*.

13. Complete the following argument that proves that parallel secants intercept congruent arcs.

Given: Secants $\overleftrightarrow{AC}$ and $\overleftrightarrow{BD}$ are parallel.
To prove: $\widehat{AB} \cong \widehat{CD}$
Argument: Sample is given.

Conclusions	Justifications
1. m∠1 = m∠2	// lines ⇒ AIA ≅
2. m∠1 = $\frac{1}{2}$m$\widehat{AB}$; m∠2 = $\frac{1}{2}$m$\widehat{CD}$	Inscribed Angle Thm.
3. $\frac{1}{2}$m$\widehat{AB}$ = $\frac{1}{2}$m$\widehat{CD}$	Substitution
4. m$\widehat{AB}$ = m$\widehat{CD}$	Mult. Prop. of Equality
5. $\overline{AB} \cong \overline{CD}$	Arc-Chord ≅ Thm. (1)

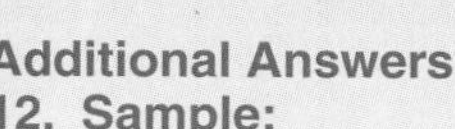

Additional Answers
12. Sample:

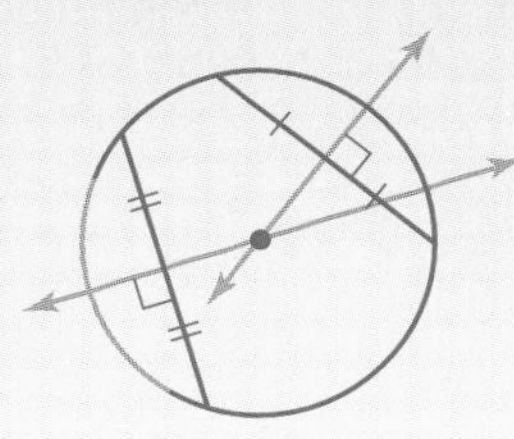

Adapting to Individual Needs

Challenge

1. Have students explain how the Inscribed Angle Theorem of Lesson 14-2 can be considered to be a special case of the Angle-Chord Theorem. [If the chords intersect on the circle, one of the intersected arcs has a measure of zero. That implies that the measure of the angle formed by the chords is one half the

(Challenge continues on page 822.)

Notes on Questions

Question 14 With this given information, the Angle-Chord and Inscribed Angle Theorems enable a person to find the measure of any angle formed by the lines containing two diagonals of the pentagon, whether the lines intersect in the interior of or on the circle.

Question 18 Some problems involving lengths of tangents and secants in Lesson 14-7 involve solving quadratic equations.

Question 19 Suppose a star is formed by extending the sides of an inscribed heptagon. What is the sum of the measures of the angles between the secants? [Students may be surprised that the sum is still 180.]

Questions 19–20 Technology Connection These questions are appropriate to be explored with an automatic drawer or with a Logo program.

Additional Answers

16. Suppose there are two 95° angles in a triangle. Thus, the sum of the interior angles of this triangle will be greater than 180, which contradicts the Triangle Sum Theorem. It implies that the supposition is false. Therefore, no triangle in Euclidean geometry can have two 95° angles.

13. Suppose you want to photograph the entire front of the house at the right with a camera that has a picture angle of 118°. At least how far in front of the middle of the house shown would you need to stand? *(Lesson 14-2)* ≈ 15.6 ft

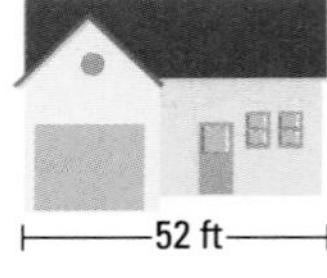

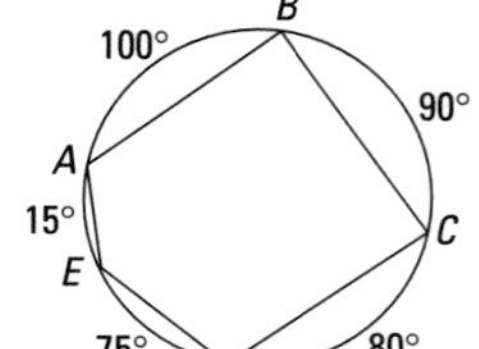

14. Find the measure of each angle of pentagon $ABCDE$ at the left. *(Lesson 14-2)* $m\angle A = 122.5$, $m\angle B = 85$, $m\angle C = 95$, $m\angle D = 102.5$, $m\angle E = 135$

15. A chord is 7 inches away from the center of a circle whose radius is $12\frac{1}{2}$ inches. Find the length of the chord. *(Lesson 14-1)* $2 \cdot \sqrt{107.25} = 20.71$ in.

16. Use indirect reasoning to explain why no triangle in Euclidean geometry can have two 95° angles. *(Lesson 11-4)* See margin.

17. What is the value of y in the figure at the right? *(Lesson 5-7)* 112° 20′

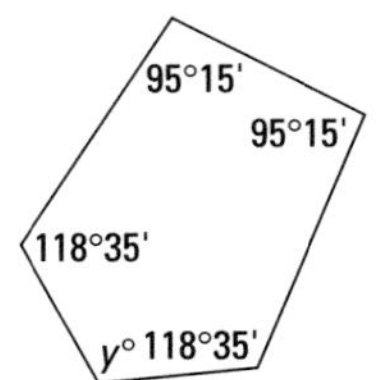

18. **a.** State the Quadratic Formula.
b. Use the Quadratic Formula to solve $2x^2 + 5x - 1 = 0$. *(Previous course)* See left.

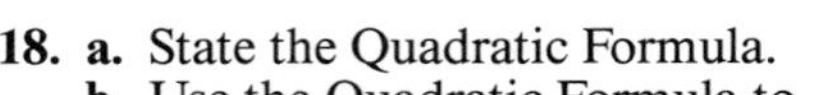

18a) If $ax^2 + bx + c = 0$, then $x = \frac{-b \pm \sqrt{b^2 - 4ac}}{2a}$.
b) $a = 2$, $b = 5$, $c = -1$, so $x = \frac{-5 \pm \sqrt{33}}{4} \approx$ 0.19 or −2.69.

Exploration

19. At the right the sides of an inscribed pentagon $ABCDE$ are extended to form a five-pointed star.
a. What is the sum of the measures of angles F, G, H, I, and J if $ABCDE$ is regular? 180
b. What is the largest and smallest this sum can be if $ABCDE$ is not regular? The sum is always 180.

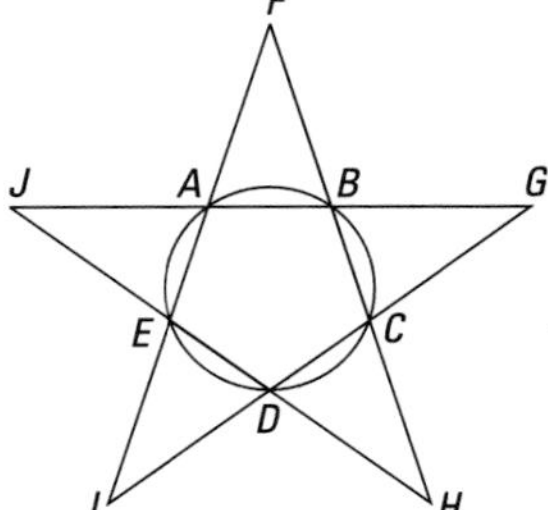

20. Repeat Question 19 for a five-pointed star inscribed in a circle.
a) 180
b) The sum is always 180.

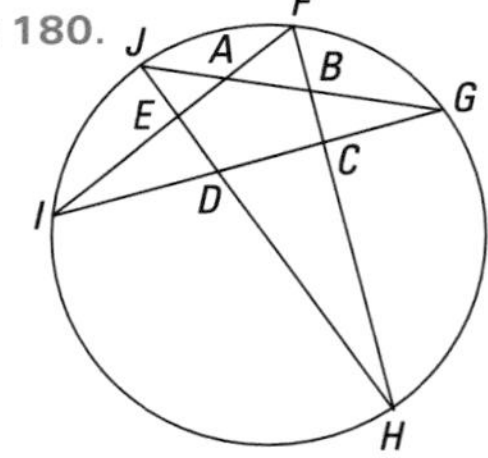

measure of the other intersected arc, which is what the Inscribed Angle Theorem states.]

2. Have students show that any two intersecting perpendicular chords of a circle divide that circle into two pairs of supplementary arcs—arcs whose measures add to 180°. [According to the Angle-Chord Theorem, the sum of the measures of a pair of opposite arcs is twice that of the angle between the chords. So the sum of the measures of the opposite arcs is 180.

Setting Up Lesson 14-5

Materials Students can use a computer to explore **Question 23** in Lesson 14-5.

LESSON

14-5

Tangents to Circles and Spheres

❶ **How far can you see?** *Shown are Barbra Streisand and Jack Nicholson in a scene from the movie* On A Clear Day You Can See Forever, *but even on a clear day you cannot see forever because Earth is round. See the Example.*

What Is a Tangent to a Circle?

The word *tangent* comes from the Latin word meaning "touching." It has two meanings in geometry. One meaning is a ratio of sides in a right triangle. A second meaning is more directly related to touching. Think of a wheel (circle) as tangent to a ramp (a line) as it rolls up or down the ramp. If the wheel and the ramp are very hard, they are thought to have only one point in common in a given plane.

Definition
A **tangent to a circle** is a line in the plane of the circle which intersects the circle in exactly one point (the **point of tangency**).

Tangents to circles can be constructed easily, due to the following theorem.

Theorem
If a line is perpendicular to a radius of a circle at the radius's endpoint on the circle, then the line is tangent to the circle.

Lesson 14-5

Objectives

F Make deductions from properties of radii and tangents, and know sufficient conditions for radii to be perpendicular to them.

J Determine the maximum distance that can be seen from a particular elevation.

Resources

From the ***Teacher's Resource File***

- Lesson Master 14-5A or 14-5B
- Answer Master 14-5
- Teaching Aid 182: Warm-up
- Activity Kit, Activity 29

Additional Resources

- Visual for Teaching Aid 182

Teaching Lesson 14-5

Warm-up

Use a compass to draw a large circle. Mark the center of the circle. Then draw any line that intersects the circle at only one point. Next draw a segment joining this point on the circle with the center of the circle. Use a protractor to measure the angle that this segment makes with the first line that you drew. Repeat the process. What do you discover? The angle is always a right angle.

Notes on Reading

❶ **Music Connection** The musical play *On a Clear Day You Can See*

Lesson 14-5 Overview

Broad Goals This lesson shows the proofs that a line is tangent to a circle if and only if it is perpendicular to a radius at the point of intersection of the radius and the circle. The theorem is then applied to find the distance to the horizon from a point above the surface of the earth.

Perspective Both parts of the Radius-Tangent Theorem are deduced with the help of the Law of Indirect Reasoning. This theorem is important for future work in mathematics. In calculus, the concept of the tangent to a curve at a point provides the main geometric picture of the derivative. The perpendicular to that tangent at the point of contact gives the direction of the *radius of curvature*.

Forever was produced in 1965 from a script by Alan Jay Lerner with a score by Burton Lane. Lerner had a string of Broadway successes throughout his career, most of which were written in collaboration with Frederick Loewe. These included *Brigadoon* (1947), *Paint Your Wagon* (1951), *My Fair Lady* (1956), and *Camelot* (1960), all of which were subsequently made into movies.

Students should finish this lesson knowing two relationships involving tangents. (1) A segment from a point outside a circle to the circle is a tangent if and only if it is perpendicular to the radius drawn to the point of intersection with the circle. The proof of this if-and-only-if statement is given in two parts. Do not expect students to be able to replicate these indirect proofs. (2) When the two tangents from an external point are drawn and the radii are drawn to the points of tangency, a kite is formed. This is **Question 16.** The proof is easy and should be discussed.

❷ Activity 1 of *Optional Activities* extends the **Activity** on page 825. If you use Activity 1, use it before **Question 16.**

In the figure below, you may wish to call quadrilateral *XOYP* the *tangent kite* for the point *P* and the circle *O*. It is special. Its congruent angles are right angles and the symmetry diagonal is the line from *P* to the center. If the vertices of the right angles are connected, a *chord triangle* is formed, and the triangle and kite have the same symmetry line. The figure for the Chord-Center Theorem from Lesson 14-1 is part of this figure.

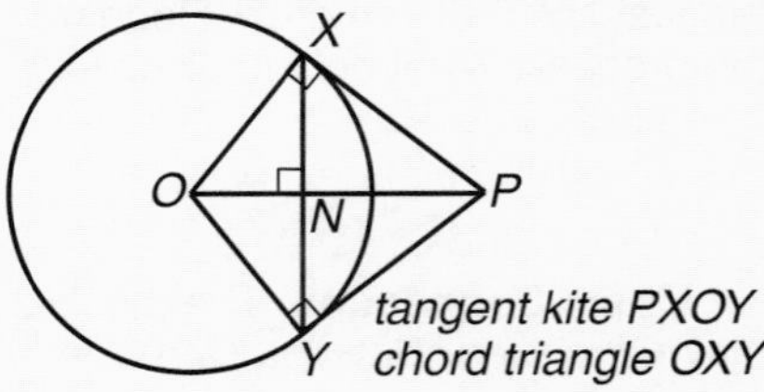

Proof

Drawing: Here is the theorem restated in terms of a figure.

Given: $\odot O$ with point P on it, $\overline{OP} \perp \ell$.

To prove: ℓ is tangent to the circle.

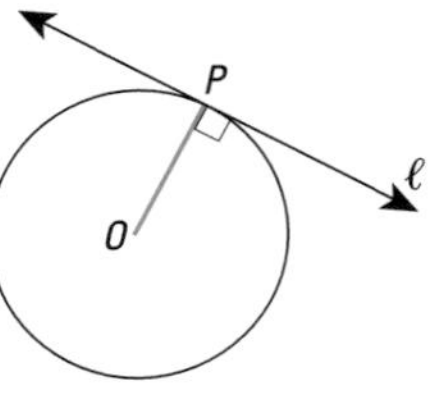

Argument:
Either ℓ is tangent (it intersects the circle at P only), or ℓ also intersects the circle at another point Q. Suppose Q is another point on ℓ and on the circle. Since Q is on ℓ, $\triangle OPQ$ is a right triangle with hypotenuse $\overline{OQ}$. So $OQ > OP$. But since Q is on the circle, $OQ = OP$. The statements $OQ > OP$ and $OQ = OP$ are contradictory. By the Law of Indirect Reasoning, the supposition must be false. Thus, ℓ is tangent to the circle.

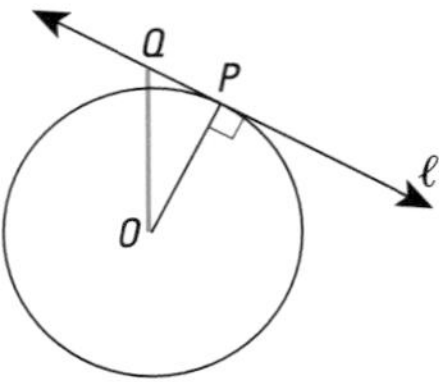

The converse of this theorem is true, but its proof is longer. Again we use an indirect argument.

Theorem
If a line is tangent to a circle, then it is perpendicular to the radius containing the point of tangency.

Proof

Drawing: What is given and what is to be proved are stated in terms of the figure at the right.

Given: m is tangent to $\odot O$ at point P.

To prove: $\overline{OP} \perp m$.

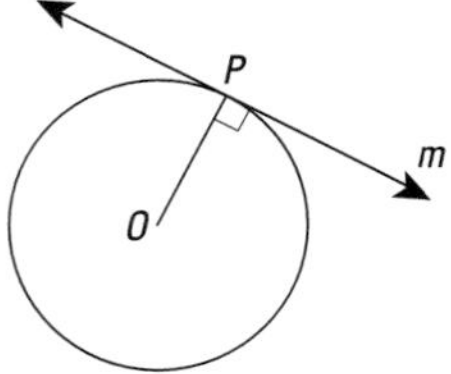

Argument:
Suppose $\overline{OP}$ is not perpendicular to m. Then there is a different segment $\overline{OQ}$, with $\overline{OQ} \perp m$ and Q on m. Locate R on m so that Q is between R and P and $QR = QP$. Then $\triangle OQR \cong \triangle OQP$ because of the SAS Congruence Theorem. So $OR = OP$ by the CPCF Theorem. This means R is on $\odot O$ (it is the same distance from O as P is). So m contains two points on the circle. Thus m is not a tangent, which contradicts the given. So, by the Law of Indirect Reasoning, $\overline{OP} \perp m$.

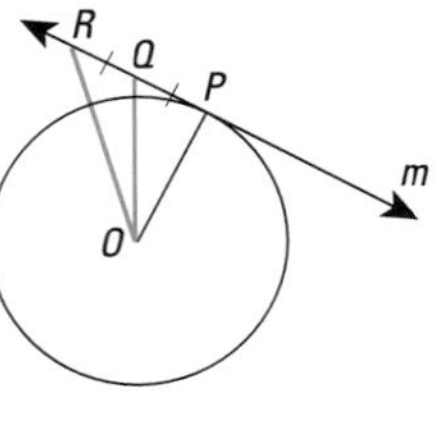

The two theorems of this lesson can be combined into one biconditional.

Radius-Tangent Theorem
A line is tangent to a circle if and only if it is perpendicular to the radius at the radius's endpoint on the circle.

Optional Activities

Activity 1
Before assigning **Question 16**, you might have students extend the **Activity** on page 825 by measuring the lengths of the tangents from points *A*, *B*, and *C*. They should discover that two tangents to a circle from the same point have the same length, which is proved in **Question 16.**

Activity 2
You may use *Activity Kit, Activity 29*, as a follow-up to the lesson. In this activity, students make a sundial.

Adapting to Individual Needs

Extra Help
You might point out to students that some lines *look* as if they are tangent to a circle when they actually have two points in common with the circle. For example, a line might intersect a circle in two points that are very close together on the circle. At first glance, the line might seem to be a tangent, but it is a tangent if and only if it has exactly one point in common with the circle.

❷ Activity

Trace or copy this circle. Draw the lines tangent to the circle at points A, B, and C.

See page 826 Additional Answers 11. a–b.

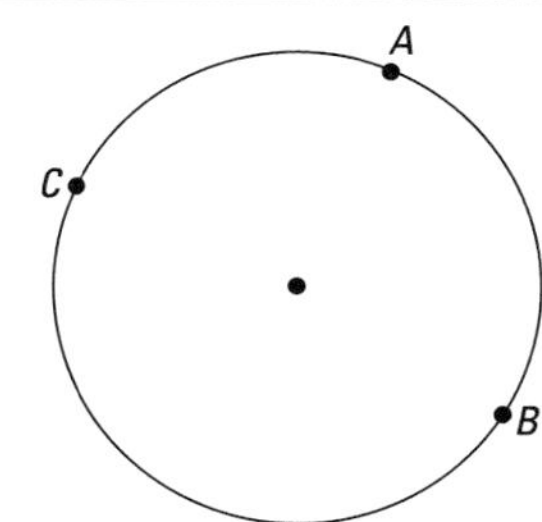

❸ Tangents to Spheres

As you know, many properties of 2-dimensional figures extend to 3-dimensional figures. The idea of tangency extends very easily to spheres. A **tangent to a sphere** is a line or a plane which intersects the sphere in exactly one point. A common example of a plane tangent to a sphere is a ball in one of its positions as it rolls down a ramp.

You can apply the Radius-Tangent Theorem to calculate how far you can see from the top of a building or hill (assuming nothing blocks your view).

Example

How far is it to the horizon from a point P that is 200 feet above the ground?

Solution

We assume Earth is a sphere with center C and radius 3960 miles. Any tangent line from P to Earth intersects Earth at what we call the horizon. Let T be a point on the horizon and X be the point on Earth directly below P. We wish to calculate PT.

P, C, and T determine a plane. Drawn here is part of the cross-section of Earth determined by that plane. Notice that the figure drawn here is *very* distorted to fit everything into it.

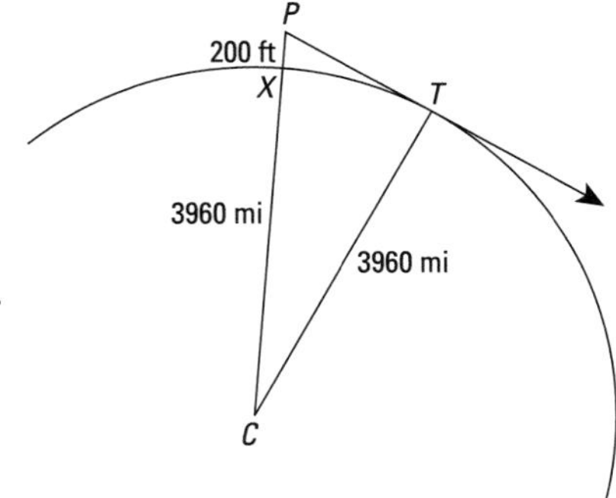

Because of the Radius-Tangent Theorem, $\angle CTP$ is a right angle. So PT can be found by using the Pythagorean Theorem. To find CP, start by converting the 200 ft to miles.

$$200 \text{ ft} = 200 \text{ ft} \cdot \frac{1 \text{ mi}}{5280 \text{ ft}} = \frac{200}{5280} \text{ mi} \approx 0.038 \text{ mi}$$

▶

❸ Tangents often occur in applications. Disks and solid spheres may not allow themselves to be broken by secants, but they can be supported by tangent lines and planes. Note that the ball touches the ramp not at its bottom but at the foot of the perpendicular from its center to the ramp. The **Example** shows how tangents can help to determine the distance to the horizon. Emphasize that the picture is distorted because if it were drawn to scale, P would be so close to T and the circle that one could not distinguish them.

At this point, students do not have the background to understand the importance of tangents to the graph of a function at a particular point on that graph. Nor can they understand the relationship of the tangent to the derivative. However, you still might draw a parabolic path of a projectile and point out that the slope of a tangent to that parabola is positive as the ball goes up, zero when it hits its peak, and negative when it comes down. Conclude therefore that the slope of the tangent gives information about the path of a projectile.

Have students record the results of the **Activity** for use with **Question 11** on page 827.

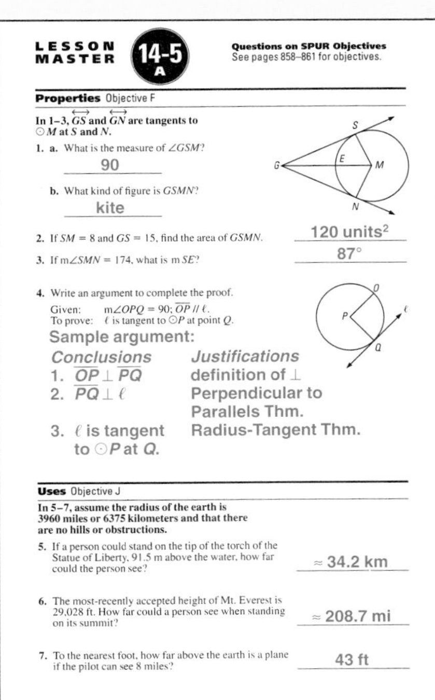

LESSON MASTER 14-5 A

Questions on SPUR Objectives
See pages 858–861 for objectives.

Properties Objective F

In 1–3, $\overleftrightarrow{GS}$ and $\overleftrightarrow{GN}$ are tangents to $\odot M$ at S and N.

1. a. What is the measure of $\angle GSM$? 90

   b. What kind of figure is $GSMN$? kite

2. If $SM = 8$ and $GS = 15$, find the area of $GSMN$. 120 units^2

3. If $m\angle SMN = 174$, what is $m\,SE$? 87°

4. Write an argument to complete the proof.

   Given: $m\angle OPQ = 90$; $\overline{OP} \parallel \ell$.
   To prove: ℓ is tangent to $\odot P$ at point Q.

   Sample argument:

Conclusions	*Justifications*
1. $\overline{OP} \perp \overline{PQ}$	definition of $\perp$
2. $\overline{PQ} \perp \ell$	Perpendicular to Parallels Thm.
3. ℓ is tangent to $\odot P$ at Q.	Radius-Tangent Thm.

Uses Objective J

In 5–7, assume the radius of the earth is 3960 miles or 6375 kilometers and that there are no hills or obstructions.

5. If a person could stand on the tip of the torch of the Statue of Liberty, 91.5 m above the water, how far could the person see? ≈ 34.2 km

6. The most-recently accepted height of Mt. Everest is 29,028 ft. How far could a person see when standing on its summit? ≈ 208.7 mi

7. To the nearest foot, how far above the earth is a plane if the pilot can see 8 miles? 43 ft

English Language Development You might illustrate the meaning of tangent to students with limited English proficiency by holding a meter stick on a wheel. Point out that the stick touches, or intersects, the wheel at one and only one point. Contrast this with other positions of the stick that suggest secants.

Challenge

Tell students to let (a, b) be any point on the circle centered at the origin with radius r. Then ask these questions.

1. What is the slope of the tangent line to the circle at that point? $[-\frac{a}{b}]$
2. Write an equation, in slope-intercept form, of the tangent line to the circle at that point. $[y = -\frac{a}{b}x + \frac{a^2}{b} + b]$

Additional Examples

1. From the roof of a school 30 feet high, about how far can you see to the horizon? $\approx$ 6.7 miles
2. Circle O has radius 5 and $OP = 12$. How long is either tangent from point P to circle O? $\sqrt{119}$
3. Describe how to construct a tangent to a circle O at a given point T on it. Draw $\overline{OT}$. Then draw the $\perp$ to $\overline{OT}$ at T. The construction works because the perpendicular to a radius at its endpoint is tangent to the circle.

Additional Answers

11a–b. The center of the circle is on all of them.

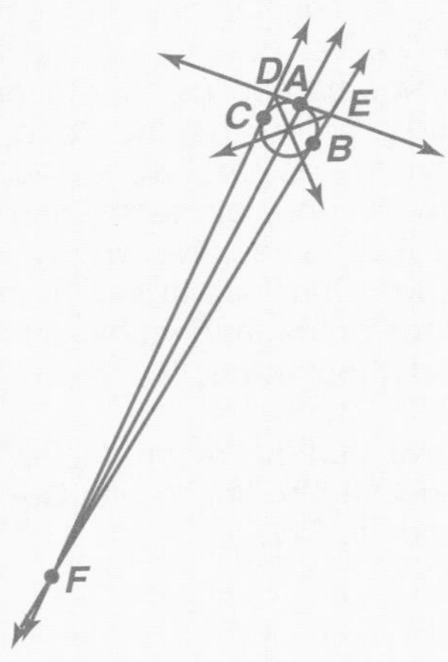

LESSON MASTER 14-5 B — Questions on SPUR Objectives

Vocabulary

1. a. Define *tangent to a circle.* a line in the circle's plane which intersects the circle in exactly one point

b. Define *tangent to a sphere.* a line or a plane which intersects the sphere in exactly one point

Properties Objective F: Make deductions from properties of radii and tangents, and know sufficient conditions for radii to be perpendicular to them.

In 2 and 3, complete the statement using the diagram at the right.

2. If $\overline{MG} \perp \overleftrightarrow{GP}$, then __?__. $\overleftrightarrow{GP}$ is tangent to $\odot M$ at G

3. If $\overleftrightarrow{GP}$ is tangent to $\odot M$ at G, then __?__. $\overleftrightarrow{GP}$ is perpendicular to $\overline{MG}$

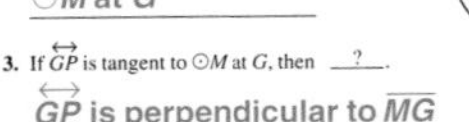

4. Refer to $\odot W$ with tangents $\overline{ZY}$ and $\overline{ZX}$.

a. What kind of triangles are $\triangle XZW$ and $\triangle YZW$? right

b. Justify your answer to Part a. Sample: By the Radius-Tangent Thm., $\overline{WY} \perp \overline{YZ}$ and $\overline{WX} \perp \overline{XZ}$.

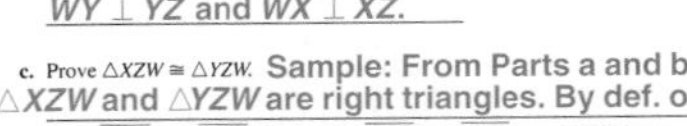

c. Prove $\triangle XZW \cong \triangle YZW$. Sample: From Parts a and b, $\triangle XZW$ and $\triangle YZW$ are right triangles. By def. of circle, $\overline{WY} \cong \overline{WX}$. Since $\overline{WZ} \cong \overline{WZ}$, $\triangle XZW \cong \triangle YZW$ by the HL Congruence Thm.

d. What does Part c imply about $\overline{ZY}$ and $\overline{ZX}$? Why? Sample: $\overline{ZY} \cong \overline{ZX}$ because CPCFC.

This means that $CP \approx 3960.038$ miles. The little amount .038 is important. Don't round here!

From the Pythagorean Theorem,

$$PT^2 + 3960^2 \approx 3960.038^2.$$
$$PT^2 \approx 3960.038^2 - 3960^2$$
$$\approx 301$$

So $$PT \approx \sqrt{301} \approx 17.3.$$

It is approximately 17 miles to the horizon from a point 200 feet high.

The numbers in the Example are difficult to deal with. It would be nice to have a formula that gives the distance to the horizon from a point h units above the surface of Earth. For these reasons, it is desirable to use variables to obtain a general formula. But then, why work only with Earth? Letting r be the radius of any sphere and h be the height above the sphere (in some units), the distance to the horizon can be shown to be $\sqrt{2rh + h^2}$. (In the Example, $r = 3960$ mi and $h = 0.038$ mi.) You are asked to derive this formula in Question 15.

QUESTIONS

Covering the Reading

1a) when it intersects the circle in exactly one point

1. a. According to the definition, when is a line tangent to a circle?
   b. According to the Radius-Tangent Theorem, when is a line tangent to a circle? If it is perpendicular to the radius at the radius' endpoint on the circle. a) See left.
2. At the left, ℓ is tangent to $\odot O$ at P. Must ℓ be perpendicular to $\overline{OP}$? Yes
3. In the proof of the first theorem of this lesson, what contradiction is reached? $OQ = OP$ and $OQ > OP$
4. *Multiple choice.* The first two theorems of this lesson are a
   (a) converses of each other. (b) inverses of each other.
   (c) contrapositives of each other. (d) negations of each other.
5. To prove the theorems in this lesson, what logical principle was applied? Law of Indirect Reasoning
6. Refer to the Example.
   a. Why is $\overline{PT} \perp \overline{TC}$? $\overleftrightarrow{PT}$ is tangent to Earth.
   b. Where does the distance 3960 miles come from? It is the radius of Earth.
7. If Earth were flat, how far could you see from a point 2 meters above ground level, assuming nothing was in the way? infinitely far (on a clear day, you could see forever . . .)
8. How far is the horizon from the observation deck of the Society Center in Cleveland, Ohio, which is 888 feet above ground level? $\approx$ 36.50 miles

3. Where did you use the information that the point of tangency is on the circle? [Since the tangent line is perpendicular to the radius, its slope is the negative reciprocal of the slope of the line through the center and the point of tangency.]
4. Where did you use the information that the radius is r? [nowhere]

Additional Answers, continued

16. Sample argument:

Conclusions	Justifications
1. $\overline{PX} \perp \overline{NX}$, $\overline{PY} \perp \overline{NY}$	Radius-Tangent Theorem
2. $NX \cong NY$	definition of circle
3. Draw $\overline{PN}$.	Point-Line-Plane Postulate

In 9 and 10, give a real-world example of the given mathematical idea.

9. a line tangent to a circle
Sample: a wheel on a ramp

10. a plane tangent to a sphere
Sample: a ball on a floor

Applying the Mathematics

11. a. Show your drawing from the Activity in this lesson.
b. Label the triangle formed by the tangent lines $\triangle DEF$. Then draw the angle bisectors of $\triangle DEF$. What is their point of concurrency?
a, b) See margin.

12. In the figure at the left, $\overrightarrow{ZI}$ is tangent to sphere P at point I. How many other rays from point Z are tangent to sphere P?
infinitely many

13. a. Extend the Radius-Tangent Theorem of this lesson to apply to spheres. A plane is a tangent to a sphere if and only if it is perpendicular to the radius at the radius's endpoint on the sphere.
b. Is the extension true?
Yes

14. Determine how far it is to the horizon from a point 100 meters above the surface of the moon. (The radius of the moon is about 1750 kilometers.) $\approx$ 18.7 km

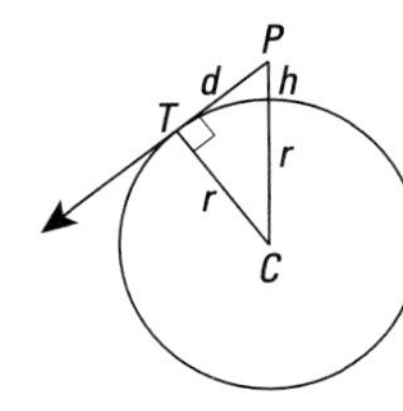

15. Use the figure at the left to show that if $\overline{PT}$ is tangent to circle C at point T, then $d = \sqrt{2rh + h^2}$. See margin.

16. Refer to the figure at the right and write a proof argument. See margin.

Given: Point P outside $\odot N$; $\overline{PX}$ and $\overline{PY}$ are tangent to $\odot N$ at points X and Y.

To prove: $PXNY$ is a kite. (This will prove that the two tangents to circle N from any point P have the same length. This is a result you should remember.)

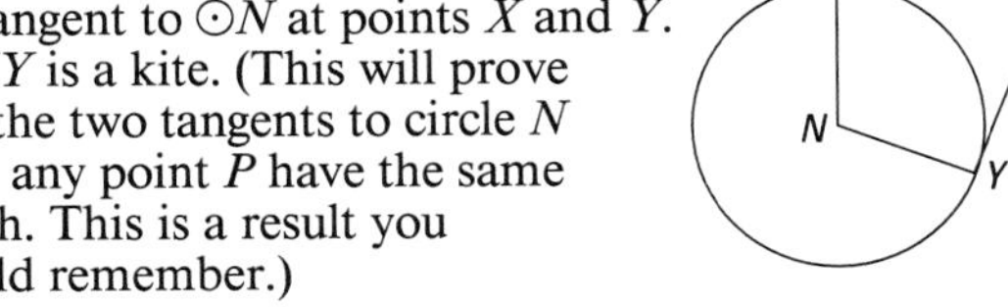

17. Copy the figure below and draw the four tangents that circles O and P have in common. These are called **common tangents** to the circles.

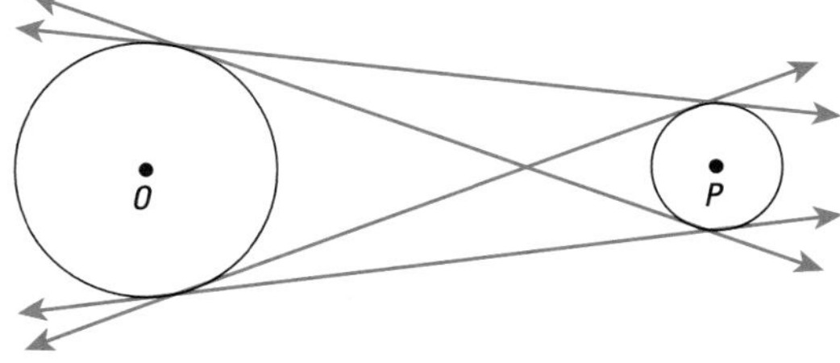

18. At the right, $\overline{PT}$ is tangent to $\odot O$ at T. $PT = 12$ and $PO = 15$.
a. What is the area of the circle?
b. What is the distance from P to N, the nearest point on the circle? 6 units
a) $81\pi \approx 254.5$ units^2

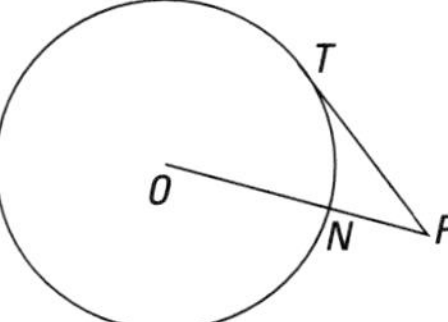

(Unique Line Assumption)

4. $NP = NP$	Reflexive Property of Equality
5. $\triangle PNX \cong \triangle PNY$	HL Congruence Theorem
6. $\overline{PX} \cong \overline{PY}$	CPCF Theorem
7. $PXNY$ is a kite.	definition of kite

Notes on Questions

Questions 9–10 Cooperative Learning You might want students to discuss these questions in groups. Encourage students to also make up other examples which are appropriate.

Question 16 This question involves the tangent kite. (See the *Notes on Reading.*) The result to be remembered is that tangents from an external point to a circle have the same length.

15.

Conclusions	Justifications
1. $\overline{PT} \perp \overline{CT}$	Radius-Tangent Theorem
2. $\triangle PTC$ is a right triangle.	definition of right triangle
3. $d^2 + r^2 = (r + h)^2$	Pythagorean Theorem
4. $d^2 + r^2 = r^2 + 2rh + h^2$	Distributive Property
5. $d^2 = 2rh + h^2$	Addition Property of Equality
6. $d = \sqrt{2rh + h^2}$	definition of square root

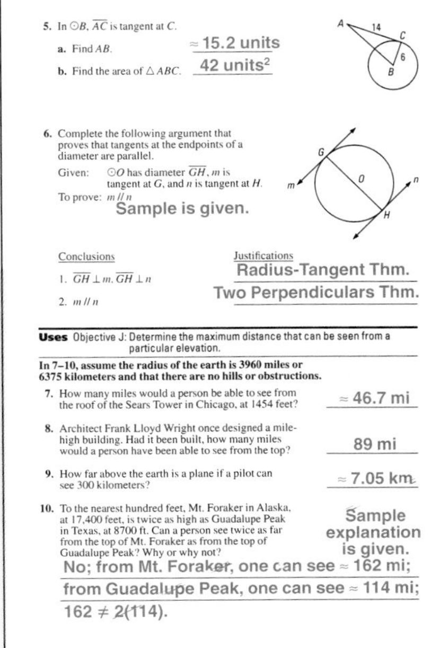

▶ **LESSON MASTER 14-5B** *page 2*

5. In $\odot B$, $\overline{AC}$ is tangent at C.
a. Find AB. $\approx$ 15.2 units
b. Find the area of $\triangle ABC$. 42 units^2

6. Complete the following argument that proves that tangents at the endpoints of a diameter are parallel.
Given: $\odot O$ has diameter $\overline{GH}$, m is tangent at G, and n is tangent at H.
To prove: $m \parallel n$
Sample is given.

Conclusions	Justifications
1. $\overline{GH} \perp m$, $\overline{GH} \perp n$	Radius-Tangent Thm.
2. $m \parallel n$	Two Perpendiculars Thm.

Uses Objective J: Determine the maximum distance that can be seen from a particular elevation.

In 7–10, assume the radius of the earth is 3960 miles or 6375 kilometers and that there are no hills or obstructions.

7. How many miles would a person be able to see from the roof of the Sears Tower in Chicago, at 1454 feet? $\approx$ 46.7 mi

8. Architect Frank Lloyd Wright once designed a mile-high building. Had it been built, how many miles would a person have been able to see from the top? 89 mi

9. How far above the earth is a plane if a pilot can see 300 kilometers? $\approx$ 7.05 km

10. To the nearest hundred feet, Mt. Foraker in Alaska, at 17,400 feet, is twice as high as Guadalupe Peak in Texas, at 8700 ft. Can a person see twice as far from the top of Mt. Foraker as from the top of Guadalupe Peak? Why or why not? Sample explanation is given.
No; from Mt. Foraker, one can see $\approx$ 162 mi; from Guadalupe Peak, one can see $\approx$ 114 mi; $162 \neq 2(114)$.

Notes on Questions

Question 23 Technology Connection You might have interested students explore the statements in **Question 23** using a computer drawing program.

Follow-up for Lesson 14-5

Practice

For more questions on SPUR Objectives, use **Lesson Master 14-5A** (shown on page 825) or **Lesson Master 14-5B** (shown on pages 826–827).

Assessment

Oral/Written Communication Have students **work in pairs.** First have each student draw a circle with one point marked on the circle. Then have them exchange drawings and construct a tangent to the circle at the labeled point. [Students correctly construct a tangent to a circle at a given point.]

Extension

Planes can be tangent to spheres. Discuss whether the theorems of this lesson are true if the word *line* is replaced by *plane* and the word *circle* is replaced by *sphere.* [Yes] Then ask how many planes are there that are tangent to a sphere and contain a given point outside the sphere? [Infinitely many]

Project Update Project 1, *Cutting Down on Waste*, Project 3, *Circles Associated with Triangles*, and Project 5, *Japanese Temple Geometry Theorems,* on pages 853–854, relate to the content of this lesson.

Review

19. Use the figure below. Find the measure of the indicated angle. *(Lessons 14-2, 14-4)*

a. $\angle 1$ 65 **b.** $\angle 2$ 92.5 **c.** $\angle 3$ 87.5 **d.** $\angle E$ 22.5

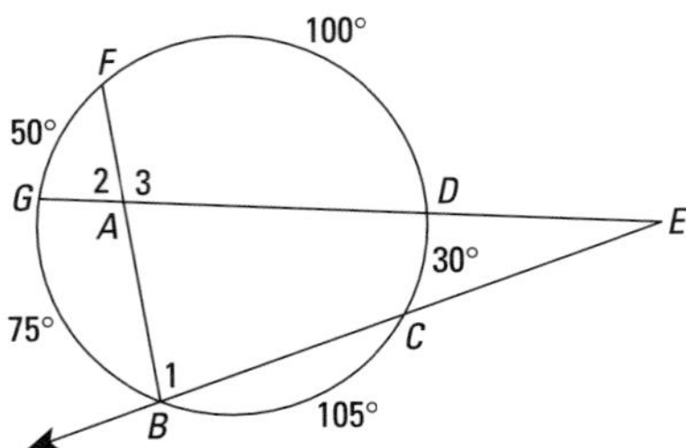

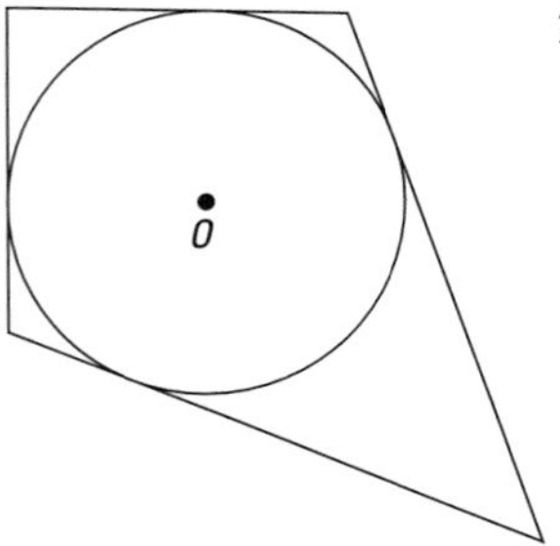

20. An 8″ chord is 3″ from the center of the circle as shown at the left. What is the area of the circle? *(Lessons 8-8, 14-1)* $25\pi \approx 78.5$ in^2

21. Below, $ABCD \sim JKHG$. Find as many missing lengths and angle measures as you can. *(Lesson 12-5)* $m\angle G = 81$; $BC = 15$; $GJ = 16$

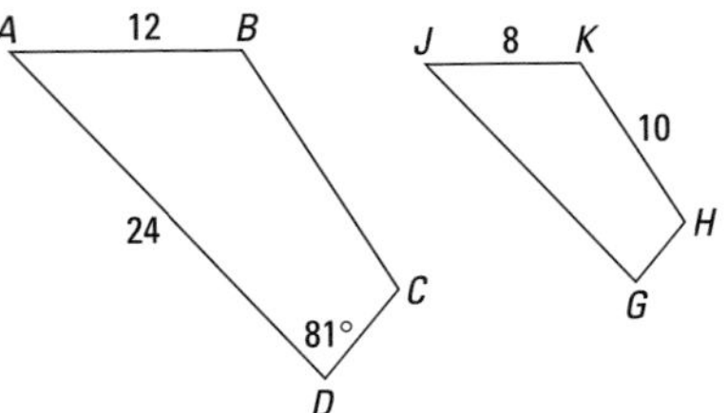

22. The measures of the exterior angles of a quadrilateral are $4x$, $8x - 23$, $9x + 7$, and $5x - 40$.

a. What is x? 16

b. What is the measure of each interior angle? *(Lesson 7-9)*

116; 75; 29; 140

Exploration

23. A polygon is circumscribed about a circle if each of its sides is tangent to the circle. At the left, a quadrilateral has been circumscribed about circle O.

a. Experiment with various circles and polygons. Tell whether you think these conjectures are *true or false.*

i. If a quadrilateral is circumscribed about a circle, then at least two of its sides are congruent. False

ii. If a parallelogram is circumscribed about a circle, then it is a square. False

iii. If an isosceles trapezoid is circumscribed about a circle, then it is a rectangle. False

iv. A polygon with an odd number of sides greater than 3 cannot be circumscribed about a circle. False

b. Prove at least one of the conclusions you make. See margin.

Additional Answers

23b. Sample: A counterexample for statement iv. is shown at the right: when $n = 5 > 3$; the pentagon is circumscribed about $\odot O$.

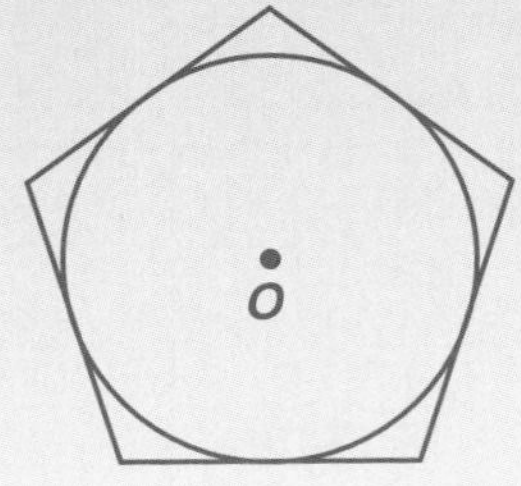

LESSON

14-6

Angles Formed by Tangents

Big wheels. *On most bicycle wheels that have ever been built, spokes are tangent to a circular axle in the middle of the wheel.*

Angles Formed by a Tangent and a Chord

In Lesson 14-4, angles were formed by chords or secants. In this lesson, angles which have at least one side tangent to a circle are explored. Consider first the angle formed by a tangent and a chord. Suppose $\overleftrightarrow{BC}$ is tangent to $\odot O$ at B and $m\widehat{AB} = 75°$, as pictured here.

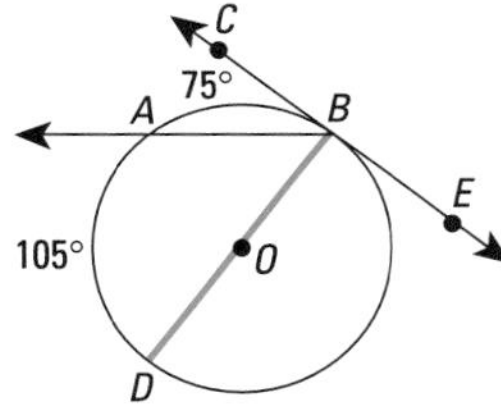

To find $m\angle ABC$, draw the diameter containing B and O. The semicircle $\widehat{BAD}$ has measure 180°, so $m\widehat{AD} = 105°$. Thus $m\angle ABD = \frac{1}{2} \cdot 105 = 52.5$. Now, since $\overleftrightarrow{CB} \perp \overline{BD}$, $\angle CBA$ is complementary to $\angle ABD$. So $m\angle CBA = 37.5$. In general,

$$\begin{aligned} m\angle ABC &= 90 - m\angle ABD \\ &= \tfrac{1}{2} \cdot 180 - \tfrac{1}{2} \cdot m\widehat{AD} \\ &= \tfrac{1}{2}(180 - m\widehat{AD}) \\ &= \tfrac{1}{2} m\widehat{AB}. \end{aligned}$$

This argument proves the following theorem.

Lesson 14-6

Objectives

C Calculate the measures of angles between chords, secants, or tangents from measures of intercepted arcs, and vice versa.

F Make deductions from properties of radii and tangents, and know sufficient conditions for radii to be perpendicular to them.

G Make deductions from properties of angles formed by chords, tangents, or secants.

Resources

From the ***Teacher's Resource File***

- Lesson Master 14-6A or 14-6B
- Answer Master 14-6
- Assessment Sourcebook: Quiz for Lessons 14-4 through 14-6
- Teaching Aids
  183 Warm-up
  188 Additional Examples
- Activity Kit, Activity 30
- Technology Sourcebook, Computer Master 25

Additional Resources

- Visuals for Teaching Aids 183, 188
- Videodisc

Teaching Lesson 14-6

Warm-up

For each of Questions 1–7, draw a diagram to illustrate the situation. **Sample diagrams are shown.**

1. A circle with a central angle

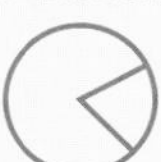

(Warm-up continues on page 830.)

Lesson 14-6 Overview

Broad Goals This lesson extends the results of Lesson 14-4 to tangents. It enables students to have a second day to assimilate the relationships between arc and angle measures.

Perspective All of the circle/angle relationships can be summarized with the following statement: If the vertex of the angle is inside or on the circle, you add the intercepted arcs and divide by two, and if the vertex is outside the circle, you subtract the intercepted arcs and divide by two. Notice that the statement applies to all circle angles, including central angles, inscribed angles, and tangent-chord angles. For inscribed angles and tangent-chord angles, one of the arcs has measure 0° since the vertex is on the circle.

Video

Wide World of Mathematics The segment, *Solar Eclipse*, describes a 1994 occurrence of a solar eclipse (when the moon moves directly between the earth and the sun). The segment may be used to show students the significance of tangent lines in a real-world situation. Related questions and an investigation are provided in videodisc stills and in the Video Guide. A related CD-ROM activity is also available.

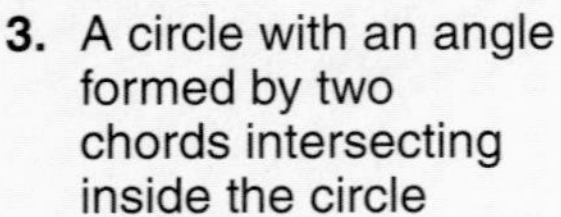

2. A circle with an inscribed angle

3. A circle with an angle formed by two chords intersecting inside the circle

4. A circle with an angle formed by two secants intersecting outside the circle

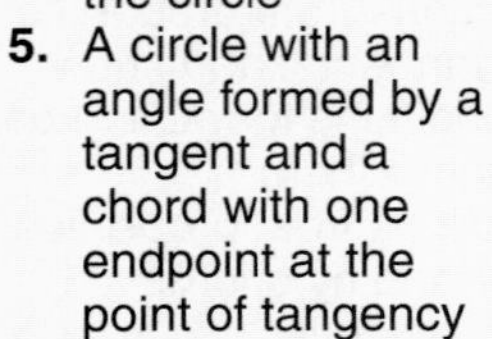

5. A circle with an angle formed by a tangent and a chord with one endpoint at the point of tangency

6. A circle with an angle formed by a tangent and a secant with the vertex of the angle outside the circle

7. A circle with an angle formed by two tangents

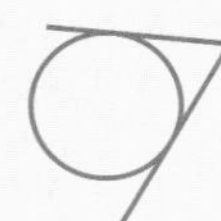

8. For which of the situations in Questions 1–7 have you already studied a theorem that allows you to determine the angle's measure from the measures of given arcs. **The angles described in Questions 1–4**

Notes on Reading

A tangent can be considered as the limit of a sequence of secants whose two points of intersection with the circle have become closer and closer until they are one. Point out that the measure of the angle formed by a tangent and a secant, or between two tangents, is just like the angle between two secants. The angle between a tangent and a chord is the limit of an inscribed angle.

Example 3 is a surprise to many students—one angle measure determines the measures of two arcs.

Tangent-Chord Theorem
The measure of an angle formed by a tangent and a chord is half the measure of its intercepted arc.

Example 1

In the figure at the right, $\overleftrightarrow{AB}$ is tangent to circle O at A. If $m\angle BAC = 80$, find $m\overset{\frown}{AC}$.

Solution

From the Tangent-Chord Theorem,

$$m\angle BAC = \tfrac{1}{2}m\overset{\frown}{AC}.$$
$$80° = \tfrac{1}{2}m\overset{\frown}{AC}$$
$$160° = m\overset{\frown}{AC}$$

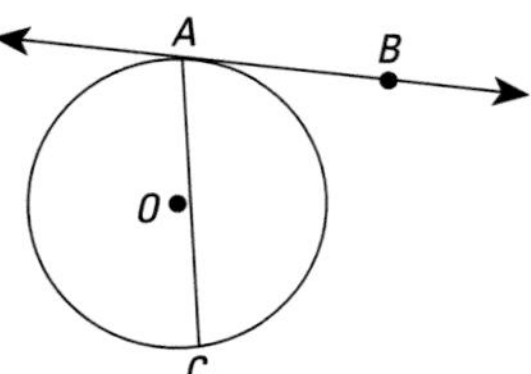

Angles Formed by Tangents and Secants

Measures of angles between tangents and secants are calculated the same way we calculate measures of angles between secants.

Tangent-Secant Theorem
The measure of the angle between two tangents, or between a tangent and a secant, is half the difference of the intercepted arcs.

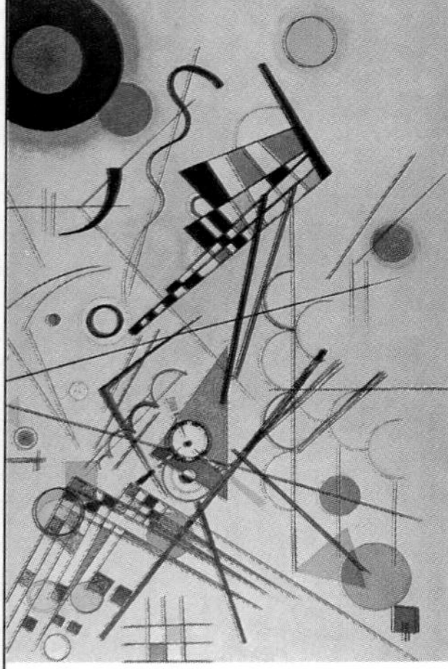

Composition 8 by Russian artist Wassily Kandinsky (1866-1944)

Proof

Here is a proof for an angle between a secant and tangent. The proof for an angle between two tangents is similar. It is left to you as Question 10.

Drawing: Secant $\overleftrightarrow{EB}$ and tangent $\overleftrightarrow{EC}$ form $\angle E$, as shown below.

Given: $m\overset{\frown}{AC} = x°$ and $m\overset{\frown}{BC} = y°$.

To prove: $m\angle E = \frac{1}{2}(x - y)$.

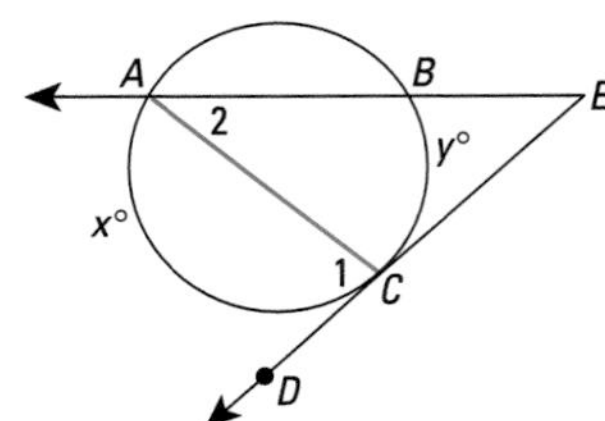

Optional Activities

Videodisc Bar Codes

Search Chapter 69

Play

Activity 1
You may use *Activity Kit, Activity 30,* either before or after the lesson. In this activity, students learn a few of the basic constructions found in windows of gothic architecture.

Activity 2
After completing the lesson, you can use the following activity. Show students the first design at the right. Point out that the entire figure is composed of line segments. Yet a curve seems to appear in the drawing. Then have students experiment with making their own line designs. [One example is shown. Point out that a circle seems to appear in the center, but in reality, the figure is a polygon with 40 sides.]

Argument:

Conclusions	Justifications
1. Draw $\overline{AC}$.	Point-Line-Plane Postulate
2. $m\angle 1 = \frac{1}{2}x$	a
3. $m\angle 2 = \frac{1}{2}y$	b
4. $m\angle 1 = m\angle 2 + m\angle E$	c
5. $m\angle E = m\angle 1 - m\angle 2$	d
6. $m\angle E = \frac{1}{2}x - \frac{1}{2}y$	e
7. $m\angle E = \frac{1}{2}(x - y)$	f

Question 8 asks you for the justifications for steps 2–7.

Example 2

Refer to the figure below. $\overrightarrow{AB}$ is tangent to the circle at B. Find $m\angle A$.

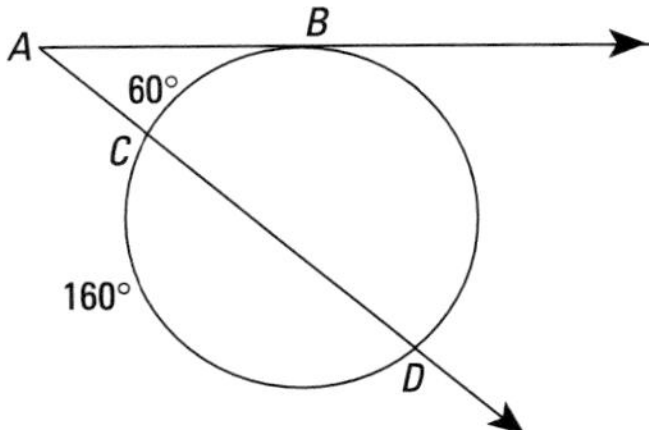

Solution

The circle measures 360°, so

$m\widehat{BD} = 360° - 160° - 60°$
$= 140°.$

$m\angle A = \frac{1}{2}(m\widehat{BD} - m\widehat{BC})$
$= \frac{1}{2}(140° - 60°) = 40°$

Angles Formed by Two Tangents

The two tangents to a circle from a point determine the measure of a smaller intercepted arc, a larger intercepted arc, and the angle formed by the tangents. If you know any one of these, you can find the other two.

Example 3

In the figure at the right, $m\angle P = 30$. What is $m\widehat{QSR}$?

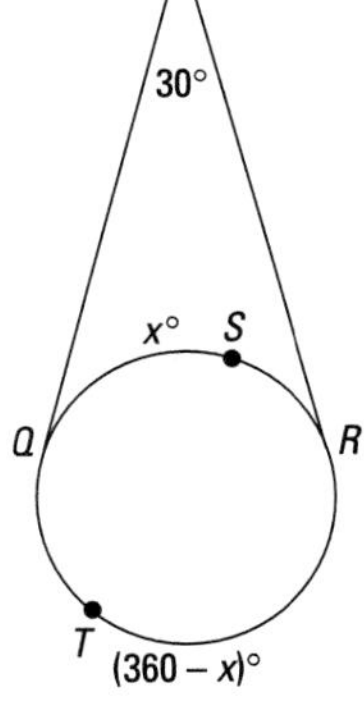

Solution

Let $m\widehat{QSR} = x°$. Then $m\widehat{QTR} = (360 - x)°$.
By the Tangent-Secant Theorem,

$m\angle P = \frac{1}{2}(m\widehat{QTR} - m\widehat{QSR})$
$= \frac{1}{2}((360 - x) - x)$

Substitute for $m\angle P$ and solve for x.

$30 = \frac{1}{2}(360 - 2x)$
$30 = 180 - x$

So $x = 150°$.

Check

When $x = 150$, then $360 - x = 210$. Does $m\angle P$ equal half the difference of the two arcs? Yes, 30 is half of $210 - 150$.

Additional Examples

These examples are also given on **Teaching Aid 188.**

1. A chord $\overline{AB}$ in a circle forms an angle of 65° with the tangent to the circle at A. Draw a possible situation and determine the measures of the major and minor arcs with endpoints A and B. **Sample drawing: 130° and 230°**

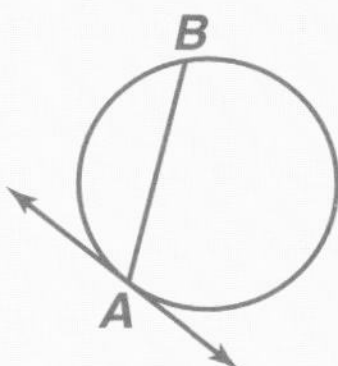

2. In the diagram below, $\overleftrightarrow{LM}$ is tangent to the circle at M and $m\widehat{MK} = 48°$. Find $m\angle L$. **47**

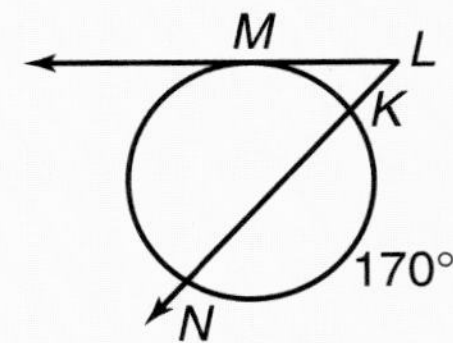

3. The measure of major arc DFE is 290°. $\overleftrightarrow{CD}$ and $\overleftrightarrow{CE}$ are tangents to the circle. What is $m\angle C$? **110**

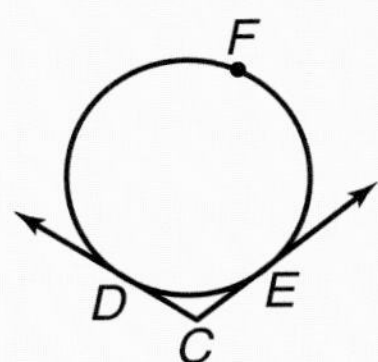

Activity 3 Technology Connection
In *Technology Sourcebook, Computer Master 25*, students explore various properties of tangents to circles. Then they apply some of these properties to developing a method for constructing a tangent, using compass and straightedge.

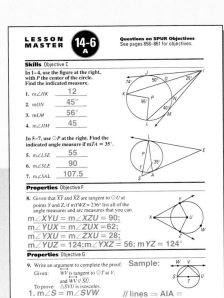

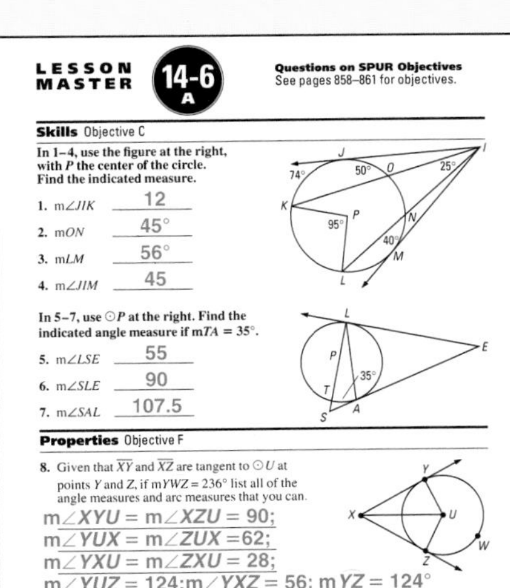

LESSON MASTER 14-6 A — **Questions on SPUR Objectives** See pages 858–861 for objectives.

Skills Objective C

In 1–4, use the figure at the right, with P the center of the circle. Find the indicated measure.

1. $m\angle JIK$ 12
2. $m\widehat{ON}$ 45°
3. $m\widehat{LM}$ 56°
4. $m\angle JIM$ 45

In 5–7, use $\odot P$ at the right. Find the indicated angle measure if $m\widehat{TA} = 35°$.

5. $m\angle LSE$ 55
6. $m\angle SLE$ 90
7. $m\angle SAL$ 107.5

Properties Objective F

8. Given that $\overline{XY}$ and $\overline{XZ}$ are tangent to $\odot U$ at points Y and Z, if $m\widehat{YWZ} = 236°$ list all of the angle measures and arc measures that you can.
$m\angle XYU = m\angle XZU = 90$; $m\angle YUX = m\angle ZUX = 62$; $m\angle YXU = m\angle ZXU = 28$; $m\angle YUZ = 124$; $m\angle YXZ = 56$; $m\widehat{YZ} = 124°$

Properties Objective G

9. Write an argument to complete the proof. Sample:
Given: $\overleftrightarrow{WV}$ is tangent to $\odot T$ at V, and $\overleftrightarrow{WV} \parallel \overline{SU}$.
To prove: $\triangle SVU$ is isosceles.

1. $m\angle S = m\angle SVW$ — // lines ⇒ AIA ≅
2. $m\angle SVW = \frac{1}{2}m\widehat{SV}$ — Tangent-Chord Thm.
3. $m\angle U = \frac{1}{2}m\widehat{SV}$ — Inscribed Angle Thm.
4. $m\angle S = m\angle U$ — Transitivity and Sub.
5. $\triangle SVU$ is isos. — def. of isos. △

Notes on Questions

Questions 1–2 These questions point out how the measure of the angle between a tangent and a chord can be found without remembering any formula. Draw the auxiliary diameter $\overline{EB}$. $m\widehat{DE} = 70°$, so $m\angle EBD = 35$ by the Inscribed Angle Theorem. Thus, $m\angle DBC = 55$. This is the reasoning that is generalized in the proof of the Tangent-Chord Theorem.

Question 5 $m\angle P$ can be found in two ways. One way is to use the Tangent-Secant Theorem. Another way is to see that $m\angle R = 36$ and that $m\angle RST = 54$. Thus, $m\angle RSP = 126$. This gives the measures of two of the angles in $\triangle RSP$, and $m\angle P$ is the third.

Question 12 Discuss this question so students can determine if they know the formulas. It can also be used to review terminology.

Question 14 Ask if anyone can prove or disprove that $\triangle ABC$ is equilateral. [$AB = AC$ and $m\angle BAC = 60$ implies that $\triangle ABC$ is equilateral.]

(Notes on Questions continue on page 834.)

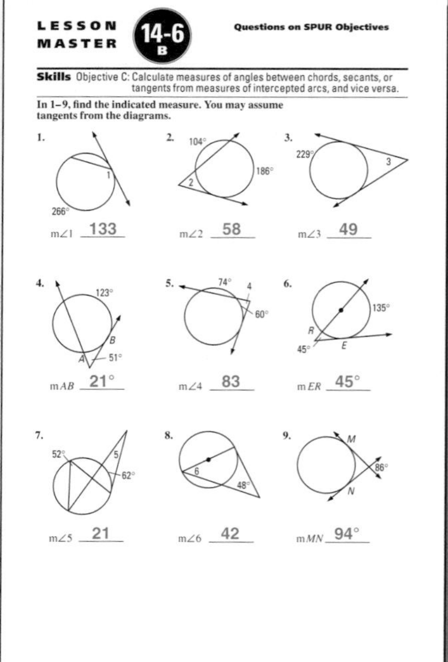
LESSON MASTER 14-6 B Questions on SPUR Objectives

Skills Objective C: Calculate measures of angles between chords, secants, or tangents from measures of intercepted arcs, and vice versa.

In 1–9, find the indicated measure. You may assume tangents from the diagrams.

1. m∠1 133
2. m∠2 58
3. m∠3 49
4. mAB 21°
5. m∠4 83
6. mER 45°
7. m∠5 21
8. m∠6 42
9. mMN 94°

You now have studied all the measures of angles made by lines that intersect a circle. You are asked to summarize the relevant theorems in Question 12.

QUESTIONS

Covering the Reading

In 1 and 2, use the diagram at the right in which $\overleftrightarrow{BC}$ is tangent to $\odot A$ at B, and $m\widehat{BD} = 110°$.

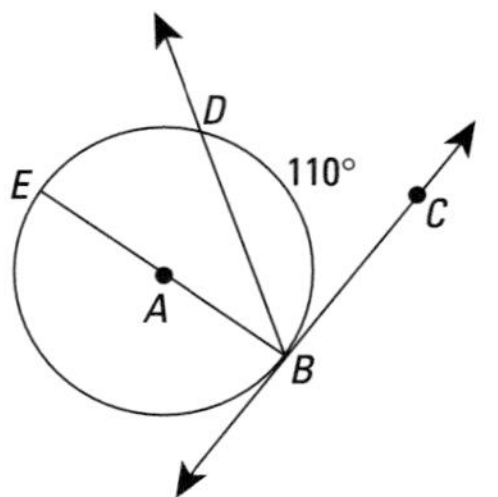

1. Find $m\angle ABC$. 90

2. Find $m\angle DBC$. 55

3. Below, $\overleftrightarrow{ST}$ is tangent to $\odot X$ at T. If $m\angle RTS = 125$, find $m\widehat{TPR}$. 250°

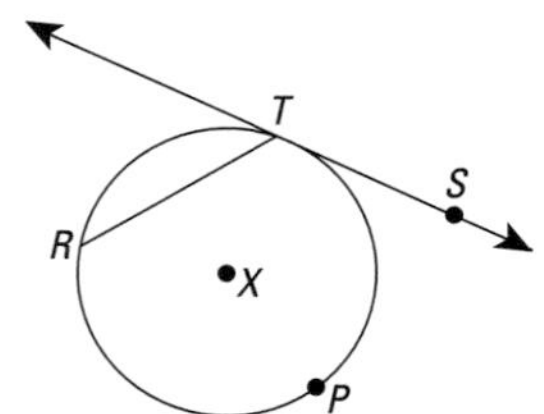

4. Find $m\angle Q$ in the circle below. 40

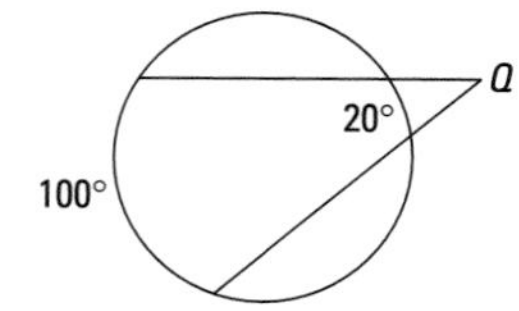

In 5–7, use the drawing at the right. $\overline{PT}$ is tangent to circle O at point S.

5. $m\angle P = (\underline{\ ?\ })$ 18

6. $m\angle TSR = (\underline{\ ?\ })$ 54

7. *True or false.* True
$m\angle RSP = \frac{1}{2}m\widehat{RQS}$

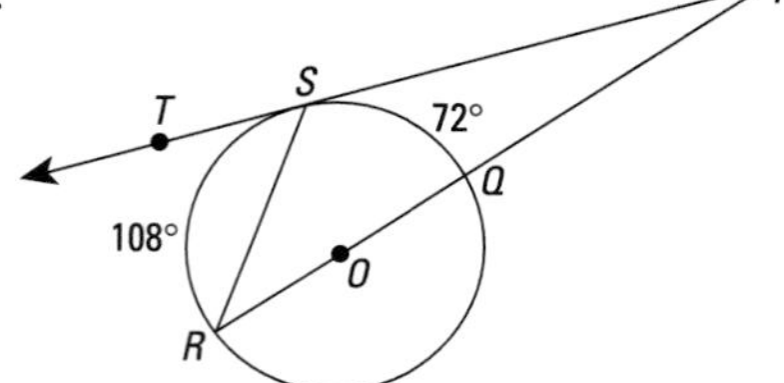

8. Give the justifications for Steps 2–7 in the proof argument of the Tangent-Secant Theorem on page 831. See left.

8a) Tangent-Chord Thm.
b) Inscribed Angle Thm.
c) Exterior Angle Thm.
d) Addition Prop. of =
e) Substitution
f) Distributive Property

9. $\overline{PS}$ and $\overline{PT}$ are tangents to $\odot O$. Find $m\angle TPS$. 80

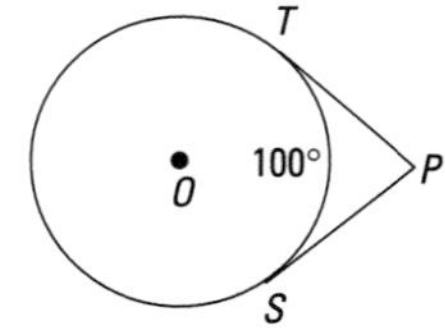

Adapting to Individual Needs

Challenge

Ask students to draw a circle and two tangents to the circle from point P outside the circle. Tell them to label the points of intersection of the tangents and the circle A and B. Then ask them to prove that the distance from P to either point of tangency is the same. [Draw the chord from A to B. According to the Tangent-Chord Theorem, the measure of $\angle PAB$ is half the measure of the intercepted arc. The same is true about the measure of $\angle PBA$. So $\angle PAB$ and $\angle PBA$ have the same measure. Therefore, $\triangle PAB$ is isosceles and $PA = PB$.]

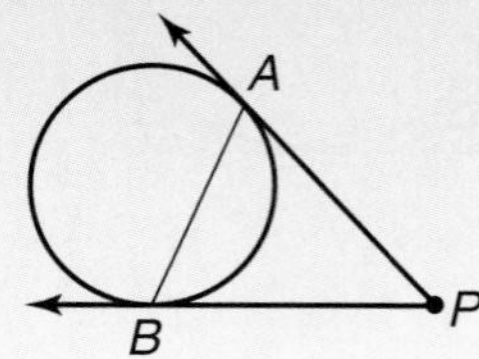

In 10 and 11, use the drawing below in which $\overrightarrow{PQ}$ and $\overrightarrow{PR}$ are tangents to $\odot O$ at points Q and R.

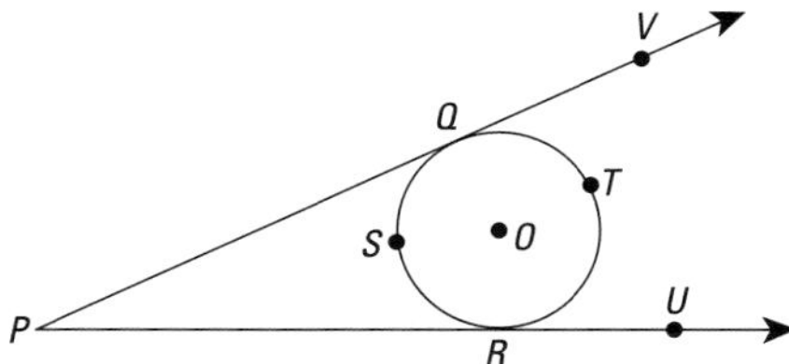

10. Prove the second part of the Tangent-Secant Theorem. That is, prove that $m\angle P = \frac{1}{2}(m\overset{\frown}{QTR} - m\overset{\frown}{QSR})$. See margin.
(Hint: Draw $\overline{QR}$ and use an exterior angle of $\triangle PQR$.)

11. If $m\angle P = 25$, find the measures of arcs $\overset{\frown}{QSR}$ and $\overset{\frown}{QTR}$.
$m\overset{\frown}{QSR} = 155°$; $m\overset{\frown}{QTR} = 205°$

Applying the Mathematics

12. Match each angle at the left with a way to compute its measure at the right.

a. angle between two chords (iii)
b. angle between two secants (iv)
c. angle between two tangents (iv)
d. angle between secant and tangent (iv)
e. angle between chord and tangent (ii)
f. inscribed angle (ii)
g. central angle (i)

(i) the intercepted arc
(ii) $\frac{1}{2}$ the intercepted arc
(iii) $\frac{1}{2}$ the sum of the intercepted arcs
(iv) $\frac{1}{2}$ the difference of the intercepted arcs

13. In the figure at the right, $\overrightarrow{PR}$ is tangent to $\odot O$ at R. $\overrightarrow{PQ}$ contains O. If $m\angle P = 41$, what is $m\overset{\frown}{QR}$? 49°

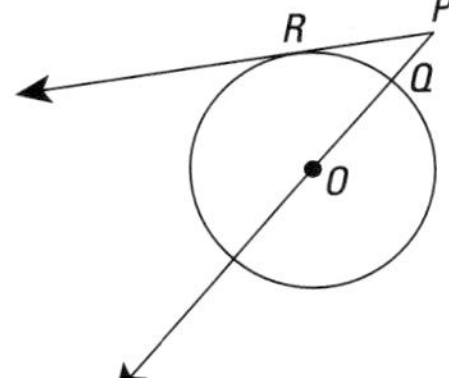

14. At the right, $\overline{AB}$ and $\overline{AC}$ are tangents to the circle and arc measurements are as marked. Find the measures of the indicated angles.

a. $\angle ABD$ 142.5
b. $\angle CAB$ 60
c. $\angle ACD$ 97.5

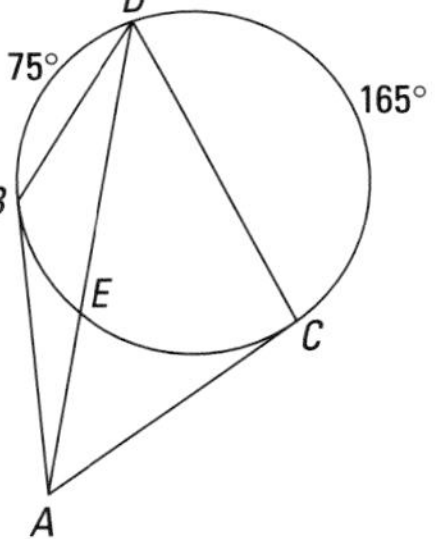

Follow-up for Lesson 14-6

Practice

For more questions on SPUR Objectives, use **Lesson Master 14-6A** (shown on page 831) or **Lesson Master 14-6B** (shown on pages 832–833).

Assessment

Quiz A quiz covering Lessons 14-4 through 14-6 is provided in the *Assessment Sourcebook*.

Oral/Written Communication Have students **work in groups**. Refer them to **Question 12**. For each type of angle described in **parts a–g**, have them draw a diagram labeled with correct angle measures and arc measures to illustrate the various relationships involved. [Students provide diagrams that illustrate the relationships among tangents, secants, chords, and their intercepted arcs.]

(Follow-up continues on page 834.)

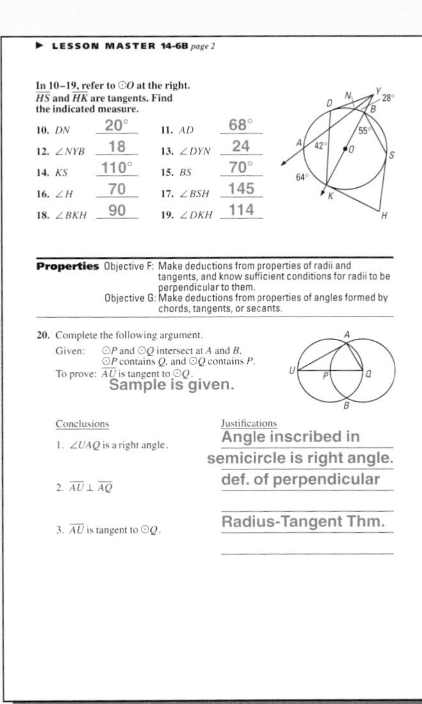

▶ **LESSON MASTER 14-6B** *page 2*

In 10–19, refer to $\odot O$ at the right. $\overline{HS}$ and $\overline{HK}$ are tangents. Find the indicated measure.

10. DN	20°	11. AD	68°
12. $\angle NYB$	18	13. $\angle DYN$	24
14. KS	110°	15. BS	70°
16. $\angle H$	70	17. $\angle BSH$	145
18. $\angle BKH$	90	19. $\angle DKH$	114

Properties Objective F: Make deductions from properties of radii and tangents, and know sufficient conditions for radii to be perpendicular to them.
Objective G: Make deductions from properties of angles formed by chords, tangents, or secants.

20. Complete the following argument.
Given: $\odot P$ and $\odot Q$ intersect at A and B. $\odot P$ contains Q, and $\odot Q$ contains P.
To prove: $\overline{AU}$ is tangent to $\odot Q$.
Sample is given.

Conclusions	Justifications
1. $\angle UAQ$ is a right angle.	Angle inscribed in semicircle is right angle.
2. $\overline{AU} \perp \overline{AQ}$	def. of perpendicular
3. $\overline{AU}$ is tangent to $\odot Q$.	Radius-Tangent Thm.

Additional Answers

10. Draw $\overline{QR}$.

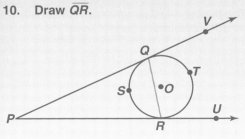

$m\angle VQR = \frac{1}{2}m\overset{\frown}{QTR}$, and $m\angle PRQ = \frac{1}{2}m\overset{\frown}{QSR}$ by the Tangent-Chord Theorem. And since $\angle VQR$ is an exterior angle of $\triangle PQR$, $m\angle P = m\angle VQR - m\angle PRQ$. So, by substitution, $m\angle P = \frac{1}{2}m\overset{\frown}{QTR} - \frac{1}{2}m\overset{\frown}{QSR} = \frac{1}{2}(m\overset{\frown}{QTR} - m\overset{\frown}{QSR})$.

Extension

Have students discuss the following optical illusions, both of which involve circles. Then have them find other examples of optical illusions.

[In the first drawing, both circles are the same size, but their position inside the angle makes them look non-congruent. In the second drawing, the circle seems distorted, but it is not.]

Project Update Project 5, *Japanese Temple Geometry Theorems*, on page 854, relates to the content of this lesson.

Notes on Questions

Question 15 The result of this question may surprise some students. Give a specific example, such as when m∠C = 43, m$\overset{\frown}{BD}$ = 137°. Note that the proof leads to the generalization that the sum of the measures of an angle formed by two tangents and its minor arc is 180°.

Question 22 This question will help prepare students for **Example 4** of Lesson 14-7.

15) Draw $\overline{AB}$ and $\overline{AD}$. By the Quadrilateral Sum Theorem, m∠A + m∠B + m∠C + m∠D = 360. By the Radius-Tangent Theorem and substitution, m∠A + 90 + m∠C + 90 = 360, so m∠A + m∠C = 180. But m∠A = m$\overset{\frown}{BD}$, so m$\overset{\frown}{BD}$ + m∠C = 180

17) Let $\overline{BC}$ be a diameter of ⊙O. By the Radius-Tangent Theorem, each tangent is perpendicular to $\overline{BC}$. By the Two-Perpendiculars Theorem, the two tangents are parallel.

18)

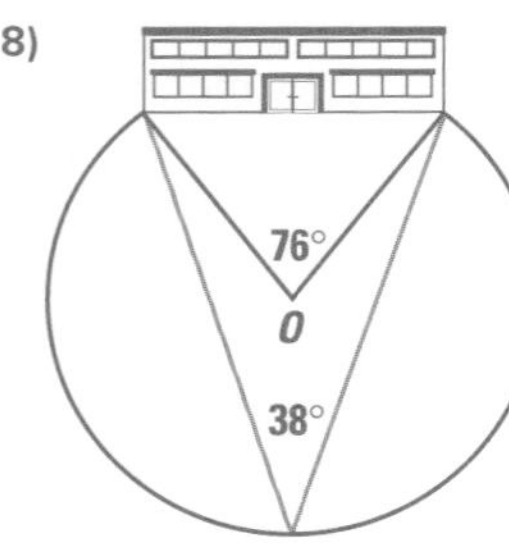

You can stand anywhere along the part of circle O drawn.

15. Write a proof argument.

Given: $\overrightarrow{CB}$ and $\overrightarrow{CD}$ are tangent to ⊙A, as shown below.
To prove: m$\overset{\frown}{BD}$ + m∠C = 180. See left.

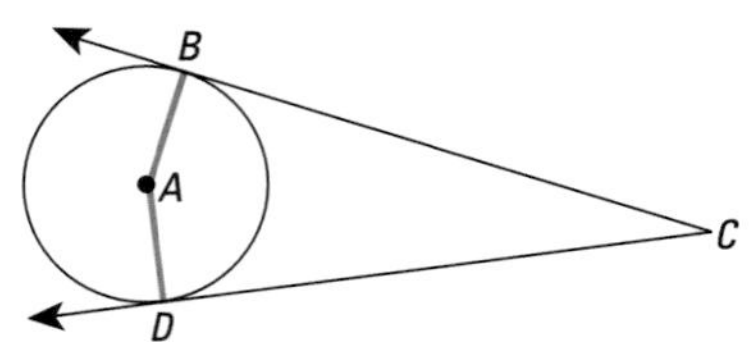

Review

16. You are in a plane at 35,000 feet on a cloudless day. How far is it from the plane to a point on the horizon? *(Lesson 14-5)* ≈ 229.2 miles

17. Prove that the tangents to a circle at the endpoints of a diameter are parallel. *(Lesson 14-5)* See left.

18. Suppose you have a camera with a picture angle of 38°. Trace the building below. Then show all the places where you could stand so that the building's front just fits into your picture. *(Lesson 14-2)* See left.

19. In right △ABC at the right, $\overline{BD}$ is the altitude to the hypotenuse. If AD = 3 and AC = 15, what is BD? *(Lesson 13-4)* 6

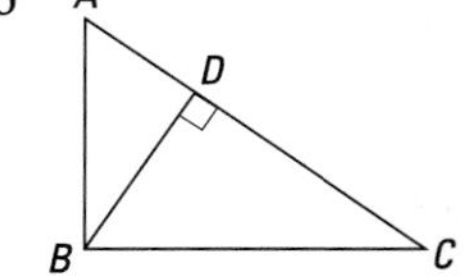

20. a. What is the mean of 10 and 20? 15

b. What is the geometric mean of 10 and 20? *(Lesson 11-8)* $\sqrt{200} \approx 14.14$

21. If $\frac{4}{x} = \frac{q}{10}$, write three other true proportions involving 4, q, x, and 10. *(Lesson 12-4)* $\frac{x}{4} = \frac{10}{q}$, $\frac{4}{q} = \frac{x}{10}$, $\frac{10}{x} = \frac{q}{4}$

22. Find all solutions to the equation $4x^2 + 10x = 6$. *(Previous course.)* $-3, \frac{1}{2}$

Exploration

23. Refer to the figure at the left. $\overrightarrow{CD}$ and $\overrightarrow{CB}$ are tangent to ⊙A at D and B, respectively. See margin.

a. On a number line, graph the possible measures of angle C.

b. Prove your result using the result in Question 15.

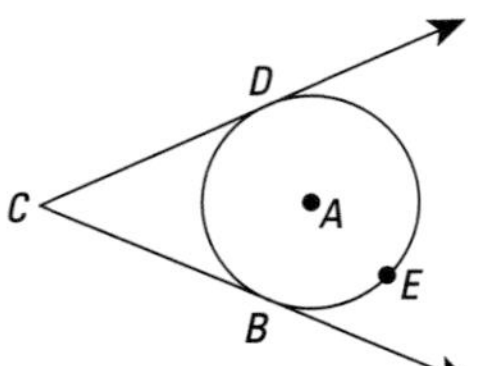

Additional Answers

23a.

b. From the result in Question 15, m$\overset{\frown}{BD}$ + m∠C = 180. By the Equation to Inequality Postulate, 0 < m∠C < 180.

Setting Up Lesson 14-7

The In-class Activity on page 835 should be done before you begin Lesson 14-7. You may wish to do this activity with an automatic drawer. Also, **Question 22** on page 834 should be discussed to review the Quadratic Formula, which students will use in **Example 4** on page 839.

Introducing Lesson 14-7

Investigating Lengths of Chords, Secants, and Tangents

IN-CLASS ACTIVITY

Work on this activity with a partner. You will need either an automatic drawer or a ruler and compass.

Chords, secants, and tangent segments to a circle have lengths that are related in simple ways. This activity explores those lengths.

1 Draw a circle with a radius of at least 4 cm. Identify four points A, B, C, and D in order on it so that $ABCD$ is not a trapezoid. Draw the quadrilateral and the diagonals $\overline{AC}$ and $\overline{BD}$. Call their point of intersection E. You should have a figure that looks something like this.

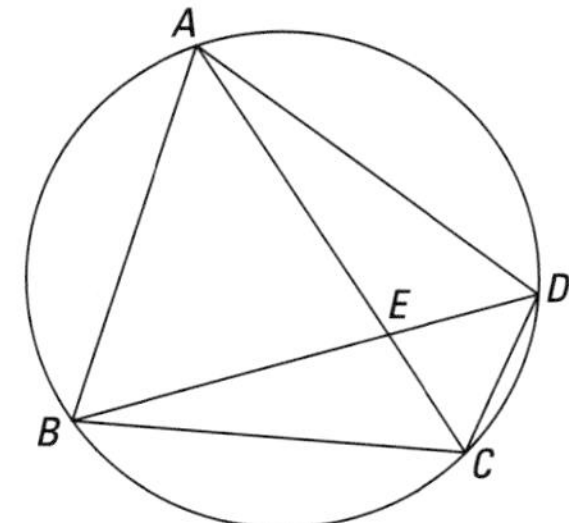

2 Measure AE, BE, CE, and DE. Multiply and divide pairs of these measures. Do you get any equal products or equal quotients? If so, write them down. See margin.

3 Extend the sides $\overline{AD}$ and $\overline{BC}$ of the quadrilateral. Call their point of intersection F. You should have a figure that looks something like this.

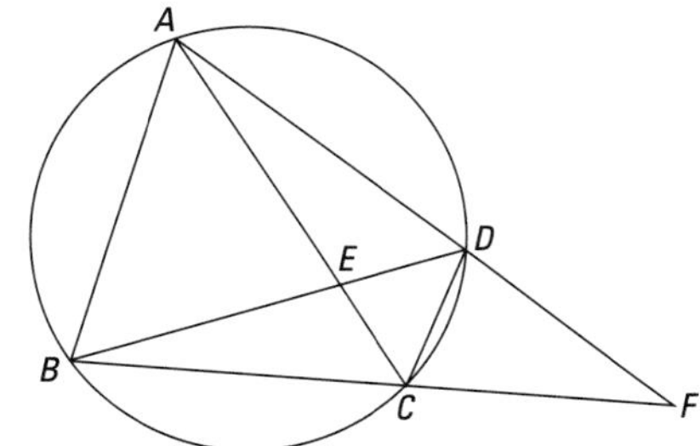

4 Measure AF, BF, CF, and DF. Again multiply and divide the measures. Do you get any equal products or equal quotients this time? See margin.

5 Move A, B, C, and D to different positions on the circle and repeat Steps 1-4. See margin.

In-class Activity

Resources

From the ***Teacher's Resource File***

- Answer Master 14-7
- Teaching Aid 189: Investigating Lengths of Chords, Secants, and Tangents

This In-class Activity has students explore the lengths of chords, secants, and tangents, and thus prepares them for the next lesson.

In Steps 2 and 4, products and quotients of four numbers are to be explored. Since there are four numbers, there are six possible products. Two of these products should be nearly equal. There are twelve possible quotients, since division is not commutative. There will be four pairs of roughly equal quotients, since when $ad = bc$, not only does $\frac{a}{b} = \frac{c}{d}$, but also $\frac{a}{c} = \frac{b}{d}$, $\frac{b}{a} = \frac{d}{c}$, and $\frac{c}{a} = \frac{d}{b}$.

Additional Answers

Step 2. $AE \approx 2.8$ cm; $CE \approx 1.1$ cm; $BE \approx 2.5$ cm; $DE \approx 1.2$ cm; $AE \cdot CE \approx 3.1$; $AE \cdot BE \approx 7.0$; $AE \cdot DE \approx 3.4$; $BE \cdot CE \approx 2.8$; $BE \cdot DE \approx 3.0$; $CE \cdot DE \approx 1.3$. Thus $AE \cdot CE \approx BE \cdot DE$. There are 12 quotients of these lengths. Equal quotients correspond to the equal products. Since $AE \cdot CE \approx BE \cdot DE$, it follows that $\frac{BE}{CE} \approx \frac{AE}{DE}$, and arithmetic shows $\frac{BE}{CE} \approx 2.3$ and $\frac{AE}{DE} \approx 2.3$.

TEACHING AID 189
In-class Activity

Investigating Lengths of Chords, Secants, and Tangents

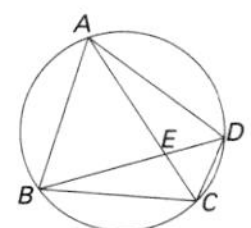

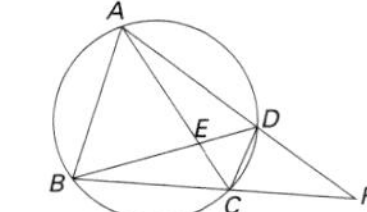

Additional Answers, continued

Step 4. $AF \approx 5.7$ cm; $BF \approx 5.6$ cm; $CF \approx 2.5$ cm; $DF \approx 2.4$ cm; $AF \cdot DF \approx 13.7$; $AF \cdot BF \approx 31.9$; $AF \cdot CF \approx 14.3$; $BF \cdot CF \approx 14.0$; $BF \cdot DF \approx 13.4$; $CF \cdot DF \approx 6.0$. Thus $AF \cdot DF \approx BF \cdot CF$. As in Step 2, equal quotients come from equal products. Since $AF \cdot DF \approx BF \cdot CF$, it follows that $\frac{AF}{BF} \approx \frac{CF}{DF}$, and arithmetic shows $\frac{AF}{BF} \approx 1.02$ and $\frac{CF}{DF} \approx 1.04$.

Step 5. Sample: $AE \approx 1.3$ cm; $CE \approx 1.8$ cm; $BE \approx 0.9$ cm; $DE \approx 2.6$ cm; $AF \approx 1.8$ cm; $DF \approx 4.1$ cm; $BF \approx 2.1$ cm; $CF \approx 3.6$ cm; $\frac{AF}{BF} \approx 0.9$; $\frac{CF}{DF} \approx 0.9$; $\frac{AE}{DE} \approx 0.5$; $\frac{BE}{CE} \approx 0.5$. Thus, $AE \cdot CE \approx BE \cdot DE$; $AF \cdot DF \approx BF \cdot CF$; $\frac{AF}{BF} = \frac{CF}{DF}$; $\frac{AE}{DE} = \frac{BE}{CE}$.

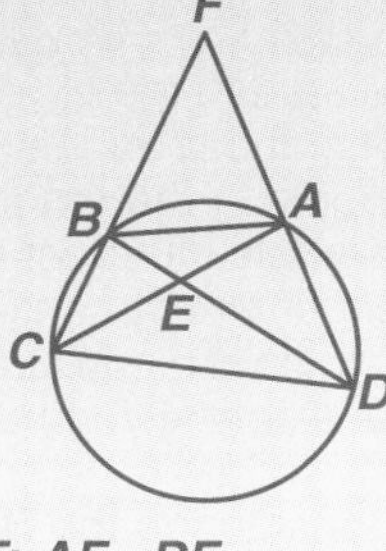

Lesson 14-7

Objectives

E Apply the Secant Length Theorem and the Tangent Square Theorem.

Resources

From the ***Teacher's Resource File***
- Lesson Master 14-7A or 14-7B
- Answer Master 14-7
- Teaching Aids
  183 Warm-up
  190 Additional Examples

Additional Resources
- Visuals for Teaching Aids 183, 190

Teaching Lesson 14-7

Warm-up

Find the geometric mean of each pair of numbers. Round to the nearest hundredth.

1. 4 and 25 10
2. 6 and 10 7.75

Solve each quadratic equation.

3. $x(x + 3) = 10$ $x = -5$ or 2
4. $x^2 - 5x + 1 = 0$ $x = \frac{5 \pm \sqrt{21}}{2}$
5. $3x^2 - 2x = 4$ $x = \frac{1 \pm \sqrt{13}}{3}$

Notes on Reading

❶ **Cooperative Learning** After students have measured the relevant segments in the In-class Activity on page 835, discuss the proof of the Secant Length Theorem. Students will understand how these theorems relate to previous ideas (inscribed angles, similar triangles, and proportions) if they can repeat the proof.

LESSON

14-7 *Lengths of Chords, Secants, and Tangents*

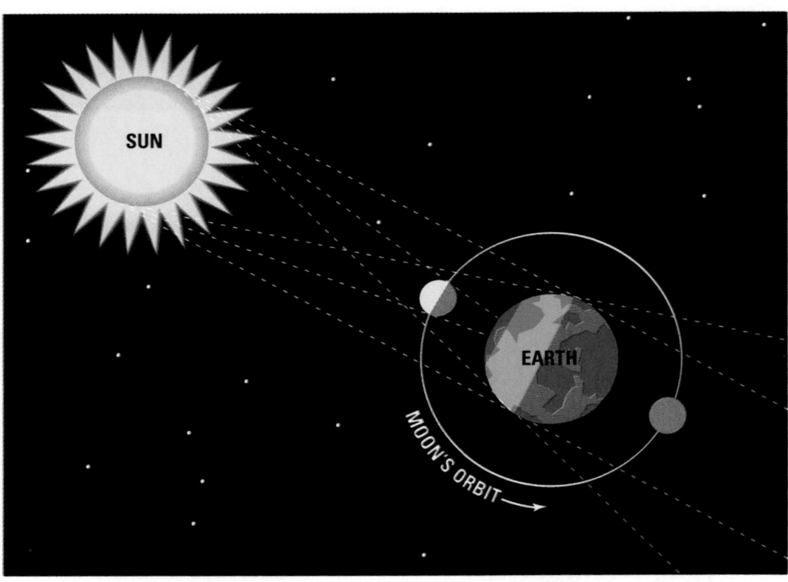

In the shadow. *Tangents outline regions of eclipses.*

A Simple Relationship Among Lengths of Segments in a Circle

The theorem relating the lengths of the segments of the In-class Activity is simple and amazing, and was known to Euclid. We still use his proof. The surprise is that the same proof works, letter for letter, for two quite different figures.

> **Secant Length Theorem**
> Suppose one secant intersects a circle at A and B, and a second secant intersects the circle at C and D. If the secants intersect at P, then
> $$AP \cdot BP = CP \cdot DP.$$

Proof
Given: $\odot O$; secants $\overleftrightarrow{AB}$ and $\overleftrightarrow{CD}$ intersect at P.
To prove: $AP \cdot BP = CP \cdot DP$.
Drawing: There are two figures, depending on whether P is inside or outside the circle.

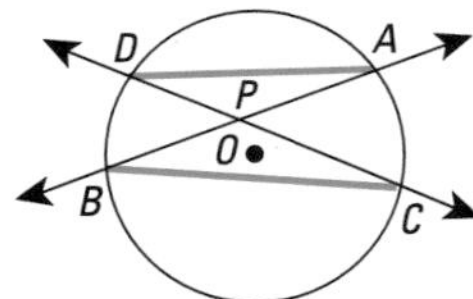

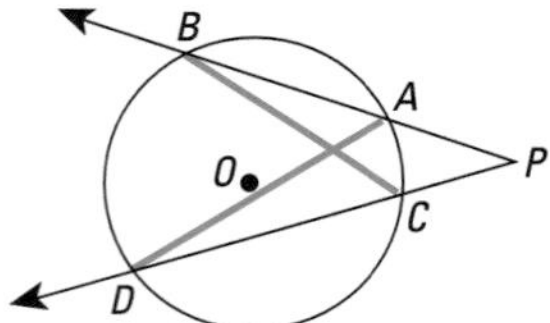

Lesson 14-7 Overview

Broad Goals This lesson is based on the relationships found in one theorem, the Secant Length Theorem. In one guise, this theorem asserts the equal products of segments of intersecting chords; in another, it is the equality of the products of any of the secants and their external segments.

Perspective The Secant Length Theorem in some books is considered as two unrelated theorems. (1) In a circle, if two chords intersect, the product of the segments of one chord equals the product of the segments of the other. (2) In a circle, if two secants intersect *outside* a circle, the product of one secant and its external segment equals the product of the other secant and its external segment.

Considering the Secant Length Theorem as two unrelated theorems disguises the fact that they are two cases of the same theorem.

A special case of the Secant Length Theorem is that the square of the length of a tangent to a circle equals the product of the length of a secant from that point and its external segment.

Quadratic equations arise frequently in situations that apply this theorem.

Argument:

$AP \cdot BP$ will equal $CP \cdot DP$ if it can be proved that $\frac{AP}{CP} = \frac{DP}{BP}$. This suggests forming triangles and trying to prove them similar. Follow the conclusions and justifications first for the figure at the left, then for the figure at the right replacing $\angle PAD \cong \angle PCB$ in Step 2 with $\angle P \cong \angle P$ (Reflexive Property).

Conclusions	Justifications
1. Draw $\overline{DA}$ and $\overline{BC}$.	Two points determine a line.
2. $\angle PAD \cong \angle PCB$, $\angle ADP \cong \angle CBP$	In a circle, inscribed angles intercepting the same arc are congruent.
3. $\triangle DPA \sim \triangle BPC$	AA $\sim$ Theorem (Step 2)
4. $\frac{AP}{CP} = \frac{DP}{BP}$	Corresponding sides of similar figures are proportional.
5. $AP \cdot BP = CP \cdot DP$	Means-Extremes Property

Example 1

Given chords $\overline{AB}$ and $\overline{CD}$ intersecting at P, with lengths as shown, find PB.

Solution

In general, $PA \cdot PB = PC \cdot PD$.

Substitute, $3 \cdot PB = 5 \cdot 6$.

$3 \cdot PB = 30$

$PB = 10$

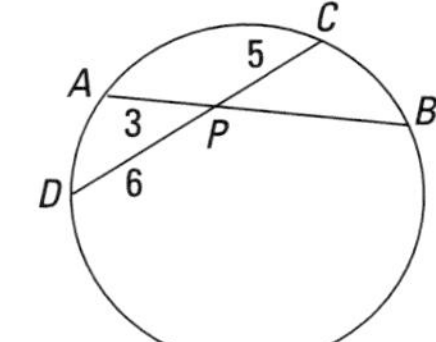

Example 2

Given secants $\overleftrightarrow{A_1B_1}$ and $\overleftrightarrow{A_2B_2}$ intersecting at E, with lengths as shown, find A_2B_2.

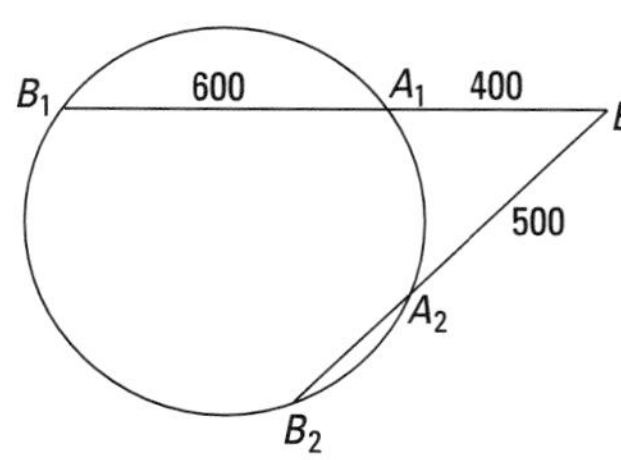

Solution

A_2B_2 is found by first getting EB_2 and then subtracting EA_2.

$EA_1 \cdot EB_1 = EA_2 \cdot EB_2$

Substituting, $400 \cdot 1000 = 500 \cdot EB_2$.

$800 = EB_2$

Since $A_2B_2 = EB_2 - EA_2$,

$A_2B_2 = 800 - 500 = 300$.

The justification for step 2 in the proof is the theorem proved in **Question 16** on page 811 of Lesson 14-2.

The Tangent Square Theorem on page 838 may be restated as follows: The length of the tangent to a circle from a point *P* is the geometric mean of the lengths of any secant from *P* to its points of intersection with the circle.

History Connection Swiss geometer Jacob Steiner was born in 1796, received no formal schooling, and in fact did not learn to read or write until he was 14. At the age of 18, he enrolled in school and went on to perform brilliant mathematical research. In 1832 he received an honorary doctorate from the University of Königsberg, and two years later became chair of geometry at the University of Berlin.

Additional Examples

These examples are also given on on **Teaching Aid 190.**

1. Three of the segments formed by two intersecting chords have lengths 4, 5, and 7 as shown below. What is the length of the fourth segment? $\frac{35}{4} = 8.75$

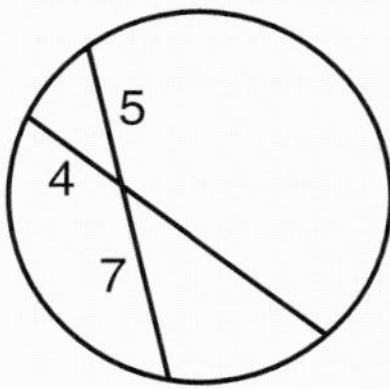

(Additional Examples continue on page 838.)

Optional Activities

Find the value of *x*. [$x = 4$ or $x = 6$]

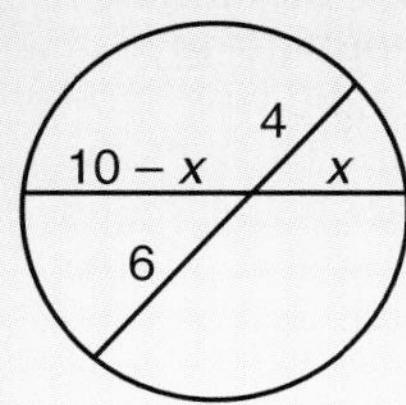

2. Given secants $\overleftrightarrow{RS}$ and $\overleftrightarrow{UV}$ intersecting at T, with lengths as shown, find UV. 275

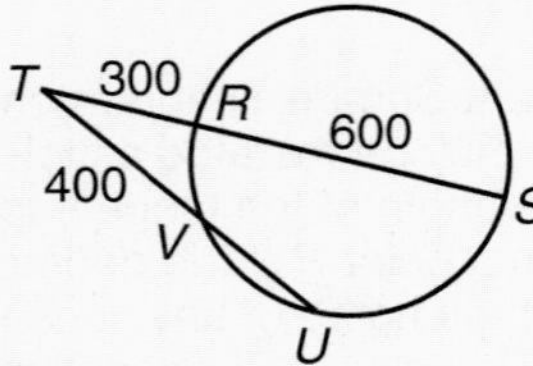

3. $\overleftrightarrow{QW}$ is tangent to the circle at W. If $QW = 10$ and $QE = 5$, find QD and DE. $QD = 20$, $DE = 15$

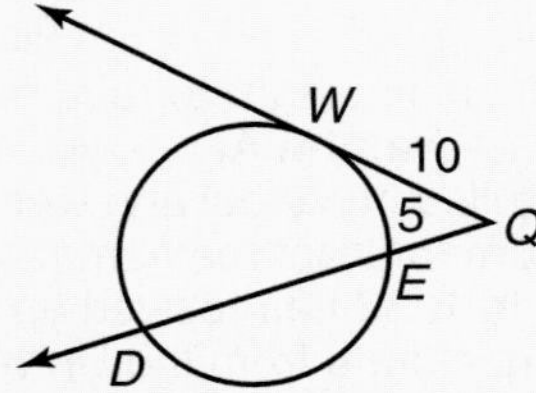

4. Given: $PA = 6$ and $\overline{PA}$ is tangent to the circle at A. If $BC = 7$, find PB. Let $x = PB$. Then $x(x + 7) = 6^2$, so $x = \frac{-7 + \sqrt{193}}{2} \approx 3.45$

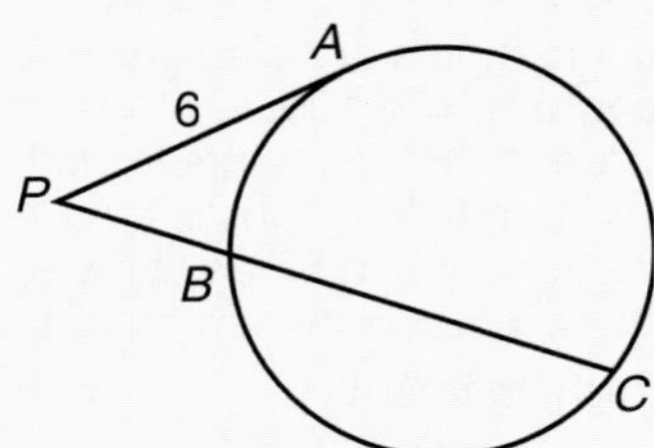

5. In the circle above, what is the power of point P? 36

(Notes on Questions begin on page 841.)

The Secant Length Theorem has a surprising application. Examine the drawing below.

$$PA_1 \cdot PB_1 = PA_2 \cdot PB_2$$
$$PA_1 \cdot PB_1 = PA_3 \cdot PB_3$$
$$PA_1 \cdot PB_1 = PA_4 \cdot PB_4$$

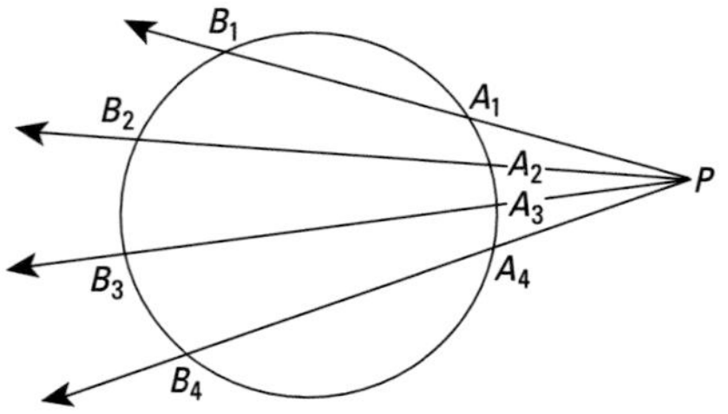

Suppose a circle and a point P are given. For any secant through P intersecting the circle in two points A and B, there is a product $PA \cdot PB$. This product is the *same* number for every secant through P. In Example 2, it is the number 400,000. In Example 1, it is the number 30.

The Swiss geometer Jacob Steiner (1796–1863) called the product the **power of the point P for the circle O.**

The Length of a Tangent from a Point to a Circle

The power of a point external to a circle is easily calculated if you know the length of a tangent from P to $\odot O$.

Tangent Square Theorem
The power of point P for $\odot O$, is the square of the length of a segment tangent to $\odot O$ from P.

Proof

Given: Point P outside $\odot O$, and $\overleftrightarrow{PX}$ tangent to $\odot O$ at T.

To prove: The power of point P for $\odot O$ is PT^2.

Drawing: A figure is shown at the right.

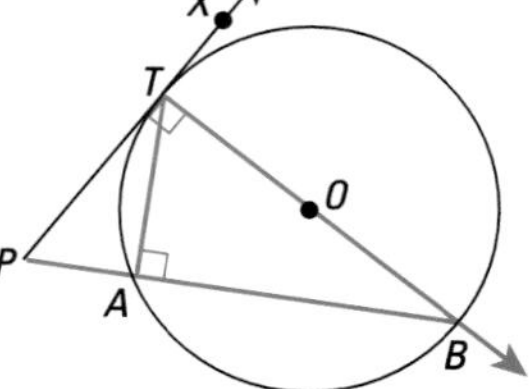

Argument:
Draw $\overrightarrow{TO}$ which intersects $\odot O$ at B. Let $\overline{PB}$ intersect $\odot O$ at A and B. Since $\overline{PT} \perp \overline{TB}$ and since $\angle TAB$ is inscribed in a semicircle, $\triangle PTB$ is a right triangle with altitude $\overline{TA}$. Thus $PT^2 = PA \cdot PB$ by the Right Triangle Altitude Theorem. Thus the power of point P for $\odot O$ is PT^2.

Since $PT^2 = PA \cdot PB$, $PT = \sqrt{PA \cdot PB}$. Thus the length of a tangent $\overline{PT}$ to the circle from a point is the geometric mean of the lengths of segments of any secant drawn from that point.

Adapting to Individual Needs

Extra Help
Show students the figure at the right. A common error students make when applying the Secant Length Theorem to secants that intersect outside the circle is to use the chord lengths AB and CD instead of PB and PD for the calculations. To help them overcome this tendency, point out that $10 \cdot 6 \neq 4 \cdot 8$, but $6 \cdot 16 = 8 \cdot 12$.

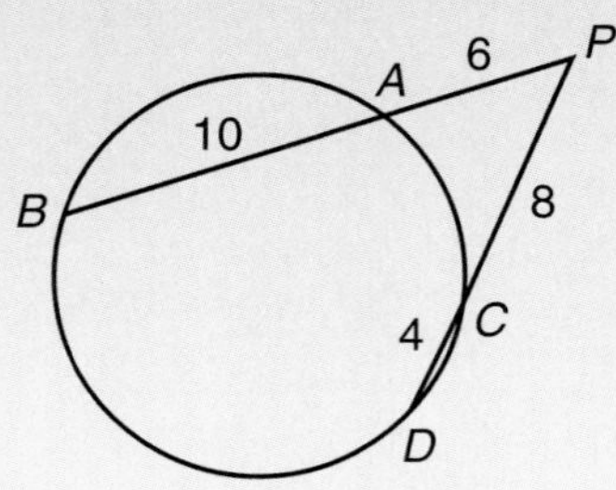

English Language Development
Students with limited English proficiency may be confused with the terminology "power of the point P" since the word *power* usually refers to an exponent. Discuss the definition of *power of the point P* with students using examples.

Example 3

At the right, $\overleftrightarrow{AR}$ is tangent to the circle at R. If $AP = 3$ and $AR = 6$, find AQ and PQ.

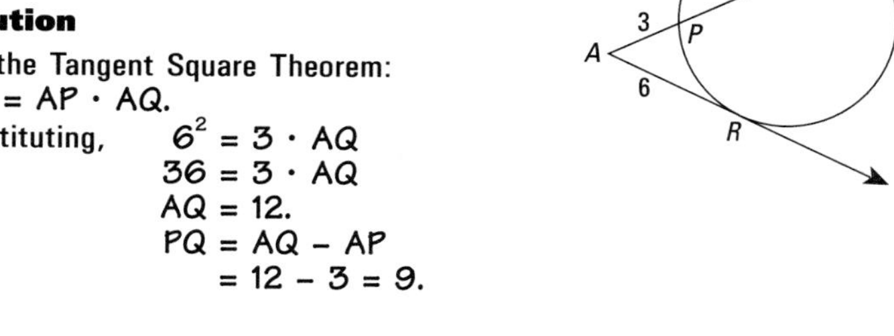

Solution

Use the Tangent Square Theorem:
$AR^2 = AP \cdot AQ.$

Substituting, $6^2 = 3 \cdot AQ$
$36 = 3 \cdot AQ$
So $AQ = 12.$
Then $PQ = AQ - AP$
$= 12 - 3 = 9.$

Some problems involving the power of a point require the solving of a quadratic equation.

Example 4

In the figure below, $\overleftrightarrow{BT}$ is tangent to the circle at T, $BT = 12$, and $ER = 32$. Find BE.

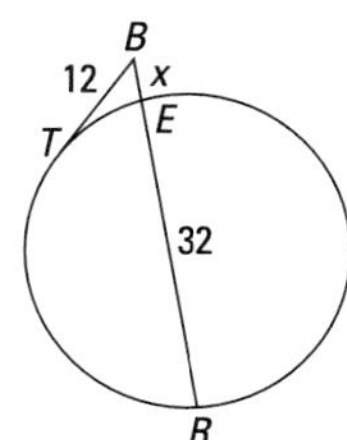

Solution

From the Tangent Square Theorem,
$$BE \cdot BR = BT^2$$
$$BE \cdot (BE + ER) = BT^2.$$
Let $BE = x$. Substituting for BT, BE, and ER,
$$x(x + 32) = 12^2.$$
So $x^2 + 32x - 144 = 0.$
We use the Quadratic Formula:
$$x = \frac{-32 \pm \sqrt{1024 + 576}}{2} = \frac{-32 \pm \sqrt{1600}}{2} = \frac{-32 \pm 40}{2}.$$
So $x = 4$ or $x = -36$. Since BE is a length and can not be negative, $BE = 4$.

QUESTIONS

Covering the Reading

In 1 and 2, refer to the figure at the right.

1. $AT \cdot TQ = \underline{\ ?\ }$. $PT \cdot TR$

2. If $AT = 6$, $TQ = 4$ and $TR = 3$, then $TP = \underline{\ ?\ }$. 8

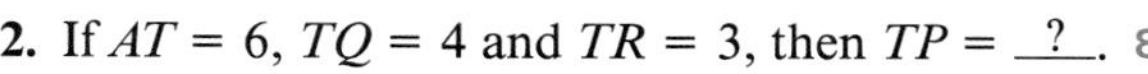

3. In the figure at the left, $DP \cdot DT = \underline{\ ?\ }$. $DU \cdot DV$

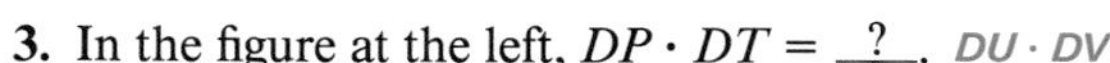

4. Refer to the figure at the right. Let $TW = 3$, $WX = 3$ and $TU = 2$.
   a. Calculate TV. 9
   b. What is the power of point T for this circle? 18
   c. Calculate UV. 7

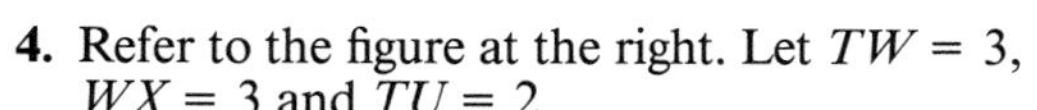

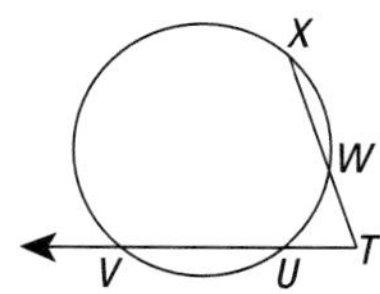

Follow-up for Lesson 14-7

Practice

For more questions on SPUR Objectives, use **Lesson Master 14-7A** (shown on page 839) or **Lesson Master 14-7B** (shown on pages 840–841).

Assessment

Oral/Written Communication
Have students **work in groups.** For each example in the lesson, have them write a new example with different labels and measures, along with the solution. Then have members of each group exchange papers and check each others' work. Encourage students to resolve any differences through a group discussion. [Students write meaningful examples and correct solutions.]

(Follow-up continues on page 840.)

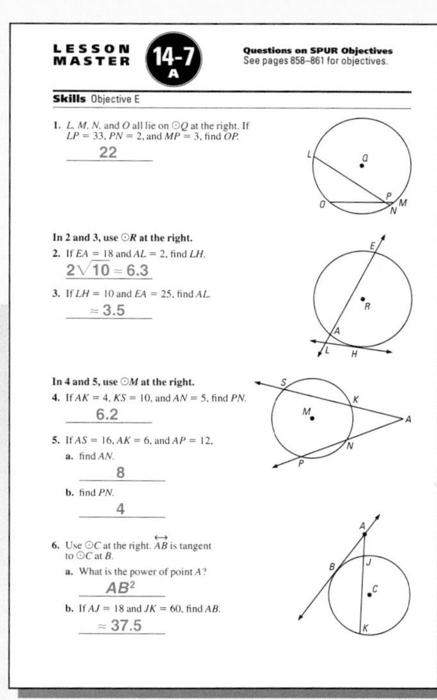

LESSON MASTER 14-7 A — Questions on SPUR Objectives. See pages 858–861 for objectives.

Skills Objective E

1. L, M, N, and O all lie on $\odot Q$ at the right. If $LP = 33$, $PN = 2$, and $MP = 3$, find OP. 22

In 2 and 3, use $\odot R$ at the right.

2. If $EA = 18$ and $AL = 2$, find LH. $2\sqrt{10} \approx 6.3$

3. If $LH = 10$ and $EA = 25$, find AL. ≈ 3.5

In 4 and 5, use $\odot M$ at the right.

4. If $AK = 4$, $KS = 10$, and $AN = 5$, find PN. 6.2

5. If $AS = 16$, $AK = 6$, and $AP = 12$,
   a. find AN. 8
   b. find PN. 4

6. Use $\odot C$ at the right. $\overleftrightarrow{AB}$ is tangent to $\odot C$ at B.
   a. What is the power of point A? AB^2
   b. If $AJ = 18$ and $JK = 60$, find AB. ≈ 37.5

Adapting to Individual Needs

Challenge
Give students the diagram at the right, in which the circle is circumscribed about $\triangle STU$. Have students prove that the radius of the circumscribed circle is given by the formula $r = \frac{stu}{4A}$, where A is the area of the triangle. [Using the formulas $A = \frac{1}{2}st \sin U$ from Lesson 13-8 and $u = 2r \sin U$ from *Challenge* in Lesson 14-2,

$$\frac{stu}{4A} = \frac{st(2r \sin U)}{4(\frac{1}{2}st \sin U)} = r]$$

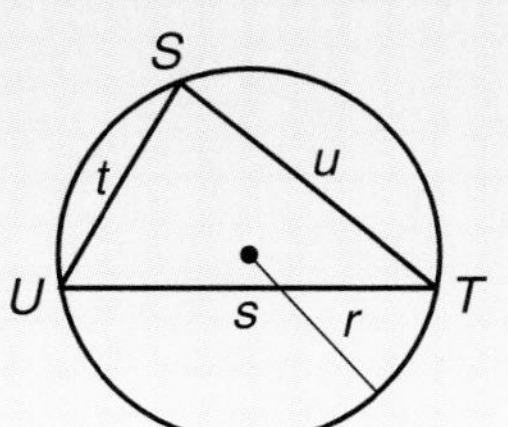

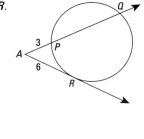

Extension

Give students the figure below. The figure shows circle O with tangents $\overline{PT}$ and $\overline{PS}$ and diameter $\overline{AB}$. (Note that $OB = OA = OT = OS$.)

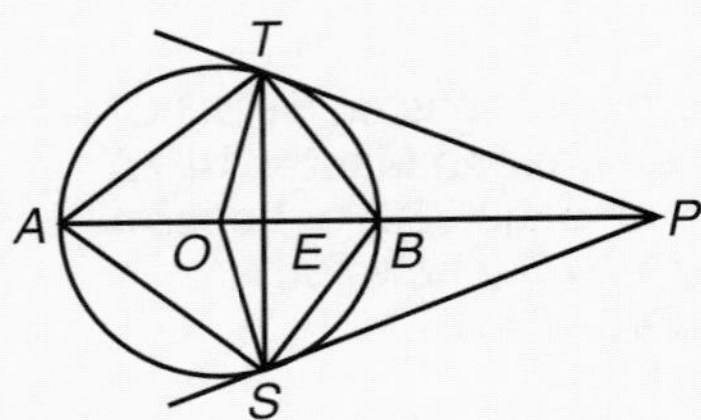

Ask students to identify as many segments which are geometric means of lengths of other segments as they can. [*PT* and *PS* are geometric means of *PB* and *PA*. *OT*, *OS*, *OB*, and *OA* are geometric means of *OE* and *OP*. *TE* and *SE* are geometric means of *OE* and *PE*. *AT* and *AS* are geometric means of *AE* and *AB*. *BT* and *BS* are geometric means of *BE* and *AB*. *TE* and *SE* are geometric means of *AE* and *BE*. Thus $OE \cdot PE = AE \cdot BE$.]

Project Update Project 1, *Cutting Down on Waste*, on page 853, relates to the content of this lesson.

LESSON MASTER 14-7 B Questions on SPUR Objectives

Skills Objective E: Apply the Secant Length Theorem and the Tangent Square Theorem.

In 1–3, refer to $\odot O$ at the right.

1. If $UV = 6$, $VR = 4$, and $VS = 12$, find VT. 2
2. If $TS = 27$, $UV = 9$, and $VR = 8$, find VS. 24
3. For the measures given in Question 2, what is the power of point V? 72

In 4–6, refer to $\odot Q$ at the right.

4. If $HK = 10$, $HM = 32$, and $HN = 12$, find HJ. 38.4
5. If $KJ = 14$, $MN = 9$, and $HN = 8$, find HK. ≈ 6.6
6. For the measures given in Question 5, what is the power of point H? 136

In 7–9, refer to $\odot C$ at the right.

7. If $AB = 14$ and $BG = 20$, find BF. 9.8
8. If $BF = 6$ and $FG = 9$, find AB. ≈ 9.5
9. For the measures in Question 8, what is the power of point B? 90

10. Consider $\odot O$ with radius 10.
    a. What is the power of point O? 100
    b. What is the power of point P, if P is 2 units from O? 96
    c. What is the power of point Q, if Q is 7 units from O? 51
    d. As a point inside a circle gets farther and farther from the center, what appears to happen to the power of the point? Sample: It grows smaller and smaller.
    e. What is the power of a point *on* $\odot O$? zero

5. In the In-class Activity, what were your equal products and quotients
a. in Step 2? **b.** in Step 4?
See page 835.

6. Refer to the figure at the left, with two intersecting chords.
a. $x =$ __?__ 9
b. The power of P in this circle is __?__. 18

In 7 and 8, refer to the figure at the right.

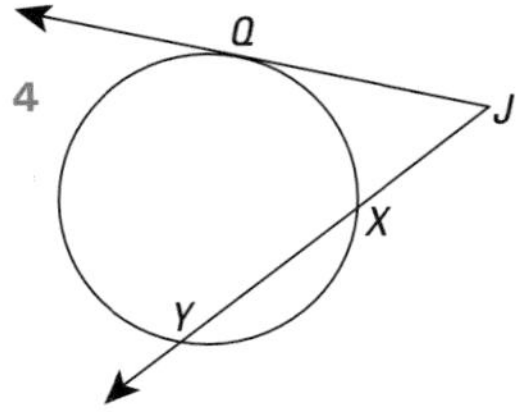

7. a. If $JX = 2$ and $XY = 6$, then $JQ =$ __?__. 4
b. What is the power of point J? 16

8. JQ is the geometric mean of __?__ and __?__.
JX, JY

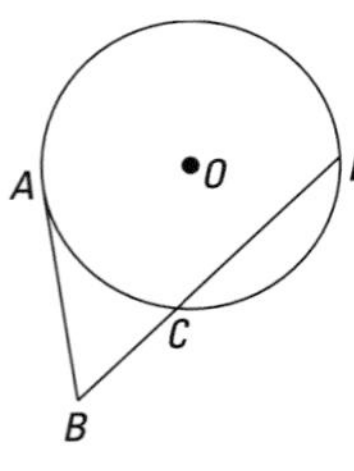

9. In the figure at the left, $\overleftrightarrow{BA}$ is tangent to $\odot O$ at A. If $AB = 15$ and $CD = 45$, find BC. ≈ 4.5 units

Applying the Mathematics

10. In $\odot K$ at the right, $\overleftrightarrow{JB}$ is tangent to $\odot K$ at B. Suppose $JI = 10$, $JA = 8$, and $AE = 12$.
a. Find HI. 6
b. Find JB. ≈ 12.65
c. What is the power of point J? 160

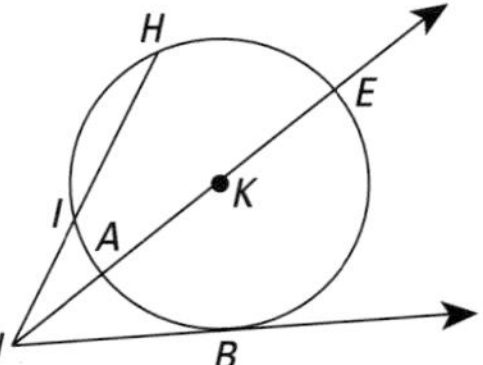

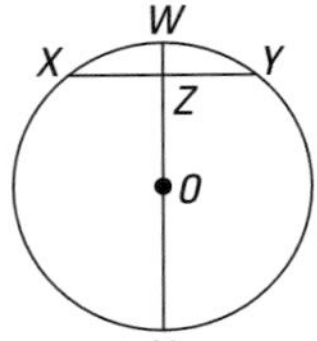

11. In $\odot O$ at the left, diameter $WV = 16$. If $\overline{XY} \perp \overline{WV}$ and $XY = 10$, find WZ. $8 \pm \sqrt{39} \approx 1.76$ or 14.24 units

12. Use the figure at the right in which $\overline{BD}$ and $\overline{AC}$ intersect at P.
Prove or disprove:
If $PA = PD$, then $PB = PC$.
See left.

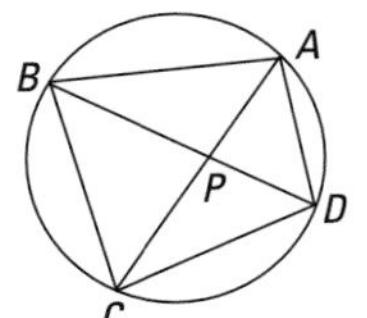

12) It is given that $PA = PD$. By the Secant Length Theorem, $PB \cdot PD = PA \cdot PC$. Using the given and the Substitution Property, $PB \cdot PA = PA \cdot PC$. Applying the Multiplication Property of Equality gives $PB = PC$.

13. Is the Secant Length Theorem true if the word "circle" in it is replaced by "sphere"? That is, if A, B, C, and D are points on a sphere, does $PA \cdot PB = PC \cdot PD$? Explain your answer.
See margin.

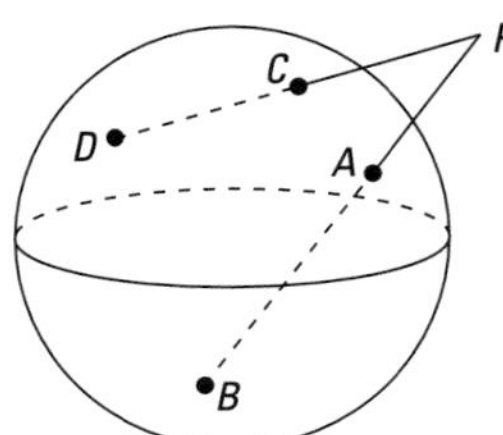

Review

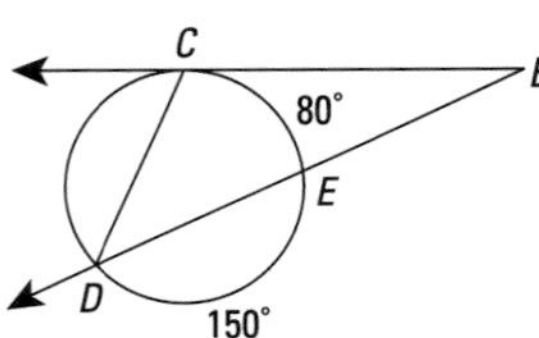

14. Find the measures of the angles of $\triangle BDC$ at the left.
(Lessons 14-2, 14-6) $m\angle B = 25$, $m\angle CDB = 40$, $m\angle DCB = 115$

840

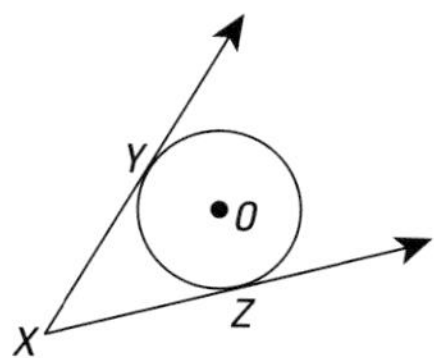

15. At the left, $\overrightarrow{XY}$ and $\overrightarrow{XZ}$ are tangent to $\odot O$ at the left. If $m\angle X = 45$, find $m\widehat{YZ}$. *(Lesson 14-6)* **135°**

16. From a point P above Earth, the horizon is 43 miles away. How high above Earth is P? *(Lesson 14-5)* **≈ 1233 feet**

17. Find the measure of $\angle A$ below. *(Lesson 14-4)* **42.5**

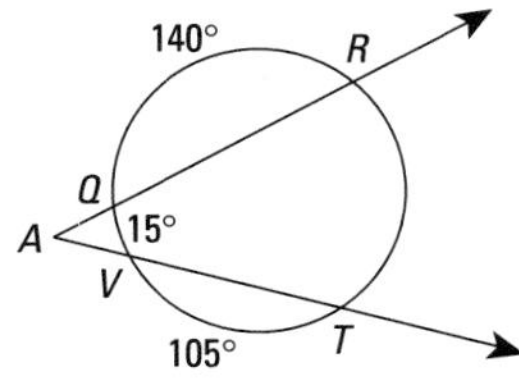

In 18 and 19, suppose you have a camera with a 64° picture angle. A top view of a building is shown below. Trace the diagram.

18) You can stand anywhere on the part of the circle drawn.

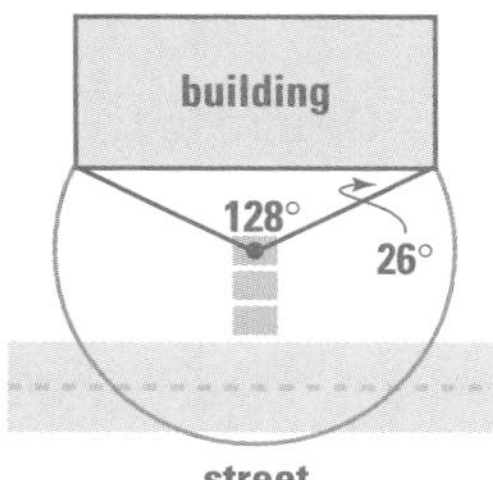

18. Draw the set of locations where you can stand so that the entire front of the building just fills your picture. *(Lesson 14-2)* **See left.**

19. If the building is 48 meters across, at least how far in front of the middle of the building would you need to stand so the building just fills your picture? *(Lesson 14-2)* **≈ 38.4 m**

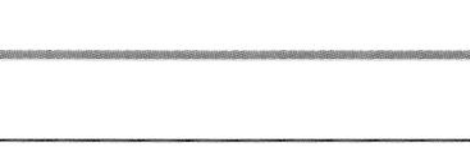

20. In right triangle ABC at the left, find

a. AC. **20**

b. $\tan B$. **$\frac{20}{21} \approx 0.952$**

c. $\sin A$. **$\frac{21}{29} \approx 0.724$**

d. $\cos B$. *(Lessons 8-6, 13-6, 13-7)* **$\frac{21}{29} \approx 0.724$**

Exploration

21. a. Is the Secant Length Theorem true if the secants intersect on the circle? **Yes**

b. If true, prove it. If not true, show a counterexample. **See margin.**

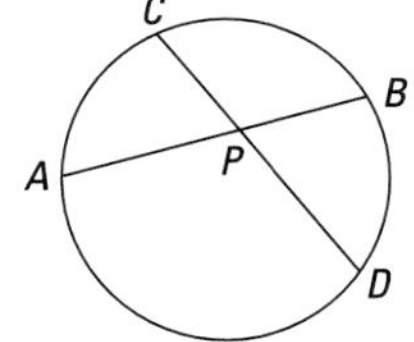

22. Two chords intersect, as shown at the left. Is it possible for the lengths AP, BP, CP, and DP to be four consecutive integers? **See margin.**

Notes on Questions

Question 6 Ask students if the chords must be perpendicular. [No]

Question 11 Students should get the equation $x^2 - 16x + 25 = 0$; there are two solutions, $x = 8 + \sqrt{39}$ and $x = 8 - \sqrt{39}$, to this equation. However, from the figure, $VZ > WZ$; therefore, they should choose $WZ = 8 - \sqrt{39} \approx 1.76$. Point out that $VZ = 8 + \sqrt{39} \approx 14.24$ and $VZ + WZ = WV = 16$.

Question 13 Another amazing characteristic of the Secant Length Theorem is that it is also true for a sphere. The key to the proof is to realize that the five points A, B, C, D, and P lie on two intersecting lines, and thus are coplanar. The 3-dimensional situation reduces to a 2-dimensional situation in which the Secant Length Theorem is known to hold.

Question 22 With four consecutive positive integers, the product of the least and greatest cannot equal the product of the middle two.

Additional Answers

13. Yes; since D, C, and P are collinear and B, A, and P are collinear, then D, C, P, B, and A are coplanar. Points D, C, A, and B lie on the circle which is the intersection of that plane and the sphere. Apply the Secant Length Theorem to this circle.

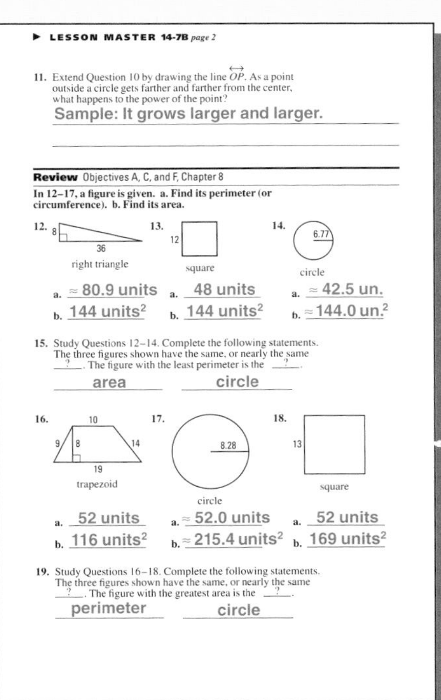

▶ **LESSON MASTER 14-7B** *page 2*

11. Extend Question 10 by drawing the line $\overleftrightarrow{OP}$. As a point outside a circle gets farther and farther from the center, what happens to the power of the point?
Sample: It grows larger and larger.

Review Objectives A, C, and F, Chapter 8

In 12–17, a figure is given. a. Find its perimeter (or circumference). b. Find its area.

12. right triangle (8, 36)
a. ≈ 80.9 units
b. 144 units²

13. square (12)
a. 48 units
b. 144 units²

14. circle (6.77)
a. ≈ 42.5 un.
b. ≈ 144.0 un.²

15. Study Questions 12–14. Complete the following statements. The three figures shown have the same, or nearly the same __?__. The figure with the least perimeter is the __?__.
area; circle

16. trapezoid (10, 9, 8, 14, 19)
a. 52 units
b. 116 units²

17. circle (8.28)
a. ≈ 52.0 units
b. ≈ 215.4 units²

18. square (13)
a. 52 units
b. 169 units²

19. Study Questions 16–18. Complete the following statements. The three figures shown have the same, or nearly the same __?__. The figure with the greatest area is the __?__.
perimeter; circle

Additional Answers, continued

21b. $PA = PC = 0$, so $PA \cdot PB = 0$ and $PC \cdot PD = 0$, so $PA \cdot PB = PC \cdot PD$.

22. No. Suppose it were the case that $AP \cdot BP = CP \cdot DP$ and the four lengths are consecutive integers. Then the segments on one chord have lengths x and $x + 3$, and the segments on the other chord have lengths $x + 1$ and $x + 2$. (Otherwise the products are clearly not equal.) Then $x(x + 3) = (x + 1)(x + 2)$, so $x^2 + 3x = x^2 + 3x + 2$. This yields $0 = 2$, which is impossible. Thus, by the Principle of Indirect Reasoning, the supposition is false. So the given conditions are impossible.

Lesson 14-8

Objectives

H Apply the Isoperimetric Theorems and the Isoperimetric Inequality to determine which figures have the greatest or least area or perimeter.

K Apply the Isoperimetric Theorems and Isoperimetric Inequality in real situations.

Resources

From the ***Teacher's Resource File***
- Lesson Master 14-8A or 14-8B
- Answer Master 14-8
- Teaching Aid 184: Warm-up

Additional Resources
- Visual for Teaching Aid 184

Teaching Lesson 14-8

Warm-up

1. Find all the possible different quadrilaterals that can be formed by connecting four of the eight equally spaced points on a circle. (Note: quadrilaterals that are formed by rotating a given quadrilateral do not count as different quadrilaterals.)

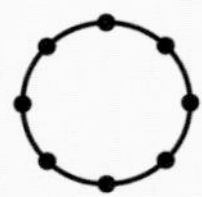

LESSON

14-8 *The Isoperimetric Inequality*

Can a corner spectator see center court? *The best view of a sporting event is not from the corner of an arena.* *See page 845.*

What Figure Has the Maximum Area for a Given Perimeter?

A basketball court is rectangular in shape, and it is easier to put benches in straight rows than in circles. So why are large basketball arenas often circular? The reason is due to an important property of circles involving areas and perimeters.

Activity

Here are 4 figures, each with a perimeter of 12 units. Calculate the area of each. (Hint: Divide the regular hexagon into six equilateral triangles.)

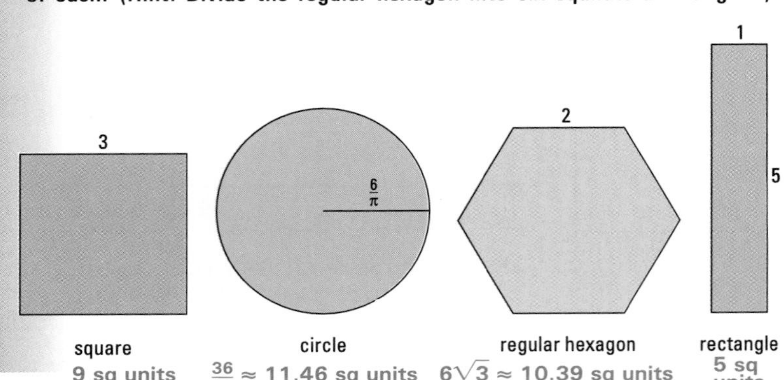

These figures are drawn to the same scale, so you can compare their areas by sight. It looks as if the circle has the maximum area. Your calculations should bear this out. That the circle has the most area for a particular perimeter is known as the Isoperimetric Theorem. *Isoperimetric* means "having equal perimeters."

Lesson 14-8 Overview

Broad Goals The basic idea of this lesson is that the area and perimeter of plane figures cannot be any two numbers. If the perimeter is fixed, the area cannot be greater than a particular number; this is the Isoperimetric Inequality. If the area is fixed, the perimeter cannot be less than a particular number; this is the alternate statement of the Isoperimetric Inequality. These bounds are reached if the figure is a circle; this is the Isoperimetric Theorem.

Perspective The purpose of this lesson and the next is three-fold. First, the Isoperimetric Theorems and Isoperimetric Inequality are important results. Second, these results can be used to explain a variety of natural phenomena. For instance, the plane version explains why the water level in a paper cup goes up if the cup is squeezed (the circular cross-sections become noncircular and lose area; the lost areas add to lost volume, so the water has no place to go but up and out of the cup.) Third, the inequality continues to reinforce the idea that area and perimeter are different concepts.

The basic idea of the Isoperimetric Inequality is that the area of a figure with a given perimeter p is no greater than $\frac{p^2}{4\pi}$. That bound is reached if and only if the figure

Isoperimetric Theorem
Of all plane figures with the same perimeter, the circle has the maximum area.

The proof of this theorem requires advanced calculus, a subject usually not studied until college. The reason the proof is difficult is that it requires discussing all sorts of curves.

Pictured below are two such curves. At the left is an ellipse which is close to circular and thus encloses a substantial area for its perimeter. At the right is a non-convex curve with the same perimeter as the ellipse. As you can see, it encloses very little area for its perimeter.

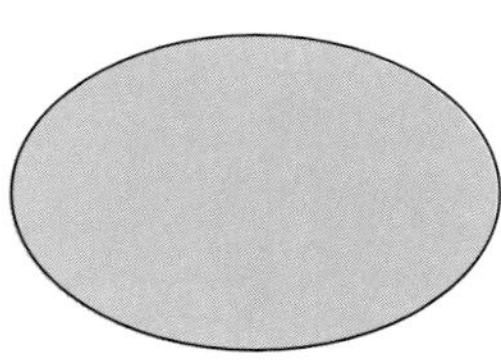

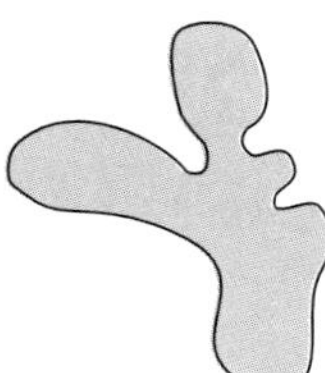

When limited to polygons with a given number of sides, regular polygons have the maximum area for their perimeter. As the number of sides increases, these regular polygons look more and more like circles.

How Large Can the Area Be?

Using the Isoperimetric Theorem, the maximum area enclosed by any perimeter p can be found. The result is known as the *Isoperimetric Inequality.*

Isoperimetric Inequality
If a plane figure has area A and perimeter p, then $A \leq \frac{p^2}{4\pi}$.

Proof
Given: A plane figure with area A and perimeter p.
To prove: $A \leq \frac{p^2}{4\pi}$.
Argument:
Consider a circle with area A and perimeter (circumference) p. Then $p = 2\pi r$. So its radius equals $\frac{p}{2\pi}$ and its area $A = \pi r^2 = \pi\left(\frac{p}{2\pi}\right)^2 = \pi \cdot \frac{p^2}{4\pi^2} = \frac{p^2}{4\pi}$. So for a circle, $A = \frac{p^2}{4\pi}$. By the Isoperimetric Theorem, the area of any other plane figure must be less than $\frac{p^2}{4\pi}$, so for any plane figure, $A \leq \frac{p^2}{4\pi}$.

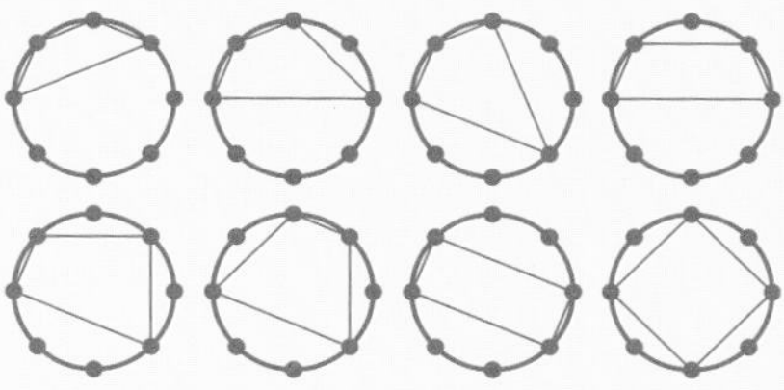

2. Which quadrilateral that you drew seems to have the greatest area? The least area? **The last quadrilateral; the first quadrilateral**

Notes on Reading

Reading Mathematics You might want to read this lesson with your students.

Have students record the results of the **Activity** for use with **Question 1** on page 845.

There are thousands of theorems involving figures that can be proved from the postulates stated in this book. However, some of the theorems we have stated require concepts (such as limit) whose detailed discussion is beyond the scope of the course. The theorems of this lesson and the next lesson are in this category.

We give no proofs, just numerical arguments here, and that is what we think teachers should do. The actual inequality is *not* to be memorized, but the ideas in the two shaded rectangles labeled "Isoperimetric Theorem" should be learned.

❶ The use of figures like these brings home the point that the theorems of this lesson apply to *all* possible simple closed curves.

is a circle. By solving $A \leq \frac{p^2}{4\pi}$ for p, as is done on page 844, we find that the perimeter of a figure with a given area A is no smaller than $\sqrt{4\pi A}$. That bound is again reached if and only if the figure is a circle. The Isoperimetric Inequality is not found in many secondary-school geometry texts for two main reasons: (1) it was not in Euclid's *Elements*; (2) its proof requires advanced calculus. However, the theorem for the plane was known at least to the ancient Carthaginians well before Euclid lived, for the problem of finding the maximum area for a given perimeter is attributed to Dido, the founder of Carthage, and called *Dido's Problem* after her. (Carthage is thought to have been founded in the 9th century B.C. See **Question 22** of Lesson 14-9.)

All that is usually covered in secondary-school mathematics (and seldom in geometry) is that of all rectangles with the same perimeter, the square has the most area. (See **Question 14.**) From that, some students get the wrong impression that the square has the most area for its perimeter.

❷ **Error Alert** It is likely that some students have not ever solved a quadratic inequality. To help them with the argument, you can ask the following question: Suppose $9 = x^2$ and x is positive. What is the value of x? [3] Now suppose $9 < x^2$ and x is positive. What are the possible values of x? [Any number greater than 3] Now suppose $A < x^2$ and x is positive. What are the possible values of x? [Any number greater than $\sqrt{A}$] In the text, $4\pi A$ replaces A and p replaces x.

❸ **Sports Connection** Circular arenas can seat so many more people closer to the center that they are preferred by many developers even though in many ways it is more difficult to construct a circular building than to construct one that is rectangular. Ask students what is the significance of the three numbers 107', 106', and 84' in the figures. [These are the distances to the person seated farthest from the center of the arenas.]

Additional Examples

1. A square and an equilateral triangle each have perimeter 30 meters. Which has the greater area? Explain why. The square has area 56.25 square meters and the equilateral triangle $25\sqrt{3} \approx 43.3$ square meters; thus, the square has the greater area. (The square is more like a circle than is the equilateral triangle.)
2. Describe the region of least perimeter that encloses 100 square yards. A circle with radius $\sqrt{\frac{100}{\pi}} \approx 5.6$ yards

(Notes on Questions begin on page 846.)

Playing with a full deck. *In India, playing cards called* ganjifa *are traditionally circular. These ganjifa are handpainted.*

Example 1

Suppose a figure has perimeter 30 cm.

a. What is its maximum possible area?

b. What is its minimum possible area?

Solution

a. The maximum possible area is given by the Isoperimetric Inequality with $p = 30$.

$$A \le \frac{30^2}{4\pi}$$

$$A \le \frac{900}{4\pi}$$

$$A \le 71.6 \text{ sq cm (approximately)}$$

The maximum possible area is about 71.6 sq cm, when the figure is a circle.

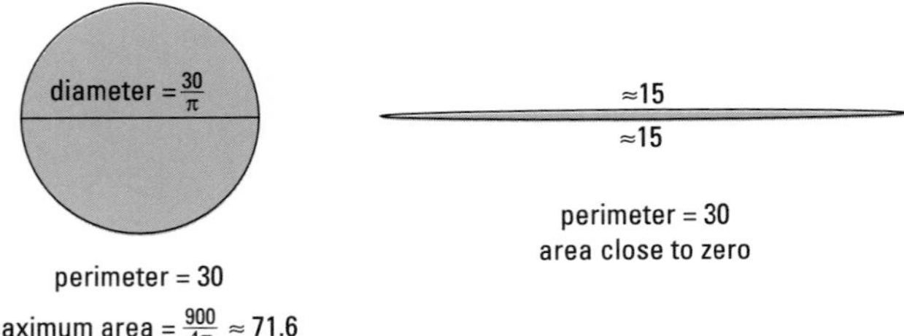

b. The area can be as small as you want, but not zero. The minimum is as close to zero as you like.

What Is the Least Perimeter Possible for a Given Area?

❷ The inequality $A \le \frac{p^2}{4\pi}$ gives the range of possible areas A for a fixed perimeter p. By solving the inequality for p, we obtain the range of possible perimeters when the area is fixed. Here is how:

Multiply both sides by 4π.	$4\pi A \le p^2$
Rewrite the inequality to put p^2 on the left.	$p^2 \ge 4\pi A$
Take the positive square root of each side.	$p \ge \sqrt{4\pi A}$

Thus of all plane figures with a given area A, the perimeter p is at least $\sqrt{4\pi A}$. This result is another way of stating the Isoperimetric Theorem.

> **Isoperimetric Theorem (alternate statement)**
> **Of all plane figures with the same area, the circle has the least perimeter.**

If the area of a circle is A, the perimeter (circumference) of the circle is exactly $\sqrt{4\pi A}$. Any other figure with this area has a greater perimeter.

Optional Activities

✎ **Writing** You may want to use this activity after completing the lesson. Have students research why most houses in industrial countries use the rectangle as the basic room shape even though a circular shape gives the greatest area for a given perimeter. Students should provide a written explanation. [Answers will vary.]

Adapting to Individual Needs

Extra Help

Some students will not recognize that the two inequalities presented in the lesson are different forms of the same inequality. Stress that the first one is solved for A in terms of p, and the second is solved for p in terms of A, but they both represent the same relationship between p and A.

Example 2

Suppose a square and a circle both have an area of 25 sq ft. Verify that the perimeter (circumference) of the circle is less than the perimeter of the square.

Solution

The square's area is 25 sq ft, so a side is 5 ft, and its perimeter is 20 ft. For the circle, if A = 25, then $p = \sqrt{4\pi(25)} = \sqrt{100\pi}$, or about 17.72 ft. Since 17.72 < 20, the circle needs less perimeter to enclose the same area.

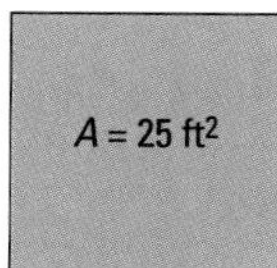

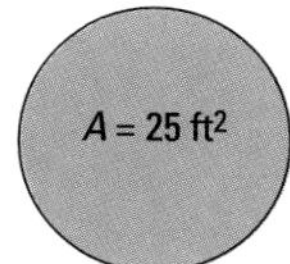

❸ The restatement of the Isoperimetric Theorem explains why the circle is a popular shape for arenas. In an arena, people like to sit close to the action. Since each person takes up about the same amount of space, each person can be thought of as one unit of area. To minimize the farthest distance from seats to the center of the court, the perimeter enclosing them should be as small as possible. The smallest perimeter is given by a circle. Another way of stating this is: Of all figures with a given area, the circle has the smallest width.

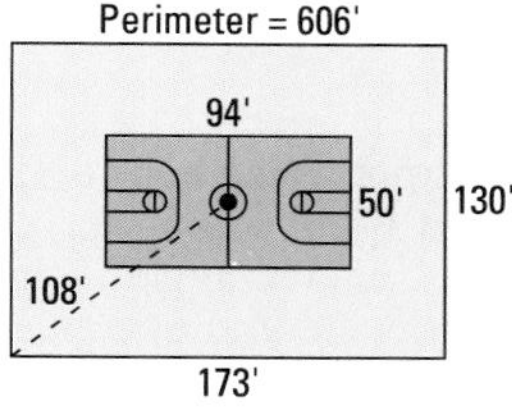

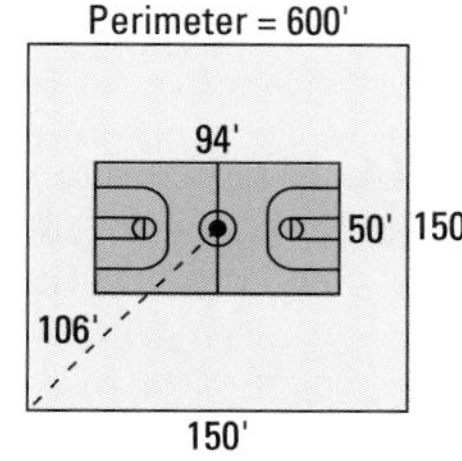

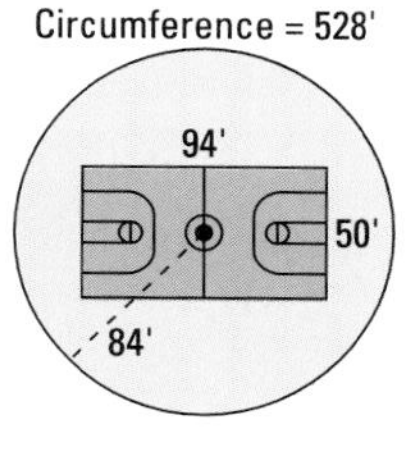

Each of these arenas has an area of about 22,500 ft^2.

QUESTIONS

Covering the Reading

1. Refer to the Activity in this lesson. Give the area of the figure.
   a. square 9 sq units
   b. circle $\frac{36}{\pi} \approx 11.46$ sq units
   c. regular hexagon $6\sqrt{3} \approx 10.39$ sq units
   d. rectangle 5 sq units
2. Of all figures with perimeter 12, which has the maximum area? the circle
3. Of all figures with perimeter 12, which has the least area? See left.

3) No particular figure has the least possible area; the area can be made as small as one wishes.

Follow-up for Lesson 14-8

Practice

For more questions on SPUR Objectives, use **Lesson Master 14-8A** (shown on page 845) or **Lesson Master 14-8B** (shown on pages 846–847).

Assessment

Written Communication Have students write a paragraph explaining in their own words the Isoperimetric Inequality. Have them use numerical examples or diagrams if necessary. [Students provide a reasonable explanation of the Isoperimetric Inequality.]

Extension

Writing The perimeters of the base of a cylinder and of a rectangular prism are the same. Both the cylinder and the prism have the same height. Which has the greater volume? Explain. [Cylinder; By the Isoperimetric Theorem, the area of the circular base of the cylinder is greater than the area of the rectangular base of the prism. Since the area of each base is multiplied by the same number to determine the respective volume of each 3-dimensional figure, the volume of the cylinder is greater than the volume of the prism.]

(Follow-up continues on page 846.)

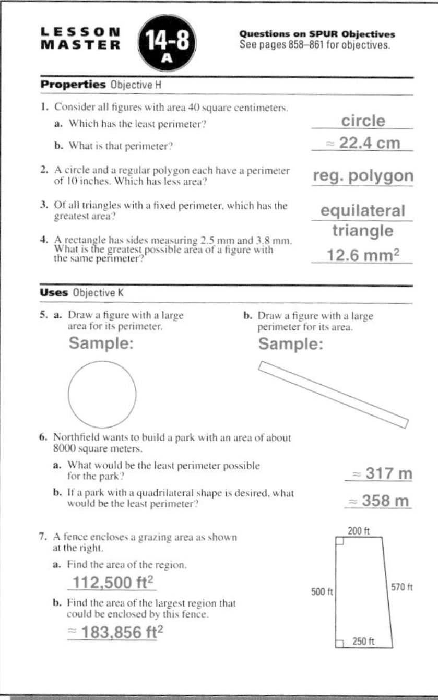
LESSON MASTER 14-8 A

Questions on SPUR Objectives
See pages 858–861 for objectives.

Properties Objective H

1. Consider all figures with area 40 square centimeters.
   a. Which has the least perimeter? circle
   b. What is that perimeter? ≈ 22.4 cm
2. A circle and a regular polygon each have a perimeter of 10 inches. Which has less area? reg. polygon
3. Of all triangles with a fixed perimeter, which has the greatest area? equilateral triangle
4. A rectangle has sides measuring 2.5 mm and 3.8 mm. What is the greatest possible area of a figure with the same perimeter? 12.6 mm^2

Uses Objective K

5. a. Draw a figure with a large area for its perimeter. Sample:
   b. Draw a figure with a large perimeter for its area. Sample:
6. Northfield wants to build a park with an area of about 8000 square meters.
   a. What would be the least perimeter possible for the park? ≈ 317 m
   b. If a park with a quadrilateral shape is desired, what would be the least perimeter? ≈ 358 m
7. A fence encloses a grazing area as shown at the right.
   a. Find the area of the region. 112,500 ft^2
   b. Find the area of the largest region that could be enclosed by this fence. ≈ 183,856 ft^2

200 ft
500 ft
570 ft
250 ft

Adapting to Individual Needs

Challenge

Ask students these questions.

1. If a circle and a square have the same perimeter, the area of the circle is how many times the area of the square? [$\frac{4}{\pi}$]
2. Suppose a circular pizza and a square pizza have the same area. Both are placed in square boxes of least possible dimensions. Which pizza requires the larger box? [The circular pizza]

Project Update Project 4, *The Universe*, on page 853, relates to the content of this lesson.

Notes on Questions

Questions 6–7 Cooperative Learning These are important questions to help students understand the isoperimetric relationships. You might want students to draw many examples and discuss them with other students.

Question 8 Error Alert Students may not realize that the radius must be calculated before they can find the circumference.

Question 13 The pentagon has perimeter 90 feet. A square with the same perimeter has area 506.25 square feet. So this pentagon encloses more land for its perimeter than a square would. The more sides a regular polygon has, the closer it is to a circle and the more area it has for its perimeter, but there are nonregular polygons of any number of sides that have small areas for their perimeters.

Question 15 The main room in traditional igloos is often a hemisphere, which has a circular base and provides a more efficient use of the 3-dimensional space for a given surface area than either a cylinder or cone. This idea can be used to lead in to Lesson 14-9.

5) 

6)

12) People like to sit close to the action. If we consider each person as one unit of area, and we want to put those areas close together in a perimeter as small as possible. The smallest perimeter is given by a circle.

15) There is only so much area that can be covered by an animal skin. The circular base allows for the largest floor area per animal skin.

4. Of all triangles with perimeter 12, which has the maximum area? the equilateral triangle

5. Draw a non-polygonal figure whose area is small for its perimeter. See left.

6. Draw a polygon whose area is small for its perimeter. See left.

7. Consider all figures with area 600 square meters. Which has the least perimeter? circle

8. A circle has area 9π sq cm. What is its circumference? $6\pi \approx 18.8$ cm

9. A square has area 9π sq cm. What is its perimeter? $12\sqrt{\pi} \approx 21.3$ cm

10. Which answer should be larger, that for Question 8 or that for Question 9? Question 9

11. Complete the statements. a) circle, least
  a. Of all figures with the same area, the __?__ has the __?__ perimeter.
  b. Of all figures with the same perimeter, the __?__ has the __?__ area. circle, most

12. What is an advantage of making a large basketball arena circular rather than rectangular? See left.

Applying the Mathematics

13. a. A fence encloses pentagonal region *ABCDE* at the right. Find the area of this region. 540 ft^2
  b. Find the area of the largest region that could be enclosed by this amount of fencing. $\frac{2025}{\pi} \approx 645$ ft^2

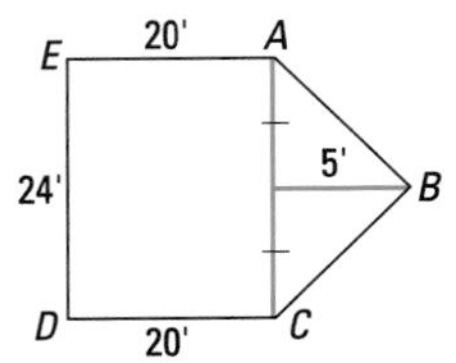

14. If a rectangle has perimeter $4s$, then its sides can be called $s - t$, $s + t$, $s - t$, and $s + t$.
  a. What is the area of this rectangle? $s^2 - t^2$
  b. For what value of t is the area the greatest? 0

15. Many nomads of Mongolia today live in yurts, cylindrical tents that are made of animal skins and are easy to put up or take down. Some Native Americans used to live in tepees, cone-shaped tents with the same properties as the yurts. Explain why the circular base is a wise shape.

LESSON MASTER 14-8 B Questions on SPUR Objectives

Vocabulary

1. What does *isoperimetric* mean? having equal perimeters

Properties Objective H: Apply the Isoperimetric Theorems and the Isoperimetric Inequality to determine which figures have the greatest or least area or perimeter.

2. Consider the figures below.
(a) (b) (c) (d)
  a. For which figure is the ratio $\frac{\text{area}}{\text{perimeter}}$ greatest? a
  b. For which figure is the ratio $\frac{\text{perimeter}}{\text{area}}$ greatest? c

3. Consider all figures with an area of 15 ft^2.
  a. Which has the least perimeter? circle
  b. What is the perimeter of the figure in Part **a**? ≈ 13.7 ft

4. Consider all figures with a perimeter of 28 meters.
  a. Which has the greatest area? circle
  b. What is the area of the figure in Part **a**? ≈ 62.4 m^2

5. A circle and a regular octagon both have the same perimeter. Which figure has the least area? regular octagon

6. Of all pentagons with a perimeter of 60 cm, which has the greatest area? regular pentagon

7. A triangle has sides of 4.3 m, 7 m, and 9.6 m. What would be the greatest possible area of a figure with the same perimeter? ≈ 34.8 m^2

8. Let A be the area of a figure with perimeter 16. Give the range of possible values for A. $0 < A \le \approx 20.4$

Additional Answers

22a. If our class has done every lesson in this book, then we will have finished the next lesson.
  b. If we do not finish the next lesson, then our class will not have done every lesson in this book.
  c. If our class has not done every lesson in this book, then we have not finished the next lesson.

25. Sample: A regular hexagon with perimeter 100 feet has area $\frac{1250}{3}\sqrt{3} \approx 722$ ft^2.

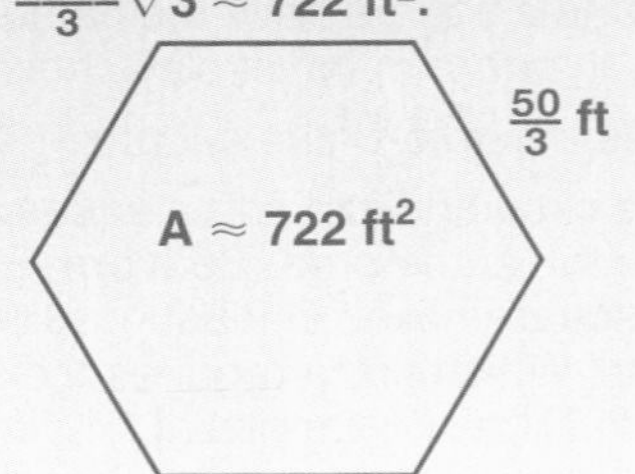

Review

16. In $\odot O$ below, suppose $XY = 8$, $YZ = 20$, and $XW = 10$.
 a. Find WV. 12.4 units
 b. What is the power of point X for $\odot O$? *(Lesson 14-7)* 224

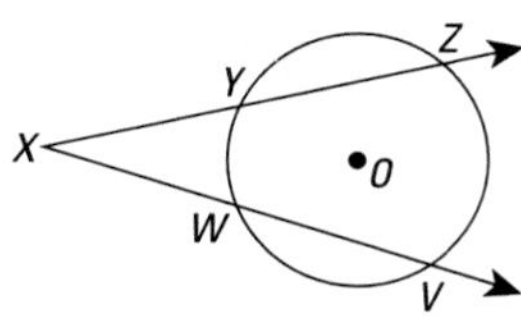

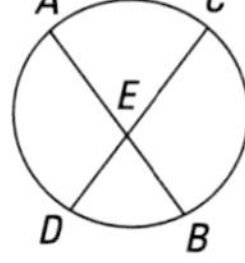

17. In the circle at the left, $AE = 16$, $BE = 14$, and $CE = 18$. Find DE. *(Lesson 14-7)* $\approx$ 12.4 units

In 18 and 19, refer to the figure at the right. $\overrightarrow{AB}$ is tangent to $\odot O$ at point B and $m\angle A = 40$. *(Lesson 14-6)*

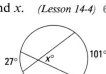

18. Find each measure.
 a. $m\widehat{BD}$ 130°
 b. $m\widehat{BC}$ 50°

19. Find $m\angle CBD$. 90

20. In the figure below, find x. *(Lesson 14-4)* 64

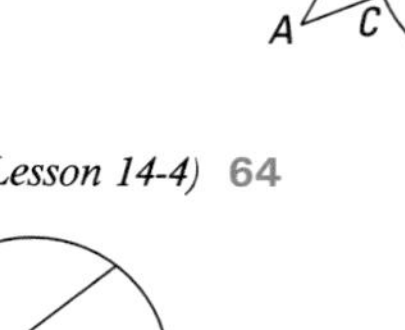

21. a. What is the volume of a right square pyramid with base area of 80 sq ft and height 16 ft? $426\frac{2}{3} \approx 426.7$ ft³
 b. If the pyramid in part **a** undergoes a transformation by $S_{\frac{2}{5}}$, what is the volume of its image? *(Lessons 10-7, 12-6)* ≈ 27.3 ft³

22. State **a.** the converse, **b.** the inverse, and **c.** the contrapositive of the following statement: *If we finish the next lesson, our class will have done every lesson in the book.* *(Lessons 2-2, 11-2)* See margin.

23. a. What is the volume of a sphere with radius 7 cm? $\frac{1372}{3}\pi$ cm³ ≈ 1436.8 cm³
 b. What is the surface area of this sphere? *(Lessons 10-8, 10-9)* See below.

24. Estimate $\sqrt[3]{\pi}$ to the nearest hundredth. *(Lesson 10-3)* 1.46

23b) 196π cm² ≈ 615.8 cm²

Exploration

25. Give the dimensions and a diagram of a polygon whose perimeter is 100 feet and whose area is greater than 625 square feet. See margin.

Multicultural Connection The term *nomad* comes from a Greek word meaning "one who wanders," and is used to describe groups of people who move periodically to find hunting grounds, pastures, or markets for their goods. There are three general types of nomads. One group, nomadic hunters and gathers, travel in search of game, food, and water. This group includes Mongolian tribes, African Pygmies, Australian Aborigines, and at one time, some American Indians. A second group, pastoral nomads, move in search of pastures and water for their livestock. The Bedouins of the Middle East, the Fulani of western Africa, and the Tuareg tribes of the Sahara are pastoral nomads. The best known members of the third group, the tinker or trader group, are the Gypsies, who make and sell simple products and hire out as laborers. While most Gypsies live in eastern Europe, they are found all around the world.

Question 25 Notice that it is easy to draw a polygon whose perimeter is 100 feet and whose area *equals* 625 square feet. Just draw a square. This is a good question for exploration with an automatic drawer.

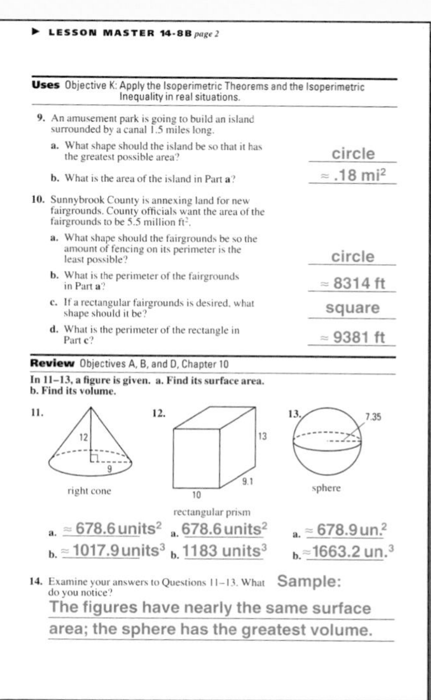

▶ **LESSON MASTER 14-8B** *page 2*

Uses Objective K: Apply the Isoperimetric Theorems and the Isoperimetric Inequality in real situations.

9. An amusement park is going to build an island surrounded by a canal 1.5 miles long.
 a. What shape should the island be so that it has the greatest possible area? circle
 b. What is the area of the island in Part **a**? $\approx$ .18 mi²

10. Sunnybrook County is annexing land for new fairgrounds. County officials want the area of the fairgrounds to be 5.5 million ft².
 a. What shape should the fairgrounds be so the amount of fencing on its perimeter is the least possible? circle
 b. What is the perimeter of the fairgrounds in Part **a**? $\approx$ 8314 ft
 c. If a rectangular fairgrounds is desired, what shape should it be? square
 d. What is the perimeter of the rectangle in Part **c**? $\approx$ 9381 ft

Review Objectives A, B, and D, Chapter 10

In 11–13, a figure is given. a. Find its surface area. b. Find its volume.

11. right cone (12, 9)
 a. $\approx$ 678.6 units²
 b. $\approx$ 1017.9 units³

12. rectangular prism (13, 9.1, 10)
 a. 678.6 units²
 b. 1183 units³

13. sphere (7.35)
 a. $\approx$ 678.9 un.²
 b. $\approx$ 1663.2 un.³

14. Examine your answers to Questions 11–13. What do you notice? Sample: The figures have nearly the same surface area; the sphere has the greatest volume.

Setting Up Lesson 14-9

Materials Students using *Optional Activities* on page 849 will need empty soft-drink cans, juice boxes, and various other empty food containers. If possible, have a sphere and a cylinder with the same surface area, to be filled with sand or water. (See the diagram at the top of page 849.)

Lesson 14-9

Objectives

H Apply the Isoperimetric Theorems and the Isoperimetric Inequality to determine which figures have the greatest or least surface area or volume.

K Apply the Isoperimetric Theorems and Isoperimetric Inequality in real situations.

Resources

From the ***Teacher's Resource File***

- Lesson Master 14-9A or 14-9B
- Answer Master 14-9
- Teaching Aid 184: Warm-up

Additional Resources

- Visual for Teaching Aid 184
- A sphere and a cylinder with the same surface area that can be filled with sand or water
- Empty soft-drink cans, juice boxes, a variety of empty food containers

Teaching Lesson 14-9

Warm-up

Find the surface area of a cube whose volume is 125 cubic feet.
150 square feet

LESSON

14-9 *The Isoperimetric Inequality in Three Dimensions*

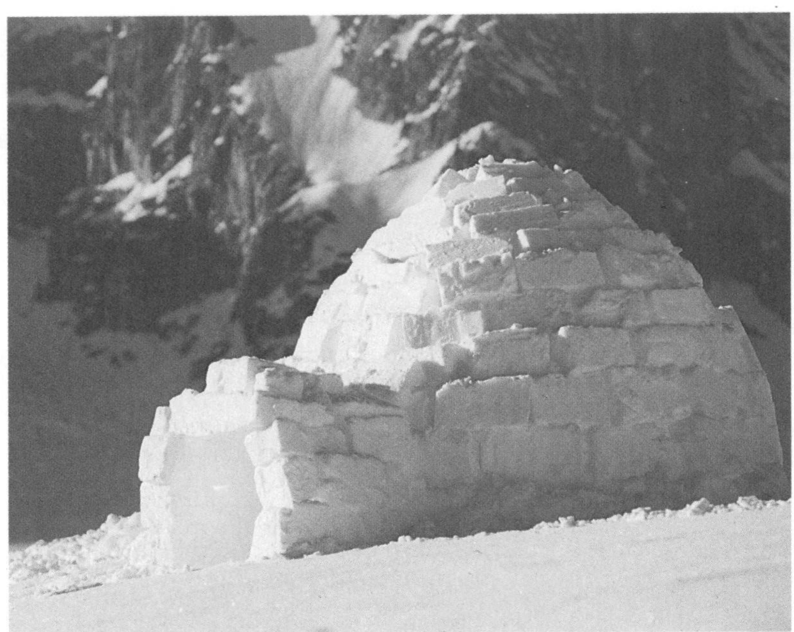

Ice house but warm! *Inuits who build igloos capitalize on the fact that the sphere is an efficient figure.*

The Shape of Igloos

Some Inuits of the northern islands of Canada live in igloos in the winter. Ice for the igloo is always available, so an igloo can be built anywhere. Also, a small igloo can be built in about an hour. (How long do you think it took to build the building you live in?) A large igloo, which takes only a little longer to build, usually has an entranceway leading to a smaller part and then to a main part of the igloo. Usually the bases of the smaller and main parts are circles. As you have learned, this shape gives the maximum floor area for a given perimeter.

Both the smaller and main parts of the igloo have the shape of a hemisphere. By using a hemisphere, Inuits can enclose more space with the same amount of ice than with a cylinder, cone, or polyhedron that covers the same base. The sphere plays the same role in 3-dimensional relationships between surface area and volume as the circle does in 2-dimensional relationships between perimeter and area. To emphasize the sameness of the roles, mathematicians use the same term, "isoperimetric," to indicate "same boundary."

> **Isoperimetric Theorem (3-dimensional version)**
> **Of all solids with the same surface area, the sphere has the largest volume.**

Lesson 14-9 Overview

Broad Goals This is a companion lesson to Lesson 14-8. The basic idea of this lesson is that the volume and surface area of space figures cannot be any two unrelated numbers. If the surface area is fixed, the volume cannot be greater than a particular number. This is the Isoperimetric Inequality, not in the lesson itself, but in **Question 23**. If the volume is fixed, the surface area cannot be less than a particular number. These bounds are reached if the figure is a sphere. This is the Isoperimetric Theorem.

Perspective Analogous to the plane version, the space version of the Isoperimetric Inequality reinforces the idea that the surface area and volume measures of physical objects are very different concepts.

The space version of the Isoperimetric Theorems tends to have more applications than the plane version. In addition to the examples mentioned in the lesson, you might point out that leaves on trees need surface area to receive light from the sun; they are flat to get more surface area for their volume. Consequently, leaves are very unlike the shape of spheres.

Fore! Water. *This 25,000-gallon water tank is spherical because that shape holds the most water for its surface area.*

Verifying that the Sphere Has the Maximum Volume

Like its counterpart in two dimensions, a proof of the space version of the Isoperimetric Theorem requires advanced mathematics. But the theorem can be verified in different ways. First is with an example. The sphere and the cylinder below have the same surface area, 144π square units.

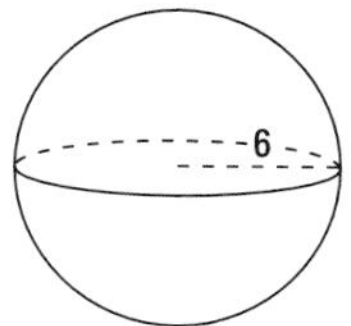

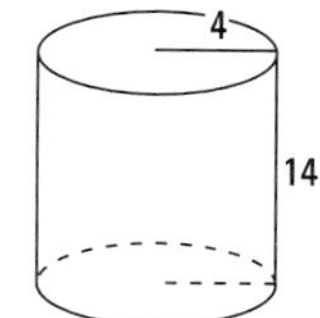

S.A. of sphere $= 4\pi r^2$
$= 144\pi$ sq units

S.A. of cylinder $=$ L.A. $+ 2B$
$= 2\pi rh + 2\pi r^2$
$= 144\pi$ sq units

Which has the greater volume? Their volumes can be easily found from formulas.

volume of sphere $= \frac{4}{3}\pi r^3$
$= 288\pi$ units^3

volume of cylinder $= Bh$
$= \pi r^2 h$
$= 224\pi$ units^3

The sphere has 64π units^3, almost 30% more volume than the cylinder. In fact, the sphere is the most efficient container. You would see spherical containers everywhere if they didn't roll!

A common experience provides a second verification. Suppose you blow air into a plastic bag. The bag, being unable to stretch to change its surface area, will tend to assume a shape as close to a sphere as it can. If you blow in more air than the sphere can hold, the bag will burst.

What Figure Has the Minimum Surface Area for a Given Volume?

Now, rather than a constant boundary, keep the capacity of the figure constant. To do this, consider shapes with the same volume. Soap bubbles consist of some soapy water and a fixed volume of air trapped inside. Because of surface tension, the bubble takes a shape to minimize the surface area surrounding the trapped air. That shape is a sphere.

> **Isoperimetric Theorem (alternate 3-dimensional version)**
> **Of all solids with the same volume, the sphere has the least surface area.**

For instance, a plastic container that would hold a gallon of milk, but use the least amount of plastic, would be shaped like a sphere. The Example verifies the alternate statement of the theorem numerically.

Notes on Reading

Reading Mathematics You might want to read this lesson with your students.

If it is possible to demonstrate that the sphere has greater volume than a cylinder with the same surface area, as illustrated in this lesson, it would be very effective. Water or sand can be poured into the appropriate containers for the demonstration.

Point out to students that for a given volume, the surface area can be as large as one wants. In fact, a sponge has an exceedingly large surface area for its volume. Because water adheres to the surface, the great amount of surface enables the sponge to hold a lot of water.

Additional Examples

1. A box with dimensions 3 in., 4 in., and 18 in. has a volume of 216 cubic in., the same as that of a cube with edge 6 in. Which has the greater surface area? **The box, 276 in^2 versus 216 in^2 for the cube. It is less like a sphere.**
2. Describe the solid of least surface area that can enclose a cubic meter. **A sphere with radius $\sqrt[3]{\frac{3}{4\pi}}$ meters**

(Notes on Questions begin on page 850.)

LESSON MASTER 14-9 A

Questions on SPUR Objectives
See pages 858–861 for objectives.

Properties Objective H

1. Consider all figures in space with a surface area of 100 square feet.
   a. Which has the greatest volume? **sphere**
   b. What is this volume? **≈ 94.0 ft^3**
2. A sphere and a square-based pyramid each have a volume of 2400 cm^3. Which has the greater surface area? **pyramid**
3. Of all regular pyramids or cones with equal surface area, which has the greatest volume? **cone**
4. Of all the rectangular prisms with a fixed volume, which has the least surface area? **cube**

Uses Objective K

5. a. Draw an object with a large volume for its surface area. **Sample:**
   b. Draw an object with a large surface area for its volume. **Sample:**
6. A container is to be designed for 36 in^3 of butter. Find its surface area if the container is
   a. a cube. **≈ 65.4 in^2**
   b. a sphere. **≈ 52.7 in^2**
   c. a right cone with height 4 inches. **≈ 72.7 in^2**
7. Give two reasons why the cube would be the best container in Question 6. **Samples: It stacks efficiently; its surface can be printed upon accurately.**
8. A jeweler has enough gold to cover a surface area of 3 cm^2 with a particular thickness of gold.
   a. What is the volume of the largest bead she could cover? **$\approx .489$ cm^3**
   b. What is the volume of the largest prism-shaped bead she could cover? **$\approx .354$ cm^3**

Optional Activities

Use Physical Models

Materials: Empty soft-drink cans, juice boxes, various other empty food containers

Have students discuss the reasons for various shapes of containers and compare the volumes of the containers. For example, compare the volume of a can of soda and its surface area with the volume and surface area of a juice box. Ask: What are the advantages to the shape of the juice box? What are the advantages to the shape of a soft-drink can? Have students continue the discussion with other food containers. [Rectangular boxes are easier to stack and leave no gaps when stored. Also, cardboard is cheaper than aluminum. Cylindrical cans give a greater volume for a given amount of metal, but metal is more expensive than cardboard.]

Notes on Questions

Question 8 You might want to ask students for real-world examples of other objects with large surface areas. A good example is the alveoli of lungs. Also, two small ice cubes cool faster than one larger one with the same volume because they have more surface area.

Question 12 Science Connection Filters trap particles. For instance, a cigarette filter traps tar and nicotine. A filter with a large surface area can trap more particles than one with a small surface area.

(Notes on Questions continue on page 852.)

Follow-up for Lesson 14-9

Practice

For more questions on SPUR Objectives, use **Lesson Master 14-9A** (shown on page 849) or **Lesson Master 14-9B** (shown on pages 850–851).

LESSON MASTER 14-9 B **Questions on SPUR Objectives**

Properties Objective H: Apply the Isoperimetric Theorems and the Isoperimetric Inequality to determine which figures have the greatest or least surface area or volume.

1. Consider the figures below.

(a) (b) (c) (d)

a. For which figure is the ratio $\frac{\text{surface area}}{\text{volume}}$ greatest? d

b. For which figure is the ratio $\frac{\text{volume}}{\text{surface area}}$ greatest? b

2. Consider all figures with a surface area of 210 ft^2.

a. Which has the greatest volume? sphere

b. What is the volume of the figure in Part **a**? $\approx 286.2\ ft^3$

3. Consider all figures with a volume of 800 cm^3.

a. Which has the least surface area? sphere

b. What is the surface area of the figure in Part **a**? $\approx 416.8\ cm^2$

4. a. What is the volume of the right square pyramid at the right? $400\ units^3$

b. What figure with the same volume has the least surface area? sphere

c. Find the surface area of the figure in Part **b**. $\approx 262.5\ units^2$

12

5

d. What is the surface area of the right square pyramid? $360\ units^2$

e. What figure with the same surface area has the greatest volume? sphere

f. Find the volume of the figure in Part **e**? $\approx 642.3\ units^3$

Example

A cube and a sphere each have volume 1000 cubic meters. Calculate the surface area for each figure.

Solution

First draw figures and write down relevant formulas.

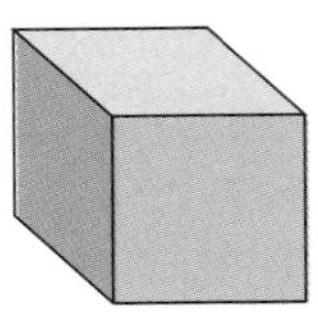

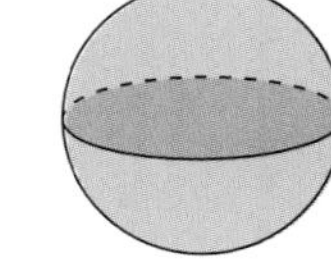

$V = s^3$ $\quad$ $V = \frac{4}{3}\pi r^3$

$S.A. = 6s^2$ $\quad$ $S.A. = 4\pi r^2$

For the cube, $1000 = s^3$, so $s = \sqrt[3]{1000} = 10$.
The surface area of the cube is $6s^2 = 600$ square meters.

For the sphere,

$$1000 = \frac{4}{3}\pi r^3$$
$$\frac{750}{\pi} = r^3$$
$$238.7 \approx r^3$$

Take the cube root to find $r \approx 6.2$.
The surface area of the sphere is $4\pi r^2 \approx 4 \cdot \pi \cdot 6.2^2 \approx 483$ square meters. The sphere has considerably less surface area than the cube.

The cube "wastes" surface near its edges and corners.

Figures with Large Surface Areas for a Given Volume

Just as a 2-dimensional figure can have a large perimeter and a small area, so a 3-dimensional figure can have a large surface area and a small volume. Think of sponges like the natural and artificial ones pictured at the left. The artificial sponge has the shape of a rectangular solid with volume 12 cubic inches, whereas the natural sponge has a more irregular shape. Both sponges are nonconvex curved spaces whose volume is quite small in comparison to their surface areas. The holes give the sponges their large surface areas. This large irregular surface enables the sponges to hold a lot of water. Some water is held because in almost any position of the sponge some of the sponge is under the water, cupping it. Other water clings to the large surface just the way the inside of a glass remains wet after you pour out its contents.

Concluding Remarks

The Isoperimetric Theorems involve square and cube roots, π, polygons, circles, polyhedra, and spheres. They explain properties of arenas, fences, soap bubbles, and sponges. They demonstrate the broad applicability of geometry and the unity of mathematics.

Adapting to Individual Needs

English Language Development
Students with limited English proficiency may better understand the terminology *isoperimetric in three dimensions* if you stress that this phrase refers to surface area, not perimeter.

Many people enjoy the way mathematics connects diverse topics. Others like mathematics for its uses. Still others like the logical way mathematics fits together and grows. The Isoperimetric Theorems exemplify all of these properties of mathematics. We hope that you have found it to be an enjoyable way to end your study of geometry using this book.

1) Both the smaller and main parts of the igloo have the shape of hemispheres, which enclose more space with the same amount of ice than a cylinder, cone, or polyhedron that covers the same base area.

9) the way it connects diverse topics; its uses; the logical way mathematics fits together and grows.

QUESTIONS

Covering the Reading

1. Why is an igloo an efficient dwelling? See left.
2. Of all solids with the same surface area, the _?_ has the maximum _?_. sphere, volume
3. The surface area of a solid is 600 square meters. To the nearest 100 cubic meters, what is the maximum possible volume of the solid? 1400 m^3
4. Of all solids with the same volume, the _?_ has the least _?_. sphere, surface area
5. Which statement, that of Question 2 or Question 4, explains the shape of a soap bubble? Question 4
6. In Question 3, what is the least possible volume of the solid? The minimum volume is as close to zero as you like.
7. A cube has volume 8 cubic units. What is its surface area? 24 units^2
8. Explain why sponges are able to hold so much water. See margin.
9. List three reasons given in this lesson why people enjoy mathematics. See left.
10. The plastic milk container that would have the least material for a given amount of milk would be shaped like a sphere. Why are milk containers *not* shaped like spheres? Sample: They do not fit on a shelf or in a packing crate without rolling or wasting space.

Applying the Mathematics

11a) $36\pi \approx 113$ m^2
b) Sample: radius of 2 m, height of 9 m; surface area: $44\pi \approx 138$ m^2
c) Sample: radius of 6 m, height of 3 m; surface area: $36\pi + 6\pi\sqrt{45} \approx 240$ m^2

11. **a.** A sphere has volume 36π cubic meters. What is its surface area?
b. Give possible dimensions for a cylinder with volume 36π cubic meters. What is the surface area of the cylinder you identified?
c. Give dimensions for a right cone with volume 36π cubic meters. What is its surface area? a, b, c) See left.
d. According to the Isoperimetric Inequality, the surface area in part **a** is _?_ than the surface areas in part **b** or **c**. less
12. A sink-side water purifier depends on a cylindrical charcoal filter of diameter 3 inches and height 8.25 inches. The manufacturer claims the filter has over 100 acres of surface area.
a. Can this claim possibly be true? Yes
b. If so, why would anyone want to have so much surface area? If not, why can't the claim be true? To filter as much water as possible.

Assessment

Written Communication Have students write a paragraph explaining why it may be advantageous to have the greatest possible volume for a fixed surface area in some cases, while in other cases it would be advantageous to have the greatest possible surface area for a fixed volume. [Students give at least one example of each type, and recognize that a sphere gives the greatest volume if the surface area is fixed and the least surface area if the volume is fixed.]

Extension

Writing Consumer Connection Have students write a paragraph that explains some of the factors other than surface area and volume that are considered by manufacturers when developing a package for a product. Students should include possible reasons for such decisions. [Sample: cost, weight, durability, ease of storage, portability, recyclability of material]

Project Update Project 4, *The Universe*, on page 853, relates to the content of this lesson.

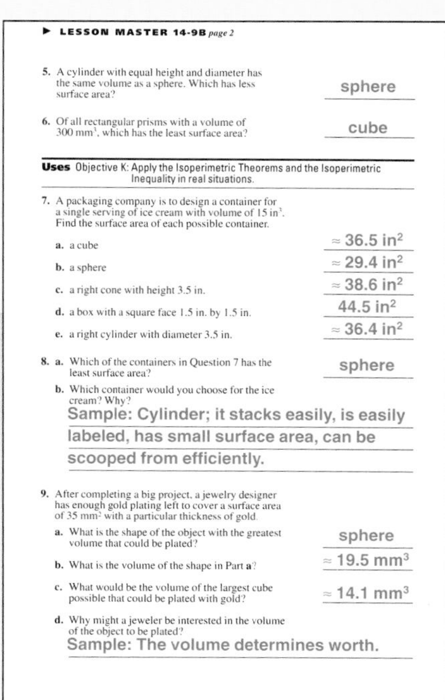

LESSON MASTER 14-9B *page 2*

5. A cylinder with equal height and diameter has the same volume as a sphere. Which has less surface area? sphere
6. Of all rectangular prisms with a volume of 300 mm^3, which has the least surface area? cube

Uses Objective K: Apply the Isoperimetric Theorems and the Isoperimetric Inequality in real situations.

7. A packaging company is to design a container for a single serving of ice cream with volume of 15 in^3. Find the surface area of each possible container.
a. a cube ≈ 36.5 in^2
b. a sphere ≈ 29.4 in^2
c. a right cone with height 3.5 in. ≈ 38.6 in^2
d. a box with a square face 1.5 in. by 1.5 in. 44.5 in^2
e. a right cylinder with diameter 3.5 in. ≈ 36.4 in^2
8. **a.** Which of the containers in Question 7 has the least surface area? sphere
b. Which container would you choose for the ice cream? Why? Sample: Cylinder; it stacks easily, is easily labeled, has small surface area, can be scooped from efficiently.
9. After completing a big project, a jewelry designer has enough gold plating left to cover a surface area of 35 mm^2 with a particular thickness of gold.
a. What is the shape of the object with the greatest volume that could be plated? sphere
b. What is the volume of the shape in Part **a**? ≈ 19.5 mm^3
c. What would be the volume of the largest cube possible that could be plated with gold? ≈ 14.1 mm^3
d. Why might a jeweler be interested in the volume of the object to be plated? Sample: The volume determines worth.

Adapting to Individual Needs

Challenge

Suppose that a sphere and a cube have the same surface area. Then the volume of the sphere is how many times as much as the volume of the cube? [$\sqrt{\frac{6}{\pi}}$, or about 1.382; Note that this problem requires a great deal of work with radicals. If students cannot give the exact answer, have them work with decimal approximations.]

Additional Answers

8. The holes give the sponge a large surface area, which enables the sponge to hold a lot of water. Some water has sponge surface area under it; other water clings to the sponge's surface area.

Notes on Questions

Question 23 This is a difficult question. If a figure has volume V, then because of the Isoperimetric Inequality, its surface area is at least equal to the surface area of a sphere.

Additional Answers

18. $AC \cdot CB = CD \cdot CE$ by the Secant Length Theorem, and $AC = CB$ by the Chord-Center Theorem, part (1). Substitution gives $AC \cdot AC = CD \cdot CE$ or $\frac{CD}{AC} = \frac{AC}{CE}$. Thus, AC is the geometric mean of CD and CE.

19. Sample:

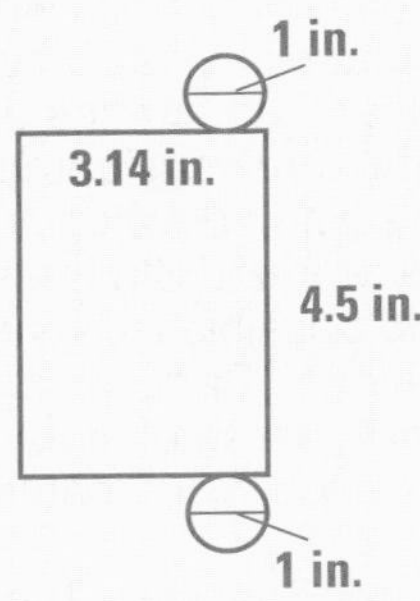

20. Isometry and isosceles; in each, there are things that are equal. In "isometry" there are equal distances; in "isosceles" there are sides of equal length.

22b. According to legend, Dido was granted all the land that could be surrounded by a piece of cowhide. She cut the cowhide into narrow strips and made a circle to surround the land which became Carthage.

23. Sample: Choose a sphere. In a sphere with radius r, the volume $V = \frac{4}{3}\pi r^3$, so $r = \sqrt[3]{\frac{3V}{4\pi}}$. The S.A. $= 4\pi r^2 = 4\pi \cdot (\sqrt[3]{\frac{3V}{4\pi}})^2$, which simplifies to $\sqrt[3]{36\pi V^2}$. So, in any 3-dimensional figure with volume V and surface area S.A., S.A. $\geq \sqrt[3]{36\pi V^2}$. Equality occurs if and only if the figure is a sphere.

13. A sphere has surface area πx. Find its volume in terms of x. $\frac{\pi\sqrt{x^3}}{6}$ units^3

Review

14. Consider all figures with area 12 square meters.
a. Which has the least perimeter? circle
b. What is the perimeter? *(Lesson 14-8)* $4\pi\sqrt{\frac{3}{\pi}} \approx 12.28$ meters

15. A circle and a square both have perimeters 96 inches.
a. Calculate their areas. circle $\frac{2304}{\pi} \approx 733$ in^2; square; 576 in.^{2}
b. Which has the smaller area? *(Lesson 14-8)* square

16. $\overleftrightarrow{QM}$ is tangent to $\odot X$ at L below. If $NQ = 6$ and $PN = 12$, find QL. *(Lesson 14-7)* $\sqrt{108} \approx 10.39$ units

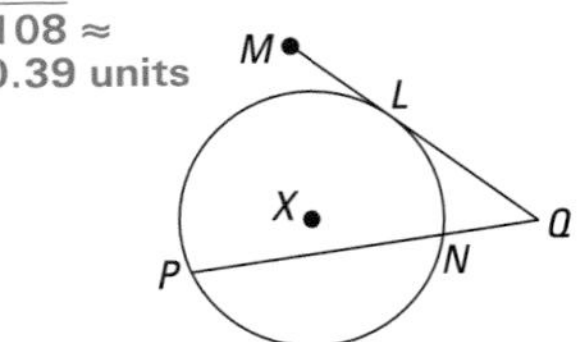

17. $\triangle ABC$ is inscribed in the circle below. What are the measures of its angles? *(Lesson 14-2)* $m\angle A = 39.5$, $m\angle B = 98$, $m\angle C = 42.5$

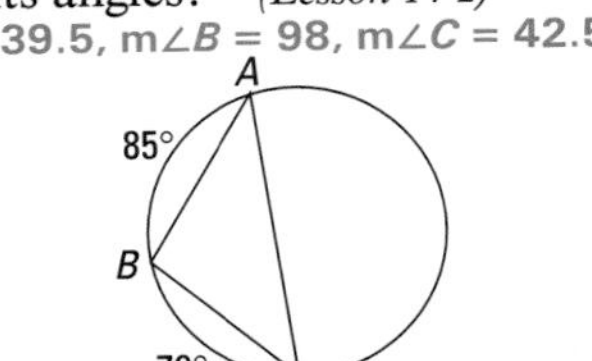

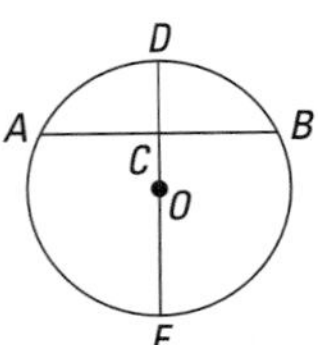

18. In the figure at the left, $\overline{DE}$ is a diameter of $\odot O$ and $\overline{AB} \perp \overline{DE}$. Prove that AC is the geometric mean of CD and CE. *(Lessons 14-1, 14-7)* See margin.

19. Draw a net for a juice can. *(Lesson 9-7)* See margin.

20. The prefix "iso-" in "isoperimetric" is found in two other mathematical terms you have studied this year. What are these terms and why is this prefix appropriate for each of them? *(Lessons 2-6, 4-7)* See margin.

21. According to the 1995 *Rand McNally World Atlas,* the distance between Greensburg and Pittsburgh, two cities in Pennsylvania, is 31 miles. The distance between Pittsburgh and Philadelphia is 308 miles. The distance between Greensburg and Philadelphia is not listed in that atlas, but what can you deduce about it? *(Lesson 2-7)* The distance is from 277 to 339 miles

Exploration

Dido and Aeneas.

22. According to legend, the first person to use the Isoperimetric Inequality was Dido, the queen of Carthage.
a. Where is, or was, Carthage? a) on the north coast of Africa, on the Bay of Tunis
b. How did Dido use this inequality? (Hint: Look in an encyclopedia or dictionary under Dido.) See margin.

23. Develop an Isoperimetric Inequality for three dimensions. That is, find a relationship between the volume V and surface area S.A. of any 3-dimensional figure. See margin.

A project presents an opportunity for you to extend your knowledge of a topic related to the material of this chapter. You should allow more time for a project than you do for typical homework questions.

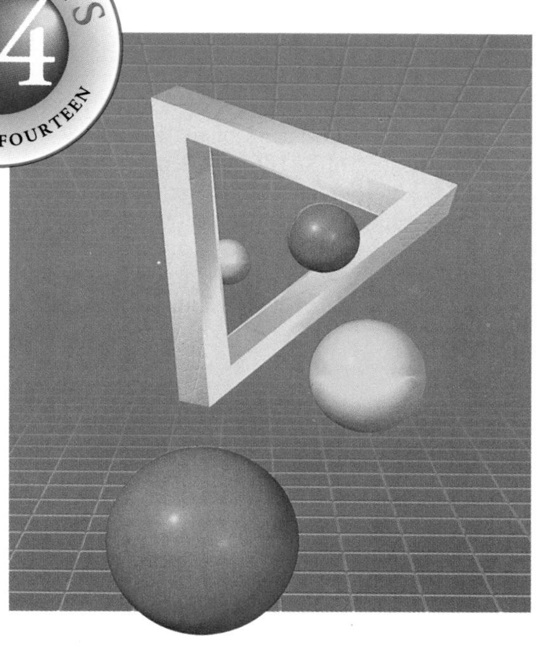

1 Cutting Down on Waste

You wish to cut five discs out of a square piece of tin. The discs can be any size. If you want to use as much tin as possible, where should the discs be located in the square, and what should be their radii? Explain how you have come to your conclusion. Then, demonstrate your results by cutting comparable disks out of a square piece of cardboard or wood.

2 Picture Angles

For this project you need a camera. Choose a large object such as a building. Measure the width of the building and the distance to a point where you can stand so as to fit just the building in a picture. Determine the picture angle of the camera. Draw a diagram indicating where you will stand. Then take shots from five different locations so that the building just fits into your picture, and display them on a poster.

3 Circles Associated with Triangles

Mathematicians have studied properties of many circles associated with triangles. For instance, the *circumcircle* of a triangle is the circle that passes through its vertices. Every triangle also has an *incircle,* three *excircles,* and a *nine-point circle.* Find out where these circles are located for a given triangle, and draw all of them for at least two different scalene triangles.

4 The Universe

Earlier in this chapter, you read the quote of Galileo: ". . . the universe . . . is written in the language of mathematics, and its characters are triangles, circles, and other geometrical figures, without which it is humanly impossible to understand a single word of it; without these, one is wandering about in a dark labyrinth." Write an essay supporting or criticizing this claim of Galileo. Illustrate your essay with examples.

▶

Chapter 14 Projects

The projects relate chiefly to the content of the lessons of this chapter as follows:

Project	Lesson(s)
1	14-1, 14-5, 14-7
2	14-1, 14-2, 14-3
3	14-3, 14-5
4	14-1, 14-8, 14-9
5	14-5, 14-6

1 Cutting Down on Waste To cut five discs out of a square piece of material and use as much of the material as possible, begin with a square with side length $2r$. Then, the first and largest circle will have radius r, and will be tangent to the four sides. Next, draw in the diagonals of the square. The four remaining circles will have center points on these diagonals. Now mark the points on the circle where the diagonals have intersected the circle. Draw in lines which are perpendicular to the diagonals at the points of intersection. This will provide four isosceles right triangles. The inscribed circles (see Project 4) for these four triangles are those needed to maximize the area removed from the material.

2 Picture Angles The methods used in Lesson 14-3 are appropriate for use here. Students can find the picture angle of their cameras by looking at the information which accompanies the purchase of the camera, or by consulting a photography store.

3 Circles Associated with Triangles The "centers" of triangles have special names—the *incenter* of a triangle is the point of intersection of the angle bisectors; the *orthocenter* of a triangle is the point of intersection of the altitudes of a triangle; the *centroid* of a triangle is the point of intersection of the medians of the triangle; the *circumcenter* of a triangle is the point of intersection of the perpendicular bisectors of a triangle. Thus, the incircle of a triangle has the incenter of the triangle as its center; and the circumcircle of a triangle has as its center the circumcenter.

4 The Universe The student responses for this project will vary greatly. A sample essay is given, but allow all reasonable student responses. The important thing is that they demonstrate that mathematics is found everywhere in the world.

(Possible responses begin on page 854.)

5 Japanese Temple Geometry Theorems This project asks for *drawings*, not *constructions*. But the drawings need to be accurate, and it is best if they are larger than the drawings shown.

Possible responses

1. **The actual demonstration cannot be exact due to measurement error and imprecision due to cutting the material.**

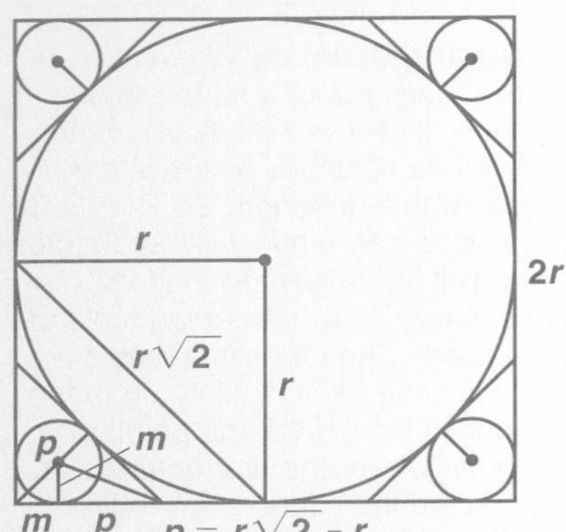

$m \quad p \quad p = r\sqrt{2} - r$

$m + p = \frac{\sqrt{2}}{2} \cdot 2(r\sqrt{2} - r) =$
$\sqrt{2}(r\sqrt{2} - r)$
$m = \sqrt{2}(r\sqrt{2} - r) - r\sqrt{2} + r =$
$3r - 2r\sqrt{2}$.
Area of the large circle $= \pi r^2$;
Area of the 4 small circles $=$
$4(\pi(3r - 2r\sqrt{2})^2) =$
$4\pi(9r^2 - 12r^2\sqrt{2} + 8r^2)$
$\frac{\text{amount removed}}{\text{total amount}} =$
$\frac{\pi r^2 + 4\pi r^2(17 - 12\sqrt{2})}{4r^2} =$
$\frac{\pi}{4} \cdot [1 + 4(17 - 12\sqrt{2})] \approx 0.88$.
About 88% of original material was removed.

2. **Responses will vary. The methods used in Lesson 14-3 are appropriate here.**

(continued)

5 Japanese Temple Geometry Theorems

In the Edo period of the history of Japan (1603–1867), when Japan isolated itself from the rest of the world, there was a tradition of posing geometry problems on tablets hung under the roofs of shrines and temples. Many of the theorems involve tangent lines and circles and were unknown outside of Japan until recently, and many are astounding. Here are four of these theorems, with the dates of their appearance given in parentheses. In these problems the radius of circle O_1 is r_1, of circle O_2 is r_2, and so on. Pick at least two of them and draw two different accurate drawings verifying the relations in the theorem.

a. (1824) If circle O_1, is tangent to circle O_2, and if circle O_3 is tangent to the two circles O_2 and O_1 and to their common tangent $\overleftrightarrow{AB}$, then

$$\frac{1}{\sqrt{r_3}} = \frac{1}{\sqrt{r_1}} + \frac{1}{\sqrt{r_2}}$$

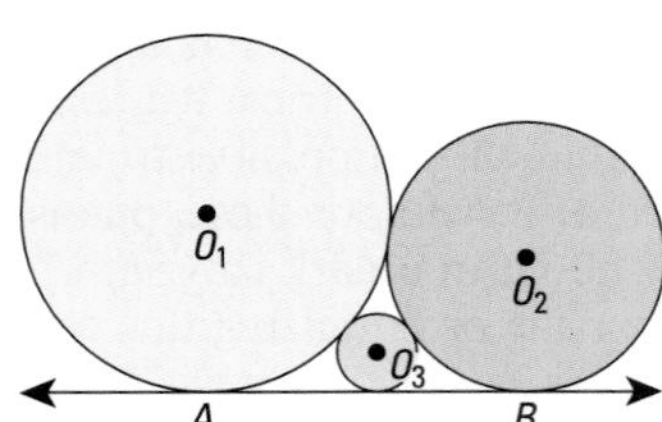

b. (1842) If $\overline{AB}$ is a chord of circle O with radius r, the five circles O_1 to O_5 are each tangent to each other, to the chord, and to circle O, and if

$r_1 = r_5$, $r_2 = r_4$, and $4r_3 = r$, then

$$r_1 = \tfrac{4}{9}r_3.$$

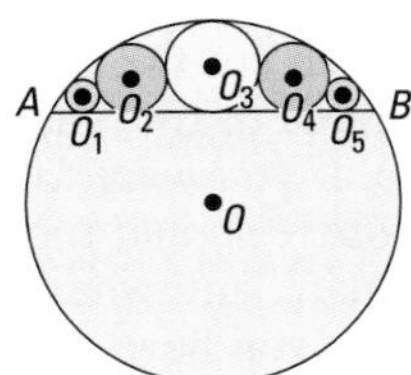

c. (1782) If circles O_1 to O_4 (of different sizes) are tangent to each other and to circle O at points A, B, C, and D, then

$$AB \cdot CD = AD \cdot BC.$$

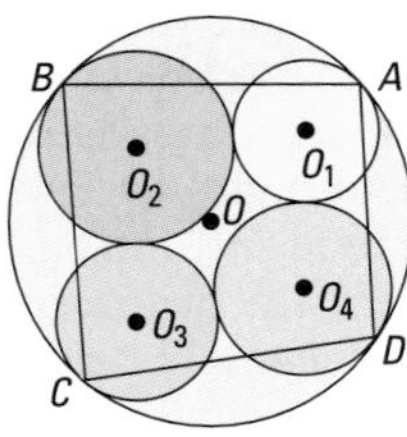

d. (1791) Let $\overline{AC}$ and $\overline{BD}$ be any two chords of a circle. Let r_1, r_2, r_3, and r_4 be the radii of the largest circles that can be drawn in the 4 regions determined by $\overline{AC}$ and $\overline{BD}$, as shown below. (The circles are tangent to the chords, the blue circle, and the pink circle.) Then

$$\frac{1}{r_1} + \frac{1}{r_3} = \frac{1}{r_2} + \frac{1}{r_4}$$

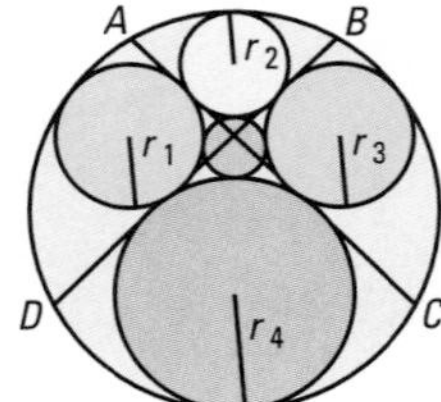

3. **The circumcircle of a triangle is the circle that contains all three vertices. Its center is the intersection of the perpendicular bisectors of each side of the triangle, and the radius is the distance from the center to any of the three vertices.**

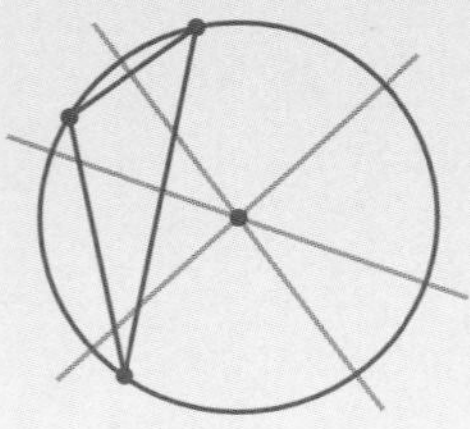

Circumcircle

The incircle, or inscribed circle, of a triangle is the circle which is tangent to all three sides of the triangle. Its center is the intersection of the angle bisectors of the angles formed by the vertices of the triangle, and its radius is the perpendicular distance of the center to one of the sides of the triangle.

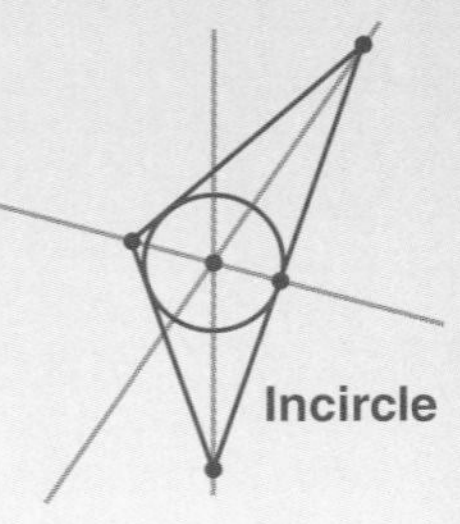

Incircle

SUMMARY

The theorems and applications of this chapter are related to many of the ideas in earlier chapters.

Perpendicular lines are important in circles. A line perpendicular to a chord bisects the chord if and only if it contains the center of the circle. If the sides of an inscribed angle are perpendicular, then the angle intercepts a semicircle. These theorems give ways of finding the center of a circle. A line perpendicular to a radius at its endpoint on a circle is tangent to the circle. All other lines through that point are secants to the circle.

The chapter also applies congruence and similarity. In a circle or in congruent circles, arcs of the same measure are congruent if and only if they have congruent chords. Inscribed angles which intercept the same arc are congruent. If two chords $\overline{AB}$ and $\overline{CD}$ intersect at point E, $\triangle EAC$ and $\triangle EDB$ are similar. As a result, $AE \cdot BE = CE \cdot DE$. This theorem holds if the word "secant" is substituted for "chord" and A, B, C, and D are the points at which two secants intersect the circle. $AE \cdot BE$ or $CE \cdot DE$ is the power of point E with respect to the circle.

Relationships between measures of angles and arcs are all derived from the definition that the measure of an arc is equal to the measure of its central angle. The measure of an inscribed angle is half the intercepted arc. From this property, you can find all the places to take a photo so that an object just fills the photo. The measure of an angle between two chords is half the sum of the intercepted arcs. The angle between secants or tangents is half the difference of the intercepted arcs.

The Isoperimetric Theorems relate perimeters and areas, or surface areas and volumes. In two dimensions: (1) of all figures with the same perimeter, the circle has the maximum area; (2) of all figures with the same area, the circle has the least perimeter. In three dimensions: (1) of all figures with the same surface area, the sphere has the maximum volume; (2) of all figures with the same volume, the sphere has the least surface area. Many properties of real objects can be explained by these inequalities.

VOCABULARY

Below are the most important terms and phrases for this chapter. For the starred (*) terms you should be able to give a definition of the term. For the other terms you should be able to give a general description and a specific example of each.

Lesson 14-1
intercepted arc
Arc-Chord ≅ Theorem
Chord-Center Theorem

Lesson 14-2
picture angle of a camera lens
*inscribed angle
Inscribed Angle Theorem

Lesson 14-3
right-angle method to find the center of a circle

Lesson 14-4
Angle-Chord Theorem
*secant to a circle
Angle-Secant Theorem

Lesson 14-5
*tangent to a circle
point of tangency
Radius-Tangent Theorem
tangent to a sphere
common tangents

Lesson 14-6
Tangent-Chord Theorem
Tangent-Secant Theorem

Lesson 14-7
Secant Length Theorem
power of a point P for a circle
Tangent Square Theorem

Lesson 14-8
Isoperimetric Theorem
Isoperimetric Inequality
Isoperimetric Theorem (alternate statement)

Lesson 14-9
Isoperimetric Theorem (3-dimensional version)
Isoperimetric Theorem (alternate 3-dimensional version)

Summary

The Summary gives an overview of the entire chapter and provides an opportunity for students to consider the material as a whole. Thus, the Summary can be used to help students relate and unify the concepts presented in the chapter.

Vocabulary

Terms, symbols, and properties are listed by lesson to provide a checklist of concepts a student must know. Emphasize to students that they should read the vocabulary list carefully before starting the Progress Self-Test. If students do not understand the meaning of a term, they should refer back to the indicated lesson.

Possible responses, continued

An excircle, or escribed circle, of a triangle is a circle which is tangent to one of the sides of the triangle, and is tangent to the extensions of the other two sides of the triangle. There are three escribed circles for any one triangle. To find the center of an escribed circle of a triangle, choose a side and extend the other legs. Then find the center of the excircle, which is the intersection of two angle bisectors—one opposite the chosen leg and one of the exterior angles of the triangle formed when the sides are extended. The radius is the perpendicular distance from the center to any side.

Excircle

The nine-point circle of a triangle is the circle through any one of three sets of three points: the feet of the three altitudes of the triangle, the midpoints of the three sides of the triangle; and the midpoints of the segments formed by the intersection of the three altitudes and the vertices of the triangle. The center and radius of the nine-point circle can be determined in the following way: using the three midpoints of the sides and the three points on the altitudes which are not at the feet, form two overlapping rectangles. The diagonal which is common to both rectangles is the diameter of the circle. So, find the midpoint of the diagonal, and this is the center. The radius is the distance from this center point to any of the nine known points of the circle.

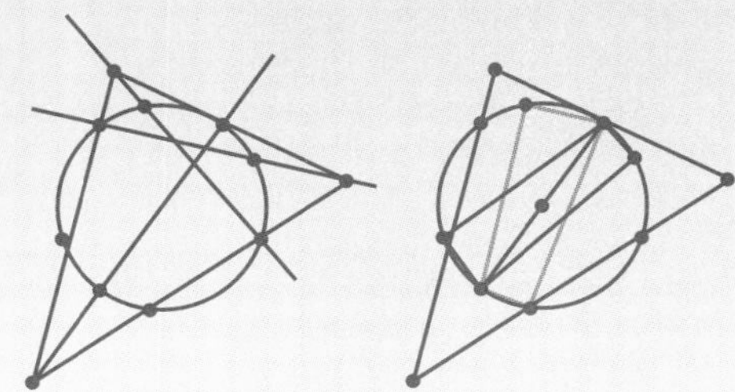

Nine-Point Circle

(Responses continue on page 856.)

CHAPTER FOURTEEN

Progress Self-Test

For the development of mathematical competence, feedback and correction, along with the opportunity to practice, are necessary. The Progress Self-Test provides the opportunity for feedback and correction; the Chapter Review provides additional opportunities and practice. We cannot overemphasize the importance of these end-of-chapter materials. It is at this point that the material "gels" for many students, allowing them to solidify skills and understanding. In general, student performance should be markedly improved after these pages.

Assign the Progress Self-Test as a one-night assignment. Answers to all questions are in the Selected Answers section of the student book. Encourage students to take the Progress Self-Test honestly, grade themselves, and then be prepared to discuss the test in class.

Advise students to pay special attention to those Chapter Review questions (pages 858–861) which correspond to questions missed on the Progress Self-Test.

Additional Answers

9. **$\ell \perp \overline{OQ}$ since a tangent is perpendicular to a radius through the point of tangency. $\overline{XY} \perp \overline{OQ}$ because a radius that bisects a chord is perpendicular to it. Thus, $\ell \parallel \overline{XY}$ because two lines perpendicular to the same line are parallel.**

PROGRESS SELF-TEST

Directions: Take this test as you would take a test in class. Then check your work with the solutions in the Selected Answers section in the back of the book. You will need a straightedge, compass, and protractor.

1. In a circle with radius 210 mm, find the length of a chord of a 120° arc. **$210\sqrt{3} \approx 363.7$ units**
2. Trace the figure below. Then find the center of the circle that contains points C, D, and E.

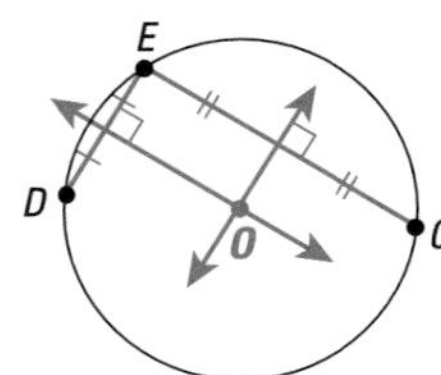

3. Square $JKLM$ is inscribed in $\odot P$ below. If the radius of $\odot P$ is 30, find the perimeter of $JKLM$. **$120\sqrt{2} \approx 169.7$ units**

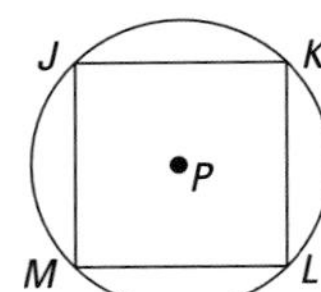

In 4 and 5, use the figure below, in which $m\widehat{DC} = 80°$ and $m\angle DEC = 100$.

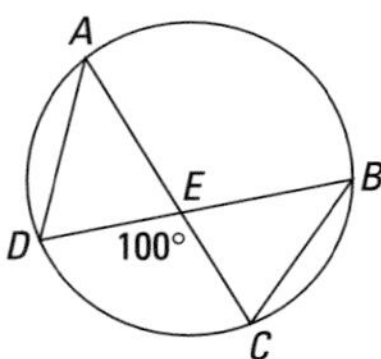

4. Find $m\angle B$. **$m\angle B = 40$**
5. Find $m\widehat{AB}$. **$m\widehat{AB} = 120°$**
6. In $\odot Z$ below, $m\widehat{US} = 30°$, $m\widehat{UV} = 80°$, and $m\widehat{ST} = 140°$. Find $m\angle R$. **$m\angle R = 40$**

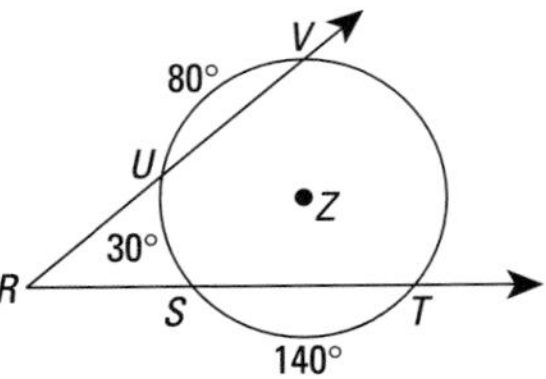

7. In circle O below, if $AQ = 19$, $BQ = 40$, and $CQ = 38$, find QD. **$QD = 80$ units**

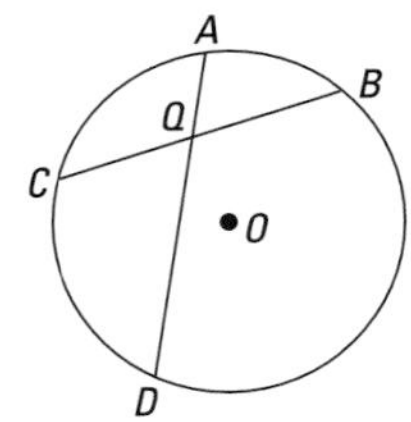

8. In $\odot G$ below, if $WX = 12$, $XY = 16$, and $WZ = 10$, find ZV. **$ZV = 23.6$**

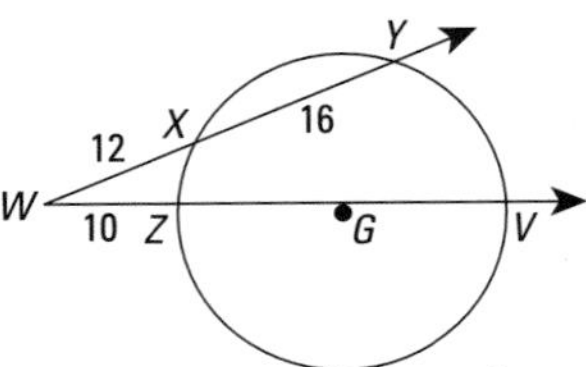

9. In the figure below, ℓ is tangent to $\odot O$ at Q. If $\overline{OQ}$ intersects chord $\overline{XY}$ at the midpoint M of $\overline{XY}$, prove that $\ell \parallel \overline{XY}$. **See margin.**

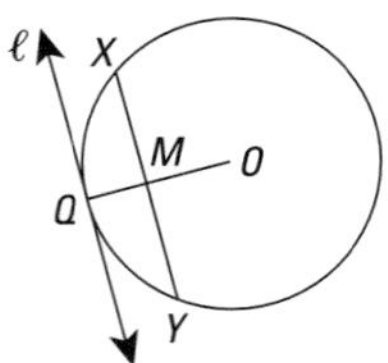

Additional responses, page 853

4. **Sample: In order to understand the universe in which we live, we must be able to describe our surroundings; and many, if not most, descriptions include notions of geometry which have been examined in this book. In everyday life, we describe our surroundings in terms of their characteristics, which include their size and shape, distance from a given point, or location in relation to a given point. For example:**

1. **We speak of the shape of the planets as spheres, rainbows as arches, columns as cylinders, and faces of buildings as rectangles, and so on.**
2. **We see signs, like road signs, in which the shape determines the meaning—octagons imply stop (stop signs), and triangles imply caution (yield signs).**
3. **We draw figures to explain or to inquire, using straight and curved lines for everything from drawing a map for directions to sketching a football play.**
4. **We write words and sentences in approximations of parallel discrete lines with the letters as points on those lines.**
5. **We speak of heights of objects as perpendicular distances from the object to a point on line.**

PROGRESS SELF-TEST

In 10 and 11, use the figure below. $\overrightarrow{PT}$ and $\overrightarrow{PU}$ are tangents to ⊙O at T and U.

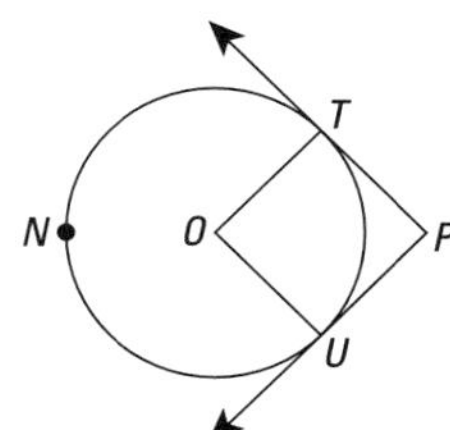

10. a. *True or false.* If m$\widehat{UT}$ = 90°, then $PUOT$ is a square. True

b. Explain your answer to part **a.** See margin.

11. If m∠P = 92, find m$\widehat{TNU}$. m$\widehat{TNU}$ = 272°

12. Write a proof argument using the given figure. See margin.

Given: $\overline{BC} \parallel \overline{AD}$.

To prove: m$\widehat{AB}$ = m$\widehat{CD}$.

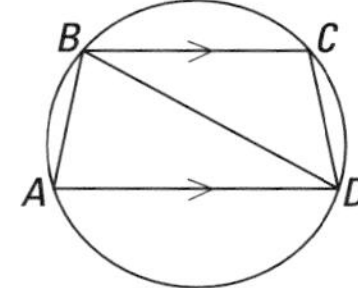

13. A clerk has a 30-cm strip of wire screen to fence in some supplies on a desk.

a. How should the screen be shaped to fence in the most area? a circle

b. What is this area? ≈ 71.6 cm^2

14. A sphere and a cube each have volume 240 cubic feet. Which has the larger surface area and why? See below.

15. Refer to the stage below which is 60 feet wide. You have a camera lens with a 64° picture angle.

a. Draw a picture indicating where you can stand so that the entire stage will just be seen in your picture. See below.

b. If you are standing in front of the center of the stage, how near to the center of the stage can you be and still photograph the entire stage? ≈ 48 ft

16. How far can you see from a 100-foot high tower if there are no obstructions? ≈ 12.2 miles

14) The cube, because of all solids with the same volume, the sphere has the least surface area.

15a)

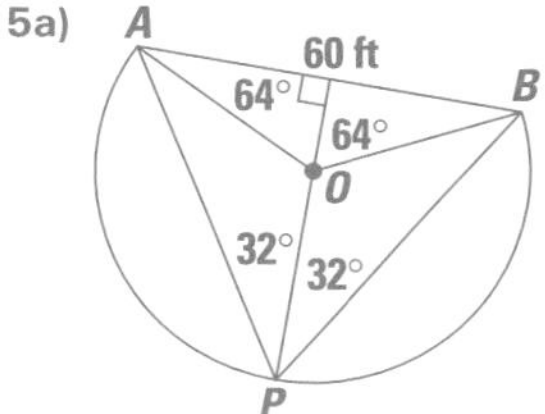

Stand on the part of the circle drawn, or outside the circle and below $\overleftrightarrow{AB}$.

Additional Answers

10b. Sample: ∠O is a 90° angle since m$\widehat{UT}$ = 90° (given). ∠PTO and ∠PUO are 90° angles since a tangent is perpendicular to a radius through the point of tangency. So ∠TPU is a 90° angle by the Quadrilateral-Sum Theorem. So $PUOT$ is a rectangle. Furthermore, OU = OT since both are radii of ⊙O. Since opposite sides of a rectangle are congruent, $PUOT$ has four sides of equal length. Therefore, by the definition of a square, $PUOT$ is a square.

12.

Conclusions	Justifications
0. $\overline{BC} \parallel \overline{AD}$	Given
1. m∠CBD = m∠ADB	// lines ⇒ AIA ≅ Thm.
2. m∠CBD = $\frac{1}{2}$m$\widehat{CD}$, m∠ADB = $\frac{1}{2}$m$\widehat{AB}$	Inscribed Angle Thm.
3. m$\widehat{AB}$ = m$\widehat{CD}$	Transitive Prop. of =

Additional responses, page 854

5. Errors in students' drawings will result from measurement inaccuracy, pencil thickness, and drawing inaccuracy. Sample measurements are described for each situation.

a. Suppose that for the circles, r_1 = 1.4 and r_2 = 1.9, then r_3 ≈ 0.4.

Is $\frac{1}{\sqrt{0.4}} = \frac{1}{\sqrt{1.4}} + \frac{1}{\sqrt{1.9}}$?

Yes, 1.58 ≈ 1.57.

b. Suppose that for circles O_1–O_5, $r_1 = r_5 = 0.35$ and $r_3 = 0.8$, then $r_2 = r_4 \approx 0.6$ and $r = 4r_3 = 3.2$. Is $r_1 = 0.35 = \frac{4}{9}(0.8)$? Yes, 0.35 ≈ 0.36.

c. If AB = 4.0, BC = 3.8, CD = 2.9, we get AD ≈ 3.1. Is (4.0)(2.9) ≈ (3.1)(3.8)? Yes, 11.6 ≈ 11.8.

d. When r_1 = 19 mm, r_2 = 25 mm, r_3 = 39 mm, and r_4 = 26.5 mm, is $\frac{1}{19} + \frac{1}{39} \approx \frac{1}{25} + \frac{1}{26.5}$? Yes, .0782 ≈ .0778.

Chapter 14 Review

Resources

From the ***Teacher's Resource File***

- Answer Master for Chapter 14 Review
- Assessment Sourcebook: Chapter 14 Test, Forms A–D Chapter 14 Test, Cumulative Form Comprehensive Test, Chapters 1–14

Additional Resources

- Quiz and Test Writer

The main objectives for the chapter are organized in the Chapter Review under the four types of understanding this book promotes—Skills, Properties, Uses, and Representations.

Whereas end-of-chapter material may be considered optional in some texts, in UCSMP *Geometry* we have selected these objectives and questions with the expectation that they will be covered. Students should be able to answer these questions with about 85% accuracy after studying the chapter.

You may assign these questions over a single night to help students prepare for a test the next day, or you may assign the questions over a two-day period. If you work the questions over two days, then we recommend assigning the *evens* for homework the first night so that students get feedback in class the next day, then assigning the *odds* the night before the test, because answers are provided to the odd-numbered questions.

CHAPTER REVIEW

Questions on SPUR Objectives

SPUR stands for **S**kills, **P**roperties, **U**ses, and **R**epresentations. The Chapter Review questions are grouped according to the SPUR Objectives for this chapter.

SKILLS DEAL WITH THE PROCEDURES USED TO GET ANSWERS.

Objective A: *Calculate lengths of chords and arcs.* (*Lesson 14-1*) 2) ≈ 104.6mm

In 1 and 2, a circle has a radius of 55 mm.

1. Find the length of a 60° arc. ≈ 57.6 mm

2. Find the length of a chord of a 144° arc.

3. *ABCD* is a square inscribed in ⊙*O* below and *OA* = 12.

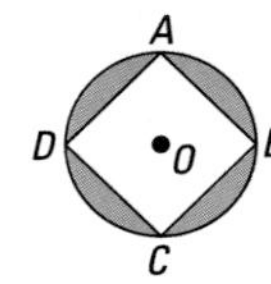

a. Find *AB*. ≈ 17.0 units

b. Find the area of the shaded region. ≈ 164.4 units²

4. In ⊙*P*, *RT* = 18, and $\overline{RT}$ is 7 units away from the center. What is *PT*? ≈ 11.4 units

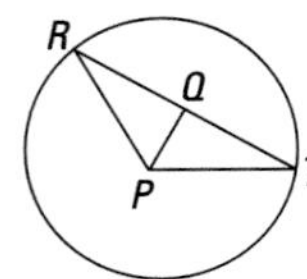

5. Regular octagon *STOPZIGN* is inscribed in ⊙*Q* at the right.

a. What is m$\widehat{IZ}$? 45°

b. If *QT* = 15, find the perimeter of the octagon. ≈ 91.8 units

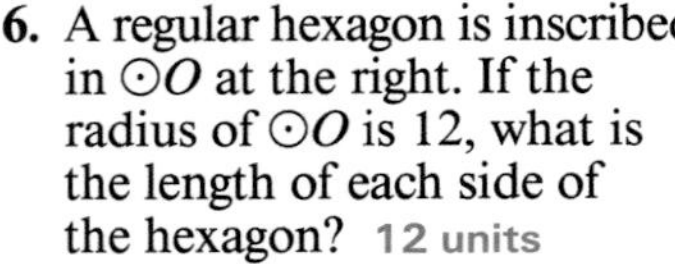

6. A regular hexagon is inscribed in ⊙*O* at the right. If the radius of ⊙*O* is 12, what is the length of each side of the hexagon? 12 units

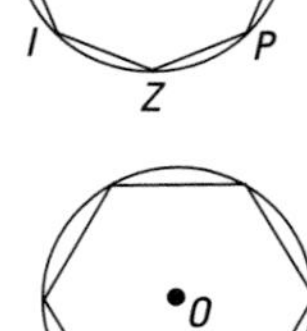

Objective B: *Calculate measures of inscribed angles from measures of intercepted arcs, and vice versa.* (*Lesson 14-2*)

In 7 and 8, use the circle at the right.

7. Find m$\widehat{CB}$. 106°

8. Find m$\widehat{ABC}$. 182°

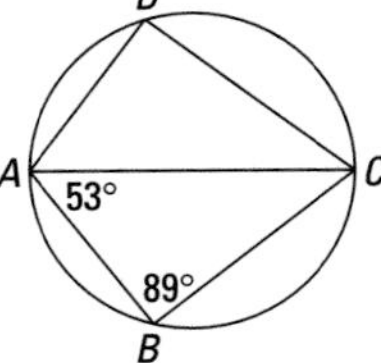

In 9 and 10, △*PQR* is inscribed in the circle at the right.

9. Find m∠*Q*. 81

10. Find m∠*P*. 52

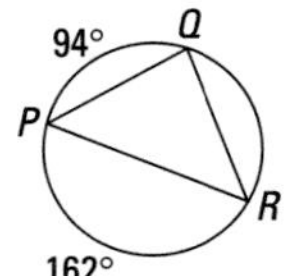

Objective C: *Calculate measures of angles between chords, secants, or tangents from measures of intercepted arcs, and vice versa.* (*Lessons 14-2, 14-4, 14-6*)

In 11 and 12, use circle *Z* at the right.

11. If m$\widehat{DG}$ = 100° and m$\widehat{EF}$ = 140°, what is m∠*EHF*? 120

12. If m∠*EHD* = 51 and m$\widehat{GF}$ = 37°, what other arc measure can be found, and what is that measure? m$\widehat{DE}$ = 65°

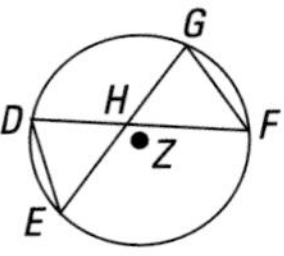

CHAPTER FOURTEEN

13. In the figure below, m$\widehat{BC}$ = 30°, and m$\widehat{DE}$ = 125°. Find the measures of as many angles in the figure as you can. See margin.

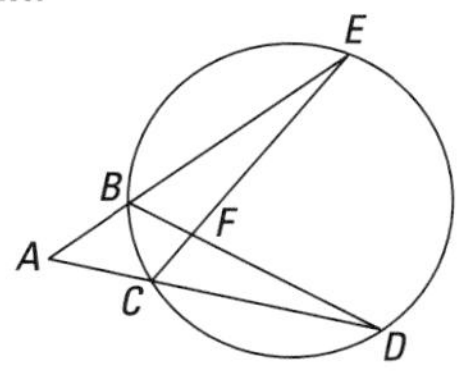

In 14–16, use ⊙L with measures as marked.

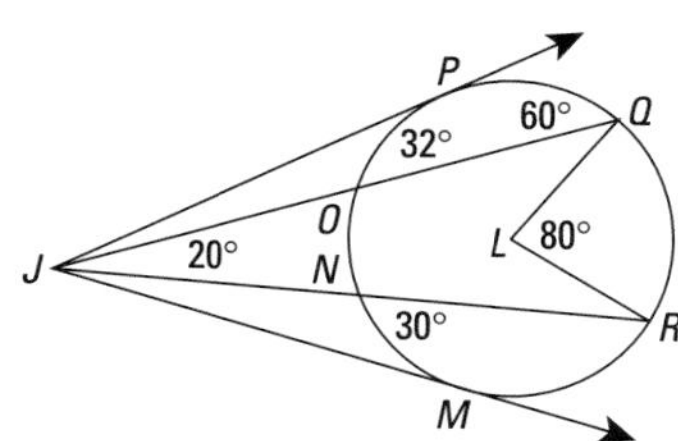

14. Find m∠PJQ. 14

15. Find m$\widehat{ON}$. 40°

16. Find m∠PJM. 78

Objective D: *Locate the center of a circle given sufficient information.* *(Lesson 14-3)*

17. Trace the figure below. Then find the center of the circle using the right angle method.

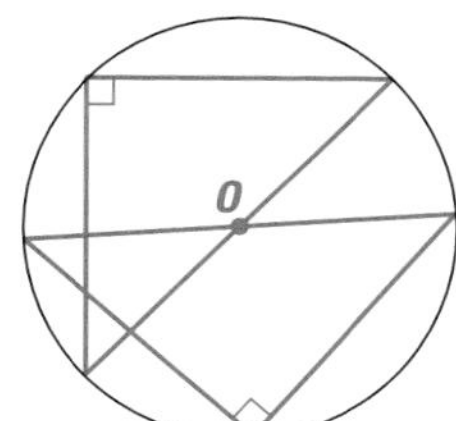

18. Trace the circular arc below. Find the center of the circle containing the circular arc. Then draw the entire circle. See margin.

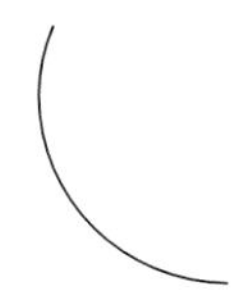

19. Trace the three points below at the left. Draw the circle through points A, B, and C.

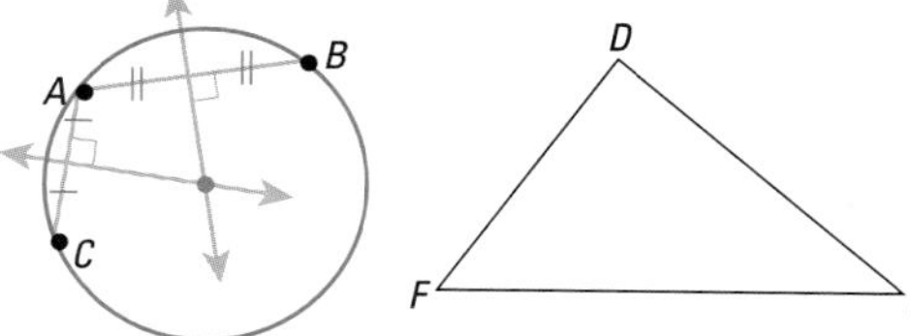

20. Trace $\triangle DEF$ above at the right. Draw the circle containing all the vertices of $\triangle DEF$. See margin.

Objective E: *Apply the Secant Length Theorem and the Tangent Square Theorem.* *(Lesson 14-7)*

21. In the figure below, A, B, C, and D all lie on ⊙O. If $AX = 12$, $XB = 40$, and $DX = 48$, find CX. 10 units

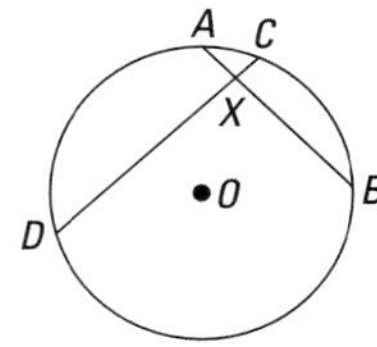

22. In the figure below, $\overleftrightarrow{QR}$ is tangent to ⊙Z at R. If $QR = 8$ and $QX = 4$, find YX. 12 units

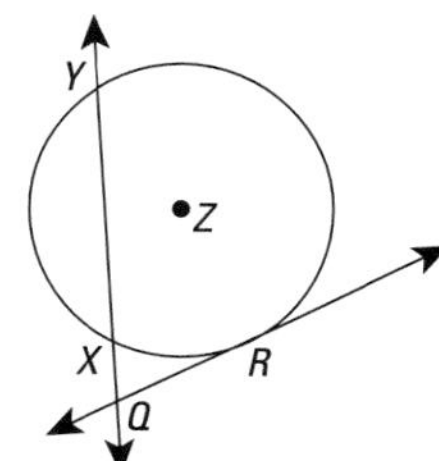

In 23 and 24, refer to ⊙O below.

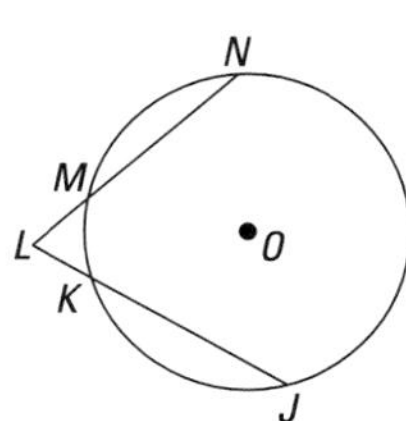

21 units

23. If $LN = 20$, $MN = 15$, and $LJ = 25$, find KJ.

24. If $LM = 6$, $MN = 7$, and $KJ = 8$, find LK. ≈ 5.7 units

It is effective to ask students which questions they still do not understand and use the day or days as a total class discussion of the material which the class finds most difficult.

Assessment

Evaluation The *Assessment Sourcebook* provides five forms of the Chapter 14 Test. Forms A and B present parallel versions in a short-answer format. Forms C and D offer performance assessment. The fifth test is Chapter 14 Test, Cumulative Form. About 50% of this test covers Chapter 14; 25% of it covers Chapter 13, and 25% covers earlier chapters. In addition to these tests, Comprehensive Test, Chapters 1–14 gives roughly equal attention to all chapters.

Additional Answers

13. m∠EFD = m∠BFC = 77.5; m∠EBD = m∠ECD = 62.5; m∠BAC = 47.5; m∠CEB = m∠CDB = 15; m∠BFE = m∠CFD = 102.5; m∠ABD = m∠ACE = 117.5.

18.

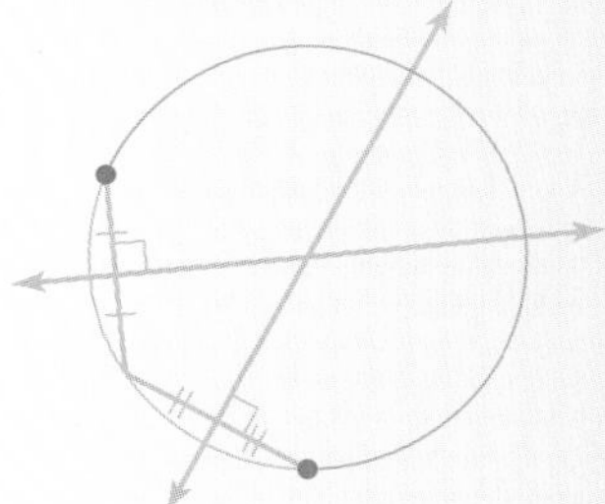

20.

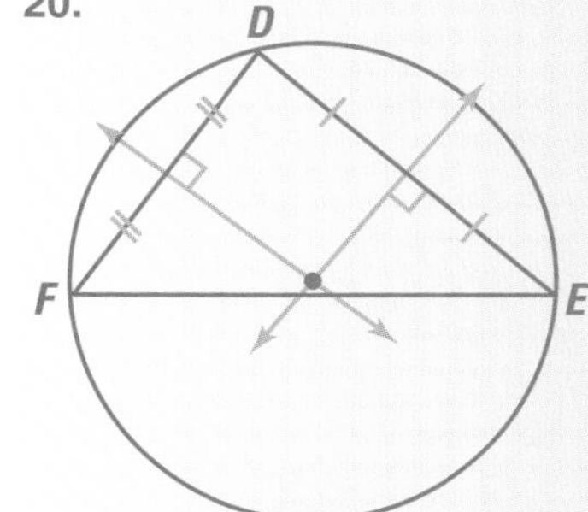

Feedback After students have taken the test for Chapter 14 and you have scored the results, return the tests to students for discussion. Class discussion of the questions that caused trouble for the most students can be very effective in identifying and clarifying misunderstandings. You might want to have them write down the items they missed and work, either in groups or at home, to correct them. It is important for students to receive feedback on every chapter test, and we recommend that students see and correct their mistakes.

Additional Answers

26. $\ell \perp \overline{AB}$ by the Radius-Tangent Theorem. From the given we have $\overline{CD} \perp \overline{AB}$. Therefore, $\ell \parallel \overline{CD}$ by the Two Perpendiculars Theorem

27. $m\widehat{YZ} = m\widehat{XY} = m\widehat{XZ}$, so $ZX = ZY = XY$ by the Arc-Chord Congruence Theorem. Therefore, by the definition of equilateral triangle, $\triangle XYZ$ is equilateral.

28.

Conclusions	Justifications
1. $\overline{ZV}$ is $\perp$ bisector of $\overline{XY}$.	Chord-Center Thm.
2. $ZY = ZX$	Perpendicular Bisector Theorem
3. $\triangle ZYX$ is isosceles.	def. of isosceles $\triangle$

29. $m\angle BAD = 15$, $m\angle DAC = 15$, $m\angle BAC = 30$, $m\angle ABD = 90$, $m\angle BDC = 150$, $m\angle ACD = 90$, $m\angle ADB = 75$, and $m\angle ADC = 75$.

30. Sample argument:

Conclusions	Justifications
0. $\overline{AB}$ and $\overline{AC}$ are tangent to $\odot D$ at points B and C.	Given
1. $AB = AC$	Two tangents to a circle from any point have the same length.
2. $BD = CD$	def. of circle
3. $AD = AD$	Reflexive Property of Equality
4. $\triangle ABD \cong \triangle ACD$	SSS Congruence Thm.

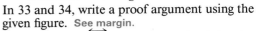

PROPERTIES DEAL WITH THE PRINCIPLES BEHIND THE MATHEMATICS.

Objective F: *Make deductions from properties of radii, chords, and tangents, and know sufficient conditions for radii to be perpendicular to them.* *(Lessons 14-1, 14-5, 14-6)*

In 25 and 26, refer to $\odot O$ below. $\overline{AB}$ is a diameter, $\overline{AB} \perp \overline{CD}$ and ℓ is tangent to $\odot O$ at point A.

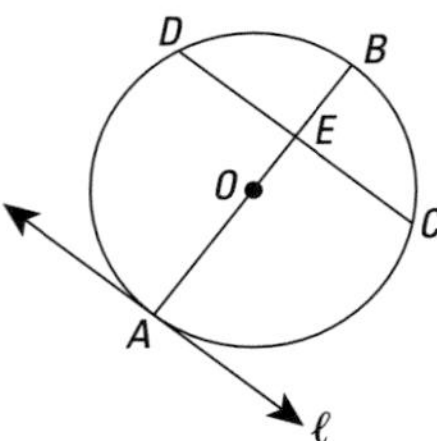

25. Justify: $DE = EC$. Chord-Center Theorem, part 1

26. Write an argument that proves $\ell \parallel \overline{CD}$. See margin.

In 27 and 28, write a proof argument using the given figure. 27–30) See margin.

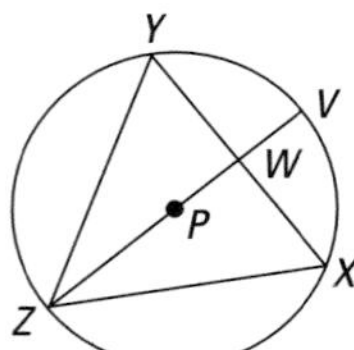

27. Given: $m\widehat{YZ} = m\widehat{XY} = m\widehat{XZ}$.
To prove: $\triangle XYZ$ is equilateral.

28. Given: W is the midpoint of $\overline{XY}$.
To prove: $\triangle ZYX$ is isosceles.

In 29 and 30, $\overline{AB}$ and $\overline{AC}$ are tangent to $\odot D$ at points B and C in the figure below.

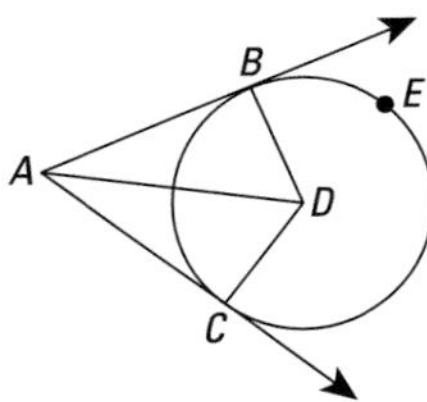

29. Find all angle measures that can be found, if $m\widehat{BEC} = 210°$.

30. Write an argument to prove $\triangle ABD \cong \triangle ACD$.

Objective G: *Make deductions from properties of angles formed by chords, tangents, or secants.* *(Lessons 14-2, 14-4, 14-6)*

In 31 and 32, $ABDC$ at the right is a rectangle.

31. Explain why $\overline{BC}$ is a diameter. See margin.

32. Suppose $m\widehat{AB} = x$. What is $m\angle ACB$? $\frac{x}{2}$

In 33 and 34, write a proof argument using the given figure. See margin.

33. Given: $\overleftrightarrow{AB}$ is tangent to circle O at B.
To prove: $m\angle ABD = m\angle C$.

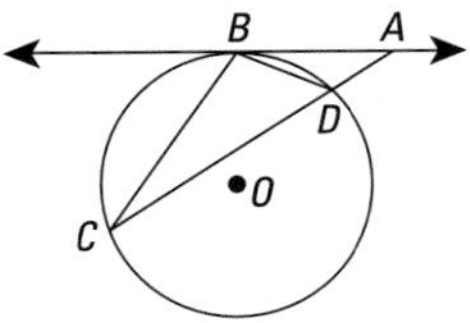

34. Given: $\overrightarrow{XW}$ and $\overrightarrow{XY}$ are tangent to $\odot P$ below at W and Y, respectively.
To prove: $m\angle X = 180 - m\widehat{WY}$.

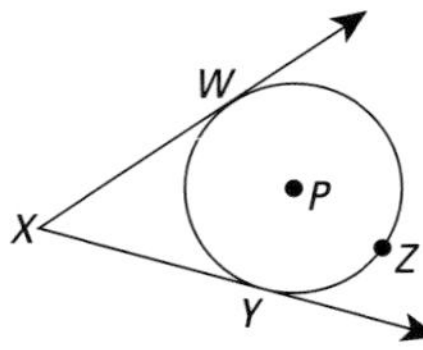

Objective H: *Apply the Isoperimetric Theorems and the Isoperimetric Inequality to determine which figures have the greatest or least area, perimeter, or volume.* *(Lessons 14-8, 14-9)*

35. Consider all figures with area 800 square feet.
- **a.** Which has the least perimeter? circle
- **b.** What is the perimeter of the figure in part **a**? ≈ 100.3 ft

36. **a.** Of all figures with perimeter 2000 centimeters, which has the most area? a circle
- **b.** What is that area? ≈ 318,310 cm^2

Additional Answers, continued

31. $\angle A$ and $\angle D$ are right angles, so they intercept semicircles.

33. By the Inscribed Angle Theorem, $m\angle C = \frac{1}{2} m\widehat{BD}$. By the Tangent-Chord Theorem, $m\angle ABD = \frac{1}{2} m\widehat{BD}$. By Transitivity of Equality, $m\angle ABD = m\angle C$.

34. Draw $\overline{WP}$ and $\overline{PY}$. $m\angle XWP = m\angle XYP = 90°$ since $\overrightarrow{XW}$ and $\overrightarrow{XY}$ are tangent to $\odot P$. The sum of the measures of four angles in quadrilateral $XWPY$ is 360. Thus, $m\angle X = 360 - 90 - 90 - m\angle WPY = 180 - m\angle WPY = 180 - m\widehat{WY}$.

37. The surface area of a solid is 10,000 square meters. What figure has the largest volume for this surface area? a sphere

38. A circle and a square both have perimeters of 32 inches. square 64 in^2; circle: ≈ 81.5 in^2

a. Calculate their areas.

b. Which has the larger area? the circle

39. a. Of all solids with surface area 48 square feet, which has the maximum volume? a sphere

b. What is that volume? ≈ 31.3 cu ft

40. A sphere and a cylinder both have volume 20,000 cubic meters.

a. Can you tell which has the larger surface area? Yes, the cylinder

b. Why or why not? See margin.

USES DEAL WITH APPLICATIONS OF MATHEMATICS IN REAL SITUATIONS.

Objective I: *Given the angle width of a lens and the width of an object, determine the set of points from which the object just fits in the picture.* *(Lesson 14-3)* 41a, 42a) See margin.

In 41 and 42, a photographer wants to take a picture showing the entire length of a football field (from A to B). A scale drawing is shown. The 50-yard line bisects the segment connecting the goal posts at C, and $AB = 120$ yards.

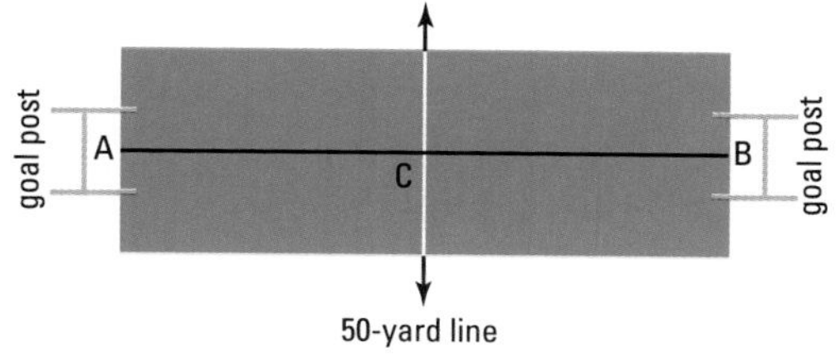

41. a. Locate all points where the photographer could stand to exactly fit $\overline{AB}$ if the camera lens has a picture angle of 62°.

b. At least how far from C will the photographer be if he or she stands on the extended 50-yard line? ≈ 99.9 yards

42. a. Locate all points where the photographer could stand to exactly fit $\overline{AB}$ if the camera lens has a picture angle of 84°.

b. At least how far from C will the photographer be standing on the extended 50-yard line? ≈ 66.6 yards

Objective J: *Determine the maximum distance that can be seen from a particular elevation.* *(Lesson 14-5)* 43) ≈ 61.8 km 44) 84.1 km

In 43–46, assume the radius of Earth is 3960 miles, or 6373 kilometers, and assume there are no hills or obstructions.

43. How far can you see from the top of the Eiffel Tower in Paris, 300 meters up?

44. How far can you see from the top of the CN Tower in Toronto, the world's tallest self-supporting structure, 555 meters up?

45. How far can you see if you are standing on the ground and your eyes are 5 feet above the ground? ≈ 2.74 miles

46. How far can you see from a plane 4 miles high? ≈ 178 miles

47–48) See margin.

Objective K: *Apply the Isoperimetric Theorems and the Isoperimetric Inequality in real situations.* *(Lessons 14-8, 14-9)*

47. a. Of all containers that can hold a liter of orange juice, what is the shape of the container that has the least surface area?

b. Why is this shape seldom used?

48. A farmer is making a pigpen with 60 feet of fencing. What is the area of the shape that gives the most room for the pigs?

49. Draw a figure with a large perimeter for its area.

50. Identify a figure with a large surface area for its volume. Sample: a sheet of notebook paper

REPRESENTATIONS DEAL WITH PICTURES, GRAPHS, OR OBJECTS THAT ILLUSTRATE CONCEPTS.

There are no Representation Objectives for this chapter.

40b. Of all solids with the same volume, the sphere has the least surface area.

41a. All points shown in the diagram on ⊙O.

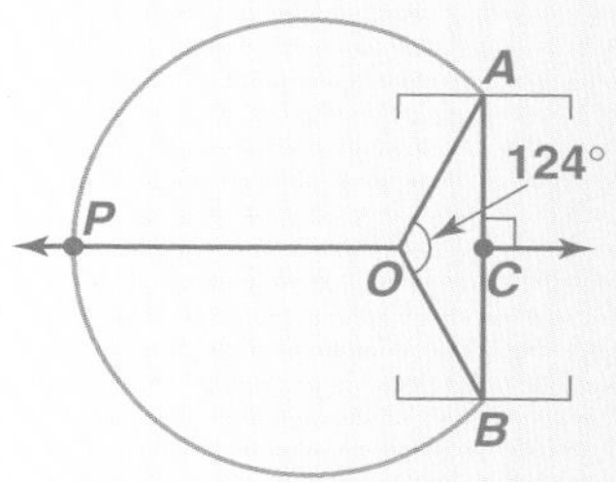

42a. All points shown in the diagram on ⊙O.

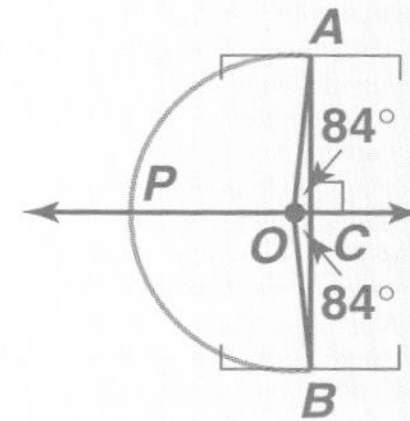

47a. a sphere

b. Sample: The container could easily roll off a shelf

48. A circle with area $\frac{900}{\pi} \approx$ 286 $feet^2$

APPENDIX A

Theorems

Theorems are statements that have been proved, or can be proved, from the postulates. They are given here in order of appearance.

Chapter 1

Line Intersection Theorem: Two different lines intersect in at most one point. *(Lesson 1-7, p. 43)*

Chapter 3

Linear Pair Theorem: If two angles form a linear pair, then they are supplementary. *(Lesson 3-3, p. 140)*

Vertical Angles Theorem: If two angles are vertical angles, then they have equal measures. *(Lesson 3-3, p. 141)*

Parallel Lines and Slopes Theorem: Two nonvertical lines are parallel if and only if they have the same slope. *(Lesson 3-6, p. 158)*

Transitivity of Parallelism Theorem: In a plane, if $\ell \parallel m$ and $m \parallel n$, then $\ell \parallel n$. *(Lesson 3-6, p. 158)*

Two Perpendiculars Theorem: If two coplanar lines ℓ and m are each perpendicular to the same line, then they are parallel to each other. *(Lesson 3-7, p. 162)*

Perpendicular to Parallels Theorem: In a plane, if a line is perpendicular to one of two parallel lines, then it is also perpendicular to the other. *(Lesson 3-7, p. 162)*

Perpendicular Lines and Slopes Theorem: Two nonvertical lines are perpendicular if and only if the product of their slopes is -1. *(Lesson 3-7, p. 162)*

Chapter 4

Figure Reflection Theorem: If a figure is determined by certain points, then its reflection image is the corresponding figure determined by the reflection images of those points. *(Lesson 4-2, p. 192)*

Two Reflection Theorem for Translations: If $m \parallel \ell$, the translation $r_m \circ r_\ell$ has magnitude two times the distance between ℓ and m, in the direction from ℓ perpendicular to m. *(Lesson 4-4, p. 206)*

Two Reflection Theorem for Rotations: If m intersects ℓ, the rotation $r_m \circ r_\ell$ has center at the point of intersection of m and ℓ and has magnitude twice the measure of the non-obtuse angle formed by these lines, in the direction from ℓ to m. *(Lesson 4-5, p. 211)*

Chapter 5

Corresponding Parts of Congruent Figures (CPCF) Theorem: If two figures are congruent, then any pair of corresponding parts is congruent. *(Lesson 5-1, p. 245)*

A-B-C-D Theorem: Every isometry preserves Angle measure, Betweenness, Collinearity (lines), and Distance (lengths of segments). *(Lesson 5-1, p. 246)*

862

Equivalence Properties of ≅ Theorem: For any figures F, G, and H:
Reflexive Property of Congruence: $F \cong F$.
Symmetric Property of Congruence: If $F \cong G$, then $G \cong F$.
Transitive Property of Congruence: If $F \cong G$ and $G \cong H$, then $F \cong H$. *(Lesson 5-2, p. 251)*

Segment Congruence Theorem: Two segments are congruent if and only if they have the same length. *(Lesson 5-2, p. 252)*

Angle Congruence Theorem: Two angles are congruent if and only if they have the same measure. *(Lesson 5-2, p. 252)*

Euclid's First Theorem: If circle A contains point B and circle B contains point A and the circles intersect at C, then $\triangle ABC$ is equilateral. *(Lesson 5-4, p. 264)*

// Lines ⇒ AIA ≅ Theorem: If two parallel lines are cut by a transversal, then alternate interior angles are congruent. *(Lesson 5-4, p. 265)*

AIA ≅ ⇒ // Lines Theorem: If two lines are cut by a transversal and form congruent alternate interior angles, then the lines are parallel. *(Lesson 5-4, p. 266)*

AEA ≅ ⇒ // Lines Theorem: If two lines are cut by a transversal and form congruent alternate exterior angles, then the lines are parallel. *(Lesson 5-4, p. 267)*

Perpendicular Bisector Theorem: If a point is on the perpendicular bisector of a segment, then it is equidistant from the endpoints of the segment. *(Lesson 5-5, p. 271)*

Uniqueness of Parallels Theorem (Playfair's Parallel Postulate): Through a point not on a line, there is exactly one line parallel to the given line. *(Lesson 5-6, p. 277)*

Triangle-Sum Theorem: The sum of the measures of the angles of a triangle is 180°. *(Lesson 5-7, p. 282)*

Quadrilateral-Sum Theorem: The sum of the measures of the angles of a convex quadrilateral is 360°. *(Lesson 5-7, p. 283)*

Polygon-Sum Theorem: The sum of the measures of the angles of a convex n-gon is $(n - 2) \cdot 180°$. *(Lesson 5-7, p. 284)*

Chapter 6

Flip-Flop Theorem:
(1) If F and G are points and $r_\ell(F) = G$, then $r_\ell(G) = F$.
(2) If F and G are figures and $r_\ell(F) = G$, then $r_\ell(G) = F$. *(Lesson 6-1, p. 301)*

Segment Symmetry Theorem: Every segment has exactly two symmetry lines: (1) its perpendicular bisector, and (2) the line containing the segment. *(Lesson 6-1, p. 302)*

Side-Switching Theorem: If one side of an angle is reflected over the line containing the angle bisector, its image is the other side of the angle. *(Lesson 6-1, p. 303)*

Angle Symmetry Theorem: The line containing the bisector of an angle is a symmetry line of the angle. *(Lesson 6-1, p. 303)*

Circle Symmetry Theorem: A circle is reflection-symmetric to any line through its center. *(Lesson 6-1, p. 303)*

Symmetric Figures Theorem: If a figure is symmetric, then any pair of corresponding parts under the symmetry is congruent. *(Lesson 6-1, p. 304)*

Isosceles Triangle Symmetry Theorem: The line containing the bisector of the vertex angle of an isosceles triangle is a symmetry line for the triangle. *(Lesson 6-2, p. 310)*

Isosceles Triangle Coincidence Theorem: In an isosceles triangle, the bisector of the vertex angle, the perpendicular bisector of the base, and the median to the base determine the same line. *(Lesson 6-2, p. 310)*

Isosceles Triangle Base Angles Theorem: If a triangle has two congruent sides, then the angles opposite them are congruent. *(Lesson 6-2, p. 310)*

Equilateral Triangle Symmetry Theorem: Every equilateral triangle has three symmetry lines, which are the bisectors of its angles (or equivalently, the perpendicular bisectors of its sides). *(Lesson 6-2, p. 312)*

Equilateral Triangle Angle Theorem: If a triangle is equilateral, then it is equiangular. *(Lesson 6-2, p. 312)*

Corollary: Each angle of an equilateral triangle has measure 60°. *(Lesson 6-2, p. 312)*

Quadrilateral Hierarchy Theorem: Every property true of all figures of one type on the hierarchy is also true of all figures of all the types below it to which the first type is connected. *(Lesson 6-3, p. 319)*

Kite Symmetry Theorem: The line containing the ends of a kite is a symmetry line for the kite. *(Lesson 6-4, p. 324)*

Kite Diagonal Theorem: The symmetry diagonal of a kite is the perpendicular bisector of the other diagonal and bisects the two angles at the ends of the kite. *(Lesson 6-4, p. 325)*

Rhombus Diagonal Theorem: Each diagonal of a rhombus is the perpendicular bisector of the other diagonal. *(Lesson 6-4, p. 325)*

Theorem: If a quadrilateral is a rhombus, then it is a parallelogram. *(Lesson 6-4, p. 326)*

Trapezoid Angle Theorem: In a trapezoid, consecutive angles between a pair of parallel sides are supplementary. *(Lesson 6-5, p. 330)*

Isosceles Trapezoid Symmetry Theorem: The perpendicular bisector of one base of an isosceles trapezoid is the perpendicular bisector of the other base and a symmetry line for the trapezoid. *(Lesson 6-5, p. 330)*

Isosceles Trapezoid Theorem: In an isosceles trapezoid, the non-base sides are congruent. *(Lesson 6-5, p. 331)*

Rectangle Symmetry Theorem: The perpendicular bisectors of the sides of a rectangle are symmetry lines for the rectangle. *(Lesson 6-5, p. 331)*

Theorem: If a figure possesses two lines of symmetry intersecting at a point P, then it is rotation-symmetric with a center of symmetry at P. *(Lesson 6-6, p. 337)*

Center of a Regular Polygon Theorem: In any regular polygon there is a point (its center) which is equidistant from all of its vertices. *(Lesson 6-7, p. 343)*

Regular Polygon Symmetry Theorem: Every regular n-gon possesses (1) n symmetry lines, which are the perpendicular bisectors of each of its sides and the bisectors of each of its angles, (2) n-fold rotation symmetry. *(Lesson 6-7, p. 344)*

Chapter 7

Theorem: If two angles in one triangle are congruent to two angles in another triangle, then the third angles are congruent. *(Lesson 7-1, p. 366)*

SSS Congruence Theorem: If, in two triangles, three sides of one are congruent to three sides of the other, then the triangles are congruent. *(Lesson 7-2, p. 370)*

SAS Congruence Theorem: If, in two triangles, two sides and the included angle of one are congruent to two sides and the included angle of the other, then the triangles are congruent. *(Lesson 7-2, p. 372)*

ASA Congruence Theorem: If, in two triangles, two angles and the included side of one are congruent to two angles and the included side of the other, then the two triangles are congruent. *(Lesson 7-2, p. 373)*

AAS Congruence Theorem: If, in two triangles, two angles and a non-included side of one are congruent respectively to two angles and the *corresponding* non-included side of the other, then the triangles are congruent. *(Lesson 7-2, p. 374)*

Isosceles Triangle Base Angles Converse Theorem: If two angles of a triangle are congruent, then the sides opposite them are congruent. *(Lesson 7-3, p. 380)*

HL Congruence Theorem: If, in two right triangles, the hypotenuse and a leg of one are congruent to the hypotenuse and a leg of the other, then the two triangles are congruent. *(Lesson 7-5, p. 390)*

SsA Congruence Theorem: If two sides and the angle opposite the longer of the two sides in one triangle are congruent, respectively, to two sides and the corresponding angle in another triangle, then the triangles are congruent. *(Lesson 7-5, p. 392)*

Properties of a Parallelogram Theorem: In any parallelogram, (a) opposite sides are congruent; (b) opposite angles are congruent; (c) the diagonals intersect at their midpoints. *(Lesson 7-7, p. 405)*

Theorem: The distance between two given parallel lines is constant. *(Lesson 7-7, p. 406)*

Parallelogram Symmetry Theorem: Every parallelogram has 2-fold rotation symmetry about the intersection of its diagonals. *(Lesson 7-7, p. 407)*

Sufficient Conditions for a Parallelogram Theorem: If, in a quadrilateral, (a) one pair of sides is both parallel and congruent, or (b) both pairs of opposite sides are congruent, or (c) the diagonals bisect each other, or (d) both pairs of opposite angles are congruent, then the quadrilateral is a parallelogram. *(Lesson 7-8, p. 413)*

Exterior Angle Theorem: In a triangle, the measure of an exterior angle is equal to the sum of the measures of the interior angles at the other two vertices of the triangle. *(Lesson 7-9, p. 417)*

Exterior Angle Inequality: In a triangle, the measure of an exterior angle is greater than the measure of the interior angle at each of the other two vertices. *(Lesson 7-9, p. 417)*

Unequal Sides Theorem: If two sides of a triangle are not congruent, then the angles opposite them are not congruent, and the larger angle is opposite the longer side. *(Lesson 7-9, p. 419)*

864

Unequal Angles Theorem: If two angles of a triangle are not congruent, then the sides opposite them are not congruent, and the longer side is opposite the larger angle. *(Lesson 7-9, p. 419)*

Chapter 8

Equilateral Polygon Perimeter Formula: The perimeter p of an equilateral n-gon with sides of length s is given by the formula $p = ns$. *(Lesson 8-1, p. 438)*

Right Triangle Area Formula: The area of a right triangle is half the product of the lengths of its legs. *(Lesson 8-4, p. 453)*

Triangle Area Formula: The area of a triangle is half the product of a side (the base) and the altitude (height) to that side. *(Lesson 8-4, p. 454)*

Trapezoid Area Formula: The area of a trapezoid equals half the product of its altitude and the sum of the lengths of its bases. *(Lesson 8-5, p. 460)*

Parallelogram Area Formula: The area of a parallelogram is the product of one of its bases and the altitude to that base. *(Lesson 8-5, p. 461)*

Pythagorean Theorem: In any right triangle with legs of lengths a and b and hypotenuse of length c, $a^2 + b^2 = c^2$. *(Lesson 8-6, p. 467)*

Pythagorean Theorem (alternate statement): In any right triangle, the sum of the areas of the squares on its legs equals the area of the square on its hypotenuse. *(Lesson 8-6, p. 467)*

Pythagorean Converse Theorem: If a triangle has sides of lengths a, b, and c, and $a^2 + b^2 = c^2$, then the triangle is a right triangle. *(Lesson 8-6, p. 469)*

Circle Circumference Formula: If a circle has circumference C, diameter d, and radius r, then $C = \pi d$, or $C = 2\pi r$. *(Lesson 8-7, p. 475)*

Circle Area Formula: The area A of a circle with radius r is πr^2. *(Lesson 8-8, p. 481)*

Chapter 9

Line-Plane Perpendicularity Theorem: If a line is perpendicular to two different lines at their point of intersection, then it is perpendicular to the plane that contains those lines. *(Lesson 9-2, p. 501)*

The Four-Color Theorem: Suppose regions which share a border of some length must have different colors. Then any map of regions on a plane or a sphere can be colored in such a way that only four colors are needed. *(Lesson 9-9, p. 547)*

Chapter 10

Right Prism-Cylinder Lateral Area Formula: The lateral area, L.A., of a right prism (or right cylinder) is the product of its height h and the perimeter (circumference) p of its base. *(Lesson 10-1, p. 565)*

Prism-Cylinder Surface Area Formula: The surface area, S.A., of any prism or cylinder is the sum of its lateral area L.A. and twice the area B of a base. *(Lesson 10-1, p. 566)*

Pyramid-Cone Surface Area Formula: The surface area, S.A., of any pyramid or cone is the sum of its lateral area L.A. and the area B of its base. *(Lesson 10-2, p. 570)*

Regular Pyramid-Right Cone Lateral Area Formula: The lateral area, L.A., of a regular pyramid or right cone is half the product of its slant height ℓ and the perimeter (circumference) p of its base. *(Lesson 10-2, p. 573)*

Cube Volume Formula: The volume V of a cube with edge s is s^3. *(Lesson 10-3, p. 579)*

Prism-Cylinder Volume Formula: The volume V of any prism or cylinder is the product of its height h and the area B of its base. *(Lesson 10-5, p. 590)*

Pyramid-Cone Volume Formula: The volume V of any pyramid or cone equals $\frac{1}{3}$ the product of its height h and its base area B. *(Lesson 10-7, p. 601)*

Sphere Volume Formula: The volume V of any sphere is $\frac{4}{3}\pi$ times the cube of its radius r. *(Lesson 10-8, p. 605)*

Sphere Surface Area Formula: The total surface area S.A. of a sphere with radius r is $4\pi r^2$. *(Lesson 10-9, p. 610)*

Chapter 11

Distance Formula on the Coordinate Plane: The distance d between two points (x_1, y_1) and (x_2, y_2) in the coordinate plane is given by the formula $d = \sqrt{(x_2 - x_1)^2 + (y_2 - y_1)^2}$. *(Lesson 11-6, p. 652)*

Equation for a Circle: The circle with center (h, k) and radius r is the set of points (x, y) satisfying $(x - h)^2 + (y - k)^2 = r^2$. *(Lesson 11-7, p. 657)*

Number Line Midpoint Formula: On a number line, the coordinate of the midpoint of the segment with endpoints a and b is $\frac{a + b}{2}$. *(Lesson 11-8, p. 662)*

Coordinate Plane Midpoint Formula: In the coordinate plane, the midpoint of the segment with endpoints (x_1, y_1) and (x_2, y_2) is $\left(\frac{x_1 + x_2}{2}, \frac{y_1 + y_2}{2}\right)$. *(Lesson 11-8, p. 663)*

Midpoint Connector Theorem: The segment connecting the midpoints of two sides of a triangle is parallel to and half the length of the third side. *(Lesson 11-8, p. 664)*

Three-Dimension Distance Formula: The distance d between two points (x_1, y_1, z_1) and (x_2, y_2, z_2) is given by the formula $d = \sqrt{(x_2 - x_1)^2 + (y_2 - y_1)^2 + (z_2 - z_1)^2}$. *(Lesson 11-9, p. 669)*

Box Diagonal Formula: In a box with dimensions ℓ, w, and h, the length d of the diagonal is given by the formula $d = \sqrt{\ell^2 + w^2 + h^2}$. *(Lesson 11-9, p. 671)*

Equation for a Sphere: The sphere with center (h, k, j) and radius r is the set of points (x, y, z) satisfying $(x - h)^2 + (y - k)^2 + (z - j)^2 = r^2$. *(Lesson 11-9, p. 671)*

Three-Dimension Midpoint Formula: In space, the midpoint of the segment with endpoints (x_1, y_1, z_1) and (x_2, y_2, z_2) is $\left(\frac{x_1 + x_2}{2}, \frac{y_1 + y_2}{2}, \frac{z_1 + z_2}{2}\right)$. *(Lesson 11-9, p. 672)*

Varignon's Theorem: If the midpoints of consecutive sides of any quadrilateral are connected, then the quadrilateral so formed is a parallelogram. *(Chapter 11 Projects, p. 676)*

Chapter 12

Properties of S_k Theorem: Let S_k be the transformation mapping (x, y) onto (kx, ky). Then, under S_k,
(1) a line and its image are parallel, and
(2) the distance between two image points is k times the distance between their preimages.
(Lesson 12-1, p. 688)

S_k Size-Change Theorem: When $k > 0$, the transformation S_k, where $S_k(x, y) = (kx, ky)$, is the size change with center $(0, 0)$ and magnitude k. *(Lesson 12-2, p. 694)*

Size-Change Distance Theorem: Under a size change with magnitude $k > 0$, the distance between any two image points is k times the distance between their preimages. *(Lesson 12-3, p. 699)*

Size-Change Preservation Properties Theorem: Every size transformation preserves (1) angle measure, (2) betweenness, and (3) collinearity. *(Lesson 12-3, p. 699)*

Figure Size-Change Theorem: If a figure is determined by certain points, then its size-change image is the corresponding figure determined by the size-change images of those points. *(Lesson 12-3, p. 701)*

Means-Extremes Property: If $\frac{a}{b} = \frac{c}{d}$ then $ad = bc$. *(Lesson 12-4, p. 706)*

Similar Figures Theorem: If two figures are similar, then: (1) corresponding angles are congruent, and (2) corresponding lengths are proportional. *(Lesson 12-5, p. 713)*

Theorem: If $G \sim G'$ and k is the ratio of similitude, then

(1) $\text{Perimeter}(G') = k \cdot \text{Perimeter}(G)$ or $\frac{\text{Perimeter}(G')}{\text{Perimeter}(G)} = k$,

(2) $\text{Area}(G') = k^2 \cdot \text{Area}(G)$ or $\frac{\text{Area}(G')}{\text{Area}(G)} = k^2$, and

(3) $\text{Volume}(G') = k^3 \cdot \text{Volume}(G)$ or $\frac{\text{Volume}(G')}{\text{Volume}(G)} = k^3$.

(Lesson 12-6, p. 718)

Fundamental Theorem of Similarity:
If two figures are similar with ratio of similitude k, then: (a) corresponding angle measures are equal; (b) corresponding lengths and perimeters are in the ratio k; (c) corresponding areas and surface areas are in the ratio k^2; and (d) corresponding volumes are in the ratio k^3. *(Lesson 12-6, p. 719)*

Chapter 13

SSS Similarity Theorem: If the three sides of one triangle are proportional to three sides of a second triangle, then the triangles are similar. *(Lesson 13-1, p. 739)*

AA Similarity Theorem: If two angles of one triangle are congruent to two angles of another, then the triangles are similar. *(Lesson 13-2, p. 745)*

SAS Similarity Theorem: If, in two triangles, the ratios of two pairs of corresponding sides are equal and the included angles are congruent, then the triangles are similar. *(Lesson 13-2, p. 747)*

Side-Splitting Theorem: If a line is parallel to a side of a triangle and intersects the other two sides in distinct points, it splits these sides into proportional segments. *(Lesson 13-3, p. 751)*

Side-Splitting Converse Theorem: If a line intersects $\overline{OP}$ and $\overline{OQ}$ in distinct points X and Y so that $\frac{OX}{XP} = \frac{OY}{YQ}$ then $\overleftrightarrow{XY} \parallel \overleftrightarrow{PQ}$. *(Lesson 13-3, p. 752)*

Geometric Mean Theorem: The positive geometric mean of the positive numbers a and b is $\sqrt{ab}$. *(Lesson 13-4, p. 759)*

Right Triangle Altitude Theorem: In a right triangle,
(1) the altitude to the hypotenuse is the geometric mean of the segments into which it divides the hypotenuse, and
(2) each leg is the geometric mean of the hypotenuse and the segment of the hypotenuse adjacent to the leg. *(Lesson 13-4, p. 761)*

Isosceles Right Triangle Theorem: In an isosceles right triangle, if a leg is x, then the hypotenuse is $x\sqrt{2}$. *(Lesson 13-5, p. 765)*

30-60-90 Triangle Theorem: In a 30-60-90 (right) triangle, if the short leg is x, then the longer leg is $x\sqrt{3}$, and the hypotenuse is $2x$. *(Lesson 13-5, p. 767)*

SAS Triangle Area Formula: In any $\triangle ABC$, the area of $\triangle ABC = \frac{1}{2}ab \sin C$. *(Lesson 13-8, p. 786)*

Chapter 14

Arc-Chord Congruence Theorem: In a circle or in congruent circles:
(1) If two arcs have the same measure, they are congruent and their chords are congruent.
(2) If two chords have the same length, their minor arcs have the same measure.
(Lesson 14-1, p. 801)

Chord-Center Theorem:
(1) The line that contains the center of a circle and is perpendicular to a chord bisects the chord.
(2) The line that contains the center of a circle and the midpoint of a chord bisects the central angle of the chord.
(3) The bisector of the central angle of a chord is the perpendicular bisector of the chord.
(4) The perpendicular bisector of a chord of a circle contains the center of the circle.
(Lesson 14-1, p. 802)

Inscribed Angle Theorem: In a circle, the measure of an inscribed angle is one-half the measure of its intercepted arc. *(Lesson 14-2, p. 807)*

Theorem: An angle inscribed in a semicircle is a right angle. *(Lesson 14-2, p. 809)*

Theorem: In a circle, if two inscribed angles intercept the same arc, then they have the same measure. *(Lesson 14-2, p. 811)*

Angle-Chord Theorem: The measure of an angle formed by two intersecting chords is one-half the sum of the measures of the arcs intercepted by it and its vertical angle. *(Lesson 14-4, p. 818)*

Angle-Secant Theorem: The measure of an angle formed by two secants intersecting outside a circle is half the difference of the arcs intercepted by the angle. *(Lesson 14-4, p. 820)*

Theorem: If a line is perpendicular to a radius of a circle at the radius's endpoint on the circle, then the line is tangent to the circle. *(Lesson 14-5, p. 823)*

Theorem: If a line is tangent to a circle, then it is perpendicular to the radius containing the point of tangency. *(Lesson 14-5, p. 824)*

Radius-Tangent Theorem: A line is tangent to a circle if and only if it is perpendicular to the radius at the radius's endpoint on the circle. *(Lesson 14-5, p. 825)*

Tangent-Chord Theorem: The measure of an angle formed by a tangent and a chord is half the measure of its intercepted arc. *(Lesson 14-6, p. 830)*

Tangent-Secant Theorem: The measure of the angle between two tangents, or between a tangent and a secant, is half the difference of the intercepted arcs. *(Lesson 14-6, p. 830)*

Secant Length Theorem: Suppose one secant intersects a circle at A and B, and a second secant intersects the circle at C and D. If the secants intersect at P, then $AP \cdot BP = CP \cdot DP$. *(Lesson 14-7, p. 836)*

Tangent Square Theorem: The power of point P for $\odot O$ is the square of the length of a segment tangent to $\odot O$ from P. *(Lesson 14-7, p. 838)*

Isoperimetric Theorem: Of all plane figures with the same perimeter, the circle has the maximum area. *(Lesson 14-8, p. 843)*

Isoperimetric Inequality: If a plane figure has area A and perimeter p, then $A \leq \frac{p^2}{4\pi}$, and $A = \frac{p^2}{4\pi}$ only when the figure is a circle. *(Lesson 14-8, p. 843)*

Isoperimetric Theorem (alternate statement): Of all plane figures with the same area, the circle has the least perimeter. *(Lesson 14-8, p. 844)*

Isoperimetric Theorem (3-dimensional version): Of all solids with the same surface area, the sphere has the largest volume. *(Lesson 14-9, p. 848)*

Isoperimetric Theorem (alternate 3-dimensional version): Of all solids with the same volume, the sphere has the least surface area. *(Lesson 14-9, p. 849)*

Isoperimetric Inequality for Three-Dimensional Figures: If a solid has volume V and surface area s, then $V \leq \sqrt{\frac{s^3}{36\pi}}$ and $V = \sqrt{\frac{s^3}{36\pi}}$ only when the solid is a sphere. *(Lesson 14-9, p. 852)*

 APPENDIX B

Postulates

Postulates are statements that are assumed true. The postulates listed below may be different from those found in other geometry books.

Postulates of Euclidean Geometry

Point-Line-Plane Postulate

a. Unique Line Assumption: Through any two points, there is exactly one line. *(Lesson 1-7, p. 41; Lesson 9-1, p. 497)*

b. Number Line Assumption: Every line is a set of points that can be put into a one-to-one correspondence with the real numbers, with any point on it corresponding to 0 and any other point corresponding to 1. *(Lesson 1-7, p. 42; Lesson 9-1, p. 497)*

c. Dimension Assumption: (1) Given a line in a plane, there is at least one point in the plane that is not on the line. (2) Given a plane in space, there is at least one point in space that is not in the plane. *(Lesson 1-7, p. 42; Lesson 9-1, p. 497)*

d. Flat Plane Assumption: If two points lie in a plane, the line containing them lies in the plane. *(Lesson 9-1, p. 497)*

e. Unique Plane Assumption: Through three noncollinear points, there is exactly one plane. *(Lesson 9-1, p. 497)*

f. Intersecting Planes Assumption: If two different planes have a point in common, then their intersection is a line. *(Lesson 9-1, p. 498)*

Some Postulates from Arithmetic and Geometry

Distance Postulate

a. Uniqueness Property: On a line, there is a unique distance between two points. *(Lesson 1-8, p. 48)*

b. Distance Formula: If the two points on a line have coordinates x and y, the distance between them is $|x - y|$. *(Lesson 1-8, p. 48)*

c. Additive Property: If B is on $\overline{AC}$, then $AB + BC = AC$. *(Lesson 1-8, p. 49)*

Triangle Inequality Postulate

The sum of the lengths of any two sides of a triangle is greater than the length of the third side. *(Lesson 2-7, p. 103)*

Angle Measure Postulate

a. Unique Measure Assumption: Every angle has a unique measure from 0° to 180°.

b. Unique Angle Assumption: Given any ray $\overrightarrow{VA}$ and any real number r between 0 and 180, there is a unique angle BVA in each half-plane of $\overleftrightarrow{VA}$ such that $m\angle BVA = r$.

c. Zero Angle Assumption: If $\overrightarrow{VA}$ and $\overrightarrow{VB}$ are the same ray, then $m\angle AVB = 0$.

d. Straight Angle Assumption: If $\overrightarrow{VA}$ and $\overrightarrow{VB}$ are opposite rays, then $m\angle AVB = 180$.

e. Angle Addition Property: If $\overrightarrow{VC}$ (except for point V) is in the interior of $\angle AVB$, then $m\angle AVC + m\angle CVB = m\angle AVB$. *(Lesson 3-1, p. 126)*

Postulates of Equality

For any real numbers a, b, and c:

Reflexive Property of Equality: $a = a$.

Symmetric Property of Equality: If $a = b$, then $b = a$.

Transitive Property of Equality: If $a = b$ and $b = c$, then $a = c$. *(Lesson 3-4, p. 145)*

868

Postulates of Equality and Operations

For any real numbers a, b, and c:

Addition Property of Equality:
If $a = b$, then $a + c = b + c$.

Multiplication Property of Equality:
If $a = b$, then $ac = bc$.

(Lesson 3-4, p. 145)

Postulates of Inequality and Operations

For any real numbers a, b, and c:

Transitive Property of Inequality:
If $a < b$ and $b < c$, then $a < c$.

Addition Property of Inequality:
If $a < b$, then $a + c < b + c$.

Multiplication Properties of Inequality:
If $a < b$ and $c > 0$, then $ac < bc$.
If $a < b$ and $c < 0$, then $ac > bc$.

(Lesson 3-4, p. 146)

Postulates of Equality and Inequality

For any real numbers a, b, and c:

Equation to Inequality Property: If a and b are positive numbers and $a + b = c$, then $c > a$ and $c > b$.

Substitution Property: If $a = b$, then a may be substituted for b in any expression.

(Lesson 3-4, p. 147)

Corresponding Angles Postulate

Suppose two coplanar lines are cut by a transversal.

a. If two corresponding angles have the same measure, then the lines are parallel.

b. If the lines are parallel, then corresponding angles have the same measure.

(Lesson 3-6, p. 156)

Reflection Postulate

Under a reflection:

a. There is a 1-1 correspondence between points and their images.

b. Collinearity is preserved. If three points A, B, and C lie on a line, then their images A', B', and C' are collinear.

c. Betweenness is preserved. If B is between A and C, then the image B' is between the images A' and C'.

d. Distance is preserved. If $\overline{A'B'}$ is the image of $\overline{AB}$, then $A'B' = AB$.

e. Angle measure is preserved. If $\angle A'C'E'$ is the image of $\angle ACE$, then $m\angle A'C'E' = m\angle ACE$.

f. Orientation is reversed. A polygon and its image, with vertices taken in corresponding order, have opposite orientations. *(Lesson 4-2, pp. 191, 193)*

Area Postulate

a. Uniqueness Property: Given a unit region, every polygonal region has a unique area.

b. Rectangle Formula: The area A of a rectangle with dimensions ℓ and w is ℓw.

c. Congruence Property: Congruent figures have the same area.

d. Additive Property: The area of the union of two nonoverlapping regions is the sum of the areas of the regions.

(Lesson 8-2, p. 442)

Volume Postulate

a. Uniqueness Property: Given a unit cube, every polyhedral region has a unique volume.

b. Box Volume Formula: The volume V of a box with dimensions ℓ, w, and h is found by the formula $V = \ell wh$.

c. Congruence Property: Congruent figures have the same volume.

d. Additive Property: The volume of the union of two nonoverlapping solids is the sum of the volumes of the solids.

(Lesson 10-3, p. 577)

e. Cavalieri's Principle: Let I and II be two solids included between parallel planes. If every plane P parallel to the given planes intersects I and II in sections with the same area, then Volume(I) = Volume(II). *(Lesson 10-5, p. 589)*

Trichotomy Law: Of two real numbers a and b, either $a < b$, $a = b$, or $a > b$, and no two of these can be true at the same time. *(Lesson 11-3, p. 637)*

Postulates of Logic

Law of Detachment: From a true conditional $p \Rightarrow q$ and a statement or given information p, you may conclude q. *(Lesson 11-1, p. 623)*

Law of Transitivity: If $p \Rightarrow q$ and $q \Rightarrow r$ are true, then $p \Rightarrow r$ is true. (also known as Transitivity Property of Implication) *(Lesson 11-1, p. 623)*

Law of the Contrapositive: A conditional ($p \Rightarrow q$) and its contrapositive ($not\text{-}q \Rightarrow not\text{-}p$) are either both true or both false. *(Lesson 11-2, p. 630)*

Law of Ruling Out Possibilities: When p or q is true and q is not true, then p is true. *(Lesson 11-3, p. 634)*

Law of Indirect Reasoning: If valid reasoning from a statement p leads to a false conclusion, then p is false. *(Lesson 11-4, p. 641)*

APPENDIX C

Formulas

In this book, we use many measurement formulas. The following symbols are used: a, b, c = sides; A = area; B = area of base; b_1, b_2 = bases; C = circumference; d = diameter; d_1, d_2 = diagonals; e = edge; h = height; ℓ = slant height (in conics); ℓ = length; L.A. = lateral area; n = number of sides; p = perimeter; r = radius; s = side; S.A. = surface area; V = volume; w = width; θ = measure of angle.

Two-Dimensional Figures

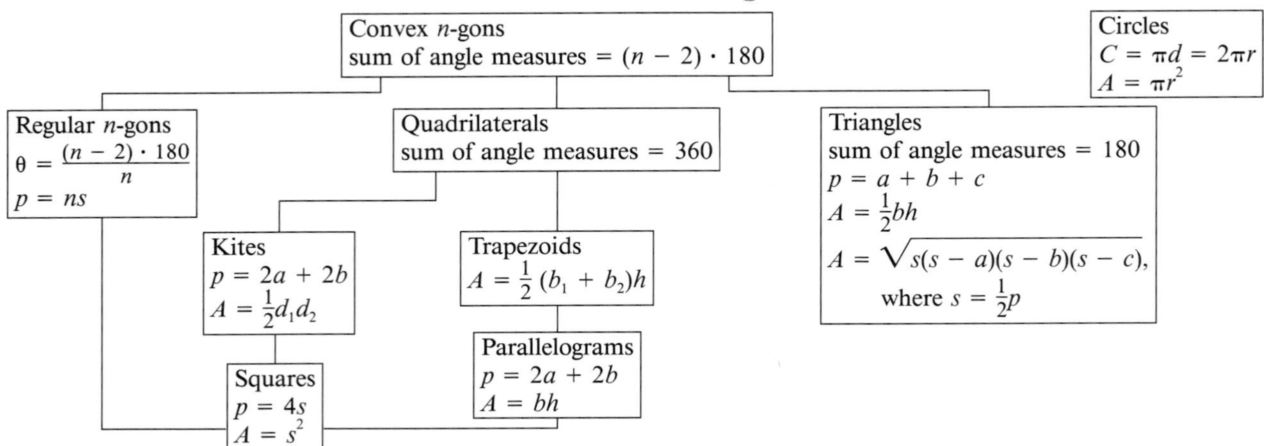

Convex n-gons
sum of angle measures = $(n - 2) \cdot 180$
Circles
$C = \pi d = 2\pi r$
$A = \pi r^2$
Regular n-gons
$\theta = \frac{(n-2) \cdot 180}{n}$
$p = ns$
Quadrilaterals
sum of angle measures = 360
Triangles
sum of angle measures = 180
$p = a + b + c$
$A = \frac{1}{2}bh$
$A = \sqrt{s(s-a)(s-b)(s-c)}$, where $s = \frac{1}{2}p$
Kites
$p = 2a + 2b$
$A = \frac{1}{2}d_1d_2$
Trapezoids
$A = \frac{1}{2}(b_1 + b_2)h$
Parallelograms
$p = 2a + 2b$
$A = bh$
Squares
$p = 4s$
$A = s^2$

Three-Dimensional Figures

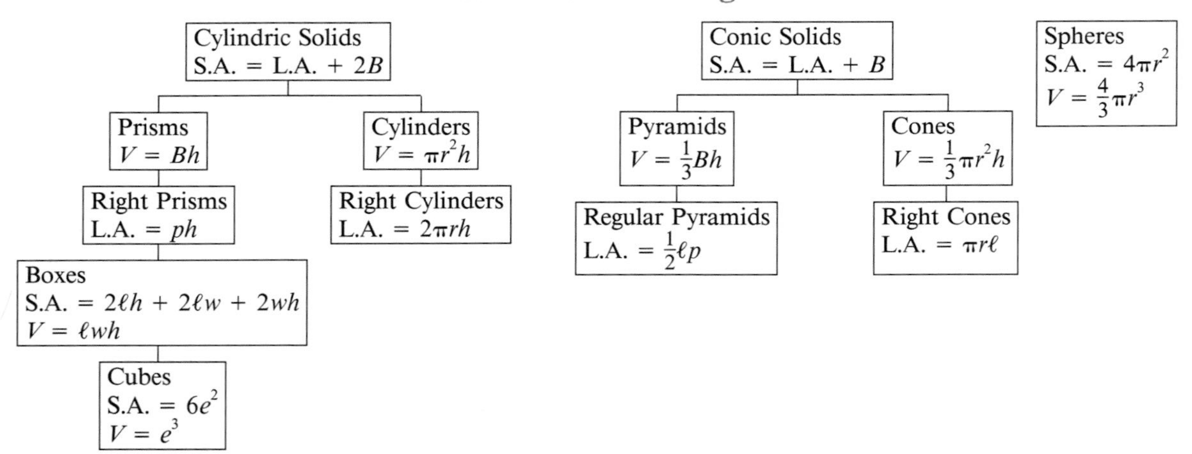

Coordinate Geometry	**Two Dimensions**	**Three Dimensions**
Distance	$d = \sqrt{(x_2 - x_1)^2 + (y_2 - y_1)^2}$	$d = \sqrt{(x_2 - x_1)^2 + (y_2 - y_1)^2 + (z_2 - z_1)^2}$
Midpoint of a segment	$M = \left(\frac{x_1 + x_2}{2}, \frac{y_1 + y_2}{2}\right)$	$M = \left(\frac{x_1 + x_2}{2}, \frac{y_1 + y_2}{2}, \frac{z_1 + z_2}{2}\right)$
Slope of a line	$m = \frac{y_2 - y_1}{x_2 - x_1}$	

870

Conversion Formulas

	Customary	Metric
Length	ft = foot, in. = inch, yd = yard, mi = mile 1 ft = 12 in. 1 yd = 3 ft 1 mi = 5280 ft	cm = centimeter, mm = millimeter, m = meter, km = kilometer 1 cm = 10 mm 1 m = 100 cm 1 km = 1000 m
	1 in. = 2.54 cm 1 ft = 0.3048 m 1 yd = 0.9144 m 1 mi ≈ 1.609 km	
Area	1 sq ft = 144 sq in. 1 sq yd = 9 sq ft	1 sq cm = 100 sq mm 1 sq m = 10,000 sq cm
	1 sq in. = 6.4516 sq cm 1 sq yd ≈ 0.836 sq m 1 sq mi ≈ 2.5889 sq km	
Land Area	1 sq mi = 640 acres	1 hectare = 10,000 sq m
	1 hectare ≈ 2.471 acres	
Volume	1 ft^3 = 1728 in^3 1 yd^3 = 27 ft^3	1 cm^3 = 1000 mm^3 1 m^3 = 1,000,000 cm^3
	1 in^3 ≈ 16.387 cm^3 1 yd^3 ≈ 0.765 m^3	
Liquid Volume	pt = pint, qt = quart, gal = gallon, oz = ounce 1 pt = 28.875 in^3 = 16 oz 1 qt = 57.75 in^3 = 32 oz 1 gal = 231 in^3 = 128 oz	mL = milliliter, L = liter 1 mL = 1000 mm^3 1 L = 1000 cm^3
	1 oz ≈ 29.574 mL 1 qt ≈ 0.946 L 1.057 qt ≈ 1 L	
Weight (Mass)	lb = pound, oz = ounce 1 lb = 16 oz 1 ton = 2000 lb	g = gram, kg = kilogram, mg = milligram 1 g = 1000 mg 1 kg = 1000 g 1 metric ton = 1000 kg
	1 oz ≈ 28.350 g 1 lb ≈ 0.4536 kg 2.2 lb ≈ 1 kg 1 ton ≈ 1.016 metric ton	

LESSON 8-1 (pp. 436–440)
13. 1.25 ft **15. a.** $8s + 18m + 2\ell$ **b.** 1300 meters **17. a.** See below. **b.** $x + y = 8$ ($x > 0$ and $y > 0$) **c.** Sample: $x = 4.5$, $y = 3.5$ **19. (d) 21.** Yes **23.** $\approx$ .79 inch **25.** 1.5 **27.** No; Sample counterexample: If $x = -1$, $(x + 1)(2x - 3) = 0$, but $2x^2 - 3 = -1$. **29. a.** $\approx$ 63 mph **b.** $\approx$ 55 mph **c.** Sample: one route has more stops or slower speed limits.

17. a.

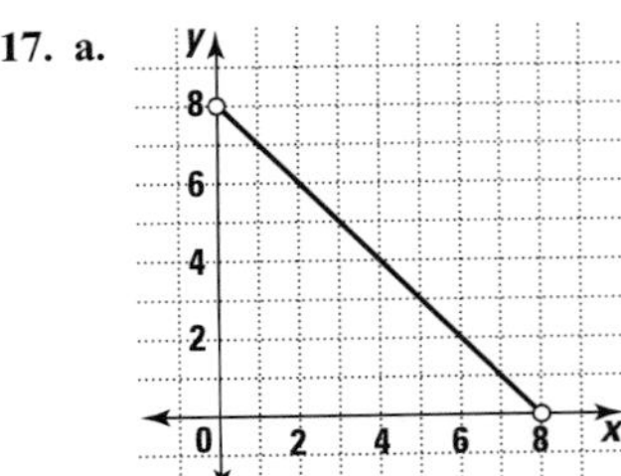

LESSON 8-2 (pp. 441–446)
9. a. 100 units^2 **b.** k^2 units^2 **11.** $\frac{1}{2}$ yard **13. a.** 288 sq in. **b.** 2 sq ft **c.** 144 **15.** 6000 **17.** 46 cm, 46 cm, 185 cm **19. a.** 230 m **b.** 6.25 m **21.** $x = \pm 4$ **23.** See right. $ABCB'$ is a rectangle.

23.

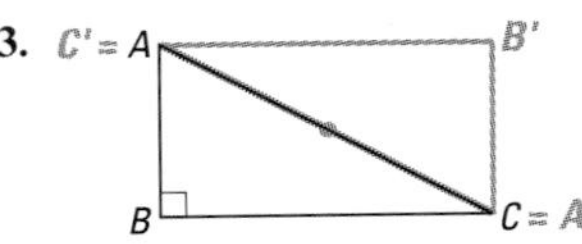

LESSON 8-3 (pp. 447–452)
7. 4096 dots/in^2 **9.** $\approx$ 66.5 km^2 **11.** about 34% **13.** farm in U.S. **15. a.** Its area is multiplied by 100. **b.** Its perimeter is multiplied by 10. **17.** 56 units

19.

Conclusions	Justifications
1. $\triangle PQA \cong \triangle DRA$	AAS Congruence Theorem (Given)
2. $\overline{PA} \cong \overline{DA}$	CPCF Theorem
3. $\triangle PAD$ is isosceles.	definition of isosceles $\triangle$

21. False

LESSON 8-4 (pp. 453–458)
11. 9000 ft^2 **13.** 3 in. **15. a.** 32 m **b.** 48 m^2 **17.** 23 units^2 **19. a.** 286,650 square miles; answers may vary by $\pm$4900 square miles. **b.** 266,400 square miles; answers may vary by $\pm$ 1225 square miles. **21.** 124 units^2

23.

Conclusions	Justifications
0. $\angle ABD \cong \angle BDC$	Given
1. $\overline{DC} \parallel \overline{AB}$	AIA $\cong \Rightarrow \parallel$ lines
2. $ABCD$ is a trapezoid.	definition of trapezoid

25. (a)

LESSON 8-5 (pp. 459–464)
13. a., b. See below. **c.** rectangle **d.** 160 units^2 **e.** Yes **15.** $\frac{1}{2}bc$ units^2

17. a. Sample Argument:

Conclusions	Justifications
1. $AF = BC$	Isosceles Trapezoid Theorem
2. $\angle F = \angle C$	definition of isosceles trapezoid
3. $m\angle AEF = 90$, $m\angle BDC = 90$	definition of perpendicular
4. $m\angle AEF = m\angle BDC$	Substitution
5. $\triangle AEF \cong \triangle BDC$	AAS Congruence Theorem (Steps 1, 2, 4)
6. $FE = DC$	CPCF Theorem

b. 52.5 units^2 **19.** (b) **21.** Place a grid over the shape. Add the number of squares entirely inside the figure to half the number of squares partially covering the figure, and multiply the result by the area of each square. **23.** 108 **25.** $3\sqrt{3}$

13. a., b.

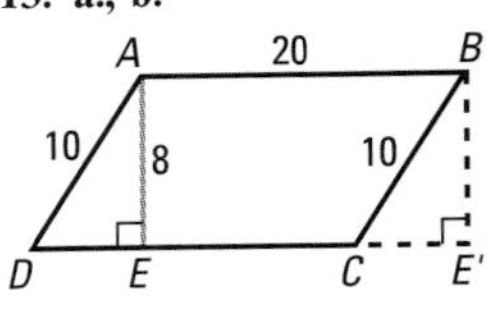

LESSON 8-6 (pp. 466–472)
19. $\sqrt{109} \approx 10.4$ miles **21.** $\sqrt{60} \approx 7.75$ feet **23.** 100 **25.** 270 units^2 **27.** 4.5 units^2 **29.** See below.

29. Sample:

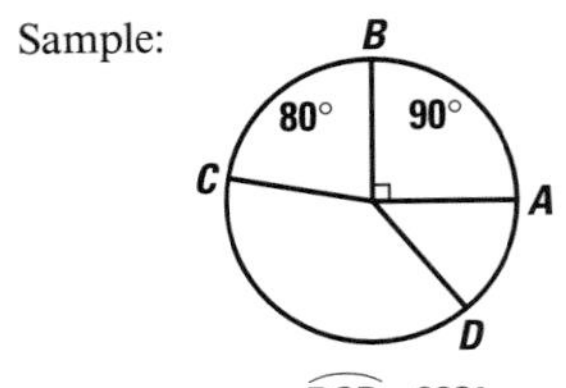

LESSON 8-7 (pp. 474–478)
11. $10\pi \approx 31.4$ m **13.** $\frac{110}{\pi}$ or about 35 seconds **15.** 20 units **17.** $A = \frac{1}{2}h(b_1 + b_2)$ **19.** $p = 4s$ **21.** 2000 units^2 **23. a.** Its perimeter is multiplied by 6. **b.** Its area is multiplied by 36. **25.** (d)

LESSON 8-8 (pp. 480–484)
7. a. 11,300 sq meters **b.** 377 m **9. a.** What is the area of Farmer Bob's field? **b.** $90{,}000\pi$ m^2 $\approx$ 282,600 m^2 **11. a.** $\frac{1}{16}$ **b.** $\frac{15}{16}$ **13. a.** 72° **b.** $6\pi \approx 18.8$ units **15.** about 466 **17. a.** $18x^2$ units^2 **b.** $(13 + \sqrt{97})x \approx 22.8x$ units **19.** 7.1 units **21.** 48 units^2 **23.** 38 cm

CHAPTER 8 PROGRESS SELF-TEST (pp. 488–489)
1. $2(40 + 15) = 110$ units **2.** $\frac{1}{2} \cdot 80 \cdot 210 = 8400$ units^2 **3.** $A = \frac{1}{2}h(a + c)$ **4.** $\frac{q}{6}$ **5.** $\ell w = 200$ m $= 25w$; $w = 8$ m **6.** $48 = \frac{1}{2} \cdot 6 \cdot (9 + b)$; $16 = 9 + b$; $b = 7$ units **7. a.** $C = 12\pi''$; $A = \pi \cdot 6^2 = 36\pi$ in^2 **b.** 38″; 113 in^2 **8. a.** $40\pi \cdot \frac{45}{360} = 5\pi \approx$ 15.7 units **b.** $400\pi \cdot \frac{45}{360} = 50\pi \approx 157$ units^2 **9.** $\sqrt{41^2 - 9^2} = \sqrt{1681 - 81} = \sqrt{1600} = 40$ **10.** $20 + 21 + \sqrt{20^2 + 21^2} = 20 + 21 + 29 = 70$ **11. a.** Yes **b.** Because $121 + 3600 = 3721 = 61^2$, meeting the condition of Pythagorean Converse Theorem. **12.** $\left(27 + \frac{21}{2}\right) \cdot 25 = 937.5$ sq miles (Answers may slightly vary.) **13.** $12^2 - 36\pi \approx 30.90$ units^2 **14. a.** $P = 2(\ell + w)$; $P' = 2(4\ell + 4w) = 4 \cdot 2(\ell + w) = 4 \cdot P$; its perimeter is multiplied by 4. **b.** $A = \ell w$; $A' = (4\ell)(4w) = 16\ \ell w$; $A' = 16A$; its area is multiplied by 16. **15.** $16 \cdot 2 + 21 \cdot 2 = 74''$ **16.** $1.8^2 + b^2 = 5^2$; $b^2 = 21.76$; $b \approx 4.7$ meters **17.** $80^2\pi \approx$ 20,100 square miles **18.** $\frac{9}{3} \cdot \frac{15}{3} = 3 \cdot 5 = 15$ sq yd **19.** $\left(\frac{2640}{4}\right)^2 = 660^2 = 435{,}600$ sq ft **20.** $\frac{\pi \cdot 6^2}{\pi \cdot 18^2} = \frac{36\pi}{324\pi} = \frac{1}{9}$ **21.** Area $= \frac{1}{2}bh = \frac{1}{2} \cdot 9 \cdot 1 = 4.5$ units^2 **22.** Area $= 9 \cdot 11 - (3 \cdot 4 + 3 \cdot 3) = 99 - 21 = 78$ units^2 **23.** Sample: Greek, Chinese, Babylonian

The chart below keys the **Progress Self-Test** questions to the objectives in the **Chapter Review** on pages 490–493 or to the **Vocabulary** (Voc.) on page 487. This will enable you to locate those **Chapter Review** questions that correspond to questions students missed on the **Progress Self-Test.** The lesson where the material is covered is also indicated on the chart.

Question	**1**	**2**	**3**	**4**	**5**	**6**	**7**	**8**	**9**	**10**
Objective	A	C	C	A	C	C	F	F	D	A, D
Lesson	8-1	8-4	8-5	8-1	8-2	8-5	8-7, 8-8	8-7, 8-8	8-6	8-1, 8-6
Question	**11**	**12**	**13**	**14**	**15**	**16**	**17**	**18**	**19**	**20**
Objective	E	B	G	A, C	H	H	J	I	H, I	J
Lesson	8-6	8-3	8-2, 8-8	8-1, 8-2	8-1	8-6	8-8	8-2	8-1, 8-2	8-8
Question	**21**	**22**	**23**							
Objective	K	K	L							
Lesson	8-4	8-2	8-6							

CHAPTER 8 REVIEW (pp. 490–493)

1. 32 units **3.** 235 meters **5.** 10 cm **7.** 12.5 units and 25 units **9.** 13,950 m^2 (Answers may slightly vary.) **11.** 37,500 sq miles (Answers may slightly vary.) **13.** 4.55 cm^2 **15.** 72 $units^2$ **17.** $\approx$ 153.2 $units^2$ **19.** 3.5 units **21.** 12 units **23.** $\sqrt{5} \approx 2.24$ units **25.** $\approx 22.2x$ units **27.** 75 cm **29.** No **31.** Yes **33. a.** 20π units, 100π $units^2$ **b.** 62.83 units, 314.16 $units^2$ **35.** $\approx 6.4x$ meters **37. a.** 41.9 units **b.** $\approx$ 39.27 $units^2$ **39.** Area of trapezoid: $A = \frac{1}{2}h(b_1 + b_2)$, but in a parallelogram, $b_1 = b_2 = b$, so $A = \frac{1}{2}h(b + b) = \frac{1}{2} \cdot h \cdot 2b = hb$. **41.** $49\pi - 98$ **43.** $3\pi x^2$ $units^2$ **45.** $\approx$ 4.4 ft **47.** $8k$ units **49.** 14 minutes **51.** 44,100 m^2 **53.** 780,000 sq ft **55.** 28.3 km^2 **57.** $\frac{100}{\pi} \approx 31.8$ ft **59.** 2025 $units^2$ **61.** 32 $units^2$ **63.** (a) **65.** True

LESSON 9-1 (pp. 496–499)

9. Yes **11.** Yes **13.** Because a plane has no thickness. **15. a.** True **b.** False **17.** A circle is the set of all points in a plane at a certain distance (its radius) from a certain point (its center). **19.** $x = 67.5$, $y = 112.5$

LESSON 9-2 (pp. 500–504)

11. Sample: the floor, north wall, and east wall **13.** Sample: If two planes are perpendicular to the same plane, then they are parallel. No. **15.** Sample: ℓ and m are skew lines. **See below.** **17. a.** 90° **b.** 30° **19.** No; by Intersecting Planes Assumption, their intersection is a line. **21. a.** 1599 $units^2$ **b.** about 49.2 units **23. See below.**

15.

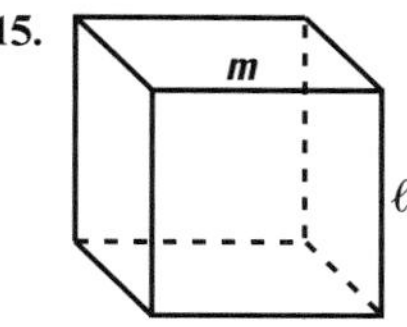

23. Sample:

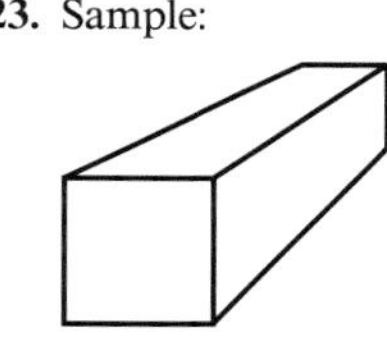

LESSON 9-3 (pp. 505–510)

13. Sample: solid right prism (often hexagonal) or a solid right circular cylinder **15.** Sample: **See right.** **17. a.** 5 units **b.** 13 units **c.** 30 $units^2$ **19. a.** 60 units **b.** If one edge has length s, then the length of all edges is $12s$. **21.** Sample: **See right.** **23.** infinitely many **25. See right.**

15.

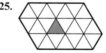

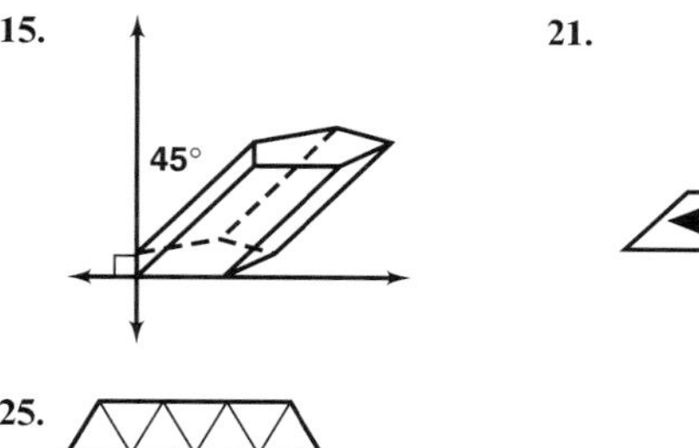

21.

25.

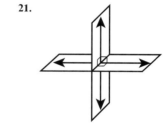

LESSON 9-4 (pp. 511–516)

11. the height of the pyramid, slant height, length of a lateral edge **13. a.** n **b.** $n + 1$ **c.** n **d.** $2n$ **15.** Sample: a platform that elephants stand on **17. a.** $2\pi'' \approx 6.28''$ **b.** 1.0″ exactly **19.** Sample: **See below.** **21.** In a right cylinder, the direction of the translation is perpendicular to the base; in an oblique cylinder, it is not. **23.** 150 $units^2$ **25. a.** 240 $units^2$ **b.** about 18.5 units

19.

LESSON 9-5 (pp. 517–524)

13. a. Sample: **See page 893.** **b.** Sample: **See page 893.** **c.** Part **a** is a rectangle; part **b** is a rectangle. **15. a.** Sample: **See page 893.** **b.** Sample: **See page 893.** **c.** part **a** is a circle and part **b** is an ellipse **17.** sphere **19. a.** Reflexive Property of Congruence **b.** definition of sphere **c.** HL Congruence Theorem **d.** CPCF Theorem **21. a.** 8 units **b.** 136 units^2 **23.** 376 units^2 **25.** The point Q is the reflection image of P over a line ℓ when P is not on ℓ if and only if ℓ is the perpendicular bisector of $\overline{PQ}$.

13. a.

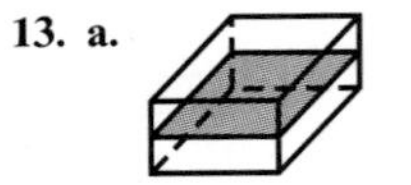

13. b.

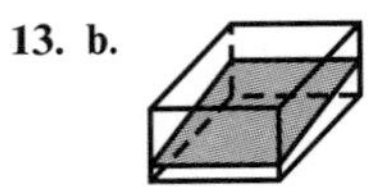

15. a.

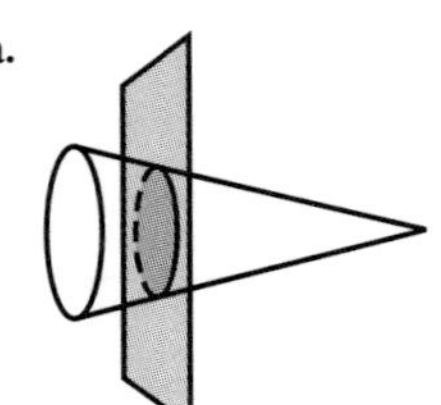

15. b.

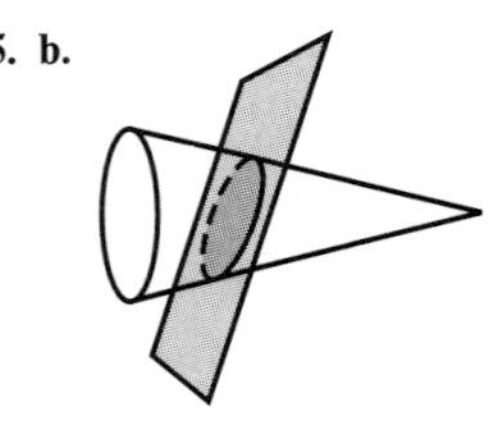

LESSON 9-6 (pp. 525–530)

11. See below. 13. False. A symmetry plane parallel to the bases will have a cross section congruent to the bases. **15. a.** Sample: **See below. b.** Sample: **See below. c.** Part **a** is a circle; part **b** is an ellipse. **17. a.** Sample: **See below. b.** 12 units **19.** box without its top **21.** 240 units^2 **23.** This has more information than is necessary.

11.

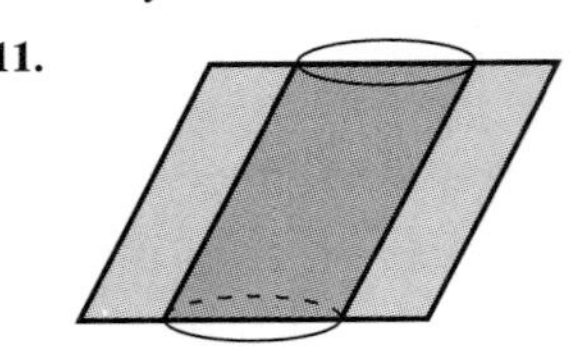

15. a.

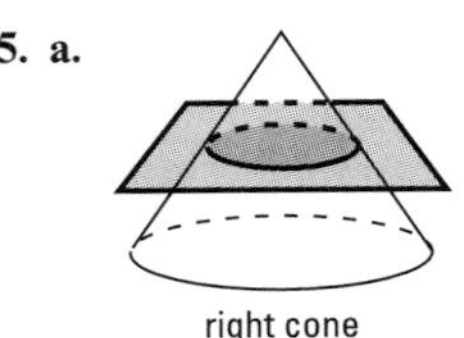

right cone

15. b.

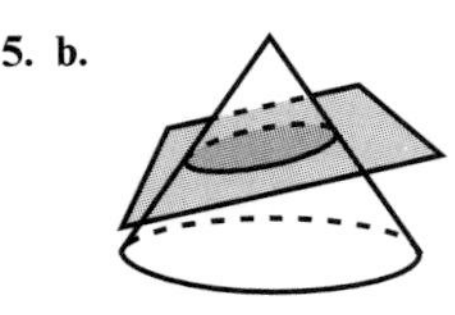

17. a.

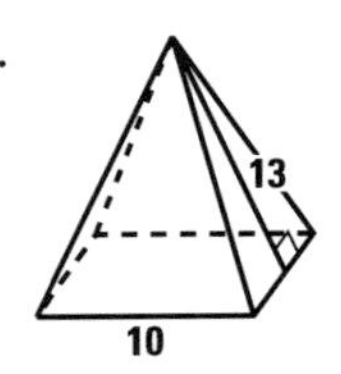

LESSON 9-7 (pp. 531–535)

11. ≈ 25 ft **13. See below. 15. a.** 2 **b. See below. 17.** 6 units **19.** one **21.** about 270 mi **23.** a correspondence between two sets of points such that (1) each point in the preimage set has a unique image, and (2) each point in the image set has exactly one preimage

13.

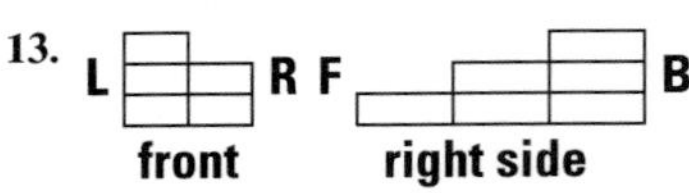

15. b.

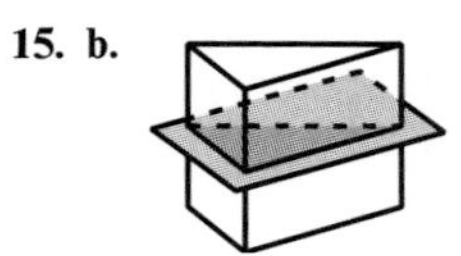

LESSON 9-8 (pp. 537–542)

9. regular octahedron **11.** (d) **13.** Sample: **See below. 15.** about 56.5 square inches **17. See below. 19. See below. 21. a.** $V = 9$, $E = 16$, $F = 9$ **b.** $V = 16$, $E = 24$, $F = 10$ **c.** $V = n + 1$, $E = 2n$, $F = n + 1$ **d.** $V = 2n$, $E = 3n$, $F = n + 2$ **e.** (c) **f.** pyramid: $(n + 1) + (n + 1) - 2n = 2n + 2 - 2n = 2$ prism: $(n + 2) + (2n) - (3n) = 3n + 2 - 3n = 2$ **23.** about 24.3 inches **25.** $t = 95$

13.

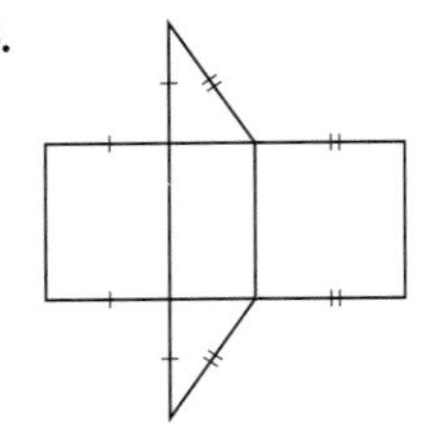

17.

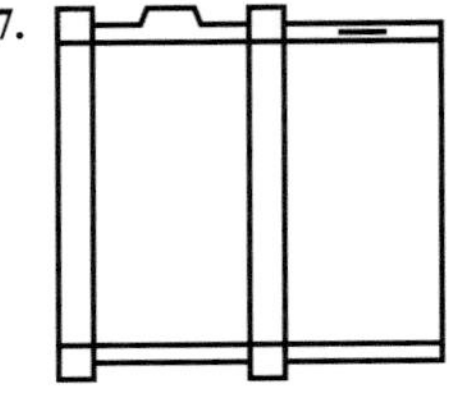

19.

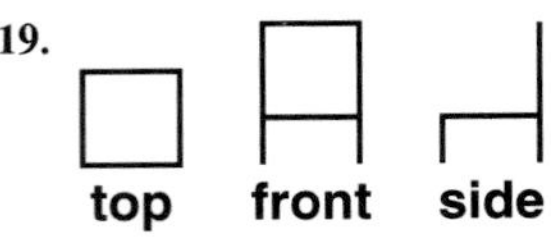

LESSON 9-9 (pp. 544–551)

11. all of them **13.** Sample: **See below. 15.** Sample: **See below. 17.** Sample: **See below. 19. See below. 21. See below. 23.** lateral surface of cylinder **25. a.** $\sqrt{136} \approx 11.7$ units **b.** $12\sqrt{2} \approx 17.0$ units **c.** $\sqrt{172} \approx 13.1$ units **d.** $\frac{1}{2} \cdot 10 \cdot 6\sqrt{2} = 30\sqrt{2} \approx 42.4$ units^2

13.

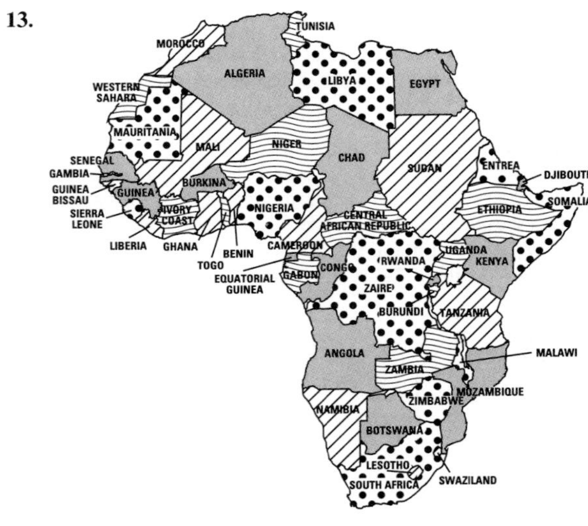

15.

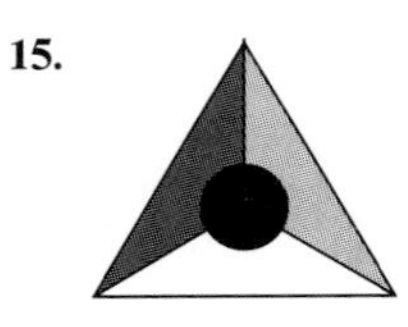

17.

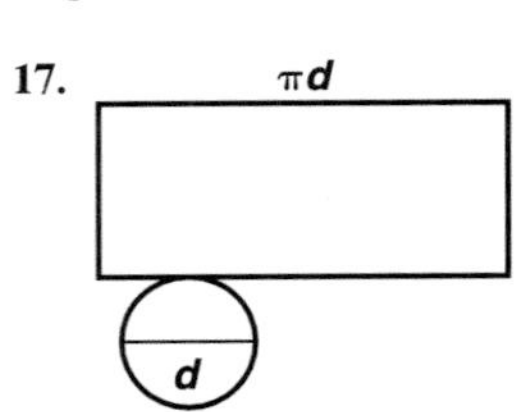

19.

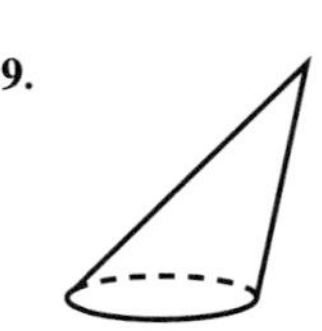

21.

CHAPTER 9 PROGRESS SELF-TEST (pp. 556–557)

1. **See below.** **2.** Sample: **See below.** **3.** **See below.** **4.** Sample: The endpoint of one leg does not lie in the plane determined by the endpoints of the other three legs. **5. a.** Sample: **See below.** **b.** Sample: **See right.** **c.** Part **a** is a square. Part **b** is a quadrilateral. **6.** 4 **7. a.** **See right.** **b.** a great circle **8.** **See right.** **9. a–c.** **See right.** **10.** infinitely many **11.** circumference $= 2\pi r = 28\pi$; $\frac{28\pi}{2\pi} = r$; $r = 14$ cm **12. a.** $\sqrt{34^2 - 16^2} = 30$ cm **b.** $10^2\pi = 100\pi \approx 314.16$ cm^2 **13. a.** Area($EGHJ$) $= 9 \cdot 22 = 198$ in^2 **b.** Area($\triangle EFG$) $= \frac{1}{2} \cdot EF \cdot FG = \frac{1}{2} \cdot 4 \cdot \sqrt{9^2 - 4^2} = 2 \cdot \sqrt{65} \approx 16.12$ in^2 **14.** a rectangular solid **15.** a sphere; it is a surface **16. a.** 2 stories **b.** 4 sections **c.** all sections of the left side **17.** regular octagonal prism **18.** Sample: **See right.** **19.** right prism with bases shaped like a parallelogram **20.** (c) and (d) **21.** Sample: **See right.**

1.

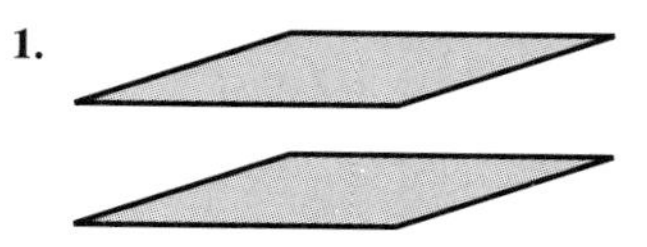

2.

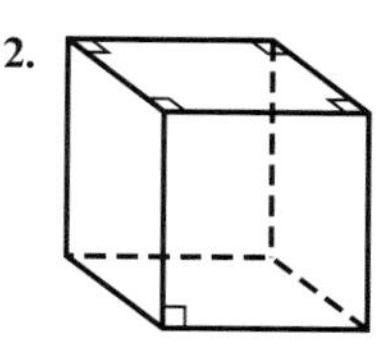

3.

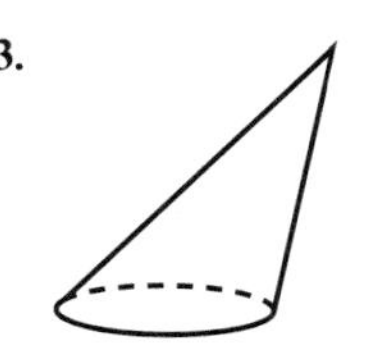

5. a.

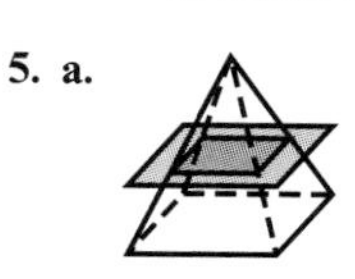

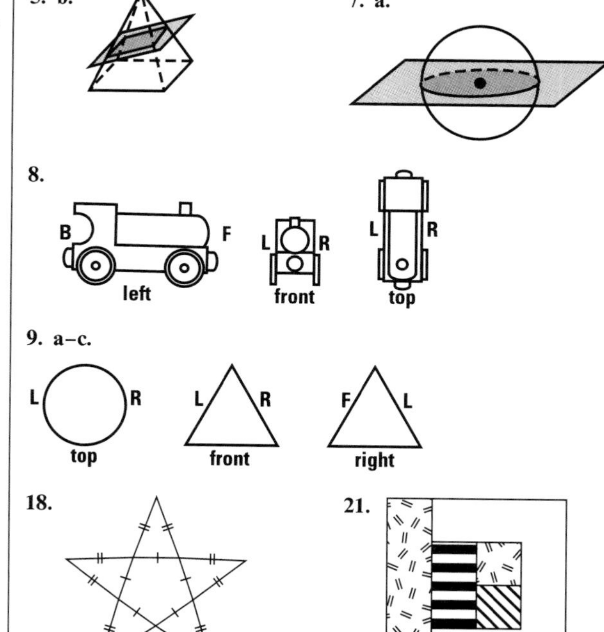

The chart below keys the **Progress Self-Test** questions to the objectives in the **Chapter Review** on pages 558–561 or to the **Vocabulary** (Voc.) on page 555. This will enable you to locate those **Chapter Review** questions that correspond to questions students missed on the **Progress Self-Test.** The lesson where the material is covered is also indicated on the chart.

Question	**1**	**2**	**3**	**4**	**5**	**6**	**7**	**8**	**9**	**10**
Objective	A	A	A	F	B	G	B	C	C	G
Lesson	9-2	9-3	9-4	9-1	9-5	9-6	9-5	9-7	9-7	9-6
Question	**11**	**12**	**13**	**14**	**15**	**16**	**17**	**18**	**19**	**20**
Objective	D	D	D	H	H	E	E	J	J	K
Lesson	9-5	9-4	9-3	9-3	9-5	9-7	9-7	9-8	9-8	9-9
Question	**21**									
Objective	I									
Lesson	9-9									

CHAPTER 9 REVIEW (pp. 558–561)

1. **See page 895.** **3.** **See page 895.** **5.** **See page 895.** **7.** **See page 895.** **9. a.** Sample: **See page 895.** **b.** Sample: **See page 895.** **c.** Part **a** is a circle, and part **b** is an ellipse. **11. a.** Sample: **See page 895.** **b.** Sample: **See page 895.** **c.** Part **a** is a regular pentagon and part **b** is a pentagon. **13. a.–c.** **See page 895.** **15. a–c.** **See page 895.** **17. a.** 36 units **b.** 48 units^2 **19. a.** $9\pi \approx 28.3$ cm^2 **b.** $\sqrt{32} \approx 5.7$ cm **21. a.** **See page 895.** **b.** $49\pi \approx 153.9$ mm^2 **23. a.** 34 units **b.** 350 units^2 **25. a.** 2 **b.** 2 **c.** back left-hand side **27.** solid right cone **29.** a line **31.** Yes; if a line is $\perp$ to two different lines in space at the same point, then it is $\perp$ to the plane containing those lines. **33.** not necessarily **35. a.** Yes **b.** infinitely many **37.** 9 **39.** solid sphere **41.** rectangular solid **43.** Sample: **See page 895.** **45.** Sample: **See page 895.** **47.** Sample: **See page 895.** **49.** Sample: **See page 895.** **51. a.** 12 units **b.** $20\pi \approx 62.8$ units **53.** Sample: Connected parts of countries may appear disconnected on different gores. **55.** Distances are not preserved.

1. 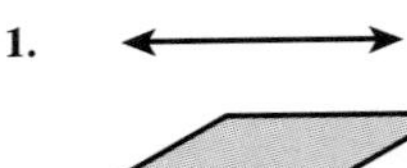

3. 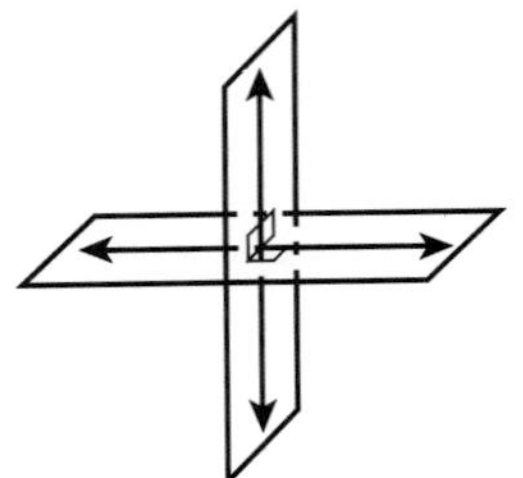

5. 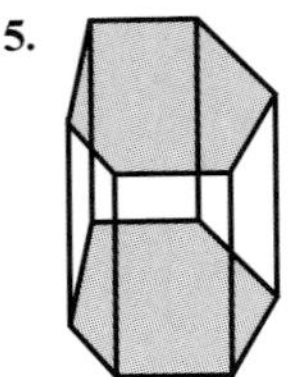

7. 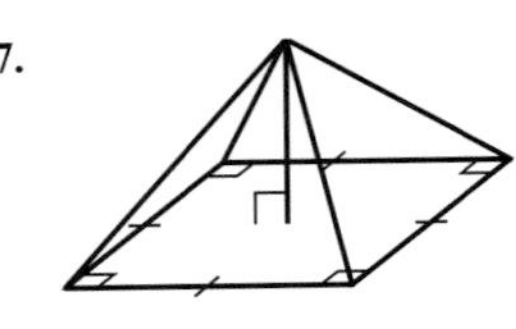
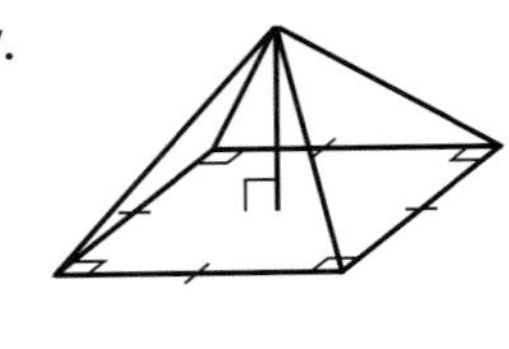

9. a. 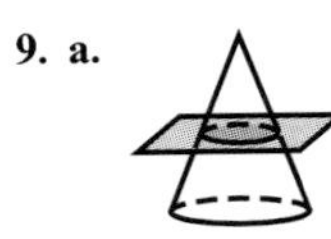

9. b. 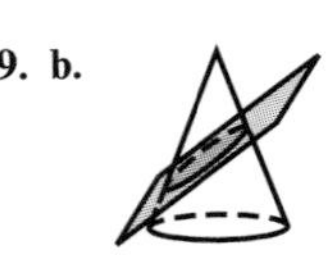

11. a. 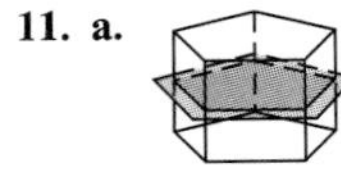

11. b. 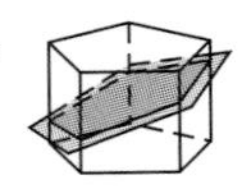

13. a–c. 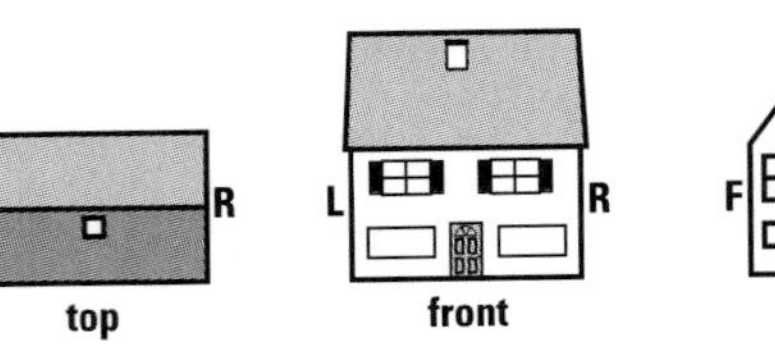

15. a–c. 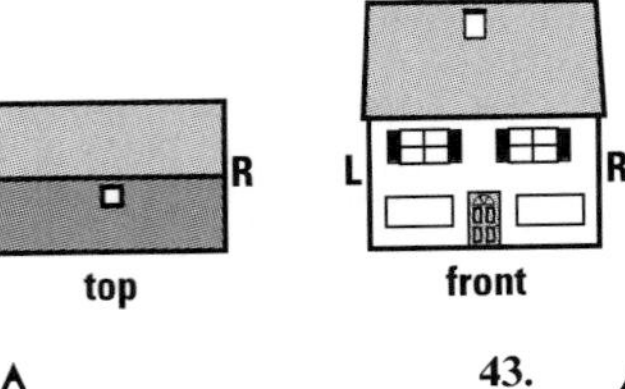

21. a. 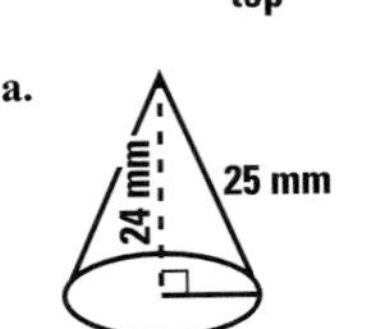

43. 

45. 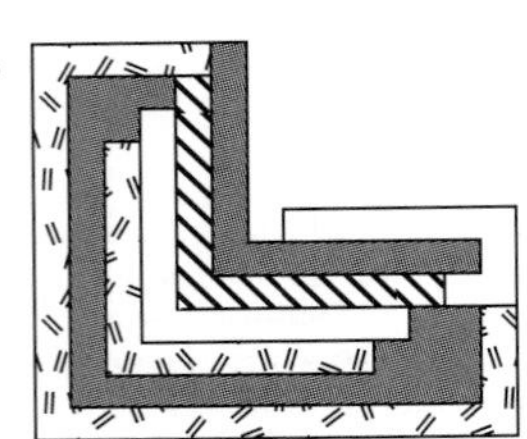

47. 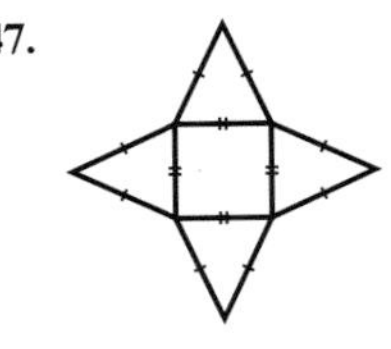

49. 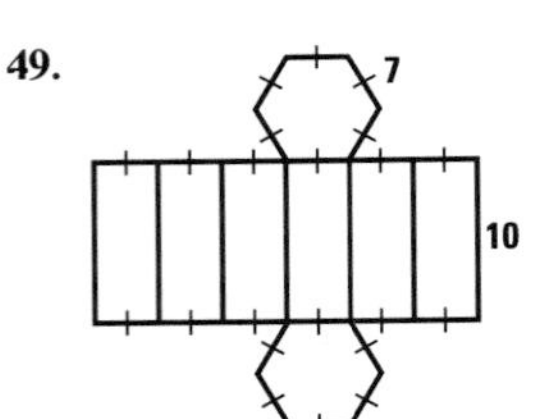

LESSON 10-1 (pp. 564–568)
13. a. right triangular prism **b.** 108 cm^2 **c.** 120 cm^2 **15.** $2(LW + LH + WH)$ **17.** $100\pi \approx 314.16$ cm^2 **19. a.** 214 $units^2$ **b.** 856 $units^2$ **c.** 4 **d.** 278, 1112, 4 **21.** Sample: **See below. 23.** Find the point of intersection of either the perpendicular bisectors of any two sides or the bisectors of any two angles.

21.

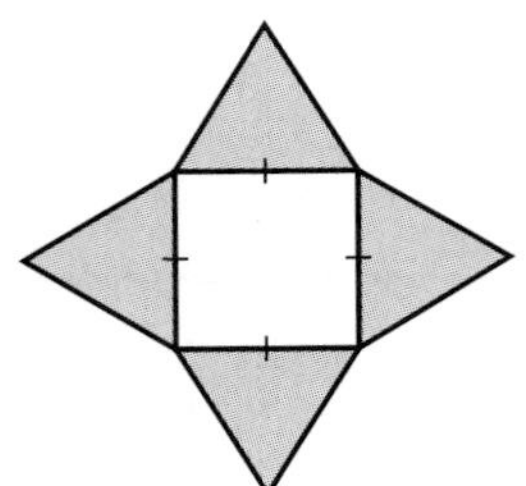

LESSON 10-2 (pp. 570–575)
13. a. Sample: **See right. b.** 1000 $units^2$ **c.** 1100 $units^2$ **15. a.** Sample: **See right. b.** $175\pi \approx 550$ $units^2$ **c.** $224\pi \approx 704$ $units^2$ **17.** 1332 sq in. = 9.25 sq ft **19.** Sample: **See right. 21.** Uniqueness Property - every polygonal region has a unique area; Rectangle Formula - the area of a rectangle with dimensions ℓ and w is ℓw; Congruence Property - congruent figures have the same area; Additive Property - if A and B are non-overlapping regions, than Area($A \cup B$) = Area(A) + Area(B). **23. a.** $x = 61$ **b.** $y = \frac{64}{3}$ **c.** $z = 4$

13. a. 

15. a. 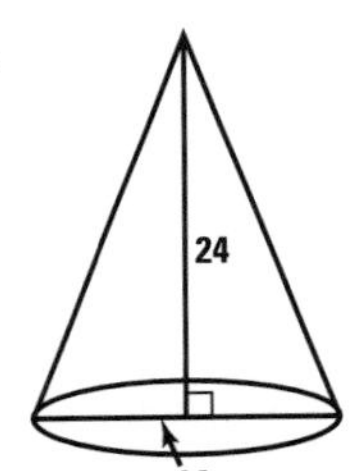

19. 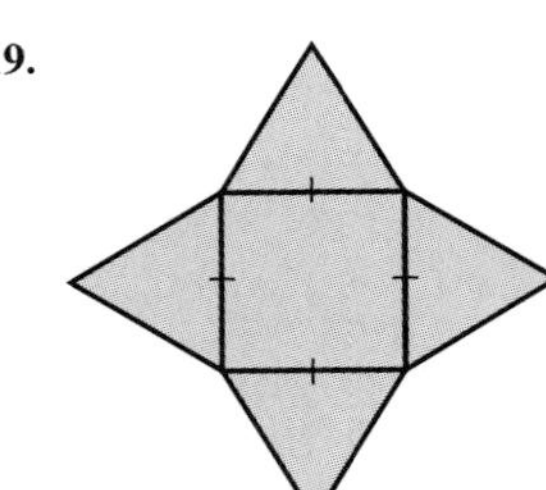

LESSON 10-3 (pp. 576–581)
15. 12 inches **17. a.** area of a base **b.** The area of the base is ℓw, so the formula $V = Bh$ is equivalent to $V = \ell wh$. **19. a.** $\frac{1}{16}$ **b.** $\frac{1}{64}$ **21. a.** 3 **b.** 9 **c.** 27 **23. a.** $156\pi \approx 490$ in^2 **b.** 4 square feet **25. a.** $5\sqrt{11} \approx 16.6$ ft^2 **b.** $84 + 24\sqrt{11} \approx 163.60$ ft^2

LESSON 10-4 (pp. 582–586)
15. $x + 3$ **17.** $33\frac{1}{3}$ cm **19.** Yes, if s is the side length of the original cube and $s = 20$, then $s \cdot (s + 5) \cdot (s - 4) = s^3$. **21.** 1.46 **23.** ≈ 1.8 cm^3 **25.** 2.88 units^2

LESSON 10-5 (pp. 587–592)
13. $\pi r^2 h$ **15.** 9.5 m^2 **17. a.** Yes **b.** For the second glass, $V \approx 2.7\pi h$. For the first glass $V \approx 1.3\pi h$. **19.** The first cylinder has four times the volume of the second cylinder. **21.** $4x^2 + 3xy + 28x - 10y^2 - 35y$ **23.** 20 cm^3 **25.** $A = \frac{1}{2}h(b_1 + b_2)$; $A = bh$; $A = \ell w$; $A = s^2$

LESSON 10-6 (pp. 593–597)
11. a. L.A. $= \frac{1}{2}\ell(2\pi r) = \pi r\ell$ **b.** S.A. $= \pi r\ell + \pi r^2 = \pi r(\ell + r)$ **13. a.** $192 + 192x$ units^2 **b.** S.A. = L.A. + $2B$ **15. a.** $144wz$ units^3 **b.** $V = Bh$ **17.** 54 cm **19.** The volume is decreased by $8k^2$. See below. **21.** $\pi(R^2 - r^2)$ **23.** $-\frac{b}{a}$

19.

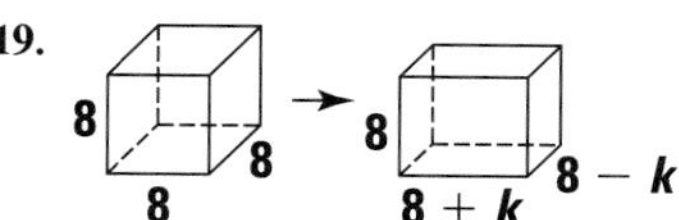

LESSON 10-7 (pp. 599–603)
11. $V = \frac{\pi r^2 h}{3}$ **13.** The volume is multiplied by 31.8. **15. a.** $\frac{72\pi}{3} \approx 75$ cm^3 **b.** 14 **c.** $3\pi\sqrt{73} \approx 81$ cm^2 **17.** at least 817 square inches **19.** volume = 216 units^3; S.A. $= 174 + 8\sqrt{117} \approx 261$ units^2 **21.** $\approx 26\%$

LESSON 10-8 (pp. 604–608)
7. 4 m **9. a.** $48\pi \approx 151$ cm^3 **b.** 37.5% **11.** $V = \frac{\pi}{6}d^3$ units^3 **13.** ≈ 449 units^3 **15.** cones, pyramids **17.** $2xyz + 8xy + 6yz + 24y$ **19.** 2.7
21.

Conclusions	Justifications
1. $AB = CB$	definition of equilateral △
2. $OB = OB$	Reflexive Property of Equality
3. $OA = OC$	definition of sphere
4. $\triangle OBC \cong \triangle OBA$	SSS Congruence Theorem
5. $m\angle OCB = m\angle OAB$	CPCF Theorem

23. $4\pi r^2$

LESSON 10-9 (pp. 609–612)
7. $\approx 1.83\%$ **9.** $\approx \$464{,}704$ **11.** $36\pi \approx 113$ m^2 **13. a.** ≈ 26 square inches **b.** ≈ 13 square inches **15.** 24 units **17.** The shorter jar holds twice as much jam. **19.** 65.0 units **21. a.** 2250 cm^2 **b.** 7200 cm^2

CHAPTER 10 PROGRESS SELF-TEST (p. 616)

1. a. L.A. $= ph = (16 + 20 + \sqrt{20^2 - 16^2}) \cdot 30 = (36 + \sqrt{144}) \cdot 30 = 48 \cdot 30 = 1440$ units^2 **b.** Volume $= Bh = \frac{1}{2} \cdot (16 \cdot \sqrt{20^2 - 16^2} \cdot 30 = \left(\frac{1}{2} \cdot 16 \cdot \sqrt{144}\right) \cdot 30 = 2880$ units^3 **2.** Because $ph = 14\pi h = 84\pi$, $h = \frac{84\pi}{14\pi} = 6$ inches **3.** Volume $= 400 = \ell wh = \ell \cdot 5 \cdot 10 = 50\ell$; $\ell = \frac{400}{50} = 8$ cm **4. a.** L.A. $= \frac{1}{2}\ell p = \frac{1}{2} \cdot 26 \cdot (4 \cdot 20) = 1040$ units^2 **b.** $h = \sqrt{26^2 - 10^2} = 24$; $V = \frac{1}{3} \cdot 400 \cdot h = \frac{1}{3} \cdot 400 \cdot 24 = 3200$ units^3 **5.** Volume $= \frac{1}{3}Bh = \frac{1}{3} \cdot 8^2\pi \cdot 15 = 320\pi \approx 1005.3$ units^3 **6.** Volume $= 96$ cm^3 $= \frac{1}{3}Bh = \frac{1}{3}B \cdot 18 = 6B$; $B = \frac{96}{6} = 16$ cm^2 **7.** S.A. $= 4\pi \cdot 19^2 \approx 4536$ units^2 $V = \frac{4}{3}\pi \cdot 19^3 \approx 28731$ units^3 **8.** S.A. $= 100\pi$ sq units $= 4\pi r^2$; $r^2 = \frac{100\pi}{4\pi} = 25$; $r = \sqrt{25} = 5$ units **9.** $\sqrt[3]{400} \approx 7$

10. L.A. $= \frac{1}{2}\ell p = \frac{1}{2} \cdot \ell \cdot 2\pi r = \pi r\ell$ **11. a.** S.A. $= 6 \cdot (9t)^2 = 6 \cdot 81t^2 = 486t^2$ units^2 **b.** $V = (9t)^3 = 729t^3$ units^3 **12.** $7^3 = 343$; so the volume of the larger box is 343 times that of the smaller one. **13.** Let e = diameter of Earth; then the diameter of Jupiter $= 11e$. S.A. of Earth $= 4\pi r^2 = 4\pi\left(\frac{e}{2}\right)^2 = \pi e^2$. S.A. of Jupiter $= 4\pi r^2 = 4\pi\left(\frac{11e}{2}\right)^2 = 121\pi e^2$. Jupiter's area is 121 times that of Earth. **14. a.** Yes **b.** They have congruent bases and heights, and both volumes are $64\pi h$ units^3. **15.** Volume(Prism) $= Bh$; Volume(Pyramid) $= \frac{1}{3}Bh$; the volume of the pyramid is one-third the volume of the prism. **16.** $2(0.9 \cdot 0.7 + 0.9 \cdot 0.2 + 0.7 \cdot 0.2) = 2 \cdot 0.95 = 1.9$ m^2 **17.** L.A. $= \frac{1}{2}p\ell = \frac{1}{2} \cdot 8\pi \cdot 18 = 72\pi \approx 226$ in^2 **18.** $V = \frac{d^3}{6}\pi = \frac{(485)^3}{6}\pi \approx 59{,}734{,}000$ miles^3 **19.** $V = Bh = \pi r^2 h = 9 \cdot 20\pi \approx 565$ cm^3 **20.** $(3x + 1)(2x + 8) = 3x \cdot 2x + 3x \cdot 8 + 1 \cdot 2x + 1 \cdot 8 = 6x^2 + 24x + 2x + 8 = 6x^2 + 26x + 8$ **21.** $(y + 2)(x + 1)(z + 6)$; $xyz + yz + 2xz + 2z + 6xy + 6y + 12x + 12$

The chart below keys the **Progress Self-Test** questions to the objectives in the **Chapter Review** on pages 617–619 or to the **Vocabulary** (Voc.) on page 615. This will enable you to locate those **Chapter Review** questions that correspond to questions students missed on the **Progress Self-Test.** The lesson where the material is covered is also indicated on the chart.

Question	**1**	**2**	**3**	**4**	**5**	**6**	**7**	**8**	**9**	**10**
Objective	A	A	A	B	B	B	D	D	C	F
Lesson	10-1, 10-5	10-1	10-3	10-2, 10-7	10-7	10-7	10-8, 10-9	10-9	10-3	10-6
Question	**11**	**12**	**13**	**14**	**15**	**16**	**17**	**18**	**19**	**20**
Objective	F	E	E	G	F	H	H	I	I	J
Lesson	10-6	10-4	10-9	10-5	10-6	10-1	10-2	10-8	10-5	10-4
Question	**21**									
Objective	J									
Lesson	10-4									

CHAPTER 10 REVIEW (pp. 617–619)
1. a. $72\pi \approx 226$ units^2 **b.** $104\pi \approx 327$ units^2 **c.** $144\pi \approx 452$ units^3 **3.** 720 units^3 **5.** 150 units^2 **7. a.** $3e$ units **b.** $27e^3$ units^3 **9.** S.A. ≈ 155 units^2; $V \approx 128.3$ units^3 **11. a.** 50 units **b.** 8000 units^2 **c.** 14,400 units^2 **13.** 200 units^2 **15.** ≈ 6.6 ft **17.** 30 **19.** 5.31 **21.** S.A. $= 20{,}736\pi \approx 65{,}144$ units^2; $V = 497{,}664\pi \approx$ 1,563,458 units^3 **23.** 6 units **25. a.** It is multiplied by 9. **b.** It is multiplied by 27. **27.** The new volume is 4 times as large. **29. a.** $2s\ell$ **b.** $s^2 + 2s\ell$ **31. a.** $\pi r^2 + \pi r\ell$ **b.** $\frac{1}{3}\pi r^2\sqrt{\ell^2 - r^2}$ **33.** Plane sections at any level other than the base do not have the same area. **35. a.** No **b.** Plane sections at any level do not have the same area. **37.** 320 square inches **39.** $\approx 14{,}142$ cubits^2 **41.** $\approx 1.13 \cdot 10^8$ km^2 **43.** 15.625 in^3 **45.** ≈ 282.7 m^3 **47.** $\approx 167{,}000$ cubits^3 **49.** ≈ 73.6 cm^3 **51.** $20xy + 15x + 8y + 6$ **53.** $(2x + 7)(x + 12) = 2x^2 + 31x + 84$ **55.** $(a + 15)(b + 9)(c + 8)$; $abc + 8ab + 9ac + 72a + 15bc + 120b + 135c + 1080$

LESSON 11-1 (pp. 622–627)
11. Pete Sampras is world-class. **13.** No conclusion can be made. **15.** Thayer is 16 or older. **17.** Nothing can be concluded. **19.** Yes **21.** $GH^2 = FG^2 + FH^2$, but $FH^2 = HI^2 + FI^2$, so by substituting, $GH^2 = FG^2 + HI^2 + FI^2$. But $FI^2 = IE^2 + EF^2$, so by substituting, $GH^2 = FG^2 + HI^2 + IE^2 + EF^2$. **23.** Sample: **See below. 25. a.** $\frac{2}{5}$ **b.** $\frac{b}{a}$ **c.** -1

23.

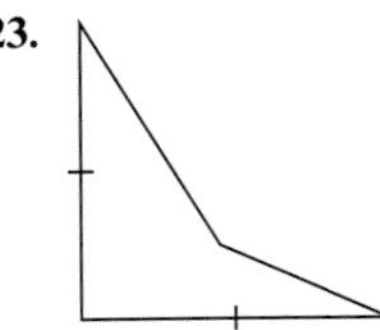

LESSON 11-2 (pp. 628–633)
15. a. $x \neq 3$ **b.** Detachment and Contrapositive **17.** Yes; Let a = Joanne apologized and d = Joanne went on her date. Her mother said not-$a \Rightarrow$ not-d. It is true, so $d \Rightarrow a$ is also true, and d is true, so you can conclude a: Joanne apologized. **19.** $\triangle ABC$ is not equilateral. **21.** From a true conditional $p \Rightarrow q$ and a statement or given information p, you may conclude q. **23.** $\sqrt{130}$ **25.** (b) **27.** 12, −22 **29.** $a^2 + b^2$; $a^2 + b^2$; 2; $a^2 + b^2$.

LESSON 11-3 (pp. 634–638)
9. $\overline{BC}$ and $\overline{AD}$ are not parallel. **11.** Catherine Voila: secretary, Edgar Guinness: manager, Wilbur Farmer: teller, Marjorie Landis: guard, Shirley Edwards: bookkeeper **13.** Converse: If I eat my hat, then my cousin is a good cook. Inverse: If my cousin is not a good cook, then I will not eat my hat. Contrapositive: If I don't eat my hat, then my cousin is not a good cook. **15.** Diagonals in a square are perpendicular.

17.

Conclusions	Justifications
1. $AC = BC$, $DC = EC$	definition of isosceles $\triangle$
2. $\angle ACD \cong \angle BCE$	Vertical Angles Theorem
3. $\triangle ACD \cong \triangle BCE$	SAS Congruence Theorem (steps 1 and 2)

19. a. $y = 11$ **b.** $x = h$ **c.** $(h, 11)$ **21.** $4z$

LESSON 11-4 (pp. 639–644)
9. Suppose that a triangle has two right angles. Then the sum of the interior angles is bigger than 180°, which contradicts the Triangle-Sum Theorem. So the supposition is false. Therefore, a triangle cannot have two right angles. **11.** Suppose that x is on the $\perp$ bisector of $\overline{PQ}$. By the Perpendicular Bisector Theorem, $PX = QX$, which contradicts the given information. So the supposition is false. Therefore, x is not on the $\perp$ bisector of $\overline{PQ}$. **13.** Suppose that two different lines intersect in more than one point, for instance, two points P and Q. This contradicts the Unique Line Assumption of the Point-Line-Plane Postulate. So the assumption is false. Therefore, two different lines intersect in at most one point. **15.** Isobel: 5′11″ and brunette; Mary: 5′10″ and black; Ruth: 5′8″ and auburn; Marcia: 5′7″ and blond; Grace: 5′6″ and red **17.** $\triangle ABC$ is not congruent to $\triangle DEF$. **19. a.** If a surface is not a box, then it is not a prism. **b.** If a surface is a box, then it is a prism. **c.** If a surface is not a prism, then it is not a box. **d.** its converse and inverse (The original statement is not true.) **21.** True

LESSON 11-5 (pp. 645–650)
9.

Conclusions	Justifications
1. The slopes of $\overline{EF}$ and $\overline{GH}$ are 1. The slopes of $\overline{EH}$ and $\overline{FG}$ are −1.	definition of slope
2. $\overline{EF} \parallel \overline{GH}$, $\overline{EH} \parallel \overline{FG}$	Parallel Lines and Slopes Theorem
3. $EFGH$ is a parallelogram.	definition of parallelogram

11. The slope of $\overline{EG} = \frac{-7}{3}$, and the slope of $\overline{FH} = \frac{-3}{7}$. $\frac{-7}{3} \cdot \frac{-3}{7} = 1 \neq -1$, so $\overline{EG}$ is not perpendicular to $\overline{FH}$. **13. a.** Sample: **See below. b.** The slope of $\overline{BD}$ is 1, and the slope of $\overline{AC}$ is −1. Therefore, the product of the slopes is −1. By the Perpendicular Lines and Slopes Theorem, $\overline{AC} \perp \overline{BD}$. **15.** Either $\sqrt{39{,}600} = 199$ or $\sqrt{39{,}600} \neq 199$. Suppose $\sqrt{39{,}600} = 199$. Then, squaring both sides: $39{,}600 = 199^2$. However, by the definition of square, $199^2 = 199 \cdot 199 = 39601$. This contradicts $39{,}600 = 199^2$. By the Law of Indirect Reasoning, the supposition is false. Thus $\sqrt{39{,}600} \neq 199$. **17.** Julie walks to school. **19. a.** ≈ 785 sq ft **b.** $\approx 25{,}656$ bushels **21. a.** 450 units **b.** 450 units **23.** cannot be simplified

13. a.

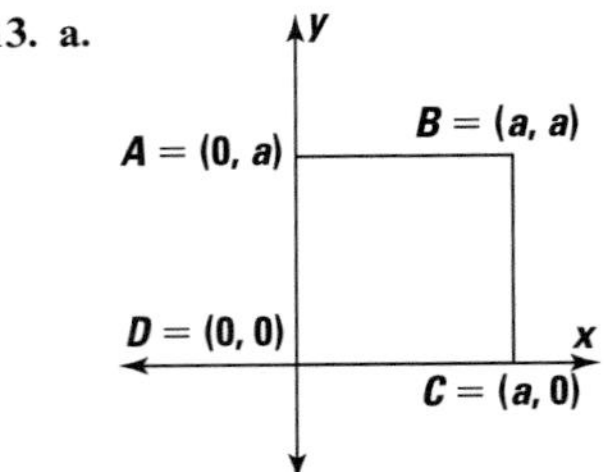

LESSON 11-6 (pp. 651–655)
11. a. **See page 898.** **b.** $\sqrt{9.49} \approx 3.08$ miles **13.** Given: Parallelogram $WXYZ$ in the convenient position as shown below, with $a > 0$. **See page 898 for drawing.** To Prove: $WX = YZ$ and $WZ = YX$. According to the Distance Formula, $WX = a$, $YZ = \sqrt{(a + b - b)^2 + (c - c)^2} = \sqrt{a^2} = a$, $WZ = \sqrt{(0 - b)^2 + (0 - c)^2} = \sqrt{b^2 + c^2}$, and $XY = \sqrt{(a + b - a)^2 + (c - 0)^2} = \sqrt{b^2 + c^2}$. Thus, by the Transitive Property of Equality, $WX = YZ$ and $WZ = YX$. Therefore, each pair of opposite sides are congruent. **15.** The slope of $\overline{PQ} = \frac{2z - 4z}{7z - 3z} = -\frac{1}{2}$ and the slope of $\overline{QR} = \frac{-8z - 2z}{2z - 7z} = 2$ by the definition of slope. $-\frac{1}{2} \cdot 2 = -1$. So $\overline{PQ} \perp \overline{QR}$ by the Perpendicular Lines and

Slopes Theorem. Thus, $\triangle PQR$ is a right triangle by the definition of right triangle. **17.** Richard Nixon did not win the majority of electoral votes. **19.** The area of the triangle is one-half the area of the parallelogram. **21.** $\frac{a-b}{2}$

11. a.

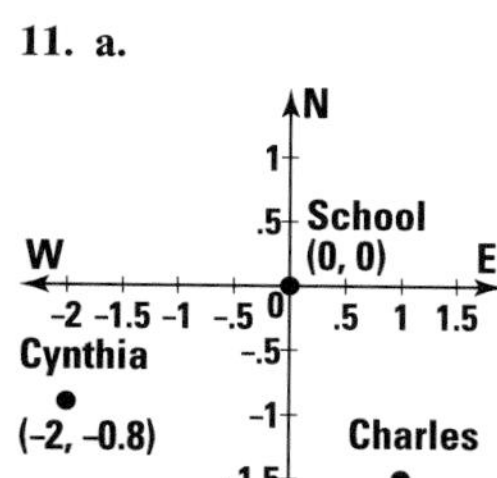

13.

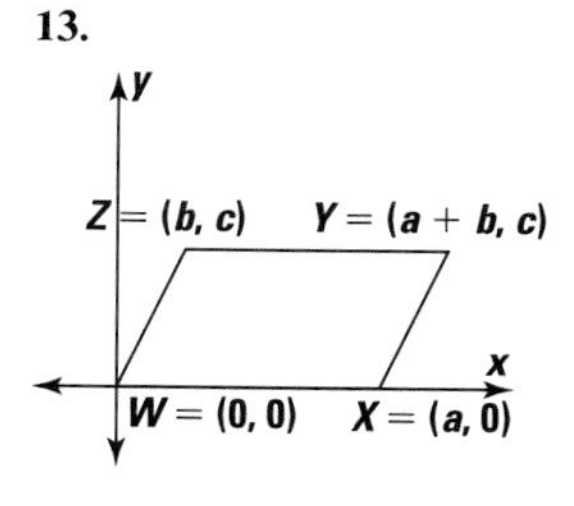

LESSON 11-7 (pp. 656–660)

9. a. (−1, 0) **b.** $\sqrt{2}$ **c.** Sample: (0, 1) **11. a.** (−6, −2) **b.** 1 **c.** Sample: (−6, −3) **13.** 22π units **15. a. See right. b.** (2, 0) **c.** $(x-2)^2 + (y+1)^2 = 1$ **d.** π square units **17.** $41x$ **19.** Given: $Q = (9a, 4b)$; $R = (6a, 2b)$, $S = (a, -7b)$, and $T = (-a, -14b)$. To prove: $QRST$ is a trapezoid.

Conclusions	Justifications
1. slope of $\overline{TQ}$ = $\frac{-14b-4b}{-a-9a} = \frac{-18b}{-10a}\frac{9b}{5a}$	definition of slope
2. slope of $\overline{SR}$ = $\frac{-7b-2b}{a-6a} = \frac{-9b}{-5a} = \frac{9b}{5a}$	definition of slope
3. $\overline{TQ} \parallel \overline{SR}$	Parallel Lines and Slopes Theorem
4. $QRST$ is a trapezoid.	definition of trapezoid

21. By the definition of isosceles triangle, $YX = ZX$. V is the midpoint of $\overline{XY}$, Therefore, $XV = VY = \frac{1}{2}XY$, $XW = WZ = \frac{1}{2}XZ$. Therefore, by the Transitive Property of Equality, $XV = XW$. By the definition of isosceles triangle, $\triangle XVW$ is isosceles. **23.** They are collinear.

15. a.

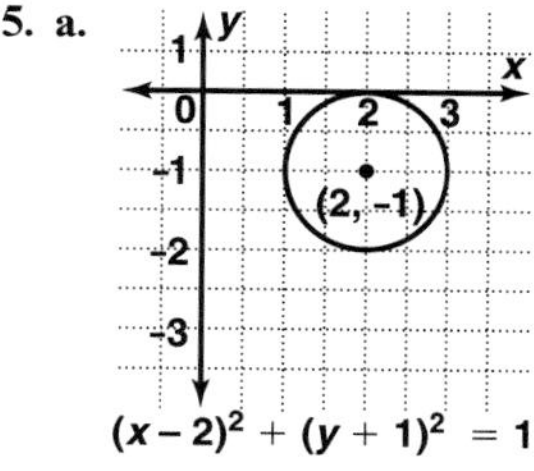

LESSON 11-8 (pp. 662–667)

13. $BC = 6$ **15.** $\overline{AB} \parallel \overline{NC}$ and $\overline{AN} \parallel \overline{CB}$ by the Midpoint Connector Theorem. Therefore, $ANCB$ is a parallelogram. **17. a.** (1986, 12.25) **b.** In 1986 one might estimate that there were 12.25 million African-American, Hispanic, and Asian families in the United States. **19.** Either the diagonals of $MNOP$ bisect each other or they do not. Suppose they do. Thus, $\overline{MO}$ and $\overline{NP}$ have the same midpoint. The midpoint of $\overline{MO} = \left(\frac{8+-4}{2}, \frac{0+6}{2}\right) = \left(\frac{4}{2}, \frac{6}{2}\right) =$ (2, 3). The midpoint of $\overline{NP} = \left(\frac{-8+4}{2}, \frac{0+6}{2}\right) = \left(\frac{-4}{2}, \frac{6}{2}\right) = (-2, 3)$. These midpoints are not the same. Thus the supposition has led to a false conclusion. Consequently, by the Law of Indirect Reasoning, the diagonals of $MNOP$ do not bisect each other. **21. a.** (1, −2.5) **b.** 8.5 units **c.** $(x-1)^2 + (y+2.5)^2 = 72.25$ **23.** $(x+2)^2 + y^2 = 25$ **25.** Birthday cake does not agree with me. **27.** Sample: **See below.**

27.

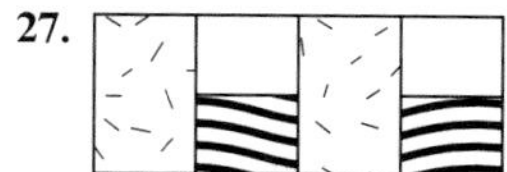

LESSON 11-9 (pp. 668–674)

11. a. $A = (10, 0, 6)$, $B = (0, 0, 6)$, $C = (0, 1, 6)$, $E = (10, 0, 0)$, $G = (0, 1, 0)$, $H = (10, 1, 0)$ **b.** 60 units^3 **c.** 152 units^2 **13.** $\overline{AB}$: (3, −.5, 1); $\overline{BC}$: (−3.5, 4, −1.5); $\overline{AC}$: (−4.5, 3.5, 4.5) **15.** $x^2 + y^2 + z^2 = 25$ **17. a.** (14, 5) **b.** $\sqrt{109} \approx 10.44$ units **19. a.** $\sqrt{10}$ **b.** $(x-3)^2 + (y+2)^2 = 10$ **21.** p **23. a.** $x = \frac{55}{2} = 27.5$ **b.** $y = 1.15$ **c.** $z = 3.9$

CHAPTER 11 PROGRESS SELF-TEST (p. 679)

1. $PQ = \sqrt{(30-7)^2 + (-7-15)^2} = \sqrt{1013} \approx 31.8$ units **2.** $M\left(\frac{30+7}{2}, \frac{-7+15}{2}\right) = M(18.5, 4)$ **3.** $RS =$ $\sqrt{(8-3)^2 + (4-4)^2} = \sqrt{5^2 + 0^2} = 5$; $RT =$ $\sqrt{(11-3)^2 + (8-4)^2} = \sqrt{8^2 + 4^2} = \sqrt{80}$; $ST =$ $\sqrt{(11-8)^2 + (8-4)^2} = \sqrt{3^2 + 4^2} = 5$. So the perimeter of $\triangle RST = RS + RT + ST = 5 + \sqrt{80} + 5 \approx 18.94$ units. **4. a. See page 899. b.** $AO = \sqrt{(5-0)^2 + (-6-0)^2 + (8-0)^2} = \sqrt{125} \approx 11.18$ units **c.** $\left(\frac{5+0}{2}, \frac{-6+0}{2}, \frac{8+0}{2}\right) = (2.5, -3, 4)$ **5. a.** $\angle A$ is a right angle. **b.** Law of Ruling Out Possibilities **6. a.** The volume of figure Q is the area of its base times its height. **b.** Law of Detachment **7. a.** If a figure is a polygon, then it is a hexagon. False **b.** If a figure is not a hexagon, then it is not a polygon. False **c.** If a figure is not a polygon, then it is not a hexagon. True **8.** Either $\triangle ABC$ has all angles with measures under 60 or it does not. Suppose that there exists a $\triangle ABC$ where $m\angle A < 60$, $m\angle B < 60$, and $m\angle C < 60$. Then by the Addition Property of Inequality, $m\angle A + m\angle B + m\angle C < 180$. But this contradicts the Triangle-Sum Theorem. So by the Law of Indirect Reasoning, there is no triangle with three angles all with measures less than 60. **9.** Either $\sqrt{80} = 40$ or $\sqrt{80} \neq 40$. Suppose $\sqrt{80} = 40$. Then squaring both sides, $80 = 1600$. This is a false statement. By the Law of Indirect Reasoning, the supposition $\sqrt{80} = 40$ is false. So $\sqrt{80} \neq 40$. **10.** $HM = \sqrt{6^2 + 8^2} = 10$; $RB = \sqrt{(16-10)^2 + (8-0)^2} = 10$; $HR =$ $\sqrt{(16-6)^2 + (8-8)^2} = 10$; $MB = \sqrt{10^2 + 0^2} = 10$ So, $HM = RB = HR = MB$. Therefore, $RHMB$ is a rhombus. **11.** By the Midpoint Formula, the midpoint of $\overline{XZ}$ is $\left(\frac{2a+2b}{2}, \frac{0+2c}{2}\right) = (a+b, c)$, and the midpoint of $\overline{YW}$ is $\left(\frac{2a+2b+0}{2}, \frac{2c+0}{2}\right) = (a+b, c)$. So the two midpoints are identical. **12.** $\overline{DF} \parallel \overline{BE}$ by the Midpoint Connector Theorem; $\overline{EF} \parallel \overline{BD}$ by the Midpoint Connector Theorem. By the definition of a parallelogram, $BDFE$ is a parallelogram. **13.** $AE = EB = DF = \frac{1}{2}AB = 5.5$; $EF = BD = DC = \frac{1}{2}BC = 11.15$

SELECTED ANSWERS

14. Let b = someone is a baby, h = someone is happy, and t = someone is teething. The statements translate to (1) $b \Rightarrow h$, (2) $t \Rightarrow b$, (3) Nate is not-h. By the Law of the Contrapositive, (1) implies not-$h \Rightarrow$ not-b and (2) implies not-$b \Rightarrow$ not-t. Applying the Law of Transitivity, not-$h \Rightarrow$ not-t. With this statement and the Law of Detachment, we can conclude Nate is not teething. **15.** Let q = Queen, k = King, j = Jack, a = Ace and > mean older than. The statements can be interpreted (1) $q > k$, (2) $j > q$, (3) $a > j$. By the Transitive Property of Inequality, $a > j > q > k$. Thus we conclude that the Ace is from the 17th century, the Jack is from the 18th century, the Queen is from the 19th century and the King is from the 20th century. **16.** If we consider Selkirk to be the origin, then Goodland is $G = (-12, 60)$ and Garden City is $C = (34, -36)$. So the flying distance $GC = \sqrt{46^2 + 96^2} = \sqrt{11332} \approx 106.5$ miles. **17.** $\sqrt{7^2 + 12^2 + 17^2} = \sqrt{482} \approx 21.95''$ **18.** **See right.** **19.** $x^2 + (y + 19)^2 + (z - 4)^2 = 36$ **20.** Sample: $(-a, 0), (a, 0), (b, c), (-b, c)$

4. a. **18.**

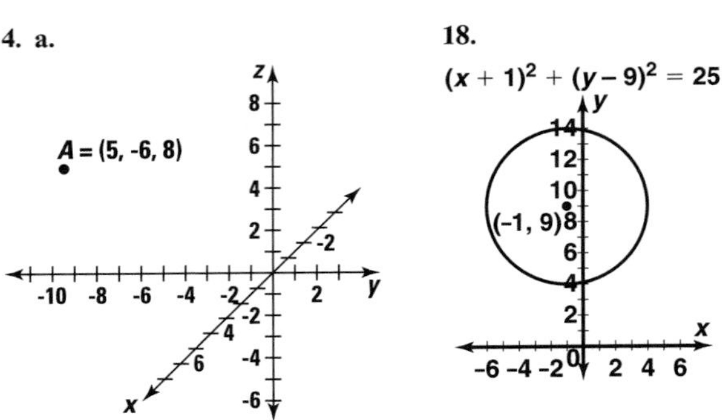

The chart below keys the **Progress Self-Test** questions to the objectives in the **Chapter Review** on pages 680–683 or to the **Vocabulary** (Voc.) on page 678. This will enable you to locate those **Chapter Review** questions that correspond to questions students missed on the **Progress Self-Test.** The lesson where the material is covered is also indicated on the chart.

Question	**1**	**2**	**3**	**4**	**5**	**6**	**7**	**8**	**9**	**10**
Objective	A	A	A	C	D	D	E	F	F	G
Lesson	11-6	11-8	11-6	11-9	11-3	11-1	11-2	11-4	11-4	11-6
Question	**11**	**12**	**13**	**14**	**15**	**16**	**17**	**18**	**19**	**20**
Objective	G	B	B	H	H	I	I	J	J	K
Lesson	11-8	11-8	11-8	11-1, 11-2	11-1	11-6	11-9	11-7	11-9	11-5

CHAPTER 11 REVIEW (pp. 680–683)

1. $\sqrt{136} \approx 11.66$ units **3.** $(-2, -6)$ **5.** 19.49 units **7.** $\sqrt{x^2 + y^2}$ **9.** $WX = 41$, $VX = 82$, $VZ = 80$ **11.** Applying the Midpoint Connector Theorem to $\triangle BCD$, $\overline{EF} // \overline{DB}$. Thus, $BDEF$ is a trapezoid by the definition of trapezoid. **13.** **See right.** **15. a.** $(-1, -1, 3.5)$ **b.** ≈ 9.64 units **17. a.** *LOVE* is a trapezoid. **b.** Law of Detachment **19. a.** $x = 11$ **b.** Law of Ruling Out Possibilities **21. a.** (d) **b.** (b) **23. a.** If $x^2 = 9$, then $x = 3$. **b.** If $x \neq 3$, then $x^2 \neq 9$. **c.** If $x^2 \neq 9$, then $x \neq 3$. **d.** original, contrapositive **25. a.** All people in the U.S. live in New York. **b.** If a person is not a New Yorker, then that person does not live in the U.S. **c.** If a person does not live in the U.S., then that person is not a New Yorker. **d.** original, contrapositive **27.** Either quadrilateral $ABCD$ has four acute angles or it does not. Suppose that in quadrilateral $ABCD$, $\angle A$, $\angle B$, $\angle C$, and $\angle D$ are acute. Thus, $m\angle A < 90$, $m\angle B < 90$, $m\angle C < 90$, and $m\angle D < 90$. So $m\angle A + m\angle B + m\angle C + m\angle D < 360$, which contradicts the Quadrilateral-Sum Theorem. So by the Law of Indirect Reasoning, the supposition is false. Thus a quadrilateral cannot have four acute angles. **29.** Either $\sqrt{2} = \frac{239}{169}$ or $\sqrt{2} \neq \frac{239}{169}$. Suppose $\sqrt{2} = \frac{239}{169}$. Then $2 = \left(\frac{239}{169}\right)^2 = \frac{57{,}121}{28{,}561}$. Then $2 \cdot 28{,}561 = 57{,}121$; so $57{,}122 = 57{,}121$. This is a false conclusion; so by the Law of Indirect Reasoning, the supposition is false. So $\sqrt{2} \neq \frac{239}{169}$. **31.** Either $ABCD$ is a trapezoid or it is not. Suppose $ABCD$ is a trapezoid. Then by the definition of trapezoid, either $\overline{AB} // \overline{CD}$ or $\overline{AD} // \overline{BC}$. Slope of $\overline{AB} = \frac{10}{8} = \frac{5}{4}$; slope of $\overline{CD} = \frac{12}{14} = \frac{6}{7}$. So, by the Parallel Lines and Slopes Theorem, $\overline{AB}$ is not parallel to $\overline{CD}$. Then by the Law of Ruling Out Possibilities $\overline{AD} // \overline{BC}$ is the other possibility. Slope of $\overline{AD} = \frac{-5}{-1} = 5$; slope of $\overline{BC} = \frac{3}{-5} = -\frac{3}{5}$. So by the Parallel Lines and Slopes Theorem, $\overline{AD}$ is not parallel to $\overline{BC}$. Therefore, the supposition is false and by the Law of Indirect Reasoning, $ABCD$ is not a trapezoid. **33.** $AB = \sqrt{145}$; $AC = \sqrt{145}$. Since $AB = AC$, $\triangle ABC$ is isosceles by definition of isosceles triangle. **35.** Slope of $\overline{XY} = \frac{-2}{7}$; slope of $\overline{YZ} = \frac{10}{3}$; slope of $\overline{ZW} = \frac{-2}{7}$; slope of $\overline{WX} = \frac{10}{3}$. By the Parallel Lines and Slopes Theorem, $\overline{XY} // \overline{ZW}$ and $\overline{YZ} // \overline{WX}$. Thus, $XYZW$ is a parallelogram by the definition of a parallelogram. **37.** Slope of $\overline{WY} = \frac{s-0}{s-0} = \frac{s}{s} = 1$; slope of $\overline{XZ} = \frac{s-0}{0-s} = \frac{s}{-s} = -1$. Since $1 \cdot -1 = -1$, by the Perpendicular Lines and Slopes Theorem, $\overline{WY} \perp \overline{XZ}$. **39.** I have not finished my homework. **41.** No bat can live on the moon. **43.** All the names on this list are melodious. **45.** $\sqrt{146} \approx 12.1$ miles **47.** 28 inches **49.** $(x - 8)^2 + (y + 1)^2 = 225$ **51.** **See below.** **53.** $(x - 4)^2 + (y + 3)^2 + z^2 = 100$ **55.** Sample: $(-a, 0), (a, 0), (0, b)$ **57.** Sample: $(-a, 0), (a, 0), (0, b), (0, -c)$

13.

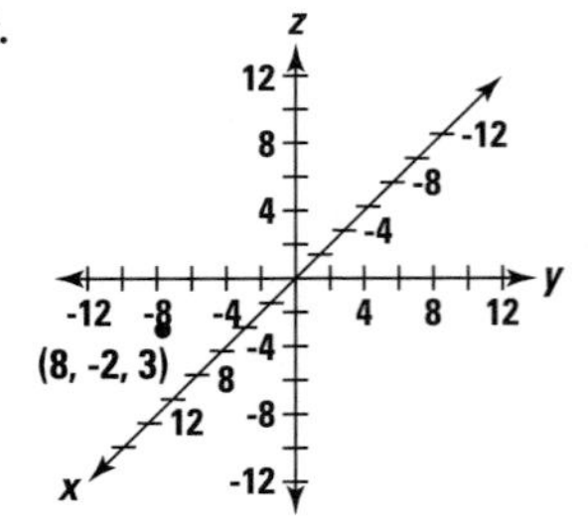

51.

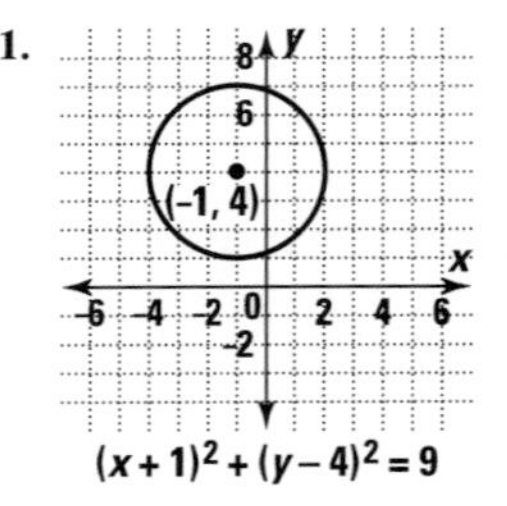

LESSON 12-1 (pp. 686–690)

9. a. (-6, 21) **b.** $OA = \sqrt{53}$, $AA' = 2\sqrt{53}$, $OA' = 3\sqrt{53}$. Thus, $OA + AA' = OA'$ **c.** By the Properties of S_k Theorem (a), the slopes of OA and OA' are the same. Also, $OA' > OA$. Thus, A is between O and A'. **11. See below. 13.** 144 inches or 12 feet **15.** $P' = (0, 0)$, $R' = (2a, 0)$, $Q' = (2b, 2c)$ **17.** Every isometry preserves Angle measure, Betweenness, Collinearity (lines), and Distance (lengths of segments). **19.** E, $G^{\#}$, B, D **21.** $x = 13.5$ **23.** $AB = 36$

11.

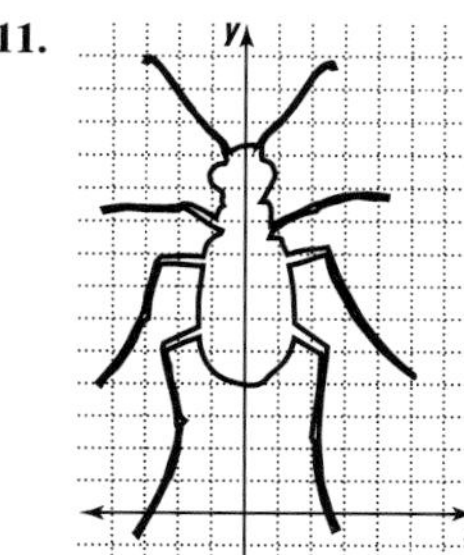

LESSON 12-2 (pp. 692–697)

13. a. expansion **b.** 1.4 **15.** $\frac{3}{5}$ **17.** (0, 0), 2 **19. See below.**
21. a. slope of $\overline{PQ} = \frac{8-2}{-4-9} = \frac{6}{-13}$, slope of $\overline{QR} = \frac{-10-8}{35--4} = -\frac{18}{39} = -\frac{6}{13}$, so P, Q, and R are collinear since $\overline{PQ} \parallel \overline{QR}$ and they share Q. **b.** $PQ = \sqrt{205}$; $QR = \sqrt{1845} = 3\sqrt{205}$; $PR = \sqrt{820} = 2\sqrt{205}$. Since $PQ + PR = QR$, P is between Q and R. **c.** $P' = (36, 8)$, $Q' = (-16, 32)$, $R' = (140, -40)$ **d.** slope of $\overline{P'Q'} = \frac{32-8}{-16-36} = \frac{24}{-52} = -\frac{6}{13}$, slope of $\overline{Q'R'} = \frac{-40-32}{140--16} = \frac{-72}{156} = -\frac{6}{13}$, so P', Q', and R' are collinear since $\overline{P'Q'} \parallel \overline{Q'R'}$ and they share Q'. **e.** $P'Q' = \sqrt{3280} = 4\sqrt{205}$, $Q'R' = \sqrt{29520} = 12\sqrt{205}$, and $P'R' = \sqrt{13120} = 8\sqrt{205}$. Since $P'Q' + P'R' = Q'R'$, P' is between Q' and R'. **23.** Yes; A to D to C to A to B to C **25. a.** $z = 0.5$ **b.** $M = \pm\sqrt{30} \approx \pm 5.48$

19.

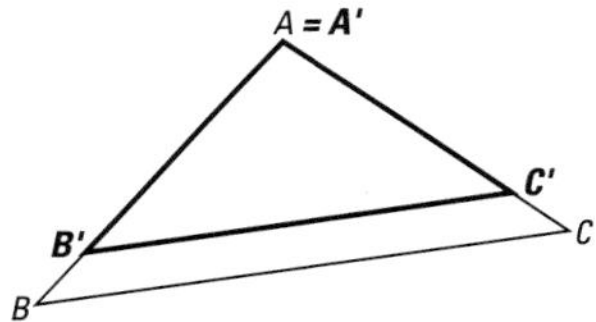

LESSON 12-3 (pp. 698–704)

13. a. $\frac{5}{8} = 0.625$ **b.** M **c.** 7.5 units **d.** 20.8 units **15. See right. 17. a.** 1.4 **b.** 16.8 cm **c.** 60 cm^2 and 117.6 cm^2 **d.** 1.96 **e.** 1.4 **19. See right.** $k \approx .7$ **21.** $k = \frac{1}{2}$, $Q' = (-4.5, 6)$, $R = (10, 26)$, $T' = (0, -4)$ **23.** composites of 2 reflections are translations and rotations; the other isometry is glide reflections **25.** $k = \frac{2}{b}$

15.

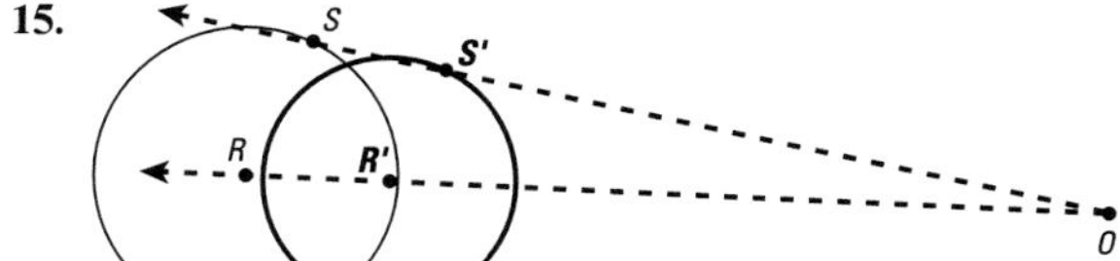

19.

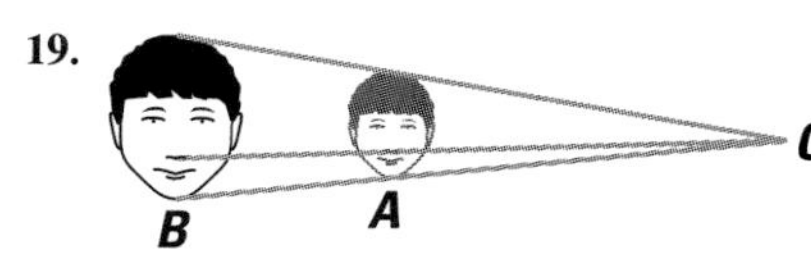

LESSON 12-4 (pp. 705–710)

13. $x = \frac{ac}{b}$ **15.** $\approx$ \$4.16 **17.** 112.5 mm **19.** $S(A) = (8, -3)$, $S(B) = (5, 4)$, $AB = \sqrt{6^2 + 14^2} = \sqrt{232} = 2\sqrt{58}$; length of $S(\overline{AB}) = \sqrt{3^2 + 7^2} = \sqrt{58}$; $\sqrt{58} = \frac{1}{2} \cdot 2\sqrt{58}$ **21.** 10 in.
23. a. Since $GHJKL$ is regular, $\overline{GL} \cong \overline{HJ}$. Since $\triangle FGL$ and $\triangle HIJ$ are regular polygons, they are equilateral (definition of regular polygon) and so $\overline{FG} \cong \overline{FL} \cong \overline{GL}$ and $\overline{HI} \cong \overline{JI} \cong \overline{HJ}$. Thus, by the Transitive Property of Congruence, all six of these segments are congruent. So, by the SSS Congruence Theorem, $\triangle FGL \cong \triangle HIJ$. **b.** 168

LESSON 12-5 (pp. 711–716)

15. 6 units **17.** 810″ or 67.5 ft **19. a.** False; for example: under a rotation of magnitude other than 0°, 180°, or -180°, the image of a line intersects its preimage. **b.** True, since if any two figures do not intersect, their images cannot intersect. (Here is a proof of the contrapositive: If their images intersected, then each point of intersection would have a preimage on both figures, so the preimages would have had to intersect.) **21.** 2.5 **23.** $\frac{244\pi}{3} \approx 256\ cm^3$

LESSON 12-6 (pp. 717–723)

11. a. $V = 3025\pi$ $units^3$; S.A. $= 792\pi$ $units^2$ **b.** 27, 9 **c.** $V = 81{,}675\pi$ $units^3$; S.A. $= 7128\pi$ $units^2$ **13. a.** 337.5 in^3 **b.** ≈ 29.63 in^3 **15. a.** 3 or $\frac{1}{3}$ **b.** 9 or $\frac{1}{9}$ **17.** $\frac{3}{2}$ **19.** $1\frac{1}{2}$″ **21.** $33\frac{1}{3}$%

LESSON 12-7 (pp. 724–728)

13. 15.625 kg **15.** $\approx$ 62 cm **17.** $\approx$ 123 lb **19.** 11.2 $units^2$
21. Two figures are similar if and only if there is a composite of size changes and reflections mapping one onto the other.
23.

Conclusions	Justifications
1. $\overline{FK} \cong \overline{KJ}$	definition of midpoint
2. $\angle FKG \cong \angle KJI$, $\angle KFG \cong \angle JKI$	// Lines ⇒ corr. ∠s ≅
3. $\triangle FGK \cong \triangle KIJ$	ASA Congruence Theorem (steps 1 and 2)

CHAPTER 12 PROGRESS SELF-TEST (p. 732)

1. Draw rays from O through A, B, and C. Measure $\overline{OA}$ and calculate $\frac{3}{4} \cdot OA$ to determine OA'. Mark A' on ray $\overrightarrow{OA}$. Draw parallel segments through A' for $\overline{A'B'}$, $\overline{A'C'}$, and draw $\overline{B'C'}$. **See page 901. 2. See page 901. 3.** Measure $\overline{FE}$. Calculate $1.5 \cdot FE$ for length of $\overline{FE'}$. Measure $\overline{FD}$. Calculate $1.5 \cdot FD$ for FD'. Use $\overline{E'D'}$ as radius and draw circle E'. **See page 901. 4. See page 901.** $OP = 5.6$ cm, $OP' = 3.4$; so the magnitude is $\frac{3.4}{5.6}$, about 0.6 **5.** $m\angle AUQ = 37$; $DA = \frac{3}{4} \cdot 27 = 20.25$; $OU = \frac{4}{3} \cdot 24 = 32$ **6.** $\frac{WY}{VZ} = \frac{WX}{XV}$; $\frac{4}{12} = \frac{6}{XV}$; $XV = 18$. **7. a.** contraction **b.** X **8.** (a) **9.** Two figures F and G are similar if and only if there is a composite of size changes and reflections mapping F onto G.

10. area($\triangle P'Q'R'$) = 5^2 · area($\triangle PQR$) = 25 · area($\triangle PQR$) **11.** $\frac{V}{729} = \left(\frac{1}{3}\right)^3$; $V = \frac{729}{27} = 27 \text{ cm}^3$ **12. a.** $\frac{QR}{VT} = \frac{OS}{VU}$, $\frac{x}{3x} = \frac{OS}{6y}$. Thus, $QS = 2y$. **b.** $\frac{QR}{VT} = \frac{RS}{TU}$, $\frac{x}{3x} = \frac{2x}{TU}$. Thus, $TU = 6x$. **13.** $\frac{3}{25} = \frac{5}{x}$; $3x = 125$; $x = \frac{125}{3} = 41\frac{2}{3} \approx 41.7$ cm **14.** $\frac{41}{28} = \frac{100}{x}$; $x \approx 68$ minutes. **15.** $\left(\frac{4}{12}\right)^3 = \left(\frac{1}{3}\right)^3 = \frac{5}{w}$; $w = 5 \cdot 3^3$ or 135 lb **16.** $\frac{2 \text{ m}}{0.4 \text{ m}} = \frac{33 \text{ cm}}{y \text{ cm}}$; $2y = 13.2$; $y = 6.6$ cm **17.** 6^3 or 216, 6^2 or 36 **18.** $S_{\frac{1}{3}}(A) = (2, -2)$, $S_{\frac{1}{3}}(B) = (3, 0)$, $S_{\frac{1}{3}}(C) = \left(-2, \frac{10}{3}\right)$ **See right.** **19.** $S_8(P) = (40, -8)$, $S_8(Q) = (8, 16)$; The distance between $S_8(P)$ and $S_8(Q) = \sqrt{(40-8)^2 + (-8-16)^2} = \sqrt{32^2 + (-24)^2} = \sqrt{1600} = 40$; $PQ = \sqrt{(5-1)^2 + (-1-2)^2} = \sqrt{4^2 + (-3)^2} = \sqrt{25} = 5$. Therefore, the distance between $S_8(P)$ and $S_8(Q)$ is $8 \cdot PQ$. **20.** $K' = (0, 4b)$, $I' = (4a, 0)$, $T' = (0, -4c)$, $E' = (-4a, 0)$

1.
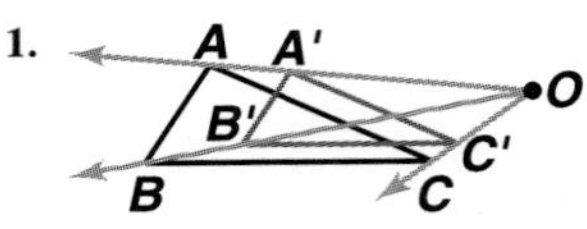

2.
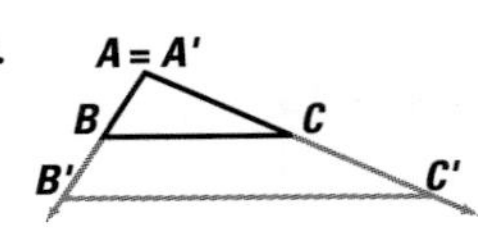

3.
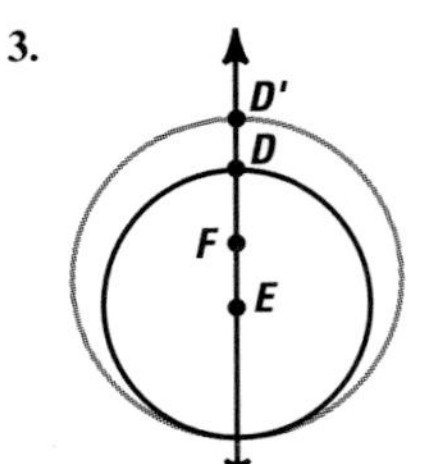

4.
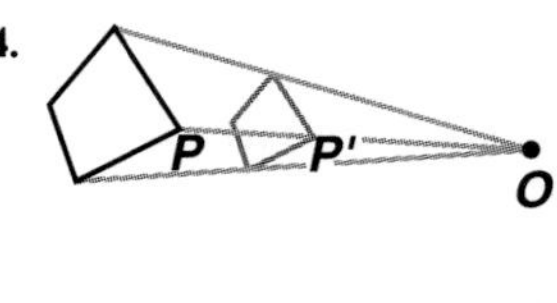

18.
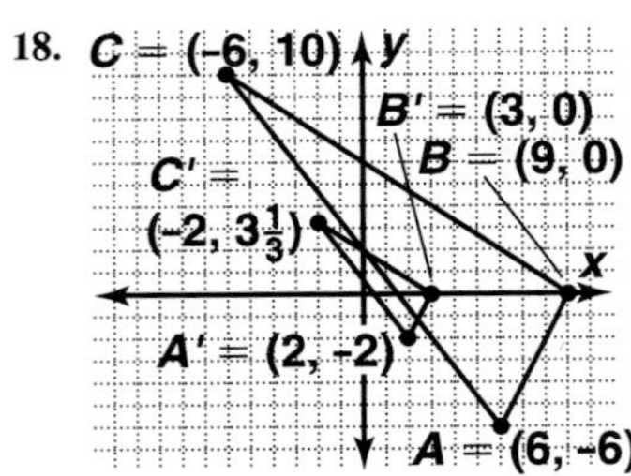

The chart below keys the **Progress Self-Test** questions to the objectives in the **Chapter Review** on pages 733–735 or to the **Vocabulary** (Voc.) on page 731. This will enable you to locate those **Chapter Review** questions that correspond to questions students missed on the **Progress Self-Test.** The lesson where the material is covered is also indicated on the chart.

Question	**1**	**2**	**3**	**4**	**5**	**6**	**7**	**8**	**9**	**10**
Objective	A	A	A	C	B	B	C	C	Voc.	D
Lesson	12-2	12-2	12-2	12-2	12-5	12-5	12-2	12-3	12-5	12-6
Question	**11**	**12**	**13**	**14**	**15**	**16**	**17**	**18**	**19**	**20**
Objective	D	B	E	E	F	E	F	G	G	G
Lesson	12-6	12-5	12-4	12-4	12-7	12-5	12-7	12-1	12-1	12-1

CHAPTER 12 REVIEW (pp. 733–735)

1. See below. 3. See below. 5. See right. 7. $m\angle H = 100$, $PE = 4.1\overline{6}$, $OU = 7.92$ **9.** $VU = 12$ units **11. a.** $\frac{2}{3}y$ **b.** $3z$ **13. a.** N **b.** 71 **c.** 44 **15. See right. 17. a.** contraction **b.** True **19.** area($\triangle A'B'C'$) = 121 · area($\triangle ABC$) **21.** $\approx 35.6 \text{ cm}^2$ **23.** 6.25″ **25.** ≈ 20.2″ **27.** 3.2″ **29.** ≈ 12.3 kg **31.** 144 **33.** 512, 64 **35. See right. 37.** $A' = (6k, -5k)$, $B' = (-10k, 0)$, $C' = (-3k, 8k)$, $D' = (12k, 20k)$ **39.** $S(E) = \left(\frac{1}{2}a, \frac{1}{2}b\right)$, $S(H) = \left(0, \frac{1}{2}c\right)$, $S(G) = \left(-\frac{1}{2}a, -\frac{1}{2}b\right)$

1.
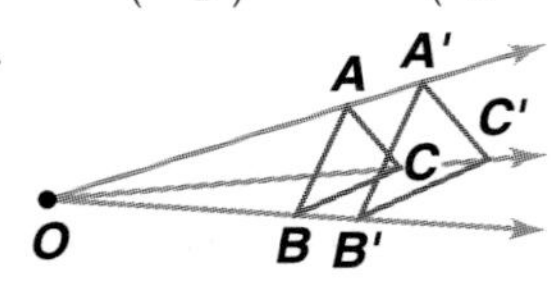

3.
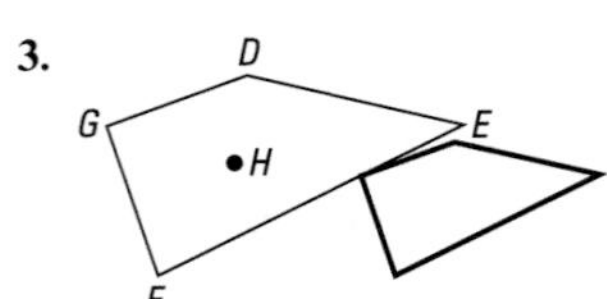

5.
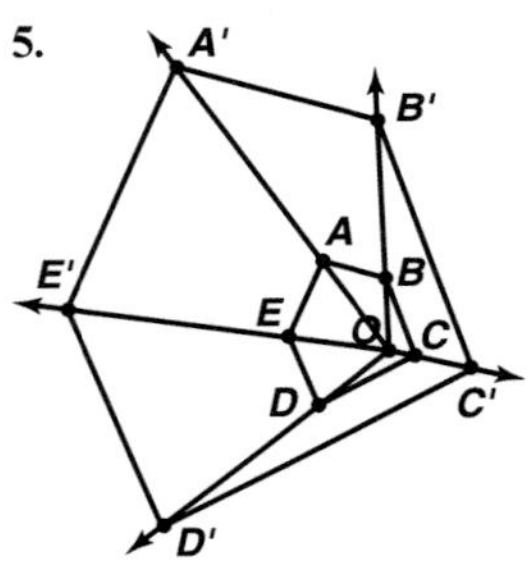

15.

35.
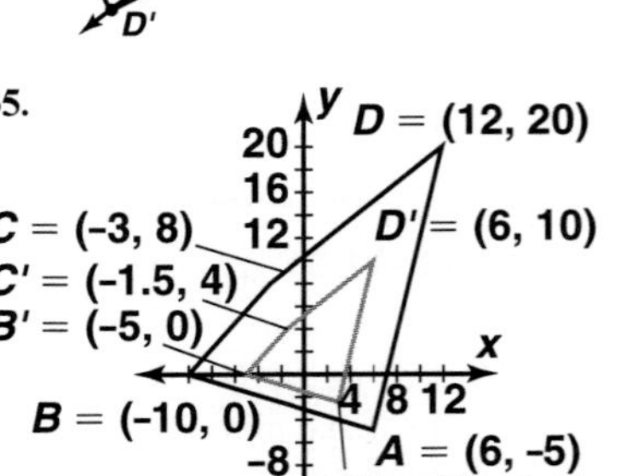

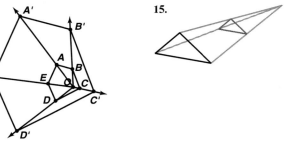

LESSON 13-1 (pp. 738–743)

9. a. $\triangle DEF \sim \triangle UVW$ **b.** $\frac{10}{33}$ or $\frac{33}{10}$ **c.** $UV = 7.\overline{57} \approx 7.6$; $VW = 9.\overline{69} \approx 9.7$ **11. a.** Yes **b.** Using the Pythagorean Theorem, $AC = 39$ and $DF = 32$. Since $\frac{24}{39} = \frac{32}{52} = \frac{40}{65}$, $\triangle ABC \sim \triangle EFD$ by the SSS Similarity Theorem.

13.

Conclusions	Justifications
1. $WX = \frac{1}{2}WY$ $WV = \frac{1}{2}WZ$	definition of midpoint
2. $XV = \frac{1}{2}YZ$	Midpoint Connector Theorem
3. $\frac{WX}{WY} = \frac{1}{2}, \frac{WV}{WZ} = \frac{1}{2}$, $\frac{XV}{YZ} = \frac{1}{2}$	Multiplication Property of Equality
4. $\frac{WX}{WY} = \frac{WV}{WZ} = \frac{XV}{YZ}$	Transitive Property of Equality
5. $\triangle WXV \sim \triangle WYX$	SSS Similarity Theorem (step 4)

15. $\frac{1}{5}$ **17.** surface area of a box with sides ℓ, w, h **19.** volume of a cylinder of height h and base of radius r **21. a.** 180 **b.** $\frac{360}{41} \approx 8.78$ **23.** (b) **25.** $\pm 10\sqrt{2}$

LESSON 13-2 (pp. 744–750)

13. a. No **b.** $\frac{12}{24} \neq \frac{5}{7} \neq \frac{13}{25}$ **15. a.** Yes **b.** SSS Similarity Theorem **c.** $\triangle XVW \sim \triangle AZY$ **17.** $\angle ABC \cong \angle EDC$, and $\angle BAC \cong \angle DEC$ from the // Lines ⇒ AIA ≅ Theorem. Thus, $\triangle CED \sim \triangle CAB$ by the AA Similarity Theorem. **19.** $AB = 1.5$ **21.** $n = 48$

23.

Conclusions	Justifications
0. $\frac{a}{b} = \frac{c}{d}$	Given
1. $ad = bc$ $\frac{d}{c} = \frac{b}{a}$	Multiplication Prop. of =
2. $\frac{b}{a} = \frac{d}{c}$	Symmetric Prop. of =

24. front **25.** $25\sqrt{2} \approx 35.4$ meters

LESSON 13-3 (pp. 751–757)

11. a. 7.5 **b.** 9 **c.** supplementary **d.** $\frac{BD}{DA} = \frac{FA}{CF}$ **13.** $x = 125$ m; $y = 100$ m **15.** No judgement can be made. **17.** Yes, $\triangle STO \sim \triangle XYZ$ by the SSS Similarity Theorem.

19.

Conclusions	Justifications
1. $\angle ABE \cong \angle CBD$	definition of angle bisector
2. $\triangle ABE \sim \triangle CBD$	AA Similarity Theorem (step 1 and given)

21. (a) **23.** No, the three angle measures are approximately 30, 70, and 30.

LESSON 13-4 (pp. 759–764)

9. $x = \frac{16}{5} = 3.2$, $y = \frac{9}{5} = 1.8$, $h = \frac{12}{5} = 2.4$ **11. a.** part (1) **b.** ≈ 17.8 feet **13.** $a = 3\sqrt{10}$, $b = 3\sqrt{15}$, $CD = 3\sqrt{6}$

15.

Conclusions	Justifications
1. $\overline{WX} \parallel \overline{ZY}$	definition of trapezoid
2. $\angle XWU \cong \angle ZYU$ $\angle WXU \cong \angle YZU$	// lines ⇒ AIA ≅ Theorem
3. $\triangle WXU \sim \triangle YZU$	AA Similarity Theorem

17. a. No **19. a.** 3 **b.** 3 **c.** 4 **21.** It is circular reasoning to use a theorem to prove itself.

LESSON 13-5 (pp. 765–770)

15. $7\sqrt{3} \approx 12.12$ **17.** 60 **19.** $OP = 4.5$ **21.** $y = 9$; $x = \sqrt{80} \approx 8.94$ **23.** $\triangle CBA$, $\triangle BPA$, $\triangle CPB$ (and also $\triangle ADC$)

LESSON 13-6 (pp. 772–776)

11. $\frac{9}{40} = .225$ **13. a.** $\angle 4$ **b.** $\angle 1$ **15. a.** $\frac{600}{\sqrt{3}} \approx 346.41$ units **b.** $\frac{10000}{\sqrt{3}} \approx 5773.50$ units^2 **17.** 24 **19. a.** No. Suppose a trapezoid is as below, where no two sides of $\overline{AB}$, $\overline{BC}$, $\overline{DC}$, and $\overline{AD}$ are equal. Therefore no two of the triangles are congruent. **See below. b.** Yes. Use the trapezoid in part **a.** Because $\overline{AD} \parallel \overline{BC}$, $\angle DAO \cong \angle BCO$ and $\angle ADO \cong \angle CBO$ (// Lines ⇒ AIA ≅ Theorem). Therefore, by the AA Similarity Theorem, $\triangle ADO \sim \triangle CBO$. **21. See below.**

19. a.

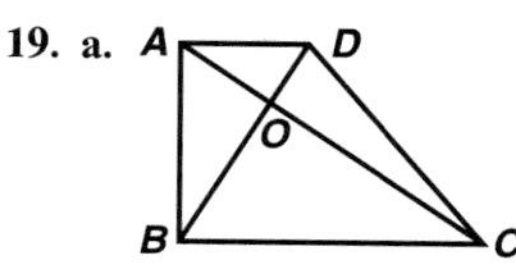

21.

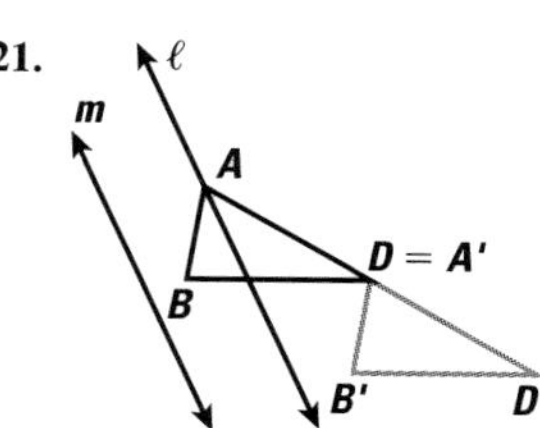

LESSON 13-7 (pp. 777–783)

13. a. Sample: $\sin B \approx \frac{14}{34} \approx .412$; $\sin B' \approx \frac{10}{24} \approx .417$ **b.** Yes; they probably will not be equal, due to measurement error, but very close. **15.** ≈ 20.1 ft **17.** ≈ 6.76 feet **19.** $\sqrt{2} - 1 \approx 0.414$ **21. a.** converse: If $m\angle ABC = m\angle DEF$, then $\triangle ABC \sim \triangle DEF$. inverse: If $\triangle ABC$ is not similar to $\triangle DEF$ with vertices in that order, then $m\angle ABC \neq m\angle DEF$. contrapositive: If $m\angle ABC \neq m\angle DEF$, then $\triangle ABC$ is not similar to $\triangle DEF$ with vertices in that order. **b.** The contrapositive is true. **23. See below.**

23.

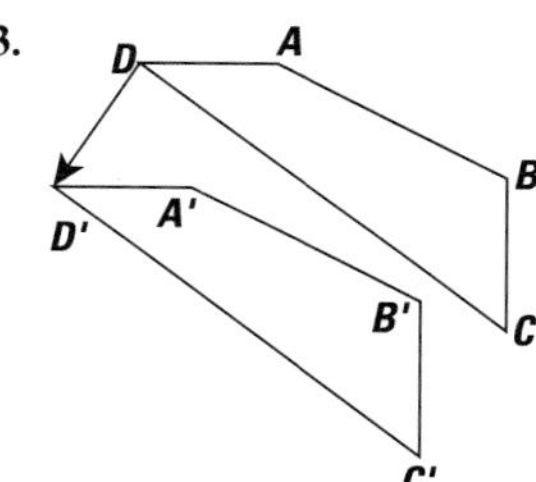

LESSON 13-8 (pp. 784–788)

11. a. ≈ 59.44 cm^2 **b.** ≈ 19 cm^2 **13.** 63 km **15.** $\sin B = \frac{11}{\sqrt{170}}$; $\cos B = \frac{7}{\sqrt{170}}$; $\tan B = \frac{11}{7}$ **17.** $\frac{60}{13}, \frac{144}{13}, \frac{25}{13}$ **19.** Rudolph is both a y and z, but not an x.

CHAPTER 13 PROGRESS SELF-TEST (pp. 792–793)

1. $\frac{BD}{BC} = \frac{BC}{AB}$ by the Right-Triangle Altitude Theorem; $\frac{2}{6} = \frac{6}{AB}$; $AB = \frac{36}{2} = 18$ 2. $\frac{75}{ZX} = \frac{ZX}{ZW}$ by the Right-Triangle Altitude Theorem; $75 \cdot ZW = ZX^2 = YZ^2 - XY^2$; $75 \cdot ZW = 75^2 - 60^2$; $ZW = 27$ 3. $\frac{VW}{VY} = \frac{VX}{VZ}$; $\frac{11}{24} = \frac{VX}{30}$; $\frac{330}{24} = VX$; $VX = 13.75$ 4. $\frac{VW}{VW + WY} = \frac{WX}{YZ}$; $\frac{8}{20} = \frac{VW}{15 + VW}$; $VW = 10$ 5. a. $BC = AB = 7$ b. $AC = 7\sqrt{2}$ 6. $h = 15\sqrt{3} \approx 25.98$ 7. Yes; because $\frac{9}{12} = \frac{12}{16} = \frac{15}{20}$, the triangles are similar by the SSS Similarity Theorem. 8. Area($\triangle TRI$) $= \frac{1}{2} \cdot TR \cdot RI \cdot \sin 55° \approx \frac{1}{2} \cdot 36 \cdot 11 \cdot .81915 \approx 162$ units^2 9. Since $\overleftrightarrow{AB} \parallel \overleftrightarrow{DE}$, $\angle A \cong \angle E$, $\angle B \cong \angle D$ because of the // Lines ⇒ AIA ≅ Theorem. Therefore, $\triangle ABC \sim \triangle EDC$ by the AA Similarity Theorem. 10. ≈ 0.855 11. $\frac{\sqrt{3}}{2}$ 12. $\tan B = \frac{AC}{BC}$ 13. $\angle 3$ 14. $\cos A = \frac{AC}{AB} = \sin B = \frac{9}{11}$ 15. $\sin E = \frac{DF}{DE} = \frac{14}{50} = \frac{7}{25} = .280$ 16. $\frac{165 \text{ m}}{150 \text{ m}} = \frac{x \text{ m}}{200 \text{ m}}$; $x = \frac{33000}{150} = 220$ m 17. $(\sin 80) \cdot 15 \approx 0.98 \cdot 15 \approx 14.8$ ft 18. $\frac{100 \text{ cm}}{21 \text{ cm}} = \frac{x \text{ m}}{67 \text{ m}}$; $x \approx 319$ m 19. a. See below. b. $\sqrt{6.2^2 + 4.8^2} \approx 7.84$ km 20. height of tree $= 5 + 40 \cdot \tan 35 \approx 5 + 0.70 \cdot 40 \approx 33$ ft

19. a.

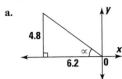

The chart below keys the **Progress Self-Test** questions to the objectives in the **Chapter Review** on pages 794–797 or to the **Vocabulary** (Voc.) on page 791. This will enable you to locate those **Chapter Review** questions that correspond to questions students missed on the **Progress Self-Test.** The lesson where the material is covered is also indicated on the chart.

Question	**1**	**2**	**3**	**4**	**5**	**6**	**7**	**8**	**9**	**10**
Objective	B	B	A	A	C	C	F	D	F	E
Lesson	13-4	13-4	13-3	13-3	13-5	13-5	13-1	13-8	13-2	13-7
Question	**11**	**12**	**13**	**14**	**15**	**16**	**17**	**18**	**19**	**20**
Objective	E	G	D	G	D	H	I	H	J	I
Lesson	13-7	13-6	13-6	13-7	13-7	13-3	13-7	13-2	13-8	13-6

CHAPTER 13 REVIEW (pp. 794–797)

1. a. 10.5 b. 2.5 3. No; since $\frac{2}{4} \neq \frac{6}{9}$. 5. 8 7. 6 9. ≈ 14.42 11. $AC = 4\sqrt{3} \approx 6.93$; $BC = 8$ 13. $6\sqrt{3} \approx 10.39$ 15. a. $7\sqrt{2} \approx 9.90$ b. 7 c. $7\sqrt{3} \approx 12.12$ d. 14 17. Sample: $m\angle A \approx 35$, $\tan A \approx .69$, $\sin A \approx .60$, and $\cos A \approx .82$. 19. $\angle 1$ 21. $\frac{24}{26} = \frac{12}{13}$ 23. ≈ 34.4 units^2 25. .843 27. $\frac{1}{2}$ 29. 1 31. a. Yes b. by the SSS Similarity Theorem 33. Yes, by the AA Similarity Theorem

35.

Conclusions	Justifications
1. $\angle BAE \cong \angle DCE$ $\angle ABE \cong \angle CDE$	// Lines ⇒ AIA ≅ Theorem
2. $\triangle ABE \sim \triangle CDE$	AA Similarity Theorem (step 1)

37. $\frac{AC}{AB}$ 39. $\frac{BC}{AC}$ 41. sine 43. $\frac{AC}{BC}$ 45. 15 m 47. a. $\frac{50}{3} \approx 16.67$ units b. $70 - \frac{70}{3} \approx 46.67$ units 49. ≈ 365 feet 51. ≈ 11.1 meters 53. northern component: ≈ 57 knots; eastern component: ≈ 18.5 knots

LESSON 14-1 (pp. 800–805)

15.

Conclusions	Justifications
1. $OB = OC$, $OA = OD$	definition of circle
2. $\triangle AOB \cong \triangle DOC$	SSS Congruence Theorem (step 1 and given)
3. $m\angle AOB = m\angle DOC$	CPCF Theorem
4. $m\angle AOB = m\widehat{AB}$, $m\angle DOC = m\widehat{CD}$	definition of arc measure
5. $m\widehat{AB} = m\widehat{CD}$	Transitive Property of Equality

17. a., b. See below. c. at the center of the circle d. Chord-Center Theorem (part 4) 19. a. 6 units b. $6x$ units 21. ≈ 1.87 m^3 23. 84°

17. a., b.

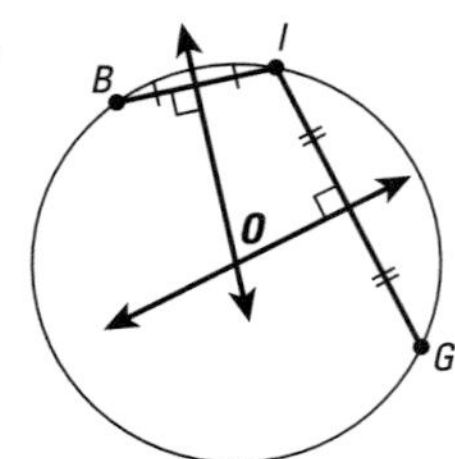

LESSON 14-2 (pp. 806–812)

13. a. n b. $\frac{n}{2}$ 15. 53°

17.

Conclusions	Justifications
1. $m\angle AXM = m\angle BXN$	Vertical Angles Theorem
2. $m\angle AMB = m\angle ANB$	If two inscribed angles intercept the same arc, then they have the same measure
3. $\triangle AXM \sim \triangle BXN$	AA Similarity Theorem (steps 1 and 2)

19. a. 72° b. $500 \sin 36° \approx 294$ units 21. $\sqrt{700} \approx 26.46$ yards 23. Line m is the perpendicular bisector of the segment with endpoints B and $r_\ell(A)$. See below. 25. 200

23.

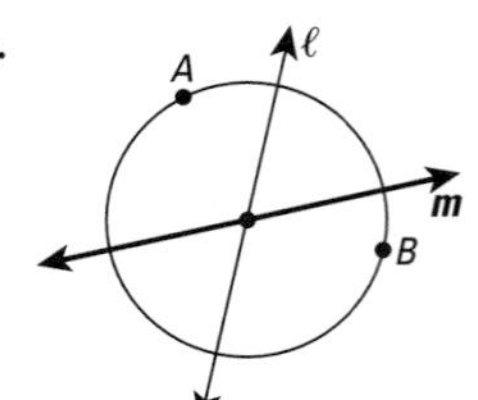

LESSON 14-3 (pp. 813–817)

7. See below. **9.** Sample: **See below.** **11. a.** All have measure 30. **b.** True **13. a.** $m\angle A = m\angle CDA = 30$, $m\angle ACD = 120$, $m\angle ADB = 90$, $m\angle BCD = m\angle BDC = m\angle CBD = 60$ **b.** x units **c.** $7\sqrt{3} \approx 12.12$ units **15.** 10 units **17.** $625\pi \approx 1963.5$ square feet

7.

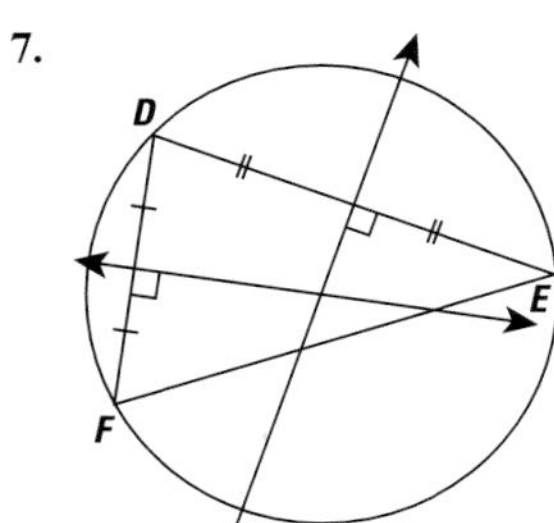

9.

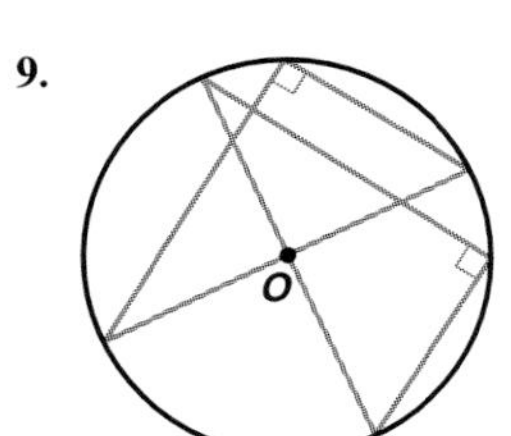

LESSON 14-4 (pp. 818–822)

9. 79 **11.** 143° **13.** ≈ 15.6 ft **15.** $2 \cdot \sqrt{107.25} \approx 20.71$ inches **17.** 112° 20′

LESSON 14-5 (pp. 823–828)

11. a., b. The center of the circle is on all of them. **See below.** **13. a.** A plane is tangent to a sphere if and only if it is perpendicular to the radius at the radius's endpoint on the sphere. **b.** Yes

15.

Conclusions	Justifications
1. $\overline{PT} \perp \overline{CT}$	Radius-Tangent Theorem
2. $\triangle PTC$ is a right triangle.	definition of right triangle
3. $d^2 + r^2 = (r + h)^2$	Pythagorean Theorem
4. $d^2 + r^2 = r^2 + 2rh + h^2$	Distributive Property
5. $d^2 = 2rh + h^2$	Addition Property of Equality
6. $d = \sqrt{2rh + h^2}$	definition of square root

17. See right. **19. a.** 65 **b.** 92.5 **c.** 87.5 **d.** 22.5 **21.** $m\angle G = 81$; $BC = 15$; $GJ = 16$

11. a., b. The center of the circle is on all of them.

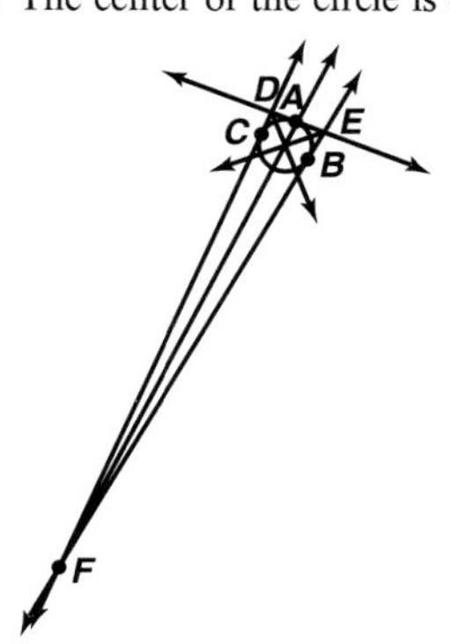

17.

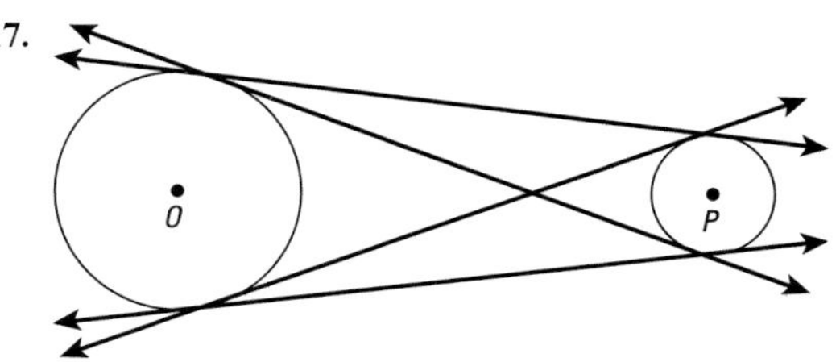

LESSON 14-6 (pp. 829–834)

13. 49° **15.** Draw $\overline{AB}$ and $\overline{AD}$. By the Quadrilateral-Sum Theorem, $m\angle A + m\angle B + m\angle C + m\angle D = 360$. By the Radius-Tangent Theorem and substitution, $m\angle A + 90 + m\angle C + 90 = 360$, so $m\angle A + m\angle C = 180$. But $m\angle A = m\widehat{BD}$, so $m\widehat{BD} + m\angle C = 180$. **17.** Let $\overline{BC}$ be a diameter of $\odot O$. By the Radius-Tangent Theorem, each tangent is perpendicular to $\overline{BC}$. By the Two-Perpendiculars Theorem, the two tangents are parallel. **19.** 6 **21.** $\frac{x}{4} = \frac{10}{q}$, $\frac{4}{q} = \frac{x}{10}$, $\frac{10}{x} = \frac{q}{4}$

LESSON 14-7 (pp. 836–841)

11. $8 \pm \sqrt{39} \approx 1.76$ or 14.24 units **13.** Yes; since D, C, and P are collinear, and B, A, and P are collinear, then D, C, P, B, and A are coplanar. Points D, C, A, and B lie on the circle which is the intersection of that plane and the sphere. Apply the Secant Length Theorem to this circle. **15.** 135° **17.** 42.5 **19.** ≈ 38.4 m

LESSON 14-8 (pp. 842–847)

13. a. 540 ft^2 **b.** $\frac{2025}{\pi} \approx 645$ ft^2 **15.** There is only so much area that can be covered by an animal skin. The circular base allows for the largest floor area per animal skin. **17.** ≈ 12.4 units **19.** 90 **21. a.** $426\frac{2}{3} \approx 426.7$ ft^3 **b.** ≈ 27.3 ft^3 **23. a.** $\frac{1372}{3}\pi$ $\text{cm}^3 \approx 1436.8$ cm^3 **b.** 196π $\text{cm}^2 \approx 615.8$ cm^2

LESSON 14-9 (pp. 848–852)

11. a. $36\pi \approx 113$ m^2 **b.** sample: radius of 2 m, height of 9 m; surface area: $44\pi \approx 138$ m^2 **c.** sample: radius of 6 m, height of 3 m; surface area: $36\pi + 6\pi\sqrt{45} \approx 240$ m^2 **d.** less **13.** $\frac{\pi\sqrt{x^3}}{6}$ units^3 **15. a.** circle: $\frac{2304}{\pi} \approx 733$ in^2; square: 576 in^2 **b.** square **17.** $m\angle A = 39.5$, $m\angle B = 98$, $m\angle C = 42.5$ **19.** Sample: **See below.** **21.** The distance is from 277 to 339 miles.

19.

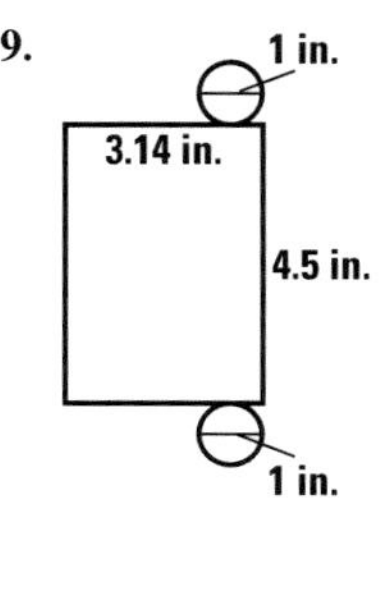

SELECTED ANSWERS

CHAPTER 14 PROGRESS SELF-TEST (pp. 856–857)

1. See right. $m\angle AOB = 120°$ $BC = 210 \sin 60° = 105\sqrt{3}$ Thus, $AB = 2BC = 210\sqrt{3} \approx 363.7$ units **2. See right.** **3.** Draw $\overline{MK}$, $MK = 60$. Because $\triangle MKL$ is a 45-45-90 triangle, $KL = \frac{60}{\sqrt{2}} = 30\sqrt{2}$. Thus the perimeter of $JKLM = 4 \cdot 30\sqrt{2} = 120\sqrt{2} \approx 169.7$ units. **4.** $m\angle B = \frac{1}{2}\, m\widehat{DC} = \frac{1}{2} \cdot 80 = 40$. **5.** $100 = \frac{1}{2}(80 + m\widehat{AB})$; $200 = 80 + m\widehat{AB}$; $m\widehat{AB} = 120$ **6.** $m\angle R = \frac{1}{2}(m\widehat{VT} - m\widehat{US}) = \frac{1}{2}(110 - 30) = \frac{1}{2}(80) = 40$. **7.** $QD \cdot QA = CQ \cdot BQ$; $QD \cdot 19 = 40 \cdot 38$; $OD = 80$ units **8.** $WV \cdot WZ = WX \cdot WY$; $WV \cdot 10 = 12 \cdot 28$; $WV = 33.6$; $ZV = 23.6$ **9.** $\ell \perp \overline{OQ}$ since a tangent is perpendicular to a radius through the point of tangency. $\overline{XY} \perp \overline{OQ}$ because a radius that bisects a chord is perpendicular to it. Thus $\ell \parallel \overline{XY}$ because two lines perpendicular to the same line are parallel. **10. a.** True **b.** Sample: $\angle O$ is a 90° angle since $m\widehat{UT} = 90°$ (given). $\angle PTO$ and $\angle PUO$ are 90° angles since a tangent is perpendicular to a radius through the point of tangency. So $\angle TPU$ is a 90° angle by the Quadrilateral-Sum Theorem. So $PUOT$ is a rectangle. Furthermore, $OU = OT$ since both are radii of $\odot O$. Since opposite sides of a rectangle are congruent, $PUOT$ has four sides of equal length. Therefore, by the definition of a square, $PUOT$ is a square. **11.** Let $x = m\widehat{TNU}$. $m\angle P = \frac{1}{2}(m\widehat{TNU} - m\widehat{TU}) = \frac{1}{2}(x - (360 - x)) = x - 180$. So $x = m\angle P + 180 = 92 + 180 = 272$.

12.

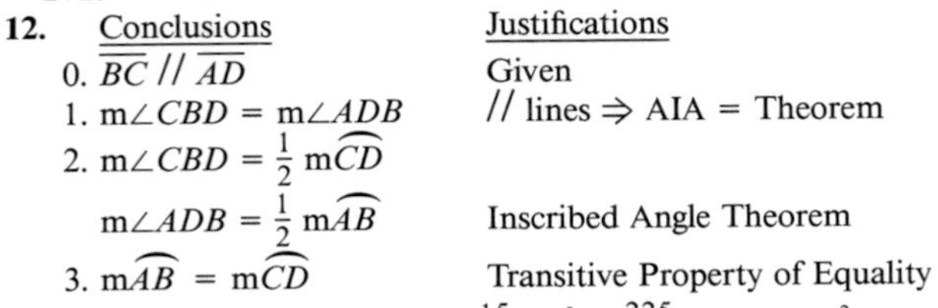

Conclusions	Justifications
0. $\overline{BC} \parallel \overline{AD}$	Given
1. $m\angle CBD = m\angle ADB$	// lines ⇒ AIA = Theorem
2. $m\angle CBD = \frac{1}{2}\, m\widehat{CD}$ $m\angle ADB = \frac{1}{2}\, m\widehat{AB}$	Inscribed Angle Theorem
3. $m\widehat{AB} = m\widehat{CD}$	Transitive Property of Equality

13. a. a circle **b.** $2\pi r = 30$; $r = \frac{15}{\pi}$; $\pi r^2 = \frac{225}{\pi} \approx 71.6 \text{ cm}^2$ **14.** The cube, because of all solids with the same volume, the sphere has the least surface area. **15. a.** Stand on the part of the circle drawn, or outside the circle and below $\overleftrightarrow{AB}$. **See right.** **b.** $\frac{30}{\tan 32°} \approx 48$ ft **16.** $100\text{ft} = \frac{100 \text{ ft}}{5280 \text{ ft}}$ mi $\approx .0189$ mi; $(\text{view to horizon})^2 + (\text{Earth's diameter})^2 = (\text{Earth's diameter} + \text{tower})^2$; view to horizon $= \sqrt{(3960 + 0.0189)^2 - 3960^2} \approx 12.2$ miles

1.

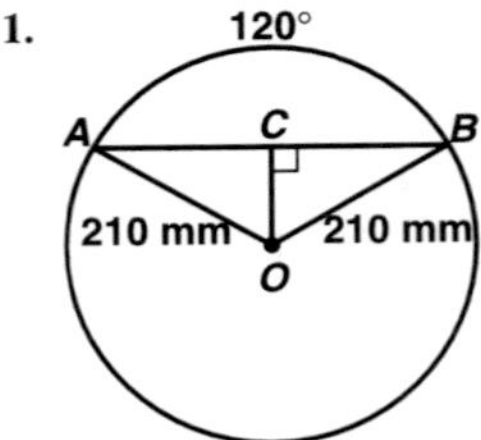

2.

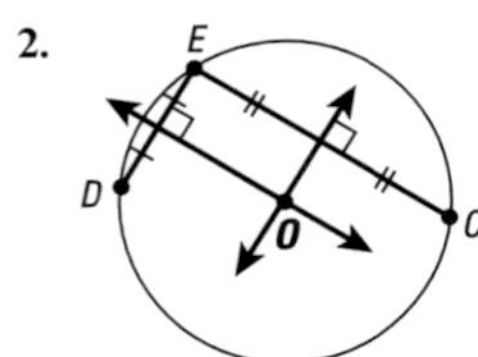

15. a.

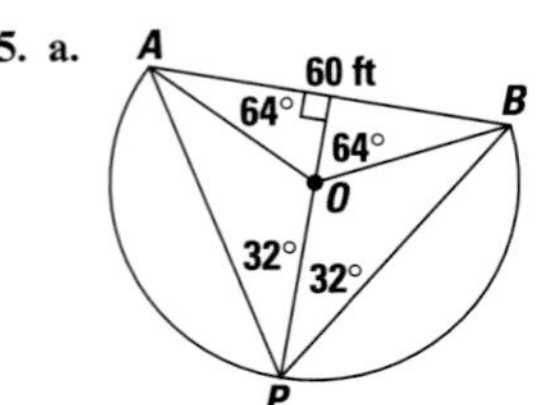

The chart below keys the **Progress Self-Test** questions to the objectives in the **Chapter Review** on pages 858–861 or to the **Vocabulary** (Voc.) on page 855. This will enable you to locate those **Chapter Review** questions that correspond to questions students missed on the **Progress Self-Test.** The lesson where the material is covered is also indicated on the chart.

Question	**1**	**2**	**3**	**4**	**5**	**6**	**7**	**8**	**9**	**10**
Objective	A	D	A	B	C	C	E	E	F	F
Lesson	14-1	14-3	14-1	14-2	14-4	14-4	14-7	14-7	14-1, 14-5	14-1, 14-5
Question	**11**	**12**	**13**	**14**	**15**	**16**				
Objective	C	G	K	H	I	J				
Lesson	14-6	14-2	14-8	14-9	14-3	14-5				

CHAPTER 14 REVIEW (pp. 858–861)

1. ≈ 57.6 mm **3. a.** ≈ 17.0 units **b.** ≈ 164.4 units^2 **5. a.** 45° **b.** ≈ 91.8 units **7.** 106° **9.** 81 **11.** 120 **13.** $m\angle EFD = m\angle BFC = 77.5$; $m\angle EBD = m\angle ECD = 62.5$; $m\angle BAC = 47.5$; $m\angle CEB = m\angle CDB = 15$; $m\angle BFE = m\angle CFD = 102.5$; $m\angle ABD = m\angle ACE = 117.5$ **15.** 40° **17. See right.** **19. See right.** **21.** 10 units **23.** 21 units **25.** Chord-Center Theorem, part (1) **27.** $m\widehat{YZ} = m\widehat{XY} = m\widehat{XZ}$, so $ZX = ZY = XY$ by the Arc-Chord Congruence Theorem. Therefore, by the definition of equilateral △, $\triangle XYZ$ is equilateral. **29.** $m\angle BAD = 15$, $m\angle DAC = 15$, $m\angle BAC = 30$, $m\angle ABD = 90$, $m\angle BDC = 150$, $m\angle ACD = 90$, $m\angle ADB = 75$ and $m\angle ADC = 75$. **31.** $\angle A$ and $\angle D$ are right angles, so they intercept semicircles. **33.** By the Inscribed Angle Theorem, $m\angle C = \frac{1}{2}\, m\widehat{BD}$. By the Tangent-Chord Theorem, $m\angle ABD = \frac{1}{2}\, m\widehat{BD}$. By Transitivity of Equality, $m\angle ABD = m\angle C$. **35. a.** a circle **b.** ≈ 100.3 ft **37.** a sphere **39. a.** a sphere **b.** ≈ 31.3 cu ft **41. a.** All points shown in the diagram on ⊙O. **See right.** **b.** ≈ 99.9 yards **43.** ≈ 61.8 km **45.** ≈ 2.74 miles **47. a.** a sphere **b.** Sample: the container could easily roll off a shelf. **49.** Sample: **See right.**

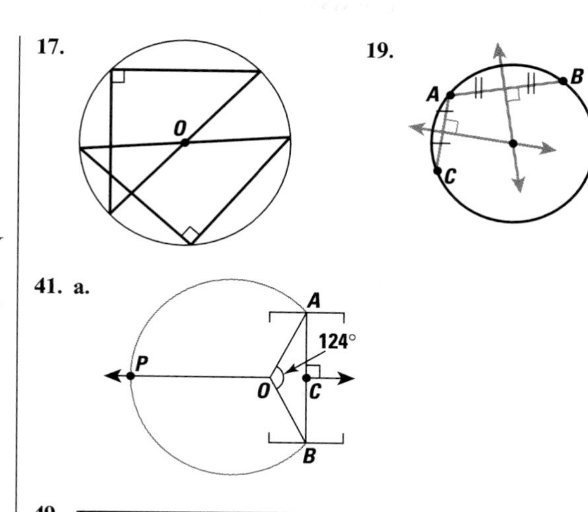

acre A unit of area often used to measure plots of land. One acre is equivalent to exactly 43,560 square feet or about 4047 square meters. (451)

acute angle An angle whose measure is greater than 0 and less than 90. (137)

adjacent angles Two nonstraight and nonzero angles with a common side interior to the angle formed by the noncommon sides. (139)

adjacent sides See *consecutive sides.*

adjacent vertices See *consecutive vertices.*

algorithm A finite sequence of steps leading to a desired end. (168)

alternate exterior angles Angles formed by two lines and a transversal whose interiors are not between the two lines and are on different sides of the transversal. (267)

alternate interior angles Angles formed by two lines and a transversal whose interiors are partially between the two lines and on different sides of the transversal. (265)

altitude In a triangle or trapezoid, the segment from a vertex perpendicular to the line containing the opposite side; also, the length of that segment. In a prism or cylinder, the distance between the bases. In a pyramid or cone, the length of a segment from the vertex perpendicular to the plane of the base. Also called *height*. (454, 460, 506, 513)

analytic geometry A geometry in which points are represented by coordinates and where algebraic methods of reasoning are utilized. (621)

angle The union of two rays (its sides) that have the same endpoint (its **vertex**). (124)

angle bisector The ray with points in the interior of an angle that forms two angles of equal measure with the sides of the angle. (127)

angle of depression An angle measured from the horizontal plane downward from an observer's eye to a given point below the plane. (782)

angle of elevation An angle measured from the horizontal plane upward from an observer's eye to a given point above the plane. (504, 773)

angle of inclination See *angle of elevation.*

antecedent The "if" clause of a conditional. Also called *hypothesis.* (69)

apothem The perpendicular segment from the center to the side of a regular *n*-gon to one of its sides.

arc A path from one point (node) of a network to another point (its endpoints or vertices). A part of a circle connecting two points (its endpoints) on the circle. (23, 132)

area The number of nonoverlapping unit squares or parts of unit squares that can be fit into a region. (441)

arithmetic mean The result of adding the *n* numbers in a data set and dividing the sum by n. Also called the *average* or *mean.* (759)

automatic drawer Computer software or calculator that enables geometric figures to be constructed from input by the user. (101)

auxiliary figure A figure that is added to a given figure, often to aid in completing proofs. (276)

average See *arithmetic mean* or *mean.*

axis A line of reference in a coordinate system. Plural: **axes**. (17, 669)

axis of a cone The line through the cone's vertex and the center of its base. (512)

base See *cylindric solid.* See *conic solid.*

base angles of an isosceles triangle Two angles of an isosceles triangle whose vertices are the endpoints of a base of the triangle. (309)

base angles of a trapezoid Two angles whose vertices are the endpoints of a base of the trapezoid. (318)

base of an isosceles triangle The side opposite the vertex angle. (309)

base of a trapezoid Either of two parallel sides of a trapezoid. (318)

base of a triangle The side of a triangle to which an altitude is drawn. (454)

betweenness of numbers A number is between two others if it is greater than one of them and less than the other. (46)

betweenness of points A point is between two other points on the same line if its coordinate is between their coordinates. (46)

biconditional statement A statement that includes a conditional and its converse. It may be written in the form $p \Rightarrow q$ and $q \Rightarrow p$, or $p \Leftrightarrow q$, or "*p* if and only if *q*." (82)

bilateral symmetry A space figure has bilateral symmetry if and only if there is a plane over which the reflection image of the figure is the figure itself. (526)

binomial An algebraic expression with exactly two terms. (583)

bisector A point, line, ray, or plane which divides a segment, angle, or figure into two parts of equal measure. (85)

bisector of an angle The ray in the interior of an angle that divides the angle into two angles of equal measures. (127)

bisector of a segment A line, ray, or segment which intersects a segment at its midpoint but does not contain the segment. (168)

box A right prism whose faces are rectangles. (505)

capacity See *volume*.

Cartesian plane Name given to the plane containing points identified as ordered pairs of real numbers. Also called *coordinate plane*. (17)

center See *circle, rotation, size change, sphere.*

center of a regular polygon The point equidistant from the vertices. (343)

center of symmetry For a rotation-symmetric figure, the center of a rotation that maps the figure onto itself. (335)

central angle of a circle An angle whose vertex is the center of the circle. (132)

centroid of a triangle The point at which all medians of a triangle intersect. (315)

characteristics The designated qualities of the defined term in a conditional. (83)

chord A segment whose endpoints are on a given circle. (347)

circle The set of points in a plane at a certain distance (its **radius**) from a certain point (its **center**). (83)

circularity The "circling back" that sometimes occurs when one tries to define basic terms; returning to the word which one is trying to define. (36)

circumference The perimeter of a circle, which is the limit of the perimeters of inscribed polygons. (473)

circumscribed circle A circle which contains all the vertices of a given polygon. (790)

circumscribed polygon A polygon whose sides are tangent to a given circle. (790, 828)

clockwise orientation The orientation "walking" around a figure keeping its interior to the right. (193)

clockwise rotation The direction in which the hands move on a nondigital clock, designated by a negative magnitude. (134)

coincident lines Lines that contain exactly the same points. (44)

collinear points Points that lie on the same line. (36)

common tangent A line which is tangent to two or more distinct circles. (827)

compass An instrument for drawing circles. (168)

complementary angles Two angles the sum of whose measures is 90. (138)

composite of two transformations The transformation $t_2 \circ t_1$, under which the image of a point or figure F is $t_2(t_1(F))$. (204)

composition The operation, denoted by the symbol $\circ$, of combining two transformations S followed by T by mapping each point or figure F onto $T(S(F))$. (204)

concentric circles Two or more circles that lie in the same plane and have the same center. (133)

conclusion The "then" clause of a conditional. The result of a deduction in a proof. Also called *consequent*. (69, 257)

concurrent Two or more lines that have a point in common. (222)

conditional A statement of the form If . . . then . . . . (69)

cone The surface of a conic solid whose base is a circle. (511)

congruence transformation A transformation that is a reflection or composite of reflections; also called an *isometry*. (229)

congruent figures A figure F is congruent to a figure G if and only if G is the image of F under a reflection or a composite of reflections. (228, 526)

conic section The intersection of a plane with the union of two right conical surfaces that have the same vertex and whose edges are opposite rays; either an ellipse, a parabola, or a hyperbola. (521)

conic solid The set of points between a given point (its **vertex**) and all points of a given region (its **base**), together with the vertex and the base. (511)

conic surface The boundary of a conic solid. (511)

conjecture An educated guess or opinion. (108)

consecutive angles In a polygon, two angles whose vertices are endpoints of the same side. (318)

consecutive sides In a polygon, two sides with an endpoint in common. (96)

consecutive vertices In a polygon, endpoints of a side. (96)

consequent The "then" clause of a conditional, also called the *conclusion*. (69)

construction A drawing which is made using only an unmarked straightedge and a compass following certain prescribed rules. (168)

continuous A figure made up of points with no space between them. (13)

contraction A size change with magnitude between 0 and 1. (693)

contradiction A situation in which there exist contradictory statements. (640)

contradictory statements Two statements that cannot both be true at the same time. (640)

contrapositive A conditional resulting from negating and switching the antecedent and consequent of the original conditional. (629)

convenient location A general location for a figure on a coordinate plane in which its key points are described with the fewest possible variables. (646)

converse The conditional statement formed by switching the antecedent and consequent of a given conditional. (76)

convex polygon A polygon whose polygonal region is a convex set. (97)

convex set A set in which every segment that connects points of the set lie entirely in the set. (66)

coordinate The number or numbers associated with the location of a point on a line, a plane, or in space. (13, 17, 668)

coordinate axes A pair of perpendicular coordinatized lines in a plane that intersect at the point with coordinate 0; three mutually perpendicular coordinatized lines in space that are concurrent at the point with coordinate 0. (17, 668)

coordinate geometry See *analytic geometry*.

coordinate plane See *Cartesian plane.*

coordinatized line A line on which every point is identified with exactly one number and every number is identified with a point on the line. (13)

coplanar Figures that lie in the same plane. (36)

corollary A theorem that is easily proven from another theorem. (312)

corresponding angles A pair of angles in similar locations when two lines are intersected by a transversal. (155)

corresponding parts Angles or sides that are images of each other under a transformation. (244)

cosine of an angle The ratio $\frac{\text{leg adjacent to the angle}}{\text{hypotenuse}}$ in a right triangle. Abbreviated *cos*. (777)

counterclockwise orientation The orientation "walking" around a figure keeping its interior to the left. (193)

counterclockwise rotation The direction opposite that which the hands move on a nondigital clock, designated by a positive magnitude. (134)

counterexample A specific case of a conditional for which the antecedent is true but the consequent is false. An example which shows a conjecture to be false. (71)

cube A box whose dimensions are all equal. (506)

cube root, $\sqrt[3]{\ }$ A real number x is the cube root of a real number y, written $x = \sqrt[3]{y}$, if and only if $x^3 = y$. (579)

cylinder The surface of a cylindric solid whose base is a circle. (507)

cylindric solid The set of points between a region (its **base**) and its translation image in space, including the region and its image. (506)

decagon A polygon with ten sides. (96)

deduction The process of making justified conclusions. (258, 621)

definition A description that clearly and uniquely specifies an object or a class of objects. (81)

degree measure of a major arc *ACB* of $\odot O$ $360 - m\overset{\frown}{AB}$. (133)

degree measure of minor arc *AB* of $\odot O$ The measure of the central angle *AOB*. (133)

degree A unit of measure used for the measure of an angle, arc, or rotation. (125)

dense A set with the property that between two elements of the set there is at least one other element of the set. (13)

diagonal of a polygon A segment connecting nonconsecutive vertices of the polygon. (96)

diameter of a circle or a sphere A segment connecting two points on the circle or sphere and containing the center of the circle or sphere; also, the length of that segment. (84, 518)

dihedral angle The angle formed by the union of two half-planes with the same edge. (503)

dimensions of a box The lengths of three edges of the box which meet at the same vertex. (505)

dimensions of a rectangle The lengths of two sides of the rectangle which meet at a single vertex. (437)

direction of translation The direction given by the vector from any preimage point to its image point in a translation. (205, 217)

directly congruent Figures which are congruent and have the same orientation. (229, 526)

direct reasoning (proofs) Reasoning (proofs) using the Law of Detachment and/or the Law of Transitivity. (639)

discrete figure A figure made up of points with space between them. (8)

discrete geometry The study of points as dots separated from each other, and lines made up of these points. (8)

distance between parallel planes The length of a segment perpendicular to the planes with an endpoint in each plane. (502)

distance between two parallel lines The length of a segment that is perpendicular to the lines with an endpoint on each of the lines. (196)

distance between two points The absolute value of the difference of their coordinates on a coordinatized line. (13)

distance from a point to a line The length of the perpendicular segment connecting the point to the line. (502)

distance from a point to a plane The length of the perpendicular segment from the point to the plane. (502)

dodecagon A polygon with twelve sides. (341)

dodecahedron A polyhedron with twelve faces. (537)

edge Any side of a polyhedron's faces. (506)

elevations Planar views of three-dimensional figures given from the top, front, or sides. (531)

ellipse The conic section formed by a plane which intersects only one of the right conical surfaces. (522)

empty set See *null set*.

endpoint See *arc*; *segment*; *ray*.

ends of a kite The common vertices of the equal sides of the kite. (324)

equiangular polygon A polygon with all angles of equal measure. (312)

equidistant At the same distance. (82, 271)

equilateral polygon A polygon with all sides of equal length. (342)

equilateral triangle A triangle with all three sides of equal length. (97)

Euclidean geometry The collection of propositions about figures which includes or from which can be deduced those given by the mathematician Euclid around 250 B.C. (41)

even node A node which is the endpoint of an even number of arcs in a network. (24)

expansion A size change with magnitude greater than one. (693)

extended ratio A sequence of three or more numbers representing the relative sizes of the numbers (or quantities). (282)

exterior angle An angle formed by two lines and a transversal whose interior contains no points between the two lines. An angle which forms a linear pair with an angle of a given polygon. (265, 416)

exterior of a circle The set of points at the distance greater than the radius from the center of the circle. (96)

exterior of a figure When a figure separates the plane into two parts, one bounded and one not, the unbounded part. (96)

exterior of an angle A non-zero angle separates the plane into two sets of points. If the angle is not straight, the non-convex set is the exterior of the angle. (125)

extremes of a proportion The first and fourth terms of the proportion. (706)

face of polyhedron Any of the polygonal regions that form the surface of the polyhedron. (505, 512, 537)

figure A set of points.

flip See *reflection*.

flow chart A diagram that shows a step-by-step progression through a procedure or system. (109)

45-45-90 triangle An isosceles right triangle whose angles measure 45, 45, and 90. (765)

fundamental region A region which is used to tessellate a plane. (398)

generalization A statement that applies to all situations of a particular type. (108)

geometric mean Given numbers *a, b,* and *g, g* is the geometric mean of *a* and *b* if and only if $\frac{a}{g} = \frac{g}{b}$. (759)

glide reflection The composite of a reflection and a translation parallel to the reflecting line; also called *walk*. (223)

gores A set of tapered sections of a net of a spherical object. (544)

grade The slope of a road, often represented as a percent or ratio. (155)

graph A picture of numbers on a number line or coordinate system. See also *network*. (13, 17, 668)

graph theory The geometry of networks. (23)

great circle of sphere The intersection of a sphere and a plane that contains the center of the sphere. (518)

half-turn A rotation of 180° about a point.

height See *altitude.*

hemisphere The half of a sphere on one side of a great circle. (518)

heptagon A polygon with seven sides. Also called *septagon*. (96)

hexagon A polygon with six sides. (96)

hexahedron A polyhedron with six faces. (537)

hidden lines Lines in a picture or a three-dimensional figure that cannot be seen, but which are marked as dashed or shaded lines so as to show existence or give a feeling of depth. (32)

hierarchy A diagram that shows how various figures or ideas are related, often with a downward direction that moves from more general to more specific. (97)

horizontal component of a vector The first component in the ordered pair description of a vector, indicating its magnitude along the x-axis of the coordinate plane. (218)

horizontal line A line with an equation $y = k$ on the coordinate plane. (18)

hyperbola The conic section formed by a plane which intersects both of the right conical surfaces. (522)

hypotenuse The longest side of a right triangle; the side opposite the right angle. (390)

hypothesis The "if" clause of a conditional, also called the *antecedent*. An assumption used as the basis for an investigation or argument. (69)

icosahedron A polyhedron with twenty faces. (537)

identity transformation A transformation that maps each point onto itself. (693)

if and only if statement A statement consisting of a conditional and its converse. Also called *biconditional*. (82)

if-then statement See *conditional*.

image The result of applying a transformation to an original figure or preimage. (134)

image of a figure The set of all images of points of a given figure. (192)

included angle Of two consecutive sides of a polygon, the angle of the polygon whose vertex is the common point of the sides. (372)

included side Of two consecutive angles of a polygon, the side of the polygon which is on both the angles. (373)

indirect reasoning (proofs) Reasoning (proofs) using the Law of the Contrapositive, the Law of Ruling Out Possibilities, or the Law of Indirect Reasoning. (641)

initial point The beginning point of a vector. (217)

inscribed angle in a circle An angle whose vertex is on the circle and whose sides each intersect the circle at a point other than the vertex. (807)

inscribed circle In a polygon, a circle which is tangent to each side of the polygon. (790)

inscribed polygon In a circle, a polygon whose vertices all lie on the circle. (790)

instance of a conditional A specific case in which the antecedent (*if* part) of the conditional is true and its consequent (*then* part) is also true. (70)

GLOSSARY

intercepted arc An arc of the circle in the interior of an angle. (800)

interior angles Angles formed by two lines and a transversal whose interiors are partially between the lines; the angles of a polygon. (265, 417)

interior of a circle The set of points at a distance less than the radius from the center of the circle. (85)

interior of a figure When a figure separates the plane into two parts, one bounded and one not, the bounded part. (96)

interior of an angle A nonzero angle separates the plane into two sets of points. If the angle is not straight, the convex set is the interior of the angle. (125)

intersecting planes Two planes that contain the same line. (498)

intersection of two sets The set of elements which are in both the sets. (87)

inverse A conditional resulting from negating the antecedent and consequent of the original conditional. (629)

isometry A transformation that is a reflection or a composite of reflections. Also called *congruence transformation* or *distance-preserving transformation*. (222)

isosceles trapezoid A trapezoid with a pair of base angles equal in measure. (318)

isosceles triangle A triangle with at least two sides equal in length. (97)

justification A definition, postulate, or theorem which enables a conclusion to be drawn. (151)

kite A quadrilateral with two distinct pairs of consecutive sides of the same length. (317)

lateral area The sum of the areas of the lateral faces of a solid. (565)

lateral edge of conic solid Any segment connecting the vertex of the solid to a point on its base. (507, 512)

lateral face of a polyhedron Any face other than a base. (507, 512)

lateral surface of a conic solid The surface of the solid excluding its base. (506, 512)

latitude Of a point P on Earth with Earth's center being C, the measure of the arc $\widehat{PQ}$, where Q is the intersection of the equator and the plane through P and the North and South Poles. The latitude is North or South according as P is between Q and the North or South Pole. Points with the same latitude lie on the same circle of latitude. (21, 52)

lattice point A point in the coordinate plane or in space with integer coordinates. (452)

leg Either side of a right triangle that is on the right angle. (390)

leg adjacent to an angle The side of the right triangle which is on the acute angle and is not the hypotenuse. (773)

leg opposite an angle The side of the right triangle which is not on the acute angle. (773)

length The distance between two points measured along the segment or an arc joining them. A dimension of a rectangle or rectangular solid. (48, 437, 577)

limit The value to which the terms of an infinite sequence get closer and closer as one goes further out in the sequence. (449, 474)

line An undefined geometric term. See *Point-Line-Plane Postulate*. (42, 497)

linear pair Two adjacent angles whose noncommon sides are opposite rays. (139)

line of reflection The line over which a preimage is reflected. Also called *reflecting line* or *mirror*. (184)

line of sight An imaginary line connecting the eye of the viewer to points on an object. (31)

line perpendicular to a plane A line perpendicular to every line in the plane which passes through the point of intersection. (501)

line segment See *segment*.

line symmetry See *reflection-symmetric figure*.

longitude Of a point P on Earth, the measure of the minor arc $\widehat{PQ}$ on its circle of latitude, where Q is the intersection of the circle with the prime meridian, the semicircle from the North Pole to the South Pole containing an observatory in Greenwich, England. (283, 524)

magnitude of rotation In a rotation, the amount that the preimage is turned about the center of rotation, measured in degrees from $-180°$ (clockwise) to $180°$ (counterclockwise), $\pm m\angle POP'$, where P' is the image of P under the rotation and O is its center. (134)

magnitude of size transformation In a size change, the factor by which length of the preimage is changed, $\frac{A'B'}{AB}$, where A' and B' are the images of A and B under the transformation. Also called a *size change factor* or *scale factor of size transformation*. (687)

magnitude of translation The distance between any point and its image. (205)

major arc AB of $\odot O$ The points of $\odot O$ that are on or in the exterior of $\angle AOB$. (133)

mapping See *transformation*.

matrix A rectangular array of rows and columns. (6)

mean The sum of a set of numbers divided by the number of numbers in the set. Also called *average* or *arithmetic mean*. See also *geometric mean*. (461, 662, 759)

means of a proportion The 2nd and 3rd terms of a proportion. (706)

measure The dimension or amount of something, usually in a system of units. (48, 125)

medial triangle The union of segments that join the midpoints of the sides of a triangle. (665)

median of a triangle The segment connecting a vertex of the triangle to the midpoint of the opposite side. (308)

menu A list of options from which a user of a computer can select an operation for the computer to perform. (102)

Mercator projection A two-dimensional map of the Earth's surface named for Gerhardus Mercator, the Flemish cartographer who first created it in 1569. (545)

midpoint of a segment The point on the segment equidistant from the segment's endpoints. (81)

minor arc *AB* of ⊙*O* The points of ⊙*O* that are on or in the interior of $\angle AOB$. (132)

***n*-fold rotation symmetry** A figure has *n*-fold rotation symmetry, where *n* is a positive integer, when a rotation of magnitude $\frac{360}{n}$ maps the figure onto itself, and no larger value of *n* has this property. (336)

***n*-gon** A polygon with *n* sides. (96)

negation of a statement A statement (called *not-p*) that is true whenever statement *p* is false and is false whenever statement *p* is true. (628)

net A two-dimensional figure that can be folded on its segments or curved on its boundaries into a three-dimensional surface. (538)

network A union of points (its **vertices** or **nodes**) and segments (its **arcs**) connecting them. Also called *graph*. (23)

node An endpoint of an arc in a network. See also *vertex.* (23)

nonagon A polygon with nine sides. (96)

nonconvex set A set in which at least one segment that connects points within the set has points that lie outside of the set. (66)

non-Euclidean geometry A geometry in which the postulates are not the same as those in Euclidean geometry. (278, 282)

nonoverlapping regions Regions that do not share interior points. (384, 443)

null set The set with no elements. Also called *empty set.* (89)

number line A line on which points are identified with real numbers. (12)

oblique cone A cone whose axis is not perpendicular to its base. (512)

oblique figure A 3-dimensional figure in which the plane of the base(s) is not perpendicular to its axis or to the planes of its lateral surfaces. (507, 512)

oblique line A line that is neither horizontal nor vertical. (8)

obtuse angle An angle whose measure is greater than 90 and less than 180. (137)

obtuse triangle A triangle with an obtuse angle. (142)

octagon A polygon with eight sides. (96)

octahedron A polyhedron with eight faces. (537)

odd node A node which is the endpoint of an odd number of arcs in a network. (24)

one-dimensional A space in which all points are collinear. (36)

one-step proof A justified conclusion of a conditional requiring a single definition, theorem, or postulate. (151)

opposite faces A pair of faces of a polyhedron whose planes are parallel to each other. (505)

oppositely congruent Figures which are congruent and have opposite orientation. (229, 526)

opposite rays $\overrightarrow{AB}$ and $\overrightarrow{AC}$ are opposite rays if and only if *A* is between *B* and *C*. (48)

ordered pair The pair of numbers (*a, b*) identifying a point in a two-dimensional coordinate system. (17)

ordered pair description of a vector The description of a vector as the ordered pair (*a*,*b*) where *a* is the **horizontal component** and *b* is the **vertical component**. (218)

ordered triple The triple of numbers (*a, b, c*) identifying a point in a three-dimensional coordinate system. (668)

order *n* rotation symmetry See *n-fold rotation symmetry.*

orientation The order of the designation of the vertices of a polygon, either *clockwise* or *counterclockwise*. (193)

overlapping figures Figures which have interior points in common. (384)

overlapping triangles Triangles that have interior points in common. (384)

pairing The assignment of two teams or individuals to compete against one another in a tournament. (349)

parabola The conic section formed by a plane parallel to an edge of the conical surface. (522)

paragraph proof A form of written proof in which conclusions and justifications are incorporated into sentences. (264)

parallel lines Two coplanar lines which have no points in common or are identical. (43)

parallelogram A quadrilateral with two pairs of parallel sides. (316)

parallel planes Planes which have no points in common or are identical. (502)

pentagon A polygon with five sides. (96)

perimeter The length of the boundary of a closed region. (435)

perimeter of a polygon The sum of the lengths of its sides. (436)

perpendicular Two segments, rays, or lines such that the lines containing them form a 90° angle. (161)

perpendicular bisector method A method for finding the center of a circle that involves drawing perpendicular bisectors of two chords. (813)

perpendicular bisector of a segment In a plane, the line containing the midpoint of the segment and perpendicular to the segment. In space, the plane that is perpendicular to the segment and contains the midpoint of the segment. (168, 525)

perpendicular planes Planes whose dihedral angle is a right angle. (503)

GLOSSARY

perspective drawing A drawing of a figure made to look as it would in the real world. (30)

pi, π The ratio of circumference to the diameter of a circle. (475)

picture angle of a camera lens An angle measure indicating how wide a field of vision can be captured in one photo. (806)

pixel A dot on a TV or computer screen or other monitor. (6)

plane An undefined geometric term. See *Point-Line-Plane Postulate*. (17, 496)

plane coordinate geometry The study of points as ordered pairs of numbers. (17, 19)

plane figure A set of points that are all in one plane. (36)

plane geometry The study of figures which lie in the same plane. (35, 38)

plane section The intersection of a three-dimensional figure with a plane. (520)

point An undefined geometric term. See *Point-Line-Plane Postulate*. (41, 497)

point of tangency The point at which a tangent intersects the curve (circle) or curved surface (sphere). (659, 823)

polygon The union of three or more coplanar segments (its **sides**) such that each segment intersects exactly two others, one at each of its endpoints (its **vertices**). (95)

polygonal region The union of a polygon and its interior. (96)

polyhedron A three-dimensional surface which is the union of polygonal regions (its **faces**) and which has no holes. Plural: **polyhedra**. (537)

polynomial An expression that is the sum or difference of two or more terms. (583)

postulate A statement assumed to be true. Also called *axiom*. (41)

power of a point for $\odot O$ For any secant through P intersecting $\odot O$ at A and B, the product $PA \cdot PB$. (838)

preimage The original figure in a transformation. (134)

preserved property Under a transformation, a property which, if present in a preimage, is present in the image. (191, 699)

prism The surface of a cylindric solid whose base is a polygon. (507)

proof A sequence of justified conclusions, leading from what is given or known to a final conclusion. (150)

proportion A statement that two ratios are equal. (706)

proportional numbers Four numbers that form a true proportion. (706)

protractor A tool commonly used to measure angles. (121)

pyramid The surface of a conic solid whose base is a polygon. (511)

Pythagorean triple A set of three numbers that can be the lengths of the sides of a right triangle. (470)

quadrilateral A polygon with four sides. (96)

radius of circle or sphere A segment connecting the center of a circle or a sphere with a point on that circle or sphere; also, the length of that segment. Plural: **radii**. (83, 517)

ratio A quotient of quantities with the same units. (705)

ratio of similitude In similar figures, the ratio of a distance or length in an image to the corresponding distance or length in a preimage. (714)

ray The ray with **endpoint A** containing B, denoted $\overrightarrow{AB}$, is the union of $\overline{AB}$ and the set of all points for which B is between each of them and A. (47)

rectangle A quadrilateral with four right angles. (316)

rectangular solid The union of a box and its interior. (505)

reflecting line The line over which a preimage is reflected. Also called *line of reflection* or *mirror*. (184)

reflecting plane The plane over which a preimage is reflected. Also called *mirror*. (526)

reflection A transformation in which each point is mapped onto its reflection image over a line or plane. (186, 526)

reflection image of a figure The set of all reflection images of the points of the original figure. (192)

reflection image of a point *P* over a line *m* If p is not on m, the reflection image of p is the point Q such that m is the perpendicular bisector of $\overline{PQ}$. If P is on m, the reflection image is point P itself. (185)

reflection image of a point *A* over a plane *M* If A is not on M, the reflection image is the point B such that M is the perpendicular bisector of $\overline{AB}$, If A is on M, the reflection image is point A itself. (525)

reflection-symmetric figure A figure F for which there is a reflection r_m such that $r_m(F) = F$. (300, 526)

region The union of a polygon or circle and its interior. More generally, any connected two-dimensional figure that has an area. (96)

regular polygon A convex polygon whose angles are all congruent and whose sides are all congruent. (341)

regular polyhedron A convex polyhedron whose faces are all congruent regular polygons and the same number of edges intersect at each of its vertices. (537)

regular prism A right prism whose base is a regular polygon. (508)

regular pyramid A right pyramid whose base is a regular polygon and whose lateral faces are congruent isosceles triangles. (512)

resolution The capability of distinguishing individual parts of an entire object or picture. (6)

rhombus A quadrilateral with four sides of equal length. (316)

right angle An angle whose measure is 90. (137)

right angle method A method for finding the center of a circle that involves constructing two inscribed right triangles. The intersection of their hypotenuses is the center. (813)

right cone A cone whose axis is perpendicular to the plane of the circular base. (512)

right cylinder A cylinder formed when the direction of translation of the base is perpendicular to the plane of the base. (507)

right prism A prism formed when the direction of translation of the base is perpendicular to the plane of the base. (507)

right pyramid A pyramid whose base is a regular polygon in which the segment connecting its vertex to the center of its base is perpendicular to the plane of the base. (512)

right triangle A triangle which contains a right angle. (142, 453)

rotation The composite of two reflections over intersecting lines; the transformation "turns" the preimage onto the final image about a fixed point (its **center**). Also called *turn*. (134, 211)

rotation-symmetric figure A figure F for which there is a composite of reflections $r_m \circ r_l$ such that $r_m(r_l(F)) = F$. (335)

round-robin tournament A tournament in which each competitor plays each other exactly once. (347)

scale factor of size transformation See *magnitude of size transformation.*

scalene triangle A triangle with no two sides of the same length. (97)

secant to a circle A line that intersects a circle in two distinct points. (819)

sector of a circle The figure bounded by two radii and the included arc of the circle. (480)

segment The set consisting of the distinct points A and B (its **endpoints**) and all points between A and B. Also called *line segment*. (47)

semicircle An arc of a circle whose endpoints are the endpoints of a diameter of the circle. (133)

side of an angle See *angle*.

side of a polygon One of the segments whose union is a polygon; also, the length of that segment. (96)

similar figures Two figures A and B for which there is a similarity transformation mapping one onto the other, written $A \sim B$. (711)

similarity transformation A composite of size changes and reflections. (712)

simple closed curve A figure that is closed and does not intersect itself. (112)

sine of an angle The ratio $\frac{\text{leg opposite the angle}}{\text{hypotenuse}}$ in a right triangle. Abbreviated *sin*. (777)

size change The transformation S such that, for a given point P and a positive real number k (its **magnitude**) and any point O (its **center**), $S(P) = P'$ is the point on $\overrightarrow{OP}$ with $OP' = k \cdot OP$. The transformation in which the image of (x, y) is (kx, ky). Also called *size transformation* or *dilation*. (693)

size change factor See *magnitude of size transformation*.

skew lines Lines that do not lie in the same plane. (504)

slant height of a regular pyramid The altitude from the vertex on any one of the lateral faces of the pyramid. (513)

slant height of a right cone The length of a lateral edge of the cone. (513)

slide See *translation*.

slope In the coordinate plane, the change in y-values divided by the corresponding changes in x-values. (157)

slope-intercept form of an equation for a line A linear equation of the form $y = mx + b$, where m is the slope and b is the y-intercept. (19)

small circle of a sphere The intersection of the sphere and a plane that does not contain the center of the sphere. (518)

solid The union of a surface and the region of space enclosed by the surface. (505)

solid geometry The study of figures in three-dimensional space. (495)

space The set of all points in a geometry. (36)

space figure A figure whose points do not all lie in a single plane. Also called a *three-dimensional figure*. (37)

sphere The set of points in space at a fixed distance (its **radius**) from a point (its **center**). (517)

square A quadrilateral with four sides of equal length and four right angles. (317)

square root, $\sqrt{\ }$ x is a square root of y if and only if $x^2 = y$. If x and y are positive, $x = \sqrt{y}$. (466)

standard form of an equation for a line An equation for a line in the form $Ax + By = C$, where A and B are not both zero. (18)

straight angle An angle whose measure is 180. (137)

straightedge An instrument for drawing the line through two points which has no marks for determining length. (168)

sufficient condition p is a sufficinet condition for q if and only if p implies q. (367)

supplementary angles Two angles the sum of whose measures is 180. (138)

surface The boundary of a three-dimensional figure. (505)

surface area The area of the boundary surface of a three-dimensional figure. (564)

symmetry diagonal (of a kite) The diagonal that connects the ends of the kite. (325)

symmetry line For a figure, a line m such that the figure coincides with its reflection image over m. (300)

symmetry plane For a figure, a plane M such that the figure coincides with its reflection image over M. (526)

synthetic geometry A geometry studied without the use of coordinates. (12)

tangent A line, ray, segment, or plane which intersects a curve or curved surface in exactly one point. (659, 823, 825)

tangent of an angle The ratio $\frac{\text{leg opposite to the angle}}{\text{leg adjacent to the angle}}$ in a right triangle. Abbreviated *tan*. (773)

tangent circles Two circles that have exactly one point in common. (853)

terminal point The endpoint of a vector. (217)

tessellation A covering of a plane with congruent nonoverlapping copies of the same region. (398)

tetrahedron A polyhedron with four faces. (537)

theorem A statement deduced from postulates, definitions, or other previously deduced theorems. (43)

30-60-90 triangle A triangle in which the three angles measure 30, 60, and 90. (766)

3-dimensional coordinate system A system of coordinates used to locate points in space by their distances and directions from three mutually perpendicular lines. (668)

three-dimensional figure A figure whose points do not all lie in a single plane. (37)

transformation A correspondence between two sets of points such that each point in the preimage set has a unique image, and each point in the image set has exactly one preimage. Also called *map*. (186)

transformation image of a figure The set of all images of the points of the figure under the transformation. (186)

translation The composite of two reflections over parallel lines. Also called *slide*. (205)

transversal A line that intersects two or more lines. (155)

trapezoid A quadrilateral with at least one pair of parallel sides. (318)

traversable network A network in which all the arcs may be traced exactly once without picking up the tracing instrument. (24)

triangle A polygon with three sides. (96)

triangulate To split a polygon into nonoverlapping triangles. (284)

trigonometric ratio A ratio of the lengths of the sides in a right triangle. (774)

trisect To divide into three congruent parts. (421)

truncated surface A part of a conic surface including its base, the intersection of a plane parallel to the base with the conic solid, and all points of the surface between these. (515)

truth value The condition of a statement in logic; either true or false. (628)

turn See *rotation*.

two-column proof A form of written proof in which the conclusions are written in one column, the justifications beside them in a second column. (264)

two-dimensional Pertaining to figures that lie in a single plane, or to their geometry. (36)

undefined terms A term used without a specific mathematical definition. (36)

union of two sets The set of elements which are in at least one of the sets. (87)

uniquely determined A situation in which there is exactly one element satisfying given conditions. (276)

unit cube A cube in which every edge has length one unit. (576)

unit square A square in which each side has length one unit. (441)

vanishing line A line containing vanishing points. (31)

vanishing point The point at which several lines of a drawing appear to meet at a distance from the viewer's eye. (30)

vector A quantity that has both magnitude and direction. (217)

velocity The rate of change of distance with respect to time. (784)

vertex See *angle*. See *conic solid*. See *network*. See *polygon*. Plural: **vertices**.

vertex angle The angle included by equal sides of an isosceles triangle. (309)

vertex of a polyhedron Any of the vertices of the faces of the polyhedron. (506, 511, 537)

vertical angles Two nonstraight and nonzero angles whose sides form two lines. (140)

vertical component of a vector The second component in the ordered pair description of a vector, indicating its magnitude along the y-axis of the coordinate plane. (218)

vertical line A line with an equation $x = h$ on the coordinate plane. (18)

volume The number of unit cubes or parts of unit cubes that can be fit into a solid. Also called *capacity*. (576)

walk See *glide reflection.*

width (of a rectangle) A dimension of a rectangle or rectangular solid taken at right angles to the length. (437, 577)

window That part of the plane that shows on the screen of an automatic grapher or automatic drawer. (102)

x-axis The line in the coordinate plane or in space, usually horizontal, containing those points whose second coordinates (and third, in space) are 0. (17, 669)

y-axis The line in the coordinate plane, usually vertical, or in space, containing those points whose first coordinates (and third, in space) are 0. (17, 669)

z-axis The line in a three-dimensional coordinate system containing those points whose first and second coordinates are 0. (668)

zero angle An angle whose measure is zero. (137)

MATHEMATICAL SYMBOLS

$>$	is greater than
$<$	is less than
$\geq$	is greater than or equal to
$\leq$	is less than or equal to
$\neq$	is not equal to
$\approx$	is approximately equal to
$\pm$	plus or minus
π	pi
$\lvert x \rvert$	absolute value of x
$\sqrt{n}$	positive square root of n
$\sqrt[3]{n}$	cube root of n
$//$	is parallel to
$\perp$	is perpendicular to
$\cong$	is congruent to
$\sim$	is similar to
r_m	reflection over line m
$\mathrm{r}_m(P)$	reflection image of point P over line m
$\mathrm{r}(P)$	reflection image of point P
$\mathrm{R}(P)$	rotation image of point P
$\mathrm{T}(P)$	transformation image of point P
$\mathrm{T}_1 \circ \mathrm{T}_2$	composite of transformation T_2 followed by T_1
S_k	size change of magnitude k
A'	image of point A
A''	image of point A'
$\Rightarrow$	if-then (implication)
$\Leftrightarrow$	if and only if
$\{\ldots\}$	set
$\{\}, \varnothing$	empty or null set
$N(E)$	the number of elements in set E
$P(E)$	probability of an event E
$\cap$	intersection of sets
$\cup$	union of sets
$\tan A$	tangent of $\angle A$
$\sin A$	sine of $\angle A$
$\cos A$	cosine of $\angle A$
$\overleftrightarrow{AB}$	line through A and B
$\overrightarrow{AB}$	ray with endpoint at A and containing B
$\overline{AB}$	segment with endpoints A and B
AB	distance from A to B
$\angle ABC$	angle ABC
$m\angle ABC$	measure of angle ABC
$\triangle ABC$	triangle with vertices A, B, C
$ABCD\ldots$	polygon with vertices $A, B, C, D, \ldots$
$\odot O$	circle with center O
⌐	right angle symbol
$n°$	n degrees
$\overset{\frown}{AB}$	minor arc with endpoints A and B
$\overset{\frown}{ADB}$	arc with endpoints A and B containing D
$m\overset{\frown}{AB}$	measure of arc AB in degrees
$\mathrm{Area}(F)$	area of figure F
$\mathrm{Volume}(F)$	volume of figure F
(x, y)	ordered pair x, y
(x, y, z)	ordered triple x, y, z
$\overrightarrow{AB}$	vector with initial point A and terminal point B
v or $\vec{v}$	vector v

Calculator Keys

± or +/–	opposite
y^x or x^y	powering function
INV, 2nd, or F	second function
EE or EXP	scientific notation
1/x	reciprocal
√	square root function
x^2	squaring function
π	pi
INV	inverse function
tan	tangent function
sin	sine function
cos	cosine function

Computer Commands

2*2	$2 \cdot 3$
4 / 3	$4 \div 3$
3 ^ 5	3^5
>=	$\geq$
<=	$\leq$
<>	not equal to
SQR(N)	$\sqrt{n}$
IF . . . THEN	THEN statement to be executed only if IF part is true.

Acknowledgments

4(c) Tim Everitt/Tony Stone Worldwide 4-5(t) Art Institute of Chicago/Bridgeman Art Library, London/Superstock, Inc. 5(b) Superstock, Inc. 6 Art Institute of Chicago/Bridgeman Art Library, London/Superstock, Inc. 7(b) ©1988 Sue Klemens/Stock Boston 7(t) David R. Frazier 9 David R. Frazier 12 Courtesy of the New Explorers, a production of Kurtis Productions, Ltd. and WTTW/CHICAGO/CARA/University of Chicago, Photo: James S. Sweitzer 13 Bob Daemmrich 15(l) Robert Frerck/Stock Market 16(b) Demetrio Carrasco/Tony Stone Worldwide 17 Esbin-Anderson/Image Works 21 Ken Hawkins/Sygma 23(t) Prenzel/Schmida/Animals Animals 27(b) Lionel Delevingne/Stock Boston 30(t) Courtesy of the Regis Collection Minneapolis, MN 31 ©1969 by Butcher Lucas. Distrubuted by King Features Syndicate 35 John Maher/Stock Market 41 Scala/Art Resource 43 "The Elements of Euclid of Megara" 46 Lowell Georgia/SS/Photo Researchers 51(t) William Johnson/Stock Boston 52(t) Leo de Wys, Inc. 52-53(b) Donovan Reese/Tony Stone Worldwide 53(t) Charly Franklin/FPG International Corp. 53(c) Superstock, Inc. 62(t) Superstock, Inc. 62(cl) Superstock, Inc. 62-63(cr) Superstock, Inc. 63(t) Superstock, Inc. 66 Jeffrey Markowitz/Sygma 69 Hugh Norton/Superstock, Inc. 73 Gahan Wilson 76 Superstock, Inc. 79(t) Boltin Picture Library 83 Superstock, Inc. 85 Superstock, Inc. 86 From The World Book Encyclopedia. ©1995 World Book, Inc. By permission of the publisher 87 Alex S. MacLean/Landslides 90(l) Frank Siteman/Tony Stone Worldwide 90(r) Reproduced by Permission MBTA, Robert L. Mabardy, Interim General Manager 92(t) Superstock, Inc. 92(b) (c)1994 Universal Press Syndicate 95 Carol M. Highsmith 96 Courtesy Watertown Historical Society 99-t ©1994 by Rand, McNally 99-b ©1994 by Rand, McNally 103 Peter Ginter/Image Bank 106 Cameramann International, Ltd. 107 Photofest 112 David Young-Wolff/PhotoEdit 113 Superstock, Inc. 114 Courtesy The Milk Foundation/©1995 National Fluid Milk Processor Promotion Board 122(t) Superstock, Inc. 122(c) Superstock, Inc. 122-123(b) Superstock, Inc. 123(t) Superstock, Inc. 123(c) Superstock, Inc. 123(cr) SF 124(t) J. Sohm/Image Works 129 Superstock, Inc. 132 Cameramann International, Ltd. 134 B. Daemmrich/Image Works 138 Courtesy of the Arthur M. Sackler Gallery, Smithsonian Institution, Washington, D.C. From the exhibition "A rural Basketmaker in Japan," Kenji Nakamura and Nakamura Yuzu Products 142(b) Superstock, Inc. 144 Joseph Thorn 150 Eric Sander/Gamma Liaison 152 Fanny Broadcast/Gamma Liaison 155 Jan Kanter 156 Myra Miller/Gamma Liaison 165 ©1994 Streetwise Maps, Inc., Amagansett, NY 166(t) Zavier Testelin/Gamma Liaison 166(b) The Dell Big Book Of Crosswords And Pencil Puzzles #5 170 Superstock, Inc. 172(r) FourByFive/Superstock, Inc. 172(l) Superstock, Inc. 173(t) Superstock, Inc. 173(br) Superstock, Inc. 182(t) Superstock, Inc. 182-183(c) Superstock, Inc. 182(bl) Superstock, Inc. 182-183(br) Superstock, Inc. 183(tl) FourByFive Inc/Superstock, Inc. 183(tr) M.C. Escher/Cordon Art-Baarn-Holland. All rights reserved. 184(t) Cameramann International, Ltd. 184(b) Scott Gibson 188 Scott Gibson 191 FPG International Corp. 195(l) Charles Gupton/Stock Boston 196 Focus on Sports, Inc. 197 Focus on Sports, Inc. 198 Vandystadt Agence de Presse 199 Bob Daemmrich 201 Superstock, Inc. 203 Myrleen Ferguson/PhotoEdit 210 Tony Stone Worldwide 214 Chris Arend/AlaskaStock 216 Rosemary Finn 220 Tony Freeman/PhotoEdit 222 Alan Oddie/PhotoEdit 225 M.C. Escher/Cordon Art-Baarn-Holland. All rights reserved. 226(b) Tracy Omar/Washington Park Arboretum 233(t) Superstock, Inc. 240 M.C. Escher/Cordon Art-Baarn-Holland. All rights reserved. 241 Bill Gallery/Stock Market 242-243(tr) Superstock, Inc. 242-243(c) FourByFive Inc/Superstock, Inc. 242(B) FourByFive Inc./Superstock, Inc. 244 Superstock, Inc. 247 Courtesy Lifetouch ®National School Studios 248 Reprinted with permission from Games World Of Puzzles Magazine (19 West 21st Street, New York, NY 10010) Copyright ©1995 B. & P. Publishing Co, Inc. 263 Stacy Pick/Stock Boston 267 Museum of the American Indian 270 John Lamb/Tony Stone Worldwide 278 Hulton/Bettmann 280(b) Ted Thai/Sygma 280(t) J.L. Atlan/Sygma 281 Kevin Galvin/Stock Boston 283 Courtesy Lands' End, Dodgeville, WI. Photo: Gary Comer 285 Jon Gray/Tony Stone Worldwide 287 Raymond B. Barnes/Tony Stone Worldwide 288(t) Superstock, Inc. 288(b) FourByFive Inc./Superstock, Inc. 297(l) Jay Syverson/Stock Boston 297(R) Cameramann International, Ltd. 298 Superstock, Inc. 298(t) Superstock, Inc. 298-299(b) Superstock, Inc. 299(t) Superstock, Inc. 299(c) Superstock, Inc. 299(tc) Courtesy ITT Sheraton Corporation 299(tr) Courtesy Mcdonald's Corporation 300 Stan Osolinski/Tony Stone Worldwide 303 Superstock, Inc. 307 Christopher Morrow/Stock Boston 309 Superstock, Inc. 314 Bob Torrez/Tony Stone Worldwide 316 Larry Lefever/Grant Heilman Photography 323 Ellis Herwig/Stock Boston 325 Sygma 329 Grant Heilman/Grant Heilman Photography 331 Focus on Sports, Inc. 334(l) Courtesy National Football League/The Pittsburgh Steelers 334(c) Courtesy Nissan Motor Corporation U.S.A. 334(r) Courtesy Minolta corporation 335 Bill Gallery/Stock Boston 336 Courtesy Chrysler Corporation 337 Superstock, Inc. 341 ` FourByFive Inc./Superstock, Inc. 346 The Pepsi Ball Design is a registered trademark for soft drinks, used courtesy of PepsiCo, Inc. 347 Michael Newman/PhotoEdit 350 Focus on Sports, Inc. 352 Superstock, Inc. 353(tr) Museum of the American Indian 353 Superstock, Inc. 353(bl) From Inversions by Scott Kim 361(l) Finn, Rosemary 361(tr) From "The Complete Stitch Encyclopedia" by Jan Eaton. Reprinted 1987 copyright © Quarto Publishing Ltd. 362-363(br) FourByFive Inc./Superstock, Inc. 362(t) Superstock, Inc. 362-363(c) Superstock, Inc. 362(bl) Superstock, Inc. 363(t) Superstock, Inc. 365 Superstock, Inc. 366 Superstock, Inc. 369 "Hidden Pictures" puzzle by Christopher Wray from Highlights For Children, July/August 1988 370 Robert Fried 371(l) Jay Wolke 374 Courtesy Divine Word International-Original American training center for Divine Word missionaries, now Techny Towers Conference Center, Techny, IL 376 Superstock, Inc. 380 Jan Kanter 381 Jan Kanter 384 Cameramann International, Ltd. 387 Superstock, Inc. 389 Phyllis Picardi/Stock Boston 390 Phyllis Picardi/Stock Boston 395 Dean Abramson/Stock Boston 396 Jim Corwin/Stock Boston 397 Cameramann International, Ltd. 399 Adam Woolfit/Woodfin Camp & Associates 401 Cameramann International, Ltd. 405 Cameramann International, Ltd. 408 Bob Daemmrich 411 Phil Long/AP/Wide World 412 Brian Smith/Stock Boston 415 Andy Sacks/Tony Stone Worldwide 416 FourByFive Inc./Superstock, Inc. 423(t) FourByFive Inc./Superstock, Inc. 423(bl) Superstock, Inc. 423(br) Superstock, Inc. 424(tl) FourByFive Inc./Superstock, Inc. 434(t) Superstock, Inc. 434(bl) Superstock, Inc. 434-435(b) Superstock, Inc. 435(t) Superstock, Inc. 437 Superstock, Inc. 439 Courtesy Commonwealth of Australia 440 Superstock, Inc. 441 Frank Lloyd Wright, American, 1867-1959, Window triptych from the Avery Coonley Playhouse, Riverside, Illinois, clear and colored leaded glass in oak frame, 1912, center panel: 88.9 x 109.2 cm; side panels: each 91.4 x 19.7 cm, Restricted gift of Dr. and Mrs. Edwin J. DeCosta and the Walter E. Heller Foundation, 1986.88, "photograph ©1995, Art Institute of Chicago. All Rights Reserved." 442 Grant Heilman/Grant Heilman Photography 446 Tony Freeman/PhotoEdit 447 Courtesy Millinocket Office of Tourism 451 Ulrike Welsch 453 Steve Rosenthal Architectural Photography 457 D.Fox/Superstock, Inc. 459 Esaias Baitel/Gamma-Liaison 464(bl) Superstock, Inc. 466 Egyptian Expedition of The Metropolitan Museum of Art, Rogers Fund, 1930. 467 Bettmann Archive 471 Thorn, Joseph 474(t) Alex MacLean/Landslides 474(b) Courtesy Studio West 475 Michael Newman/PhotoEdit 477 Phil Moughmer/Third Coast Stock Source, Inc. 480 Steve Rosenthal Architectural Photography 483 ©1995 Bill Amend/Universal Press Syndicate. All Rights Reserved. 484 Superstock, Inc. 485(t) Superstock, Inc. 485(b) Superstock, Inc. 486 Superstock, Inc. 489 R.Maiman/Sygma 494-495(t) Superstock, Inc. 494-c Superstock, Inc. 494(bl) Superstock, Inc. 494-495(b) Superstock, Inc. 495(c) Superstock, Inc. 496 Cameramann International, Ltd. 501 Superstock, Inc. 503 Steve Rosenthal 509 Cameramann International, Ltd. 510 Jim Harrison/Stock Boston 511(l) David R. Austen/Stock Boston 511(r) Superstock, Inc. 513 Cameramann International, Ltd. 516 Superstock, Inc. 517 NASA 518 Courtesy L. Meisel Gallery, New York 519 Superstock, Inc. 525 Rosemary Finn 529 Parkinson, Mary Taylor 531(all) Courtesy Simmons-Boardman Publishing Corporation 539 Finn, Rosemary 544(t) Tom Van Sant/Geosphere Project, Santa Monica/SPL/Photo Researchers 545(t) Special Publication No. 1 of the American Cartographic Assn., Copyright 1986 by the American Congress on Surveying and Mapping 545(b) Copyright ©1992 Quarto Publishing Pic, Marlboro Books Corp, a division of Barnes & Noble, Inc. 545 Special Publication No. 1 of the American Cartographic Assn., Copyright 1986 by the American Congress on Surveying and Mapping 552(t) Superstock, Inc. 552(b) Superstock, Inc. 553 Superstock, Inc. 556 Joseph Thorn 562-563(t) Superstock, Inc. 562(c) Superstock, Inc. 562(b) Superstock, Inc. 563(c) Superstock, Inc. 563(b) Superstock, Inc. 564 Paul Chesley/Tony Stone Worldwide 568 The World Of Games, Their Origins and History, How to Play Them, and How to Make Them © 1989 first English language edition by Facts on File Inc., New York and Oxford. All rights reserved. 570 Cameramann International, Ltd. 572 Superstock, Inc. 573 Bob Daemmrich/Stock Boston 575 Jan Kanter 576 Brian Yen 577 Ivory Cats ©Lesley Anne Ivory 1990, Licensee ENESCO Corporation 582 John Coletti/Stock Boston 584 Ivory Cats ©Lesley Anne Ivory 1990, Licensee ENESCO Corporation 587 FourByFive Inc./Superstock, Inc. 594 Everett Collection, Inc. 596 Chuck Keeler/Tony Stone Worldwide 599 FourByFive Inc./Superstock, Inc. 602 Roxanna Marino 609 RIchard Pasley/Stock Boston 613 Superstock, Inc. 620(cl) Superstock, Inc. 620-621(t) Superstock, Inc. 620(cr) Superstock, Inc. 620-621(b) Superstock, Inc. 621(c) FourByFive/Superstock, Inc. 622 Superstock, Inc. 624 Drawings by John Tenniel 625 Giraudon/Art Resource 626 Focus on Sports, Inc. 627 Superstock, Inc. 628 Everett Collection, Inc. 629 David Young-Wolff/PhotoEdit 631 AP/Wide World 632 Richard Hutchings/PhotoEdit 634 Hazel Hankin/Stock Boston 635 Chris Cole/Tony Stone Worldwide 637 Bob Daemmrich/Stock Boston 639 Billy Barnes/Stock Boston 644 David Young-Wolff/PhotoEdit 650 Roberto De Gugliemo/SPL/Photo Researchers 651 Eric Smith/Liaison (Gamma) 655 Focus on Sports, Inc. 656 Courtesy The House on the Rock 665 Cameramann International, Ltd. 666 Richard Hutchings/PhotoEdit 668 Bob Daemmrich/Stock Boston 674 John Elk/Tony Stone Worldwide 675(l) Superstock, Inc. 675(tr) FourByFive/Superstock, Inc. 675(b) The British Library, London/Superstock, Inc. 676 Superstock, Inc. 682 Culver Pictures Inc. 684(tl) Superstock, Inc. 684-685(tr) FourByFive/Superstock, Inc. 684-685(c) Superstock, Inc. 684-b FourByFive/Superstock, Inc. 685(b) Superstock, Inc. 685(r) Superstock, Inc. 686 Finn, Rosemary 698 Karen Stockwell 701 Joseph Thorn 703 Museum of the American Indian, Smithsonian Institution 2742 705 C.H.Rose/Stock Boston 710 Richard Pasley/Stock Boston 711 Richard Pasley/Stock Boston 717 Seth Resnick/Stock Boston 720 722 Ernst Haas/Magnum Photos 724 Bettmann Archive 725 Library of Congress 726 Jacksonville Art Museum, Florida/Superstock, Inc. 727 Everett Collection, Inc. 728 Leo Mason/Sports Illustrated 729(t) Superstock, Inc. 729(b) FourByFive/Superstock, Inc. 730(tr) Superstock, Inc. 730(br) Superstock, Inc. 736(t) Superstock, Inc. 736-737(c) FourByFive/Superstock, Inc. 736(b) Superstock, Inc. 737(t) Superstock, Inc. 737(b) Superstock, Inc. 738 Alan Levenson/Tony Stone Worldwide 742 Superstock, Inc. 744 Sovfoto/Eastfoto 746 Cameramann International, Ltd. 753 Simon Milliken 755 Frank Siteman/Stock Boston 759 Bill Gallery/Stock Boston 763 Bob Daemmrich/Stock Boston 764 Cameramann International, Ltd. 765 John Garrett/Tony Stone Worldwide 767 David R. Frazier 777 Superstock, Inc. 779 Bettmann Archive 784 Will & Deni McIntyre/Tony Stone Worldwide 787 Superstock, Inc. 789(tl) Superstock, Inc. 789(tr) Superstock, Inc. 789(bl) Superstock, Inc. 789(c) Superstock, Inc. 790 Superstock, Inc. 798(tl) Superstock, Inc. 798-799(tr) Superstock, Inc. 798-799(c) Superstock, Inc. 798(b) FourByFive/Superstock, Inc. 799(b) Superstock, Inc. 800 Maxwell Mackenzie/Tony Stone Worldwide 801 Superstock, Inc. 804 Steve Rosenthal 806 Underwood & Underwood/Bettmann Archive 809 Steve Rosenthal 812 Superstock, Inc. 814 Margaret Bourke-White/Life Magazine, Time Warner, Inc. 817 Pascal Quittemelle/Stock Boston 818 Jim Pickerell/Stock Boston 829 Everett Collection, Inc. 829 Lina Cornell/Stock Boston 830 Summit Labs/Lerner Fine Art Collections/Superstock, Inc. 842 Focus on Sports, Inc. 844 The World Of Games, Their Origins and History, How to Play Them, and How to Make Them © 1989 first English language edition by Facts on File Inc., New York and Oxford. All rights reserved. 846(l) Charles Gupton/Stock Boston 846(r) George Haling Productions/Photo Researchers 848 Jeff Schultz/AlaskaStock 849 Courtesy Chicago Bridge & Iron Company 851 Rosemary Finn 852 Bettmann Archive 853 Superstock, Inc. 854 Superstock, Inc. 857 Richard Pasley/Stock Boston

INDEX

NOTES

NOTES